Intensive Beef Prod

Other Titles in the Pergamon International Library

DILLON, J. L. The Analysis of Response in Crop and Livestock Production, 2nd Edition

DODSWORTH, T. L. Beef Production

GARRETT, S. D. Soil Fungi and Soil Fertility

GILCHRIST SHIRLAW, D. W. A Practical Course in Agricultural Chemistry

HILL, N. B. Introduction to Economics for Students of Agriculture

LAWRIE, R. A. Meat Science, 2nd Edition

LOCKHART, J. A. R. & WISEMAN, A. J. L. Introduction to Crop Husbandry, 3rd Edition

MILLER, R. & MILLER, A. Successful Farm Management

NELSON, R. H. An Introduction to Feeding Farm Livestock

PARKER, W. H. Health and Disease in Farm Animals, 2nd Edition

ROSE, C. W. Agricultural Physics

SHIPPEN, J. M. & TURNER, J. C. Basic Farm Machinery, 2nd Edition

YEATES, N. T. M., EDEY, T. N. & HILL, M. K. Animal Science: Reproduction, Climate, Meat, Wool

Intensive Beef Production

SECOND EDITION

BY

T. R. PRESTON

Ph.D.(Dunelm), D.Sc.(Newcastle)

Technical Adviser and Director of Research,
'Proyecto Nutricional Ganadero'
Comisión Nacional de la Industria Azucarera,
Humboldt No. 56-1er. piso,
México 1, D.F.

AND

M. B. WILLIS

B.Sc.(Dunelm), Ph.D.(Edin.)

Department of Agriculture,
The University,
Newcastle-upon-Tyne,
England

PERGAMON PRESS

OXFORD · NEW YORK · TORONTO
SYDNEY · PARIS · FRANKFURT

U.K.	Pergamon Press Ltd., Headington Hill Hall, Oxford OX3 0BW, England
U.S.A.	Pergamon Press Inc., Maxwell House, Fairview Park, Elmsford, New York 10523, U.S.A.
CANADA	Pergamon of Canada, Suite 104, 150 Consumers Road, Willowdale, Ontario. M2 J1P9, Canada
AUSTRALIA	Pergamon Press (Aust.) Pty. Ltd., P.O. Box 544, Potts Point, N.S.W. 2011, Australia
FRANCE	Pergamon Press SARL, 24 rue des Ecoles, 75240 Paris, Cedex 05, France
FEDERAL REPUBLIC OF GERMANY	Pergamon Press GmbH, 6242 Kronberg-Taunus, Pferdstrasse 1, Federal Republic of Germany

First edition 1970

Second edition 1974

Reprinted 1975, 1979

Library of Congress Cataloging in Publication Data

Preston, Thomas Reginald.
Intensive beef production,
1. Beef cattle. I. Willis, Malcolm Beverley,
joint author. II. Title.
SF207.P78 1974 636.2′1′3 74–5276
ISBN 0–08–017788–3 hardcase
ISBN 0–08–018980–6 flexicover

Printed in Great Britain by
Billing & Sons Limited, Guildford, London and Worcester

Contents

PART II. THE INPUTS

PART IV. THE FUTURE

List of Illustrations

List of Plates

Plates 1–15 between pages 264–265

List of Tables

Acknowledgements

The authors are grateful to Sra Lidia González for typing the draft manuscript and for assistance in compiling the index and to Srta Marta Fernández for typing the final version. We also wish to thank Mrs. Joanne Preston for typing all the tables and many of the references, for preparing several of the figures, and for assistance in proof-reading and the compilation of the index.

We wish to acknowledge the editors of the *Journal of Animal Science*, the *Journal of Dairy Science*, *Animal Production*, *Revista cubana Ciencia agrícola*, *Proceedings of the Technical Melbourne Conference on Carcass Composition and Appraisal of Meat Animals*, and the *Farmers Weekly* for permission to reproduce published material.

We are grateful to Mr. G. B. Hagelberg of the Institut für Wirtschaftsgeschichte, Deutsche Academie der Wissenschaften, Berlin, for contributing Chapter 1 and for his helpful suggestions regarding Chapter 12.

Preface to the Second Edition

Extensive revisions have been made to the sections of the book on calf rearing (Ch. 7, Rearing by suckling) and sugar cane (Ch. 9, 9.3.3, Sugar cane), in view of important recent developments in these subjects which have taken place since the original versions were written.

T. R. Preston
M. B. Willis

Introduction

THE growing and fattening of cattle for meat is undertaken in practically every country of the world and the methods employed are as varied as the people who practice them. To deal comprehensively with each and every system is beyond the scope of a single book. Nor is it desirable to attempt to treat the subject in this encyclopedic way since many of the techniques employed have only sociological or historical significance. Our original intention was to discuss modern methods of beef production, but to chronicle all the so-called recent developments would be to mislead our readers. For many "new" methods are new in name only and offer nothing to the cause of greater efficiency which, in the long term, should be the major concern of any beef-producing enterprise.

We define intensive beef production as the growing and/or feeding of cattle under conditions of confinement in which all feed is carried to the animals. Within the limits of this definition we have attempted to be comprehensive for our thesis is that meat production must become a factory operation. On this basis, like any other manufacturing process, it needs man's skill to convert raw materials into a marketable product. The market varies according to location and so, within narrow limits, do the raw materials, but the principles are the same the world over. The only variation is in degree of development which makes some countries or enterprises more efficient than others.

There are many who criticize our basic premise that growth and fattening of beef cattle should be an intensive operation. Objectors on ethical or religious grounds, as typified by Ruth Harrison and her disciples, seem to lose sight of the fact that man is superior to animals and must exploit them to survive—in the same way that one animal species exploits another. It is perhaps significant that such criticisms are generally voiced only in highly developed countries where food is plentiful and almost never in those countries where people still go hungry.

The technical objections are of two basic kinds. One school holds to the belief that because the ruminant has a biological potential to digest roughages, then *ipso facto* such feeds must be the basis of the diet. The other opinion is that roughages, particularly grass, are easier to grow and cheaper per unit of energy than carbohydrate-rich crops. This is also taken as justification for extensive research and development on these feeds. Such arguments overemphasize evolutionary processes, which in the natural state fit animals to specific environments, and ignore the more positive control of the population geneticist who by selection can fit animals to any environment. It is then a short step from defining the best environment for a particular productive process to breeding the animals specifically for it. Moreover, when economics are discussed the final decision may be governed less by the costs of growing feed and more by such things as suitability for mechanization and ease of handling, storage and feeding.

One must also accept the fact, albeit distasteful to some, that the available land area in developed countries is decreasing and with it opportunity for extensive grassland farming. In such countries maximum productivity per unit of land area becomes ever more important, and under these conditions grassland has increasing difficulty in competing with cereals. Even in the tropics, where pasture and forages have hitherto reigned supreme, the need to increase animal production is focusing attention on the fact that other crops have a vastly superior potential.

Intensive beef production is often considered to be synonymous with high grain feeding. In fact, one of the major advantages of an intensive system is that it also lends itself readily to the utilization of industrial-type feeds and byproducts. Thus protein substitutes from the chemical industry (urea and ammonia), and energy sources from oil refining (fatty acids) and sugar-beet and sugar-cane processing (molasses) are more efficiently utilized in intensive feeding systems than on pasture. There are disadvantages obviously in intensive units, not least of which are the disease hazard, the large investment in specialized facilities and the problems of faecal waste disposal. But intensification in agriculture is as inevitable as the continuing growth of cities. We have to learn to live with it and, more important, profit by it.

In line with our thesis that beef production is like any other manufacturing process, this book has been divided into four main parts. These basically set out the stages that an intending manufacturer might follow in setting up his enterprise. Thus Part I (The Product) deals with the market and factors governing the quality of the output—beef. Part II (The Inputs) covers the raw materials, i.e. the type of animal and its genetic makeup together with the nutritional principles which determine the extent to which its potential can be exploited. Part III (The Production) is concerned with details of manufacture (i.e. growth and fattening) together with the problems which arise during the process, e.g. disease. Finally, Part IV (The Future) includes ideas on economic trends and areas in which investigation might be undertaken so as to improve future efficiency.

Throughout, an international approach has been attempted, and although the United States and the United Kingdom feature prominently, this mainly reflects the fact that most work in beef production has been associated with these two countries. We have nevertheless sought to put in perspective the needs and potential of the new nations, particularly those in the tropical and subtropical regions.

The different aspects of each chapter are broken down in accordance with the factors affecting them. For example, "breed" is discussed as a factor affecting the carcass (Chapter 2), reproductive traits (Chapter 6) and growth and efficiency (Chapter 8). At times this approach has led to some duplication, but it does mean that individual sections are complete entities which we believe is an important factor in a work of reference.

If the tone of the book is at times critical of individuals, organizations and governments, this is because previously there has been too much complacency. Beef has probably the most secure future of almost all animal products, but more than most it has suffered from a reluctance to incorporate new technology and an excessive preoccupation with tradition.

Part I. The Product

CHAPTER 1

The Market

G. B. Hagelberg

1.1 INTRODUCTION

The world's cattle and buffalo population, according to FAO estimates, reached close to 1200 million in 1966, roughly one animal for every three persons. It produced around 34.6 million tons of meat or about 10 kg for each of the world's inhabitants (Table 1.1).

Unlike many other resources, the animals are broadly distributed over the major part of the globe and, on the whole, their number in relation to the human population is not significantly lower in less developed than in more developed regions. Somewhat over half is concentrated in six countries—India, the United States, the Soviet Union, Brazil, Mainland China and Argentina, in descending numerical order—corresponding fairly closely to the aggregate share of these countries in the world's human population. In addition, Colombia, Ethiopia, Mexico and Pakistan, among the developing countries, hold large numbers of cattle. More than one animal per person exists in Australia, New Zealand, Argentina, Brazil, Uruguay, Chad, Ethiopia, Malagasy Republic and Mauritania. At the other extreme, the United Kingdom and West Germany have only one head of cattle for about every four and a half inhabitants.

However, not all countries with a high animal–human ratio are large *per caput* meat producers. In general, what distinguishes the less developed from the more developed regions is the degree to which their cattle resources are exploited. Since foreign trade accounts for a relatively small slice of world meat production and a substantial part of such redistribution actually takes place among the developed countries themselves, the difference is well expressed in overall consumption terms. United States authorities have pointed out that in 1959–61 the 1100 million people in the developed countries had almost one and a half times as many calories and over five times as much high-quality animal protein per person as the 1900 million people in the developing countries (National Advisory Commission on Food and Fibre, 1967, p. 308). Because of poverty, technological backwardness and dietary tabus, the 189 million cattle and 56.5 million buffalo estimated to exist in India—roughly one animal for every two persons—contribute little to solve that country's food problem. In Africa, meat production per head of cattle was estimated to be about 17 kg per year against 62 kg in western Europe (FAO, 1965, p. 14). Additionally, the European cattle herd produced annually some 1200 kg of milk per head compared with only 100 kg in Africa.

TABLE 1.1 CATTLE NUMBERS 1965/6 AND BEEF, VEAL AND BUFFALO MEAT PRODUCTION IN 1966

Country	Cattle (million head)	Carcass weight (1000 metric tons)
India	188.8[a]	151
USA	108.9	9363
USSR	93.0[a]	3752
Brazil	90.5	1452
China, Mainland	62.8[a]	2100
Argentina	47.0	2412
Pakistan	35.6[a]	270[b]
Mexico	33.1	435[b]
Ethiopia	25.5	175[c]
France	20.6	1650
Australia	17.9	884
Colombia	15.0	415
Germany, Fed. Rep.	13.7	1081
Turkey	13.2[a]	104[d]
South Africa	12.5	390
United Kingdom	12.2	882
Canada	11.7	923
Tanzania	10.5	83
Poland	10.4	426
World	1075.2[a]	34582

[a] Plus the following buffalo numbers (millions): India 56.5; USSR 0.4; China 28.6; Pakistan 8.7; Turkey 1.2; world 120.9.

[b] Commercial production, excluding farm slaughter.

[c] Not specified whether total or inspected or commercial production only.

[d] Inspected production, i.e. from animals slaughtered under governmental supervision, only. (FAO, 1968a, Tables 101, 106, 110.)

But although much more productive, the cattle herds in the advanced countries have not, on the whole, supplied sufficient meat to satisfy the rapidly increasing demand spurred by rising incomes. Compared with modern methods of poultry production, beef raising for the most part is still on the threshold of industrialization. The problem, then, is twofold: to devise means in the developing areas which will speedily reduce the protein gap and to perfect intensive techniques in the developed countries which will further extend the frontiers of productivity, both aims to be achieved in the most economical way (FAO, 1967a; Moore *et al.*, 1967).

1.2 OUTPUT

Excluding centrally planned countries in Asia, world production of beef and veal during 1967 was estimated at 33.7 million metric tons, up 3.2% from the previous year and 36.4% above the average for 1955–7 (Table 1.2). The output of all types of meat during this period also rose by over a third, from 52.2 million tons in 1955–7 to 71.1 million tons on average in 1965–7. Stimulated by industrial production methods and the availability of low-cost feeds, the supply of poultry meat has increased fastest, doubling from an average of 5.6 million tons in 1955–7 to an estimated 11.1 million tons in 1967. On the other hand, output of pigmeat advanced by just under 36%, from 17.5 to 23.7 million tons, while mutton and lamb only grew by somewhat over a quarter, from 4.4 to 5.6 million tons, reflecting the fact that they are mostly produced by extensive methods, and their relative share in total meat output fell by about 10%.

TABLE 1.2 SHARES OF DIFFERENT MEATS IN WORLD PRODUCTION[a]

Category	1955–7 (average)	1965	1966 (preliminary)	1967 (estimate)
		(million metric tons)		
Beef and veal	24.71	30.84	32.67	33.70
Pigmeat	17.46	22.19	22.62	23.72
Poultry meat	5.58	9.65	10.42	11.13
Mutton and lamb	4.44	5.39	5.41	5.64
Total	52.19	68.07	71.12	74.19
		(%)		
Beef and veal	47.3	45.3	45.9	45.4
Pigmeat	33.5	32.6	31.8	32.0
Poultry meat	10.7	14.2	14.7	15.0
Mutton and lamb	8.5	7.9	7.6	7.6

[a] Excluding centrally planned countries in Asia. In terms of carcass weight. (FAO, 1968b, Table 19.)

Indicative of the vast differences in productivity, the United States, with roughly 10% of the world's cattle, produced 27% of the world's beef and veal in 1966 (Table 1.1). Another 11% of the total beef supply was accounted for by the Soviet Union, while the Soviet cattle population represented less than 9% of the world's herds. Although holding almost the same number of animals as the Soviet Union, Brazil's meat output amounted to only 4% of the world total. By contrast, Argentina, with a herd half the size of the Russian, produced nearly 7% of the world's beef in 1966. France, the leading west European producer, contributed just under 5% to the world total, followed by West Germany and the United Kingdom with 3 and 2.6% respectively. The principal Commonwealth source of beef and veal, Australia, was only slightly ahead of the United Kingdom notwithstanding the fact that its herd was almost half again as large as the British.

Looking at herd development during recent years, the greatest increases have taken place in Brazil and the Soviet Union, which raised their stocks from 76.2 and 82.1 million head respectively in 1961/2 to over 90 million in 1965/6. Several other countries, among them Argentina, Cuba, Mexico, Ireland and the United States, registered substantial gains in this period (FAO, 1968a, Table 101).

Beef and veal are by far the most important meats produced in the world. But, as a result of different rates of development, their share in total meat output has declined appreciably (Table 1.2). The picture is rather different, however, if poultry meat is excluded. In relation to total red meat output, the share of beef and veal shows a small rise from 53.0% in 1955–7 to 53.4% in 1965–7. The trend becomes clearer when some of the principal industrialized countries are examined individually. Thus in the United States, beef and veal accounted for 59.8% of total red meat production in 1962–6 against 55.2% in 1952–6 (FAO, 1968a, Table 110). In Italy the proportion of beef and veal rose from 55.0 to 59.1% in the respective periods. Pork continues to be the most important item in central and eastern Europe, but the gap is narrowing. In Poland the ratio of pork to beef and veal production in live weight terms diminished from 2.36:1 in 1958–60 to 1.84:1 in 1964–6 (Zaleski, 1968). In the German Democratic Republic, the ratio fell from 2.54:1 in 1958–60 to 2.09:1 in 1965–7 (Staatliche Zentralverwaltung für Statistik, 1968). In the Soviet Union, beef seems definitely to have gained the edge on pork. Despite a large increase in the output of pigmeat, beef advanced from 43.9 to 45.9% of Soviet red meat production between 1952–6 and 1962–6 and in the latter year stood at 47.7% (FAO, 1968a, Table 110). Soviet beef production in 1966 was double the average for 1952–6, pork increased by 88%, and mutton and lamb by 22%. One notable exception to this trend in recent years is the United Kingdom where beef and veal dropped from 46.6 to 45.5% of total red meat output between 1952–6 and 1962–6 as a result of a more rapid expansion of mutton and lamb as well as of pork, the latter actually overtaking beef production in 1965.

International statistics generally pool beef and veal in one category, since the latter represents a small and decreasing fraction of total output. In the United States, commercial slaughter in 1966 reached 6.6 million head, 10% less than a year earlier and the smallest number since 1918 when 6.5 million head were slaughtered (USDA, Economic Research Service, 1967), an increasing proportion of cattle being slaughtered as mature animals. In 1946 calf slaughter totalled about 33% of the calf crop; in 1956 30%; in 1966 about 15%. The major reasons for the decline in calf slaughter were attributed to the reduction in dairy cattle numbers (which in the 20 years fell 37%), the growing prominence of the cattle feeding industry and an increasing proportion of calves carried to mature weight before slaughter. In 1966 over 20 million head of cattle were moved through feedlots—up 82% from 1956. Almost 72% of the 1966 calf crop was still on farms on 1 January 1967 compared with 52% 20 years earlier. In the United Kingdom the share of veal in total output averaged only 1.3% in 1965–7 against 2.3% in 1960–2 (Central Statistical Office, 1968, Table 219). Similar tendencies to reduce the number of calves slaughtered and to increase their slaughter weight can be observed in many countries, and this is one of the reasons why beef production has risen faster than cattle numbers (Organization for Economic Cooperation and Development, 1967; Zaleski, 1968; Staatliche Zentralverwaltung für Statistik, 1968; Statistical Office of the European Communities, 1968b; FAO, 1968a, Table 113).

1.3 INTERNATIONAL TRADE

Less than a tenth of all the meat produced in the world enters international trade, although the proportion is gradually rising. Gross meat and live animal exports were valued at some 4436 million US dollars in 1966, up 3.2% from the year before and consisting of the following major categories (FAO, 1968d):

	Million US dollars	
	1965	1966
Live cattle	682.4	584.9
Live sheep, lambs and goats	84.5	89.4
Live pigs	153.7	148.1
Fresh, chilled and frozen meats	2340.2	2447.7
Canned and prepared meats	1039.9	1166.1

This listing suffices to indicate an outstanding characteristic of the meat market—its enormous complexity. Meat is traded among a large number of countries "on the hoof", as carcasses and manufactured products; fresh, chilled and frozen; sides, quarters and boneless. Its volume is subject to quotas, droughts and epidemics. Its values are influenced by a multitude of subsidies, tariffs and imposts. Our discussion will hence be confined to what seem to be the longer-range trends.

Gross world exports (excluding centrally planned countries in Asia) of fresh, chilled, frozen, canned and prepared meats of all kinds have been rising steadily and in 1967 were estimated to have reached nearly 4.6 million tons in terms of product weight, against an average of 2.5 million tons in 1955–7 (Table 1.3). Fresh, chilled and frozen meats represented three-quarters of the total in 1967 and their volume doubled in the period under review, while the volume of canned and prepared meats increased by only 37%. Although beef and veal continued to constitute the principal export category, by far the fastest growth was experienced in the pork and poultry trade.

Exports of live sheep, lambs and goats exhibit a rising tendency, but no firm conclusions can be drawn with respect to the trend of live cattle and pigs, the figure for the latter being affected, among other things, by the sharp fluctuations in Chinese exports to Hong Kong. Incomplete figures (including exports from the rest of the world to the USSR, eastern Europe and Mainland China, but not exports from these countries) for 1967 show live cattle shipments of 3.8 million head, up almost 13% from the previous year but only slightly above the 1965 level (FAO, 1968c, Annex Table 9A). In terms of value, live cattle exports also mark a rising trend, thanks to higher prices (FAO 1968d, Table 1).

The main currents of the world meat trade flow from Oceania and Latin America to western Europe and the United States (Table 1.4). A large volume of commerce also takes place between the countries of western Europe, where Denmark and the Irish Republic are the largest exporters, and Italy, the United Kingdom and West Germany the principal markets. Since 1960, Yugoslavia has also become a major exporter, while new outlets have developed in Greece, Israel, Portugal and Spain. Large numbers of live cattle are traded within the European Economic Community, only Italy making no shipments to the other members. Additionally, the EEC received in 1966 about a million head from the United Kingdom, Denmark and eastern Europe. Elsewhere in the world, substantial cattle movements take place from Canada and Mexico to the United States, from Argentina to Chile, Paraguay and

TABLE 1.3 WORLD EXPORTS OF MEAT AND LIVE ANIMALS

MEAT[a]

Category	1955–7 average (1000 tons)	%		1967 estimate (1000 tons)	%		Percent increase 1967: 1955–7
Fresh, chilled and frozen:							
Beef and veal	812	48		1560	45		92
Mutton and lamb	391	23		585	17		50
Pork	137	8		378	11		176
Poultry meat	93	6		356	10		283
Offal, game, other meat	202	12		474	14		135
Unspecified	47	3		95	3		102
Total, fresh, chilled and frozen	1682	100	67	3448	100	75	105
Canned and prepared:							
Bacon, ham, salted pork	375	46		452	40		21
Canned meat	394	48		598	53		52
Other, incl. sausages	53	6		80	7		51
Total, canned and prepared	822	100	33	1130	100	25	37
Total, all categories	2504		100	4578		100	83

LIVE ANIMALS[b]
(million head)

Category	1960	1961	1962	1963	1964	1965	1966
Cattle	3.17	4.06	3.93	4.05	3.81	4.41	4.12
Sheep, lambs and goats	3.04	5.50	5.70	6.25	6.03	6.80	7.66
Pigs	2.75	2.60	2.67	2.34	2.98	3.76	3.40

[a] Excluding centrally planned countries in Asia. In terms of product weight.

[b] Totals for 1960, especially those of sheep, lambs and goats, are not comparable with following years because of wider coverage beginning in 1961, notably the inclusion of Mongolia. (FAO, 1967b, Tables 1, 2 and 3; FAO, 1968b, Table 19; FAO, 1968d, Tables 1, 2 and 3.)

Peru, and between different countries in Africa (Commonwealth Secretariat, Commodities Division, 1967).

1.4 PRICES

With demand often outstripping supplies, meat values as a whole have trended upwards, contrary to the declining tendency shown by cereal prices until 1961 and ahead of FAO's general export price index for food and feed (Fig. 1.1). The ascent has been particularly steep since 1962 as a result of the concerted advance of all red-meat prices. A downward adjustment began in 1966, but this was not expected to get far (FAO, 1968b). Of the different categories of red meats, beef has experienced the sharpest rise, the 1965–7 level being almost double the 1955–7 values (Figs. 1.2 and 1.3).

The combined effect of greater volume and higher prices has been to lift the total value of fresh, chilled and frozen beef and veal exports from an average of \$350 million in 1955–7 to over \$1140 million in 1966 (FAO, 1968b, Table 20; excluding USSR and Mainland China). Beginning in 1958, the curve reflects large purchases by the United States and the rapid increase in the quantity of boneless beef shipped to the United States from Oceania (FAO, 1965, pp. 38–39; Thomas, 1963). The major influence on mutton and lamb export prices appears to have been the rise and fall of requirements on the part of the United Kingdom, the leading importer. Export values of pork products, on the other hand, have to a certain extent paralleled the trend of cereal prices, since grains constitute the greater part of pigmeat production costs. Poultry meat prices declined not only because of the relative cheapness of feed grains but also because of the rapid spread of large-scale industrialized production methods.

Export values, like prices and volume in general, are, of course, affected not only

TABLE 1.4 BEEF AND CATTLE TRADE OF SELECTED COUNTRIES

	1960	1961	1962	1963	1964	1965	1966	1967
	Gross exports and imports of fresh, chilled and frozen beef (thousand metric tons)							
Exporter								
Argentina	280.0	270.7	388.7	531.5	420.9	349.2	401.1	379.7
Australia	191.2	136.2	204.4	265.0	286.2	321.3	286.4	115.0
Denmark	70.9	49.7	76.7	94.5	70.0	63.5	83.7	107.6
France	62.5	103.3	154.9	98.9	70.2	65.5	87.6	91.3
Ireland	47.9	74.7	59.8	61.7	52.7	55.0	70.0	148.0
Netherlands	37.4	24.0	35.8	61.6	70.2	71.5	58.8	66.5
New Zealand	100.3	97.0	117.7	128.5	121.6	121.4	102.7	107.4
Uruguay	52.2	42.9	54.5	64.5	122.1	64.6	55.4	—
Yugoslavia	16.1	29.7	63.6	68.9	63.3	65.6	76.2	78.8
Importer								
Belgium–Luxemburg	8.5	12.5	16.9	20.4	22.8	17.7	14.2	30.1
France	27.0	10.9	9.6	15.8	72.9	59.4	36.9	35.1
Germany, Fed. Rep.	64.7	83.7	105.5	91.1	117.6	147.4	125.5	134.0
Greece	11.6	12.0	17.3	28.3	22.0	30.6	30.9	37.0
Israel	2.2	2.9	11.5	13.1	21.3	23.9	40.9	24.2
Italy	136.8	53.8	94.8	259.3	287.3	252.4	277.4	325.1
Netherlands	14.5	21.7	21.1	17.8	30.5	24.8	32.9	41.5
Portugal	7.7	10.4	6.4	10.7	9.7	9.8	10.0	25.8
Spain	11.2	3.9	42.6	83.2	19.3	68.6	87.8	106.7
Switzerland	16.1	17.2	21.2	16.7	34.1	31.2	24.9	32.7
United Kingdom	358.4	292.5	332.8	363.6	350.6	294.1	290.1	273.4
United States	187.7	258.1	391.6	448.4	320.5	266.1	348.6	382.1

TABLE 1.4 (cont.)

	1960	1961	1962	1963	1964	1965	1966
	Gross exports and imports of live cattle (thousand head)						
Exporter							
Argentina	152.1	171.1	250.3	291.8	166.1	102.0	119.1
Austria	87.6	88.4	100.3	148.7	79.9	99.9	77.9
Canada	273.0	503.2	492.4	278.7	222.9	613.1	537.3
Denmark	353.4	370.7	294.0	339.5	266.3	277.2	168.6
France	163.3	122.5	89.6	197.2	156.0	204.1	135.6
Germany, Fed. Rep.	1.3	1.4	2.1	45.1	127.1	110.7	95.7
Hungary	123.5	92.4	97.2	143.9	107.3	148.5	155.8
Ireland	542.0	722.4	575.3	662.8	793.8	596.8	624.9
Mexico	395.7	549.7	766.2	552.9	358.0	557.4	589.7
Poland	27.1	14.6	23.6	23.4	78.8	103.8	108.2
Turkey	9.3	63.6	132.6	123.5	95.2	104.6	66.4
United Kingdom	60.6	188.5	122.3	164.4	306.1	324.7	172.3
Importer							
Chile	170.9	207.1	161.0	132.5	121.3	79.9	69.5
Germany, Fed. Rep.	473.2	448.5	374.6	365.8	324.4	524.1	350.0
Hong Kong	139.6	98.8	125.3	111.7	143.9	168.3	198.7
Ireland	45.0	159.4	102.2	140.1	147.6	101.4	74.7
Italy	342.3	353.4	295.4	755.1	575.5	680.8	894.9
Lebanon	76.3	87.9	110.1	152.4	103.1	114.7	120.0
Nigeria	102.3	89.9	105.6	114.4	91.6	71.7	—
Peru	12.5	32.3	100.6	131.3	49.5	66.8	115.6
USSR	158.0	138.1	135.8	88.5	93.7	114.6	128.1
United Kingdom	508.5	692.1	567.7	639.4	706.5	511.2	566.9
United States	663.2	1042.7	1250.0	852.3	546.6	1128.4	1100.4

(FAO, 1967b, Tables 1 and 5; FAO, 1968d, Table 1; FAO, 1968, *Mo. Bull. Agric. Econ. Stat.*, Rome, **17** (9), September, 1968.)

by changes in supply and demand but also by governmental economic policies. As a rule, protective measures maintain internal producer prices in importing countries above the world market level. Import duties and quotas may limit the volume of competitive entries from abroad; guaranteed prices and subsidies are designed to stimulate domestic production. Usually applied in combination, both types of measures tend to make domestic production more profitable than it would be without protection. In addition, the producer can often count on government aid in the form of financial assistance to eliminate livestock diseases or subsidized fertilizer prices which ultimately reduce the cost of feeds, although supported grain prices may have the opposite effect.

Similarly, exporting countries can influence the market in various ways. Indirectly the market is affected by government expenditures for research and extension services designed to increase production and improve efficiency. Direct effects arise from taxes, subsidies, price and foreign exchange differentials, support purchases, price stabilization programmes and meatless days. The aim may be to encourage production, regulate the distribution between domestic and foreign consumers and/or isolate the national from the world market.

To what extent the tug of war of these measures motivated by economic, fiscal, social and political considerations finally helps to promote technical efficiency—assuming that to be the goal which in the long run benefits producers and consumers alike—or shields the inefficient, is not always easy to determine. In any event, the effect of the interplay of so many factors at different national levels is to enhance the highly complex, probabilistic character of the market, with at times rather curious results. For example, the total amount of beef and veal available for consumption in the United Kingdom in 1965 was the smallest in recent years. Not only were imports at an exceptionally low level as a consequence of a reduced Argentine surplus, but

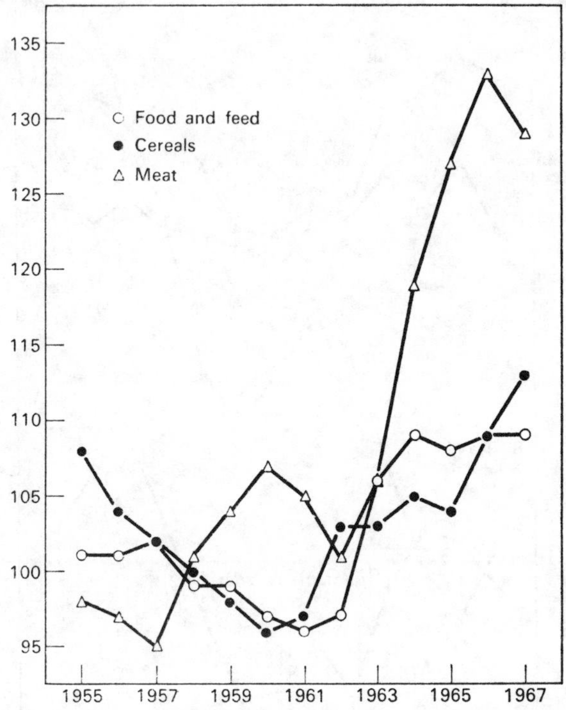

FIG. 1.1 Index numbers of world (excluding USSR, eastern Europe and Mainland China) average export unit values for food and feed, cereals and meat, 1955–67 (1957–9 Æ 100). (FAO, 1968c, Annex, Table 13.)

the shortage of animals available for domestic slaughter was aggravated by large shipments of live cattle to members of the EEC, especially West Germany and the Netherlands. Higher prices in the EEC also attracted substantial numbers of Irish stock which in normal times would have been marketed in the United Kingdom (Commonwealth Secretariat, Commodities Division, 1967, pp. 45–47).

Producer and wholesale prices of meat in the different national markets are hard to compare because of the diversity of economic conditions and technical specifications. The picture is further confused by abrupt and at times contradictory short-term fluctuations. Leaving these aside, however, some broad trends become apparent. Figure 1.4 shows that, with the notable exception of the United States, beef prices have tended to rise sharply in all the major Western national markets. Possible explanations for the different evolution of American producer and wholesale beef prices (which, as will be shown, was not matched at the retail level) are the increase of relatively cheap imports and the fact that the United States has advanced furthest in intensive meat production from grain-fed cattle under the impetus of favourable feed prices. A measure of the intensity of the rise in beef prices in other countries is supplied by a FAO survey of the development of producer prices in thirteen European countries during the decade ending 1964–5. Cattle prices, it was found, were in first

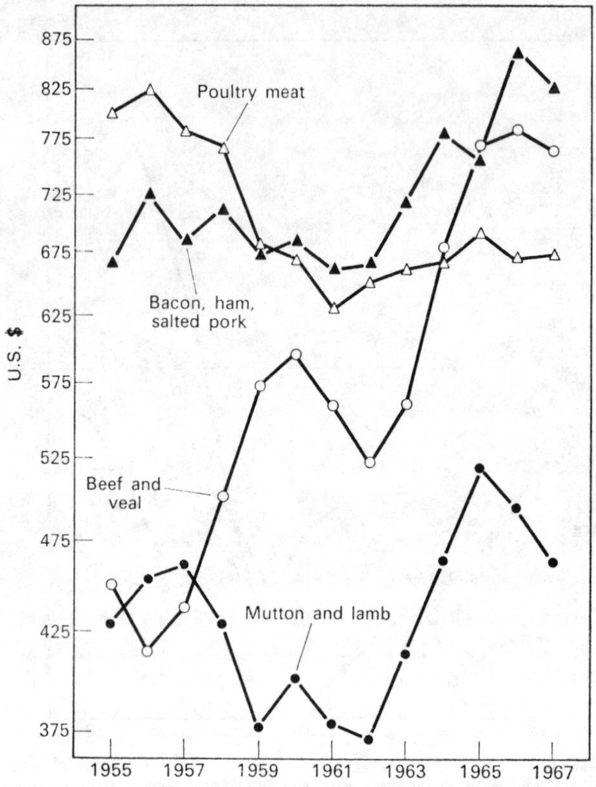

Fig. 1.2 World (excluding USSR, eastern Europe and Mainland China) average export unit values for meat, 1955–67 (US $ per ton). (FAO, 1968c, Annex, Table 13.)

or second place in terms of price increases among the ten commodities compared in eleven of the thirteen countries, and in ten countries rose faster than the general wholesale price index (Anon., 1967).

Prices of other red meats have evolved far less uniformly. The course of pork prices since 1950 has tended downward not only in the United States and Canada (notwithstanding a sudden rise in 1965–6), but also in the United Kingdom. French and Irish pork prices have fluctuated aimlessly, while slight to moderate advances can be noted in West Germany, the Netherlands, Denmark and Australia. New Zealand is one of the few countries where pork prices have shown anything like the sustained buoyancy of beef values. On the other hand, producer prices of lamb in New Zealand show a weakening tendency over the years which, however, has not been reflected in the London price for frozen New Zealand lamb carcasses nor shared by quotations in Melbourne for export quality lambs, both of which have risen. A similar divergence can be found between the downward slope of producer and wholesale lamb prices in the United States and Canada, on the one side, and increasing values in the United Kingdom and France, on the other.

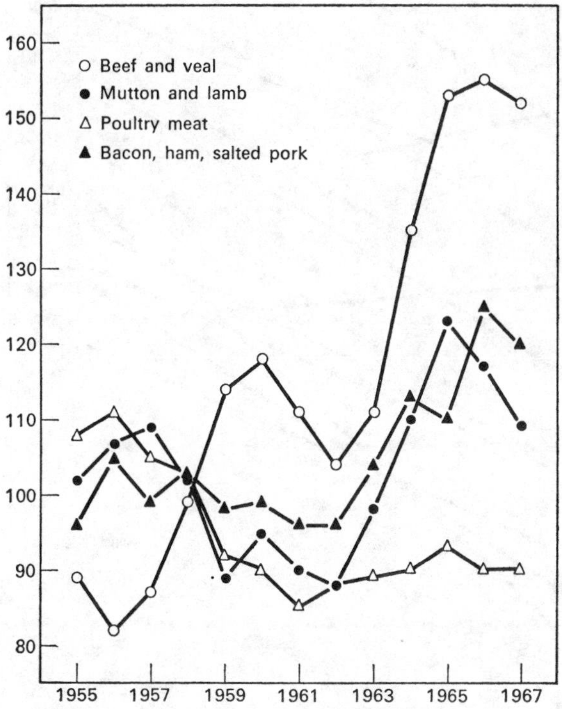

Fig. 1.3 Index numbers of world (excluding USSR, eastern Europe and Mainland China) average export unit values for different meats, 1955–67 (1957–9 = 100). (FAO, 1968c, Annex, Table 13.)

By way of contrast, poultry prices have undergone something like the uniform evolution of beef prices—but in the opposite direction. With the sole exception of Italy, chicken prices have descended in all major Western markets since the 1950's. In the United States, producers in 1964–6 received, on average, just over one half the price obtained in 1950–2 for broilers, and even less for chickens. This is undoubtedly a reflection of the technological revolution which has taken place in broiler and turkey production. Highly suggestive in this connection is the difference in the growth of labour productivity between farm-raised chicken and industrialized broiler production in the United States (Table 1.5). Both stood at approximately the same level in the mid-1930's; but since then the man-hour expenditure per 100 lb (45.4 kg) live weight of broiler meat has sunk to one-fifth of that for farm-raised chicken meat. Even so, progress in the latter has been rather faster than in beef or pork.

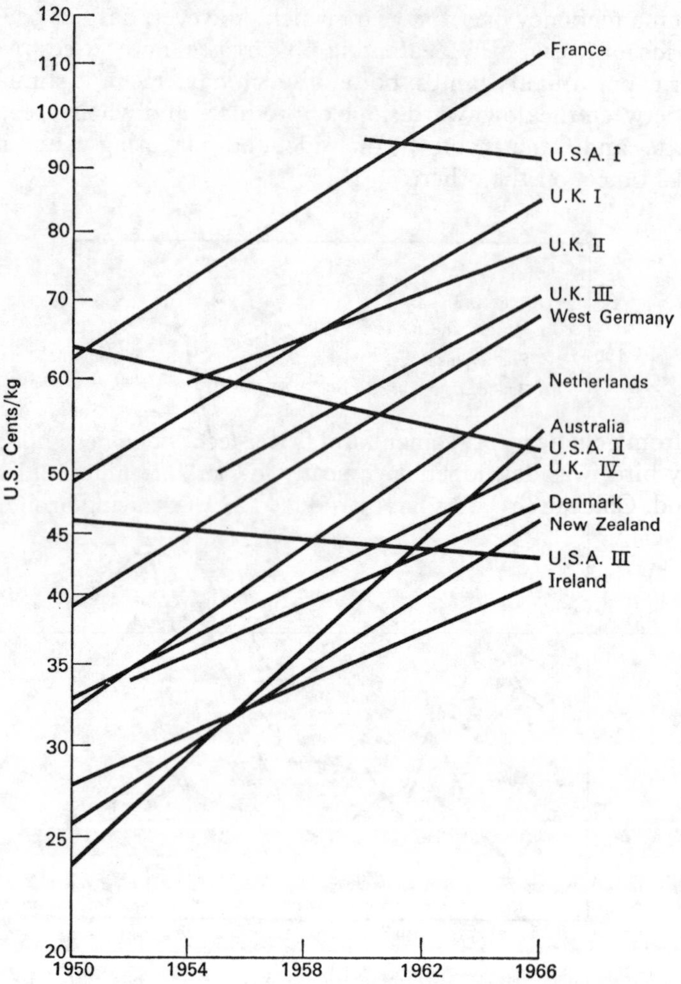

Fig. 1.4 Trends of producer and wholesale beef prices in selected countries. *France:* First quality oxen, slaughter weight, wholesale price excluding tax, Paris. *USA I:* Choice steer beef carcasses, 500–600 lb, wholesale price, Chicago. *UK I:* Chilled Argentine hindquarters, wholesale price, London. *UK II:* English longsides, wholesale price, London. *UK III:* Chilled Argentine sides, wholesale price, London. *West Germany:* Young, well-fleshed oxen, live weight, producer price, 24 markets. *Netherlands:* Second quality, live weight, producer price, leading markets. *Australia:* Oxen, first and second export quality, 650–700 lb, wholesale price, Brisbane. *USA II:* Choice steers, live weight, wholesale price, Chicago. *UK IV:* Certified steers and heifers, average price at live weight auctions, including payments under Fatstock Guarantee Scheme. *Denmark:* Best quality steers for export, live weight, wholesale price, Copenhagen. *New Zealand:* Ox and heifer, quarter beef, good average quality, slaughter weight, opening schedule price for meat operators and exporters, North Island. *USA III:* Live weight, average producer price. *Ireland:* Fat cattle, 2–3 years old, live weight, wholesale price at fairs. (FAO, 1968a.)

TABLE 1.5 LABOUR PRODUCTIVITY IN LIVESTOCK PRODUCTION IN THE UNITED STATES

Man hours per 100 lb of live weight	1910–14	1925–9	1935–9	1945–9	1955–9	1960–4
Beef	4.6	4.3	4.2	4.0	3.2	2.7
Hogs	3.6	3.3	3.2	3.0	2.4	2.1
Chickens (farm-raised)	9.5	9.4	9.0	7.7	6.7	4.5
Chickens (broiler)	—	—	8.5	5.1	1.3	.9
Turkeys	31.4	28.5	23.7	13.1	4.4	2.9

(National Advisory Commission on Food and Fibre, 1967, p. 155.)

In addition to modern housing, labour-saving devices, management expertise and the economies of scale afforded by large units, the efficiency of poultry production has benefited from genetic improvement and better feeds. The Beltsville white turkey, a small, meaty bird, was developed specifically for small families and has become a year-round food. Chicken breeders have produced a fast-growing broiler, much more thrifty in converting feed to meat, whether fed on an old-fashioned diet or on a modern formula.

As in the case of labour productivity, the rate of improvement in feed conversion has been more rapid for poultry than for red meats. US Department of Agriculture data (Table 1.6) show some decline in the feed unit requirements to produce beef and pigmeat during the early fifties followed by a rise which completely nullified the gains. In the case of beef, this is probably to be explained by the change in herd composition with the reduction in dairy cattle numbers, the increase in slaughter weight and the decline of calf slaughter, and in both cases changes of system and liberal feeding practices confound the picture. Broiler production, however, shows a steady improvement in feed efficiency, and in 1960–4 it took 37% fewer feed units to produce 100 lb of broilers than 20 years earlier. By 1964 the broiler industry in the United States had progressed to the extent of being able to produce birds of 3.5 lb (roughly 1.6 kg) in 65 days (Hodgson and Bayley, 1964), which indicates the potential gains to be achieved with other animals.

Finally, meat prices at the producer and wholesale level are affected by three production factors. The first is the growing utilization of grain and other high-energy feeds in livestock diets. In 1960–1 about half of the world's cereal consumption

TABLE 1.6 FEED UNIT[a] EQUIVALENT OF ALL FEEDS CONSUMED PER 100 lb PRODUCED BY DIFFERENT CLASSES OF LIVESTOCK

Livestock	1940–4	1945–9	1950–4	1955–9	1960–4
Cattle and calves	1001	993	930	1002	999
Hogs	545	546	527	534	579
Broilers	467	427	358	323	296

[a] A feed unit is the equivalent in feeding value of a pound of maize. (US Dept. of Agriculture, 1963, Table 544; US Dept. of Agriculture, 1966, Table 542.)

(excluding rice) was estimated to be in this form (FAO, 1965, pp. 81–82). While grain feeding has advanced furthest in the United States, the practice is also making headway in Europe. In the EEC area 43% more grain was employed for feed in the 3-year period 1964/5–1966/7 than in 1955/6–1957/8 and the proportion of total domestic grain (excluding rice) so consumed rose from 49 to 57% (Statistical Office of the European Communities, 1968a). Not only poultry and pigs, but also cattle are increasingly being raised on grain. Lower cereal prices have stimulated the development of new feeding techniques which eventually may reduce the economic advantage of the grasslands systems in the traditional exporting countries and provoke changes similar to the shift from pasture to dry lot observed in pig nutrition (Hanson, 1958). Costs are, or course, not the only consideration, but also the capacity to meet market requirements in quantity and quality. However, large differences still exist among different countries with respect to the relation between prices for livestock products and for grains and other feedstuffs (Table 1.7), to the extent that in many developing countries grain feeding is virtually precluded. The picture may change as a result of the introduction of new high-yielding varieties of cereals which offer the perspective of lowering production costs and hence prices sufficiently to make livestock feeding with grain economic.

Apart from cereals, ever greater supplies of livestock feeds are becoming available as a byproduct of the constant expansion of the food industry. For example, about 170,000 tons of dried sugar-beet pulp are annually consumed by livestock in the United States (Moore *et al.*, 1967). Wet beet pulp is also fed in areas adjacent to sugar

TABLE 1.7 RELATIONSHIP BETWEEN BEEF AND FEED GRAIN PRICES, 1964–5 AVERAGE

Country	Beef[ab]	Feed grain[a]		Ratio
	US $ per 100 kg			
United Kingdom	81.4	Sorghum	5.6	14.5
Syrian Arab Republic	63.9	Barley	5.0	12.8
United States	54.3[c]	Sorghum	4.5	12.1
South Africa	52.4	Maize	4.6	11.6
Argentina	30.0[cd]	Barley	2.7[d]	11.1
Yugoslavia	59.5[ce]	Maize	5.9[e]	10.1
Australia	51.1	Barley	5.6	9.1
Iraq	81.2	Wheat	8.9	9.1
Kenya	42.9[d]	Maize	4.7[d]	9.1
France	64.0[c]	Oats	7.8	8.2
Tanzania	32.2	Sorghum	4.9	6.6
Pakistan	46.3	Sorghum	7.2	6.4
Germany, Fed. Rep.	62.1[c]	Oats	10.5	5.9
Chile	44.9	Oats	8.1	5.5
Sudan	24.9	Maize	4.7	5.3
India	28.4	Sorghum	9.5	3.0

Note: Where price data are available for several feed grains, the cheapest has been selected.
[a] Wholesale price. [b] Slaughter weight. [c] Live weight. [d] Producer price. [e] Supported price.
(FAO, 1968c, p. 98.)

mills. Some 500 million US gallons of molasses (2,680,000 metric tons), equivalent in carbohydrate value to about 2 million tons of maize, were available for livestock feed in the United States in 1966 (USDA, Consumer and Marketing Service, 1967). More recently it has been suggested that, particularly in tropical countries, sugar—in the form of cane juice, invert or final molasses—offers an attractive alternative to cereals in intensive beef production both from the point of view of the favourable price relation between sugar and meat and because of the much higher hectare yields of energy obtainable from sugar cane, as compared with cereals (Preston and Hagelberg, 1967). Due to this advantageous price relationship, the use of sugar as such for livestock feeding has made rapid headway in various countries. In West Germany 281,000 tons (refined value)—13.4% of total domestic sugar consumption—were so employed in 1966/7, while in France 66,000 tons—equivalent to 4% of total consumption—were fed to animals (Statistical Office of the European Communities, 1968a).

The second production factor is in part derived from the first inasmuch as a concomitant of the increasing use of grain has been the rapid growth of a feed-processing industry. This in turn has led, especially in American broiler production, to a vertical integration whereby feed manufacturers or dealers, hatcherymen or poultry processors contract with "bird-tenders" to raise the chicks. The contractors provide chicks, feed and drugs (which are administered in accordance with their directions) and subsequently market the finished product. Together with integration, the size of the operations makes possible efficiencies which have resulted in the steady reduction of consumer prices. Although progress in this direction has been greatest in the United States, poultry and pigmeat production in all developed countries, East and West, is tending towards large-size units, specialization and integration (e.g. Jannermann and Gussek, 1966). Advocates are not lacking who urge that the same methods must be applied to beef production in order to maintain costs at a competitive level (Barnett, 1967).

The third factor operates specifically in those European countries in which dairy cattle provide most of the beef produced. In this case the meat industry is obviously linked to the economics of milk production and the relation between milk and meat prices and between the latter and fattening costs. The meat output is contingent, among other things, on the number of cows and their milk yield, the birth rate and the percentage of calves available for fattening in each generation. The question of increasing meat production faster than milk production in diary herds consequently hinges on the possibilities of raising the birth-rate and of developing new systems such as fattening cows for slaughter after the first lactation (FAO, 1965, pp. 85–88; EWG-Kommission, Generaldirektion Landwirtschaft, 1966; Borsody, 1966).

1.5 CONSUMPTION

The annual *per caput* supply of all types of meat ranges from less than 5 kg in large parts of Asia to over 90 kg in the United States, Argentina, Uruguay, Australia and New Zealand. Real *per caput* income, meat prices *per se* and in relation to those of other articles, cultural attitudes and social conditions are the main factors governing consumption on an individual level, while total demand on a national basis is primarily a function of population. As personal income rises, more money is spent on food in absolute terms, although in accordance with Engel's law the proportion of the total budget allocated for food purchases decreases. At the same time, the pattern of consumption tends to change with economic development, high-quality foods such as meat, dairy products and fruit becoming preferred over inexpensive carbohydrates such as grains and potatoes.

The relationship between changes in demand and income is called the income elasticity of demand. It is measured by an income elasticity coefficient established by studying family budgets which can refer either to physical quantity or money value, the other variable—price—being held constant. Similarly, from statistical market data it is possible to determine the price elasticity of demand in which the variable—income—is assumed to be constant. Thus an income elasticity coefficient of 0.36 means that an increase of 10% in income will cause an increase of 3.6% in the demand (in terms of quantity or value, as the case may be) of the product concerned; a price elasticity coefficient of −0.36 signifies a drop of 3.6% in the demand for a 10% increase in price; and a price elasticity coefficient with respect to a substitute product (such as beef in relation to pork) of 0.36 implies that, *ceteris paribus*, demand of the first will go up by 3.6% if the price of the alternate item rises by 10%. (For an introduction to demand curves; see Lange, 1962.)

As a preferred item of the diet, meat usually has a higher income elasticity than most other foods (FAO, 1965, pp. 68–69). Demand coefficients are closely correlated with *per caput* consumption levels. Generally speaking, the smaller the consumption, the greater the elasticity, i.e. the less meat is eaten the greater the desire to eat more, and vice versa. Data referring to the period 1959–61 with respect to thirty-three countries grouped in four categories according to the income elasticity of the quantitative demand for meat are set out in Table 1.8.

TABLE 1.8 AVERAGES OF INCOME ELASTICITIES FOR MEAT, ANNUAL *per caput* MEAT CONSUMPTION AND INCOME IN 33 COUNTRIES, 1959–61

Country group	Average income elasticity	Average meat consumption (kg)	Average *per caput* income (US $)
Low income elasticities (up to 0.2)	0.15	106	990
Low to medium elasticities (0.35–0.6)	0.50	60	1075
Medium to high elasticities (0.7–1.3)	1.00	24	320
High elasticities (above 1.3)	1.50	10	130

(FAO, 1965, pp. 69–70 and Appendix Table 21.)

The reason why the group of countries with the highest meat consumption placed second with regard to income is that it included Argentina where income is relatively low but meat traditionally cheap and abundant.

National estimates of the income elasticities of demand for beef and veal in terms of quantity ranged from a low of 0.25–0.35 in the United Kingdom to a high of

1.0–1.3 in Greece, Italy, Portugal, Spain, Turkey and Yugoslavia (FAO, 1965, p. 72). A larger number of countries is covered in FAO (1967c, vol. II, pp. 28–33), while detailed data for the United Kingdom can be found in Ministry of Agriculture, Fisheries and Food (1968). An investigation of 160 budgets of single workers in Moscow in 1960 revealed an income elasticity for beef and veal (quantity) of 1.05, against 0.79 for eggs, 0.65 for animal fat and 0.58 for potatoes and sugar (Shvirkov, 1964). As elsewhere, consumption of bread and potatoes tended to decline with a rising standard of living, while the demand for meat, eggs, milk and fruit increased.

On a national plane, however, changes in individual demand are overshadowed by the demographic factor. There is a high correlation between population and the estimated increase in total national consumption. Differences in the expected increase of *per caput* consumption are rarely large enough to overcome this. Hence, taking into account population, present consumption levels and income elasticity coefficients, the largest absolute increases in the total volume of meat consumed for each 1% rise in *per caput* national income could be expected in the United States, West Germany, Brazil, the United Kingdom, France, Italy and Japan (FAO, 1965, p. 71).

The retail price elasticity of total meat demand in the principal importing countries was considered to be of the order of −0.6 plus or minus 0.1. For beef, estimates ranged from −0.7 to −0.8 in West Germany to −1.0 in the United Kingdom (FAO, 1965, p. 74). The flexibility of substitution between different kinds of meat is apparently rather low unless price differences are quite substantial, as in the case of chicken prices (FAO, 1965, pp. 77–78; Ministry of Agriculture, Fisheries and Food, 1968). However, developments in the United Kingdom during 1964–6 would seem to indicate that while consumer demand is relatively quick to switch to cheaper kinds of meat, especially pork and poultry, when beef is dear and scarce, it is slower to readjust when beef again becomes more plentiful. In fact, data for various countries show a growing gap between red meat and poultry prices (Table 1.9), with pork also tending to become relatively cheaper in some cases.

Implicit in these demand relationships and the physical limit of the amount of food that can be consumed by one person is the fact that as income grows, there is a gradual saturation of the quantitative *per caput* demand for a given product. The evolution of meat consumption in the United States (Table 1.10) suggests that possibly only relatively small increments may be expected once the 90 kg mark is reached and that at this point substitutions become rather more important. There is a sustained consumer demand for beef. The rise of 23–24% in the retail prices of pork chops and loin roast between 1960 and 1966 compared with increases of only up to 8% in the prices of representative beef cuts (Tables 1.9 and 1.13), helps to explain the considerable drop in pigmeat consumption, while the demand for chicken has obviously been encouraged by declining prices.

The *per caput* meat consumption of several European countries is shown in Table 1.11. As was to be expected, under favourable economic conditions, consumption grew relatively faster in those countries which took off from an inferior level. Hence it is not surprising that in three of the four principal west European countries, total *per caput* meat consumption during recent years increased not only in absolute terms but also relatively with respect to the United States, with the fastest growth shown by Italy. In contrast, the United Kingdom level in 1964–6, although slightly higher than in 1960 in absolute terms, fell away from the peak reached in 1962–3 and the

TABLE 1.9 RETAIL MEAT VALUES IN THE UK, US AND WEST GERMANY

	1960	1961	1962	1963	1964	1965	1966
Trends in deflated average prices[a] in the United Kingdom							
Beef and veal	100	97	96	95	102	108	108
Mutton and lamb	100	95	94	94	99	100	100
Pork	100	98	92	90	93	90	92
Poultry	100	90	86	81	83	75	73
Average retail prices in the United States (in cents/lb)							
Sirloin steak	108.8	107.0	110.8	109.7	106.3	113.7	117.2
Pork chops	85.8	87.9	89.8	88.2	88.0	97.3	106.3
Pork roast	62.8	63.0	64.1	62.5	61.0	68.7	77.2
Frying chicken	42.7	38.5	40.7	40.1	37.8	39.0	41.3
Labour time (in minutes) necessary for purchase of 1 kg in West Germany[b]							
Beef stewmeat	115	106	96	90	92	93	88
Pork belly	92	85	77	75	71	64	65
Pork chops	145	139	128	126	121	112	113
Frying chicken	124	107	91	89	83	74	70

[a] After deflation by the Index of Retail Prices.

[b] Calculated on the basis of the yearly average of gross hourly wages of industrial workers and consumer price data collected by the Federal Statistical Office. (Ministry of Agriculture, Fisheries and Food, 1968; US Bureau of the Census, 1966, p. 362; US Bureau of the Census, 1967, p. 359; Sackur, 1968.)

TABLE 1.10 CIVILIAN *per caput* CONSUMPTION OF MEATS IN THE UNITED STATES

Year	Total (kg)	Beef	Veal	Lamb and mutton	Pork excl. lard	Chicken	Turkey
		Carcass weight (%)				Ready to cook (%)	
1930	66.3	33.4	4.4	4.6	45.8	10.7	1.0
1940	72.3	34.4	4.6	4.1	46.1	8.8	1.8
1950	76.8	37.4	4.7	2.4	40.9	12.2	2.4
1960	88.5	43.6	3.1	2.5	33.3	14.4	3.2
1961	89.9	44.3	2.8	2.6	31.3	15.2	3.7
1962	90.8	44.4	2.7	2.6	31.8	15.0	3.5
1963	93.9	45.6	2.4	2.4	31.6	14.9	3.2
1964	96.6	46.8	2.4	2.0	30.7	14.7	3.4
1965	94.2	47.8	2.5	1.8	28.3	16.0	3.6
1966 prel.	96.1	48.3	2.2	1.9	27.1	16.9	3.7

(US Bureau of the Census, 1966, p. 86; US Bureau of the Census, 1967, p. 88. For greater detail, including regional differences, see USDA, Agricultural Marketing Service, 1960.)

gap in relation to the United States actually widened. Beef and veal as well as mutton and lamb consumption declined, while that of pigmeat and poultry increased. Indeed, pork displaced beef as the most popular meat in Britain in 1964–6 (Commonwealth Secretariat, Commodities Division, 1967). That this reflects inadequate supplies rather than consumers' choice is shown by the similar, albeit more moderate, fluctuations in beef consumption in other west European countries.

TABLE 1.11 *Per caput* MEAT CONSUMPTION IN SELECTED EUROPEAN COUNTRIES (kg)

	1964/5	1965/6	1966/7
Belgium–Luxemberg			
Beef and veal	22.1	22.8	23.7
Pigmeat	22.4	23.4	24.1
Poultry	7.8	7.6	6.8
All meats, incl. edible offal	61.7	63.7	65.4
France			
Beef and veal	26.5	27.1	27.6
Pigmeat	22.8	23.1	25.4
Poultry	11.2	12.0	12.3
All meats, incl. edible offal	76.4	78.6	80.7
Germany, Fed. Rep.			
Beef and veal	20.8	21.3	21.8
Pigmeat	33.7	33.5	33.3
Poultry	6.0	6.3	6.8
All meats, incl. edible offal	66.0	66.5	67.5
Italy			
Beef and veal	15.1	17.2	18.4
Pigmeat	8.0	7.7	7.9
Poultry	7.3	7.4	7.4
All meats, incl. edible offal	34.9	36.8	38.6
Netherlands			
Beef and veal	17.1	18.7	19.7
Pigmeat	18.4	20.0	19.4
Poultry	3.8	4.4	4.5
All meats, incl. edible offal	45.2	49.2	49.7

(Statistical Office of the European Communities, 1968b)

Coming now to the form in which meat is consumed, there are substantial national differences between, for example, the United Kingdom, on the one hand, and the United States and West Germany, on the other, with regard to the proportion of meat purchased in the natural state or processed as sausages, etc. (FAO, 1965, pp. 78–79). Against this, the spread of supermarkets and centralized retail packaging throughout the world, as well as the wider ownership of home refrigeration and deep-freezing appliances, would appear to constitute a unifying influence. The belief has been expressed that the growth of self-service shops favours beef over pork on the ground that the former looks more attractive in packaged cuts (FAO, 1965, p. 80). The same factor was thought to operate in favour of higher quality cuts with respect to inferior. In any event, increased standardization as a result of the development of big shopping centres and the concentration of wholesale buyers can be expected to lead to greater pressure on the producers to furnish carcasses of uniform size and quality. In the United Kingdom there is an unmistakable trend towards a greater consumption of boned-out beef, which rose from an average of 3.7% of total supplies in 1960–1 to 9.9% in 1965–6 (Commonwealth Secretariat, Commodities Division, 1967, p. 47).

Higher incomes not only result in increased meat consumption but also in a preference for the more tender cuts from young animals. As an example of such consumer discernment, FAO (1965) cited the growing gap between the average retail prices for different beef cuts from prime quality domestic animals in the United Kingdom (Table 1.12). FAO (1965) thought that similar consumer preferences in the United States could not be deduced from retail price developments there on the ground that the intense promotion of processed meats supported the demand for

TABLE 1.12 AVERAGE RETAIL PRICES (IN PENCE/LB) PAID IN MID-OCTOBER FOR FIRST-QUALITY HOME-KILLED BEEF CUTS IN SEVEN LARGE UNITED KINGDOM TOWNS

Year	(A) Sirloin (without bone)	(B) Brisket (with bone)	Ratio A/B
1955	52.6	25.4	2.07
1956	50.5	22.5	2.24
1957	53.4	22.5	2.37
1958	63.5	27.4	2.32
1959	64.3	26.6	2.42
1960	65.0	26.9	2.42
1961	62.3	24.5	2.54
1962	66.3	26.2	2.53
1963	68.1	27.4	2.49

(FAO, 1965, p. 79.)

beef of inferior quality. In addition, the American grading system, which tends to associate higher quality and prices with fatness notwithstanding consumer aversion to fat, may well constitute a confounding factor (cf. Brady, 1957). However, a juxtaposition of American round steak, chuck roast and hamburger prices indicates a comparable trend, which evidently began somewhat earlier than in the United Kingdom (Table 1.13).

This tendency lends added weight from the producer point of view to the economic importance of small variations in carcass composition. As Everitt (1963) pointed out, while such variations may mean less than a penny a pound in meat trade terms, they may spell the difference between profit or loss on a 500 lb carcass. A survey made by Everitt of the prices paid at different body weights at auction markets in the East Anglian area of England in 1956–7 showed that butchers buying cattle on the hoof tended to penalize excess fat by lower prices, reflecting consumer preference for lean meat. In general, price per pound fell as body weight increased, the differences in the

TABLE 1.13 RETAIL PRICES (IN CENTS/LB) FOR SELECTED CUTS IN THE UNITED STATES

Year	(A) Round steak	(B) Chuck roast	(C) Ham-burger	Ratio A/B	Ratio A/C
1940	36.4	23.5	—	1.55	—
1950	93.6	61.6	56.6	1.52	1.65
1955	90.3	50.1	39.5	1.80	2.29
1960	105.5	61.6	52.4	1.71	2.01
1961	103.6	59.4	51.2	1.74	2.02
1962	107.8	62.3	52.1	1.73	2.07
1963	106.4	60.3	51.3	1.76	2.07
1964	103.9	56.8	49.5	1.83	2.10
1965	108.4	59.5	50.8	1.82	2.13
1966	110.7	62.2	54.2	1.78	2.04

(US Bureau of the Census, 1966, p. 362; US Bureau of the Census, 1967, p. 359.)

pattern of the price-weight relations between sexes within breeds, and between breeds, being ascribed largely to the proportion of fatty tissue to be expected in the carcass at different weights.

1.6 PROJECTIONS

Based on trends, estimated income elasticities and assumed rates of growth in population and in *per caput* income, projections are worked out of future production and consumption. A selection of such projections made by FAO, the EEC Commission and the Organization for Economic Cooperation and Development with respect to beef and veal production and consumption in 1970, 1975 and 1985, is reproduced in Table 1.14. It will be noted that the figures differ rather widely in some cases, which underlines the caution that because of short-term changes in production and cyclical medium-term trends, on the one hand, and the various assumptions that can be made with regard to income and population growth, on the other, such forecasts should be taken to indicate tendencies, rather than the balance to be expected in any given year. Moreover, different methods have been employed in elaborating the projections, and the reader interested in making closer comparisons is advised to consult the notes on methodology in the sources cited.

Keeping these reservations in mind, the forecasts provide a guide to the probable course of developments. It seems likely that world demand for meat of all types—and specifically beef and veal—will rise faster than production. Although the industrialized countries of Europe and North America as a whole can be expected to meet the bulk of the increased demand from domestic production, their total deficit will probably grow. This means that the world meat trade will continue to expand, that there will be a sustained import demand for beef and that beef prices will pursue an upward trend, further improving their position in relation to most other agricultural products. Of course the generally favourable outlook for producers and exporters, particularly with respect to beef, does not rule out the possibility of temporary marketing difficulties when a sudden rise of production in the main importing areas coincides with increased supplies from the exporting countries. Among the latter,

TABLE 1.14 PROJECTIONS OF BEEF AND VEAL PRODUCTION AND DEMAND IN SELECTED COUNTRIES: 1970, 1975 and 1985
(1000 tons in terms of carcass weight)

Country	1970		1975		1985		Source
	Production	Demand	Production	Demand	Production	Demand	
Argentine	2648–2695	2095–2129					FAO, 1965
	2640	2050	2800	2050			EWG, 1966
			2942–3020	2237			FAO, 1967c
Australia	1075–1095	678–690					FAO, 1965
	1170	750	1240	750			EWG, 1966
			1250–1300	670–700			FAO, 1967c
			1228	626	1582	742	OECD, 1968
Canada	832–879	817–864					FAO, 1965
	850	840					OECD, 1967
			1008–1060	939–981			FAO, 1967c
			1003	1027	1173	1371	OECD, 1968
Denmark	280–290	85–88					FAO, 1965
	330	100	350	100			EWG, 1966
	235	90					OECD, 1967
			305–315	110–116			FAO, 1967c
			210	99	201	111	OECD, 1968
EEC	4682	4737–5021					FAO, 1965
	4695	5200	5160	5740			EWG, 1966
	4280	4880					OECD, 1967
			4555–4760	5093–5398			FAO, 1967c
			4374	5170	4924	5894	OECD, 1968
France	2074	1628–1692					FAO, 1965
	2090	1800	2340	1900			EWG, 1966
	1900	1800					OECD, 1967
			1990–2100	1826–1916			FAO, 1967c
			1978	1882	2307	2087	OECD, 1968
Germany, F.R.	1257	1404–1487					FAO, 1965
	1245	1600	1300	1770			EWG, 1966
	1250	1440					OECD, 1967
			1320–1340	1546–1638			FAO, 1967c
			1315	1504	1448	1663	OECD, 1968

Greece	38–42	63–70					FAO, 1965
	61	101	81	128			EWG, 1966
	75	115					OECD, 1967
			56–62	88–96			FAO, 1967c
			69	133	102	175	OECD, 1968
Ireland	255–260	50–52					FAO, 1965
	350	125	370	125			EWG, 1966
	375	50					OECD, 1967
			345–355	57–59			FAO, 1967c
			365	56	392	70	OECD, 1968
Italy	802	1185–1280					FAO, 1965
	770	1220	850	1420			EWG, 1966
	580	1050					OECD, 1967
			660–710	1122–1218			FAO, 1967c
			525	1170	590	1435	OECD, 1968
Japan	260–280	290–315					FAO, 1965
	250	275					OECD, 1967
			246–265	377–476			FAO, 1967c
			242	346	451	557	OECD, 1968
New Zealand	330–335	140–145					FAO, 1965
	340	170	370	180			EWG, 1966
			365–403	154			FAO, 1967c
			419	151	524	182	OECD, 1968
Spain	190–200	225–240					FAO, 1965
	210	290	240	340			EWG, 1966
	255	390					OECD, 1967
			260–275	348–388			FAO, 1967c
			230	374	280	478	OECD, 1968
UK	940–970	1610–1645					FAO, 1965
	950	1430	1040	1520			EWG, 1966
	900	1485					OECD, 1967
			1015–1065	1574–1619			FAO, 1967c
			883	1275	1016	1446	OECD, 1968
USA	9165–9580	9565–10080					FAO, 1965
	8850	9570	10450	11150			EWG, 1966
	9600	10200					OECD, 1967
			10460–10780	11350–11720			FAO, 1967c
			9875	11217	12677	14020	OECD, 1968
Yugoslavia	290–310	195–205					FAO, 1965
	305	180	340	200			EWG, 1966
	270	160					OECD, 1967
			325–350	228–255			FAO, 1967c
			284	232	385	302	OECD, 1968

Australia and New Zealand may be counted on to increase their exportable surplus, possibly in part at the cost of stagnation or even reduction of their *per caput* consumption of beef in favour of other meats and fish. Consumption restraints on beef in favour of exports are also likely to operate in Denmark, Ireland and Yugoslavia. But these increased supplies are not expected to be sufficient to meet the additional demand of the developed countries. Moreover, Canada is projected to switch from the surplus to the deficit column. The main potential source is Latin America, but it is considered doubtful whether Latin America, with its own rapidly increasing population, will be in a position to meet the additional needs, even at rising prices. As a matter of fact, although the projections provide for only a modest *per caput* increase of meat consumption in the developing countries, while the growth of production is estimated higher than the rate in the past, it is expected that the internal demand in this group of countries will rise considerably faster than supplies. Because many of these countries lack foreign exchange to import meat, this deficit does not necessarily represent an effective import demand, but is likely to hold back the growth of *per caput* consumption.

The projections thus emphasize the need for technical progress in meat and particularly beef production. More efficient methods of feeding, reduction of the time required for fattening and increased meat yield per animal have caused production in the developed regions to rise faster than in the traditional exporting countries. To achieve a balance between supply and demand internationally at a reasonable price level and provide sufficient food for a growing world population, more intensive methods of beef production will have to be adopted everywhere.

REFERENCES

ANON. (1967) Agricultural producer prices in Europe, *Mo. Bull. Agric. Econ. Stat.*, FAO Rome, **16** (5), 16–20 (May 1967).

BARNETT, B. D. (1967) Vertical integration: Is it good or evil?, *Feedstuffs*, Minneapolis, Minn., 23 September 1967.

BORSODY, L. (1966) Beef and veal production in western Europe: Trends and prospects, *Mo. Bull. Agric. Econ. Stat.*, FAO Rome, **15** (12), 9–18 (December 1966).

BRADY, D. E. (1957) Results of consumer preference studies, *J. Animal Sci.*, **16,** 233.

CENTRAL STATISTICAL OFFICE (1968) *Annual Abstract of Statistics*, No. 105, 1968, HMSO, London.

COMMONWEALTH SECRETARIAT, COMMODITIES DIVISION (1967) *Meat: A review of production, trade, consumption and prices relating to beef and veal, mutton and lamb, pigmeat, poultry meat, offals, canned meat*, London, July 1967.

EVERITT, G. C. (1963) Beef carcase appraisal by jointing, in Tribe, D. E. (ed.), *Carcase Composition and Appraisal of Meat Animals*, Commonwealth Scientific and Industrial Research Organization, East Melbourne, September 1964.

EWG-KOMMISSION, GENERALDIREKTION LANDWIRTSCHAFT (1966) *Lage und Tendenzen der Weltmärkte der wichtigsten Agrarerzeugnisse: Rinder, Rindfleisch*, Hausmitteilungen über Landwirtschaft No. 14, August 1966.

FAO (1965) *The World Meat Economy*, Commodity Bulletin Series No. 40, Rome.

FAO (1967a) *Protein: At the heart of the world food problem*, World Food Problems No. 5, Rome.

FAO (1967b) *Trade Yearbook* 1966, Vol. 20, Rome.

FAO (1967c) *Agricultural Commodities—Projections for 1975 and 1985*, Rome.

FAO (1968a) *Production Yearbook 1967*, Vol. 21, Rome.

FAO (1968b) *Commodity Review 1968*, Rome.

FAO (1968c) *The State of Food and Agriculture 1968*, Rome.

FAO (1968d) *Trade Yearbook 1967*, Vol. 21, Rome.

HANSON, L. E. (1958) Fifty years of progress in swine nutrition, *J. Animal Sci.*, **17,** 1029.

HODGSON, R. E. and BAYLEY, N. D. (1964) Problems in animal husbandry, in *Farmer's World: The yearbook of agriculture 1964*, USDA, Washington, DC.

JANNERMANN, G. and GUSSEK, K.-D. (eds.) (1966) *Grundriss der Ökonomik sozialistischer Landwirtschaftsbetriebe*, Deutscher Landwirtschaftsverlag, Berlin.

LANGE, O. (1962) *Introduction to Econometrics*, Pergamon, Oxford, and Polish Scientific Publishers, Warsaw.

MINISTRY OF AGRICULTURE, FISHERIES AND FOOD (1968) *Household Food Consumption and Expenditure* 1966, annual report of the National Food Survey Committee, HMSO, London.

MOORE, L. A., PUTNAM, P. A. and BAYLEY, N. D. (1967) Ruminant livestock: their role in the world protein deficit, *Agric. Sci. Rev.*, Washington, DC, **5** (2), 1–7.

NATIONAL ADVISORY COMMISSION ON FOOD AND FIBRE (1967) *Food and Fibre for the Future*, report, Washington, DC, July 1967.

ORGANIZATION FOR ECONOMIC COOPERATION AND DEVELOPMENT (1967) *The Market for Beef and Veal and its Factors*, Paris.

ORGANIZATION FOR ECONOMIC COOPERATION AND DEVELOPMENT (1968) *Agricultural Projections for 1975 and 1985: Europe, North America, Japan, Oceania: Production and consumption of major food stuffs*, Paris.

PRESTON, T. R. and HAGELBERG, G. B. (1967) Turning sugar into meat, *New Scientist, London*, 5 October 1967.

SACKUR, M. (1968) Die landwirtschaftlichen Märkte 1967 im Rahmen der Gesamtwirtschaft, in Hasselbach, W. von (ed.), *Die Agrarmärkte 1967 BR Deutschland, EWG und Weltmarkt: Vieh und Fleisch*, Zentrale Markt- und Preisberichtstelle der Deutschen Landwirtschaft GmbH, Bad Godesberg.

SHVIRKOV, V. V. (1964) Coefficients of the elasticity of demand and of consumption, in *Problems of Economic Dynamics and Planning: Essays in honour of Michal Kalecki*, Polish Scientific Publishers, Warsaw.

STAATLICHE ZENTRALVERWALTUNG FÜR STATISTIK (1968) *Statistisches Jahrbuch 1968 der Deutschen Demokratischen Republik*, Staatsverlag der Deutschen Demokratischen Republik, Berlin.

STATISTICAL OFFICE OF THE EUROPEAN COMMUNITIES (1968a) *Agricultural Statistics*, Luxemburg, No. 1, 1968.

STATISTICAL OFFICE OF THE EUROPEAN COMMUNITIES (1968b) *Agricultural Statistics*, Luxemburg, No. 7, 1968.

THOMAS, F. (1963) Relation of beef production economics to carcase appraisal, in Tribe, D. E. (ed.), *Carcase Composition and Appraisal of Meat Animals*, Commonwealth Scientific and Industrial Research Organization, East Melbourne, September 1964.

US BUREAU OF THE CENSUS (1966) *Statistical Abstract of the United States: 1966*, US Government Printing Office, Washington, DC.

US BUREAU OF THE CENSUS (1967) *Statistical Abstract of the United States: 1967*, US Government Printing Office, Washington, DC.

US DEPARTMENT OF AGRICULTURE (1963) *Agricultural Statistics 1962*, US Government Printing Office, Washington, DC.

US DEPARTMENT OF AGRICULTURE (1966) *Agricultural Statistics 1966*, US Government Printing Office, Washington, DC.

USDA, AGRICULTURAL MARKETING SERVICE (1960) *Meat Consumption: Trends and Patterns*, Agricultural Handbook No. 187, Washington, DC.

USDA, CONSUMER AND MARKETING SERVICE (1967) *Molasses Marketing News, Annual Summary 1966*, C&MS–2 (1966), Washington, DC, March 1967.

USDA, ECONOMIC RESEARCH SERVICE (1967) *Livestock and Meat Situation*, LMS–154, Washington, DC, March 1967.

ZALESKI, J. (1968) Haupttendenzen innerhalb der Fleischproduktion Polens, *Internationale Zeitschrift der Landwirtschaft*, Standing Commission for Agriculture, Council for Mutual Economic Assistance, Sofia, No. 4, 1968, 399–401.

CHAPTER 2

Carcass Composition and Quality

2.1 INTRODUCTION

A major theoretical and practical problem of beef production is the lack of an objective definition of what is meant by quality. Barton (1958) considered the butcher to be "the arbiter of carcass quality" and postulated that knowledge of the factors which influenced his assessment of quality was a necessary prerequisite to any beef studies. Pearson (1960) described quality as "that combination of physical, structural and chemical characteristics of meat which results in maximum desirability from the standpoint of appearance and eatability". Neither of these definitions differs materially from the subjective views of Hammond and Mansfield (1936) that quality was "that which members of the public like and butchers can sell best" or of Hammond (1952a) as "that for which the consumer is consistently prepared to pay the most". These very general definitions must, of course, be qualified in relation to specific markets, national tastes, price considerations and the effect of advertising and presentation. For example, in these days of increasing supermarket sales, the consumer is much less personally advised by the butcher as to what is quality, but responds to multiple motivations, among them convenience, previous experience and economy.

Assuming that the consumer is the ultimate arbiter of quality, we are still faced with the difficulty of catering for widely differing consumer requirements. Broadly speaking, there are three classes of consumer:

(1) general (usually a housewife);
(2) luxury (the hotel and shipping trades and butchers supplying an exclusive clientele);
(3) processing industry.

The interest of the manufacturer is confined almost exclusively to the degree of leanness. The average consumer places equal emphasis on the absence of fat, but also looks for eatability and attractiveness. The luxury trade, on the other hand, is concerned first and foremost with eatability to the extent of accepting an extensive fat cover in the belief that this is necessary for best flavour and juiciness.

In real terms, therefore, the intensive beef producer has to provide primarily carcasses with minimum fat content and concern himself to a lesser extent with qualities of attractiveness and eatability. The requirements of the luxury trade, as it is constituted at the moment, are best left to the small-scale traditional farmer to whom enterprise costing is less important than the aesthetic satisfaction of raising "quality" cattle.

The four major elements determining the quality of the beef animal are: size or weight, body composition, attractiveness of the meat and eatability. In the ensuing discussion each of these is considered separately in relation to the factors which influence it.

2.2 BODY WEIGHT

2.2.1 Requirements

If unit value remained constant over the whole range of live weight, it would be most efficient, purely from the point of view of marketing, to produce as heavy an animal as possible. However, prices vary widely. In a study of some 12,000 cattle in East Anglia, Everitt (1958) showed live weight to be the most important determinant of price. Prices per unit of live weight declined as live weight increased, but more so in heifers than in steers. Prices varied less between grades than between live weights and the effect of breed or cross was least important. Everitt considered the price–weight variations to be largely a reflection of the expected fat content of the carcass. However fatness is not the only factor, since within a given carcass grade the price per kg of meat declines with increasing carcass weight. This trend is illustrated in the average wholesale prices at major markets in the UK in October, 1969 (Table 2.1). The preference for a comparatively small carcass is related to the growing supermarket trade, for which too large a muscle mass necessitates extra cutting with its resultant packaging problems.

TABLE 2.1 CARCASS WEIGHT IN RELATION TO AVERAGE WHOLESALE PRICES OF FIRST QUALITY BEEF AT PRINCIPAL MARKETS IN THE UK FOR THE WEEK ENDING 4 OCTOBER 1969 (COURTESY OF THOS. BORTHWICK & SONS, LONDON)

Carcass weight (kg)	Average price (cents/kg)
204	92.4
227	90.2
250	88.0
272	85.8
295	83.6
318	82.4

2.2.2 Dressing percentage

Almost all measures of efficiency pertaining to commercial production are related to final live weight at the farm or feedlot. It is, however, the weight of the cold carcass which ultimately determines the price paid to the producer. The relationship between live weight and cold carcass weight, i.e. the dressing percentage, is therefore supremely important.

2.2.2.1 Nutrition. The most important determinant of dressing percentage is the type of diet. Stobo (1964) found an association in calves between fibre content of the diet and rumen fill (Table 2.2) which, in adult animals, would result in large differences in dressing percentage. Reid *et al.* (1963) showed that the contents of the gastro-intestinal tract could account for up to 30% of live weight, depending on the nutritional regime. The significance of these findings is demonstrated by results from

Table 2.2 Effect of Diet on the Contents of the Alimentary Tract of Calves (after Stobo, 1964)

Age (months)	Live weight (kg)	Type of diet	Contents of alimentary tract (% of live weight)
3–4	110	Cow's milk	3.6
4	106	All-concentrate	10.8
3	77	Hay plus 2.30 kg concentrates	14.7
3	70	Hay plus 1.40 kg concentrates	18.6
3	59	Hay plus 0.45 kg concentrates	23.3
4	69	Hay only	26.9

Brahman cattle which on high forage diets had an average dressing percentage of 52.0 compared with 55.8 when only concentrates were given (Preston and Willis, 1969). Similar results were obtained by McCroskey *et al.* (1961), who compared roughage/concentrate ratios of 4:1 and 1:4, and Swann and Lamming (1967), who fed Friesian steers on complete pelleted diets with different proportions of ground barley straw. The differences in dressing percentage reported by Palmer *et al.* (1957) in steers on pasture or drylot given *ad libitum* or restricted concentrates also probably stem from variations in rumen fill.

Even with high energy diets with minimal roughage, an increase in energy concentration is known to raise dressing percentage (Guenther *et al.*, 1962, 1965; Bucy and Bennion, 1962; Luitingh, 1963; Preston *et al.*, 1963a; Breidenstein *et al.*, 1965). These higher carcass yields were associated with increased fat deposition and it has been shown by Guilbert *et al.* (1944), Winchester *et al.* (1957) and Hendrickson (1962) that when carcass weight and fatness are held constant, dressing percentage is not affected by plane of energy nutrition *per se*. It is probable that the reported changes in dressing percentage due to differences in protein content in isocaloric diets (Summers *et al.*, 1960; Carroll *et al.*, 1964) can also be explained by dietary effects on carcass weight and fatness.

Compensatory growth is not considered to have any effect upon dressing percentage (Winchester and Howe, 1955; Carroll *et al.*, 1963a; Meyer *et al.*, 1965). The reduction observed by Butterfield (1966) was confounded with a lower carcass fatness.

2.2.2.2 Age and Live Weight. It is axiomatic that carcass weight increases with live weight and a linear relationship ($r = 0.83 \pm 0.03$) for these two variables has been given by Willis *et al.* (1968). A similar linear relation between carcass weight and empty body weight in sheep has been described by Tulloh (1964), who showed further that the plot of dressing percentage against empty body weight took the form of a hyperbola (Fig. 2.1). Seebeck and Tulloh (1966) quoted additional data to substantiate the claim that dressing percentage increased with live weight, as did Field and Schoonover (1967) and Breidenstein *et al.* (1965). (See Tables 2.3 and 2.11.)

TABLE 2.3 RELATIONSHIP BETWEEN LIVE WEIGHT AND DRESSING PERCENTAGE (AFTER FIELD AND SCHOONOVER, 1967)

Live weight range (kg)	No. of animals	Dressing percentage (of starved live weight)
91–135	3	51.4
136–180	8	52.4
181–226	27	52.4
227–271	26	55.7
272–317	64	56.3
318–362	97	56.4
363–407	52	57.8
448–453	18	59.1
454–498	26	58.8
499–543	23	60.3
544–589	10	59.9

Willis *et al.* (1968) were not able to demonstrate any such relation in 137 Brahman cattle over the more limited range of 350–430 kg live weight, but their cattle varied little in fatness and, as shown by Helser *et al.* (1930), Callow (1949) and Good *et al.* (1961), a major determinant of dressing percentage is carcass fatness.

Since body weight generally increases with age, one would expect a positive relation between age and dressing percentage. Levi *et al.* (1967) with 525 Holstein bulls demonstrated an increase in dressing percentage with increasing age, even though weight was held constant and carcass weight excluded non-saleable fat.

2.2.2.3 SEX. In a comparison between Holstein bulls and steers slaughtered at 360 or 450 kg live weight, the former had lower dressing percentages due to heavier hides and reduced fatness (Nichols *et al.*, 1964). Heavier hides in bulls have also been reported by Peregoncuk (1962) and Ivanov and Zahariev (1964). Using Friesian dizygous twins, Preston *et al.* (1968b) reported no difference in dressing percentage between bulls and steers slaughtered at the same live weight and significant advantages in favour of bulls when slaughter was at the same age and the bulls were heavier. Field *et al.* (1964b) reported similar findings, as did Cahill *et al.* (1956), Harte *et al.* (1965), Ivanor *et al.* (1966), Bailey *et al.* (1966a) and Harte and Curran (1967) for bulls and steers killed at the same live weight.

Heifers are usually slaughtered at lighter weights than steers, but despite such weight differences Preston *et al.* (1963c) reported that they had higher dressing percentages; their carcasses were also much fatter.

2.2.2.4 HORMONES. The general consensus of opinion, covering innumerable reports with a wide variety of diets, is that dressing percentage in steers is reduced by the feeding or implantation of DES or hexoestrol.

Where contradictory results have been obtained, these can often be explained by higher carcass weights in the treated animals. Implantation of bulls with DES did not affect dressing percentage in the experiments carried out by Cahill *et al.* (1956) but gave a 2% advantage for bulls in the work reported by Bailey *et al.* (1966a). Fewer experiments have been done with synthetic oestrogens in heifers, but in general the effect on dressing percentage appears to be similar to that with steers (Clegg and Carroll, 1956).

2.2.2.5 Breed. Traditional beef breeds (Hereford, Angus and Shorthorn) have a higher dressing percentage than dairy cattle, which is to be expected from the greater fat content of the former (Branaman *et al.*, 1962; Preston *et al.*, 1963c; Pearson, 1966).

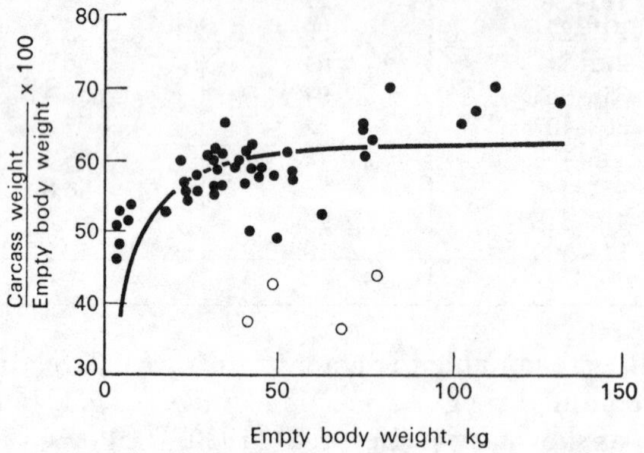

Fig. 2.1 Dressing percentage compared with empty body weight. Hollow circles are data from pregnant ewes. (From Tulloh, 1964.)

Seebeck and Tulloh (1966) found the dressing percentage of Herefords to be lower than that of Angus and Shorthorn. Powell *et al.* (1961) confirmed the superiority of the Angus over the Hereford and attributed this in part to the Hereford's heavier hide. This latter characteristic was also noted by Butler *et al.* (1962), although the difference in dressing percentage did not reach significance.

There is complete agreement as to the superiority in dressing percentage of Brahman × Herefords over Herefords. The difference is consistently between 2 and 4 percentage units and appears to be caused by the lower weights of viscera and rumen fill (Black *et al.*, 1934; Carroll *et al.*, 1955; Hubbert *et al.*, 1955; Butler *et al.*, 1956b, c; Damon *et al.*, 1960; Cole and Ramsey, 1961). Increasing the proportion of Brahman relative to Shorthorn "blood" from 25 to 100% also reduced visceral contents, but a greater weight of hide and heavier feet compensated for this, so that dressing percentages remained fairly constant (Carpenter *et al.*, 1961). It is surprising that Jones *et al.* (1955) reported Brangus steers to dress lower than Herefords since both Angus and Brahman are superior to Hereford for this trait.

Crossbred cattle sired by Charolais bulls had higher dressing percentages than crosses sired by Angus or Hereford, but were similar to Brahman crossbreds (Damon *et al.*, 1960). In Britain the Charolais was superior to the Shorthorn when crossed with Ayrshire cows (Broadbent *et al.*, 1967) and to the Hereford and Friesian when mated with dairy breeds (Edwards *et al.*, 1966). Our own data in Cuba (Willis and Preston, 1969b) with 400 kg bulls slaughtered on completion of performance tests, indicated that Charolais were superior to Brahmans and other breeds. In all these reports the Charolais carcasses contained less fat. Cahill *et al.* (1962) did not observe advantages in dressing percentage for Charolais as compared to Hereford, but there appeared to have been almost twice as much fat in the Hereford carcasses.

2.2.2.6 CONFORMATION. Muscular hypertrophy in Piedmont cattle has been associated with a higher than normal dressing percentage (Raimondi, 1961). This was due to thinner hides and reduced viscera in addition to their greater muscle development. Lighter bone, less fat, thinner hides and smaller feet have also been reported in affected cattle of other breeds (Kidwell *et al.*, 1952; Mackellar, 1960). Mason (1963) agreed with these findings, although in his sample of heterozygous animals dressing percentage was the same.

Lush (1932) and Good *et al.* (1961) have reported relationships between dressing percentage and width between the eyes, while McMeekan (1956) reported decreasing percentage with increasing circumference of the cannon bone. There seems to be no anatomical or physiological explanation for these correlations and they are probably spurious.

2.2.2.7 TRANQUILLIZERS. It is well known that cattle transported long distances to slaughter lose weight on the journey. In the main, loss is in gut contents but tissues can also be depleted particularly if there is associated stress. Tranquillizers have been used in attempts to reduce stress susceptibility, but there is no evidence that at the low levels used there is any consistent benefit (Kercher, 1959, 1960a; Marion, 1959). Moreover there is the risk of inducing a state of semi-sedation which might render the animal incapable of standing, and thus susceptible to suffocation.

2.3 BODY COMPOSITION

2.3.1 Requirements

Since the consumer seeks leanness above all other attributes of meat quality (Sloop *et al.*, 1952; Seltzer, 1955; Prescott and Hinks, 1968) it is obvious that the producer must aim for an animal which at the specified carcass weight (Table 2.1), performs most satisfactorily on this score. Leanness is a very general term and has been interpreted to mean muscle *per se*, or edible meat which includes intra- and some intermuscular and subcutaneous fat. This latter is usually trimmed to a specified thickness in accordance with particular market requirements.

Although knowledge of the total muscle in a carcass has academic interest, the beef producer is only concerned with what is saleable and at what price. It is impossible to envisage a situation in which carcasses are paid for on the basis of total muscle content. But it is quite feasible that one day (it is hoped this point is not so far distant) carcasses will be paid for on the basis of their content of edible meat, with bonuses for attractiveness and eatability.

In the remainder of this section we are concerned with yield of edible meat which is defined as the carcass weight from which bone and obvious tendons and connective tissue and all excess fat have been removed. Acceptable fat cover on meat varies slightly from a maximum of approximately 1 cm for the US market (Bray, 1963) to nearer 0.5 cm in Europe (Brewster, 1968).

Edible meat, as defined above, is subdivisible into two parts which we will refer to as first and second quality meat. This subdivision has economic significance since first quality meat includes those big muscles which by virtue of their intrinsic quality (particularly tenderness and juiciness) are suitable for grilling or roasting and thus command a high price. The remaining second quality meat does have some thick muscles, but is mainly made up of thin muscle or small pieces of muscle of low intrinsic

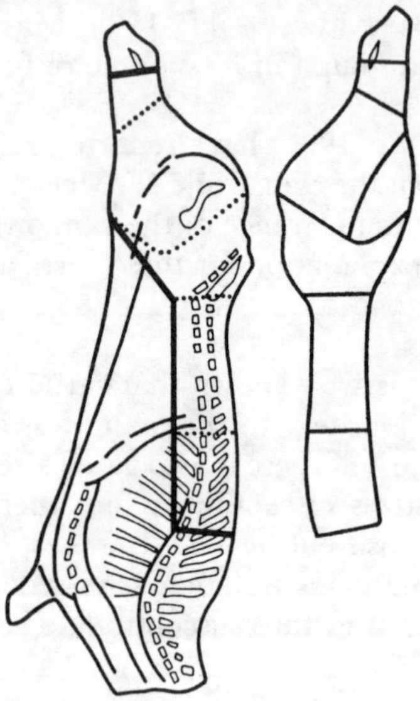

FIG. 2.2 The *pan traité* cut (area within heavy lines) according to Le Guelte *et al.* (1964).

quality. Such second-quality meat is suitable for stewing, boiling or, increasingly, for manufacture into hamburgers, sausages, etc.

The desirable muscles which make up first-quality meat are situated in the proximal parts of the hind limbs and the dorsal area posterior to the 5th rib. If so desired, these parts can be removed in one piece from the remainder of the carcass, thus providing physical as well as economic parameters for carcass evaluation. The advantage of this form of carcass division has been recognized for some time in certain markets and the French *pan traité*, Scottish *gun* and Latin American *pistola* make use of this broad classification. It must be clearly understood that the above separations are general ones and, as commonly applied, still include bone and excess fat. To obtain yield of first-quality meat, these major cuts must be subdivided into smaller joints for removal of bone and excess fat.

Figure 2.2 illustrates the position of the *pan traité* according to Le Guelte *et al.*

(1964). A New Zealand version of this is given in Fig. 2.3 and the Latin American *pistola* cut in Fig. 2.4. The Scottish *gun* approximates to that in Fig. 2.3.

The traditional methods of cutting found in the UK and the US are shown in Figs. 2.5 and 2.6.

The *pan traité* has obvious advantages over the more traditional US and UK systems in that the parts containing the first-quality meat are clearly separated from the inferior sections of the carcass. The major criticism of all these methods is that the cuts still include bone and excess fat—which have negligible value in relation to the edible meat. Elliot *et al.* (1961) attempted to overcome this deficiency by removing the excess fat from their foreshortened version of the *pan traité*. Bone was not removed since primary distribution of meat in the US (i.e. at the wholesale stage) is based on joints with "bone-in".

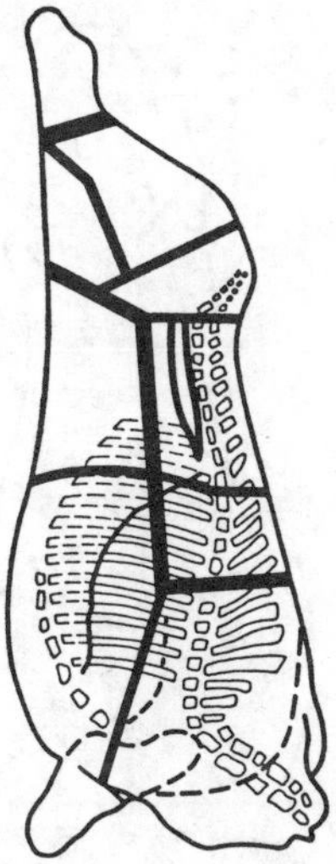

FIG. 2.3 New Zealand version of the *pan traité* (region within the thick cutting line) according to Everitt and Jury (1963).

The anachronistic methods of marketing which still persist in most parts of Europe and the US have undoubtedly retarded progress in beef production. Accurate analysis of carcass worth (i.e. total edible meat) is only possible by carcass dissection. This currently involves financial loss which inevitably limits such evaluations to small-scale operations. It is often argued that the presence of bone at the retail consumer level enables the butcher to classify to some degree the age of the animal, while it is also felt that cooking meat with the bone improves flavour. Since the retail butcher is steadily being replaced by fluorescent display counters and there is no scientific evidence that bone influences flavour, there is less and less economic justification for marketing "bone-in" beef. Indeed, quite apart from the increased transport and refrigeration costs, the bones could be more productively utilized as bone meal for animal feeding instead of ending up in the garbage bin.

Fortunately, marketing methods are changing, and in Australia the increase in boneless beef sales has led to cheaper and more accurate evaluation of edible meat production. It is therefore not surprising that Australian scientists are responsible for many of the recent developments in our understanding of carcass composition.

We have stressed the importance of assessing carcass worth in terms of edible meat and particularly that part which we have defined as first quality. In a later section we deal specifically with the factors affecting edible meat content of the carcass. However, many of these factors are themselves determined by the way in which the animal grows and the interrelations of muscle, fat and bone. For this reason the following sub-sections deal respectively with growth and carcass composition.

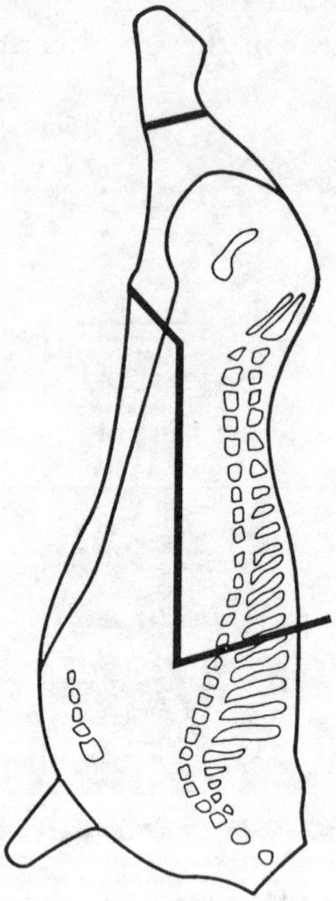

FIG. 2.4 The pistola style of cutting (after Willis and Preston, 1967).

2.3.2 Growth

Our present understanding of growth mechanisms in cattle has its origins in the pioneering work of Sir John Hammond and his associates at Cambridge University.

The major research findings of Hammond and his associates were summarized by Palsson (1955). He postulated that as animals grow, not only do they increase in weight but their body proportions (conformation) change due to different rates of growth of the constituent parts. Palsson described a primary wave of growth which proceeds from the cranium to the facial part of the head and caudally to the lumbar region, while a secondary wave, beginning in the distal parts of the limbs, passes to the ventral region of the trunk, also ending in the lumbar region. The lumbar region was considered by the Hammond school to be the part of the body which matures last.

In addition to this anatomical order of precedence, Hammond and his co-workers stated (Hammond, 1944) that priorities also existed in the allocation of nutrients to the different tissues. The brain, central nervous system and digestive tract had first claim, followed by bone, muscle and fat in that order. It was further claimed, on the basis of work by McMeekan (1940a, b, c; 1941), Brookes and Vincent (1950) and Palsson and Verges (1952a, b), that while mature form and composition were ultimately under genetic control, nutrition—particularly energy level—was the major determinant of both conformation and composition while growth was still active. These theories in turn led to various recommendations: for example, "that it pays to feed the young calf well up to eight months of age for it can then be fattened more profitably than one reared badly" (Brookes and Vincent, 1950); "that major

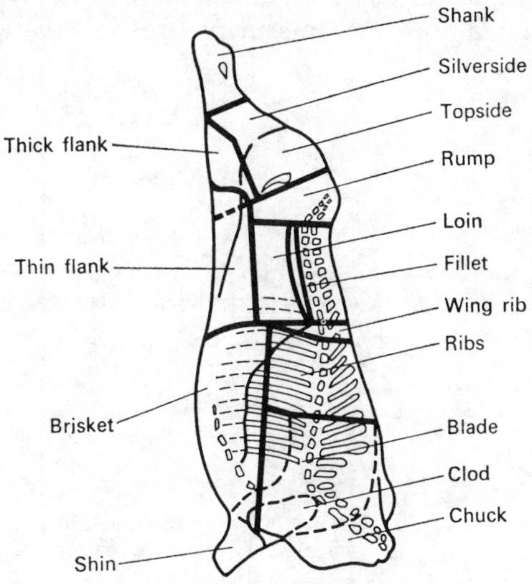

FIG. 2.5 Method of cutting for the UK market (from Everitt and Jury, 1963).

development of back and thigh muscles does not take place until fifteen to twenty months of age" (Hammond, 1960); and that "the most valuable parts of the carcass increased proportionally with increasing age and plane of nutrition" (Hammond, 1952a).

Luitingh (1962) in South Africa was the first to challenge some of these theories, particularly that the loin and lumbar region was the last to develop, and that high levels of nutrition led to greater proportions of high-priced joints (i.e. first-quality meat). His criticism was strengthened by that of New Zealand and Australian workers who employed individual muscle dissection techniques (Walker, 1961; Butterfield, 1964a). Butterfield (1964b) showed that, of the expensive muscles, those in the distal part of the hind limb developed at a relative rate of 90% compared with total muscle, while those surrounding the spinal column grew at the same rate as total muscle (Table 2.4); and that the abdominal—not the loin—muscles developed last. Butterfield further showed that there were no differences in the rate of development of the two parts of the longissimus dorsi muscle, taking the tenth/eleventh rib as the dividing point.

As an animal gets older it increases in body weight and it becomes fatter. All three processes are interrelated and it is impossible to discuss one separately from the others. The rates of increase of live weight and fat deposition are, as indicated by Hammond and his associates, ultimately under genetic control. For example, if Aberdeen Angus and Friesian steers are fed *ad libitum* the same diet, then at any given weight or age the former will, on average, have a fatter carcass (Preston *et al.*, 1963c). This comes about because the Angus is earlier maturing, i.e. it possesses the genetic capacity to synthesise fatty tissue at an earlier age than the Friesian. A similar relationship has been described for Herefords and Friesians by Anon (1966b). The extent to which this genetic potential is expressed in any breed will depend upon the level of energy that is fed, assuming the diet is adequate in other essential nutrients.

The advantages claimed for early maturity are only valid if one accepts the

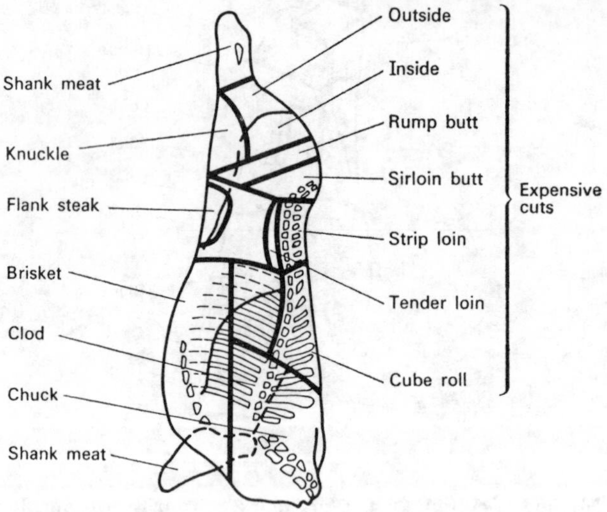

FIG. 2.6 Method of cutting for the US market (from Everitt, 1964).

TABLE 2.4 RELATIVE GROWTH OF MUSCLE GROUPS FROM BIRTH TO 4 YEARS (FROM BUTTERFIELD, 1964b)

Muscle group	Growth relative to total muscle = 100
Distal foreleg	60
Distal hind leg	70
Proximal foreleg	90
Total muscle	100
Muscle surrounding spinal column	100
Thorax and neck muscles attaching foreleg to trunk	103
Proximal hind leg	104
Abdominal	135

Hammond theory that the expensive cuts of meat are late maturing and do not attain maximum development until the overall rate of muscle growth begins to decline in favour of rapid fat deposition. Hammond (1960) postulated that this stage was not reached by beef animals until about 15–20 months. Butterfield (1964b) has shown, however, that not only do the expensive muscles grow with age at the same relative rate as total muscle, but that the major changes in muscle distribution occur before 240 days of age (Table 2.5). Relative changes in the different muscle groups due to age are shown in Fig. 2.7.

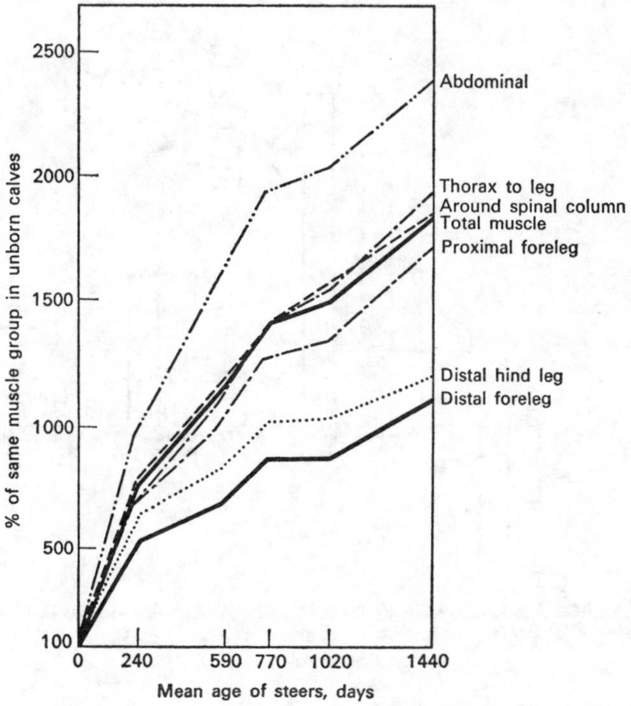

FIG. 2.7 The percentage weight increase of "standard muscle groups" with increase in age: the weight of each muscle group is expressed as a percentage of the same muscle group in unborn calves (after Butterfield, 1964).

TABLE 2.5. CHANGES IN MUSCLE-WEIGHT DISTRIBUTION WITH AGE (AFTER BUTTERFIELD, 1964b)

Age period (days)	Coefficient of variation of percentage weight increase of "standard muscle groups"
0–240	17.5
241–590	8.4
591–770	2.6
771–1020	3.9
1021–1440	3.2

The teaching of the Hammond school that the loin area was the last to develop implies that as animals become bigger, and therefore fatter, the proportion of desirable joints increases. Luitingh (1962), while confirming that fattening increased with age and plane of nutrition, demonstrated that these changes led to a relatively lighter hindquarter and ever-smaller porportions of expensive butcher's joints. However, these changes are to be expected from a study of Butterfield's "fat index" (Fig. 2.8) which shows that as overall fatness increases, the expensive muscles decrease in relation to total muscle. By comparison, the proportion of less desirable muscle rises.

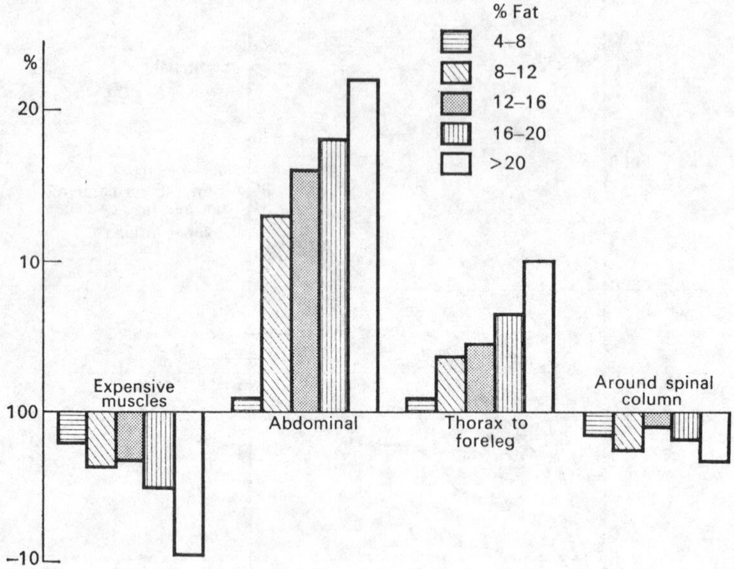

FIG. 2.8 Weights of some muscle groups as percentages of total muscle in steers of different fatness: expressed as deviations from carcass of 0–4% dissectable fat = 100 (after Butterfield, 1964b).

Butterfield (1964b, 1966) also challenged the generalization of Brookes and Vincent (1950) that a high nutritional plane early in life was essential for the proper development of the beef animal. He in fact showed that a period of starvation had virtually no effect upon the relative development of the spinal muscles and the proximal muscles of the hind leg—which produce the first-quality meat—but severely retarded the less valuable abdominal and thorax muscles (Fig. 2.9).

Comparing breeds of widely different external conformation (Fig. 2.10), namely, Poll Hereford, Hereford, Angus, 3/4 and 1/2 Brahman and unimproved Shorthorn (54 animals in total), Butterfield found that the percentage of expensive muscles varied only from 55.4 to 56.8 amongst the breeds, there being no significant breed difference (Table 2.6).

2.3.3 Carcass composition

The work of Butterfield on individual muscle dissection has undoubtedly been one of the most important contributions in the last two decades to our understanding of

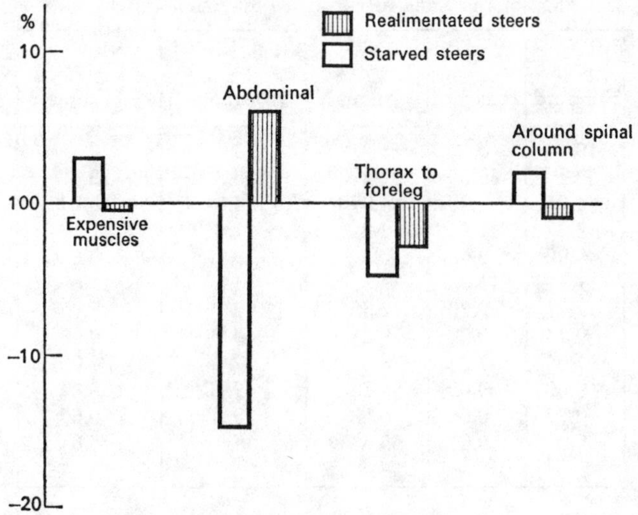

FIG. 2.9 Weights of some muscle groups as percentages of total muscle in starved and realimentated animals; expressed as deviations from control animals = 100 (after Butterfield, 1964b).

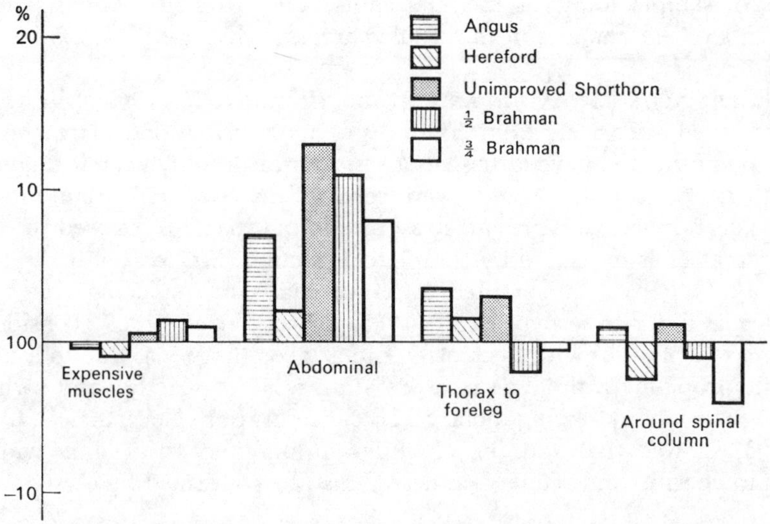

FIG. 2.10 Weights of some muscle groups as percentages of total muscle in steers of different breeds; expressed as deviations from Poll Hereford = 100 (after Butterfield, 1964b).

TABLE 2.6 "STANDARD MUSCLE GROUPS" AS A PERCENTAGE OF TOTAL SIDE MUSCLE IN STEERS (FROM BUTTERFIELD, 1964b)

	Poll Hereford	Hereford	Angus	$\frac{3}{4}$ Brahman	$\frac{1}{2}$ Brahman	Unimproved Shorthorn
No. of carcasses	19	8	5	5	9	8
Proximal hind leg	32.2	32.6	32.2	33.2	33.8	32.2
Distal hind leg	4.95	5.20	4.87	4.61	5.07	4.46
Spinal	12.2	11.9	12.2	11.8	12.1	12.3
Abdominal	9.90	9.69	10.5	9.20	8.85	8.65
Proximal foreleg	11.5	11.0	11.3	11.6	11.0	11.7
Distal foreleg	2.71	2.79	2.66	2.75	2.75	2.57
Thorax/leg	9.14	9.32	9.51	9.09	8.98	9.48
Neck/leg	7.03	7.06	6.61	7.64	7.00	7.42
Neck and thorax	9.59	9.69	9.66	9.70	9.84	10.6
Waste	0.77	0.66	0.58	0.63	0.67	0.70
Expensive muscles	55.9	55.6	55.6	56.4	56.8	56.1

growth as it affects carcass composition. However, a vast amount of research has been done, particularly in the US, on the way carcass composition is affected by the many genetic, nutritional and environmental factors encountered in beef production. Examination of this work is necessary, for although we have stressed the importance of evaluating carcasses in terms of edible meat yield, this parameter itself depends on the interrelations of muscle, fat and bone.

The majority of beef production experiments do not include data on complete separation of whole carcasses and results are more frequently measured on the basis of analysis of sample joints or measurements. The extent to which samples and measurements reflect changes in the whole carcass is discussed in § 2.5.

2.3.3.1 ENERGY CONCENTRATION AND INTAKE. Preston *et al.* (1963c), in studies with Friesian steers fed intensively from 3 months of age, showed that increasing the ME concentration of the diet gave fatter carcasses, as measured by chemical composition of the tenth rib cut. Similar results were reported by Swan and Lamming (1967), who diluted cereal diets with ground straw and found that this reduced the separable fat in the carcasses as measured by complete dissection. McCroskey *et al.* (1961) and Martin *et al.* (1966b) also obtained fatter carcasses by replacing roughage with concentrates as did Klosterman *et al.* (1965a). Weiss *et al.* (1967) considered that increasing carcass fatness with decreasing dietary roughage was due to a narrowing of the acetic/propionic ratio. The interpretation was not strictly valid owing to the confounding effect of increasing dietary ME concentration. Nevertheless, Oltjen and Davis (1963) showed that addition of buffers to all-concentrate diets widened the acetic/propionic ratio and reduced fatness. This was confirmed by Wise *et al.* (1961, 1965).

Reducing total energy intake by increasing the stocking rate on pasture was found by Hull *et al.* (1961) to decrease carcass fatness. The observations of Church and Ralston (1963) that individually fed animals were leaner than those fed in groups can also be attributed to differences in energy intake.

Perhaps of greater importance is the effect of increasing dietary energy concentration, or intake, upon bone content of the carcass. On a weight constant basis, Guenther *et al.* (1965) found that Hereford steers fed on a high plane of nutrition always had less bone than contemporaries given diets of lower energy content. In a study with Holstein steers slaughtered at 454 kg, Martin *et al.* (1966b) obtained a reduction from 20.6 to 17.6% in the bone in the 9th–10th–11th rib joint with increasing energy level. Similar findings were observed by Klosterman *et al.* (1965a) and Swan and Lamming (1967).

These nutritional effects on carcass composition support the tissue priority theory of growth propounded by Hammond (1952b).

2.3.3.2 Compensatory growth. A moderate reduction in energy intake early in life appears to have no effect on ultimate carcass composition provided the restricted animals are allowed to recover on the same diet as their controls (Winchester and Howe, 1955; Winchester and Ellis, 1956; Aitken *et al.*, 1963; Lawrence and Pearce, 1964a, b; Wardrop, 1966). Maintenance feeding between 10 and 15 months, followed by realimentation, had no effect on intramuscular fat, moisture, total protein and ash of psoas major and the semitendinosus muscles in a study carried out by Hill (1967).

The situation would appear to be somewhat different when the restriction is more extreme either in degree (to the extent of weight loss) or in length of time. Meyer *et al.* (1965) and Butterfield (1966) showed that during severe restriction there is depletion of fat reserves; while under extreme conditions, as in the arid regions of Australia, there is also depletion of muscle (Robinson and Lambourne, 1968). In these cases, subsequent realimentation to the same live weight as controls did not restore carcass composition. Fat growth was, however, faster during realimentation which implies that comparable carcass composition would have been achieved if the final live weight had been higher. Pinney *et al.* (1962a) and Carroll *et al.* (1963a) also reported that realimentated animals were leaner than controls but the latter were heavier.

2.3.3.3 Protein. Little critical work has been undertaken in cattle on carcass effects due to variation in protein/energy ratio. Preston *et al.* (RRI, 1965) reported significantly fatter carcasses in Friesian steers fed increasing levels of protein in all-concentrate diets, but attributed these to differences in rumen fermentation, since the protein was in excess of requirements.

Trends towards greater fatness with increasing protein level can be seen in the data of Kelly *et al.* (1963), Keith *et al.* (1965), Haskins *et al.* (1967) and Kay *et al.* (1968). On the other hand, adding urea to a basal all-concentrate diet, deficient in protein, significantly increased the muscle and reduced the fat content in bulls (Preston *et al.*, 1967b) and steers (Morris, 1966).

2.3.3.4 Sex. Comparative US and UK data for bulls and steers are given in Table 2.7. The unanimous agreement that bulls have more lean meat and less fat is confirmed by many other reports (e.g. Matsushima and Sprague, 1963; Rostovcev *et al.*, 1964; Anon, 1965a; Ivanov *et al.*, 1966). Bone content appears to be either the same or slightly higher in bulls.

TABLE 2.7 EFFECT OF SEX ON CARCASS COMPOSITION

Carcass weight (kg)		Lean (%)		Fat (%)		Bone (%)		Authors
Bulls	Steers	Bulls	Steers	Bulls	Steers	Bulls	Steers	
220	221	72.5[a]	61.3[a]	10.1[a]	23.7[a]	17.4[a]	15.0[a]	Raven *et al.*, 1966
227	228	67.8[a]	57.7[a]	16.5[a]	28.3[a]	15.7[a]	14.0[a]	Raven *et al.*, 1966
205	205	64.0	60.9	18.8	23.9	18.1	16.1	Nichols *et al.*, 1964
256	259	63.0	60.0	18.8	23.9	18.1	16.1	Nichols *et al.*, 1964
259	254	51.8[a]	44.1[a]	30.8[a]	40.1[a]	17.4[a]	15.8[a]	Bailey *et al.*, 1966a
276	272	—	—	19.3[b]	28.9[b]	—	—	Bailey *et al.*, 1966a
246	228	—	—	22.7[c]	31.7[c]	4.00[d]	3.99[d]	Preston *et al.*, 1968b
229	237	—	—	20.6[c]	32.7[c]	4.19[d]	4.06[d]	Preston *et al.*, 1968b

[a] 9th-10th-11th rib joint.
[b] From specific gravity.
[c] Ether extract in 10th rib joint.
[d] Ash in 10th rib joint.

The Russian technique of partial castration (Baiburtcjan, 1963) appears to give results intermediate between bulls and steers as regards carcass composition (Robertson and Laing, 1965; Wawrzynczak, 1965). That heifers are even fatter than steers is widely known and has been shown experimentally by Warner *et al.* (1965), Williams *et al.* (1965), Bradley *et al.* (1966a) and Riggs *et al.* (1967).

2.3.3.5 Hormones. The two papers giving complete half side separations of oestrogen treated steers are those of Cahill *et al.* (1956) and Ogilvie *et al.* (1960). The conclusions from these reports that oestrogen treatment, by feeding or implantation, increases the proportion of muscle, or protein, at the expense of fat is supported by a vast body of data based on sample joint separation or chemical analysis (Clegg and Cole, 1954; Andrews *et al.*, 1956; Aitken and Crichton, 1956; Beeson *et al.*, 1956a; Kastelic *et al.*, 1956; Clegg and Carroll, 1956; Everitt and Carter, 1961, 1963; Wallentine *et al.*, 1961; Wilson *et al.*, 1963a, amongst others). In an analysis of the longissimus dorsi muscle of six control and six hexoestrol implanted steers, Lawrie (1960) showed that the major effect of hormone treatment was to decrease intramuscular fat from 3.37 to 2.42%.

There is a dearth of information on carcass effects in bulls fed or implanted with oestrogens. The five American studies that have been carried out (Cahill *et al.*, 1956; Casas and Raun, 1964; Wipf *et al.*, 1964; Bailey *et al.*, 1966a; Hunsley, 1967) show clearly that the effect is quite different to that in steers in that treated bulls were not leaner than controls; the extra fatness, while consistent, was marginal.

As with bulls, there is little information on the effect of exogenous hormones on carcass composition of heifers. Early work with DES implied that there was either no effect or some slight reduction in fatness (Clegg and Carroll, 1956; Kastelic *et al.*, 1956; Kolari *et al.*, 1960). With progesterone-type hormones, such as MGA, all the evidence so far indicates no carcass effect even though growth stimulation has been more consistent with this compound than with the synthetic or natural oestrogens (Bloss *et al.*, 1966; Young *et al.*, 1967; O'Brien and Baumgardner, 1967; Davis and Truesdale, 1968; O'Brien *et al.*, 1968).

2.3.3.6 Breed. In a large-scale trial Damon *et al.* (1960) studied crosses of Angus, Brahman, Brangus, Hereford, Charolais and Shorthorn bulls, mated to cows of the first four breeds in all possible combinations. The data relating to measures of carcass fatness (Table 2.8) show the superior leanness of the Charolais, while steers with Brahman breeding ranked intermediate between Charolais and the traditional British breeds. Similar findings (Table 2.9) were reported by Abraham *et al.* (1968).

In an analysis of 2436 carcasses of steers exhibited at the International Livestock Exposition in Chicago (1956–65), Kauffman *et al.* (1968) confirmed the higher fat content of the Angus, Shorthorn and Hereford relative to all other breeds (Table 2.9).

Kennick *et al.* (1965) and Martin *et al.* (1965) found that Charolais × Hereford had less fat than Hereford, a finding supported by the work of Carroll and Rollins (1965) with Charbray and Hereford, albeit few sires were involved in the latter experiment.

Significantly less separable and chemical fat in the carcass with increasing amounts of Brahman blood ranging from $\frac{3}{4}$ Shorthorn $\frac{1}{4}$ Brahman to pure Brahman—at the

TABLE 2.8 CARCASS CHARACTERISTICS OF STEERS ACCORDING TO THE BREED OF SIRE (AFTER DAMON *et al.*, 1960)

Breed of sire	No. of steers	Slaughter weight[a] (kg)	Fat thickness	Kidney knob	Marbling in L. dorsi
				Scores[b]	
Charolais	44	354	7.3	8.9	4.2
Brahman	42	341	8.5	8.9	4.3
Brangus	43	322	8.3	9.9	5.5
Hereford	47	342	10.2	10.2	6.2
Angus	49	323	10.3	10.3	7.2
Shorthorn	50	344	11.1	11.4	7.2

[a] Adjusted for age of dam and age of steer.
[b] Increasing number indicates more fat.

TABLE 2.9 EFFECT OF BREED ON FATNESS

Breed	No. of steers	Carcass weight (kg)	Marbling (score[a])	Fat-thickness (cm)	L. dorsi area (cm^2)
Kauffman *et al.*, 1968					
Angus	1219	292[b]	8.1	2.4	74.8
Shorthorn	407	293[b]	7.5	2.4	67.1
Hereford	563	297[b]	7.1	2.2	74.2
Red Poll	37	301[b]	6.5	1.5	76.8
Others	210	299[b]	6.2	1.5	76.1
Abraham *et al.*, 1968					
Angus	170	259[c]		1.93[d]	62.3[d]
Hereford	371	186[c]		1.52[d]	60.5[d]
Brahman[e]	37	205[c]		1.47[d]	59.5[d]
Santa Gertrudis[f]	56	239[c]		1.14[d]	58.6[d]
Brown Swiss[f]	36	212[c]		1.12[d]	62.2[d]
Charbray[f]	20	281[c]		0.99[d]	58.3[d]
Charolais[f]	59	250[c]		0.91[d]	64.9[d]

[a] 1 = devoid; 10 = abundant. [b] Hot. [c] Chilled. [d] Adjusted to constant carcass weight of 235 kg. [e] 75% or greater. [f] 50% or greater.

same age and live weight—was also reported by Carpenter *et al.* (1961) and Hargrove *et al.* (1961).

Kidwell and McCormick (1956) analysed the 9th–10th–11th rib joints from 35 Hereford and 39 Holstein steers and obtained significantly more muscle and bone, and less fat, in the dairy breed, which also had slightly heavier carcasses. In complete separations of half carcasses Branaman *et al.* (1962) found significant differences only with respect to bone, which was higher in Holsteins, while Callow (1961) found 3%

more muscular tissue in Friesians than Herefords. However in both these studies the dairy steers were older and heavier at slaughter. Latham and Rogers (1961) claimed that Angus × Friesian steers were fatter than Dairy Shorthorn steers, which in turn were fatter than pure Friesians; however, their measurements were subjective, uncorrected for differences in carcass weight and the feeding systems confounded with breed. Nevertheless there is confirmation of their findings in the more exact study of McCullough and Chestnutt (1965) wherein, at the same carcass weight, the Dairy Shorthorn was significantly fatter than the Friesian.

In a more comprehensive study (Anon., 1966a) Hereford and Friesians were reared alike and slaughtered at fixed age intervals up to 2 years. At each age the Friesians had a heavier carcass, a greater weight of muscle and bone and the same amount of fat. Berg and Butterfield (1968) converted this data by plotting the relevant tissue weight against that of muscle plus bone and found that the two breeds had identical growth patterns for muscle and fat development but that fattening began earlier in the Hereford. The same conclusion was reached by Kruger and Meyer (1967) in a study with Hereford and Black Pied Lowland cattle in Germany.

Complete carcass separations on Charolais × Ayrshires and Shorthorn × Ayrshires showed the former to be significantly leaner (Broadbent *et al.*, 1967). In a large-scale trial in the UK (Edwards *et al.*, 1966) the Charolais × Friesian had 59.3% lean and 21.6% fat compared with 52.3 and 29.5% respectively for Hereford × Friesians. There was little difference in bone (14.6 vs. 13.8%). Since the carcasses of the Charolais crosses were heavier, correction of the data to the same carcass weight would have magnified the differences in leanness.

In Italy, Curto *et al.* (1965) compared Charolais, Chiani and Red Pied Lowland fattened from 180 days to 540–590 kg live weight. The fat in the 7th rib cut was 15.6, 18.4 and 20.7% for the three breeds respectively.

Comparisons within a breed were reported by Gallagher (1963) who showed that progeny of fast-growing Angus sires had more fat than those from slow-growing sires; but correction of his data for carcass weight eliminated these differences. Bradley *et al.* (1966a), comparing a Hereford sire of fast gain and high feed efficiency against a slow-growing sire, found that the progeny of the former had less fat and more lean in the 9th–10th–11th rib cut. This difference existed in absolute terms and per 100 kg body weight. Cartwright *et al.* (1958a) found the opposite effect, in that there was a negative correlation between the percentage of lean in the 9th–10th–11th rib cut and live weight for age at 180 days post-weaning. However, their data were not adjusted to constant carcass weight and, since the steers with the highest live weight per day of age were heavier, their conclusion that "selection for gain should improve carcass grade" is without foundation.

Comprest and conventional Hereford were found to have the same proportions of lean, fat and bone in the 9th–10th–11th rib cut (Skinner *et al.*, 1959). Similarly, Hereford steers and heifers, sired by three long-bodied or three short-bodied bulls, showed no differences in composition of the 9th–10th–11th rib cut when adjustments were made for differences in carcass weight (Cahill *et al.*, 1959).

The above evidence shows that at the same carcass weight the traditional British beef breeds (Angus, Hereford and Shorthorn) are fatter than the Friesian. The data for Charolais imply that it is leaner than either the dairy breeds (Friesian and Ayrshires), the British beef breeds or Brahmans.

2.3.4 Edible meat

2.3.4.1 THE CONCEPT. We have already emphasized the importance of evaluating carcass composition in terms of edible meat content. The studies on growth and carcass composition (§§ 2.3.2 and 2.3.3) enable a better understanding of the theoretical basis of meat production. But although the separable lean and total weight of the muscles are related to edible meat, they are not synonymous. The supermarket does not advertise longissimus dorsi or biceps femoris, nor is it ever likely to. In economic terms, we are primarily interested in the quantity of edible meat in the carcass, particularly that part designated as first quality. With all its imprecision and variability, edible meat must be our yardstick since this is what is bought and sold; and as Miller *et al.* (1965) have shown, edible meat content is highly correlated ($r = 0.87$) with retail value.

The concept of edible meat yield is relatively new. It was introduced by Kropf and Graf (1959b) under the title of "boneless beef yield" and subsequently developed by Durham and his co-workers in Texas and Everitt in New Zealand.

The other measure of carcass quality which has vital economic importance is the proportion of "expensive" meat (Figs. 2.2, 2.3 and 2.4). Early attempts to measure this began in the US in the late 1940's. The term "high-priced cuts" was coined and related to the proportion of round, rump, loin and chuck as separated by commercial wholesale cutting procedures, i.e. including bone and all fat. In 1959 King *et al.* introduced the use of "fat trim and boning-out" and pointed out the significant discrepancy between the proportion of high-priced cuts separated by this method compared with the standard wholesale cutting procedure. Confirmation of such differences came from Brungard and Bray (1963).

Two main definitions appear in the literature as to what constitutes high-priced or first quality meat:

First-quality retail yield (US) refers to round, rump, loin, chuck up to and including the 4th rib. We refer to this as "first quality (RLRC)".

First-quality meat (most other countries) derives from the *pan traité* cut and does not include all the chuck. This is referred to as "first quality".

A somewhat different approach to the study of first-quality meat yield is that of Martin *et al.* (1966a). They separated total muscle into thick (steaks and roasts) and remaining thin muscle. The former contained muscles in the hindquarter which were thicker than 5.1 cm and in the forequarter thicker than 7.5 cm. Applying this technique to ten pairs of choice or standard grade carcasses, they claimed a significantly higher percentage of thick muscle for the former. Aside from the arbitrary assumption that these dimensions categorize first- or second-quality edible meat, the work can be faulted on other grounds. The sample was small and differed markedly in those characteristics for which pairing was claimed, namely, eye-muscle area, fat thickness and carcass weight. The claim that choice carcasses were superior did not take account of the excess fat trimmed from the carcasses and omitted from the analyses, which would have been greater for the choice carcasses. Moreover, the most relevant criteria, namely total muscle as a percentage of carcass weight and thick muscle as percentage of total muscle, were not calculated.

2.3.4.2 Age and live weight. There is little point in discussing age effects on edible meat yield since animals are marketed on the basis of live or carcass weight together with some index of fatness, e.g. visual appearance, grade, etc.

The first comprehensive study of the effect of carcass weight on edible meat yield was that of Kropf and Graf (1959b). They examined 324 carcasses from steers, heifers and cows of varying degrees of fatness and weights ranging from 181 to 408 kg; fat was trimmed to a maximum of 1.25 cm. With increasing carcass weight there were significant decreases in the proportions of edible meat and bone; the percentage of excess fat rose, as did the edible meat/bone ratio. There was no significant change in the relation of first quality meat (steaks and roasts) to total edible meat, i.e. it decreased as a percentage of total carcass weight (Table 2.10).

Table 2.10 Effect of Carcass Weight upon Edible Meat Yield from Steers Grading Good or Choice (after Kropf and Graf, 1959b)

Item	Carcass weight range (kg)			Significant differences
	181–227 (1)	272–318 (2)	363–408 (3)	
No. of carcasses	40	40	40	
Edible meat (% in carcass)	65.4	65.0	62.3	1, 2 > 3
Excess fat (% in carcass)	16.2	17.9	21.1	3 > 2 > 1
Bone (% in carcass)	16.3	15.1	14.5	1 > 2 > 3
Edible meat/bone	4.03	4.33	4.32	2, 3 > 1
Total steaks and roasts (% in edible meat)	57.9	58.9	58.1	NS

Willis *et al.* (1968), in a study of 107 Brahman cattle varying in live weight from 350 to 430 kg and fed concentrates and molasses/urea *ad libitum*, reported that the percentage of total edible meat (fat trimmed to a maximum of 0.5 cm) remained unchanged, but the proportions of first-quality edible meat and bone decreased significantly, while that of excess fat rose significantly with increasing carcass weight.

Over a broader live weight range, Breidenstein *et al.* (1965) reported that the percentage of edible meat did fall with increasing live weight and in other aspects found similar results to Kropf and Graf (Table 2.11).

In an analysis of 307 Hereford steers, Busch *et al.* (1966) found that 75–88% of the variation in edible meat yield was controlled by slaughter weight. Suess *et al.* (1966a) obtained similar results. Nichols *et al.* (1964), using 60 bulls and steers, observed significant reductions in the proportions of hindquarter and round (untrimmed, bone-in) as the carcass weight rose from 201 to 256 kg.

The economic significance of slaughter weight is well illustrated by the work of Stringer *et al.* (1967) who slaughtered cattle in groups of 40 at 28 day intervals beginning at 179 days post-weaning. Over the overall slaughter period of 112 days there was a carcass weight increase of 53.5 kg of which only 29% was edible meat (trimmed retail joints). There was a reduction of 7% in edible meat between the first and last slaughter groups.

Table 2.11 Effect of Live Weight on Edible Meat Yield (after Breidenstein *et al.*, 1965)

Item	Live weight at slaughter (kg)			
	307	386	466	545
No. of steers	32	32	32	32
Dressing percentage	54.5	56.1	57.4	59.1
Carcass weight (kg)	167	217	268	322
Edible meat (%[a])	65.3	64.0	60.6	58.2
First quality (RLRC) (%[a])	50.9	49.3	47.0	44.9
Ether-extractable fat (%[a])	14.4	17.6	24.0	28.6
Bone (%[a])	17.6	16.4	14.9	13.5

[a] % in carcass.

2.3.4.3 Fatness. In the above studies, weight was confounded with fatness. As Everitt (1961) showed, when comparisons are made at similar levels of fatness, the percentage of edible meat does not change with increasing live weight. Bull *et al.* (1930) reported a decline, particularly noticeable in heifers, in the proportion of expensive cuts as the level of fatness rose. Comparing commercial, good and choice grades, i.e. in increasing order of fatness, Kropf and Graf (1959b) showed trends similar to those observed with increasing live weight, except that they were more pronounced (Table 2.12). In the study with Brahmans, Willis *et al.* (1968) found a significant correlation of -0.72 ± 0.05 between the proportions of edible meat and excess fat, which means that some 50% of the variation in yield of edible meat is due to variation in the amount of excess fat. The correlation between first-quality meat and excess fat was -0.76 ± 0.04. Correlations between the percentages of excess fat and first-quality meat (RLRC) of -0.66 and -0.81 were obtained by Zinn *et al.* (1962, 1963a).

Table 2.12 Effect of Fatness (Grade) on Edible Meat Yield (after Kropf and Graf, 1959b)

Item	Grade			Significant differences
	Commercial (1)	Good (2)	Choice (3)	
No. of carcasses	75	80	80	
Range of carcass weight (kg)	181–318	181–318	181–318	
Edible meat (% in carcass)	66.1	64.5	62.9	1 > 2 > 3
Excess fat (% in carcass)	14.9	17.8	20.7	3 > 2 > 1
Bone (% in carcass)	17.1	15.7	14.4	1 > 2 > 3
Edible meat/bone	3.87	4.10	4.37	3 > 2 > 1
Total steaks and roasts (% of edible meat)	58.1	58.4	58.3	NS

Martin *et al.* (1966b) reported no differences in the percentage of wholesale joints from Holstein steers of the same live weight given different concentrate/roughage ratios. There were, however, highly significant differences in carcass fatness and had they applied retail cutting techniques, they would certainly have encountered differences in first-quality meat in favour of the leaner carcasses. The earlier findings of Luitingh (1962) are in general agreement with those given above, as are the conclusions of Tayler (1964) that fattening is detrimental to carcass value since increase in fatness depresses the proportions of both total and first-quality edible meat.

Interesting findings in support of the concept of high plane feeding from weaning were those of Hansen and Zinn (1968) from a study with 128 Hereford steers. There were three fattening regimes, high energy from 192 kg to slaughter or two high roughage diets from 192 to 272 kg followed by high energy. The cattle were slaughtered at 45 kg increments between 272 and 454 kg. At all slaughter weights the percentage first-quality (RLRC) and percentage total edible meat did not differ between treatment groups, but continuous high energy diets also gave greater fat thickness and a larger eye-muscle area.

2.3.4.4 Sex. The effect of sex on some carcass components can be seen in Table 2.13. Steer carcasses yielded significantly higher proportions of edible meat and bone and less excess fat than heifers and cows, but the content of steaks and roasts in total edible meat was the same (i.e. in relation to carcass weight, the yield of steaks and roasts was greater for steers). Comparisons between bulls, steers and heifers (Tables 2.14 and 8.3 (p. 287)) reveal a direct relation between the percentage of edible meat yield and daily gain in favour of bulls followed by steers, with poorest results for heifers. Koger *et al.* (1960), Wipf *et al.* (1964) and Schneeberger (1966) also found that bulls grew faster and yielded a significantly higher proportion of edible meat than steers. Similar results were observed by Field *et al.* (1964b), but it is interesting to note that steers yielded more *untrimmed* wholesale cuts (RLRC) than bulls.

Preston *et al.* (1968b) found significantly more high-priced cuts (rib, loin, rump and round, including bone and excess fat) in bulls as compared with steers. Nichols *et al.* (1964) also reported significant advantages for bulls in terms of the proportion of round, but no difference in that of rib and loin.

TABLE 2.13 EFFECT OF SEX ON EDIBLE MEAT YIELD (AFTER KROPF AND GRAF, 1959b)

Items	Sex			Significant differences
	Steers (1)	Heifers (2)	Cows (3)	
No of carcasses	61	54	60	
Range of carcass weight (kg)	181–318	181–318	181–318	
Edible meat (% in carcass)	65.7	61.3	62.5	1 > 2, 3
Excess fat (% in carcass)	16.2	22.1	20.7	2, 3 > 1
Bone (% in carcass)	16.1	14.6	14.7	1 > 2, 3
Edible meat/bone	4.09	4.21	4.25	2, 3 > 1
Total steaks and roasts (% of edible meat)	58.7	58.7	58.5	NS

TABLE 2.14. EFFECT OF SEX ON EDIBLE MEAT AND EXCESS FAT

Carcass weight (kg)			Edible meat (%)			Excess fat (%)			Authors
Bulls	Steers	Heifers	Bulls	Steers	Heifers	Bulls	Steers	Heifers	
	253	255		62.9	60.0				Breidenstein *et al.*, 1963
			76.1	69.9		8.4	15.4		Cahill *et al.*, 1956
			74.3	69.6					Champagne *et al.*, 1964
234	215		70.4	65.5		12.9	17.3		Harte & Curran, 1967
216	208		71.1	66.2		9.1	13.7		Harte & Curran, 1967
194	176		73.2	71.7		4.6	7.2		Harte *et al.*, 1965
	271	258		71.9	70.1		12.3	15.5	Klosterman *et al.*, 1955
			74.6	67.1	62.7	15.7	22.4	29.0	Warner *et al.*, 1965

The effect of pregnancy in heifers was studied by Brookes and O'Byrne (1965). They claimed no differences between heifers fattened after calving (suckling their calves for 10 weeks or not suckling) and control heifers. Unfortunately their data were not statistically analysed and there was considerable confounding of slaughter weight with treatment and the carcasses were only partially deboned.

The situation with regard to bulls and steers and edible meat yield is well summarized by the work of Bidart *et al.* (1967) in Nebraska which involved 218 Angus bulls and steers. Partial regression analyses showed that bulls consumed 4.57 and steers 8.32 Mcal DE for every kilogram of edible product. In economic terms Riggs *et al.* (1967) considered that bulls produced edible meat at less cost per unit weight than did steers.

2.3.4.5 HORMONES. In a trial with Angus steers, Everitt and Duganzich (1965) found that the implantation of hexoestrol increased the proportion of edible meat due to a related drop in excess fat. Different doses of hormone (30 or 40 mg) had no effect on meat or fat, although the higher level appeared to increase bone content. There were no differences due to hormone treatment in the percentage of edible meat in the *pan traité* area, but lean meat trimmings were significantly higher. As a result, monetary value per unit of edible meat was less with hormone treatment, although this was compensated for by a greater total yield. Cahill *et al.* (1956), Koger *et al.* (1960) and Breidenstein *et al.* (1965) all observed a greater proportion of edible meat in the carcass when steers were implanted. The average effect of hormone treatment in all these trials was some 2–4% increase in edible meat yield. There appears to be no effect in bulls (Cahill *et al.*, 1956; Koger *et al.*, 1960).

In an analysis of 24 Aberdeen Angus steers, Everitt and Jury (1964) found that the *pan traité* cut was heavier in implanted steers than in controls, but no allowance was made for differences in carcass weight which, in fact, accounted for the differences ascribed to treatment. The same error vitiates their findings that the weight of valuable cuts was higher in implanted steers. The only logical conclusion from this experiment is that oestrogen implantation increased rate of gain and hence carcass weight.

Alder *et al.* (1964), using the London and Home Counties method of cutting, reported increases in the proportion of round and rump as a result of hexoestrol treatment. Although they found no effect on the proportion of loin and forerib, these areas carried more fat cover in the control animals. This emphasizes the need in carcass studies to separate edible meat from excess fat if conclusions of economic worth are to be drawn.

Implanting three levels of DES in 80 yearling steers, Ogilvie *et al.* (1960) observed no effect on the proportion of bone and slight non-significant increases in that of rump, foreshank and brisket.

2.3.4.6 Breed. It is a considered opinion of breeders, judges and cattlemen in general that the traditional beef breeds (Hereford, Shorthorn and Angus), because of their so-called "improved" live animal conformation, produce carcasses with higher proportions of the more valuable cuts of meat than undeveloped breeds and dairy animals.

Scientists have sought for many years to verify this belief. Neither Willey *et al.* (1951) nor Stonaker *et al.* (1952) were able to detect differences in the percentage of high-priced wholesale cuts between such widely differing live animal shapes as Comprest and conventional Herefords. Subsequently, Kidwell and McCormick (1956) found only small differences among animals of dissimilar size and shape, but the same weight. No significant differences were encountered between traditional British beef breeds and Brahman crossbreds (Carroll *et al.*, 1955; Riggs and Maddox, 1955; Butler *et al.*, 1956c; Carpenter *et al.*, 1961) or between Herefords and Holsteins (Branaman *et al.*, 1962).

On the other hand, in Sweden, Brännäng (1966b) found that at the same live weight the Friesian had 1.5% more hindquarter than the Red and White which, in turn, had 1.5% more than the Swedish Poll (the hindquarter did not include kidney fat).

Butler (1957), Pierce (1957), Kidwell *et al.* (1959) and Goll *et al.* (1961b) all concluded that hereditary differences in yield of high-priced wholesale cuts were small or non-existent, the major determining factor being degree of "finish" or fatness. Butler (1957) obtained a correlation of −0.5 between estimated fatness and yield of high-priced cuts in animals of different conformation and concluded that "the animal breeder has considerable latitude in selecting animals of different shapes without encountering great changes in the proportion of wholesale cuts".

In Tennessee, Cole *et al.* (1963, 1964) studied wholesale cuts of British and Brahman beef cattle together with dairy cattle and noted few differences. The percentage of wholesale round was significantly less in Angus (21.9) and Jersey (22.3) than in Hereford (23.7), Brahman crosses (24.3) and Santa Gertrudis (23.9). The Hereford was also poorer for this characteristic than Brahman or Holstein (24.7). This confirmed earlier findings of Kunkle and Cahill (1959).

As we have pointed out, the percentage of wholesale cuts does not necessarily reflect edible meat yield. It is true that the studies of Everitt (1964b) indicated no significant variation in edible meat yield due to breed (two pure breeds and three crosses) but he used calves whose carcass weights ranged from only 34 to 114 kg (Fig. 2.11).

That there are variations in total edible meat yield can be seen from the data in Table 2.15. In comparisons between Hereford and Angus the former has always yielded better. There is further support for the conclusion in the data of Powell

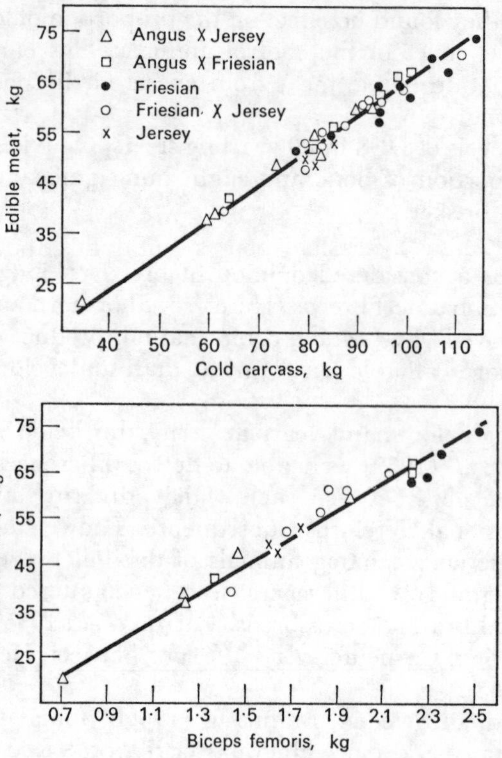

FIG. 2.11 Relation of edible meat yield from 10-month-old calves with (a) cold carcass weight, and (b) weight of right biceps femoris muscle (after Everitt, 1964).

TABLE 2.15 BREED DIFFERENCES IN YIELD OF EDIBLE MEAT (% OF CARCASS)

Carcass weight (kg)	Angus	Brahman	Hereford	Holstein	Shorthorn	Charolais	Authors
235	48.8[a]	51.0[ab]	49.8[a]			51.8[ac]	Abraham *et al.*, 1968
254			27.4[d]	27.7[d]			Branaman *et al.*, 1962
242	60.0			63.0			Breidenstein *et al.*, 1965
242	46.7[a]			48.6[a]			Breidenstein *et al.*, 1965
254	48.6[a]		48.9[a]				Butler *et al.*, 1962
245	64.7		67.1		60.0		Gregory *et al.*, 1966c
245	52.8[a]		55.4[a]		49.4[a]		Gregory *et al.*, 1966c
259	66.1[e]			72.1[e]			Judge *et al.*, 1965
	48.4[a]		47.0[a]			49.1[a]	Kirchner *et al.*, 1968
233, 290			68.3			72.5	Klosterman *et al.*, 1965a
—[f]	61.5[a]		62.7[a]			65.7[a]	Sagebiel *et al.*, 1967b
230		27.4[g]		29.8[g]		32.0[g]	Willis & Preston, 1969b
230		71.5		73.6		76.6	Willis & Preston, 1969b

[a] First quality (RLRC).
[b] 75% Brahman or greater.
[c] 50% Charolais or greater.
[d] Trimmed sirloin, round and porterhouse steaks.
[e] Edible meat in round, loin and rib.
[f] Constant age.
[g] First quality (*pistola* cuts).

et al. (1961) which involved 48 steers of each breed. Although there were no differences in feedlot performance, the Herefords had significantly more meat in the higher-priced cuts. The workers considered "... that the superior Angus conformation scored by the USDA grader actually was related to poorer cutout." Data from 835 steers of 10 breed groups, including Angus, Brahman, Charolais, Charbray, Hereford and Santa Gertrudis were analysed by Abraham *et al.* (1968). Cutability (RLRC as % of carcass) was highest for the Charolais and Charbray with Brahman only slightly poorer; Angus steers had poorest cutability and most fat. Cutability estimated by a variation of the equation of Murphy *et al.* (1960), was higher for steers by Charolais bulls than those by Angus, Hereford, Brahman or Brangus. Steers by Shorthorn bulls were poorest for this characteristic (Brown *et al.*, 1961).

The differences between breeds for this characteristic are almost entirely due to variations in fatness but they are none the less real in that at the same carcass weight, an early maturing breed, e.g. Angus, will yield less edible meat than a later maturing breed such as Holstein.

Dikeman *et al.* (1968c) did not find this to be the case when British breeds and Holsteins were slaughtered at very high weights (318–340 kg carcass). However, they were selected on the basis of comparable fatness, and no data were given regarding nutritional regimes.

The traditional cattleman will still argue that the point at issue is not total edible meat but its distribution, i.e. the proportion found in those cuts considered to be of first quality. Breidenstein and his associates, however, still found no difference in edible meat distribution between Holstein and Angus (Table 2.14). In Switzerland, Schneeberger (1966) also observed no differences in edible meat distribution between Brown Swiss or Simmental cattle. The theoretical reasons why one should not expect differences in yield or distribution of edible meat due to breed or conformation have been explained by Butterfield (1964b) on the basis of his muscle-dissection studies (§ 2.3.2).

It is significant that hitherto published work on edible meat yields has been almost entirely confined to dairy breeds, Brahmans or British beef breeds. With the exception of the work of Dumont *et al.* (1961b), the pure Charolais has been conspicuously absent from meat studies. Data obtained in Cuba (Willis and Preston, 1969b) from performance-tested bulls fed high-energy diets from weaning at 90 days to slaughter at 400 kg live weight show that breeds do differ in their meat distribution (Table 2.16). The results indicate that the Charolais has a significantly greater proportion of first-quality meat relative to total meat then either the Brahman or the Santa Gertrudis.

If, as seems likely, the Charolais is also superior to the traditional beef breeds with respect to edible meat distribution in the carcass, the reason may lie in its evolution. The Charolais, like other breeds originating in western and central Europe (e.g. Limousin and Piedmont), was originally a draught animal and hence early selection should have led to development of a musculature specific to the function of work, particularly the drawing of carts and ploughs. Such musculature would obviously differ from that developed for the show ring. Evolutionary pathways of this nature are in line with the conclusions of Butterfield (1964b) that "the distribution of muscle weight in the carcasses of cattle is the result of functional demands by the animal to meet the challenges of its environment".

TABLE 2.16 THE EFFECT OF BREED ON EDIBLE MEAT CONTENT OF BULL CARCASSES (AFTER WILLIS AND PRESTON, 1969b)

	Santa Gertrudis	Brahman	Criollo	Charolais	Significance level
No. of bulls	8	16	16	19	
Carcass weight (kg)	225	228	231	235	
Dressing (%)	55.2[a]	56.8[a]	57.0[ab]	58.0[b]	*
Edible meat (%)	69.9[a]	71.8[a]	74.8[b]	76.4[c]	***
First quality (%)	26.9[a]	27.6[a]	29.8[b]	32.1[c]	***
Excess fat (%)	13.8[a]	11.5[b]	9.8[c]	7.1[d]	***
Bone (%)	16.2	16.6	15.5	16.6	
Conformation index[e]	38.3[a]	38.4[a]	39.9[b]	42.0[c]	***
Meat/bone ratio	4.34[a]	4.36[a]	4.94[b]	4.60[ab]	**

[abcd] Means in the same row with the same letter do not differ significantly.
[e] First quality as % of total edible meat.
* $P < 0.05$. ** $P < 0.01$. *** $P < 0.001$.

2.4 ATTRACTIVENESS

2.4.1 Introduction

The modern consumer almost certainly is more influenced by the presentation and appearance of meat than formerly, a change probably related to the transition from the butcher's shop to the self-service display counter. Impulse buying is a new feature in marketing and can be exploited by improving the attractiveness of the product.

In the US, Pearson (1960) considered that the four factors contributing to attractiveness of meat were: colour of lean, colour of fat, firmness of cut, and texture. Similar priorities with regard to colour of lean were indicated in the study by Prescott and Hinks (1968) of supermarket sales in the north of England. However, fat colour—while thought to be important in rolled sirloin roasts—was less so for topside round, and had no influence in choice of frying steak.

With respect to colour the consumer, at least in developed countries, tends to have preconceived ideas as to what constitutes desirable colour in meat and fat. Most of us seek in beef a bright cherry red in the lean and white, or creamy white fat which is firm to the touch. Deviations from these popular images are often thought to be due to spoilage or inferior quality although there is evidence that freezing can also affect colour of lean *per se* (Lewis *et al.*, 1968a). Spoilage caused by bad handling and inefficient storage and changes due to freezing technique are problems of the wholesale/retail trade and have been discussed in detail by Lawrie (1966); our concern is with those aspects of attractiveness which can be related to production through to the point of slaughter.

2.4.2 Colour of lean

2.4.2.1 DARK-CUTTING. Although a bright cherry red has been tentatively suggested as the preferred colour, there is almost certainly a fairly wide range of colour acceptance. The one clear exception is beef of a dark red colour—known in the meat trade as dark-cutting beef—which is definitely not wanted. The lightness or darkness of meat is known to be related to its pH. Hall *et al.* (1944) showed that lean tissues were bright at pH of 5.6 and less, and above this became dull and shady, while above 6.5 the meat was dark. Confirmation of the fact that higher-than-normal pH produces a dark colour comes from Howard and Lawrie (1957b) and Bouton *et al.* (1957). Although the latter were unable to detect any change in colour within the pH range of 5.2–5.8, significant darkening was noted by Lewis *et al.* (1962) when pH rose from 5.6 to 5.8.

According to Lawrie (1966) a high pH leads to greater surviving activity of the cytochrome enzymes and since the muscle proteins are above their isoelectric point the water is tightly bound causing packing of the muscle fibres. These two factors prevent the entry of oxygen to the meat and hence predominance of the purplish-red myoglobin rather than the bright-red oxymyoglobin.

2.4.2.2 Stress. The subject of dark-cutting has been studied extensively in pigs since the pioneer work of Callow (1936) who showed that pH and associated differences in colour of lean could be induced experimentally by subjecting pigs to mild transport stress prior to slaughter. The relation between pH and meat colour is now well established (Wismer-Pedersen and Briskey, 1961). It is known that muscle colour in pork is affected by the rate of post-mortem glycolysis and by ante-mortem environmental temperature, feeding and management practices, since all of these affect final muscle pH (Briskey *et al.*, 1960; Briskey and Wismer-Pedersen, 1961; Sayre *et al.*, 1961). The causal factor in raising pH is the reduction of glycogen in the muscle—by extended exercise or stress prior to slaughter—and the concomitant reduction in lactic acid production (Bate-Smith, 1948).

Effects of stress on ultimate pH are more marked in pigs than cattle due to greater glycogen stores (1.5–2.0% of fresh muscle; Howard, 1964a) and resistance to depletion of the latter. Pigs by comparison have glycogen ranging from 0.25 to 0.8%, with the higher value necessitating special sugar feeding prior to slaughter (Briskey *et al.*, 1960). Even fasting steers for 28 days did not reduce glycogen reserves below the critical level (Howard, 1964a), nor did long-continued exercise (Mitchell and Hamilton, 1933). Only prolonged excitement over at least 24 hr, caused by repeated adrenalin injections, or continual goading with an electric probe, consistently produced high muscle pH and dark colour (Hedrick *et al.*, 1959, 1961; Lewis *et al.*, 1962, 1964a). Recovery from this degree of stress was slow and up to 3–4 days were necessary to regain low pH in the meat and the corresponding bright red colour.

There is also the possibility that animals of a highly excitable nature produce dark meat without artificial stress (Bouton *et al.*, 1957).

2.4.2.3 Age and nutrition. It is well known that meat darkens as the animal ages. This has been demonstrated by Tuma *et al.* (1962a) in studies on the longissimus dorsi from cattle aged from 6 to 90 months. Ageing of the meat tended to lower pH with resultant lightening of the colour. Romans *et al.* (1965b) found that the Munsell test value (i.e. darkness) increased with maturity, while hue (i.e. colour) rose with increasing marbling.

Yeates (1965) considered "... that most steers of 18 months would provide meat red enough to merit the description *beef*, while steers as young as 12 months would need to have been pasture reared to do so". Quite aside from the fact that pasture will not provide a sufficiently high plane of nutrition to produce a slaughter live weight of 400 kg at 12 months or less (the norm for "barley" beef) the available evidence (Craig *et al.*, 1959, 1966) shows there is no difference in myoglobin, residual haemoglobin or total pigment between steers fed on pasture or in drylot. Moreover, if anything, the greater intra-muscular fat content of the grain-fed animal, by increasing light reflectance, will tend to make the meat brighten—which is a desirable property. Yeates's opinion that exercise would *improve* the colour of beef is known to be without foundation (Bull and Rusk, 1942).

There is an isolated report that delayed growth due to protein deficiency led to carcasses with paler flesh (Simone *et al.*, 1961), but we found no indication of this in Brahman bulls given diets deficient, or adequate, in protein and slaughtered at the same live weight (Preston *et al.*, 1967b). There is some suggestion that freezing leads to darkening of colour in cooked meat, but the data are not extensive (Howard and Lawrie, 1957a; Lewis *et al.*, 1968a).

2.4.2.4 Sex. A frequent criticism against the use of entire bulls for meat production is that this will lead to a greater incidence of dark-cutting beef. The criticism is probably justified in the case of pasture-reared bulls slaughtered at some 15–18 months. A significantly higher pH was obtained in ribs and silverside from such young bulls, as compared with steers, but there was no evidence of darker colour (Jones *et al.*, 1964b).

Preston *et al.* (1968b) found no differences in the colour of lean between bulls and steers fed all-concentrate diets to slaughter at less than 14 months and similar findings have been reported elsewhere (Anon., 1965b). According to this latter report, semi-intensively reared bulls given rationed concentrates and *ad libitum* roughage and killed at 16–18 months had darker meat than comparable steers. However, Champagne *et al.* (1964) found that lean colour was an acceptable cherry red in bulls and late and early castrates slaughtered at about 14 months. There was an indication of lighter colour in those castrated early but no difference between bulls and late castrates.

2.4.2.5 Hormones. Such evidence as is available on the implantation of steers with hormones suggests that this practice does not affect the colour of lean meat (Williams, 1959; Wilson *et al.*, 1963a). This implies that meat colour differences between aged bulls and steers are not likely to be due to sex hormones *per se*, but rather to their indirect effect of making the animals more excitable.

2.4.2.6 Breed. Breed differences in muscle colour are well established in pigs (Duckworth *et al.*, 1966), but in cattle the picture is less clear. There is some evidence of darker colour in Friesians compared with Hereford crosses (Anon., 1965b), and Damon *et al.* (1960) found a tendency to lighter lean in Charolais crosses compared with Hereford and Angus. On the other hand, Carroll and Rollins (1965) working with Charbrays, Herefords and crosses between them, encountered no evidence of colour differences. Gallagher (1963) found no difference in muscle colour in the progeny of fast or slow-growing Angus sires. It is likely that where breed effects have been found these have been due to differences in the content of intramuscular fat rather than in lean colour *per se*.

2.4.3 Colour of fat

Although US consumer studies by Branson (1957) and Van Syckle and Brough (1958) indicated that yellow fat *per se* was not objectionable, there is little doubt that prejudice against yellow fat is fairly widespread at the wholesale and retail level. Maynard (1937) showed that the yellow colour, particularly in Jersey and Guernsey cattle, was due to storage of vitamin A reserves in the form of carotenoids. Diet also plays a part and grass-fed cattle produce yellower fat than those fed concentrates (Craig *et al.*, 1959). The prejudice is purely aesthetic since yellow fat, by virtue of its carotenoids, must have a higher nutritive value.

Fat colour, as might be expected, does not appear to be influenced by sex (Anon., 1965b), hormones (Williams, 1959), or genetic merit for growth rate (Gallagher, 1963). There is some evidence that blast-freezing produces whiter fat than normal freezing (Howard and Lawrie, 1957a).

2.4.4 Firmness

Soft, watery meat is not liked by the consumer. However, little is known about the factors determining this characteristic. Wismer-Pedersen (1959) and Briskey and Wismer-Pedersen (1961) have shown that soft muscle is associated with the rate of post-mortem glycolysis, ante-mortem environmental temperature, feeding practice and post-mortem rate of carcass cooling. In cattle, Swift and Berman (1959) demonstrated differences in firmness for various muscles and considered water retention to be an effective index. Unfortunately, water retention is improved by high muscle pH (Hamm, 1963) and therefore somewhat antagonistic to eatability (§ 2.5).

Pearson (1966) considered that firmness increases with age, but this may be an effect of increase in fatness (particularly in the intra-muscular fat) and in connective tissue, since Pilkington *et al.* (1960) obtained a correlation of 0.70 between firmness and fat content. Damon *et al.* (1960) observed that steers by Shorthorn sires had firmer lean than those by sires of five other breeds; steers of Brahman breeding ranked lowest. These changes in firmness of lean tended to reflect variation in fat content of the 9th–10th–11th rib cut.

It is to be expected that the firmness of fat will in turn affect the firmness of muscle. Edwards *et al.* (1961) have established that changes in the fatty acid composition of fat depots in cattle can be related to the type of dietary fat, but such effects are less marked than in pigs because of the modifying influence of rumen micro-organisms, whose capacity to hydrogenate unsaturated fatty acids has been demonstrated by Reiser (1951) and Edwards *et al.* (1961).

2.4.5 Texture

This characteristic has declined in importance with the advent of prepackaging as the consumer is less able to measure it at the time of sale. Pearson (1966) implied that coarse-textured cuts are high in connective tissue and are therefore tougher, but it may be that perhaps cuts are coarse-textured because they have more connective tissue! Kropf and Graf (1959a) obtained a correlation of −0.54 between visual texture rating and mechanical shear, which supports the previous point that texture and toughness are related.

There is some evidence that meat from bulls is more coarse-textured than that from steers (Anon., 1965b; Nichols *et al.*, 1964). But treatment of steers with synthetic oestrogens had no effect according to Williams (1959). No differences have been obtained between Herefords and Holsteins (Branaman *et al.*, 1962) nor between progeny of fast- or slow-growing Angus bulls (Gallagher, 1963). However, Damon *et al.* (1960) reported finer texture in meat from steers sired by Angus, Hereford and Shorthorn, as opposed to Charolais, Brangus and Brahman bulls. Similar results relating to Brahmans, Herefords and Shorthorns were observed by Black *et al.* (1934).

2.4.6 Blood drip

The presence of blood drip, i.e. the aqueous exudate from the muscle surface, is of considerable importance in the meat trade and particularly so with respect to pre-packaging and display.

An early report (Alexander and Clark, 1939) was that blood-drip increased with increasing carcass grade (i.e. fatness). It is generally considered that blood-drip is greater when frozen carcasses and cuts are thawed, than with fresh or chilled beef. Marsh (1952) found that the capacity of muscle proteins to retain fluid was improved by slowing down the breakdown of adenosine triphosphate (ATP) during conversion of glycogen to lactic acid. It is well established that blood-drip is less when muscle pH is increased (e.g. Bouton *et al.*, 1957). Unfortunately, increases in pH of meat are also negatively correlated to tenderness, flavour and overall acceptability (Howard, 1964a).

One method of reducing drip without affecting eating quality was to blast freeze before the onset of rigor mortis, using a special blast tunnel operating at −40°C and 305 m/min (Howard and Lawrie, 1957a). However, this has little commercial significance.

2.5 EATABILITY

2.5.1 Definition

Eatability refers to the physical and aesthetic sensations caused by meat in the course of mastication. The characteristics of meat which influence eatability are tenderness, juiciness, aroma and flavour, all of which are affected by production methods. No one combination of these factors is acceptable to all consumers and the very diversity of demand makes improvement and standardization of production difficult. Since eatability concerns the taste and smell of the cooked meat, the consumer can only judge this attribute in retrospect. Early attempts to find some visual indication of eatability led to the choice of marbling, and this still persists, particularly in US evaluation systems, as the main criteria of quality. In many ways this choice was an unfortunate one, for marbling has since been shown to be poorly related to any parameter of eatability other than juiciness, and to this only moderately (§§ 2.5.2.2 and 2.5.3.1).

No alternative visual method of determining eatability has been put forward and this is not surprising in view of the complex nature of the subject. The only way in which the consumer could obtain guidance regarding eatability would be by knowledge of the history of the meat in terms of animal age, method of feeding, post-slaughter treatment, etc. How these factors influence eatability is discussed in the following sections.

Unlike the other aspects of meat quality which lend themselves to some degree of objective measurement, eatability depends mainly on subjective methods, either by taste panels trained to recognize and evaluate tenderness, juiciness and flavour, or consumer preference panels which merely indicate overall acceptability.

2.5.2 Tenderness

2.5.2.1 THE NATURE OF TENDERNESS. It would seem that tenderness (Brady, 1937; Seltzer, 1955) has been and still is (Prescott and Hinks, 1968) the most important single characteristic influencing the acceptability of beef. A great deal of work has accumulated with regard to the physical expression of tenderness and the factors affecting it, but the biochemical and biological changes which decide the degree of tenderness are still imperfectly understood. The problem is further complicated by the fact that the method of cooking can exert a considerable modifying effect (Braniff *et al.*, 1961; King *et al.*, 1968).

It has long been assumed that tenderness is determined by the amount of connective tissue in meat (mainly present as collagen). As far back as 1907, Lehman (cited by Mitchell *et al.*, 1928) considered that connective tissue, rather than muscle fibre, was the major determinant of toughness. Mitchell and his co-workers themselves affirmed that more tender cuts generally had a lower collagen content. Husaini *et al.* (1950a) encountered a significant negative correlation between the amount of alcohol-insoluble protein and tenderness, while Hiner *et al.* (1955), after a histological study of connective tissue, concluded that collagenous fibre influenced tenderness. A significant correlation between hydroxyproline (found to be related to connective tissue by Wierbicki and Deatherage, 1954) and tenderness was reported by Loyd and Hiner (1959). They also found that hydroxyproline content was less in veal than beef and that it increased with age.

The lack of unanimity on the subject is demonstrated by the fact that in 1954 Wilson *et al.* reported a greater collagen content in the longissimus dorsi of veal than of cows or steers, concluding that collagen did not necessarily reflect the degree of toughness. Wierbicki *et al.* (1954, 1955) and Hunsley *et al.* (1967b) also found little connection between tenderness and hydroxyproline, while McClain (1965) did not obtain a significant relation between tenderness and acid, or salt-soluble, collagen. Goll *et al.* (1963) reported no significant changes in the hydroxyproline content of muscle with growing age, although tenderness steadily decreased.

That connective tissue *per se* is not solely responsible for toughness was shown by the work of Hill (1966a, b). Although he obtained a significant correlation of 0.68 between intramuscular collagen and the Warner-Bratzler shear value, he also demonstrated that this was considerably modified by the chemical structure of the collagen and particularly the degree of solubility. For instance, in muscles from 98 cattle between 2 and 84 months of age, there was no relation between total

TABLE 2.17 PERCENTAGE TOTAL COLLAGEN AND PERCENTAGE OF TOTAL COLLAGEN SOLUBILIZED BY HEATING, AS RELATED TO AGE: STERNOMANDIBULARIS MUSCLE OF 42 FRIESIAN STEERS (FROM HILL, 1966b)

No. of animals	Approx. age (months)	Total collagen (%)	Total collagen solubilized by heating 1 hr at 77°C (%)
2	2	2.21 ± 0.31	21.9 ± 0.57
8	4	1.21 ± 0.06	24.6 ± 1.06
5	4.5	1.31 ± 0.11	20.7 ± 1.16
5	4–6	1.75 ± 0.11	21.1 ± 1.16
14	10	1.30 ± 0.26	12.9 ± 0.61
3	22	1.74 ± 0.16	8.5 ± 0.95
1	30	1.51	3.6
1	36	1.67	3.7
2	42	1.20 ± 0.13	4.5 ± 0.41
1	54	1.25	3.7

collagen and age, but a very close agreement between the percentage of collagen solubilized by heating for one hour at 77°C and chronological age (Table 2.17). A decrease in the solubility of collagen with increasing animal age has also been observed in pigs by Carpenter *et al.* (1963).

Verzor (1963) postulated that since collagen does not have a metabolic turnover, molecular movements eventually bring the polypeptide chains closer together and assist cross linkages. Jackson and Bentley (1960) also pointed out that with time the collagen molecule becomes more firmly cross-linked. Goll *et al.* (1964a, b, c), using bovine biceps femoris muscle, noted that the susceptibility of collagenous residues to collagenase digestion decreased with chronological age; the thermal shrinkage temperature of collagen (i.e. the point at which large quantities of soluble collagen are released) was 55°C for veal, rising to 70°C for aged cows.

Joubert (1956a) demonstrated that the number of muscle fibres did not increase after birth, but that there were differences between breeds and crosses in fibre diameter. Several workers have shown, however, that fibre diameter is poorly correlated with tenderness, particularly when the age effect is removed (Brady, 1937; Strandine *et al.*, 1949; Hiner *et al.*, 1953; Tume *et al.*, 1962b; Romans *et al.*, 1965a). This is not surprising in view of the fact that fibre diameter itself varies considerably within the same muscle (Swanson *et al.*, 1965). On the other hand, direct evidence linking fibre diameter with tenderness was given by Yeates (1964) in that emaciated animals exhibited shrinkage of the muscle-fibre diameter and had tougher meat. Subsequent realimentation, however, reinflated the muscle fibres and restored tenderness. Yeates attributed the greater toughness of starved animals to a greater concentration of connective tissue.

Other structural properties of the muscle seem to be more closely concerned with tenderness. For example, cutting muscles from their attachment to the skeleton prior to rigor mortis results in increased toughness, compared with leaving them in place while rigor sets in (Ramsbottom and Strandine, 1949; Paul *et al.*, 1952; Locker,

1960). On the other hand, Marsh (1964) found that neck muscles removed immediately after slaughter, placed in boiling water and cooked for 30 min, were more tender than after normal rigor mortis. These effects were almost certainly due to the changes brought about by contraction of the muscle during rigor mortis.

Confirmation of this thesis comes from the work of Eisenhut *et al.* (1965) and Herring *et al.* (1965b), who reported increased tenderness following stretching of the muscle fibres, while Gothard *et al.* (1966) noted decreased tenderness in muscle which contracted most. The state of contraction of muscles, whether induced experimentally or occurring naturally, was also found by Herring *et al.* (1965a) to be associated with tenderness. Similarly, blast-freezing of muscles, clamping them before rigor mortis, or allowing rigor mortis to take place at 15°C (at which temperature shortening is at a minimum), all prevent the loss of tenderness which accompanies normal rigor mortis (Ramsbottom and Strandine, 1949; Paul *et al.*, 1952). The actual extensibility of muscle fibre is not of importance in determining tenderness according to Wang *et al.* (1956).

The nature of the changes taking place when muscles shorten during rigor mortis is not fully understood, but is certainly related to the composition and state of the muscle proteins, particularly the contractile or myofibrillar proteins, myosin and actin (Szent-Gyorgyi, 1945). Existing knowledge on the role of the various muscle proteins in relation to meat tenderness has been reviewed by Donnelly *et al.* (1966). Protein composition is clearly an important determinant of the biophysical properties of meat, but at the present time no definite conclusions can be drawn.

2.5.2.2 Age. In view of the foregoing findings it is to be expected that tenderness will be closely correlated with age. This has been confirmed experimentally, many workers reporting that meat becomes less tender as animal age increases (see Helser *et al.*, 1930; Brady, 1937; Hiner and Hankins, 1950; Hiner *et al.*, 1955; Jacobson and Fenton, 1956; Dunsing, 1959; Simone *et al.*, 1959; Wellington and Stouffer, 1959; Blackmon, 1960; Tuma *et al.*, 1962a, 1963; Adams and Arthaud, 1963; Goll *et al.*, 1963; Webb *et al.*, 1964; Walter *et al.*, 1965a; Romans *et al.*, 1965a; Kyomo *et al.*, 1966). Over limited age ranges, differences due to age have been less noticeable (Nelson *et al.*, 1930; Graham *et al.*, 1959b; Palmer, 1963, Moe *et al.*, 1964; Ritchey and Hostetler, 1964).

In a study with 134 bulls and 84 steers and heifers, Field *et al.* (1966a) found that age was not an important factor in the tenderness of steers and heifers, but that it was inversely related to tenderness in bulls.

2.5.2.3 Nutrition, fattening and marbling. When animals slaughtered at the same age have been exposed to different levels of nutrition, their carcasses invariably differ in fatness. Thus, in the main, nutritional effects are confounded with fatness and it is more convenient to discuss changes as due to fattening. We put marbling in the same context, since marbling scores, in themselves, reflect different levels of carcass fatness (Good *et al.*, 1961).

The case against marbling as a reliable indicator of tenderness goes back to 1936 and the work of Hostetler and his associates. They were supported subsequently by Hankins and Ellis (1939) who failed to find a significant correlation between intramuscular fat in the longissimus dorsi and shear value. Ramsbottom *et al.* (1945)

encountered no relationship between intramuscular fat and the shear value of raw or cooked meat from 50 different muscle samples. These findings have been substantiated by many other workers and the general consensus is that only 5–11% of the variation in tenderness can be attributed to marbling *per se* (Husaini, 1950b; Cover *et al.*, 1956, 1958; Cartwright *et al.*, 1958b; Loyd and Hiner, 1959; Wellington and Stouffer, 1959; Walter *et al.*, 1963, 1965a, b; Romans *et al.*, 1965a; Gilpin *et al.*, 1966; Slinger *et al.*, 1966). The distribution of the marbling fat also appears to have no relation with the chemical, physical or organoleptic properties of the meat (Moody *et al.*, 1965; Reddy *et al.*, 1968).

Some correlations of tenderness with marbling and other measures of fatness are given in Table 2.18. It is clear from the low correlations in this table that in the normal range of carcasses, fatness has little to do with tenderness.

Where better correlations between tenderness and marbling have been reported, the carcasses were at the extreme ends of the marbling range. Thus Rogers *et al.* (1966) in a study of 305 rib steaks found tenderness to differ significantly as between "devoid" or "traces" and higher scores and between "slightly abundant" and lower scores. The correlations observed by Doty and Pierce (1961) also referred to very fatty

TABLE 2.18 CORRELATIONS BETWEEN TENDERNESS AND VARIOUS MEASURES OF FATNESS

Item	Test	No. of carcasses	Correlation coefficient	Authors
Marbling score	S	84	−.28	Field *et al.*, 1966a
	S	36	−.11	Matthews & Bennett, 1962
	S	96	−.08	Zinn *et al.*, 1961
	S	60	−.05	Reddy *et al.*, 1968
	S	134	.02	Field *et al.*, 1966a
	S	24	.18	Matthews & Bennett, 1962
	P	24	−.13	Matthews & Bennett, 1962
	P	36	−.08	Matthews & Bennett, 1962
	P	536	.11	Palmer *et al.*, 1958
	P	134	.15	Field *et al.*, 1966a
	P	122	.22	Suess *et al.*, 1966b
	P	101	.24	Legg *et al.*, 1965
	P	84	.34	Field *et al.*, 1966a
	P	176	.40	Harris *et al.*, 1965
Ether extract	S	200	NS	Zinn *et al.*, 1963b
	P	60	NS	Cobb *et al.*, 1961
		176	−.38	Harris *et al.*, 1965
		32	.16	Simone *et al.*, 1958a
Separable fat (%)	S		NS	Bowman *et al.*, 1958
	P	98	NS	Kidwell *et al.*, 1959
	P	36	.11	Matthews & Bennett, 1962
		40	.50	Pilkington *et al.*, 1960
Fat thickness	S	330	−.37	McBee & Wiles, 1967
	P	330	.20	McBee & Wiles, 1967
Specific gravity	S		NS	Bowman *et al.*, 1958
	P	100	−.04	Cole *et al.*, 1960b

S = Warner-Bratzler shear. P = Taste panel.

carcasses in the higher grades. It is possible that muscles devoid of marbling come from animals on a low nutritional plane, in which event muscle development *per se* might affect tenderness (see Yeates, 1964). That muscle-fibre diameter was greater in longissimus dorsi steaks with moderate rather than low marbling (Tuma *et al.*, 1967) lends further support to this thesis.

Cooking improves tenderness by hydrolysing collagen (Cover, 1959), and Wang *et al.* (1954) noted that more hydrolysing of collagen occurred in the fattier areas. Blumer (1963) postulated that this might be due to the high heat-carrying capacity of the fat. If Blumer is correct, improved tenderness through marbling would be expected more frequently in very well-marbled carcasses, as in fact was found by Doty and Pierce (1961) and Rogers *et al.* (1966). However, there are little other data to support this.

TABLE 2.19 CORRELATIONS BETWEEN FATNESS AND TENDERNESS AND JUICINESS IN 38 STEERS (FROM COVER *et al.*, 1956)

Cut and method of cooking	Independent variable	Juiciness	Tenderness	
			Panel score	Warner–Bratzler shear
Loin, broiled	Carcass fat[a]	.48**	.24	−.25
	Marbling	.37*	.27	−.22
	Ether extract in *L. dorsi*	.51**	.34*	−.33*
	Ether extract in loin	.38*	.20	−.24
Loin, braised	Carcass fat	.10	.06	−.22
	Marbling	.13	.14	−.19
	Ether extract in *L. dorsi*	.36*	.30	−.34*
	Ether extract in loin	.20	.17	−.28
Bottom round, broiled	Carcass fat	.22	.19	−.15
	Marbling	.34*	.35*	−.28
	Ether extract in *L. dorsi*	.39*	.50**	−.35*
	Ether extract in round	.23	.44**	−.16
Bottom round, braised	Carcass fat	.09	.18	−.20
	Marbling	.15	.37*	−.33*
	Ether extract in *L. dorsi*	.25	.55***	−.52***
	Ether extract in round	.24	.51**	−.52***

[a] Estimated from 9th–10th–11th rib cut. * P< ·05 ** P< ·01 *** P< ·001

Evidence of interaction with the method of cooking is provided by the report of Cover *et al.* (1956) that marbling accounted for more variation in tenderness in rounds that were braised than in loin steaks that were grilled (Table 2.19).

While high planes of nutrition must result in increased fatness, it does not follow that this is always reflected in greater marbling. A high plane of nutrition is beneficial to meat tenderness as shown by results from Texas, Iowa and Cornell (quoted by

Pearson 1963a), Virginia (Graham *et al.*, 1959b; Fontenot *et al.*, 1959) and Florida (Huffman *et al.*, 1962). In all cases, animals on the higher plane of nutrition had more tender meat. Martin *et al.* (1966b) used three diets ranging from *ad libitum* concentrates/limited hay to *ad libitum* hay restricted concentrates and found that the high forage diet led to tougher steaks and, although the animals were leaner, cooking losses were greater. Similar results from replacing forage with concentrates were noted by Graham *et al.* (1959b), Howard (1964b), Riggs *et al.* (1967) and Skelly *et al.* (1968).

In contrast, Wellington *et al.* (1954) observed little relationship between gains and tenderness, neither did Mathews and Bennett (1962), comparing fast and slow preslaughter gains in young animals. Interesting findings were reported by Davis *et al.* (1963a) in that extended feeding to the same fat thickness over the rib, as compared to a continuous high concentrate system, increased marbling but decreased tenderness as measured by shear values.

Exact interpretation of all this research is made difficult by the inevitable confounding of age, fatness and plane of nutrition. Nevertheless, since tenderness undoubtedly decreases with age and is little affected by fatness (5–11% of the variation), it would seem likely that high planes of nutrition—and therefore rapid rates of growth—have a beneficial effect on this characteristic.

Hill (1967) observed that animals subjected to compensatory growth exhibited the same degree of tenderness as did control steers. Although the number of animals involved (10) was too few to permit general conclusions, the data are in agreement with the findings of Yeates (1964).

2.5.2.4 Sex. Early US research on the effect of sex upon tenderness indicated that steers were superior to bulls (Klosterman *et al.*, 1954; Wierbicki *et al.*, 1955). These findings are borne out by some subsequent work summarized in Table 2.20. There are several reports indicating no significant differences in meat tenderness of bulls and steers (Champagne *et al.*, 1964; Wipf *et al.*, 1964; Warner *et al.*, 1965; Woodham and Trower, 1965), and others which describe only minimal differences (Brown *et al.*, 1962a; Lewis *et al.*, 1965), but the general inference is that castration of the male is beneficial for this characteristic. Age is clearly an important factor in expression of tenderness as between bulls and steers, since in the large-scale study reported by Field *et al.* (1966a) differences did not become apparent until after 400 days of age.

Differences in tenderness do not necessarily imply that meat from bulls is always less acceptable (Woodham and Trower, 1965). In a consumer acceptance study in Wyoming, Field *et al.* (1964a, c) placed unmarked rump, rib and chuck roasts and rib, round and loin steaks in six self-service stores at the same price. There were no differences in order of selection except in the case of the chuck roast which was in fact preferred from bulls. Out of 931 replies to a questionnaire, as to whether or not the buyer would purchase the same type of meat again, 89% were in the affirmative for bulls and 91% for steers.

The three experiments reported in Table 2.20 imply that heifers are intermediate between bulls and steers. More recently Riggs *et al.* (1967) considered that while steers and heifers were generally superior to bulls there were negligible differences between them.

TABLE 2.20 EFFECT OF SEX ON TENDERNESS SCORE

No.	Age (months)	Bulls	Steers	Heifers	Test	Authors
27	14	12.3	9.8	11.0	S	Adams & Arthaud, 1963
24	15	13.7	11.2	12.4	S	Adams & Arthaud, 1963
100		4.9	5.8	5.4	P[a]	Legg *et al.*, 1965
20	11–16	5.1	3.9		S	Jones *et al.*, 1964b
94	*c.* 15	7.2	6.4		S	Bailey *et al.*, 1966b
94		6.3	7.6		P	Bailey *et al.*, 1966b
20	*c.* 16	5.0	5.7		P[b]	Cahill *et al.*, 1956
20	*c.* 16	7.5	7.0		P[c]	Cahill *et al.*, 1956
68	12	2.81	3.12		S	Field *et al.*, 1966a
		5.28	5.38		P	Field *et al.*, 1966a
39	15	3.60	3.01		S	Field *et al.*, 1966a
		4.99	5.71		P	Field *et al.*, 1966a
63	18	2.45	3.31		S	Field *et al.*, 1966a
48	22	6.29	4.87		P	Field *et al.*, 1966a
		2.72	3.36		S	Field *et al.*, 1966a
		6.36	4.73		P	Field *et al.*, 1966a
24	14	3.76	3.81		P	Raven *et al.*, 1966

[a] Overall acceptability. [b] 3 days post mortem. [c] 13 days post mortem. S = Warner–Bratzler shear. P = Taste panel.

2.5.2.5 HORMONES. While depriving males of their sex hormones by castration generally leads to improved meat tenderness, the administration of synthetic sex hormones to steers or bulls appears to have no such consistent effect. In steers there is certainly no evidence of improvement in tenderness as a result of hormone treatment and, except for Wierbicki *et al.* (1956) Simone *et al.* (1958b), and Riggs *et al.* (1967), who reported that treatment reduced tenderness, most workers have been unable to detect any changes (Klosterman *et al.*, 1955; Cahill *et al.*, 1956; Deans *et al.*, 1956; Pilkington *et al.*, 1959; Jones *et al.*, 1964a; Bailey *et al.*, 1966b; Hill, 1966a; Hunsley *et al.*, 1967c).

2.5.2.6 BREED. One advantage frequently claimed for traditional beef cattle (Hereford, Angus, Shorthorn) is that they produce meat of better quality than dairy animals. Kennedy *et al.* (1903) were early propounders of this philosophy. However, if tenderness is the major yardstick of meat quality, the claim has only limited support.

Husaini *et al.* (1950a) found the meat of common-grade Holsteins and choice Herefords of the same age to be equally tender. Similar conclusions with respect to these two breeds were reached by Branaman *et al.* (1962). No differences in tenderness between beef and dairy-type steers were observed by Cole *et al.* (1958), while in later work by the same group (Ramsey *et al.*, 1963) the pure Jersey produced more tender meat than some of the beef breeds (Table 2.21). There were also no differences between Angus and Holstein, killed at the same live weight, according to Judge *et al.* (1965). The only evidence in favour of beef versus dairy animals is that of Heck *et al.* (1968). However, the data related to bulls and the dairy animals were heavier.

TABLE 2.21. EFFECT OF BREED ON TENDERNESS: 151 STEERS (FROM RAMSEY *et al.*, 1963)

Breed	Shear values			Laboratory panel score			Family panel score	
	Loin steaks	Round steaks	6th–7th rib roasts	Loin steaks	Round steaks	6th–7th rib roasts	Loin steaks	Round steaks
Jersey	4.40^{b}	5.01^{ab}	12.5	8.09^{b}	7.06^{b}	8.17^{a}	7.59	6.89^{b}
Hereford	5.09^{ab}	4.93^{a}	14.5^{a}	7.58^{ab}	6.68^{ab}	7.72^{a}	6.80^{a}	6.59^{ab}
Angus	5.61^{a}	5.55^{ab}	14.9^{ab}	7.34^{a}	6.30^{ac}	7.66^{a}	6.74^{ab}	6.41^{a}
Holstein	5.24^{ab}	5.25^{ab}	16.4^{b}	7.05^{a}	6.36^{ac}	6.99^{c}	6.67^{ab}	6.47^{ab}
Brahman X	5.41^{ab}	5.89^{bc}	17.4^{bc}	6.83^{a}	5.96^{cd}	6.71^{bc}	6.13^{bd}	6.51^{a}
Santa Gertrudis	6.67^{c}	5.43^{ab}	17.6^{bc}	6.90^{a}	6.47^{ac}	5.90^{b}	5.94^{cd}	6.75^{c}
Brahman	7.09^{c}	6.35^{c}	19.3^{c}	6.07	5.75^{d}	6.11^{b}	5.45^{c}	5.53^{c}

Means in the same column with different superscripts are significantly different ($P < 0.05$).

Within beef breeds and their crosses, Crockett *et al.* (1959) observed the same degree of tenderness in broiled loin steaks from Angus, Santa Gertrudis, Brahman × Hereford and Charolais × Brahman steers. Powell *et al.* (1961) and Butler *et al.* (1962) found no differences between Angus and Hereford, nor did Klosterman *et al.* (1965a) among Charolais, Hereford and their crosses, while in the Argentine, Cabrini and Cavandoli (1964) found Charolais crosses to be equal to those by British breeds. Damon *et al.* (1960) noted that Hereford and Angus were similar to Charolais, both pure and as crossbreds, and that all had more tender meat than Brahman. Dissentient findings are those of Jones (1968) and Ziegler *et al.* (1968). In a comprehensive study in the UK involving 132 animals and 5 different taste panels, the former reported that meat from Holstein and Ayrshire crosses was significantly less tender when Charolais sires were used as compared with Hereford or Devon. The American workers also found meat from Charolais steers to be less tender than that from British breeds.

There is general agreement as to the inferiority of the Brahman with respect to tenderness as compared with other breeds and crosses (Tables 2.22 and 2.23). Supporting evidence can be found in the results of Ramsey *et al.* (1963) (Table 2.21), Huffman *et al.* (1962) and Kincaid (1962) who showed that shear values increased with the percentage of Brahman "blood" in crosses with British breeds. In defence of the Brahman, Howard (1964a) indicated that it performed better with regard to tenderness than the Hereford or Shorthorn—but it also grew faster under what were, possibly, bad environmental conditions.

TABLE 2.22 EFFECT OF BREED ON PANEL TENDERNESS (AFTER PALMER, 1963)

Breed	No. of cattle	% cattle giving score[a] of				
		1–2	2–3	3–4	4–5	5–6
Angus	84	—	2	11	27	59
Devon	12	—	—	—	42	58
Hereford	48	—	2	11	48	40
Shorthorn	122	2	4	38	37	20
Brangus	18	—	5	38	48	10
Brahman	196	3	21	40	27	9

[a] 1 = inedible; 6 = excellent.

Alsmeyer *et al.* (1958) did find that offspring of certain Brahman bulls produced more tender meat than the European-type breeds. Similar differences in tenderness between progeny of particular sires within breeds were observed by Carpenter *et al.* (1955), Cover *et al.* (1957), Cartwright *et al.* (1958a), Means and King (1959) and Meyer (1966). Epley *et al.* (1968a) found that sire differences existed, as judged by Warner–Bratzler shear values and taste panel scores, although these could not be detected in consumer studies. Genetic selection for tenderness is being undertaken at Michigan State University (Magee *et al.*, 1968), but it is doubtful whether this will be of more than academic interest.

TABLE 2.23 EFFECT OF *Bos indicus* "BLOOD" ON TENDERNESS

Test	Brahman	Crossbreds				Santa Gertrudis	Shorthorn	Hereford	Angus	Authors
		Brahman Angus	Sindhi crosses	Africander Angus	Brahman Hereford					
S	12.3	8.8				9.1		8.4	8.6	Burns *et al.*, 1958
S	25.8	19.0	19.7	16.6					15.5	De Rouen *et al.*, 1961
S					9.0			8.1		Cover *et al.*, 1967
P	3.5						4.2			Alsmeyer *et al.*, 1958
S	20.4	15.3			15.7			14.4	14.4	Damon *et al.*, 1960

S = Warner-Bratzler shear (higher value = less tender). P = Taste panel (higher value = more tender).

Genetic differences in tenderness almost certainly exist, but it is probable that these are largely due to genetic variation in growth rate, and selection for faster-growing cattle is both simpler and economically more justified. However, the possibility of a relationship between tenderness and temperament cannot be ruled out, and attention to docility might result in improved tenderness.

2.5.2.7 STRESS FACTORS. The effect of muscle pH on tenderness has been documented by Howard (1964a) (Fig. 2.12). Increasing pH first reduces tenderness and then beyond pH 6.0 tenderness improves again, but with associated "mushiness". The most important cause of high muscle pH (discussed previously in § 2.3.1) is stress. Deleterious effects of periodic electrical stimulation for 24 hr prior to slaughter on the tenderness of the longissimus dorsi have been described by Lewis *et al.* (1962, 1964, 1965). Not all muscles were similarly affected, and the interaction of stress and the method of cooking is an important source of variation (Lewis *et al.*, 1964).

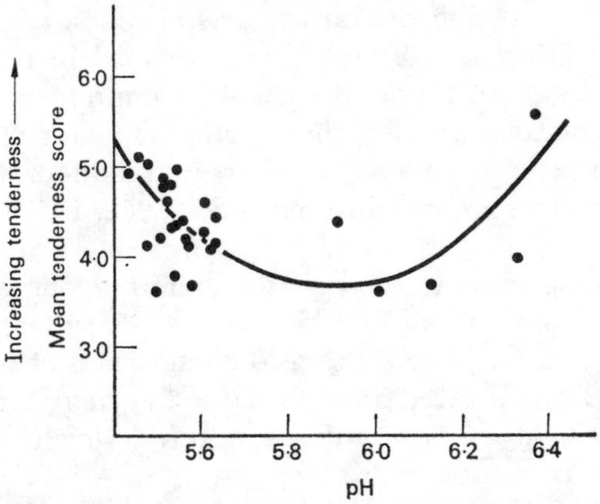

FIG. 2.12 Relation between tenderness and pH (from Howard, 1964).

The importance of temperament in relation to stress was discussed by Howard (1964a) who showed that highly excitable animals had a higher muscle pH in the carcass which gave rise to darker meat. Earlier, Cover *et al.* (1957) in Texas observed that the Brahman bull whose offspring had the most tender meat was gentle and easily handled. In contrast, the bull whose progeny had the toughest meat was unruly and pugnacious. The relationship between the temperament score of heifer progeny from four sires and tenderness ratings of the steer progeny is given in Table 2.24. There is a suggestion that the two traits are related. The thesis is given further support from the findings of Shirley *et al.* (1957) that muscle glycogen—which is indirectly related to ultimate muscle pH—was less with increasing Brahman "blood". In our experience, the Brahman is more excitable than other breeds and its meat is undoubtedly tougher (Table 2.22).

2.5.2.8 SLAUGHTER PRACTICES. There have been two approaches to the problem of improving tenderness by artificial means. Durham *et al.* (1961) injected, under pressure, edible beef tallow into the muscles of the carcass. Injected steaks had lower

TABLE 2.24. RELATION BETWEEN TEMPERAMENT AND TENDERNESS (FROM COVER *et al.*, 1957)

Sires in descending order according to desirable temperament of female offspring	Tenderness (mean of 4 measures)	
	Panel score	Shear force
H 7	7.5	8.4
B 113	6.0	10.0
B 117	7.2	8.5
B 119	5.2	10.9

shear values than controls, but whether this was due to expansion of the muscle or the physical effect of the perforated needles used in the operation is not known. The technique does not seem to have found commercial acceptance.

The second method, involving the intravenous injection of papain (a proteolytic enzyme) immediately prior to slaughter was developed in the US by Beuk *et al.* (1959). Huffman *et al.* (1960) reported significant improvements in tenderness, as evaluated by panel or shear tests, after the injection of 22 mg of crude papain or 0.2 mg crystalline papain per kg live weight. Livers and kidneys were over-tenderized. In later reports by the same group (Huffman *et al.*, 1962, 1967a, b) over-tenderizing was not a problem.

The practice of ageing meat to increase tenderness is long established and finds scientific justification in the work of Wierbicki *et al.* (1955, 1956), Wilson *et al.* (1960) and Doty and Pierce (1961). Differences in the tenderness of bull and steer meat 3 days post mortem had disappeared after 13 days of ageing (Wierbicki *et al.*, 1955). Blast-freezing at −40°C and 305 m/min air velocity, which took 18 hr, produced more tender meat than conventional freezing at −5° to −15°C for 2–3 days or −12° to −18°C for 3–5 days (Howard and Lawrie, 1957a). Freezing *per se* at temperatures ranging from −6° to −29°C had little effect on tenderness according to McBee and Naumann (1959).

2.5.3 Juiciness

Although juiciness is often rated second to tenderness as a contributory factor of eatability, such ranking is purely arbitrary and probably reflects the fact that juiciness is easier to define and test than flavour. According to Weir (1960), juiciness relates both to the initial impression of wetness, due to the rapid release of meat fluid and the longer lasting effect brought about by the stimulating action of fat on the salivary glands.

2.5.3.1 MARBLING. Intra-muscular fat has been shown to contribute little to tenderness. However, a considerable body of work indicates that it is more highly associated with juiciness (Cover *et al.*, 1956; Wellington and Stouffer, 1959; McBee and Wiles, 1967). Doty and Pierce (1961) supported these findings up to the point of a moderate amount of marbling, after which the relationship became less obvious. Romans *et al.* (1965a) also found moderately marbled steaks significantly more juicy than those only slightly marbled. The only dissenting reports were by Tuma *et al.* (1962a) and

Walter *et al.* (1965b), who found no connection between these variables. In a review of the subject, Blumer (1963) reported that although the relationships between marbling and intramuscular fat and juiciness were low ($r = 0.38$ and 0.39 respectively), they were consistent. It appears, therefore, that some 16% of the variation in juiciness is due to marbling fat within the muscle. Some correlations between juiciness and carcass traits are given in Tables 2.19 and 2.25.

TABLE 2.25 CORRELATIONS BETWEEN JUICINESS AND OTHER CARCASS TRAITS

Item	No. of carcasses	Correlation coefficient	Authors
Marbling score	134	.26	Field *et al.*, 1966a
	101	.28	Legg *et al.*, 1965
	84	.32	Field *et al.*, 1966a
Ether extract in longissimus dorsi	32	.33	Simone *et al.*, 1958b
	16	.42	Morgan, 1967
Fat in 12th rib cut (%)	128	−.13 to .03	Suess *et al.*, 1966b
	32	.33	Simone *et al.*, 1958b
Fat depth over longissimus dorsi	330	.24	McBee & Wiles, 1967
Specific graviy of rib cut	100	−.35	Cole *et al.*, 1960a
Total moisture (%)	32	−.35	Simone *et al.*, 1958b
	16	−.19	Simone *et al.*, 1961
Bound moisture (%)	16	.86	Simone *et al.*, 1961
Free moisture (%)	16	−.32	Simone *et al.*, 1961
Water-holding capacity	32	−.44	Moe *et al.*, 1964
Panel tenderness	84	.52	Field *et al.*, 1966a
	80	.53	Romans *et al.*, 1965a
	134	.67	Field *et al.*, 1966a
Shear force	134	−.38	Field *et al.*, 1966a
	84	−.35	Field *et al.*, 1966a
	80	−.32	Romans *et al.*, 1965a
Colour	32	.45	Moe *et al.*, 1964
Firmness	330	.32	McBee & Wiles 1967

2.5.3.2 MOISTURE. Surprisingly, total moisture content does not appear to be linked with juiciness. In pork, Hardy and Noble (1945) did obtain a relationship, but it was low. Wierbicki and Deatherage (1958) had some evidence of a relationship between water-binding capacity and juiciness, and this is supported by data from Kaufman (1961) that the proportion of expressible water was inversely related to juiciness and marbling. Simone *et al.* (1961) also reported a high correlation (Table 2.25) between the percentage of bound moisture and juiciness.

2.5.3.3 pH. It is clear from Fig. 2.13 that pH has no consistent effect on juiciness; this contrasts markedly with the changes it induces in tenderness and flavour (Bouton *et al.*, 1957).

2.5.3.4 AGE. Tuma *et al.* (1962a) and Field *et al.* (1966a) could find no relationship between juiciness and age, and although Helser *et al.* (1930) considered that age increased both the quantity and quality of juice, the effect was clearly one of fatness rather than age *per se* (Table 2.26).

TABLE 2.26 EFFECT OF AGE AND FATNESS ON JUICINESS (FROM HELSER *et al.*, 1930)

Type of cattle	Juiciness score	
	Quality[a]	Quantity[a]
Weaned calves		
Growing ration	11.1	5.7
Fattening ration	11.4	7.4
Yearlings		
Growing ration	11.6	5.6
Fattening ration	11.9	8.0
Two-year-olds		
Growing ration	12.4	6.3
Fattening ration	13.1	8.0

[a] Higher value is more desirable.

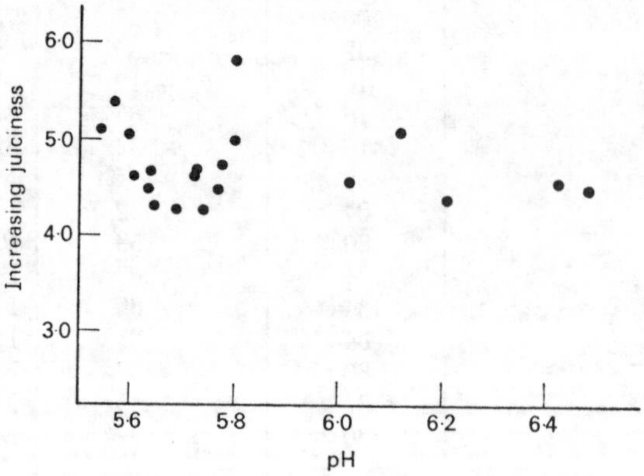

FIG. 2.13. Relationship between juiciness and pH (after Bouton *et al.*, 1957).

2.5.3.5 SEX AND HORMONES. Castration of bulls was found by Jones *et al.* (1964b) to enhance juiciness, but these findings were confounded with marbling. A similar tendency was reported by Raven *et al.* (1966) although the differences did not reach significance. A more comprehensive study by Field *et al.* (1966a) with bulls and steers of widely differing age groups showed no difference in juiciness until the age range of 600–700 days, when steers and heifers were superior to bulls. Again the degree of fatness confuses the picture, but it seems probable that killed early, before marked differences in fatness develop, bulls are as acceptable as steers for this characteristic.

Oestrogen implantation was found by Preston *et al.* (1961) to have no effect on juiciness, and although Simone *et al.* (1958b) observed that treated animals tended to be poorer for this trait, the effect was not significant. In contrast, Forrest and Sather (1965), working with Holstein steers killed at 340, 522, or 703 kg live weight, reported that treated animals were less juicy in the two heavier ranges. Ignoring hormone treatment, the two heavier groups had juicier meat than the light animals. All of these effects can be explained by differences in fatness.

2.5.3.6 BREED. Branaman *et al.* (1962) observed greater juiciness in beef from Herefords as opposed to Holsteins as did Prescott and Hinks (1968) between Angus and Friesian. Differences among beef breeds have been reported by Damon *et al.* (1960) and, although Carroll and Rollins (1965) found no differences between Charolais, Hereford and crosses between them, Jones (1968) found that meat from Charolais crosses was less juicy than that from crosses with Devon and Hereford. This confirmed an earlier finding by Cabrini and Cavandoli (1964) in the Argentine relative to Charolais and British breeds and is supported by American data (Ziegler *et al.*, 1968). As with age and sex effects, it is probable that breed differences merely reflect variations in the rate of fattening.

2.5.4 Flavour and aroma

2.5.4.1 THE NATURE OF THE EFFECT. Flavour is affected by cooking much more than any other component of eatability. This is particularly noticeable in those countries where spices and sauces are integral components of most meat dishes. The frequent criticism that modern, intensively produced meat lacks the flavour of the traditional product could imply that cooking techniques may have to be adjusted to the new production methods. Nevertheless, flavour is an intrinsic quality of meat and the factors controlling it need to be understood in order that natural meat flavour can be exploited when the economic situation warrants it.

Flavour cannot easily be separated from aroma, and Crocker (1948) and Kramlich and Pearson (1958) considered that the flavour of cooked beef consisted more of odour than taste.

Cramer (1963) refers to three schools of thought as to the source of flavour compounds:

(1) That they are derived from muscle and therefore include amino acids, nitrogen bases and ammoniacal and sulphur compounds.
(2) That they are derived from fat.
(3) That basic meat flavours emanate from muscle and species differences are derived from fat.

In Fig. 2.14 are listed some of the compounds and precursors that contribute to meat flavour and aroma. Much of present research aims to determine which of these are important and in what way they serve to differentiate classes and types of meat.

That both fat and muscle contribute to flavour is clear from the reviews of Bender and Wood (1956) and Hornstein and Crowe (1964). Work by Kramlich and Pearson (1958), Yueh and Strong (1960) and Hornstein *et al.* (1960, 1963) showed that most flavour precursors were water-soluble. Freeze-drying of a water extract from beef yielded a powdered concentrate which on heating developed an aroma similar to that of cooked beef. The volatile fraction contained carbonyls, ammonia and hydrogen sulphide. An oily viscous liquid of low vapour pressure but strong aroma was also isolated. Later the same workers (Anon., 1962a) extracted carbonyls from the fatty tissues of lamb and found that when this fat was heated it no longer produced the characteristic odour of mutton. A variety of carbonyls are probably also produced during cooking, due to the transamination and decarboxylation of amino acids and oxidation of fatty acids, but it is clear they also exist in fatty tissue *per se*. Hornstein and Crowe (1964) concluded that the meat flavour of all species is basically the same and that differences are due to the volatiles associated with the fatty tissues.

2.5.4.2 FATNESS. Barbella *et al.* (1939) showed that among age, breeding, sex and fatness, the last-named accounted for 41% of the total variance for desirable flavour, although for intensity of flavour fat contributed only 5% of the variation. It is important to note that the meat studied included subcutaneous as well as inter- and intra-muscular fat and that such relationships may not necessarily hold for the type of lean meat preferred today. However, Simone *et al.* (1958a) and Kropf and Graf (1959a) supported the thesis that flavour increased with fatness, as did Cole *et al.* (1960d) in a consumer preference study of ground beef in Tennessee.

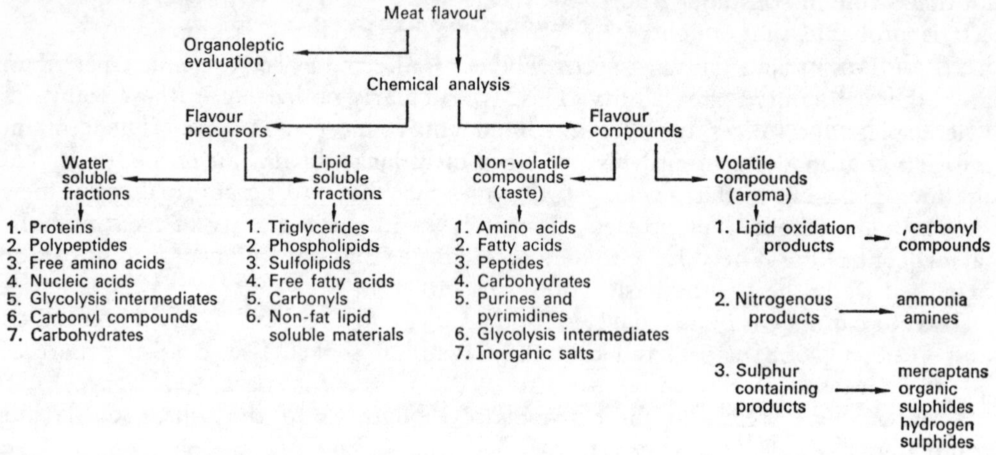

FIG. 2.14. Some chemical components contributing to flavour in meat (from Cramer, 1963).

2.5.4.3 AGE, BREED, SEX AND HORMONES. Field *et al.* (1966a) found no difference in flavour between steers, heifers and bulls until an age of 600–700 days when the meat of bulls became less acceptable. In animals up to 440 days of age at slaughter Raven *et al.* (1966) found similar ratings for bulls and steers. On the other hand, Jones *et al.* (1964b), Bailey *et al.* (1966b) and Forrest (1966) all provided evidence that steers had better flavour than bulls. Implanting steers with hexoestrol improved flavour in roast ribs of low-grade animals, but had the opposite effect in stewed neck muscles from the same cattle; in better finished animals, no effect on flavour was observed from hormone treatment (Jones *et al.*, 1964a).

A comprehensive study of the effect of different doses of DES, oestradiol/progesterone and testosterone was made by Kennick *et al.* (1961a, b). The 10th–11th rib roast occasionally had a significantly greater aroma in carcasses from treated animals, but otherwise there were no significant differences.

Improved flavour with increasing age has been reported by Helser *et al.* (1930),

Dunsing (1959) and Simone *et al.* (1959), although Romans *et al.* (1965a) found that greater maturity of steaks, associated with larger muscle fibres, reduced their acceptability. The same group of workers (Tuma *et al.*, 1962a) earlier had failed to note a relation between flavour and age.

Differences in flavour between beef-type and dairy-type cattle have been observed by Branaman *et al.* (1962), and among beef breeds by Damon *et al.* (1960) but not by Cabrini and Cavandoli (1964) or Carroll and Rollins (1965). In studies in the US (Judge *et al.*, 1965) and the UK (Prescott and Hinks, 1968) there were no differences between Angus/Angus crosses and Holstein/Friesian. There was an indication from the work of Jones (1968) that meat from Charolais crosses on Friesians and Ayrshires had less flavour than when Hereford and Devon sires were used. Ziegler *et al.* (1968) also found Charolais meat to have less flavour than that from British breeds. In a study with 200 steers by 12 sires, Epley *et al.* (1968) found that flavour intensity, according to taste panels, was significantly affected by sire. These differences were not detectable in consumer studies.

It is probable that much of the reported effects on flavour attributed to age, breed and sex are, in reality, manifestations of different degrees of carcass fatness. Comparisons at similar levels of carcass fatness are necessary to gain new insights in this area. Some correlations between flavour and various carcass parameters are given in Table 2.27.

2.5.4.4 Ageing and pH effects. The reported effects on flavour by ageing meat after slaughter vary between nil (Tuma *et al.*, 1962a), slight reduction (Tuma *et al.*, 1963) and significantly less acceptability after a period of 3 weeks (Meyer *et al.*, 1960a).

Meat pH appears to have a critical effect on flavour, the latter decreasing linearly with increasing pH (Fig. 2.15).

2.5.5 Palatability

Some studies have sought to assess overall palatability, but this contributes little to our understanding of the constituent elements of eatability.

Since the factors determining tenderness tend to be antagonistic to those controlling juiciness and flavour, assessments of palatability must of necessity have poor repeatability. This is not to say that overall palatability is not important, but for purposes of comparison one must know why one meat is more palatable than another.

2.6 CARCASS EVALUATION

2.6.1 Subjective methods of assessing carcass composition

2.6.1.1 Live animal judgement. Awards in the show ring are still a major incentive to breeders of beef cattle, and the champion beef animal at Smithfield, Perth or Chicago is still regarded as the epitome of beef type. According to Darlow (1958), the judge's duty is to get "the best compromise between what is wanted by the consumer and what a breeder can afford to produce. . . . This has resulted in the type of meat animal we have today." Without livestock shows, "we would have only a few of the desirable animals rather than many". More specifically he asserted that the average dairy animal will not produce as much, or as high quality, meat as a beef animal. It is

TABLE 2.27 CORRELATIONS BETWEEN FLAVOUR AND OTHER CARCASS TRAITS

Item	No. of carcasses	Correlation coefficient	Authors
Marbling score	101	.18	Legg *et al.*, 1965
	134	.20	Field *et al.*, 1966a
	84	.57	Field *et al.*, 1966a
Ether extract in *L. dorsi* (%)	16	.67	Morgan, 1967
	32	.77	Simone *et al.*, 1958b
Fat in 12th rib cut (%)	32	.20	Simone *et al.*, 1958b
Specific gravity	100	—.28	Cole *et al.*, 1960a
Total moisture (%)	32	.12	Simone *et al.*, 1958b
Juiciness	80	.47	Romans *et al.*, 1965a
	16	.52	Morgan, 1967
	84	.54	Field *et al.*, 1966a
	134	.64	Field *et al.*, 1966a
	380	.70	McBee & Wiles, 1967
Quality of juice	98	.79	Kidwell *et al.*, 1959
Panel tenderness	84	.55	Field *et al.*, 1966a
	330	.65	McBee & Wiles, 1967
	134	.67	Field *et al.*, 1966a
	80	.68	Romans *et al.*, 1965a
Shear force	80	—.48	Romans *et al.*, 1965a
	84	—.37	Field *et al.*, 1966a
	134	—.33	Field *et al.*, 1966a
Colour	32	.86	Moe *et al.*, 1964

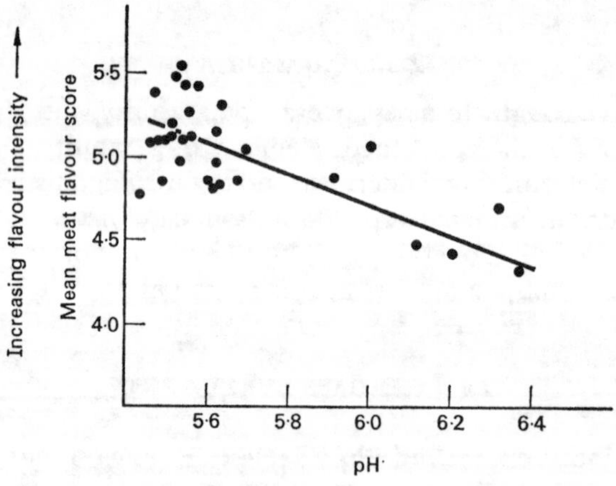

FIG. 2.15 Relation between meat flavour and pH (from Howard, 1964).

perhaps appropriate that in the same journal Cole *et al.* (1958) reported that at the same live weight (410 kg) steers from the dairy breeds (Holsteins, Jersey and Guernsey) had a higher percentage of rib, loin and round than beef breeds (Brahman, Angus and Hereford) and that the breef breeds were superior only in degree of fatness. Thus differences in type, for which judges and breeders may take credit—or accept responsibility—are really no more than differences in fatness due to variation in the rate of maturity. The reasons why this should be so have been explained by Butterfield (1964b) (§ 2.3.2).

The futility of livestock judging as a means of assessing the true attributes of carcass composition has been amply demonstrated by a number of workers. Gregory *et al.* (1962) were unable to find any meaningful relationship between live animal assessment and any aspect of carcass conformation or quality. On 688 cattle, Wheat and Holland (1960) could only obtain a correlation of 0.22 between live grade and carcass grade. Wilson *et al.* (1964) reported attempts of six judges to assess, independently, fat thickness, rib eye area, percentage of kidney fat, dressing percentage and carcass grade of 135 steers fed in the same drylot. Not surprisingly, the correlations obtained were too low to be of any practical use. Similar conclusions were reached by Davis *et al.* (1964) on comparing the visual ranking of three judges with subsequent carcass analysis. Vitlo and Magee (1965) found that judges were incapable of assessing the percentage of preferred cuts, although the same judges had moderate success in assessing eye-muscle area. Similarly, Gregory *et al.* (1964) found that three experienced live animal graders could only account for 35% of the variation in cutability.

This is not to say that it is impossible to assess some carcass traits in the live animal. People with such talents certainly exist. Thus Lewis *et al.* (1968b) found that the estimates of experienced live-animal judges accounted for 75% of the variation in fat thickness whereas inexperienced operators were only half as effective. The problem is that such an "eye" for cattle only comes from long experience; it cannot really be taught or passed on.

2.6.1.2 GRADE. Carcass grading is a subjective method of estimating quality. Several countries have developed their own grading methods and scales of merit. The most widely known is the system of the US Department of Agriculture (USDA), which consists of the following seven major grades in descending order of merit: prime, choice, good, commercial, utility, cutter and canner. Brief descriptions of these grades, adapted from Pearson and Kirk (1954), are as follows:

Prime. This is supposed to be the highest quality meat available, approaching perfection in flavour and tenderness. It comes only from steers and heifers which are blocky, compact and very well finished. The beef is used mostly by restaurants, hotels, airlines and passenger liners; it is generally too expensive and carries too much fat for the average housewife.

Choice. This meat is also considered to have superior eating qualities, although it does not meet all the requirements of prime grade. Fat trim is still considerable with this grade of meat.

Good. This is the type of meat found in most retail butchers' shops since for the majority it represents an acceptable compromise between eating quality and economy. The meat has still a fair amount of exterior fat covering and a slight amount of marbling. Young cows may appear in this grade, as well as steers and heifers.

Commercial. Beef of this grade is quite variable in conformation, finish and quality. It includes young cows, steers and heifers that are considered to be lacking in conformation and finish. Generally, meat of commercial grade should be cooked with moist heat or be ground into hamburgers or sausages.

Utility. This grade is markedly inferior in conformation, finish and quality. While a small proportion finds its way into retail channels, it is not suitable for roasting or grilling. However, it produces excellent pot roast, stewing meat, and meat for grinding and processing for which finish is not essential.

Cutter and canner. These are the two poorest grades of meat and do not appear on the market in carcass form. Most of this meat is canned, processed or used as ground beef.

In many countries the grading system influences economic return, e.g. by advertising as in the US, and by being linked to price-support systems as in the UK. Grading would be advantageous if grades accurately reflected economic worth, i.e. edible meat and eatability. In reality, grades do little more than subjectively assess the degree of fatness and of the desirable attributes of eatibility; they are probably correlated only with juiciness.

Cole *et al.* (1960a) investigated fat thickness in 100 12th-rib cuts, equally divided among prime, choice, good, standard and commercial grades. They found that the higher the grade the greater the marbling and fat cover. Specific gravity tests showed a concomitant decrease in the percentages of lean and bone and of protein. Meyer *et al.* (1960b) established a similar relationship by specific gravity techniques and estimated fat percentages in the carcasses of 8.8, 13.5, 18.7 and 23.6 for utility, standard, good and choice grades, respectively. The correlations in Table 2.28 show clearly that grade is a useful measure only for fatness and bears no relationship to eatability.

Vilstrup (1964), quoting Iowa data, found that lower grade steers with less fat were more profitable than "choice" or "good" steers. This appears logical in view of the findings of Kidwell *et al.* (1959) that carcass grade was positively correlated with excess fat, which is known to be negatively related to the percentage of edible meat (Willis *et al.*, 1968). As far back as 1960, the economic significance of carcass grading was questioned by the American Meat Institute, which considered it an outmoded concept, since "prime" and "choice" meat, i.e. the top grades, were too fat to please the modern consumer.

Accepting McMeekan's (1956) argument that the function of carcass appraisal is to provide a connecting link between consumer and producer, the USDA grading system is clearly anachronistic. This criticism is even more applicable to UK grading standards. For while USDA grades have no statutory link with market prices, their equivalent in the UK is used to determine fatstock guarantee payments. This results in such ludicrous situations as those reported by Anon. (1965b) in which a high proportion (47%) of bull carcasses were denied support price payment on the grounds that they did not achieve grade standards. Yet, the bulk of the evidence indicates that bulls, while they may be slightly inferior with respect to meat tenderness, are distinctly superior in most other carcass characteristics of economic significance (§ 2.3.4.4).

An attempt was made by the USDA to develop an ancillary method for assessing

TABLE 2.28 RELATION BETWEEN CARCASS GRADE AND VARIOUS CARCASS TRAITS

Item	No. of observations	Correlation coefficient	Authors
Marbling	137	.86	Wellington, 1968
	36	.88	Matthews & Bennett, 1962
	688	.89	Wheat & Holland, 1960
		.89	Dunn, 1960
	96	.89	Zinn *et al.*, 1961
	24	.93	Matthews & Bennett, 1962
		.97	Dunn, 1960
Separable fat (%)	133	.79	Ramsey *et al.*, 1962
Separable lean (%)	133	−.70	Ramsey *et al.*, 1962
Bone (%)	133	.83	Ramsey *et al.*, 1962
Panel tenderness	176	−.40	Harris *et al.*, 1965
	128	−.23	Suess *et al.*, 1966a
	24	−.02	Matthews & Bennett, 1962
	36	.25	Matthews & Bennett, 1962
	536	.28	Palmer *et al.*, 1958
Longissimus dorsi area	265	.05	Cundiff *et al.*, 1964
Longissimus dorsi area/kg carcass weight	265	−.18	Cundiff *et al.*, 1964
Edible meat (%)	103	−.12	Cobb & Ovejera, 1965
	47	−.66	Miller *et al.*, 1965
First quality (RLRC) (%)	47	−.60	Miller *et al.*, 1965

carcasses according to their likely edible meat content based on the research findings of Murphey *et al.* (1960). This technique, known as yield grading, combined fat thickness, percent kidney, pelvic and heart fat, hot carcass weight and area of *L. dorsi* in an equation to estimate cutability (edible meat yield). A dual grading system using yield grade alongside the established "quality" grading method (largely based upon marbling) was introduced in the US in 1962 but abandoned after one year.

Subjective scoring for conformation was undertaken by Dikeman *et al.* (1968a) on 120 steer carcasses. The correlation between conformation scores and the weight or percentage of total edible meat ranged from 0.09 to 0.24 and were generally non-significant.

2.6.2 Objective methods of assessing carcass composition

2.6.2.1 MEASUREMENTS IN LIVE ANIMALS. In a study of 674 steers representing three breeds, exhibited at the International Livestock Exposition in Chicago (1956–8), Good *et al.* (1961) found that width between the eyes, width of muzzle, circumference of round and circumference of cannon bone were all significantly and negatively correlated with fat cover at the 12th rib. However, their conclusion that broad-headed, heavy-boned cattle with large rounds are desirable can hardly be justified in view of the fact that the maximum correlation obtained was only −0.34, i.e. accounting for only 11.6% of variation in fat cover. Orme *et al.* (1959b) found relatively high correlations ($r = 0.43$–0.80) between measurements on the live animal and the related traits in the carcass, but prediction of first-quality cuts (untrimmed, bone-in) from live measurements were not encouraging; their best measurement, circumference of middle, accounted for only 28% of the variation in the first-quality cuts. Woodward *et al.* (1959) found that the correlations of various body measurements with carcass traits were not high enough to have much predictive value, while Bass *et al.* (1962) reported that such measurements accounted for only 19–34% of the variation in edible meat yield, and Cundiff *et al.* (1967) concluded that body weight was a better estimate of weight of first quality meat (RLRC) than any of eleven linear measurements. This is in general agreement with the earlier findings of White and Green (1952) and Yao *et al.* (1953).

Tallis *et al.* (1959) reported that the ratios of weight/height and weight/length were positively correlated with rib eye area, but negatively correlated with the percentage of edible meat. A highly significant relation between the ratio chest girth/wither height and fat content of the 10th rib cut was found by Preston and Aitken (1963) and subsequently used (Preston *et al.*, 1963c) to determine optimum time of slaughter.

Partial correlations (carcass weight held constant) between the circumference of the cannon in the live animal and the rib eye area have been reported by Weseli *et al.* (1958) and Wythe *et al.* (1961) (citing Merkel, 1950, and Arthaud, 1958), but the relationship was weak.

It would appear that the statement of Lush and Copeland that "the principal objection to the extensive use of body measurements seems not to be their inaccuracy, but their inadequacy to describe the animal in a complete way" is no less true today than when it was made in 1930.

Photogrammetry, a method developed by German scientists for determining body volume from photographs, was used by Brinks *et al.* (1964a) to predict wholesale cuts of beef. These workers obtained very accurate predictions on Hereford steers, but application of the equations to Brown Swiss was slightly less rewarding. They claimed that the method was useful in ranking sire progeny groups. However, it should be remembered that wholesale cuts, particularly in fat animals, are neither a reliable guide to body composition nor to edible meat content. It is not surprising, particularly in view of the cost of the equipment, that this system has not been widely adopted.

Ultrasonic methods have been employed in pigs with good results to predict back-fat thickness and the percentage of lean cuts (Claus *et al.*, 1957; Lauprecht *et al.*, 1957; Hazel and Kline, 1959). Stouffer *et al.* (1961) obtained correlations in several groups of cattle of 0.32–0.54 and 0.22–0.85 between ultrasonic measurements and fat thickness and eye-muscle area respectively. These were significant but lower than those obtained with pigs. Hedrick *et al.* (1962) reported similar findings. By 1964 Davis *et al.* were able to show correlations of 0.90 and 0.87 between ultrasonic estimates and fat thickness and eye muscle area, respectively. However, in 1966 these same workers reported correlations of only 0.79 for fat thickness. In Australia, Campbell and Dodd (1965) reported significant correlations between estimated fat thickness over the 10th–11th rib and the weight of separable fat in the corresponding rib cut. Ramsey *et al.* (1967) used a multiple regression technique combining live weight with an ultrasonic estimate of biceps femoris thickness and accounted for 93% of the variation in weight of first-quality meat (RLRC).

The cattle used in the majority of these studies had from 12 to 28 mm of fat over the eye muscle and it is unlikely that ultrasonics will be equally efficient in estimating fat depth in younger, lightly finished animals, where the fat cover does not exceed 10 mm. This same criticism applies to the probing of fat thickness with a hypodermic thermister needle as used by Warren *et al.* (1959) and Brackelsberg *et al.* (1967). Watkins *et al.* (1967) have in fact shown that while subcutaneous fat thickness *per se* did not reduce the accuracy of eye-muscle area estimation, it did affect determination of fatness. Fat thickness was overestimated in animals with less than 2 cm and underestimated in those with more than 2 cm of back fat thickness; prediction was also more accurate in the latter ($r = 0.84$) than the former ($r = 0.55$). In contrast Gravert (1967) found that in Friesians the correlation between actual eye-muscle area and that predicted by ultrasonic measurements was only 0.31, which would suggest that fat thickness also affects precision of estimating eye-muscle area.

Of the many other techniques tried at one time or another to estimate body composition, some are clearly unsuitable. Specific gravity measurements, although useful for carcass appraisal, have limited value in live animals (Tallis *et al.*, 1963); skinfold thickness had no relation to subcutaneous fat (Tulloh, 1961); antipyrine, to measure body water, gave too variable results (Garrett *et al.*, 1959a) and tritiated water, although more accurate (Panaretto and Till, 1963) involves subsequent destruction of the treated animals; estimates by means of potassium 40 are also too variable (Kirton and Pearson, 1963), as well as expensive and time-consuming (Kirton, 1964a); muscle biopsy techniques (Everitt and Carter, 1961; Everitt, 1964a) are still being developed owing to the problems of selecting representative sample sites, and there is the further complication that biopsy sampling may lead to fatty degeneration in the muscle (Link *et al.*, 1967).

A more complete review of these techniques and others has been given by Kirton (1964b). It would appear that at the present time the practical application of most of them is extremely limited.

2.6.2.2 CARCASS MEASUREMENTS. Early attempts to incorporate simple measurements of the intact carcass into an objective system of carcass appraisal were the New Zealand score-card system of Kneebone *et al.* (1950) and the Australian method of Yeates (1952).

Yeates's system, although more objective than that of Kneebone *et al.* (1950), still contains a subjective correction for age. Moreover, it appears to have been designed more for the show ring than commercial appraisal. The method involves the expression of carcass weight as a function of carcass length with a correction for fat-thickness. In discussing its applicability, Yeates (1965) claimed that the gross fleshing index was highly correlated (−0.82) with percentage of bone; this is not unexpected in that the range of bone content was from 12 to 24%. But if such an index is to be of value it must have a high predicting capacity over a much more restricted range of carcasses. He gives no data to support his claim that the net fleshing index is available as an estimate of the amount of trimmed meat. Moreover, the finding of Martin (1968) that edible meat and excess fat in the 9th–10th–11th rib joint were poor indicators of these components in the carcass implies that Yeates's fat correction is subject to considerable error.

The inadequacy of Kneebone's score-card and Yeates's fleshing index to describe the commercial value of a carcass was demonstrated by Everitt and Jury (1964), who found no significant association between the total score from either system and a monetary index of wholesale carcass value. In any event, the repeatability of the measurements used appears to be low, according to Bodwell *et al.* (1959a). They studied eight measurements on 15 carcasses, made by three observers, and obtained good agreement only for length of body and length of loin.

From an examination of half-carcasses of 29 Charolais steers weighing 187 ± 40 kg, Dumont *et al.* (1961b) derived the following equation to predict carcass muscle which they considered "sufficiently precise for most practicable purposes".

$$Y = 0.48Z + 0.78X_4 + 0.20X_{15} - 0.80,$$

where Y = total musculature, Z = half-carcass weight, X_4 = thickness of thigh and X_{15} weight of diaphragm. The variables were expressed as logarithms. The same group of workers (Le Guelte *et al.*, 1964) found the correlations between measurements and weight of carcass joints to be low, although they did feel that length of carcass and thickness of thigh were sufficiently important to recommend breeding for short, wide-thighed carcasses.

In a 4-year study of 130 steers of seven different breeds or crosses, Ramsey *et al.* (1966) found few carcass measurements to be related to separable muscle weight; the best were chest width ($r = 0.53$), round circumference ($r = 0.50$) and carcass length ($r = 0.42$).

These results are not very different from those of Orme *et al.* (1960). In 1959(b) this group was unable to account for more than 25% of the variation in the percentage of first quality cuts (untrimmed bone-in) due to any measurements of the carcass. In a comprehensive analysis of 74 steers, Tayler *et al.* (1961) tested many measurements, but found these to reflect differences in carcass weight more than in individual joints. When the measurements were corrected for carcass weight, they were of little use for predicting weights of joints in individual carcasses. Similar conclusions regarding the confounding of carcass weight and measurements were reported by Birkett *et al.* (1965). Harrington and Pomeroy (1959) and Goll *et al.* (1961a) had earlier commented on the poor predictive value of carcass measurements and score appraisal schemes derived from them for defining carcass quality.

2.6.2.3 Eye-muscle area. The area of the longissimus dorsi muscle has been studied for many years, particularly as an indicator of carcass muscling. It is measured relatively easily by means of tracings and a planimeter (Naumann, 1952; Bodwell *et al.*, 1959b). Riley *et al.* (1966) and Hillers *et al.* (1968) found that grids placed directly over the eye muscle gave results which were just as accurate as planimeters. Photographic methods were suggested by Schoonover and Stratton (1957) as less subject to error. Significant differences between right and left sides, reported by Butler *et al.* (1956a) and Carpenter and Palmer (1961), appear to be mainly due to cutting errors (Hedrick *et al.*, 1965). Henderson *et al.* (1966c), comparing various methods, found good correlations among different operators, but agreed with earlier workers as to the importance of cutting errors.

The choice of method would thus appear to be relatively unimportant. Of more concern is the actual value of the eye muscle area as an indicator of the commercial yield of the carcass.

Table 2.29 summarizes the findings of many workers relating to correlations between eye muscle area and various measures of carcass leanness. There is little consistency among the findings cited, but in general the correlations are low, particularly with respect to important parameters, such as the percentage of first-quality edible meat. Adjustment of eye-muscle area for carcass weight tends to lower those parameters couched in terms of weight and to increase those expressed as a percentage. The limited predictive value of eye-muscle area is demonstrated by the findings of Ramsey *et al.* (1962) that the relationship between the percentages of first-quality meat and separable meat was improved by removing eye-muscle area from the equation. Brungardt and Bray (1963) also showed that while the simple correlation of eye-muscle area with the percentage of first-quality meat was 0.45, the multiple correlation, after removing the effects of side weight, percentage kidney fat, percentage trimmed round and fat depth over the 12th rib, fell to 0.02.

TABLE 2.29 CORRELATIONS BETWEEN EYE-MUSCLE AREA AND CARCASS TRAITS

Item	No. of carcasses	Corre ation coefficients		Authors
		Simple	Partial adjustment for carcass weight	
Carcass weight	104	.12		Willis *et al.*, 1968
		.35		Dinkel *et al.*, 1965
		.43		Scarth & Bray, 1967
	32	.45		Birkett *et al.*, 1965
	135	.47		Wilson *et al.*, 1964
	90	.52		Goll *et al.*, 1961a
	99	.52		Cole *et al.*, 1960c
	60	.52		Kieffer *et al.*, 1958
	152	.70		Fitzhugh *et al.*, 1965b
	132	.74		Cole *et al.*, 1962
	835	.75		Abraham *et al.*, 1968
	354	.81		Field & Schoonover, 1967
Separable lean in carcass (%)	86	.31	.54	Henderson *et al.*, 1966a
	86	.36	.59	Henderson *et al.*, 1966a
Separable lean in carcass (wt.)	99	.43	.04	Cole *et al.*, 1960c
	130	.52		Ramsey *et al.*, 1966
	51	.59		Cole *et al.*, 1960b
	132	.59		Cole *et al.*, 1962
		.85		Bodwell *et al.*, 1959b
Separable lean in 9th–10th–11th rib (wt.)				Kropf, 1959
	29		.41	
	99	.45		Brungardt & Bray, 1963
	99	.55	.35	Cole *et al.*, 1960c
	56	.41		Woodward *et al.*, 1959
Edible meat (%)	104	.02		Willis *et al.*, 1968
	103	.18		Cobb & Ovejera, 1965
	47	.38		Hedrick *et al.*, 1965
	47	.40		Miller *et al.*, 1965
	38	.43		Gottsch *et al.*, 1961
	40	.85		Cahill *et al.*, 1956

TABLE 2.29 (cont.)

Item	No. of carcasses	Correlation coefficients: Simple	Correlation coefficients: Partial adjustment for carcass weight	Authors
Edible meat (wt.)	47	.76		Hedrick *et al.*, 1965
	835	.77		Abraham *et al.*, 1968
	47	.82		Miller *et al.*, 1965
First-quality edible (RLRC) (%)	311	.51		Busch *et al.*, 1968
	37	−.30	.21	King *et al.*, 1964
	40	−.02		Iwanaga & Cobb, 1963
	32	.00	.31	Birkett *et al.*, 1965
	42	.07	.07 to .37	Magee, 1965b
	47	.39		Hedrick *et al.*, 1965
	99	.45		Brungardt & Bray, 1963
	86	.45	.65	Henderson *et al.*, 1966a
	47	.54		Miller *et al.*, 1965
	194		.61	Stringer *et al.*, 1963
First quality edible (%)	104	.18		Willis *et al.*, 1968
First quality edible (RLRC) (wt.)	47	.24 to .47		Hedrick *et al.*, 1965
	32	.49	.25	Birkett *et al.*, 1965
		.83		Miller *et al.*, 1965
Boneless roast and steak meat (wt.)	59	.31		King *et al.*, 1965
	241	.45		DuBose & Cartwright, 1967
	152	.65	.06	Fitzhugh *et al.*, 1965b
	305	.76	.50	DuBose *et al.*, 1967
Marbling	2436	.02		Kauffman *et al.*, 1968
	137	.16		Wellington, 1968

In view of the obviously low value of eye-muscle area as a predictor of edible or total lean meat, it is surprising that this measurement still features in indices of carcass merit. This is not to say that the eye-muscle area is not important. Since it is one of the best sources of steaks for grilling, as well as roasts, it is highly desirable that eye-muscle area should be as large as possible.

That the size of the eye-muscle is a function of carcass weight is clear from the correlations between these two variables in Table 2.29. Zinn *et al.* (1962) studied 99 steers and 100 heifers slaughtered at intervals during the fattening period and found that in the heifers eye-muscle area increased for the first 120 days of fattening and then remained constant for the succeeding 150 days; by comparison, in steers, eye-muscle area increased for up to 180 days of fattening before levelling off during the remainder of the 270 day period. Field and Schoonover (1967) slaughtered 354 bulls at live weights between 91 and 589 kg (104–686 days) and reported a linear increase in eye-muscle area throughout the entire weight range (Table 2.30). The

TABLE 2.30 RELATIONSHIP OF LONGISSIMUS DORSI AREA TO LIVE WEIGHT (FROM FIELD AND SCHOONOVER, 1967)

Live weight range (kg)	No. of animals	L. dorsi area (cm^2)
91–135	3	32.11
136–180	8	37.98
181–226	27	39.80
227–271	26	48.80
272–317	64	57.50
318–362	97	63.25
363–407	52	68.00
408–453	18	79.36
454–498	26	79.25
499–543	23	88.30
544–589	10	90.29

difference between their judgement and Zinn *et al.* (1962) may reflect a growth difference between bulls and steers. That Willis *et al.* (1968) did not obtain similar high correlations for their bulls can be attributed to the narrower live weight range of their data (350–430 kg).

The inferiority of the Shorthorn relative to the Hereford and Angus, in that it had a smaller eye-muscle area at the same live weight, was noted by Field and Schoonover (1967) and confirmed by Kauffman *et al.* (1968) (Table 2.9).

In view of its relatively high heritability (Table 3.11), it would seem that the eye-muscle area is a more appropriate item in genetic improvement plans than in prediction indices of carcass leanness.

2.6.2.4 RIB JOINTS. The most widely used sample joint is the 9th–10th–11th rib cut. It was first described by Hankins and Howe (1946) who pointed out the possibility of using the composition of this cut to predict muscle, fat and bone in the entire carcass. The correlations between sample and carcass for the three tissues were, respectively, 0.90, 0.93 and 0.80. More recently, Crown and Damon (1960) reported correlations of 0.94, 0.98 and 0.73 for muscle, fat and bone in this cut and in the whole carcass. Branaman *et al.* (1962) also found the percentage of ether extract in the 9th–10th–11th rib cut to be highly correlated ($r = -0.87$) with carcass separable lean. Cole *et al.* (1962) compared actual separable lean with that calculated from the 9th–10th–11th rib cut by the equation of Hankins and Howe (1946). The correlation was 0.95 and the results agreed to within 2.3 kg. These findings were better than those of an early study (Cole *et al.*, 1960c) in which the correlation for muscle was only 0.76.

The 12th rib cut has also been used for predictive purposes (Crown and Damon, 1960). There were high correlations for muscle, fat and bone between the 12th rib and the 9th–10th–11th rib cut (0.83, 0.97 and 0.85), and the entire carcass (0.82, 0.96 and 0.75).

Ledger and Hutchinson (1962), analysing carcasses of 32 Zebu steers, claimed that the physical separation of the 10th rib was likewise a good guide to the composition of the carcass. Willis *et al.* (1968) examined 107 Brahman carcasses, but found only moderate correlations of 0.35, 0.43 and 0.43 between muscle, fat and bone in this rib cut and the percentage of edible meat, excess fat and bone, respectively; while Busch *et al.* (1968) reported that the physical separation of the 9th–10th–11th ribs joint on a percentage basis was not correlated with the weight of edible meat in the carcass. However, equations containing carcass weight and either percentage separable fat or muscle accounted for 88% of the variation in edible portion, a slight improvement over carcass weight alone (79%). Martin (1968) compared the edible meat, excess fat and bone contents of the 9th–10th–11th rib joint with corresponding data for rib plus loin. Correlations were low when calculated within a breed and he considered that a single regression equation which ignored breed would not accurately describe the relationship between the rib joint dissection and that of the whole carcass.

It is clear that sample rib joints are useful indicators of total muscle, fat and, to a lesser extent, bone in the carcass. However, they appear to be less valuable as indices of edible meat content.

2.6.2.5 OTHER JOINTS. The first attempts to use wholesale joints to estimate carcass composition were those of Cole *et al.* (1960c). They analysed 63 carcasses and obtained high correlations between the weights of separable lean in the various joints and the corresponding weights of carcass lean. The correlations for seven joints ranged from 0.70 to 0.95, the best measures being separable round lean ($r = 0.95$), chuck lean ($r = 0.93$) and foreshank lean ($r = 0.82$). Ramsey *et al.* (1966), working with a larger sample of 130 carcasses from different breeds and crosses, also reported high correlations between weight of separable muscle in the half-carcass and that in the round ($r = 0.91$), chuck ($r = 0.91$), loin ($r = 0.86$) and rib ($r = 0.77$), among others. Thornton and Hiner (1965) used the total weight of round in a study involving 104 beef and dairy steers of five breeds and reported correlations of 0.98, 0.81 and 0.90 for total separable lean, fat and bone, respectively.

In contrast to the carcass indices considered previously, the round appears to hold high promise as a predictor of edible meat (Table 2.31).

TABLE 2.31 CORRELATIONS BETWEEN TRIMMED BONELESS ROUND AND EDIBLE MEAT IN THE CARCASS

Edible meat	No. of carcasses	Round measurement		Authors
		%	wt.	
Total (%)		.59 to .90		Henderson *et al.*, 1966a
	47	.75	.18	Miller *et al.*, 1965
	38	.78		Gottsch *et al.*, 1961
First quality (RLRC) (%)	99	.57		Lewis *et al.*, 1964b
	100	.73 to .93		Magee *et al.*, 1968
	47	.74	.19	Miller *et al.*, 1965
	20	.80		Moody & Kemp, 1965
	99	.83		Brungardt & Bray, 1963
Steak and roast (wt.)	152		.92	Fitzhugh *et al.*, 1965b

A procedure for evaluating the edible meat yield with a minimum breakdown of the carcass was the "streamlined hindquarter" of Elliot *et al.* (1961), which was in effect a foreshortened version of the *pan traité*. The correlation between this component, as a percentage of the carcass, and the percentage of first-quality meat (RLRC) in 101 steers was 0.89. Everitt and Jury (1964) considered that the percentage variability of the *pan traité* was similar to that of the combined group of first-quality joints, which is to be expected since such joints are almost all situated in the *pan traité* area. Similarly, the high correlations (0.95–1.00) between weight or percentage first-quality meat (RLRC) to total edible meat obtained by Dikeman *et al.* (1968b) is to be expected since the former comprises some 60% of the latter.

After dissecting 24 steer carcasses, Callow (1962) concluded that the weight of any one tissue in a joint was not a reliable guide to its weight in the total carcass. This conclusion was criticized by Harrington and King (1963), who reanalysed Callow's data and showed that sample joints offered a useful guide to the total content of muscular tissue, provided the weight of the joint and the carcass weight were taken into account.

2.6.2.6 Muscles. Joubert (1956b) was the first to draw attention to the possibility of using the muscle-fibre diameter as an indicator of carcass composition in sheep. Possible relationships between total carcass lean and fibre diameter in longissimus dorsi and semitendinosus muscles were investigated by Tuma *et al.* (1962b), but the high, simple correlations obtained (0.83 and 0.73) were reduced to a non-significant level (0.00 and 0.35) when the effect of animal age was removed.

A more fruitful line of inquiry has resulted from dissection and weighing of individual muscles, as proposed by Orme *et al.* (1960) and Walker (1961). Butterfield (1962) found extremely close relationships between the weight of certain muscles, or muscle groups, and the total weight of muscle in the right side of the carcass. Some of the correlations and prediction equations he obtained are given in Table 2.32. Butterfield's correlation coefficients were significantly better than those given by Orme *et al.* (1960); he ascribed this to a more accurate dissection technique. This seems probable since Orme and his co-workers determined total muscle by separation of joints rather than by dissection of the individual muscles. Dumont *et al.* (1961a, b) carried out muscle dissections on Charolais steers and calculated various multiple regression equations, the most accurate of which has already been referred to (§ 2.6.2.2). Their general findings are in line with those of Butterfield, but the equations are more complex.

On the basis of the quoted correlation coefficients, individual muscles are obviously superior to rib cuts as indices. But detailed dissections are required and their predictive value for estimating edible meat in the carcass has yet to be determined. On the strength of the available evidence (Everitt, 1964b), the relation between weight of edible meat and weight of biceps femoris is not significant when carcass weight is held constant. However, Everitt's sample was atypical, being based on 20 10-month-old calves from five breeds and crosses. The value of the relation in older and fatter animals at more normal slaughter weights has yet to be investigated.

2.6.2.7 Fat-measurements. Bodwell *et al.* (1959c) first called attention to the fact that, as the thickness of fat over the eye muscle increased, the proportion of round

TABLE 2.32 CORRELATION COEFFICIENTS AND REGRESSION EQUATIONS FOR WEIGHT (g) OF CERTAIN MUSCLES, OR MUSCLE GROUPS (x), AND TOTAL WEIGHTS OF MUSCLE IN THE RIGHT HALF OF THE CARCASS (y) (FROM BUTTERFIELD, 1962)

Muscle	Correlation coefficient	Regression equation
Biceps femoris	.99	$y = 1344 + 13.66\ x$
Semimembranosus and adductor femoris	.99	$y = -926 + 14.25\ x$
Longissimus dorsi	.99	$y = 2317 + 16.75\ x$
Infra-spinatus	.98	$y = 3295 + 44.25\ x$
Shin muscle group	.98	$y = -7905 + 43.61\ x$
Semitendinosus	.96	$y = 9871 + 33.04\ x$

(which is positively correlated with lean meat yield) decreased. Subsequently Murphey *et al.* (1960) used the average fat thickness over the eye muscle in an equation to predict the percentage of first-quality meat (RLRC). This equation formed the basis of the USDA yield grade introduced to accompany carcass grading in the "dual grading" system. The original formula was:

Percentage first-quality meat (RLRC) $= 51.34 - 5.784X_1 - 0.0093X_2 - 0.462X_3 + 0.740X_4$,

where X_1 = fat thickness over eye muscle (in.), X_2 = carcass weight (lb), X_3 = kidney fat (% of carcass), X_4 = eye-muscle area (in^2).

Ramsey *et al.* (1962), investigating the efficacy of this new system, found that carcass grade and yield grade were both negatively associated with the percentages of muscle and bone, and positively associated with percentage fat. Omitting eye-muscle area from the yield grade calculations increased the negative relationship, but the association with separable fat was higher. Powell *et al.* (1968b) also found yield grade and percentage ether extract to be positively correlated ($r = 0.93$). According to Ramsey and his co-workers, a single fat-thickness measurement over the eye muscle was as effective as carcass grade or yield grade in determining separable lean or fat in the carcass (Table 2.33). They concluded that there was nothing to be gained by using several fat measurements and that eye-muscle area was less valuable than fat-thickness as an indicator of the percentage of lean and fat in the carcass. Zinn *et al.* (1961) had earlier found a similar negative relationship ($r = -0.40$) between the dual grading yield estimate and the proportion of first quality meat (RLRC), which would indicate that yield grading, as propounded by Murphey *et al.* (1960), did not serve its intended purpose. Fat-thickness, on the other hand, has proved a reliable and simple guide to carcass composition and, what is more important, edible meat yield. Table 2.34 shows the relation of fat-thickness to various carcass parameters. There is good agreement with respect to the percentages of edible and first quality meat ($r = 0.70$), which appears to be independent of carcass weight. Only King *et al.* (1964) reported findings contrary to this general trend, but their sample of 37 Santa Gertrudis cows was hardly typical.

TABLE 2.33 CORRELATION COEFFICIENTS OF PERCENTAGE LEAN, FAT AND BONE IN THE LEFT SIDE WITH CARCASS GRADE, YIELD GRADE AND FAT-THICKNESS (FROM RAMSEY *et al.*, 1962)

Parameter	Percentage		
	Lean	Fat	Bone
Carcass grade	−.70	.79	−.83
Yield grade	−.75	.73	−.51
Yield grade omitting eye-muscle area	−.79	.83	—
Fat-thickness	−.76	.82	−.76
Fat-thickness (mean of three)	−.73	.80	−.78

TABLE 2.34 CORRELATION OF FAT-THICKNESS OVER EYE MUSCLE AND VARIOUS CARCASS TRAITS

Item	Correlation coefficients			Authors
	Simple		Partial (adjusted for carcass wt.)	
	Single measure	Means/several measures		
Carcass weight	.47	.60		Abraham *et al.*, 1968
	.36	.22		Wilson *et al.*, 1964
	.45			Suess *et al.*, 1966b
		.53		Cole *et al.*, 1962
Dressing (%)	.20	.12		Wilson *et al.*, 1964
Carcass grade	.07	.02		Wilson *et al.*, 1964
	.64	.65		Abraham *et al.*, 1968
	.20 to .50			DeRouen *et al.*, 1964
Marbling score	.23			Wellington, 1968
	.20		.16	Suess *et al.*, 1966b
	.21			Kauffman *et al.*, 1968
	.13 to .57			DeRouen *et al.*, 1964
Excess fat (%)	.66	.71		Allen *et al.*, 1968
Excess fat (wt.)	.51	.59		Allen *et al.*, 1968
	.58	.57		Gottsch *et al.*, 1961
Carcass fat (%)	.65			Field *et al.*, 1966b
	.65	.63		Brungardt & Bray, 1963
	.82	.80		Ramsey *et al.*, 1962
	.90			Powell *et al.*, 1968b
	.90			Butterfield, 1964a
Kidney fat (%)	.23	.14		Wilson *et al.*, 1964
	.42	.46		Abraham *et al.*, 1968
Specific gravity in rib cut	−.57			Cole *et al.*, 1960a
Area longissimus dorsi		−.07	−.41	Cundiff *et al.*, 1964
	.00	−.10		Wilson *et al.*, 1964
	.16	.30		Abraham *et al.*, 1968
	.13 to .79			DeRouen *et al.*, 1964
	.28		−.26	Fitzhugh *et al.*, 1965b
	.41		.64	Henderson *et al.*, 1966a

TABLE 2.34 (cont.)

Item	Correlation coefficients: Simple: Single measure	Simple: Means/several measures	Partial (adjusted for carcass wt.)	Authors
		.44		Cole *et al.*, 1962
Carcass muscle (%)	−.83			Butterfield, 1964a
	−.79		−.78	Henderson *et al.*, 1966a
	−.76	−.73		Ramsey *et al.*, 1962
	−.67			Field *et al.*, 1966b
Carcass muscle (wt.)		.07		Cole *et al.*, 1962
Bone (%)	−.84			Butterfield, 1964a
Edible meat (%)	−.87			Riley *et al.*, 1968
	−.75		−.75	Henderson *et al.*, 1966a
	−.72	−.66		Abraham *et al.*, 1968
	−.58			Hedrick *et al.*, 1965
	−.57	−.64		Allen *et al.*, 1968
Edible meat (wt.)	−.26	−.27		Allen *et al.*, 1968
	−.13			Miller *et al.*, 1965
	−.10			Hedrick *et al.*, 1965
	0.25	.43		Abraham *et al.*, 1968
		0.22		Busch *et al.*, 1968
First quality meat (RLRC) (%)	−.76		−.76	Henderson *et al.*, 1966a
	−.72		−.75	Murphey *et al.*, 1963
	−.71	−.73		Brungardt & Bray, 1963
	−.60			Hedrick *et al.*, 1965
	−.60	−.78		Allen *et al.*, 1968
	−.56			Miller *et al.*, 1965
	−.64			Zinn *et al.*, 1961
	−.22			Iwanaga & Cobb, 1963
			−.61	Stringer *et al.*, 1963
		−.15		King *et al.*, 1964
First quality meat (RLRC) (wt.)	−.26			Allen *et al.*, 1968
	−.20			Miller *et al.*, 1965
	−.13			Hedrick *et al.*, 1965
Steaks and roasts (wt.)			−.54	DuBose *et al.*, 1967

2.6.2.8 OTHER MEASURES OF FATNESS. Kennick and England (1960) described a method of taking a core sample 6 mm in diameter from the 9th–10th–11th rib cut and separating it into muscle and fat. Better correlations with 9th–10th–11th rib composition were obtained by probing from the side, which missed the eye muscle, than from above, which included it. There seems to be little advantage from this complicated technique over a single measure of fat-thickness.

Some correlations of kidney fat (as a percentage of carcass weight) with various carcass parameters are set out in Table 2.35. While the relationships are consistent, their magnitude is generally less than in the case of fat-thickness over the eye muscle.

Murphey *et al.* (1960) included kidney fat in their yield grade prediction index, but is doubtful if it contributes much when fat-thickness measurements are available. This

TABLE 2.35 CORRELATION OF PERCENTAGE KIDNEY FAT AND VARIOUS CARCASS PARAMETERS

Parameters	Correlation	Authors
Carcass weight	.13	Goll *et al.*, 1961a
	.42	Abraham *et al.*, 1968
Carcass grade	.27	Goll *et al.*, 1961a
Carcass grade (adjusted for carcass weight)	.28	Goll *et al.*, 1961a
Fat (%)	.40	Brungardt & Bray, 1963
	.68	Field *et al.*, 1966b
Muscle (%)	−.34	Henderson *et al.*, 1966a
	−.65	Field *et al.*, 1966b
Edible meat (%)	−.24	Field *et al.*, 1966b
	−.60	Miller *et al.*, 1965
First quality meat (RLRC) (%)	−.25	Field *et al.*, 1966b
	−.54	Brungardt & Bray, 1963
	−.61	Stringer *et al.*, 1963
	−.61	Miller *et al.*, 1965
Eye-muscle area	−.44	Abraham *et al.*, 1968

is borne out by the findings of Henderson *et al.* (1966b) that there was no advantage from including the percentage of kidney fat in an index which already included fat-thickness, carcass weight and longissimus dorsi area.

Thackston *et al.* (1967) and Kirchner *et al.* (1968) have compared various prediction equations developed by USDA and various American universities. Sex significantly affected the accuracy of several and ranked correlations were never more than 0.85.

A few workers have computed relationships between excess fat (fat-trim) and various carcass parameters, and these are shown in Table 2.36. As might be expected, excess fat is highly correlated with the percentages of total and first quality edible meat.

Hicks and Hazel (1965) considered that excess fat when adjusted for breed, nutritional level and carcass weight accounted for 87% of the total variance in carcass value. They concluded that kidney fat and fat-depth alone, while being useful indicators, did not reflect overall carcass differences to a satisfactory degree.

2.6.2.9 BONE. The idea of using bone weights and dimensions to predict carcass composition originated with the Hammond school. The cannon bone was one of the most favoured and McMeekan (1956) stated that given the weight of this bone and of the carcass he could predict the weight of lean meat within 1%! Needless to say, subsequent workers (Orme *et al.*, 1959a) have been a little less enthusiastic about the predictive value of such measurements. Orts and King (1959) investigated the metacarpus and metatarsus bones and found both weight and weight/length ratio to be highly correlated (0.87 and 0.88) with the weight of preferred wholesale cuts. However, in the same year Cahill *et al.*, while confirming the high values for simple correlations (weight of femur to weight of edible meat had $r = 0.93$), found that on correcting for carcass weight, the correlations became non-significant. Subsequent

TABLE 2.36 CORRELATION BETWEEN PERCENTAGE EXCESS FAT AND CARCASS TRAITS

Item	Correlation coefficient	Authors
Carcass weight	.09	Allen *et al.*, 1968
	.37	Willis *et al.*, 1968
Carcass grade	.70	Zinn *et al.*, 1962
Marbling score	.74	Zinn *et al.*, 1962
Fat in carcass (%)	.75	Brungardt & Bray, 1963
Fat in 10th rib cut (%)	.43	Willis *et al.*, 1968
Bone in carcass (%)	−.77	Zinn *et al.*, 1963a
	−.94	Miller *et al.*, 1965
Edible meat (%)	−.92	Riley *et al.*, 1968
	−.72	Willis *et al.*, 1968
First quality meat (%)	−.76	Willis *et al.*, 1968
	−.91	Miller *et al.*, 1965
First quality meat (RLRC) (%)	−.90	Brungardt & Bray, 1963
	−.89	Iwanaga & Cobb, 1963
	−.81	Zinn *et al.*, 1963a
	−.66	Zinn *et al.*, 1962

work by the Orts and King group (Wythe *et al.*, 1961) yielded lower correlations than previously between bone weight and weight of edible meat, despite the fact that their sample covered a wide range of carcass weights. Later Orts *et al.* (1968) found that weight, weight/length ratio and the area of the metacarpal bone were correlated 0.47, 0.45 and 0.42 with the weight of first-quality meat (RLRC). Even total carcass bone is less well correlated with edible meat yield than such simple measurements as fat-thickness (compare Tables 2.37 and 2.34).

Zinn *et al.* (1963a) obtained partial regression coefficients of 0.62 and 0.25 for percentage excess fat and percentage bone in an equation relating to first-quality meat yield and therefore concluded that excess fat was more than twice as important as bone in predicting yield of edible meat.

TABLE 2.37 CORRELATION BETWEEN PERCENTAGE BONE AND VARIOUS CARCASS TRAITS

Item	Correlation coefficient	Authors
Carcass weight	−.35	Willis *et al.*, 1968
Bone in 10th rib cut (%)	.43	Willis *et al.*, 1968
Excess fat (%)	−.77	Zinn *et al.*, 1963
	−.31	Willis *et al.*, 1968
	−.61	Miller *et al.*, 1965
Edible meat (%)	.71	Riley *et al.*, 1968
First quality edible meat (RLRC) (%)	.45	Brungardt & Bray, 1963
	.53	Miller *et al.*, 1965
	.73	Zinn *et al.*, 1963

Highly relevant, on the other hand, is the ratio of muscle to bone (Hankins *et al.*, 1943) because of its direct effect on edible meat yield. This ratio increases with carcass weight (Moulton *et al.*, 1922; Kropf and Graf, 1959b; Zinn *et al.*, 1963a) and with fatness (Kropf and Graf, 1959b; Tayler, 1964), since carcass weight and fatness are related. It would appear from the work of Berg and Butterfield (1968) that the true determinant of the muscle/bone ratio is carcass weight rather than fatness. They found a pooled within-group correlation of 0.44 between the muscle/bone ratio and total weight of fat tissue, which was similar to the correlation of 0.38 with the percentage of fat. A multiple regression equation using carcass weight as a second independent variable showed that this accounted for all the variation associated with the muscle/bone ratio and that the percentage of fat had no effect when carcass weight was statistically controlled. Their carcasses had a wide range, but a relatively low average value, for fatness. However, re-analysis of the data of Callow (1961), where fatness was high, supported their thesis. Confirmatory evidence is to be found in the data of Zinn *et al.* (1963a, b) and the reappraisal by Elsley *et al.* (1964) of the growth studies of McMeekan and Palsson.

While a high muscle/bone ratio is desirable *per se*, the economic consequences of increased carcass weight (and associated fatness due to the higher weight) must be carefully evaluated. Optimum slaughter weight and therefore muscle/bone ratio will depend upon the genetic merit of the cattle, their nutritional plane and other environmental influences.

According to Nelms *et al.* (1968) there is no satisfactory method of predicting muscle/bone ratio other than deriving first the separate parameters. Their equations for deriving muscle weight (Y_1) and bone weight (Y_2) were:

$$Y_1 = -8.1 + 0.627X_1 - 10.1X_2 + 12.5X_3,$$
$$Y_2 = 0.39 + 0.052X_1 + 4.0X_3 + 0.59X_4 - 1.0X_5,$$

where X_1 = carcass weight (kg), X_2 = fat thickness at 12th rib (cm), X_3 = weight of forearm muscles (kg), X_4 = round depth (cm) and X_5 = per cent of kidney fat. These equations accounted for 96 and 85% of the variation in muscle and bone respectively.

2.6.2.10 Specific gravity. The use of specific gravity to estimate carcass composition is based on the hypothesis that animal tissues consist basically of fat and non-fat tissue: the latter contains water in a fixed proportion of 73–74%; the fat-free dry matter contains approximately 80% protein; water and fat are inversely related and have different densities. The formulation of these theories rests on the studies made by Moulton in Missouri in 1923 (cited by Panaretto, 1964).

The technique has been widely used in pig carcasses (e.g. Brown *et al.*, 1951; Price *et al.*, 1957; Saffle and Bratzler, 1959). It was first applied to cattle by Kraybill *et al.* (1952) and more recently the method has been described by Meyer *et al.* (1960b) and Morris and Moir (1964). Some idea of the efficacy of specific gravity for assessing carcass composition can be obtained from the correlation coefficients in Table 2.38. The data are particularly inadequate in half carcass estimations; there is an indication that the size of the correlation is linked to the weight of the sample joint and possibly its fat content.

It is perhaps significant that all the reports concerning specific gravity originate

TABLE 2.38 CORRELATION BETWEEN SPECIFIC GRAVITY AND VARIOUS CARCASS TRAITS

Item	Specific gravity in	Correlation coefficient	Authors
Carcass grade	9th–10th–11th rib	−.68	Orme *et al.*, 1958
		.17	Cole *et al.*, 1962
Marbling		.72	Cole *et al.*, 1962
Fat in carcass (%)	Carcass	−.98	Meyer *et al.*, 1960a
	Carcass	−.92	Powell *et al.*, 1968b
	Carcass	−.91	Riley *et al.*, 1968
Fat in empty body (%)	Carcass	−.84	Gil *et al.*, 1968
Excess fat (%)	Carcass	−.91	Riley *et al.*, 1968
Fat in joint (%)	9th–10th–11th rib	−.73	Kropf, 1959
	9th–10th–11th rib	−.40	Cole *et al.*, 1960
Fat thickness, 12th rib	9th–10th–11th rib	−.57	Cole *et al.*, 1960
Ether extract in longissimus dorsi (%)	Longissimus dorsi	−.36	Bieber *et al.*, 1961
	9th–10th–11th rib	−.81	Orme *et al.*, 1958
Ether extract in joint (%)	9th–10th–11th rib	−.77	Cole *et al.*, 1960
Water in carcass (%)	Carcass	.90	Riley *et al.*, 1968
Water in longissimus dorsi (%)	Longissimus dorsi	.03	Bieber *et al.*, 1961
Water in 9th–10th–11th rib (%)	9th–10th–11th rib	.74	Orme *et al.*, 1958
Protein in longissimus dorsi (%)	Longissimus dorsi	.60	Bieber *et al.*, 1961
Protein in 9th–10th–11th rib (%)	9th–10th–11th rib	.68	Orme *et al.*, 1958
Separable lean in 9th–10th–11th rib (%)	9th–10th–11th rib	.67	Cole *et al.*, 1960
	9th–10th–11th rib	.45	Kropf, 1959
Bone in joint (%)	9th–10th–11th rib	.82	Kropf, 1959
Edible meat (%)	Carcass	.72	Cobb & Ovejera, 1965
	Carcass	.82	Riley *et al.*, 1968
First quality meat (RLRC) %	Carcass	.74	Iwanaga & Cobb, 1963

from the US with carcasses characterized by a high degree of fatness. In a comprehensive study Kelly *et al.* (1968) examined 150 steers of known history and which had been raised on four diets ranging from maintenance to full feeding. The specific gravities of ten different joints were related to their physical and chemical composition. It was concluded that the use of whole carcass specific gravity to determine carcass composition was of extremely limited value and particularly so with animals whose fat content was less than 20%. On the other hand, density of the 9th–10th–11th rib joint was a reliable guide to its composition which in turn was highly related to the composition of the carcass.

2.6.2.11 CREATININE. Brody (1945) accumulated evidence to show that the level of urinary creatinine reflected the quantity of muscle in the body, and Lofgreen and Garrett (1954) reported a correlation of 0.67 between creatinine excretion and the percentage of lean in the 9th–10th–11th rib cut. Wuthier and Stratton (1957) estimated creatinine levels in blood serum and obtained a correlation of 0.55 between these and the percentage of lean in the same rib cut. Although significant, these correlations indicate that creatinine accounts for only some 40% of the variation in the lean of the rib cut, and its value as a predictor of lean in the carcass must inevitably be low.

2.6.2.12 Carcass weight. The simplest and most precise measurement of the carcass is its weight. Everitt (1964b) has said that "up to the stage where the deposition of fatty tissue in the carcass predominates in the development cycle, carcass weight is one of the most accurate biological and economic determinants of composition and quality". He showed that in animals less than 10 months of age, carcass weight was a better predictor of weight of edible meat than was the weight of the biceps femoris, a muscle considered by Butterfield (1964a) to be the best indicator of total carcass muscle. Table 2.39 illustrates this point in view of the very high correlations between carcass weight and measures of both total muscle and edible meat. In line with Everitt's postulate, the correlations were less for fat. The value of carcass weight to predict percentage composition is low.

Table 2.39 Correlation between Carcass Weight and Major Traits of the Carcass

Item	Correlation coefficient with		Authors
	Weight of trait	% trait	
Muscle	.77		Cole *et al.*, 1960b
	.99		Tulloh, 1964
Edible meat		−.32	Cobb & Ovejera, 1965
	.87	−.12	Allen *et al.*, 1968
	.89		Busch *et al.*, 1968
	.93	−.04	Willis *et al.*, 1968
Pistola	.90	−.27	Willis *et al.*, 1968
First quality	.89	−.32	Willis *et al.*, 1968
First quality (RLRC)	.89	−.11	Allen *et al.*, 1968
	.93		Cundiff *et al.*, 1967
	.94		DuBose *et al.*, 1967
	.96	−.48	Swiger *et al.*, 1964
	.97	−.52	Birkett *et al.*, 1965
	.97	−.54	Magee, 1965b
Roasts and steaks	.90		Fitzhugh *et al.*, 1965
Fat	.59		Cole *et al.*, 1960
	.97		Tulloh, 1964
Excess fat	.56	.37	Willis *et al.*, 1968
	.70	.09	Allen *et al.*, 1968
Bone	.50	−.35	Willis *et al.*, 1968
	.96		Tulloh, 1964

The growing use of carcass weight as a major component in prediction equations—which a decade ago were almost exclusively based on sample joint composition—possibly reflects the undoubted trend towards leaner carcasses and the failure of grade and score card systems to indicate much more than fatness. For example,

Butterfield (1964a) suggests the following formula to predict total muscle: $K_1 - K_2$ (fat thickness) $- K_3$ (carcass weight), where K_1, K_2 and K_3 are constants. Fitzhugh *et al.* (1965b) reported partial correlations between carcass weight and that of first-quality meat (RLRC) of 0.50 with longissimus dorsi area held constant, 0.90 with fat-thickness constant and 0.94 with kidney fat constant. In 1964 Swiger *et al.* used even simpler parameters and obtained correlations of 0.94 between the weight of first-quality meat (RLRC) and live weight plus fat-thickness over the eye muscle, recorded either on the carcass or the live animal. Henderson *et al.* (1966b) employed carcass weight and fat-thickness to estimate the percentage of first-quality meat (RLRC) and obtained a multiple correlation of 0.76. Inclusion of more measurements, for example eye-muscle area and percentage kidney fat, or trimmed round and rump, only improved the correlation to 0.83.

The future of prediction equations would thus seem to lie less in detailed measurements and/or sample joint composition than in reliance on carcass weight together with some simple measure of fatness.

2.6.3 Objective methods of evaluating attractiveness and eatability

2.6.3.1 Colour. The methods of measuring the colour of lean meat have been reviewed by Nickerson (1946), Cook (1964) and Pearson (1966). The three methods available are subjective appraisal, extraction of the pigments for spectrophotometric analysis (Fleming *et al.*, 1960) and light reflectance from the cut surface with subsequent analysis in a colorimeter (Hunter, 1948). The ultimate arbiter, however, is visual appraisal and on this basis Charpentier (1964) concluded that light reflectance was superior to the use of extracted pigments. It is nevertheless still true that there is a need for "a simple, rapid and easily understood method for measurement of lean meat colour" (Pearson, 1966).

Fat colour has been studied less, but there seems to be little objection to the technique suggested by Bunnell *et al.* (1954) of extracting the carotenoids and measuring their concentration in a spectrophotometer or colorimeter.

2.6.3.2 Firmness and texture. Although mechanical methods have been used to assess firmness (Pilkington *et al.*, 1960), there is no evidence to show that they are an improvement on subjective appraisal. The suggestion of Swift and Berman (1959) that water retention might be related to firmness also awaits verification. Texture is possibly even more difficult to measure objectively. Pearson (1966) intimated that coarse texture is due to the presence of connective tissue, but measurements of this, for example by hydroxyproline, have yet to be identified with subjective ratings. Kropf and Graf (1959a) obtained a correlation of 0.54 between the subjective appraisal of texture and Warner-Bratzler shear values, which is too low to allow measurement of texture by shear force methods.

2.6.3.3 Tenderness, juiciness and flavour. The final decision regarding eatability rests with the consumer. For this reason, most assessments of eatability rely on analytical taste panels. The method presents problems in regard to the number of tasters and the statistical control of sampling and presentation. Panel members need to be carefully selected—not everyone has a developed palate—and must be trained so as to be able to express their reactions in repeatable terms.

Analytical taste panels must not be confused with consumer preference studies. The former seek to obtain precise, repeatable measurements of specific traits according to a predetermined scale of values. The latter are invariably conducted on a larger scale and aim only to measure overall acceptability, rather than specific components of eatability. They tend to have poor repeatability (King *et al.*, 1958).

Taste panels are difficult to train and organize and inevitably impose restrictions on experimental design. For this reason, objective methods have been sought, not with the aim of replacing the taste panel, but in order to enlarge the scale and scope of eatability studies.

The only trait which has been successfully measured by objective means is tenderness. The various techniques have been reviewed by Schultz (1957) and Pearson (1963b). Many devices have been developed, but only the Warner–Bratzler shear machine seems to have found general acceptance. This machine measures the force required to slice through a sample of meat. Hence high values indicate toughness and the correlation of shear values and taste panel scores should always be negative. Some correlations between the two measurements, obtained by different groups of investigators, are given in Table 2.40. Due to the known effects of cooking on meat tenderness, it is important that shear values be made on cooked meat. Lower correlations between taste panel scores and shear values on raw meat have been reported by Cook (1964).

Tenderness is usually measured in the longissimus dorsi, a logical site since most

TABLE 2.40 CORRELATIONS BETWEEN WARNER–BRATZLER SHEAR VALUES AND TASTE PANEL SCORES

Muscle or joint	No. of samples	Correlation coefficient	Authors
Longissimus dorsi	24	−.88	Matthews & Bennett, 1962
	16	−.88	Morgan, 1967
	132	−.85	Hunsley *et al.*, 1967c
	36	−.83	Matthews & Bennett, 1962
	44	−.80	Wang *et al.*, 1956
	84	−.77	Field *et al.*, 1966a
	60	−.76	Cobb *et al.*, 1961
	80	−.73	Romans *et al.*, 1965a
	32	−.70	Moe *et al.*, 1964
	50	−.67	Webb *et al.*, 1964
	134	−.65	Field *et al.*, 1966a
Semitendinosus	13	−.51	Wang *et al.*, 1956
Various	135	−.77	Renou, 1964
	108	−.67	Renou, 1964
Loin	330	−.78	McBee & Wiles, 1967
Broiled loin	38	−.84	Cover *et al.*, 1957
Braised loin	38	−.89	Cover *et al.*, 1957
Broiled bottom round	38	−.73	Cover *et al.*, 1957
Braised bottom round	38	−.86	Cover *et al.*, 1957

steaks for grilling or broiling come from this muscle. The site must be selected carefully, Christians *et al.* (1961) having shown in a study of 176 Angus carcasses that the meat at the 12th rib was more tender than at the 8th or 9th rib. Henrickson and Mjoseth (1964) also observed substantial variation in the tenderness of the longissimus dorsi and considered the semitendinosus to be more uniformly tender. Interactions between breed and sampling site used in tenderness studies have been noted by Sharrah *et al.* (1965).

In addition to location differences, Hedrick *et al.* (1968) noted that the method of cooking also affected shear values in that broiled meat was always more tender than that cooked in deep fat. Smith *et al.* (1968) recommended that several core samples be taken from the longissimus dorsi muscle since a tenderness gradient existed over the cross-section.

Up to the present time, there are no objective methods to measure juiciness or flavour which correlate with taste panel assessments. Moreover, such a development is unlikely until more is known of the chemical and physical relationships which determine the expression of these traits.

II. The Inputs

CHAPTER 3

Genetic Improvement

3.1 INTRODUCTION

The animal breeder can change the genetic nature of the population under his control in two possible ways. He can decide which of his animals should be used as parents (selection) and how these should be mated (breeding system).

The effectiveness of selection depends upon the superiority of the selected animals in relation to the mean of the population from which they come (selection differential) and the extent to which this superiority is inherited. In any population the smaller the proportion of animals selected as parents, the greater will be the selection differential provided that those selected are at the upper end of the merit scale for the trait involved. The selection differentials resulting from different intensities of selection are given in Table 3.1.

An example of the use of Table 3.1 can be taken from the data of Willis and Preston (1968a) in respect of live weight for age at 400 kg in performance-tested Charolais bulls. The bulls averaged 1.24 ± 0.14 kg for this variable. In such a population the best 50% would have an average of 1.35 kg ($1.24 + 0.14 \times 0.80$) whereas the best 10% would average 1.49 kg ($1.24 + 0.14 \times 1.75$) and the best 1%, 1.61 kg ($1.24 + 0.14 \times 2.67$).

The possible selection intensity depends, in part, upon the sex of the animals. If a female produces only four progeny, half of which are females, then the selection intensity on the female side cannot exceed 50% and the maximum selection differential will be 0.8 times the SD of the trait. On the other hand, a bull in natural service might have 40 sons which would give a selection differential of $2.3 \times$ SD. With AI, the number of males required becomes negligible in relation to the total population, and the upper limit of selection intensity will be very high. The rate of replacement thus restricts the selection intensity, and populations or herds with lower replacement rates can be subjected to more intense selection, as can declining populations. On the other hand, in populations, breeds or herds which are expanding rapidly, or in which the replacement rate is high so that most females are retained for breeding purposes, the selection intensity—especially on the female side—is very much reduced.

In commercial practice we are mainly concerned with the response to selection per unit of time rather than per animal generation. Robertson and Rendel (1950) expressed the rate of genetic progress as

$$\Delta G = \frac{\Sigma I}{\Sigma L},$$

TABLE 3.1 SELECTION DIFFERENTIAL ATTAINABLE BY VARIOUS INTENSITIES OF SELECTION (AFTER LUSH, 1945)

Percentage of the population saved	Selection differential (in terms of standard deviations)
95	0.11
90	0.20
85	0.27
80	0.35
75	0.42
70	0.50
65	0.57
60	0.64
55	0.72
50	0.80
45	0.88
40	0.97
35	1.06
30	1.16
25	1.27
20	1.40
15	1.55
10	1.75
5	2.06
4	2.15
3	2.27
2	2.42
1	2.67

where ΔG is the rate of genetic gain per year, ΣI is the selection differential for all possible pathways and ΣL is the total generation interval. The actual pathways as defined by Rendel and Robertson (1950) are:

	Selection differential	Generation interval
Bulls to breed bulls	I_{bb}	L_{bb}
Bulls to breed cows	I_{bc}	L_{bc}
Cows to breed bulls	I_{cb}	L_{cb}
Cows to breed cows	I_{cc}	L_{cc}

The generation interval is usually calculated as the average age of the parents when their progeny are born. Longevity in parental stock will increase the generation interval although, by making available more data on the parent, it can also lead to greater accuracy of selection and an increased differential. The breeder therefore has to weigh the benefits likely to accrue from waiting for maximum data (which increases progress per generation) against the disadvantages of an increased generation interval (which could reduce progress per unit of time). A compromise solution must usually be worked out for any particular set of circumstances.

In their study with dairy cows, Rendel and Robertson (1950) found that genetic improvement in milk yield was made up as follows: I_{bb} 43%, I_{bc} 18%, I_{cb} 33%, I_{cc} 6%. This demonstrates the importance of accurate selection of bulls since 76% (43 + 33) of the total improvement came from this source. Generation interval was of the order of 4 years per pathway. By 1960 the mean generation interval in British Friesian cattle was 5.4 years (O'Connor and Willis, 1967), mainly as a result of the adoption of a progeny testing programme and the use of older, tested bulls. Similar studies have not been made in beef cattle, but one would expect generation interval to be somewhat higher in females, due to the tendency to retain older cows, and lower in males, since beef bulls are used extensively at earlier ages than dairy sires undergoing progeny tests for milk yield.

The selection differential only measures the animal's phenotypic superiority in a trait and must be multiplied by the heritability which is equivalent to the regression of the animal's breeding value upon its phenotype. By changing genic frequencies selection could also change heritability values, thus necessitating recalculation of heritability each generation. In practical terms, however, this is a minor issue and Robertson's and Rendel's (1950) formula is normally used for several generations. When selection is practised for more than one trait simultaneously, the formula of Magee (1965a) is more appropriate.

Response will be difficult, if not impossible, to predict when the selection method does not efficiently evaluate superiority. If variation in a particular character is largely environmental in nature, then heritability will be low and response will tend to be small unless selection intensity is very high. But in any given set of circumstances heritabilities cannot be calculated until a large body of data has been amassed and in order to compile data a breeding programme has usually to be initiated. This paradoxical situation leads to selection programmes being undertaken on the basis of assumed heritabilities for the particular characters under selection (using findings of other investigators). It is in such circumstances that difficulties most often arise for if evaluation of the animals is inaccurate, and more of the variation is due to environmental factors, then heritabilities will be lower than those originally taken as standard. The reverse situation, in which evaluation is more accurate and heritabilities higher than expected, presents no problems since although response measurement is inaccurate it underestimates rather than overestimates progress. These considerations have practical importance in deciding what form of testing programme should be undertaken.

To be effective, selection of animals must be undertaken in a specific rather than in a random manner. In deciding which animals shall be chosen to be the parents of the next generation the breeder can make use of various systems depending upon the information available. He can select his animals on the basis of ancestry, family relatives, individual performance or the performance of progeny, or combinations of all these factors. The efficiency of any system depends upon the nature of the character under selection in terms of its heritability, whether it is measurable in the live or the dead animal (or both) and the practical and economic problems which any system produces in particular circumstances.

3.2 HERITABILITIES

3.2.1 The concept

The first stage of any genetic improvement plan is to determine which traits are of economic importance. Their order of precedence will depend, in part, on geographic location in the sense that characteristics important in one area of the world may be of little value in another. Certain characteristics, however, such as fertility, liveability, fast growth and efficient feed conversion are fundamental. The extent to which these can be incorporated into a selection programme is partly determined by the extent to which they are inherited.

The usual measurement of the influence of heredity is the ratio of additive genetic variance to phenotypic variance; this is termed the heritability (h^2). There are several ways in which the heritability of a character can be determined (cf. Falconer, 1960b), the most usual being paternal half-sib correlation, intersire regression or offspring–parent regression. The relative efficiency of the various methods depends upon the particular population and the number of records involved in the estimate. For some mathematical discussion of the subject the reader is referred to Kempthorne and Tandon (1953), Val Vleck *et al.* (1960), McKean and Bohren (1961) and Searle (1962).

Since heritability of a trait is a function of the population in which it was calculated, it is not strictly accurate to take estimates made in one population for general application in another. Nevertheless, in broad terms, characters can be classified as having high (>0.50), medium (0.25 to 0.50) or low (<0.25) heritability.

3.2.2 Reproductive traits

Amongst these are some of the most important economic traits in beef production (Table 3.2). Unfortunately, the only characteristic which appears to be even moderately high is gestation length, and this is of negligible importance. For all practical purposes fertility will not give sufficient response to justify selection. This is not to say that fertility is not under genetic control since there are marked differences between breeds. But greater progress for this trait is more likely to come from heterosis and crossbreeding.

3.2.3 Calf liveability

The same comments apply to this trait as to reproductive rate. There are differences due to breed and also to sex (Woodward and Clark, 1959). Improvement will mostly rest with exploitation of heterosis.

3.2.4 Birth weight

Estimates given in Table 3.3 indicate that the preferred value for this trait is around 0.40; it should therefore respond to selection.

TABLE 3.2 HERITABILITY ESTIMATES FOR REPRODUCTIVE TRAITS

Trait	No. of records	Breed	h^2	Authors
Fertility	500,000		.01 to .02	Maijala, 1964
	1419	BPL	.00 to .20	Schönmuth, 1965
Reproductive performance	412		.15	Davenport *et al.*, 1965
Reproducing ability	1608	H	.45	Brinks *et al.*, 1964b
Reproductive score	2424	SG	.04	Dickey & Cartwright, 1966
Gestation length	3606	H	−.05	Lindley *et al.*, 1958
	747	H	.10	Everett & Magee, 1965
	4113		.11	Hanset, 1966
		Tharparkar	.32	Singh *et al.*, 1958
	1971–4369	Various	.33 to .57	Banerjee-Schotsman, 1964
	459	C	.37	Vianna *et al.*, 1964b
	16375	MRY	.40	Banerjee-Schotsman, 1965
	2063	Various	.42	DeFries *et al.*, 1959
	296	RD (female)	.49	Andersen, 1962
	608	A, H, S, B × H	.50	Wheat & Riggs, 1958
	351	H	.54	Lasley *et al.*, 1961
	958	H	.60	Plum *et al.*, 1965
	319	RD (male)	.83	Andersen, 1962
Twinning	500,000		.03	Maijala, 1964
Birth rate	571	B, Bx	.39	Deese & Koger, 1967b
Calving interval	152,342	H	.02 to .04	Miller *et al.*, 1966
	3989	A	.03	Schalles, 1967
	3606	H	.06	Lindley *et al.*, 1958
			.15	Schmidt, 1958
	2424	SG	.20	Dickey & Cartwright, 1966
Service period	3606	H	.03	Lindley *et al.*, 1958
	162	Tharparker	.13	Singh *et al.*, 1958
		NR	.13	Odegard, 1965
Conception rate	1406	HF	.08	Inskeep *et al.*, 1961
Age at first oestrus	192	Hariana	.38	Choudhury *et al.*, 1964
Age at first fertile oestrus	192	Hariana	.08	Choudhury *et al.*, 1964
Age at first calving	88	Zebu	−.03	Stobbs, 1966a
Mothering ability	2424	SG	.06	Dickey & Cartwright, 1966
Survival (%)	2424	SG	.05	Dickey & Cartwright, 1966
Calf survival ability	2424	SG	.03	Dickey & Cartwright, 1966

TABLE 3.3 HERITABILITY ESTIMATES FOR BIRTH WEIGHT

Location	No. of records	Breed	h^2	Authors
Virginia	175	H	.00	Thornton *et al.*, 1960
São Paulo	459	C	.11	Vianna *et al.*, 1964a
Virginia	214	A	.13	Thornton *et al.*, 1960
Texas	580	H	.15	Miguel & Cartwright, 1963
Texas	196	B	.16	Miguel & Cartwright, 1963
Sudan	275	Kenana	.18	Alim, 1964
France	7384	Limousin crosses	.19	Poujardieu & Vissac, 1966

TABLE 3.3 (cont.)

Location	No. of records	Breed	h^2	Authors
Texas	209	BH × B	.20	Miguel & Cartwright, 1963
Arizona	720	H	.20	Pahnish *et al.*, 1964
Virginia	257	S	.21	Thornton *et al.*, 1960
Nebraska	502	A, H, S	.22	Burris & Blunn, 1952
Ohio	793	H	.22	Swiger, 1961
Michigan	1064	HF	.22	Everett & Magee, 1965
Montana	177	H	.23	Knapp & Nordskog, 1946a
India	557	Sahiwal	.23	Batra & Desai, 1962
France	548	C	.24	Auriol *et al.*, 1963
France	7384	C crosses	.24	Poujardieu & Vissac, 1966
Arkansas	932	A	.24	Brown & Galvez, 1968
Russia	283	BPL	.25	Zavertjaev, 1966
Texas	146	BH × H	.26	Miguel & Cartwright, 1963
Maryland	402	SG	.29	Dawson *et al.*, 1947
S. Africa	544	Crosses	.30	Lombard, 1963
Nebraska	647	A, H, S	.30	Swiger *et al.*, 1962
New Jersey	266	HF	.32	Lal *et al.*, 1966
Nebraska	958	HF	.34	Plum *et al.*, 1965
Montana	4553	H	.35	Koch & Clark, 1955a, b
Uganda	205	Zebu	.36	Stobbs, 1966a
Nebraska	2092	A, H, S	.37	Swiger *et al.*, 1962
Illinois	1234	HF, BS, G, J, Ay	.38 to .51	Legault & Touchberry, 1962
Montana	3584	H	.38	Brinks *et al.*, 1964b
Oklahoma	295		.40	Kieffer *et al.*, 1959
Mexico	1049	B	.41	Berruecos & Robison, 1968
Nigeria		White Fulani	.42	Foster, 1960
Iowa	6000	H	.42	Koch, 1953
Arkansas	789	H	.45	Brown & Galvez, 1968
W. Africa		Ruanda	.46	Compere, 1965
UAR	235	Egyptian	.48	Ragab & Abd-el-Salam, 1963
Texas	48	H × B	.50	Miguel & Cartwright, 1963
Maryland	58	DS	.51	Dawson *et al.*, 1955
Oregon			.52	Bogart *et al.*, 1963b
Montana	880	H	.53	Knapp & Clark, 1950
Montana	615	H	.54	Shelby *et al.*, 1963
Texas	385	B × H	.55	Miguel & Cartwright, 1963
Japan	485	Japanese	.57	Kumazaki & Matsukawa, 1964
Germany	1556	BPL	.58	Rappen, 1965
Oregon			.58	Bogart *et al.*, 1963b
New Jersey	526	HF	.58	Lal *et al.*, 1966
Montana	542	H	.59	Shelby *et al.*, 1957
Oklahoma	498		.60	Kieffer *et al.*, 1958
Arizona	414	H	.67	Lasley *et al.*, 1961
Montana	635	H	.72	Shelby *et al.*, 1955
Tennessee	469	H	.88	Loganathan *et al.*, 1965
Mississippi		A	.99	Meade *et al.*, 1959a
Mississippi		H	1.00	Meade *et al.*, 1959a
Preferred value			.38	

3.2.5 Pre-weaning growth rate

Both rate of gain to weaning (Table 3.4) and weaning weight (Table 3.5) are of medium inheritance (0.30). Differences in heritability of pre-weaning growth due to sex have been reported by Meyerhoffer *et al.* (1963) and Marlowe and Vogt (1965), but management effects were probably partially responsible. In any event, growth rate during this period is of limited importance for, under systems of intensive production, most growth occurs in the feedlot.

TABLE 3.4 HERITABILITY ESTIMATES FOR PRE-WEANING GROWTH RATE (WEANING GENERALLY AT 6–8 MONTHS)

Location	No. of records	Breed	h^2	Authors
Nebraska	647	A, H, S	−.02	Swiger *et al.*, 1962
Oregon		A, H	.00	Hoornbeek & Bogart, 1966
Arizona	720	H	.05	Pahnish *et al.*, 1964
Virginia	1779	A, H	.07	Vogt & Marlowe, 1966
Japan	485	Japanese	.08	Kumazaki & Matsukawa, 1964
Iowa	6000	H	.12	Koch, 1953
Virginia	175	H	.13	Thornton *et al.*, 1960
Nebraska	2092	A, H, S	.14	Swiger *et al.*, 1962
Virginia	908	A, H, S	.18	Meyerhoeffer *et al.*, 1963
Virginia	1987	A, H, S	.20	Lehmann *et al.*, 1961
Montana	4553	H	.21	Koch & Clark, 1955a, b
Virginia	214	A	.21	Thornton *et al.*, 1960
S. Africa	544	Crosses	.22	Lombard, 1963
Virginia	1682	A, H, S	.22	Meyerhoeffer *et al.*, 1960
Pennsylvania	2019	A, H	.24 to .60	Hallman, 1966
Virginia	257	S	.25	Thornton *et al.*, 1960
Hawaii	1306	H	.26	Mahmud & Cobb, 1963
Virginia	4153	H (heifers)	.27	Marlowe & Vogt, 1964
Virginia	751	A, H, S	.28	Meyerhoeffer *et al.*, 1963
Virginia	2802	H (steers)	.31	Marlowe & Vogt, 1964
Virginia	4257	A (steers)	.31	Marlowe & Vogt, 1964
Virginia	8279	H	.31	Marlowe & Vogt, 1965
Virginia	1324	H (bulls)	.33	Marlowe & Vogt, 1964
Tennessee	469	H	.36	Loganathan *et al.*, 1965
Virginia	12,145	A	.38	Marlowe & Vogt, 1965
Montana	542	H	.40	Shelby *et al.*, 1957
Montana	3584	H	.40	Brinks *et al.*, 1964b
Virginia	6075	A (heifers)	.43	Marlowe & Vogt, 1964
New York	1648	H	.43	Cunningham & Henderson, 1965a
Mexico	1049	B	.43	Berruecos & Robison, 1968
New York	3190	A	.48	Cunningham & Henderson, 1965a
Virginia	1813	A (bulls)	.49	Marlowe & Vogt, 1964
Virginia	2638	A	.57	Schalles, 1967
Nebraska	480	A, H, S	.60	Swiger *et al.*, 1965
Oregon			.68	Bogart *et al.*, 1963b
Preferred value			.27	

TABLE 3.5 HERITABILITY ESTIMATES OF WEANING WEIGHT (BASED ON 180–240 DAYS)

Location	No. of records	Breed	h^2	Authors
Texas	241	Various	.00[a]	Dubose & Cartwright, 1967
Texas	146	BH × H	.07	Miguel & Cartwright, 1963
New Mexico	499	H	.08	Blackwell *et al.*, 1962
Virginia	212	A, H, S	.08	Carter & Kincaid, 1959a
Arizona	720	H	.10	Pahnish *et al.*, 1964
Arizona	414	H	.11	Lasley *et al.*, 1961
Arkansas	212	A	.11	Brown, 1958
Montana	177	H	.12	Knapp & Nordskog, 1946a
Japan	485	Japanese	.12	Kumazaki & Matsukawa, 1964
Florida	466	B × S	.17	Deese & Koger, 1967a
Arkansas	201	A, H, S	.18[c]	Brown & Gacula, 1964
Texas	209	BH × B	.19	Miguel & Cartwright, 1963
Iowa	600	H	.19	Koch, 1953
Louisiana	446	BA	.19	Dawson *et al.*, 1954
Virginia	1987	A, H, S	.21	Lehmann *et al.*, 1961
Texas	48	H × B	.22	Miguel & Cartwright, 1963
Kansas	265	S	.23	Gottlieb *et al.*, 1962
Montana	635	H	.23	Shelby *et al.*, 1955
Montana	4553	H	.24	Koch & Clark, 1955a, b
Montana	616	H	.24	Shelby *et al.*, 1963
Hawaii	1306	H	.24	Mahmud & Cobb, 1963
Texas	580	H	.24	Miguel & Cartwright, 1963
Texas	385	B × H	.25	Miguel & Cartwright, 1963
Ohio	748	H	.25	Swiger *et al.*, 1961b
Florida	725	B	.25	Deese & Koger, 1967a
Arkansas	255	H	.26	Brown, 1958
S. Africa	544	Crosses	.27	Lombard, 1963
Nebraska	1671	A, H, S	.28	Swiger *et al.*, 1963
Montana	880	H	.28	Knapp & Clark, 1950
Arizona	329	H	.28[b]	Pahnish *et al.*, 1961b
Michigan	326	H	.30	Magee *et al.*, 1961
Kansas	265	S	.30	Gottlieb *et al.*, 1962
S. Dakota	436	A	.32	Minyard & Dinkel, 1965b
Oklahoma	295		.32	Kieffer *et al.*, 1959
S. Dakota	336	H	.33	Wilson *et al.*, 1962
S. Dakota	1915	H	.33	Minyard & Dinkel, 1965b
Pennsylvania		Crosses	.33	Scarth *et al.*, 1965
Brazil	1168	Guzera	.35	Carneiro & Pereira, 1968
New Mexico	420	H	.38	Blackwell *et al.*, 1962
S. Dakota	473	H	.38	Wilson *et al.*, 1963b
Oklahoma	498		.39	Kieffer *et al.*, 1959
S. Dakota	679	H	.40	Busch & Dinkel, 1967
Nebraska	1121	H	.40	Koch *et al.*, 1968
California	165	H	.42	Wagnon & Rollins, 1959
Montana	3584	H	.43	Brinks *et al.*, 1964b
Montana	542	H	.43	Shelby *et al.*, 1957
Texas	196	B	.44	Miguel & Cartwright, 1963
Kansas	1861	A	.47	Hamann *et al.*, 1963
Mexico	1049	B	.47	Berruecos & Robison, 1968
Nebraska	733	A, H, S	.48	Swiger *et al.*, 1962

TABLE 3.5 (cont.)

Location	No. of records	Breed	h^2	Authors
N. Carolina	425		.54	Gregory & Stewart, 1962
38 US States	17,023	A	.54	Harricharan *et al.*, 1967
Arizona	329	H	.57[b]	Pahnish *et al.*, 1961b
California	140	H	.57	Wagnon & Rollins, 1959
Nebraska	480	A, H, S	.58	Swifer *et al.*, 1965
Virginia	212	A, H, S	.69	Carter & Kincaid, 1959a
Mississippi		A	.72	Meade *et al.*, 1959a
W. Africa		Ruanda	.75	Compere, 1965
Colorado	118	H	.81	Lindholm & Stonaker, 1957
Mississippi		H	1.00	Meade *et al.*, 1959a
Texas	241	Various	1.00	DuBose & Cartwright, 1967
Preferred value			.30	

[a] Adjusted for birth weight.
[b] 270 day weaning weight.
[c] 130 day weight (not weaning).

3.2.6 Post-weaning growth rate

The available data on this trait (Table 3.6) are almost exclusively American and based primarily on bulls that have been performance-tested or fattening steers. The preferred value is high being of the order of 0.50.

TABLE 3.6 HERITABILITY ESTIMATES FOR AVERAGE DAILY GAIN IN FEEDLOT

Location	No. of records	Days in feedlot	Breed	h^2	Authors
Virginia	175		H	.00	Thornton *et al.*, 1960
Texas	48		H × B	.00	Miguel & Cartwright, 1963
Virginia	214		A	.12	Thornton *et al.*, 1960
Ireland	271		F	.18	Vial & Mason, 1961
Virginia	257		S	.22	Thornton *et al.*, 1960
Oregon			A, H	.22 to .42	Hoornbeek & Bogart, 1966
Texas	196		B	.23	Miguel & Cartwright, 1963
Israel	1658	to 365 days	F	.33	Bar-Anan *et al.*, 1965
S. Dakota	336		H	.36	Wilson *et al.*, 1962
New Zealand	1072	to 21 months	A	.38[a]	Brumby *et al.*, 1963
Virginia	192	200	A, H, S	.38 to .49	Kincaid & Carter, 1958
S. Dakota	224	140	H	.39	Dearborn & Dinkel, 1959
Ohio	832	140	H	.40	Swiger, 1961
Germany	390	to 400 kg	BPL	.41	Heidler, 1966
Texas	146		HB × H	.42	Miguel & Cartwright, 1963
Bavaria	225	to 500 kg	Simmental	.43	Scheper, 1965

TABLE 3.6 (cont.)

Location	No. of records	Days in feedlot	Breed	h^2	Authors
S. Dakota	224	196	H	.43	Dearborn & Dinkel, 1959
S. Dakota	224	168	H	.45	Dearborn & Dinkel, 1959
S. Dakota	149	140	H	.45	Dinkel, 1958
Germany	1034	to 350 kg	F	.45	Langlet *et al.*, 1967
Montana	542	196	H	.46	Shelby *et al.*, 1960
Arkansas	371	154	A, H	.46	Brown & Gifford, 1962
28 US States	5150		A	.47	Harricharan *et al.*, 1967
Montana	616	254	H	.48	Shelby *et al.*, 1963
Germany	2295	to 1½ years	BPL	.50	Samson-Himmelstjernal, 1965
Colorado	1013			.50	McNitt *et al.*, 1966
S. Dakota	149	168	H	.52	Dinkel, 1958
S. Dakota	473	235–270	H	.52	Wilson *et al.*, 1963b
Nebraska	741	168	H	.52	Swiger *et al.*, 1962
Texas	1324			.53	Patterson *et al.*, 1955
Texas	291		B, H	.54	Warwick & Cartwright, 1955
S. Dakota	679		H	.55	Busch & Dinkel, 1967
Nebraska	733	168	A, H	.56	Swiger *et al.*, 1962
Montana	272		H	.57	Willson *et al.*, 1954
Colorado	417		H	.57	Lickley *et al.*, 1960
Germany	418	141–500	Simmental	.60	Averdunk, 1968
Nebraska	351	168	H	.63	Swiger *et al.*, 1962
Texas	56	224	H	.64	Fitzhugh *et al.*, 1967
S. Dakota	149	196	H	.65	Dinkel, 1958
Montana	880	252	H	.65	Knapp & Clark, 1950
Nebraska	1324	154–168	A, H, S	.65	Koch *et al.*, 1963
Virginia	212	168	A, H, S	.66	Carter & Kincaid, 1959a
Montana	635	252	H	.68	Shelby *et al.*, 1955
Texas	209		HB × B	.70	Miguel & Cartwright, 1963
Montana	613	252	H	.70	Knapp & Clark, 1951
Texas	241		Various	.71	DuBose & Cartwright, 1967
Texas	580		H	.74	Miguel & Cartwright, 1963
New Mexico	499	168	H	.76	Blackwell *et al.*, 1962
Arkansas	179	154	A, H, S	.77	Gacula & Brown, 1963
Germany	418	365–500	Simmental	.81	Averdunk, 1968
Oklahoma	176	180	A	.88	Christians *et al.*, 1962
Texas	385		B × H	.90	Miguel & Cartwright, 1963
Israel	525	to 425 days	F	.92	Levi *et al.*, 1967
Arkansas	201	154	A, H, S	.93	Brown & Gacula, 1964
Montana	177		H	.99	Knapp & Nordskog, 1946a
Nebraska	351	168	A, H, S	1.31	Swiger *et al.*, 1962
Preferred value				.52	

[a] On grass.

3.2.7 Final weight and weight per day of age

Most estimates for final weight after performance testing (Table 3.7) are high (average 0.65) and it is not surprising that this measurement is used as the main selection criterion in many US testing programmes. There is only one published estimate of weight per day of age in beef cattle (0.77), but our own unpublished findings, calculated on the basis of response to selection, confirm that this trait is highly heritable (0.60–0.70). It appears to be less heritable in dairy breeds but this may be a reflection of the different management systems used.

3.2.8 Feed intake and conversion

The values in Table 3.8 for feed intake are mainly in the region of 0.40. Estimates for feed conversion are much more variable, and although the average is also about

TABLE 3.7 HERITABILITY ESTIMATES OF FINAL WEIGHT AFTER PERFORMANCE TEST

Location	No. of records	Breed	h^2	Authors
UK	986	F	.12[ab]	Hodges *et al.*, 1961
California	200	H	.16	Rollins *et al.*, 1962
Arkansas	179	A, H, S	.21	Gacula & Brown, 1963
UK	911	RP, DS	.27[ab]	Mason, 1964
Israel	1563	F	.33[b]	Soller *et al.*, 1966a, b
S. Dakota	336	H	.33[c]	Wilson *et al.*, 1962
Arkansas	201	A, H, S	.37	Brown & Gacula, 1964
Germany	525	F	.40[b]	Langlet, 1965
California	200	H	.41	Rollins *et al.*, 1962
S. Dakota	224	H	.43	Dearborn & Dinkel, 1959
S. Dakota	473	H	.45	Wilson *et al.*, 1963b
Ohio	832	H	.47	Swiger *et al.*, 1961b
Texas	241	Various	.48[c]	Dubose & Cartwright,1967
Nebraska	741	H	.49[c]	Swiger *et al.*, 1961b
Montana	542	H	.55[c]	Shelby *et al.*, 1960
Montana	616	H	.55	Shelby *et al.*, 1963
Montana	616	H	.64	Shelby *et al.*, 1963
Germany	418	Simmental	.65[d]	Averdunk, 1968
New Mexico	499	H	.70	Blackwell *et al.*, 1962
Nebraska	480	A, H, S	.72	Swiger *et al.*, 1965
Colorado	417	H	.72	Lickley *et al.*, 1960
Montana	542	H	.77	Shelby *et al.*, 1960
New Mexico	499	H	.77[b]	Blackwell *et al.*, 1962
Germany	418	Simmental	.79[e]	Averdunk, 1968
Montana	177	H	.81	Knapp & Nordskog, 1946a
Montana	635	H	.84	Shelby *et al.*, 1955
Arkansas	371	A, H	.85	Brown & Gacula, 1962
S. Dakota	679	H	.85	Busch & Dinkel, 1967
Montana	880	H	.86	Knapp & Clark, 1950
Texas	241	Various	1.00	DuBose & Cartwright,1967
Preferred value			.70	

[a] On grass. [b] Weight per day of age. [c] Adjusted to the same age. [d] 420 days. [e] 364 days.

0.40, several workers have obtained much higher figures. The variable nature of the conversion data is not surprising in view of the feeding systems used in US testing programmes. The use of ill-defined and changing ratios of concentrate to roughage involves making assumptions in order to calculate feed conversion on a uniform basis (e.g. DM, TDN or ME). This results in considerable loss of precision and hence greater environmental variance.

TABLE 3.8 HERITABILITY ESTIMATES OF FEED INTAKE AND CONVERSION DURING PERFORMANCE TEST

Location	No. of records	Breed	h^2	Authors
		Feed intake		
Arkansas	179	A, H, S	.35	Gacula & Brown, 1963
Nebraska	351	H	.38	Swiger *et al.*, 1961
Oregon	290		.38	England *et al.*, 1961
Arkansas	201	A, H, S	.43	Brown & Gacula, 1964
Nebraska	660	H	.45	Swiger *et al.*, 1961b
Nebraska	480	A, H, S	.46	Swiger *et al.*, 1965
Nebraska	1324	A, H, S	.64	Koch *et al.*, 1963
Arkansas	371	A, H	.76	Brown & Gifford, 1962
		Feed conversion		
Virginia	152	A, H, S	.17	Gaines *et al.*, 1958
Arkansas	179	A, H, S	.22	Gacula & Brown, 1963
Montana	635	H	.22	Shelby *et al.*, 1955
Oregon		A, H	.22 to .46	Hoornbeck & Bogart, 1966
Colorado	417	H	.27	Lickley *et al.*, 1960
Montana	542	H	.32	Shelby *et al.*, 1960
Nebraska	1324	A, H, S	.36	Koch *et al.*, 1963
Colorado	417	H	.36[a]	Lickley *et al.*, 1960
Germany	390	BPL	.37	Heidler, 1966
Arkansas	201	A, H, S	.41	Brown & Gacula, 1964
Virginia	276	A, H, S	.63	Gaines *et al.*, 1958
Germany	1034	F	.68	Langlet *et al.*, 1967
Montana	177	H	.75	Knapp & Nordskog, 1946a
Arkansas	371	A, H	.80	Brown & Gifford, 1962
Virginia	212	A, H, S	.99	Carter & Kincaid, 1959a
Preferred values			.44 and .36	

[a] Adjusted for initial weight.

3.2.9 Carcass traits

The subjective nature of carcass grading, allied to the fact that fatness, the most variable trait in the carcass, is its major determinant, could account for the inconsistent estimates obtained (Table 3.9). There appears to be less variation in estimates for fat thickness which is quite highly heritable (about 0.50). The single estimate for excess fat is of the same order.

TABLE 3.9 HERITABILITY ESTIMATES OF MEASUREMENTS OF CARCASS FATNESS

Trait	No. of records	Breed	h^2	Authors
Carcass grade (USDA)	62	H	.00	Magee *et al.*, 1958
	635	H	.16	Shelby *et al.*, 1955
	616	H	.17	Shelby *et al.*, 1963
	212	A, H, S	.20	Carter & Kincaid, 1959a
	832	H	.33	Knapp & Clark, 1950
	499	H	.49	Blackwell *et al.*, 1962
	265	A, H	.62	Cundiff *et al.*, 1964
	58	DS	.67	Dawson *et al.*, 1955
	304	F	.70	Langlet, 1965
	257	A, H	.74	Brackelsberg *et al.*, 1968
	176	A	.78	Christians *et al.*, 1962
	241	Various	.80	DuBose & Cartwright, 1967
	177	H	.84	Knapp & Nordskog, 1946b
Yield grade	265	A, H	.36	Cundiff *et al.*, 1964
Dressing percentage	177	H	.01	Knapp & Nordskog, 1946b
	911	RP, DS	.05	Mason, 1964
	525	HF	.20	Levi *et al.*, 1967
	499	H	.25	Blackwell *et al.*, 1962
	616	H	.57	Shelby *et al.*, 1963
	58	DS	.69	Dawson *et al.*, 1955
	635	H	.73	Shelby *et al.*, 1955
	176	A	.74	Christians *et al.*, 1962
Fat thickness over longissimus dorsi	616	H	.24	Shelby *et al.*, 1963
	635	H	.38	Shelby *et al.*, 1955
	176	A	.38	Christians *et al.*, 1962
	265	A, H	.43	Cundiff *et al.*, 1964
	257	A, H	.43	Brackelsberg *et al.*, 1968
	480	A, H, S	.50	Swiger *et al.*, 1965
	679	H	.57	Busch & Dinkel, 1967
	272	H	.58	Willson *et al.*, 1954
	241	Various	.74	DuBose & Cartwright, 1967
Kidney fat	241	Various	.63	DuBose & Cartwright, 1967
Excess fat	257	A, H	.50	Brackelsberg *et al.*, 1968
Fat in 9th–10th–11th rib (%)	176	A	.31	Christians *et al.*, 1962
Fat in 9th rib (%)	227	F	.48 to .76	Gravert, 1962
Marbling	118	H	.05	Harwin *et al.*, 1961
	679	H	.31	Busch & Dinkel, 1967

The more important traits, i.e. edible and first quality meat, have only been studied since the mid-1960's, and few estimates have been published. The indications are that the heritabilities for percentage edible and first quality meat are slightly lower than those for fat thickness (Table 3.10). This is perhaps to be expected in view of the factors determining these measures (see Chapter 2).

TABLE 3.10 HERITABILITY ESTIMATES OF MEASUREMENTS OF MEAT AND BONE YIELD

Trait	No. of records	Breed	h^2	Authors
Carcass weight per day of age	271	F	.20	Vial & Mason, 1961
	304	F	.28	Langlet, 1965
	625	RP, DS	.38	Mason, 1964
	265	A, H	.39	Cundiff *et al.*, 1964
	525	HF	.49	Levi *et al.*, 1967
Edible meat (%)	679	H	.38	Busch & Dinkel, 1967
	503	A, H, S	.41	Cundiff *et al.*, 1968
First quality meat (%)	480	A, H, S	.24	Swiger *et al.*, 1965
	503	A, H, S	.30	Cundiff *et al.*, 1968
	265	A, H	.40	Cundiff *et al.*, 1964
First quality meat (wt.)	480	A, H, S	.65	Swiger *et al.*, 1965
Steak and roasts (wt.)	241	Various	.65	DuBose & Cartwright, 1967
Round and loin (wt.)	257	A, H	.81	Brackelsberg *et al.*, 1968
Semimembranosus (as % of round)		Beef	.34	Kline *et al.*, 1968
		Dairy	.45	Kline *et al.*, 1968
Lean (%)	225	Simmental	.23	Scheper, 1965
Lean in 9th–10th–11th rib (%)			.05	Cartwright *et al.*, 1958a
Round (%)	176	A	.30	Christians *et al.*, 1962
Chuck (%)	176	A	.46	Christians *et al.*, 1962
Loin (%)	176	A	.60	Christians *et al.*, 1962
Rib (%)	176	A	.46	Christians *et al.*, 1962
Bone (%)	176	A	.30	Christians *et al.*, 1962
Bone (%)	225	Simmental	.48	Scheper, 1965
Bone in 9th–10th–11th rib (%)	176	A	.41	Christians *et al.*, 1962
Carcass value	257	A, H	.53	Brackelsberg *et al.*, 1968
Carcass length	1034	F	.18	Langlet *et al.*, 1967

Heritabilities for quality factors are set out in Table 3.11. The longissimus dorsi area is apparently a highly heritable trait with a median value of 0.60–0.70.

Tenderness, as assessed by shear machine, appears to be a highly heritable trait (0.60), whereas by taste panel tests the values are low. This is difficult to explain in view of the high correlations between the two measurements (Table 2.40). It could be that they are, in reality, two different characteristics in that resistance to cutting may not be entirely the same as the multiple sensations involved in chewing meat. Estimates are few, however, and must be treated with caution, but it is interesting to note that Alsmeyer *et al.* (1958) obtained an estimate of 0.51 for taste panel score in Brahmans. It may be that tenderness is controlled by different combinations of factors in different breeds. Thus tenderness in Herefords may be primarily due to biochemical configuration of the collagen molecule, for which sire differences are probably non-existent. On the other hand, tenderness in Brahmans may be related to their temperament and the effect this has on muscle pH (Bouton *et al.*, 1957; Table 2.23).

TABLE 3.11 HERITABILITY OF CARCASS "QUALITY" FACTORS

Trait	No. of records	Breed	h^2	Authors
Longissimus dorsi area		BPL	.03	Langlet *et al.*, 1963
	227	F	.05	Gravert, 1965
	241	Various	.12	DuBose & Cartwright, 1967
	679	H	.25	Busch & Dinkel, 1967
	616	H	.26	Shelby *et al.*, 1963
	257	A, H	.40	Brackelsberg *et al.*, 1968
	60	A	.56	Kieffer *et al.*, 1958
	512	H	.68	Knapp & Clark, 1950
	177	H	.69	Knapp & Nordskog, 1946b
	635	H	.72	Shelby *et al.*, 1955
	265	A, H	.73	Cundiff *et al.*, 1964
	272	H	.73	Willson *et al.*, 1954
	176	A	.76	Christians *et al.*, 1962
	62	H	1.56	Magee *et al.*, 1958
Panel score (tenderness)	227	F	.00	Gravert, 1963
		S	.00	Alsmeyer *et al.*, 1958
		Crosses	.00	Alsmeyer *et al.*, 1958
	38	H, B × H	.28 to 1.19	Cover *et al.*, 1957
		B	.51	Alsmeyer *et al.*, 1958
Shear force (tenderness)	679	H	.00	Busch & Dinkel, 1967
	241	Various	.39	DuBose & Cartwright, 1967
			.51	Adams, 1964
	176	A	.62 to .69	Christians *et al.*, 1962
	38	H, B × H	.74 to 1.02	Cover *et al.*, 1957
	60	A	.92	Kieffer *et al.*, 1958

3.2.10 Conformation score and body measurements

In view of the subjective nature of scores and grades it is not surprising that there is considerable variation in the heritability estimates in Table 3.12. The preferred values are in the low-medium range (0.17–0.28). Body measurements, on the other hand, appear to be more highly heritable (Table 3.13). There is evidence from identical twins that the heritability of body measurements increases with increasing age (Christian *et al.*, 1965a; Taylor and Craig, 1967); this may be due to the increased accuracy of measurements on larger animals (Taylor, 1963).

TABLE 3.12 HERITABILITY ESTIMATES OF TYPE SCORE AND GRADE

Trait	No. of records	Breed	h^2	Authors
At weaning	626	H	.01	Vogt & Marlowe, 1966
	495		.04	Kieffer *et al.*, 1959
		H	.08	Robertson *et al.*, 1963
		Crosses	.11	Scarth *et al.*, 1965
	720	H	.13	Pahnish *et al.*, 1964

TABLE 3.12 (cont.)

Trait	No. of records	Breed	h^2	Authors
At weaning (cont.)	6000	H	.16	Koch, 1953
	1153	A	.17	Vogt & Marlowe, 1966
	3831	H	.18	Koch & Clark, 1955a, b
	469	H	.19	Loganathan *et al.*, 1965
	908	A, H, S	.20	Meyerhoeffer *et al.*, 1963
	1682	A, H, S	.21	Meyerhoeffer *et al.*, 1960
	616	H	.23	Shelby *et al.*, 1963
	425		.23	Gregory & Stewart, 1962
	1257	H	.24	Koger & Knox, 1952
		H	.24	Roberson *et al.*, 1963
	420	H	.26	Blackwell *et al.*, 1962
	688	H	.28	Knapp & Clark, 1950
	3584	H	.28	Brinks *et al.*, 1964b
	751	A, H, S	.29	Meyerhoeffer *et al.*, 1963
	715	A	.30	Koger & Knox, 1952
	613	H	.31	Knapp & Clark, 1951
	499	H	.31	Blackwell *et al.*, 1962
	2638	A	.31	Schalles, 1967
	1987	A, H, S	.33	Lehmann *et al.*, 1961
	8279	H	.33	Marlowe & Vogt, 1965
	2019	A, H	.34 to .60	Hallman, 1966
	544	Crosses	.35	Lombard, 1963
	1306	H	.36	Mahmud & Cobb, 1963
	577	H	.36	Rollins & Wagnon, 1956
	12,145	A	.36	Marlowe & Vogt, 1965
	1648	H	.49	Cunningham & Henderson, 1965a
	3190	A	.53	Cunningham & Henderson, 1965a
	177	H	.53	Knapp & Nordskog, 1946b
	1671	A, H, S	.53	Swiger *et al.*, 1963
	542	H	.60	Shelby *et al.*, 1957
	17,023	A	.65	Harricharan *et al.*, 1967
	326	H	.70	Magee *et al.*, 1961
As yearling		H	.04	Roberson *et al.*, 1963
		H	.13	Roberson *et al.*, 1963
		H	.16	Roberson *et al.*, 1963
	212	A, H, S	.17	Carter & Kincaid, 1959a
	420	H	.34	Blackwell *et al.*, 1962
	499	H	.40	Blackwell *et al.*, 1962
At 18 months	425		.00	Gregory & Stewart, 1962
	3584	H	.13	Brinks *et al.*, 1964b
Final	179	A, H, S	.06	Gacula & Brown, 1963
	201	A, H, S	.15	Brown & Gacula, 1964
	336	H	.39	Wilson *et al.*, 1962
	473	H	.40	Wilson *et al.*, 1963b
	679	H	.45	Busch & Dinkel, 1967
	371	A, H	.58	Brown & Gifford, 1962
Mature cows	1371	A	.42	Morrow & Marlowe, 1966

TABLE 3.13 HERITABILITY OF VARIOUS BODY MEASUREMENTS

Item	No. of records	Breed	h^2	Authors
Body length	212	A	.00	Brown, 1958
	255	H	.10	Brown, 1958
	1034	F	.35	Langlet *et al.*, 1967
	616	H	.46	Shelby *et al.*, 1963
	138	A, H	.48	Brown & Franks, 1964
	60	Japanese-Brown	.67	Okanoto *et al.*, 1966
Chest girth	1034	F	.58	Langlet *et al.*, 1967
	138	A, H	.71	Brown & Franks, 1964
Chest width		Simmental	.32	Vinnicuk, 1966
Heart girth	212	A	.06	Brown, 1958
	255	H	.44	Brown, 1958
	138	A, H	.46	Brown & Franks, 1964
	600	Japanese-Brown	.71	Okanoto *et al.*, 1966
Hip height	600	Japanese-Brown	.47	Okanoto *et al.*, 1966
	138	A, H	.69	Brown & Franks, 1964
Wither height	138	A, H	.41	Brown & Franks, 1964
	1034	F	.43	Langlet *et al.*, 1967
	600	Japanese-Brown	.57	Okanoto *et al.*, 1966
Wither length	255	H	.29	Brown, 1958
	212	A	.38	Brown, 1958

Our preferred values for the more important traits discussed in this chapter are generally based on the median, but show good agreement with the mean values calculated by Warwick (1958).

3.3 CORRELATIONS BETWEEN TRAITS

3.3.1 Introduction

The phenotypic variation in any polygenic character is divisible into genetic and environmental components. In the same way, the relationship between characters (phenotypic correlation) has genetic and environmental parts, although the latter does also include some non-additive genetic effects. Genetic correlations are mainly brought about by pleiotropy, which is the capacity of a gene (or genes) to affect two characters simultaneously. For example, the genes controlling weaning weight might also be expected to affect subsequent growth, thus leading to genetic correlation between these two measurements. On the other hand, the environmental factors affecting these two traits are quite different such that environmental correlation might be low. Since genes may affect characteristics in the same (positive) or in different (negative) directions, and as environmental correlations do not necessarily follow the same deviation, the observed phenotypic variation does not automatically give an indication of the underlying genetic correlation. If both characters have high heritabilities the genetic correlation is the more important determinant of phenotypic correlation, but when heritabilities are low the environmental correlation is the major factor.

In selection programmes there is an obvious need to know the genetic correlation between any two important economic traits, for the existence of a positive genetic correlation means that selection for one trait will also bring about progress in the other. In contrast, a negative genetic correlation necessitates simultaneous selection if progress in one character is not to be accompanied by regression in the other. Here it is relevant to discuss the various traits for which heritabilities have already been given and to examine their genetic relationship.

The phenotypic, genetic and environmental correlations given in Tables 3.14–3.19 are calculated from very many different populations, and it is not therefore surprising that differences exist, as such correlations are specific to the population in which they were calculated, much the same as are heritabilities. Values are also dependent for their accuracy on the number of animals involved in the calculation, although for ease of presentation these have been omitted. Environmental correlations have been included only when given in the papers cited, but they can be calculated from the genetic correlation and the heritabilities (Falconer, 1960b).

3.3.2 Pre-weaning growth rate

The genetic correlations between birth weight and pre-weaning growth (Table 3.14) are in the main higher than the observed phenotypic correlations, indicating that selection for birth weight should increase subsequent gain. It has been shown by High *et al.* (1959) that there is a positive correlation ($r = 0.86$) between gains from birth to 125 days and those from birth to weaning. Nevertheless, Hill *et al.* (1966) suggest that there is a negative correlation between the calf's genotype for weight gain and the dam's genotype for maternal effect. This is supported by Ray *et al.*

TABLE 3.14 GENETIC, ENVIRONMENTAL AND PHENOTYPIC CORRELATIONS OF PRE-WEANING GAIN AND OTHER TRAITS

Correlated trait	Correlation			Authors
	Genetic	Environmental	Phenotypic	
Birth weight	.11	.14	.12	Brinks *et al.*, 1962b
	.30	.18	.20	Pahnish *et al.*, 1964
	.46	.08	.23	Brinks *et al.*, 1964c
	.55		.36	Loganathan *et al.*, 1965
	.82		.32	Berruecos & Robison, 1968
	1.98	.01	.09	Pahnish *et al.*, 1964
			−.05 to .11	Flock *et al.*, 1962
			.31	Koger *et al.*, 1957
Final weight	.54	.71	.62	Brinks *et al.*, 1962b

(1968). According to Brown and Galvez (1968) the apparent antagonism between pre-natal growth of the calf and its pre-natal environment may be due to a permanent negative environmental effect.

Rapid gains to weaning are generally desirable, but the consequences in terms of increased birth weight and associated side effects such as dystokia (§ 6.6.4), must not be overlooked.

3.3.3 Weaning weight

As might be expected, both birth weight and pre-weaning gain show high genetic correlations with weaning weight (Table 3.15). More important is the high genetic correlation between weaning weight and final test weight. Such relationships only hold with late weaning (6 months or more) and no evidence is available on correlations with weaning weights at younger ages, although our data (Willis and Preston, 1967) suggest they will almost certainly be less.

TABLE 3.15 GENETIC, ENVIRONMENTAL AND PHENOTYPIC CORRELATIONS OF WEANING WEIGHT WITH OTHER TRAITS

Correlated trait	Correlation			Authors
	Genetic	Environmental	Phenotypic	
Birth weight	.21	.42	.30	Brinks *et al.*, 1962b
	.42	.42	.42	Pahnish *et al.*, 1964
	.60	.28	.41	Brinks *et al.*, 1967
	.68		.37	Shelby *et al.*, 1963
	.84		.42	Berruecos & Robison, 1968
	.99	−.13		Lasley *et al.*, 1961
	1.12	.22	.31	Pahnish *et al.*, 1964
			.37	Meade *et al.*, 1959a
			.47	Koger *et al.*, 1957
Pre-weaning gain	0.8			Harricharan *et al.*, 1967
	.90	1.13	1.08	Pahnish *et al.*, 1964
	.92		1.00	Berruecos & Robison, 1968
	.93		.97	Lehmann *et al.*, 1961
	.99	.82	.92	Brinks *et al.*, 1962b
	.99	.98	.98	Brinks *et al.*, 1962b
	1.70	.94	.94	Pahnish *et al.*, 1964
			.81	Reynolds *et al.*, 1964a
Final test weight	.33		.72	Wilson *et al.*, 1963b
	.40		.64	Wilson *et al.*, 1962
	.48	.81	.53	Blackwell *et al.*, 1962
	.67	.59	.16	Brinks *et al.*, 1962b
	.77			Nelson & Cartwright, 1968
	.86	.51	.73	Swiger *et al.*, 1965
	.86		.57	Shelby *et al.*, 1963
	.94	.82	.82	Swiger *et al.*, 1961b
Yearling weight	.63			Koch *et al.*, 1968
Feed intake	−.31		−.40	Swiger *et al.*, 1962
	.65	.30	.48	Swiger *et al.*, 1965

3.3.4 Post-weaning growth rate (gain on test)

This trait is of greater economic value than either pre-weaning gain or weaning weight which in turn are less well related to it than to each other (Table 3.16).

Weaning weight is likely to influence gain on test in a positive direction, but birth weight is of lesser importance, and the indications are that pre-weaning gain is negatively related. According to Sabin *et al.* (1961), who made a survey of 330 calves of three breeds, adjustment of daily gain on test for differences in birth weight increased genetic variance, indicating a negative correlation between these traits.

TABLE 3.16 GENETIC, ENVIRONMENTAL AND PHENOTYPIC CORRELATIONS OF TEST GAIN WITH OTHER TRAITS

Correlated trait	Correlation			Authors
	Genetic	Environmental	Phenotypic	
Birth weight	.07	.14	.11	Brinks *et al.*, 1964c
	.29		.30	Shelby *et al.*, 1963
	.71	−.16	.23	Brinks *et al.*, 1962b
Pre-weaning gain	−.50			Harricharan *et al.*, 1967
	−.08	.32	.14	Brinks *et al.*, 1962b
	.06	.26	.17	Brinks *et al.*, 1962b
			.20	Reynolds *et al.*, 1964a
			.57	Reynolds *et al.*, 1964a
Weaning weight	0.8			Harricharan *et al.*, 1967
	.22	.39	.24	Blackwell *et al.*, 1962
	.28		.15	Wilson *et al.*, 1963b
	.34		.19	Wilson *et al.*, 1962
	.47		.18	Swiger *et al.*, 1962
	.49		.32	Carter & Kincaid, 1959b
	.61	−.17	.28	Swiger *et al.*, 1965
	.77		.18	Shelby *et al.*, 1963
	.81			Dearborn & Dinkel, 1959
	.83	−.10	.20	Swiger *et al.*, 1961b
			.03	Swiger *et al.*, 1961b
Final test weight	.31			Brown & Gifford, 1962
	.39			Brown & Gifford, 1962
	.64			Lickley *et al.*, 1960
	.64			Koch *et al.*, 1963
	.70		.77	Wilson *et al.*, 1963b
	.73		.77	Wilson *et al.*, 1962
	.76	.92	.80	Brinks *et al.*, 1962b
	.93	.76	.86	Swiger *et al.*, 1963
	.96		.86	Shelby *et al.*, 1963
	.97	.49	.73	Swiger *et al.*, 1961b
	.97	.18	.76	Blackwell *et al.*, 1962
	1.09	.27	.69	Swiger *et al.*, 1965
			.73	Shah & O'Mary, 1964
Feed intake	−.94		−.65	Swiger *et al.*, 1962
			.35	England *et al.*, 1961

Not surprisingly, in view of the phenomenon of compensatory growth, these workers found some indications of increased gains on test with lower pre-weaning gains. Bogart and Frischknecht (1967) considered pre-weaning gains to bear no relation to gains on test. They concluded that simultaneous improvement of pre- and post-weaning gains necessitated simultaneous selection, and that heavy culling at weaning might be detrimental to post-weaning gains and efficiency.

Dahmen and Bogart (1952) and Pierce *et al.* (1954) also found negative relationships between pre-weaning and post-weaning gains. Thus the findings of Moore *et al.* (1961) that at the same initial weight older animals would gain less, and that at the same initial age heavier animals would gain more, must be treated with caution. This is particularly so in view of the known effects of compensatory growth (DeBaca *et al.*, 1959) and the work of England *et al.* (1961) which showed that at any given weight older calves ate more, gained more and were less efficient.

In a theoretical discussion, Taylor and Fitzhugh (1968) concluded that mass selection for rate of gain on a constant weight/age basis would be expected to increase rate of gain and mature size.

3.3.5 Final weight

Final weight has significance in those testing systems employing a fixed-age termination point. In this context it is affected by weight at weaning (Table 3.15) and at intermediate stages. DuBose *et al.* (1968) found that correlations among 205-day weaning weight, gain on test, final weight and weight per day of age ranged from 0.46 to 0.70 and were all significant. Selection for any one of these traits improved the others. It was also thought by Nelson and Cartwright (1968) that direct selection for weight at any age was a relatively effective means of increasing size at any other age.

It is to be expected that final weight should be affected by many of the factors governing gain on test, and genetic correlations support this (Table 3.16).

Weight for age at a constant weight has been little studied. In a general sense it will be affected by many of the genes determining final weight at a fixed age. However, animals assessed on the former basis will show less variation in carcass composition; thus genetic correlations with other traits, particularly feed conversion and weaning weight, will be different from those reported for final weight at a fixed age.

Gould (1966) has claimed that 55% of the variation in the 360-day weight of Charolais crosses could be accounted for by birth weight and gestation length. There is no other support for what is rather an extravagant claim and one must assume the relationship was spurious.

3.3.6 Feed conversion

Since feed conversion, expressed as feed consumed per unit of weight gain, is the reciprocal of efficiency it is negatively related to gain on test. The genetic correlations in Table 3.17 indicate that the relationship between gain and feed conversion is not so high as to obviate the need to select for this latter trait. The assumption of Taylor and Fitzhugh (1968) that selection for rate of gain would not, on average, affect intrinsic feed efficiency is not supported by the data in Table 3.17. However, as these authors subsequently contradict themselves on this aspect (Fitzhugh and Taylor, 1968) their somewhat academic mathematical exercises should not be taken too seriously.

TABLE 3.17 GENETIC, ENVIRONMENTAL AND PHENOTYPIC CORRELATION OF FEED CONVERSION ON TEST WITH OTHER TRAITS

Correlated trait	Correlation			Authors
	Genetic	Environmental	Phenotypic	
Pre-weaning gain			.33	Pepito *et al.*, 1961
Weaning weight	.43		.26	Carter & Kincaid, 1959b
Initial test age			.18	Crawford *et al.*, 1967
Initial test weight			.62	Crawford *et al.*, 1967
Test gain	−.79			Koch *et al.*, 1963
	−.69		−.45	Lickley *et al.*, 1960
	−.41		−.26	Lickley *et al.*, 1960
	−.34			Brown & Gifford, 1962
	−.32		−.50	Carter & Kincaid, 1959b
			−.21[a]	O'Mary *et al.*, 1959c
			−.38[b]	O'Mary *et al.*, 1959c
			−.47	Willis & Preston, 1967
			−.58[c]	O'Mary *et al.*, 1959c
			−.69	Crawford *et al.*, 1967
Feed intake	0.4			Koch *et al.*, 1963
	.71			Brown & Gifford, 1962
Final test weight	−.15			Lickley *et al.*, 1960
	.74			Brown & Gifford, 1962
Weight for age at 400 kg			−.34	Willis & Preston, 1967

[a] Time constant. [b] Weight constant. [c] Age constant.

3.3.7 Carcass traits

Although there are many phenotypic correlations among carcass traits (Chapter 2), there are few reports of genetic correlations between carcass traits and production characteristics, or among carcass traits. Available data are given in Tables 3.18 and 3.19.

Interpretation of the data in Table 3.18 is complicated by the fact that it derives from US performance tests, wherein a fixed test period was used. Under such circumstances those animals growing faster have heavier final weight and *ipso facto* a fatter carcass (Willis *et al.*, 1968a).

The high positive genetic correlations between test performance (gain or final weight) and measures of fatness might be taken to indicate that selection for faster growth will produce fatter carcasses. It has in fact been suggested (Taylor, 1965; Taylor and Fitzhugh, 1968) that increased rate of gain, as a result of selection, will lead to delayed maturity and larger mature size. Thus, on a within breed basis and at any fixed weight, faster growing animals will be either leaner or show no change (Willis and Preston, 1967). Cundiff *et al.* (1964) considered that genes for rapid growth were not antagonistic to those for desirable carcasses (i.e. with high edible meat content). Their opinion that increased growth might lead to slightly greater fatness stems from the feeding system used and almost certainly does not apply to testing to fixed weights.

TABLE 3.18 GENETIC, ENVIRONMENTAL AND PHENOTYPIC CORRELATIONS BETWEEN PERFORMANCE AND CARCASS TRAITS

Correlated traits	Correlation			Authors
	Genetic	Environmental	Phenotypic	
Weaning weight/ carcass grade	−.04		.09	Shelby *et al.*, 1963
	.84		.23	Carter & Kincaid, 1959b
	.92	−.13	.11	Blackwell *et al.*, 1962
Longissimus dorsi area			−.05	Brinks *et al.*, 1962a
Fat-thickness			−.26	Brinks *et al.*, 1962a
Bone (%)			.15	Brinks *et al.*, 1962a
Lean (%)			.35	Brinks *et al.*, 1962a
Fat (%)			−.36	Brinks *et al.*, 1962a
Gain on test/ carcass grade	.08	.27	.17	Swiger *et al.*, 1965
	.25		.37	Shelby *et al.*, 1963
	.78	−.30	.43	Blackwell *et al.*, 1962
	.85		.31	Carter & Kincaid, 1959b
Fat-thickness	.30		.14	Shelby *et al.*, 1963
First quality (RLRC) (%)	−.45	.01	−.16	Swiger *et al.*, 1965
Final weight/ carcass grade	.88	−.61	.36	Blackwell *et al.*, 1962
Fat-thickness	.31		.29	Shelby *et al.*, 1963
First quality (RLRC) (%)	−.25	−.23	−.21	Swiger *et al.*, 1965
Carcass weight/day of age/carcass grade	.47	−.15	.16	Cundiff *et al.*, 1964
Fat-thickness	.15	.43	.31	Cundiff *et al.*, 1964
First quality (RLRC) (%)	.02	−.43	−.26	Cundiff *et al.*, 1964
Longissimus dorsi area	−.02	.58	−.39	Cundiff *et al.*, 1964
Feed conversion/ carcass grade	.16		.16	Carter & Kincaid, 1959b

Biondini *et al.* (1968) and Sutherland *et al.* (1968) reported on a selection experiment in mice wherein lines were selected for rate of gain, feed efficiency, feed intake or at random (control). Selection for gain and particularly feed intake led to significant increases in size and fatness when slaughtered at a *fixed age* and at a stage of chemical maturity. The line selected for efficiency also increased in size and rate of gain but without change in body composition. The application of these interesting findings to cattle must be made with caution. Aside from the fact that fattening cattle are always slaughtered before reaching chemical maturity, the most important question concerns effects on composition at a fixed weight, not a fixed age, particularly when the basic parameter is feed efficiency.

Theoretical considerations, allied to our own unpublished findings, lead us to believe that selection for weight for age will, *when evaluation is at a constant weight*, bring

TABLE 3.19 PHENOTYPIC GENETIC AND ENVIRONMENTAL CORRELATIONS AMONG CARCASS TRAITS

Correlated traits	Correlation			Authors
	Genetic	Environmental	Phenotypic	
Percentage first-quality meat (RLRC) with:				
Carcass grade	−.85	−.29	−.44	Swiger *et al.*, 1965
	−.80	.11	−.34	Cundiff *et al.*, 1964
Fat-thickness	−.95	−.74	−.83	Cundiff *et al.*, 1964
Longissimus dorsi area	.28	.94	.52	Cundiff *et al.*, 1964
Longissimus dorsi area[a]	.35	.89	.70	Cundiff *et al.*, 1964
	.85		.45	DuBose & Cartwright, 1967
Fat-thickness with:				
Carcass grade	.23		.44	Shelby *et al.*, 1963
	1.00	−.40	.33	Cundiff *et al.*, 1964
Longissimus dorsi area[a]	−.02	−.63	−.41	
Longissimus dorsi area	.05		.30	Shelby *et al.*, 1963
	.08	−.30	−.07	Cundiff *et al.*, 1964

[a] Adjusted to constant carcass weight.

about, either, no change, or an increase in percentage edible meat due to reduced fatness. Selection for efficiency will definitely lead to leaner carcasses, with higher proportions of edible meat.

The selection experiment which Magee *et al.* (1968) carried out in a Hereford herd tends to support this thesis. Evaluating on a fixed age basis, they obtained a negative relationship between daily gain and percentage first-quality meat (RLR). This, however, was entirely attributable to an increase in final weight (and consequently in fatness), since adjustment to a constant carcass weight eliminated the relationship between gain and percentage first-quality meat. Similarly, Scarth *et al.* (1966), found, in an experiment with 33 steers and 43 heifers by 5 polled Hereford sires out of Angus × Holstein dams, that live weight per day of age was positively correlated with percentage trimmed round (a good indicator of edible meat yield; cf. Table 2.31) and genatively with carcass grade and marbling. It is significant that in this trial slaughter was at fixed weights of 454 and 410 kg for steers and heifers respectively. Further support is given by the work of Cundiff *et al.* (1966a) in which the progeny of a Hereford bull selected for a high gain and efficiency were compared with those from a bull with poor performance for these traits. The former had not only faster gains and higher final weights but also less fat thickness, a lower percentage of fat and more lean. Melton *et al.* (1967a) also found that bulls superior for feed efficiency had leaner carcasses.

Among carcass traits there is a pronounced antagonism between carcass grade, or fat-thickness, and percentage edible meat. Brackelsberg *et al.* (1968) considered that the high negative genetic correlations between measures of fatness and high-priced cuts indicated a basic relationship between fat and muscle rather than real differences in carcass proportions independent of fatness.

The animal breeder must therefore balance the relative advantages of a higher retail yield (i.e. edible meat content) against carcass grade which aids eatability through greater juiciness, but which at the same time reduces retail yield.

There is a suggestion from the work of Scarth *et al.* (1966) and Magee *et al.* (1968) that increased rate of gain is negatively associated with tenderness but the relationships were not high. In a study with 11 bulls and steers paired for weight and sire, Bartee *et al.* (1961) found that performance traits (birth weight, rates of gain to weaning, feed consumption and rate of gain on test) accounted for from 55 to 94% of the variation in taste panel assessments of flavour, aroma, texture, tenderness, juiciness and colour, with relationships generally being higher for steers. However, whether correlations were positive or negative was not reported. There are indications from the work of Cundiff *et al.* (1966a) that selection for faster growth results in meat with better flavour.

3.3.8 Conformation scores

Some correlations between conformation scores at weaning, or after performance test, with various production traits, appear in Table 3.20. The relationships are generally poor and often negative.

In 1958 Woodward and Rice found that body length was a highly repeatable measurement, but the correlation between this and daily gain was only 0.15. Conformation scores at different stages of growth are generally highly correlated with each other (Brown *et al.*, 1956a; Bogart and Frischknecht, 1967) but not with production traits. An exception seems to be conformation score at birth which, according to Flock *et al.* (1962), was not related to score at weaning. DuBose *et al.* (1968) found that performance traits (weaning weight, gain on test, final weight and weight for age) of bulls were not correlated to the type score of their dams and negatively correlated to those of their sires. If this is generally tenable, the continued use of conformation grading can only be detrimental to beef cattle improvement in economic terms.

3.4 SELECTION METHODS

3.4.1 The methods available

The object in most breeding programmes is to improve more than a single trait. The three principal ways of doing this (Hazel and Lush, 1942) are:

(1) Tandem selection—selection in turn for each character.
(2) Independent culling levels—selection of each character at the same time but independently, i.e. rejecting any animal which fails to reach a particular standard in any one trait regardless of its level in the others.

TABLE 3.20 GENETIC, ENVIRONMENTAL AND PHENOTYPIC CORRELATION OF LIVE ANIMAL SCORES OR GRADES WITH PRODUCTION TRAITS

Correlated traits	Correlation			Authors
	Genetic	Environmental	Phenotypic	
Weaning score with:				
Birth weight	−.48	.20	.09	Pahnish *et al.*, 1964
	−.32			Roberson *et al.*, 1963
	−.32	.25	.14	Pahnish *et al.*, 1964
	.05	.15	.15	Brinks *et al.*, 1964c
	.20	.05	.13	Brinks *et al.*, 1962b
	.99		.29	Shelby *et al.*, 1963
Pre-weaning gain	.01		.42	Lehmann *et al.*, 1961
	.16	.37	.24	Schalles, 1967
	.21		.28	Marlowe & Vogt, 1965
	.23		.23	Marlowe & Vogt, 1965
	.32	.58	.52	Pahnish *et al.*, 1964
	.36	.37	.36	Cunningham & Henderson, 1965a
	.41		.39	Loganathan *et al.*, 1965
	.61	−.95	.28	Cunningham & Henderson, 1965a
	.74	.34	.53	Brinks *et al.*, 1962b
	1.65	.52	.47	Pahnish *et al.*, 1964
Weaning weight	−.52	.52	.45	Pahnish *et al.*, 1964
	−.44		.40	Magee *et al.*, 1961
	−.28	.16	−.05	Blackwell *et al.*, 1962
	−.03		.39	Lehmann *et al.*, 1961
	.18			Harricharan *et al.*, 1967
	.21	.64	.54	Pahnish *et al.*, 1964
	.27	.59	.51	Brinks *et al.*, 1964c
	.51		.57	Shelby *et al.*, 1963
	.72	.30	.50	Brinks *et al.*, 1962b
Test gain	−.06	.16	.07	Brinks *et al.*, 1962b
	−.02		.03	Shelby *et al.*, 1963
	.23			Harricharan *et al.*, 1967
Final score with:				
Weaning weight	−.51		.20	Wilson *et al.*, 1962
	−.39		.11	Wilson *et al.*, 1963b
Test gain	.10		.32	Wilson *et al.*, 1962
	.16		.28	Wilson *et al.*, 1963b
	.29			Brown & Gifford, 1962
Feed conversion	.48			Brown & Gifford, 1962
Final weight	−.05		.31	Wilson *et al.*, 1962
	.13		.29	Wilson *et al.*, 1963b

(3) Selection index—simultaneous selection for all traits, each character being weighted according to its economic importance, its heritability and the genotypic and phenotypic correlations between it and other characters.

Selection on the basis of an index has been shown to give the most rapid progress

(Hazel and Lush, 1942), and ways of constructing such indices are described in the classical paper of Hazel (1943).

There are several ways in which these selection procedures can be used in practice. They can be applied to individuals, to families, to individuals within families or to a combination of individual and family data. The theoretical aspects of the first three methods have been adequately dealt with by Falconer (1960b) and the reader is referred to Lerner (1950) and Robertson (1955) for a theoretical appraisal of combined selection. It is sufficient here to state that, of all these methods, individual selection will, in most instances, be the easiest to apply as well as the most rewarding.

3.4.2 Pedigree evaluation

In most dairy-cattle-breeding programmes bulls are initially selected on the basis of pedigree. This is particularly true in the case of a bull for AI which is rarely purchased as a calf unless its pedigree, particularly in respect of its sire's progeny test, shows some evidence of high production of milk and/or butter-fat. AI authorities use pedigree evaluation as a screening technique, since sires with high contemporary comparisons will generally have better-than-average sons (Robertson, 1960; Willis, 1960); but the emphasis is still on subsequent testing. The situation with beef cattle is complicated by the fact that pedigrees may be little more than a list of names and herd book numbers. Such data are quite valueless for assessing the pedigree for growth rate or feed conversion. In the late 1950's and early 1960's organizations such as the Beef Recording Association in the UK and the Syndicat de Contrôle de la Précocité des Élevages Nivernais in France began growth recording on farms, and this ought to lead to more useful and more readily available data in future pedigrees. A review of some methods in operation in Europe has been given by Bergstrom (1962).

When adequate data exist pedigree evaluation can be made objective. Lush (1935) and Le Roy (1958) have described a system of calculating partial regression coefficients of the animal's breeding value on separate items of its pedigree. This method is applicable to beef cattle but is laborious. Robertson (1959) suggested a simpler system in dairy cattle which might well be applied to beef cattle once pedigrees take on a more useful form. The extent to which pedigrees will prove useful depends not only on the data they contain but also the heritability of the trait studied. If the heritability is high, little is gained by studying ancestors more remote than parents. For characters of low heritability more distant ancestors may be considered, although in such a situation pedigree study will be of limited value whichever way it is undertaken. For simple characters controlled by one or two genes (e.g. some abnormalities) pedigree evaluation may well be essential, but once the genotype of the more recent ancestors is known with certainty, further pedigree study is unnecessary.

In this section it is appropriate to deal with family selection since "family" is a term frequently used in cattle-breeding circles, although its validity is questionable. In small-animal breeding a family is a closely related group of individuals, and in this respect may be quite distinct from another family both in genetic structure and performance. In reality such families can be regarded as separate lines and some such families have been reported in beef cattle, e.g. the inbred lines of Herefords at the US Range Livestock Experiment Station in Montana (see Urick *et al.*, 1966).

The nomenclature of families in most pedigree beef herds is usually based on a matriarchal system, e.g. the Buttercup family all trace back in the tail-female line to the original Buttercup cow, and each calf is given a number corresponding to the order of birth within the family. Thus Buttercup 44 is the 44th cow born in direct female descent from the original Buttercup. Variations of this theme exist in that the cow may also have the name of her sire incorporated in her own name. In an analysis of this system in a dairy herd, Willis (1960) has shown that family groupings are valueless as means of indicating relationships. In reality a member of one family may be more closely related to members of other families than to members of her own. Selection on female families is not likely to achieve progress.

The belief that some families "nick" with others (i.e. exhibit specific combining ability) is also without foundation. In the Friesian herd studied by Willis (1960) there was no evidence of "nicking" by family, and the structure of such families made "nicking" unlikely. Some specific combining ability has been demonstrated for milk yield (Fohrman and Graves, 1933; Heizer *et al.*, 1938; Johnson *et al.*, 1940; Laben *et al.*, 1955; Willis, 1960), but this has always been on the basis of one sire "nicking" with the progeny of another. Moreover, while specific combining ability cannot be ignored it is of limited practical value since the paradoxical situation exists in which it is necessary to make certain matings in order to demonstrate that they were worth making.

3.4.3 Performance testing

3.4.3.1 Introduction. Performance testing involves the measurement of traits in the live animal. It is popularly assumed to relate primarily to the evaluation of bulls in special stations on the basis of their growth rate, feed conversion and/or conformation. The term could also be applied to assessment of growth and reproductive traits in females. However, the greater part of genetic progress comes from the selection of bulls (Rendel and Robertson, 1950), and performance testing will be discussed in this context.

The major advantage of performance testing is that it permits evaluation of the animal at a much earlier age than is possible with progeny testing. This reduces the generation interval and enables a bull to be used during his most productive years whereas progeny testing effectively inactivates a bull for at least 3–4 years. Although a performance test is less accurate than a progeny test, it allows a much greater selection intensity. If 50 bulls are required and facilities exist for 1000, a performance testing programme will yield a selection differential of 2.06 × SD of the trait (see Table 3.1). If the same facilities were used for progeny testing then, with 10 progeny per bull, 50% of the bulls would have to be retained and the selection differential would be only 0.80 × SD.

The disadvantage of performance testing is its unsuitability for traits not measurable in the live animal (e.g. carcass characteristics) or which have low heritabilities.

3.4.3.2 Testing system. Animals can be tested on a constant age basis (i.e. from one fixed age to another), during a fixed period of time, between specific live weights, or combinations of these (e.g. from a fixed age to a fixed weight). Most US tests start at or soon after weaning and finish after a fixed period, usually 140, 196 or 240 days. Such tests are not consistent in either starting or finishing points, since weaning is invariably at a particular time of year rather than at a fixed animal age. Thus considerable statistical corrections may be necessary before valid conclusions can be drawn.

O'Mary *et al.* (1959c) compared three testing systems to evaluate the rate of gain of bulls and heifers fed a pelleted ration:

Time constant—animals tested for 150 days, all starting and finishing together.
Weight constant—bulls tested from 228 to 374 kg and heifers from 228 to 342 kg.
Age constant—animals tested from 243 to 393 days of age.

Despite a range in starting age of 61 days and of over 100 kg in weight in the first system, the workers claimed no differences among the three methods of testing. This may well have been due to insufficient numbers (15 bulls and 23 heifers).

In the UK most tests also begin soon after weaning, but tend to finish at a fixed animal age of 400 days (Baker, 1965, 1966). Neither the US nor the UK methods relate to market requirements as both employ end points determined by age rather than weight. Brumby *et al.* (1962) suggested constant weight, constant "finish" or constant age as possible termination points, and considered that a constant weight was the most suitable. Since live weight is a major determinant of carcass composition and animals are invariably marketed by weight, the use of other termination points seems to us particularly inappropriate.

The specific disadvantages of a constant age termination point are obvious from the results of Lewis (1966) in which bulls ranged from 390 to 543 kg at 400 days of age, and of Tallack (1967) who reported 400 day weights in Lincoln Red bulls of up to 640 kg. Intensive beef producers would not long remain in business if they fed their animals to the weights reached by the so-called "best" bulls. This is particularly true in view of Illinois findings (Zimmerman *et al.*, 1966) regarding edible meat yields in cattle slaughtered at 505 or 654 kg. The proportion of saleable meat in the carcass was 12% less at the higher weight thus the extra 150 kg in live weight produced only 25 kg additional saleable meat, *the rest being mostly added waste*. Retail value was actually reduced more than $8.80 per 100 kg on a live weight basis.

In any performance testing programme one should select an animal on the basis of its superiority for the trait (or traits) required in its progeny. If, for example, these progeny are to be slaughtered at a particular live weight, the evaluation point in the performance test should be the same. Earlier selection may be justified in terms of reduced generation interval if performance to this stage is highly correlated with performance to the optimum weight. By comparison, testing to older ages or heavier weights than is commercially desirable is pointless both in genetic and economic terms. We have used 400 kg (Willis and Preston, 1967, 1968a) since in Cuba, where the tests were undertaken this live weight yielded, on average, the optimum carcass for export.

3.4.3.3 Length of test period. In 1959 Dearborn and Dinkel found that heritability of daily gain on test in 224 Hereford bulls was 0.39 to 0.45 in test periods of

140, 168 or 196 days—the highest value being for 168 days. For final weight, however, heritabilities were more or less equal (0.41–0.44). They considered that selection for weight after 140 days was 89% as effective as selection after 168 days and 85% as effective as selection after 196 days. This conflicts with earlier findings by Dinkel (1958) that heritability increased from 0.45 after 140 days to 0.65 after 196 days.

In UK tests, Baker (1965, 1966) and Lewis (1966) have stressed the need for a long test period (although in practice their system only allows for 140 days for some bulls). They state that after some 3–4 months the original order of merit changes, the new ranking then remaining fairly constant.

In a 140 day post-weaning test with 832 calves from a Hereford herd in Ohio, Swiger (1961) calculated the heritabilities of gain for each successive 28 day period. The values were highest for the second period (0.28) and thereafter decreased to 0.04, indicating an increasing environmental effect with time on test. This led Swiger and Hazel (1961) to conclude that the same genes affected gain in weight during different stages of growth up to one year and selection could thus be made at an earlier stage. A short post-weaning evaluation of about 3 months was considered the most suitable provided high-concentrate rations were used. These proposals are at variance with the findings of Swiger *et al.* (1961b) that accuracy was increased by time on test up to at least 168 days and with our own results (Willis and Preston, 1967) relating to Charolais bulls selected on the basis of weight for age at 400 kg, wherein correlations with weight for age at earlier stages were not high (0.42 at 200 kg; 0.81 at 300 kg). The inadvisability of making early decisions relating to the probable potential of fattening cattle is demonstrated by the findings of Riley *et al.* (1967). Of the 25 slowest-growing animals in a group of 250, as assessed at 28 days, only 9 could be so categorized after 196 days. Performance to 56 days was a no better guide to final performance.

Apart from the work of Swiger *et al.* (1961b) on the heritability of gains during different periods of the performance test, there have been other attempts to show the relationship of gain in one period to that in another. According to Cartwright and Dayhoff's (1959) analysis of 2420 bulls, steers and heifers fed on 140 day tests over a 7 year period, repeatability of gain in successive 28 day periods was low. Periodic gains tended to be cyclic and compensatorial, the correlations being negative (about −0.02 to −0.10). Accumulated gain, on the other hand, was increasingly highly correlated with total gain. Fitzhugh (1968) tested 75 steers by 15 sires over a 224 day test and found that correlations between weights at weekly intervals were in excess of 0.90. By contrast, correlations between gains in adjacent 2, 4, 8 or 16 week periods, were −0.40, −0.31, −0.24 and −0.11 respectively. According to Fitzhugh, these negative correlations could not be considered as indications of compensatory growth. However, as feed consumption in this experiment was more or less equalized for each animal, Fitzhugh's conclusions have little application in commercial practice. In our experience, daily gains over adjacent time periods vary to such an extent, and for such a wide variety of reasons, as to make these lines of enquiry somewhat valueless.

In Germany, Averdunk (1968) studied the performance of 418 Simmental bulls by 38 sires which had been artificially reared from 6 weeks of age. The heritability of weight at 140, 280, 364, 420 and 500 days was 0.51, 0.91, 0.79, 0.65 and 0.46 respectively. Heritability for gain from 141 to 500 days was 0.60 and from 365 to 500 days was 0.81. The genetic correlation between 364 and 500 day weight was 0.69 but between 364 day weight and gain from 364 to 500 days was −0.54. Averdunk considered that selection for weight at one year favoured early maturing bulls with low subsequent growth rates, whereas selection at 500 days was for a larger growing capacity. Since the animals were only given up to 3.3 kg of concentrates daily plus maize silage, the amounts being rationed according to live weight, environmental influences must have been considerable as the author admits. The quoted heritabilities are almost certainly overestimates, which casts doubt on the validity of making comparisons between them. Similarly, the contention that higher weights at one year of age reflect a capacity for early maturity is at variance with all other published work, it being established that early maturing animals are relatively slower growing owing to increased fat deposition. That the heavier bulls at 364 days of age grew slower thereafter is probably associated with the feeding system employed. Moreover, since bulls of this breed on this feeding system are likely to be ready for slaughter at 360 days, there seems to be little point in testing to higher weights, and relationships of subsequent gains to optimum slaughter weights would appear to be academic.

The major criticism of most US and UK tests is that they are not long enough due to the late entry caused by conventional late-weaning systems. A longer period on test is likely to increase variation and thus aid selection. For example, Shelby *et al.* (1960) in a review of testing at Miles City, Montana, showed that total variation in gain on test was 22% higher in steers fed 252 days than in bulls fed only 196 days.

The 400 day termination point used by the Beef Recording Association is a particularly unsatisfactory method of lengthening the test, for final weights then become quite unrealistic while feed costs—and hence costs of testing—are unnecessarily high.

Few attempts have been made to lengthen the test by weaning early. The Milk Marketing Board (1960b), Jones and Francis (1963) and Dodsworth *et al.* (1963) attempted testing from birth or thereabouts, but these pioneering efforts were effectively destroyed by the anachronistic bull licensing system in the UK wherein "breed type" was the final arbiter—irrespective of performance. There are certainly management problems in starting tests at birth due to the difficulties of raising beef calves by artificial methods. We believe that delaying weaning to 90 days overcomes this rearing hazard and, since this is the point when the milk yield of beef cows becomes the limiting factor to calf growth (Drewry *et al.*, 1959; Brumby *et al.*, 1963), weaning on to *ad libitum* concentrate feeding guarantees continued maximum expression of the genetic potential (Willis and Preston, 1968a). Under these circumstances initial weight on test is of little importance, being poorly correlated ($r = 0.14$) with weight for age at 400 kg.

Many workers attempt to overcome initial weight and age differences by adjustment of their data. That this is less effective than a fixed age of entry is shown by the fact that the correlation of weight for age at 400 kg and initial weight adjusted to 90 day entry was higher ($r = 0.61$) than the correlation with actual 90 day weight (Willis and Preston, 1967).

A further important advantage of early entry is that final selection can be made at an earlier animal age. For example, in our testing programme, many bulls have completed their tests at an earlier age than the point of entry of some of the bulls tested by Lewis (1966). By the time our best bulls were 30 months old they had tested sons ready for use. In contrast, when the termination point is 400 days, a minimum of

37 months elapses; thus, with the same selection intensity, progress per year is at least 20% slower.

3.4.3.4 Effect of initial age and weight. The choice in the UK of a 400 day termination point undoubtedly resulted from the need to allow sufficient time to permit the animals to adjust for pre-test environmental differences. In one Beef Recording Association test bulls entered at ages between 205 and 262 days with weights of 225 to 386 kg (Lewis, 1966). Even though the starting age was adjusted to 250 days we found a high correlation (0.79 ± 0.07) between final weight and adjusted 250 day weight. In a similar test undertaken by BOCM (1962), our calculations reveal a correlation of 0.92 ± 0.05 between initial and final weights. In both tests bulls came from many different farms which employed varying systems of feeding and management. The differences in initial weight may thus have reflected more environmental than genetic differences. Final weight must have been similarly influenced in view of its high correlation with initial weight.

Thomas and Cartwright (1962) found in an analysis of 1840 Hereford bulls that initial age was an important source of variation in gain during a 140 day test; they suggested that the age of entry should not exceed 7 months.

The above evidence conflicts with the previously mentioned findings of O'Mary *et al.* (1959c) that age at the start of testing was not an important factor. This latter view was also taken by Swiger and Hazel (1961) and by Brown (1963) who with Angus, Hereford, Red Poll and Polled Hereford bulls considered it unnecessary to correct daily gains for initial weight, age or condition even though initial ages ranged from 241 to 338 days. Later, however, Brown (1965) concluded that 60% of the variance in average daily gain of 122 Hereford and Angus bulls tested for 154 days was accounted for by initial weight and feed consumption. We also found that initial age and weight significantly affected the rate at which animals reached 400 kg (Willis and Preston, 1967).

The effect of initial weight on feed conversion is much greater than on gains. Thus although Bennett and Mathews (1955) found that initial weight did not affect gain on test it seriously affected feed conversion to the extent that every 0.45 kg increase in initial weight gave 0.009 kg less gain for each 45.4 kg of TDN. Similar results were obtained by Anon. (1958) in an analysis of performance tests with Angus, Hereford and Shorthorns in Canada. Starting weight (around 250 kg) did not affect daily gain on test but appeared to be related to feed conversion. Pepito *et al.* (1961) studied the data from 242 bulls starting on test at an average of 217 days and found that 66% of the variation in feed efficiency during a 154 day test was accounted for by age at the start, average weight during the test and daily gain. The contention that it is not necessary to select for both gain and efficiency may be justified when testing is over a constant weight range, since Smith *et al.* (1961) found that, under these conditions, correlations between the two traits in heifers were of the order of −0.90 while on a constant time basis the correlation was only −0.41. Although correlations for bulls were high on both systems the data were misleading in view of the small number of bulls involved.

3.4.3.5 Miscellaneous effects. According to Schalles and Marlowe (1967) bulls with "dwarfism" in their pedigree had better performance on test than those with "clean" pedigrees. It is impossible to explain this, but in view of previous work from this station (Marlowe *et al.*, 1962; Marlowe, 1964), which showed "snorter dwarfs" to be slow growing, the effect was probably spurious.

England (1959) has shown that there is no evidence that inherently slow-growing animals respond differently to DES implants than inherently fast growers. Despite this, we feel that bulls on performance test should not be given hormone treatment. For whether the hormone is fed or implanted, absorption rate is likely to vary between individual bulls, thus increasing the proportion of the growth response ascribable to environmental rather than genetic effects.

It was considered by Baily and Gilbert (1962) that age of dam had significant effects not only on initial weight at the start of testing (which is to be expected) but also on final weight. Similarly, Schalles and Marlowe (1967) reported, from an analysis of 633 group-fed animals at one station in Virginia, that age of dam affected 365 day weight, gain on test and lifetime daily gain. At another station, where bulls were fed and housed individually, there were no such effects. Our own unpublished findings in Cuba, relating to bulls weaned early and fed individually, confirm that age of dam need not be a complicating factor. It is almost certain that the problem is related to size and age at weaning. Under US conditions, age of dam significantly affects weaning weight (§ 6.5.4) and under group feeding conditions bigger calves (from older cows) have an undoubted advantage.

According to Patterson *et al.* (1955), initial conformation grade and condition score had correlations of −0.12 and −0.24 respectively with daily gain in a 140 day test. DuBose *et al.* (1968) also reported that type scores of sires or dams were not related to any performance traits in their progeny, while Schalles and Marlowe (1967) found conformation scores at the start were negatively related to performance on test.

3.4.3.6 Feeding system. There is a great lack of uniformity in the management and feeding procedures employed in performance tests (e.g. compare Brown and Arosemena, 1962; Koger *et al.*, 1962a; Jones and Francis, 1963; Crawford *et al.*, 1967; Schalles and Marlowe, 1967). Not only is there no consistency between stations, but within stations variability is also considerable. For example, Rollins *et al.* (1962) fed alfalfa hay as the test diet, but during cold weather, or when the hay was of poor quality, supplementary grain was given. Shelby *et al.* (1960) used increasing proportions of concentrates as the test progressed. Smith and O'Mary (1962) concluded that supplementing a pelleted ration with long hay had little effect on gain, but the experiment was hardly valid since, in common with many other tests, all the bulls were bedded on straw and almost certainly consumed some of it.

The object of any system of performance testing must be to evaluate, as quickly and as efficiently as possible, genetic differences between animals in terms of their phenotypic expression. The greater the variation in environment among the bulls on test the more difficult it is to attain this objective since heritability of the character is reduced. It is obvious that the higher the energy intake the faster the rate of growth and the shorter the generation interval. Procedures based on restricted feeding are particularly inappropriate since variation is reduced (Taylor and Young, 1966; Preston and Willis, 1967) and differentiation is thus made more difficult. The futility of trying to carry out performance tests under these conditions is demonstrated by the work of Carrera and Cházaro (1967) in Mexico. They fed 18 Santa

Gertrudis bulls for 140 days post-weaning on a diet the composition of which permitted a growth ceiling of only 0.8 kg/day. Nine bulls attained this level but their true potential and their order of merit could not be ascertained, for bulls of this breed are capable of daily gains in excess of 1.10 kg (Willis and Preston, 1968a).

Giving concentrates and long roughage separately complicates the issue in that bulls on the same test can consume quite different diets. Kidwell *et al.* (1955) tested 11 Hereford bulls for 91 days on a diet of hay and concentrates and although a ratio of 3 parts hay to 1 concentrates was intended, the bulls actually consumed ratios ranging from 2.95:1 up to 3.26:1. Since these workers included cost of gain in their selection index, variable hay consumption partially invalidated the index as regards cost of feed as well as actual gain. Brown and Arosemena (1962) suggested that capacity for and intake of roughages was highly heritable, and Ratcliff *et al.* (1962) found differences between sires in the ability of their daughters to consume forage. This is hardly a characteristic worthy of selection except perhaps in a predominantly pastoral country such as New Zealand. The other serious disadvantage of using roughages in test diets is their variation in quality from year to year and even within years. It is also extremely difficult to calculate feed conversions on other than a very approximate basis.

It seems to us that the advantages of complete high-energy diets are irrefutable. Firstly, voluntary intake of ME is at a maximum with ground, mixed diets containing 75% or more concentrates (see § 5.4); thus daily gain is limited only by the growth potential of the animal and generation interval is minimized. Secondly, the diet is the same for all bulls (selection of ingredients by the animals being impossible with correctly designed feeding equipment) and comparisons between years are valid if feed ingredients are carefully chosen. Thirdly, use of a complete ground feed facilitates management and self-feeding reduces labour costs and increases the accuracy of feed recording.

Such complete feeds should not be pelleted since this is likely to induce problems such as rumen parakeratosis (§ 11.3.5) unless some long roughage is also fed, an undesirable practice in performance testing for the reasons already outlined. The risk of liver abcess formation—often associated with high concentrate diets (§ 11.3.5) —does not seem to be a serious problem when calves are suckled on pasture to 90 days of age (Willis and Preston, 1968a). The incidence of bloat is probably higher on such diets, but since this trait is partly under genetic control (§ 11.3.2), selection can be practised against susceptible animals. The same is also true of certain hoof anomalies which have been observed in Herefords (Brown *et al.*, 1967a) and Brahmans (Willis and Preston, 1968a).

Baker (1965) offered the opinion, albeit without evidence, that when bulls are presented with a single coarse mixture they reject specific ingredients such as maize and protein cake. Our own experience with such diets given from correctly designed self-feeders does not support this contention. Moreover, Putnam *et al.* (1967a) showed that bulls actually preferred complete ground rations containing 75% concentrates. They ate 7 times as much of this diet as of a ground diet containing only 11% concentrates; the same diets in pelleted form were preferred least of all. There was no evidence of selection within a given diet.

The argument that high energy test diets take no account of possible genotype/environment interactions is discussed in Chapter 4.

3.4.3.7 Management and housing. In the UK the general pattern in most individual performance tests has been to create elaborate facilities in which the animals are "belly-deep" in straw. Frequently this was to placate pedigree breeders who tend to believe that such management produces superior animals. Apart from confounding feed recording, due to unknown bedding consumption, such practices are unnecessarily expensive. We have had excellent results from the use of concrete slatted-floor pens which obviate the need for bedding and reduce labour to a minimum. A pen size of 2 $\times$ 2.5 m has proved satisfactory in individual testing of over 400 bulls.

Group testing is widely practiced in the US and it is useful when testing facilities are limited; but it has several disadvantages. A pecking order exists in all animal groups (e.g. McBride, 1964; McPhee *et al.*, 1964) which could affect gains to the extent that an animal of high genetic potential but placid temperament might appear inferior due to its docility and consequent susceptibility to bullying. Feed intake and conversion measurements are not possible and although gain and feed efficiency are related valuable information is lost and overall progress reduced. Franke and Cartwright (1968) have put forward a method for estimating individual intakes of animals housed in groups. Errors of estimating weekly intakes were alleged to be small but ranged up to 2 kg. As this represents about 5% of actual consumption the method is hardly accurate enough to allow selection for feed conversion. Broadbent (1967) devised a system whereby a tuned electronic circuit attached to the animal operated an electromagnetic lock securing the entrance flap on the animal's own feed box. By this method animals can be housed in groups, but with the possibility of recording individual intakes. The procedure offers considerable promise for reducing the housing costs associated with performance testing in individual pens.

3.4.3.8 Measurements. Initial and final weights, average daily gain on test, weight for age, feed intake and feed conversion are essential parameters. Weighing at intervals is a valuable guide to the shape of growth curves as well as accustoming bulls to routine handling. Some assessment of temperament might prove useful in view of its possible association with meat quality. (§ 2.5.2.6).

In view of the low correlations between body measurements, or conformation scores, and records of performance (e.g. Black *et al.*, 1938; Cook *et al.*, 1951; Woodward *et al.*, 1959) there is little point in measuring these characteristics. In Nevada, Kidwell *et al.* (1955) pointed out that use of rate or economy of gain did not always result in the selection of "good looking" bulls, nevertheless carcass quality of their progeny was of a high order. Despite this finding, these workers went on to incorporate conformation in their selection system. Similarly, in the UK, Jones and Francis (1963) awarded 20% of the points in their selection index to visual merit, thus rating it twice as important as feed efficiency. Although this type of selection procedure makes no economic or genetic sense, these investigations were, at the time, pioneering efforts in their appropriate countries. There can, however, be no excuse for the statements by Baker (1965) in his capacity as Chief Executive Officer of the Beef Recording Association in the UK that ". . . the major present and potential uses of testing centres are to determine the weight performance and conformation scores of potential sires", that ". . . conformation assessments at the end of a test period are obviously of major importance to beef cattle and to the beef industry in general", and that "... in view of the importance of both weight for age and body conformation in beef cattle the best and simplest method of compiling a single index is to combine both of these factors in equal proportions".

Masculinity score would seem to be of negligible value in selection indices (Schalles and Marlowe, 1967). Putnam *et al.* (1965) studied the relationship between gain on test and rumen VFA concentration but as only 11–14% of the variation in gain was attributable to VFA differences, such measurements also contribute little. Johnson *et al.* (1963, 1965) found little relation between rate or efficiency of gain and digestive function or rumen fermentation. Similar results were reported by Stufflebean *et al.* (1963) for certain blood components.

The fewer the criteria under selection the more rapid the progress in any one and the most important measurement in beef production, apart from considerations of fertility and liveability, is the amount of edible meat per unit of feed consumed. Since accurate carcass evaluation is not yet possible in the live animal, alternative selection criteria must be used. Feed conversion (feed/gain ratio) is probably correlated with efficiency of edible meat production (cf. §§ 3.3.6 and 7) while weight for age is the best measure of growth rate. Although this latter has been criticized by Munro (1962), who demonstrated a spurious negative correlation between age and weight per day of age, the measure is perfectly valid when bulls are evaluated at a fixed weight. Weight for age is correlated with daily gain on test ($r = 0.71$, Willis and Preston, 1967), but the formei is more suitable since it minimizes effects of compensatory growth.

3.4.3.9 Application. Performance testing can only lead to progress when it is linked with selection. It is not sufficient merely to identify superior bulls; they must be used widely and inferior bulls eliminated. The major criticism of almost all current performance testing is that after having identified the apparently superior animals in respect of gain, feed efficiency, final weight or weight for age, little selection is actually practised. This is particularly true of UK tests where, in every instance, the bulls have been subjected to appraisal for conformation. More often than not this has resulted in the superior bulls (on the basis of performance) being refused licences or having them granted only on a limited experimental basis (MMB, 1960b; BOCM, 1962, 1963; Dodsworth *et al.*, 1963; Jones and Francis, 1963; Lewis, 1966). The futility of licensing is further demonstrated by the fact that Jones and Francis obtained no evidence of a relationship between body measurements or "visual merit" and conversion, while Dodsworth *et al.* (1963) found some suggestions that the bull with the best conformation produced the poorest progeny in terms of economic merit. The lack of relation between these traits is also shown in Lewis's (1966) data for final weight and conformation in 33 Hereford bulls (Table 3.21).

Although US tests are not officially hampered by licensing, many investigators have included type appraisal as one of their selection criteria. Responsibility for this rests, in part, with commercial producers. For instance, in a survey sent to 1235 producers in Indiana (of whom only 227 replied) the three most important factors determining selection of herd sires in a list of eleven were conformation, size and health and type for small herds; and conformation, size and reputation of the breeder for large herds (Rutherford *et al.*, 1966). In California, Rollins *et al.* (1962) found that progeny testing programmes were restricted by the reluctance of co

TABLE 3.21 NUMBER OF PERFORMANCE-TESTED BULLS IN EACH LIVE WEIGHT/CONFORMATION CATEGORY (AFTER LEWIS, 1966)

400 day weight (kg)	Conformation grade			
	Top	High average	Low average	Bottom
>499	3	3	2	1
477–499	1	1	3	2
454–477	2	2	3	2
<454	1	3	2	2

operating farmers to use a bull grading 2 minus or less, on the University of California conformation scale. But as the University was itself responsible for encouraging farmers to pay attention to type (Albaugh *et al.*, 1956; Rollins and Wagner, 1956b), it was in no position to complain.

In Mississippi, Taylor *et al.* (1960b) found correlations of 0.53 for Angus and 0.63 for Hereford between final conformation grade and sale price. Similar correlations were obtained between sale price and final weight, but correlations between the former and gain on test were negligible. Perhaps the most serious reflection on the American beef-cattle industry is the report of Marlowe and Morrow (1967). Over a 7 year period they sold at public auction in Virginia 390 Angus and 233 Hereford "record of performance" bulls. Information available to potential buyers included: the animal, name of breeder, pedigree, pre-weaning daily gain, grade, index value, 365 day weight, 140 day test gain, lifetime average daily gain and sale age and weight. Information not made available included pedigree appraisal for dwarfism and scores for masculinity development. Table 3.22 illustrates the priorities and emphasizes the commercial producers' apparent indifference to performance test data.

The high ranking of the trait "dwarfism" further indicates the preoccupation with type. In our opinion, the short-legged and blocky animal possibly owes its popularity as much to aesthetic considerations as to the mistaken belief that such a configuration

TABLE 3.22 FACTORS INFLUENCING SALE PRICE OF PERFORMANCE-TESTED ANGUS AND HEREFORD BULLS IN VIRGINIA (AFTER MARLOWE AND MORROW, 1967)

Order of importance of factor	Angus	Hereford
1	Live grade	Live grade
2	Year of birth	Year of birth
3	Breeder	Breeder
4	Dwarfism	Dwarfism
5	Sale weight	Poll condition
6	Masculinity score	365 day weight
7		Sale weight or age
8		Pre-weaning gain
No importance	Any measure of test performance	
Average sale price ($)	602	679

yields most meat. The eye appeal of the short square animal accounts for the ready acceptance in the late 1930's and early 1940's of Compact Shorthorns and Comprest Herefords which were nothing more than heterozygous expressions of lethal genes (see review by Warwick, 1958). The later defect of "snorter dwarfs" in Angus and Hereford cattle (see Johnson *et al.*, 1950) is another genetic problem unlikely to be resolved even though selection against dwarfism ranked fourth in Marlowe and Morrow's (1967) study, since breeders continue to select for square, blocky animals.

In a 10-year study of Dutch Friesians, Cazemier (1965) showed that bulls 2 cm or more lower in height than the average had sons which, in general, obtained higher points in classification for conformation. The almost universal preoccupation with conformation—apparent in developing (Muñiz and Kaspar, 1967) as well as agriculturally advanced countries—is almost certainly the reason for the abysmally slow progress in beef cattle improvement. As a positive selection criterion, conformation should be rejected. Its only justification is in the negative sense to ensure that animals with obvious serious abnormalities (e.g. leg weakness) are not used for breeding regardless of their test performance.

In contrast with the findings of Marlowe and Morrow (1967), DuBose and his co-workers (1968) sold 44 tested Angus bulls in Texas during 1967 and found that sale price was positively correlated with the most important performance traits. Since Marlowe and Morrow's findings related to the years 1959–66, this may indicate a growing and welcome awareness on the part of breeders of the value of performance testing.

The selection of bulls to breed bulls is the major avenue of progress, yet in the UK performance tests the best bulls generally return to small herds so that their impact on the nation's beef cattle is slight. When such bulls do enter AI they are no longer able to sire pure-bred sons, since the major beef breed societies in the UK and the US do not permit registration of stock bred by AI. This is hardly conducive to progress.

3.4.4 Progeny testing

Progeny testing—the selection of parents on the basis of the performance of their offspring—is the most accurate direct measure of the animal's breeding value. The major drawback of the method is the time required to obtain and evaluate sufficient progeny. In addition to increasing the generation interval, it may also reduce selection intensity in that fewer sires can be progeny-tested as compared with performance testing. Although progeny testing can be applied to both sexes it is normally only used for bulls, since for cows the time necessary to obtain sufficient progeny renders the method impractical.

For traits not measurable in the live animal, progeny testing is the only way to improvement. The major practical problem is to arrive at a compromise between the number of sires to be tested and the required number of progeny from each, i.e. whether it is better to test a large number of small families or a small number of large ones. The optimum family size for progeny testing of sires has been discussed by Robertson (1957).

Although progeny testing has been widely accepted in dairy cattle breeding there is little published evidence of its value for beef cattle improvement. Dodsworth *et al.* (1963) performance-tested 10 Shorthorn bulls and progeny-tested 3 of them. No significant differences between progeny groups were observed but there was a suggestion that the best bull on performance test had the better progeny. The failure to obtain significant differences in the progeny test may reflect on the efficiency of the method used. In Holland, Bergström (1965) progeny-tested 9 Friesian and 9 Meuse–Rhine–Yssel bulls with a total of 119 male progeny (5–10 per bull). The range of progeny-group means for the various traits studied were:

Daily gain: 1.10–1.33 kg.
Feed conversion: 3.14–3.64 kg starch equivalent per kg gain.
Dressing percentage: 57.4–62.0.
Meat/bone ratio: 4.1–4.9.
Meat/fat ratio: 9.6–5.8.

The MRY bulls were superior in conversion and meat/fat ratio, but variation within progeny groups was greater than between groups. Differences were small except for meat/fat ratio, which led Bergström to conclude that progeny testing was of doubtful value because of the large number of progeny needed. Similar difficulties were encountered by Kincaid and Carter (1958) in that the steer progeny of 19 high sires (1.02 kg/day on performance test) and 19 low sires (0.75 kg/day) only differed by 0.95 kg/day. The progeny groups were tested in pairs (low and high on each farm) with an average of from 2 to 12 progeny per sire. Better results were obtained by Gregory and Stewart (1962) with 29 bulls, performance-tested for weaning weight (192 days) and post-weaning gain in a 154 day test. Progeny of these bulls were tested for 182 day weight and grade and 18 month weight and grade. The 154 day performance-test gain was a better indicator of progeny performance than was weaning weight. As a means of identifying superior sires, 10 progeny per bull were considered adequate and even 5 were as useful as a performance test on the sire itself. Rollins *et al.* (1962) found that 10 steer progeny were sufficient to identify the better bull of a pair provided the selected trait was weight for age and not gain. Nine bulls of 4 inbred lines from the Miles City Station and 8 commercial bulls were progeny-tested by Pahnish *et al.* (1961a). Significant differences in weaning weight were obtained between progeny groups, but the number of progeny and the ranking of the sires were not given. In California, Albaugh and Elings (1964) tested 11 Hereford and 4 Angus bulls which were mated to 25–30 cows on the basis of two or three bulls per ranch. At weaning, 8–10 progeny per sire were randomly selected and fattened for 188 days under feedlot conditions. There were no apparent differences in bulls for cutability or index grade, but significant differences were found in the wholesale value of the carcasses. The highest-gaining sires produced progeny which gave most financial return.

Suggestions of economic differences between sires in terms of the carcass value of their progeny were also reported by Greiman and Taylor (1964) in Arizona, although only 4 steers were available for each of 4 sires.

Wilson *et al.* (1967) tested 13 polled Hereford sires with a total of 80 steer and 94 heifer progeny out of Angus × Holstein dams. Slaughtering at a constant weight for each sex, these workers obtained significant differences between sires for 205 day weaning weight, gain on test and weight of trimmed loin in the carcass. In a long-term breeding project in Kentucky, Bradley *et al.* (1967) reported that, with 8–10 bull progeny per sire, mean 205 day weaning weight ranged from 140 to 164 kg and weight per day of age at slaughter from 0.89 to 0.97 kg. The significance or otherwise of these differences was not given. Carcass traits for 8 or 9 bulls by each of two sires indicated a greater fatness in one group despite it being 12.5 kg lighter.

In Germany, Bogner (1966) progeny-tested 5 sires each with 22 progeny fattened to either 350, 500 or 600 kg live weight. He considered that of 37 characters examined, only longissimus dorsi area and weights of the hind and forequarters were useful selection tools. On the other hand, Heigler (1966) used 390 progeny from 40 BPL sires in East Germany and found that at 400 kg between-group variance was high. He concluded that over half of the differences in fat content of the carcass between progeny groups was genetic in origin.

An early attempt to progeny-test Angus bulls under farm conditions was that of Mason *et al.* (1962) in the UK. In the second year of a 2 year trial, 15–24 crossbred progeny were available for each of 3 bulls; there were significant differences between sires for weaning weight and subjective measures of carcass fatness and conformation of the round. The investigation showed the feasibility of testing on commercial farms, but suffered from inadequate data collection and poor methods of carcass appraisal which were unrelated to economic merit.

Large-scale progeny testing on commercial farms was subsequently undertaken in both Britain and Israel using contemporary comparison systems. The British tests were with imported Charolais and British beef bulls using their crossbred progeny from dairy cows. Interpretation of the results, which related to gestation period, birth weight, mortality, calving difficulties and live weight gains (Edwards *et al.*, 1966), was complicated by the fact that the bulls were used in groups of 3 in each of 5 geographical regions. Differences were subsequently found to exist between regions for several of the traits studied (O'Connor *et al.*, 1968), which led to some confounding, nevertheless, this system allowed identification of superior sires. The development of contemporary comparison systems, similar to those used to evaluate milk yield potential, is probably the best way of incorporating progeny testing in beef cattle improvement programmes.

In view of the promise of this first trial it is disappointing that the same organization (MMB, 1966) began using station progeny testing when more progress would result from using these facilities for performance testing. This is well illustrated by the first results of the scheme which were described by Jobst (1968). The mean daily gain from 90 days to slaughter (a carcass weight of 208 kg) for progeny groups of 17 Hereford bulls (26 steer progeny per bull) was 1.13 kg/day, the best sire being only 4% above average in terms of the daily gain of his progeny. Eleven of the 17 sires were culled on the basis of the test; thus after 3 years of operation, necessitating the housing and testing of 440 steers, only 6 sires of moderate superiority actually entered the AI stud; the realized selection differential was only 1.06 × SD of each trait considered. Had the same facilities been used for performance testing, 155 sires would have been available for AI at the same selection differential or, conversely, if only 6 bulls were needed the selection differential would have been 2.60 × SD of each trait considered.

The Israeli approach is the most effective work available to date. Bar-Anan *et al.* (1965) gave data for 44 sires based on the performance of 1658 sons on commercial farms. Contemporary comparisons for weight at 365 ± 30 days ranged from −11.3 to 25.2 kg. Although 365 days is the average slaughter age under the intensive feeding conditions practised in Israel, it would have been better from the point of view of carcass evaluation to have selected according to a fixed final weight.

Some of our data is given in Table 3.23 and relates to the progeny testing of Charolais sires using purebred sons and to Charolais and Brown Swiss sires using sons out of Brahman cows. All progeny were weaned at 90 days and fed a complete high-energy diet individually until slaughter at 400 kg live weight. Since the experiments concerned were not designed to investigate progeny testing *per se* the number of sons per bull is not high. Nevertheless significant differences for some live and carcass traits exist between sires of the same breed. Most of the sires given in Table 3.23 were foundation stock and hence there is no information on their own performance.

3.4.5 Realized response to selection

3.4.5.1 PERFORMANCE TO WEANING. Theoretical estimates of the likely response to selection for pre-weaning traits have been put forward by Brinks *et al.* (1964b) and Pahnish *et al.* (1964). According to these latter workers, direct selection for weaning weight would result in an improvement per generation of 4.4 and 1.0 kg in heifers and bulls respectively. Correlated response in birth weight would be 0.33 and 0.55 kg respectively. They considered that selection for pre-weaning gain would be no more effective than for weaning weight in improving the pre-weaning gain while correlated responses in birth weight would be less. An earlier paper by Shelby *et al.* (1963) was in good agreement with these proposals.

In practice, Flower *et al.* (1964) found that performance testing in 7 Hereford lines or cross-lines over a period of 6 years resulted in an average annual progress in weaning weight of 2.07 kg (1.23%).

Eller and Carter (1967) studied the use actually made of performance records in 12 Angus and 9 Hereford herds which had participated for at least 10 years in the Virginia Beef Cattle Improvement Programme. Available data related to 4279 Angus and 2303 Hereford heifer calves and showed annual selection differentials of 8.7 and 7.1 kg for each breed respectively in weaning weight and 0.03 kg for both breeds in adjusted daily gain. There was considerable variation between herds, but for the six traits measured the annual selection differentials were about 25% of that which would have been possible had selection been made for only single traits.

Chapman *et al.* (1968) estimated genetic change per year in a Hereford herd in Texas over a 12 year period to be effectively zero for birth weight, 1.23 kg for 180 day weaning weight and 0.009 kg in pre-weaning daily gain. In this herd there had actually been negative selection for these traits among some sires. In another Hereford herd in Nebraska, in which three lines had been selected on the basis of either weaning weight, yearling weight or an index combining muscle score and yearling weight, Koch *et al.* (1968) found that the average annual improvement was 2.6, 2.0 and 3.8% for the respective traits in each line. On the other hand, Hoornbeek and Bogart (1966) analysed the data from three Hereford and one Angus line and showed that pre- and post-weaning gains had largely declined. Some of this may have been attributable to inbreeding but selection had actually been based on an index incorporating pre- and post-weaning gain together with conformation score; it is perhaps significant that all lines had improved in conformation.

TABLE 3.23 PROGENY TEST RESULTS

Breed of progeny	Charolais			Charolais × Braham		Brown Swiss × Brahman	
Sire	San José 521	San José 638/1	ICA Alfonso[a]	ICA Alfonso[a]	ICA Atlas[b]	13R	14R
				Growth data 90 days to 400 kg live weight			
No. of sons	8	10	12	7	5	11	9
WFA at 400 kg[c]	1.20	1.31	1.31	1.14	1.27	1.11	1.24
Conversion	5.04	5.62	5.53	6.11	5.43	6.09	5.34
				Carcass data at 400 kg live weight			
No. of sons	7	7	7	7	5	10	8
Dressing (%)	57.8	59.3	58.9	57.7	57.2	55.5	55.9
Edible meat (%)	76.8	73.1	76.1	75.0	74.8	73.9	72.9
Excess fat (%)	7.1	9.7	6.9	7.8	8.8	9.4	10.7
Bone (%)	16.1	17.2	17.0	17.2	16.4	16.7	17.1

[a] Weight for age of this sire was 1.48 kg at 400 kg live weight.
[b] Weight for age of this sire was 1.57 kg at 400 kg live weight.
[c] Weight for age in kilograms per day.

In a 17 year study in Colorado where selection indices had been used for weaning weight, gain, feed conversion and grade, Armstrong *et al.* (1965) found that although environment had improved the genotype had regressed. Here again an inefficient selection index may have been responsible, but the more probable cause was high inbreeding (of the order of 30%).

3.4.5.2 Post-weaning performance. Gregory (1965) predicted that selection of 10% of sires and 50% of heifers on the basis of post-weaning daily gain alone should result in an annual improvement in this trait of 0.014 kg. Nelms and Stratton (1967) selected for final weight in a closed Hereford herd in Wyoming and reported changes of 10.9 kg (3.5%) per generation together with correlated responses of 3.0 kg (1.8%) in 180 day weaning weight and 0.05 kg/day (5.9%) in post-weaning gain. In a small closed Charolais herd we selected the best 10% bulls on the basis of weight for age at 400 kg and obtained an improvement of 0.12 kg (9.7%) in the first generation (Willis and Preston, 1969a).

Tallack (1967) analysed the relationship between the 400 day weight of 30 Lincoln Red sires and that of their progeny groups (at least 7 progeny per sire) raised on farms in the UK. Interpretation of his data is made difficult by the fact that the scatter diagram had its points inaccurately marked and the regression equation did not fit the regression line. However, our own re-analysis of the original data indicates that the author's conclusion, that for every 100 kg increase in sire weight the progeny increased 40 kg, is broadly correct. Even allowing for the fact that no adjustments were made for environmental effects and the possibility that the chosen progeny may have been out of above-average cows the heritability of the trait would appear to be high. It is therefore disconcerting to find that the average liveweight gain of Lincoln Red steers was the same in 1966–7 as it was in 1961–2 when the recording scheme started. One can only conclude that either the Beef Recording Association figures are not a good guide to genetic potential or that breeders are not using them efficiently.

3.4.5.3 Conformation. Although Krehbiel *et al.* (1958) reported on the effectiveness of selecting for type in an Angus herd, the evidence suggests that this would be economically undesirable. Willson *et al.* (1963) described results with two Hereford herds in Montana, in one of which sires were selected on the basis of performance test and in the other, visually, by breeders. The former herd performed better in pre- and post-weaning gains and in carcass grade. In Angus and Shorthorn herds selected over a 12 year period on the basis of either post-weaning growth, or type at weaning, Bovard *et al.* (1966) also found that in both breeds the growth line was the heavier and gained faster.

In Nevada, Bailey and Gilbert (1962) selected for rate or economy of gain or conformation and found that selection for either of the first two characteristics gave similar results; the "conformation" line was least efficient and also had a poorer growth rate. Subsequently (Bailey *et al.*, 1967) they found maximum selection intensity for any trait to be 0.2 × SD units per year; selection for single traits did not cause divergance of the lines within two generations. The line with greatest improvement in gain and efficiency had the highest feed intakes. It is interesting to note that all lines were considered to have improved in conformation. After two generations, selection for conformation appeared to have produced fatter animals than selection for gains or efficiency (Hammack and Bailey, 1968).

The undesirability of selecting for conformation is also emphasized by Wilson *et al.* (1963b), who calculated that to include this trait in a selection index would adversely affect progress in both daily gain and weaning weight.

3.4.5.4 Female selection and reproductive traits. The high replacement and low reproductive rate of females allows only limited progress by selection. Facilities are unlikely to be sufficient to permit individual testing of females, but group evaluation could prove useful for growth rate. The field programmes undertaken in Europe (Bergström, 1962; Tallack, 1967; Taylor, 1967) are likely to prove of limited practical value, owing to the fact that conditions are so variable even on the same farm. Biometrical correction of the data is possible but rarely within the scope of the breeder. Moreover, the small size of most beef herds in Europe makes selection programmes for females well-nigh impossible.

In California, Gregory *et al.* (1963) demonstrated considerable differences in the size of various body measurements of Hereford cows rejected or retained for breeding purposes. Some of these differences may have represented selection against the Comprest type of animal, but there is no evidence that the programme adopted had any positive effect on economic traits.

There is a belief that females should be selected for their fertility, but while it is economically justified to cull infertile cows or those with poor reproductive performance, it should not be assumed that this will lead to genetic improvement in reproductive traits. Davenport *et al.* (1965) studied the effect of culling for calf-crop percentage and found that the selection pressure ranged from 3.4% at 2 years to 10.5% at 8 years of age, but that reproductive performance was not improved.

Plasse *et al.* (1968c) studied 3938 Brahman calves in Florida and suggested that selection for reproductive performance during a short breeding season would decrease average calving interval and thus improve overall reproductive efficiency. But, in view of the difficulties associated with getting Brahmans in-calf when they are lactating (Chapter 6), it is probable that early weaning would be a more certain means of achieving this end. Selection for twinning has been undertaken from time to time, but Mechling and Carter (1962) found it to be ineffective even over a 20 year period. This is not surprising since heritability of this trait is effectively nil (Table 3.2).

3.5 BREEDING SYSTEMS

3.5.1 Introduction

It is well established that reproductive traits are of low heritability, but it is equally true that these characteristics are particularly responsive to crossbreeding. It follows from this that if we wish to improve fertility or even maintain it at a high level, the basic breeding programme must be predicated upon the exploitation of heterosis via crossbreeding. Crossbreeding to produce cattle for fattening is common in many countries particularly the UK where a high proportion of beef comes from the dairy herd (Edwards, 1963). In this case mainly Angus and Hereford bulls are used on Friesian and Ayrshire, particularly heifers, whose calves are not required for herd replacements. Although this use of crossbreeding is accepted and even actively encouraged by breeders of pedigree beef bulls, the traditional viewpoint is still that specialized beef production from beef-type herds should be based on pure-bred Angus, Hereford or Shorthorn cattle.

There are several reasons for opposing this practice. Firstly, crossbreeding of dairy cattle with beef bulls reduces selection intensity for milk production; and, secondly, there is no evidence that a better beef animal is always produced by such crossing. This is particularly true of the Friesian which, bred pure, is much more suited to intensive beef production than any of the traditional British beef breeds (Branaman *et al.*, 1962; Preston *et al.*, 1963c; Cole *et al.*, 1963, 1964). Moreover, it has been shown by Nichols and White (1964) that the use of traditional British beef breeds as compared to pure Holstein results in reduced output of beef per hectare of land per unit of time.

Our reason for advocating crossbreeding in beef herds is not the traditional one of producing animals solely for fattening but rather to produce crossbred dams with the primary aim of improving reproductive traits. This does not mean that pure breeds must be eliminated, but that their role in beef-cattle society should be brought up to date.

Any plan to improve a nation's cattle should begin with a census so as to ascertain the breed structure of the national herd. Performance testing on the lines we have outlined should then be undertaken for all major breeds with the exception of those clearly deficient in desired characteristics. Such testing should be on as large a scale as possible and, preferably, centralized under government control. In those breeds where performance, in terms of growth, feed conversion and carcass quality, is already relatively high and the variation within these traits sufficiently large, testing should continue to further improve the breed. Breeds with poor performance and the mass of commercial cattle destined for beef production should serve as the basic raw material on which selected tested sires from the pure breeds will be used according to a planned crossbreeding programme.

3.5.2 Censuses

In most agriculturally advanced countries, cattle censuses are made at regular intervals. AI organizations usually publish annual reports which include data relating to breed demand, and there are the herd books of the breed societies. Thus at any one time there exists a fairly comprehensive picture of the cattle population.

Such data rarely exist in a developing country; indeed, it is often difficult to obtain exact figures of total numbers, quite apart from a breakdown into breeds. Too often grandiose cattle improvement schemes, involving large-scale crossbreeding or massive importations of expensive cattle, are launched before any study has been made of the indigenous cattle stock in terms of numbers, breeds and intrinsic value.

It is unnecessary to describe here how a census should be carried out since this will vary according to the situation. Useful examples of censuses relating to the dairy industry, which could serve as models, have been published by the MMB (1955, 1960a, 1965).

3.5.3 Breed evaluation

In seeking to evaluate existing breeds one must bear in mind the purposes for which the cattle are required. Fertility and calf liveability are important traits in any country, but breed differences may be more marked in specific circumstances, as, for example, in tropical areas. Similarly, disease resistance or acquired immunity may be of little or no importance in Europe but vital in parts of South America, Australia and Africa. Growth rate and feed efficiency, on the other hand, must be ranked high in all circumstances. It could be argued that conformation also has economic value in those countries where markets exist for animals which excel in this trait. Even though such a market is artificial, in the sense that conformation has no productive role, it may be currently justifiable for some breeders to consider this trait in breeding programmes. It has, however, no place in any commercial fattening enterprise selling on strict carcass merit. Moreover, with increasing awareness, on the part of developing countries of what constitutes true merit in beef cattle, even the existing markets for the show bulls of Perth and similar archaic institutions will inevitably decline.

The methods of evaluating breeds must depend on the recording facilities which exist or can be made available. The herd-recording techniques used in Europe (see Bergström, 1962; Tallack, 1967; Taylor, 1967) could be adapted to obtain data on fertility, calf mortality and disease problems, provided they are applied on a sufficiently large scale and not—as is often the case—in selected herds. However, measurements of growth rate and feed efficiency on a herd basis have limited value as a means of comparing breeds, and this is best done in central testing stations. The importance of making such comparisons as part of a national performance testing programme cannot be overemphasized since it is of little value to rank bulls within a breed without at the same time ranking the breeds.

Having evaluated the breeds available, the next stage is to decide which should be retained and which incorporated into the commercial herd. Although it is frequently claimed that breeds have arisen according to need, it is clear that there is little or no economic justification for the continued existence of many of them. The UK alone has some 24 different cattle breeds of which probably only the Angus, Charolais, Friesian, Hereford, Jersey, Lincoln Red, South Devon, and Sussex need be retained for further development.

The number of pure breeds necessary in any country will depend on the relative importance of the beef and dairy industries. Where milk production has high priority there is an argument for retaining some exclusively dairy breeds. For a beef breeding programme *per se* we consider that the minimum requirement is of the order of five pure breeds specialized for beef. This could include such breeds as the Friesian and Brown Swiss which, although basically dairy animals, are well able to compete with the better beef breeds when intensive feeding regimes are employed.

If one accepts the premiss that pure breeds are necessary only as sources of bulls for use on the overall crossbred population, the number of cows in each of the selected pure breeds need not be large. Where too few breeds with sufficient merit exist, importation of the required new stock (after due consideration of their performance) does not have to be a huge financial undertaking. Where acclimatization is important, grading-up of indigenous stock is a useful means of augmenting numbers. Countries with rigid health controls can import most cheaply and with greater safety by purchasing frozen semen.

Within the chosen pure breeds, improvement should be by means of performance testing along the lines already described. We consider that with AI widely available the number required of each pure breed is about 500 cows per million mateable commercial cow population. In such circumstances regular checks must be made with regard to inbreeding within the pure herds.

Although widely used in the early development of present breeds as a means of fixing type, inbreeding now has little to recommend it. The belief that inbreeding leads to uniformity is completely erroneous; the fact that inbred lines tend to resemble one another is attributable to selection rather than inbreeding *per se*. In reality, inbreeding leads to deterioration in many economic traits. The effect in reducing milk yield is well documented (see Robertson, 1954). It also increases embryonic mortality (Hawk *et al.*, 1955) and reduces fertility in bulls (Harris *et al.*, 1960). In addition there is depression of various measurements of size and growth such as birth weight and pre-weaning performance (Alexander and Bogart, 1961; Bovard *et al.*, 1963; Brinks *et al.*, 1963), weaning weight (Harwin *et al.*, 1966; Dinkel *et al.*, 1968), post-weaning growth (Alexander and Bogart, 1961, Moore *et al.*, 1961; Swiger *et al.*, 1961a) and mature body size (Mi *et al.*, 1962). Food consumption is also known to be affected (Alexander and Bogart, 1961; Swiger *et al.*, 1961a). This is not to imply that inbreeding is always dangerous; much depends on the nature of the particular trait and the population at risk. Thus Dinkel *et al.* (1968) found it to have little effect on conformation. There is universal agreement, however, as to its damaging effect on reproductive fitness, and, when practised at high levels, inbreeding depression can be sufficiently powerful to negate selection pressure (Armstrong *et al.*, 1965) or limit its effectiveness (Alexander and Bogart, 1961).

If matings were completely at random in the suggested 500 cow pure herds and 20 sires were used in each, the increase in inbreeding according to Wright (1931) would be:

$$100 \frac{1}{8 \times 20} + \frac{1}{8 \times 500} = 0.65\% \text{ per generation.}$$

This is not particularly high and in practice would be considerably less since mating would not be at random.

3.5.4 Heterosis

When two breeds are crossed, the F_1 progeny will generally perform at a level at least midway between that of their parents. Crossbreeding is thus most useful when there are wide differences between breeds and the inferior ones are the most numerous.

An example of this is the cattle population of Cuba, composed primarily of Brahmans, but with small herds of Charolais and other European breeds. Under intensive feeding conditions from 90 days of age, the weight for age at 400 kg of Brahman bulls was 0.86 ± 0.20 compared with 1.24 ± 0.14 for Charolais (Willis and Preston, 1968a). Assuming only additive genetic effects for this trait, the F_1 could be expected to have a weight for age of 1.05 kg. To achieve this same improvement by selection within the Brahman breed would require the use of only the top

12% of animals (assumed $h^2 = 0.60$). If a population of 1 million cows were to be mated by AI and each bull provided 5000 first services, than some 1670 Brahman sires would have to be performance tested and the best 200 selected. By comparison, 200 unselected Charolais bulls would give the same degree of improvement; and if tested Charolais bulls were used (from a population of 1670) the F_1 progeny would have a weight for age of 1.09 instead of 1.05 kg without the need for any female selection. This only takes account of additive effects, whereas in practice non-additive effects are sometimes manifested and bring about in the F_1 a performance superior to the mid-parent average. This is the phenomenon known as heterosis or hybrid vigour. An early explanation of hybrid vigour was that of East (1912) who considered it to be the reverse of inbreeding depression, i.e. that reproductive fitness lost by inbreeding is replaced by crossbreeding. Other theories involving over-dominance have been put forward from time to time, but the original hypothesis based on increased heterozygosity is still the most widely accepted. Lerner (1954) has given valid reasons why natural selection tends to favour the heterozygote; and since all pure breeds have undergone some degree of inbreeding heterozygosity is invariably increased when they are crossed. The extent of the response will in part depend upon the origins of the particular breeds and their gene frequency for specific traits.

Although heterosis is often believed to be most pronounced for reproductive traits, it is also manifest in characters such as growth rate and feed consumption which have no bearing on viability. In such cases, heterosis is termed "luxuriance" (Dobzhansky, 1952).

Additive effects of crossbreeding are predictable once the contributing populations, breeds or strains have been evaluated. Since the performance of different breeds and their crosses is relevant only to the conditions under which the measurements are made, the appropriate data appear elsewhere (chapters 2, 4, 6–8). Heterotic effects, being non-additive, are unpredictable for specific circumstances; nevertheless, evidence has accumulated which serves as a guide to the possible benefits that might be expected for particular traits.

3.5.4.1 Reproduction traits. In crosses involving dairy breeds there was no heterosis for gestation length according to Rendel (1959) and Verley and Touchberry (1961). The latter also reported no benefits in calving interval, service period, age at first calving or services per conception. The data in Table 3.24 all confirm these findings in relation to gestation length.

A significant effect of crossbreeding on percentage calf crop was reported by Ellis and Cartwright (1963), but they attributed this to non-genetic causes. Large negative effects are apparent in the data of Chapman and England (1965) and are difficult to explain other than on the basis of paucity of numbers. Reynolds *et al.* (1965b) found 10% improvement in this trait which is more in line with the remaining data in Table 3.25. The very high response noted by Reynolds *et al.* (1966) almost certainly reflects the abnormally low parental fertility.

Heterosis in age and weight as puberty has been observed by Kaltenbach and Wiltbank (1962) using Angus, Hereford and Shorthorn breeds in all combinations. Crossbred heifers reached puberty 50 days earlier and were 12.3 kg lighter than purebreds. In contrast, Bellows (1968) found no heterosis in either of these traits in a similar experiment involving Angus, Hereford and Charolais cattle.

TABLE 3.24 HETEROSIS IN GESTATION LENGTH

Paternal breed	Gestation length (days)	Maternal breed	Gestation length (days)	F_1 (days)	Heterosis (%)	Authors
SD	287	Dexter	287	284	1.0	Joubert & Hammond, 1958
Cr	289	B	289	290[a]	0.4	Willis & Preston, 1969a
SD	286	Af	292	290	−0.3	Skinner & Ziervogel, 1962
A	279	C	282	284	−0.3 to 0.5	Sagebiel *et al.*, 1967a
H	285	C	282			
H	285	A	279			
RS	291	J	280	287	−0.5	McDowell *et al.*, 1959
HF	281	B	289	284[a]	−1.0	Willis & Preston, 1969a
C	289	B	289	285[a]	−1.4	Willis & Preston, 1969a

[a] Non-reciprocal cross.

TABLE 3.25 HETEROSIS IN PERCENTAGE CALF CROP

Paternal breed	Calf crop (%)	Maternal breed	Calf crop (%)	F_1	Heterosis (%)	Authors
H	88	A	89	87	−2	Wiltbank *et al.*, 1967a
A	89	S	87	87	−1	Wiltbank *et al.*, 1967a
B	56.8	Br	72.6	64.6[ad]	0	Meade *et al.*, 1959b
Simmental	87.8	Red Steppe	85.6	89.7[b]	4	Lymarj, 1956
A	78	C	73.9	86.1	6	Sagebiel *et al.*, 1967a
H	91.7	C	73.9			
H	91.7	A	78.0			
A	63	H	63	67	6	Turner *et al.*, 1968
H	63	BA	64	67	6	Turner *et al.*, 1968
A	61.2	BA	66.9	70.9	7	Kidder *et al.*, 1964
H	90	A	90	96	7	Gaines *et al.*, 1966
H	88	S	87	93.5	7	Wiltbank *et al.*, 1967a
A	90	S	76	92	11	Gaines *et al.*, 1966
B	67	BA	64	73	11	Turner *et al.*, 1968
A	63	BA	64	72	13	Turner *et al.*, 1968
B	50	A	76	71[ac]	13	Kidder *et al.*, 1964
A	61.2	H	59.8	73.4	13	Kidder *et al.*, 1964
B	65.2	BA	66.9	78.7	13	Kidder *et al.*, 1964
S	62.6	B	69.0	74.5[ac]	13	Koger *et al.*, 1962b
H	90	S	76	95	15	Gaines *et al.*, 1966
A	61.2	B	65.2	80.3	17	Kidder *et al.*, 1964
A	63	B	67	77	18	Turner *et al.*, 1968
BA	66.9	H	59.8	82.2	19	Kidder *et al.*, 1964
B	65.2	H	59.8	89.9	27	Kidder *et al.*, 1964
B	67	H	63	83	28	Turner *et al.*, 1968
B	49	A	60	78[ab]	43	Reynolds *et al.*, 1966

[a] Non-reciprocal cross. [b] F_1 dams, conception to first service. [c] At weaning.
[d] Adjusted pregnancy rate.

3.5.4.2 Calf mortality. The data in Table 3.26 demonstrate a very favourable response in calf liveability and embryonic mortality due to crossbreeding. Confirmatory evidence was supplied by Gerlaugh *et al.* (1951) with respect to viability, while Ellis and Cartwright (1963) and Reynolds *et al.* (1965b) showed that the total weight of calves weaned per cow bred was higher for F_1 dams than the parental breeds. Bellows (1967) found, in a trial involving 711 Angus, Hereford and Charolais cattle and their crosses, that although the crossbreds had an 84% calf crop compared with 80% for purebreds, the former lost more calves at birth (2.5 vs. 1.7%). In contrast, from birth to weaning crossbreds suffered fewer losses (1.1 vs. 3.5%) so that their net calf crop was higher (80.9 vs. 75.9%).

Table 3.26 Heterosis in Liveability

Paternal breed	Liveability (%)	Maternal breed	Liveability (%)	F_1	Heterosis (%)	Authors
A	92.6	B	92	87.1[c]	−6	Turner *et al.*, 1968
A	95	S	92	91.9[b]	−2	Wiltbank *et al.*, 1967a
H	92	A	95	92.9[b]	−1	Wiltbank *et al.*, 1967a
Ay	97.2	J	92.1	94.0[b]	−1	Donald, 1963
H	92	S	92	92.8[b]	1	Wiltbank *et al.*, 1967a
B	92	BA	92.4	92.7[c]	1	Turner *et al.*, 1968
BA	92.4	H	91	93.2[c]	2	Turner *et al.*, 1968
H	92	S	91	93.5[c]	2	Wiltbank *et al.*, 1967a
A	94	S	91	95.0[c]	3	Wiltbank *et al.*, 1967a
H	93.2	A	93.2	95.8[f]	3	Gaines *et al.*, 1966
A	92.6	BA	92.4	95.2[c]	3	Turner *et al.*, 1968
A	92.6	H	91	94.1[c]	3	Turner *et al.*, 1968
H	92	A	94	96.5[c]	4	Wiltbank *et al.*, 1967a
A	91.1	S	92.1	95.7[c]	5	Gaines *et al.*, 1966
B	92	H	91	96.2[c]	5	Turner *et al.*, 1968
H	86.7	A	91.1	93.8[c]	6	Gaines *et al.*, 1966
H	93.2	S	91.4	97.5[f]	6	Gaines *et al.*, 1966
F	87.5	J	92.1	95.0[b]	6	Donald, 1963
A	93.2	S	91.4	97.7[f]	6	Gaines *et al.*, 1966
F	87.5	Ay	97.2	98.2[b]	6	Donald, 1963
H	86.7	S	92.1	97.5[c]	11	Gaines *et al.*, 1966
F	82.7	G	72.2	89	15	Dickinson & Touchberry, 1961
B	76.5	H	95.7	100.0[acde]	16	Chagas *et al.*, 1966
A	11.4	C	5.6			
H	0.0	C	5.6	3.1[g]	44	Sagebiel *et al.*, 1967a
H	0.0	A	11.4			

[a] Non-reciprocal cross. [b] % live births. [c] Liveability to weaning. [d] Includes back-cross. [e] F_1 dams. [f] Liveability to 36 hr. [g] Embryonic mortality.

Table 3.26 refers to means for reciprocal crosses, but improvement may be greater in a particular cross rather than its reciprocal, due to maternal effects (Leonard *et al.*, 1967) or to selective mating by certain sires (Chapman and England, 1965).

3.5.4.3 Birth weight. Heterotic effects on birth weight are consistently positive although not high when considered on a reciprocal basis (Table 3.27). The 20% reduction over the mid-parent in birth weight reported by Joubert and Hammond (1958) for crosses between South Devons and Dexters was certainly due to maternal effects in the abnormally small Dexter. There is some suggestion that heterotic effects are greater when one of the contributing breeds is Hereford or Brahman (McCormick and Southwell, 1957) and that the Brahman is more likely to contribute to heterosis when used as a sire (Ellis *et al.*, 1965; Brown *et al.*, 1967c). In Australia, Seifert and Kennedy (1966) found that Brahman sires, when crossed with Hereford or Shorthorn dams, gave 13% heterosis, while Africanders gave only 5%. Although Hereford × Shorthorn crosses had only 3% heterosis, the inter-se matings (F_2) were superior to the F_1's. In contrast F_2's of Brahman or Africander descent showed a marked decline in heterosis, and were actually inferior to the British purebreds. Donald *et al.* (1962) found no evidence of heterosis in birth weight, while Reynolds *et al.* (1959) considered that, for this trait, maternal effects were more important than heterosis.

3.5.4.4 Pre-weaning growth and weaning weight. Both these traits respond well to crossbreeding (Tables 3.28 and 3.29). Several workers who did not encounter heterosis at birth reported it at weaning (Reynolds *et al.*, 1959; Scott and Martin, 1959; Sullivan *et al.*, 1964). There appears to be a difference in response according to the sex of the calf in that Stonaker (1963), Cornforth *et al.* (1965), Brinks *et al.* (1967) and Urick *et al.* (1968) all found greater heterosis in females. In Stonaker's analysis of 1229 calves, heterosis was almost twice as great in females; he quoted confirmatory evidence of more heterosis in the homogametic sex in turkeys. It is also significant that Dinkel *et al.* (1968) observed greater inbreeding depression in females than males.

The different responses of reciprocal crosses for pre-weaning gain and weaning weight have been discussed by England *et al.* (1963), England and Farthing (1964) and Leonard *et al.* (1967). Such differences usually spring from variation in mothering ability and milk yield. Schwulst *et al.* (1968) have demonstrated a slight heterosis for milk yield in beef cows which tended to increase with length of lactation, while a pronounced improvement in milk yield (75%) for Hereford × Brahman over the purebreds was found by Todd *et al.* (1968). In both experiments the effects were associated with higher weights in the progeny of crossbred mothers. A greater efficiency of crossbred dams (Brahman × Hereford) compared with purebred dams was shown by Maples *et al.* (1968) in that 11% fewer feed units were required per cow per unit of calf weaned for the F_1 dam than the mid-parent average.

3.5.4.5 Post-weaning traits. It would seem from the data in Table 3.30 that weight for age or daily gain to slaughter are the post-weaning traits most responsive to heterosis. There are fewer reports relating to feed intake or conversion but generally the effects are lower (Table 3.31).

TABLE 3.27 HETEROSIS IN BIRTH WEIGHT

Paternal breed	Birth weight (kg)	Maternal breed	Birth weight (kg)	F_1	Heterosis (%)	Authors
SD	45.6	Dexter	23.8	27.8	−20	Joubert & Hammond, 1958
H	34.5	A	29.8	30.5	−5	Lopez Saubidet *et al.*, 1963
SD	40.0	Africander	39.4	38.7[a]	−3	Skinner & Ziervogel, 1962a
H	31.0	C	39.0	34.4	−2	Klosterman *et al.*, 1965a
H_1[b]	33.6	H_4[b]	36.0	34.2[a]	−2	Flower *et al.*, 1963
H	34.5	S	31.7	32.6	−2	Lopez Saubidet *et al.*, 1963
H_6[b]	31.6	H_{10}[b]	36.1	33.6	−1	Brinks *et al.*, 1967
A	29.8	S	31.7	30.6	−1	Lopez Saubidet *et al.*, 1963
F	39.5	J	22.5	31.0	0	Donald *et al.*, 1962
SG	32.5	Cr	29.1	30.9	0	Muñoz & Martin, 1968
F	39.5	Ay	33.2	36.5	1	Donald *et al.*, 1962
H_4[b]	35.0	H_6[b]	31.6	33.5	1	Brinks *et al.*, 1967
H_3[b]	35.2	H_4[b]	36.0	35.9[a]	1	Flower *et al.*, 1963
Ay	33.2	J	22.5	28.1	1	Donald *et al.*, 1962
H_2[b]	35.9	H_4[b]	36.0	36.5[a]	1	Flower *et al.*, 1963
A	28.6	S	32.5	31.1	2	Gaines *et al.*, 1966
H	32.9	A	28.6	31.4	2	Gaines *et al.*, 1966
H_1[b]	36.1	H_{10}[b]	36.1	36.9	2	Brinks *et al.*, 1967
H_1[b]	36.1	H_6[b]	31.6	34.7	3	Brinks *et al.*, 1967
A	29.4	S	32.6	31.5	3	Gregory *et al.*, 1965
H_6[b]	31.6	H_9[b]	31.0	32.3	3	Brinks *et al.*, 1967
A	28.1	C	36.9			
H	31.8	C	36.9	33.5	4	Sagebiel *et al.*, 1967a
H	31.8	A	28.1			
H_1[b]	36.1	H_9[b]	31.0	34.8	4	Brinks *et al.*, 1967
H	35.3	A	29.4	33.5	4	Gregory *et al.*, 1965
H_4[b]	35.0	H_{10}[b]	36.1	37.1	5	Brinks *et al.*, 1967
H_4[b]	35.0	H_9[b]	31.0	34.6	5	Brinks *et al.*, 1967
B	27.6	Br	29.6	30.4	5	Reynolds *et al.*, 1959
H_1[b]	36.1	H_4[b]	35.0	37.4	5	Brinks *et al.*, 1967
H	32.9	S	32.5	34.6	6	Gaines *et al.*, 1966
H	35.3	S	32.6	36.1	6	Gregory *et al.*, 1965
B	27.5	SG	32.5	31.9	6	Muñoz & Martin, 1968
H	32.3	HL	28.9	32.6	7	Lawson & Peters, 1964
B	27.5	Cr	29.1	30.4	7	Muñoz & Martin, 1968
H_9[b]	31.0	H_{10}[b]	36.1	36.1	8	Brinks *et al.*, 1967
B	27.0	Cr	25.0	28.0	8	Plasse, 1968
A	30.1	Africander	28.7	32.1[a]	9	Kreft, 1962
H	32.1	B	28.3	33.5	11	Ellis *et al.*, 1965
B	26.8	H	26.8	31.8[c]	19	Maples *et al.*, 1968
B	27.0	BA	29.0	33.5[a]	20	Reynolds *et al.*, 1965a
B	29.7	H	33.0	38.2[a]	22	Brown *et al.*, 1967c
B	27.0	A	27.0	33.1[a]	23	Reynolds *et al.*, 1965a
B	27.0	AfA	31.0	35.8[a]	23	Reynolds *et al.*, 1965a

[a] Non-reciprocal cross. [b] Inbred lines. [c] Out of F_1 cows.

3.5.4.6 CARCASS EFFECTS. In 1962 Kincaid considered that there was little evidence for heterosis in those carcass traits not related to growth. The data of Klosterman *et al.* (1965a), Gregory *et al.* (1966c), Gaines *et al.* (1967) and Willis and Preston (1969c) support this statement. Several of the US workers observed differences in carcass composition, but these were invariably due to the faster growth and consequently higher carcass weights of the crossbreds.

TABLE 3.28 HETEROSIS IN PRE-WEANING DAILY GAIN

Paternal breed	Daily gain (kg)	Maternal breed	Daily gain (kg)	F_1	Heterosis (%)	Authors
H	.70	S	.78	.74	0	Gaines *et al.*, 1966
H	.68	C	.92	.81	2	Klosterman *et al.*, 1965a
H_1[a]	.78	H_{10}[a]	.76	.79	3	Brinks *et al.*, 1967
A	.80	S	.78	.82	4	Gregory *et al.*, 1965
H	.70	A	.76	.77	6	Gaines *et al.*, 1966
H	.77	S	.78	.82	6	Gregory *et al.*, 1965
H_1[a]	.78	H_6[a]	.75	.81	6	Brinks *et al.*, 1967
H_6[a]	.75	H_{10}[a]	.76	.80	6	Brinks *et al.*, 1967
H_1[a]	.78	H_9[a]	.74	.81	7	Brinks *et al.*, 1967
H_6[a]	.75	H_9[a]	.74	.80	7	Brinks *et al.*, 1967
H_4[a]	.71	H_{10}[a]	.76	.79	8	Brinks *et al.*, 1967
H	.77	A	.80	.84	8	Gregory *et al.*, 1965
A	.76	S	.78	.83	8	Gaines *et al.*, 1966
H_9[a]	.74	H_{10}[a]	.76	.81	8	Brinks *et al.*, 1967
H_4[a]	.71	H_6[a]	.75	.79	8	Brinks *et al.*, 1967
H_4[a]	.71	H_9[a]	.74	.80	10	Brinks *et al.*, 1967
B	.60	Cr	.55	.63	10	Plasse, 1968
H_1[a]	.78	H_4[a]	.71	.85	14	Brinks *et al.*, 1967

[a] Inbred lines.

There appears, nevertheless, to be some heterotic effect on longissimus dorsi area even when adjustments are made for carcass weight. Data on percentage edible meat and longissimus dorsi area are summarized in Table 3.32.

3.5.4.7 CONCLUSIONS. In a review of the subject, Mason (1966) concluded that the only real advantage of crossbreeding was the improved fertility manifested by dams carrying F_1 foetuses and the greater viability of the calves. While agreeing with him on the score of fertility, we cannot accept his premiss that the amount of heterosis for growth "is not sufficient to justify a crossbreeding programme". His error arises from the assumption that the important thing is not the superiority of the F_1 over the mid-parent average but its superiority over the better parent. Although this latter aspect is highly desirable, superiority over the poorer breed has considerable economic value in situations where the better parent breed is numerically small. Even when this is not the case, a breeder will benefit more by crossing rather then by selling his stock and purchasing a superior (and invariably more costly) breed.

TABLE 3.29 HETEROSIS IN WEANING WEIGHT (GENERALLY 180–240 DAYS)

Paternal breed	Weaning weight (kg)	Maternal breed	Weaning weight (kg)	F_1	Heterosis (%)	Authors
H	189	A	175	177	−3	Damon *et al.*, 1959a
A	175	BA	197	187	1	Damon *et al.*, 1959a
H	206	C	279	247	2	Klosterman *et al.*, 1965a
H	176	S	190	187	2	Gaines *et al.*, 1966
H	189	BA	197	199	3	Damon *et al.*, 1959a
H_1[c]	195	H_{10}[c]	191	199	3	Brinks *et al.*, 1967
A	190	S	189	196	3	Gregory *et al.*, 1965
H_3[c]	184	H_4[c]	195	195[a]	3	Flower *et al.*, 1963
Cr	203	SG	208	212	3	Muñoz & Martin, 1968
H	176	A	188	189	4	Gaines *et al.*, 1966
B	170	BA	197	191	4	Damon *et al.*, 1959a
SG	210	Cr	209	218	4	Muñoz *et al.*, 1964
H_2[c]	183	H_4[c]	195	197[a]	5	Flower *et al.*, 1963
H	190	A	190	200	5	Gregory *et al.*, 1965
H	190	S	189	200	5	Gregory *et al.*, 1965
H_6[c]	185	H_{10}[c]	191	198	5	Brinks *et al.*, 1967
H[c]	182	H[c]	182	191	5	Urick *et al.*, 1968
A	188	S	190	200	6	Gaines *et al.*, 1966
H_1[c]	195	H_6[c]	185	201	6	Brinks *et al.*, 1967
A	154	C	189			
H	153	C	189	175	6	Sagebiel *et al.*, 1967b
H	153	A	154			
H_1[c]	176	H_4[c]	195	196[a]	6	Flower *et al.*, 1963
H_1[c]	195	H_9[c]	183	201	6	Brinks *et al.*, 1967
H_6[c]	185	H_9[c]	183	196	7	Brinks *et al.*, 1967
H_4[c]	180	H_{10}[c]	191	198	7	Brinks *et al.*, 1967
H_4[c]	180	H_6[c]	185	197	8	Brinks *et al.*, 1967
H_9[c]	183	H_{10}[c]	191	203	9	Brinks *et al.*, 1967
B	190	SG	208	217	9	Muñoz & Martin, 1968
H[cd]	166	H[c]	166	181	9	Urick *et al.*, 1968
A	175	B	170	189	10	Damon *et al.*, 1959a
H_4[c]	180	H_9[c]	183	199	10	Brinks *et al.*, 1967
H	163	HL	154	174	10	Lawson & Peters, 1964
B	150	A	146	163[a]	10	Kidder *et al.*, 1964
B	190	Cr	203	218	11	Muñoz & Martin, 1968
H	189	B	170	199	11	Damon *et al.*, 1959a
SG	210	B	194	224	11	Muñoz *et al.*, 1964
B	194	Cr	209	224	12	Muñoz *et al.*, 1964
B	152	Cr	139	158	12	Plasse, 1968
H_1[c]	195	H_4[c]	180	211	13	Brinks *et al.*, 1967
B	157	H	168	183[e]	13	Maples *et al.*, 1968
B	155[b]	D	155	180	16	Koger *et al.*, 1961
B	150	D	159	181	18	Kidder *et al.*, 1964
B	168	S	140	190	23	Peacock *et al.*, 1960

[a] Non-reciprocal cross. [b] Mean of both parents. [c] Inbred lines. [d] Heifers. [e] Out of F_1 cows.

TABLE 3.30 HETEROSIS IN WEIGHT FOR AGE AT SLAUGHTER

Paternal breed	Weight for age (kg)	Maternal breed	Weight for age (kg)	F_1	Heterosis	Authors
H	.79	A	.76	.74	−5	Damon *et al.*, 1959b
Cr	1.10	B	.93	.98[a]	−3	Willis & Preston, 1969c
H	1.05	A	.98	1.00[d]	−2	Vogt *et al.*, 1967
SG	.87	A	.73	.79[a]	−1	Clyburn *et al.*, 1961
H_1[c]	.36	H_4[c]	.39	.37[ab]	0	Flower *et al.*, 1963
PH	.75	SG	.87	.81[a]	0	Clyburn *et al.*, 1961
H	1.05	S	1.00	1.03[d]	1	Vogt *et al.*, 1967
A	.86	S	.89	.88	1	Gregory *et al.*, 1966b
A	.76	BA	.77	.78	2	Damon *et al.*, 1959b
A	.98	S	1.00	1.01[d]	2	Vogt *et al.*, 1967
H_3[c]	.35	H_4[c]	.39	.37[ab]	2	Flower *et al.*, 1963
H	.71	C	.89	.83	4	Klosterman *et al.*, 1965a
H	.91	S	.89	.94	4	Gregory *et al.*, 1966b
H	.91	A	.86	.92	5	Gregory *et al.*, 1966b
H[e]	422	H[c]	422	441[f]	5	Urick *et al.*, 1968
C	1.28	B	.93	1.16[a]	5	Willis & Preston, 1969c
B	.70	BA	.77	.78	6	Damon *et al.*, 1959b
A	.73	PH	.75	.79[a]	7	Clyburn *et al.*, 1961
A	.84	C	.98			
H	.90	C	.98	.97[d]	7	Sagebiel *et al.*, 1967b
H	.90	A	.84			
H	.79	BA	.77	.84	8	Damon *et al.*, 1959b
HF	1.09	B	.93	1.09[a]	8	Willis & Preston, 1969c
B	.73	A	.76	.81[ad]	9	DeRouen *et al.*, 1961
F	.60	DS	.55	.63[b]	10	Gibson & Watson, 1963
SG	.49	Cr	.47	.53[d]	10	Muñoz *et al.*, 1964
B	.68	S	.62	.72[ad]	11	Koger *et al.*, 1962a
H_2[c]	.37	H_4[c]	.39	.42[ab]	11	Flower *et al.*, 1963
SD	.70	Gallegan	.55	.70[ae]	12	Button, 1959
A	.76	B	.70	.84	15	Damon *et al.*, 1959b
H	.79	B	.70	.86	15	Damon *et al.*, 1959b
SG	.49	B	.51	.58[d]	16	Muñoz *et al.*, 1964
B	.51	Cr	.47	.59[d]	19	Muñoz *et al.*, 1964
S	.54	B	.66	.75	25	Hargrove *et al.*, 1959

[a] Non-reciprocal cross. [b] Daily gain in heifers. [c] Inbred lines. [d] Daily gain.
[e] At 12 months. [f] Final weight on test.

Selection of pure lines (for subsequent hybridization) has been widely practised in crop plants and some success has been reported with inbred Hereford lines (Flower *et al.*, 1963; Brinks *et al.*, 1967). Some evidence for specific combining ability was put forward by Damon *et al.* (1961) who considered that, while it was of minor importance for weaning weight, it accounted for 21 and 27% of the variance among crosses in rate of gain on test and final weight per day of age respectively. However, Jilek *et al.* (1968), who mated Angus sires to dams of two breeds, were unable to demonstrate any specific combining ability among sires. We prefer to concur with

TABLE 3.31 HETEROSIS IN FEED INTAKE AND FEED CONVERSION

Paternal breed	—	Maternal breed	—	F_1	Heterosis (%)	Authors
				Feed intake		
A	4.31	S	4.56	4.49[b]	1	Gregory *et al.*, 1966b
B	2.08	S	2.24	2.19[ac]	1	Koger *et al.*, 1962a
H	4.35	A	4.31	4.47[b]	3	Gregory *et al.*, 1966b
H	4.35	S	4.56	4.65	4	Gregory *et al.*, 1966b
				Feed conversion		
S	5.50	B	4.77	4.86	−6	Hargrove *et al.*, 1959
A	6.15	S	5.84	6.08[e]	−2	Gregory *et al.*, 1966b
H	5.28	S	5.84	5.58[e]	−0	Gregory *et al.*, 1966b
A	8.49	C	8.46			
H	8.39	C	8.46	8.33	1	Sagebiel *et al.*, 1967b
H	8.39	A	8.49			
H	5.28	A	6.15	5.51[e]	4	Gregory *et al.*, 1966b
B	6.55	S	6.95	6.44[c]	5	Koger *et al.*, 1962a
H	5.62	C	5.81	5.32	7	Klosterman *et al.*, 1965a
B	10.9	S	8.7	9.1[cd]	7	Koger *et al.*, 1962a

[a] Intake per 100 kg live weight. [b] Intake TDN kg per day, weaning to 400 kg.
[c] Non-reciprocal crosses. [d] Feed per kg fat adjusted carcass. [e] TDN per kg gain, weaning to 400 kg.

Bowman (1959) that selection for this latter phenomenon is too problematical to justify its widespread use.

3.5.5 Crossbreeding systems

3.5.5.1 F_1 CROSSES. The production of F_1 crosses for the maximum exploitation of heterosis is economically feasible and commonly practised in crop plants, poultry and to some extent in pigs. It has little or no application in beef cattle breeding since the low reproductive rate of this species necessitates a greater number of purebred females than the F_1 progeny to be produced; and if these purebreds have only moderate performance the overall population average will have been improved only slightly. Moreover the maximum exploitition of the F_1 generation entails breeding from the females.

The choice of sire to use on F_1 heifers presents a serious problem. Backcrossing to one of the parent breeds has occasionally been successful in maintaining heterosis (Koger *et al.*, 1961; Ellis and Cartwright, 1963; Kidder *et al.*, 1964; Gaines *et al.*, 1966; Todd *et al.*, 1968), but a continued grading-up programme must inevitably dissipate the advantage and may even be deleterious (Bellows, 1966). Grading-up is justified on a limited scale in situations where one of the breeds is in short supply; the Charolais in the US reached its present numbers by such procedures. But when, as is most often the case, crossbreeding is instituted to improve the mass of cattle, grading-up is too slow and cumbersome.

TABLE 3.32 HETEROSIS IN PERCENTAGE EDIBLE MEAT AND THE LONGISSIMUS DORSI AREA

Breed		Breed		F_1	Heterosis (%)	Authors
Edible meat		(%)				
H	67.1	S	60.0	62.6	−1.4	Gregory *et al.*, 1966c
H	67.1	A	64.7	65.2	−1.1	Gregory *et al.*, 1966c
A	67.7	C	68.6	}		
H	65.4	C	68.6	} 66.7[b]	−0.7	Sagebiel *et al.*, 1967b
H	65.4	A	67.7	}		
Cr	74.8	B	71.5	72.9[a]	−0.3	Willis & Preston, 1969c
BS	74.9	B	71.5	73.1[a]	−0.1	Willis & Preston, 1969c
A	64.7	S	60.0	62.4	0.1	Gregory *et al.*, 1966c
HF	73.6	B	71.5	72.7[a]	0.3	Willis & Preston, 1969c
H	69.3	C	72.5	71.2	0.4	Klosterman *et al.*, 1965a
C	76.6	B	71.5	74.3[a]	0.4	Willis & Preston, 1969c
A	61.5	C	65.7	}		
H	62.7	C	65.7	} 63.6[c]	0.5	Sagebiel *et al.*, 1967b
H	62.7	A	61.5	}		
L. dorsi area per 100 kg carcass						
H	23.3	S	22.4	23.2	−2.7	Gaines *et al.*, 1967
H	26.0	C	27.4	26.8	0.4	Klosterman *et al.*, 1965a
A	28.4	S	26.0	27.4	0.7	Gregory *et al.*, 1966c
H	27.6	S	26.0	27.0	0.7	Gregory *et al.*, 1966c
A	28.4	H	27.6	28.3	1.1	Gregory *et al.*, 1966c
A	23.4	H	23.3	24.4	4.5	Gaines *et al.*, 1967
A	23.4	S	22.4	24.4	6.6	Gaines *et al.*, 1967

[a] Non-reciprocal cross. [b] After 182 days on feed. [c] After 266 days on feed.

In developing countries, where highly productive breeds are usually scarce, it is often argued (e.g. Hutchinson and Stephens, 1959) that indigenous stock can be improved by crossing with exotic "blood" for one generation, thereafter mating back to the indigenous stock. The aim is to retain the valuable high growth and efficient feed conversion of the exotic breeds without losing those traits relating to adaption and survival. Such a programme can only succeed if the desired traits introduced from the exotic breed are easily recognizable and are controlled by few genes. In fact, almost all important economic traits are polygenic in origin, thus such a policy—although perhaps promising at the start—must ultimately fail.

Inter se mating of F_1's is often mooted. The belief that this will lead to greater variation in the F_2 is without theoretical justification (Mahadevan, 1966); and in respect to birth weight Seifert and Kennedy (1966) have shown that the coefficient of variation was similar in F_1's and their *inter se* crosses. However, Kidder *et al.* (1964) found that heterosis in weaning weight of Brahman × Devons was much reduced by such mating; similar results were reported by Ellis *et al.*, (1965) in that a 11% heterosis in birth weight for F_1's dropped to 2% by *inter se* mating.

3.5.5.2 ROTATIONAL AND CRISS-CROSSING. On theoretical grounds *inter se* mating of F_1's or their back-crossing must eventually result in loss of heterosis, and experience has confirmed this. One possible way to maintain heterosis would appear to be the use of a third breed, and the logical extension of this is the use of a series of breeds in a fixed rotation. In such a scheme involving three breeds, Lush *et al.* (1939) calculated that gene frequencies rapidly approach a state of equilibrium wherein an individual derives about 57% of its genes from the breed of its sire, 29% from that of the dam's sire and 14% from the breed of the sire of the maternal grandam.

Carmon *et al.* (1956) have shown that, theoretically, when the number of breeds does not exceed four, rotational crossbreeding was likely to be superior to the crossing of several breeds followed by random mating. A variation of this theme was put forward by Lauprecht (1961) wherein 3 breeds could be combined so as to contribute equally to the genetic makeup. The plan required about 6 generations, although near-equilibrium would be reached after only 4. So far no experimental evidence exists as to the efficacy of this method as a means of preserving heterosis. It is, in fact, likely to lead to the creation of a new breed, and thus defeat its object.

Another procedure is criss-crossing whereby the F_1 progeny are back-crossed to one parental breed and their progeny to the other; this alternate mating then continues indefinitely.

Due to the time needed to evaluate such programmes and the fact that scientifically controlled crossbreeding experiments only really began in the late 1950's and early 1960's, it is too soon to pronounce on the efficiency of these schemes. Nevertheless, interim results are promising. For instance, with regard to post-weaning gain, three-breed crosses were 0.1 kg per day better than purebreds or back-crosses; the breeds involved were Angus, Brahman, Brangus and Hereford (England *et al.*, 1963a). Brown *et al.* (1967c) found in Texas that average birth weight for two- three- and four-breed crosses was 36.3, 35.0 and 37.7 kg respectively. In Georgia, McCormick *et al.* (1963) used 1036 cattle of the Angus, Polled Hereford and Santa Gertrudis breeds and their crosses to study grading-up, cross-crossing and rotational crossing. Crossbred animals gained faster than purebreds, and rotational crosses were slightly better than criss-crosses. In Texas, Tovar *et al.* (1966) studied weaning weights in a single-sire Hereford herd, a multiple-sire herd and a rotational-cross herd which began as Hereford × Brahman and in which Charolais, Angus and Shorthorn bulls were used in that order. The 205 day weaning weights (of 1527 calves) were 185, 181 and 218 kg for the three herds respectively. Rotational-cross calves exceeded single-sired Herefords by 26.8% and multiple-sired Herefords by 28.7%. In a study with Brahmans and Devons in Florida, Kidder *et al.* (1964) found that 205 day weaning weight was increased 17% by crossbreeding, and this was maintained on a criss-crossing system but declined to 10% with *inter se* mating.

Vogt *et al.* (1967) compared the three British beef breeds as purebreds, two- or three-breed combinations and back-crosses. Although there were no noticeable effects on feedlot gain, slaughter weight was 4% higher for the two- and three-breed crosses than the purebreds or back-crosses. In Friesian, Ayrshire and Jersey cattle, Donald (1963) found that the average mortality of calves from purebred heifers was 14.8% but decreased to 6.5% in the F_1 crosses, while three-breed crosses averaged 8.2%. For cows the respective figures were 2.4, 1.9 and 1.2%. Gaines *et al.* (1966), on the other hand, found that births and weaned calves per 100 cows were greater with crosses than with purebreds but that F_1 cows mated to a third breed gave slightly inferior progeny than the back-cross.

There is adequate evidence to justify crossbreeding in order to exploit heterotic effects, although the relative merits of the various systems are still not clearly defined. The F_1 is obviously the most productive in all traits, but its exploitation as a breeding animal poses serious practical difficulties. *Inter se* mating does not appear to be advisable, and while back-crosses have occasionally performed well, the practical problem is similar to that with F_1's, in that a large reserve of female purebred stock must be maintained. Rotational or criss-cross systems, on the other hand, are able to function with relatively small purebred herds (for sire production only) and offer greater scope for retaining heterotic advantages. Rotational systems have been discussed on the basis of a planned order of breed crossing. The possibilities of indiscriminate crossing coupled with the use of performance-tested pure or crossbred bulls have yet to be evaluated, although such ideas are giving encouraging results in the UK pig industry (King and Smith, 1968). In such a gene pool programme, the mass of cattle would be mated only to superior sires irrespective of their breed.

3.6 SELECTION FOR MEAT PRODUCTION IN DAIRY CATTLE

3.6.1 Introduction

In many European countries the national dairy herd is an important source of animals for meat production. For example, in the UK some 40–50% of cattle slaughtered for beef are of pure dairy breeding (Mason, 1964), and in Israel it is even higher (Hodges, 1960). Even in the US, 15–20% of all commercial steer and heifer slaughtering is made up of dairy steers (Marquart, 1964). In these same countries there are highly developed programmes for genetic improvement of milk production using the progeny testing schemes through the medium of AI. Knowledge of the relation between milk and meat traits is thus of paramount importance, for if, as is current practice in the UK, selection of dairy sires takes no account of meat traits, then the effect of this upon the efficiency of meat production will depend entirely on the nature of the relationship between the two.

The likelihood that such a relationship is sufficiently high to obviate the need for selection for meat is remote. However, simultaneous selection for meat (necessary if the genetic correlations are low or negative) will inevitably lead to a reduced intensity of selection for milk. This reduction, assuming no correlation between the traits, has been calculated by Soller *et al.* (1966a) to be equal to:

$$\tfrac{1}{4}\,(i^m - i'^m)\,h^{2m}\sigma^m,$$

where i^m = intensity of selection of dams of young bulls when performance testing is not carried out; i'^m = intensity of selection with performance testing; h^{2m} = heritability of milk production and σ^m = phenotypic standard deviation for milk production.

Despite this predicted loss in selection for milk, overall genetic progress (and *ipso facto* economic return) for milk and meat combined should be higher (Soller *et al.*, 1966a).

Although performance testing from an early age to a fixed live weight of around 400 kg would involve investment in testing facilities, it need not interfere with the practical aspects of progeny testing for milk. Most dairy bulls are not normally used in AI before they are 12 months old, and by this time the performance test could be finished; furthermore, since most AI organizations purchase their bulls soon after birth, some investment in housing is inevitable. It would cost little more to extend these facilities to allow individual performance testing. Inevitably more bulls will have to be tested if selection for meat is to be included with selection for milk. How many more must be evaluated will depend upon the correlations between the two traits, and the selection pressure it is planned to exert.

3.6.2 Body size and milk yield

The effect of body size upon milk yield has been reviewed by Johansson (1964) who concluded that live weight up to 24 months of age had little relationship to milk yield although there was a slight positive relationship between growth rate and subsequent milk yield in heifers. Holtz *et al.* (1961), however, found the relationship between rate of gain to 6 months and FCM production to be only 0.14; slightly higher figures were obtained by Martin *et al.* (1962) for these traits. In older cattle (5 years or more), Nöring (1962) obtained a correlation of only 0.07 between live weight and milk yield. A genetic correlation between live weight and milk production of the order of 0.30 was obtained by Miller and McGilliard (1959), and although Clark and Touchberry (1962) found negative genetic correlations for these traits in Holsteins, the standard errors were extremely high. Erb and Ashworth (1961) concluded that the effect of live weight on milk yield was not linear, although they did find that weight increases were generally associated with improvement in yield.

Eftimov *et al.* (1964) found a correlation in Bulgarian dual-purpose cattle of 0.38 between live weight and milk yield and comparable figures were reported by Csomos (1965) in a study of 4677 lactation records of Hungarian spotted cattle. In a still more extensive investigation in the US with 22,767 Holstein and 2174 Guernsey records, Harville and Henderson (1964) described genetic correlations between adjusted live weight and milk yield of 0.45 and 0.40 respectively. A similar genetic correlation of 0.43 between live weight at 12 months and milk yield was recorded by Wilk *et al.* (1963) who concluded that there appeared to be no evidence "of a genetic antagonism between measurements of body size and milk production" in heifers.

3.6.3 Milk and meat production

The suggestion that body size and milk yield in the same animal are positively correlated, encourages the belief that milk production may also be correlated with meat production in male relatives. The first evidence in this field was that of Cook *et al.* (1942) who obtained negative correlations between milk yield of Dairy Shorthorn cows and the carcass grade ($r = -0.20$) and fatness ($r = -0.17$) of their steer progeny; in other words, an increase in milk yield was associated with greater leanness of the carcass in the male progeny. Subsequent developments, in the main, have been in Europe probably because of the greater dependence there on meat from the dairy herd.

In a study of Danish records, Mason (1962) reported a correlation of 0.03 between milk yield in the heifer progeny of 41 sires and rate of gain to 220 kg of corresponding male progeny. A higher correlation ($r = 0.16$) between cows' milk yield and the growth rate of their male progeny was obtained by Langlet (1962). In German Fleckvieh cattle, Bogner (1962) reported a correlation of 0.13 between milk and meat performance of half sibs while in a study of Red Polls and Dairy Shorthorns in the UK (Mason, 1964) there were genetic correlations of 0.19 and 0.11 between milk yield and live weight for age and carcass weight for age respectively. These correlations were based on progeny tests for milk and beef characters. Genetic correlations for the same traits as between cows and the steer progeny were —0.01 and —0.14 respectively. The genetic correlations between milk yield and live weight for age were —0.04 for half and full sibs. Langlet (1965) reported a correlation of 0.22 between milk yield and daily gain of half-sibs in an investigation based on 236 sons and 2450 daughters of 25 German Friesian sires. A lower correlation of 0.07 for dams' milk yield and gain from 3 to 6 months of the male and female progeny was recorded by Martin and Starkenburg (1965) in a crossbreeding experiment in Indiana. The genetic correlation between these traits was 0.16.

Samson-Himmelstjerna (1965) measured milk yield in 9553 heifers and growth to 1–1½ years in 2295 bulls, but found genetic correlations between half-sibs to be essentially zero. Similar results were obtained for dam–son correlations. Suess *et al.* (1968) studied growth to 455 kg in the steer progeny of 8 Holstein bulls with high or low breeding values for milk and found that the better sires had progeny with a greater weight of first quality meat (RLRC) but within the group of 4 low sires breeding value foı milk was negatively correlated with first-quality meat yield. Groenwald (1961) obtained a correlation of 0.75 between cows' milk production and fattening capacity of their male progeny, and although this value appears excessively high, Fulkenburg *et al.* (1968) also obtained a correlation of 0.56 between daily gain in the feedlot of Holstein steers and the milk production of their dams. More recent work in Israel (Soller *et al.*, 1966b), where live weight for age at 420 days in 1563 Friesian bulls was related to milk production of female relatives, showed that the genetic correlation was not significantly different from zero.

The balance of the evidence indicates that the relationship between meat and milk is either zero or very slightly positive. In practical terms one can conclude that selection for either of these traits will not be detrimental to the other and may even improve it slightly. The need to instigate selection progıammes for meat in dairy cattle in Europe is emphasized by the work of Soller *et al.* (1966b) and in fact such a programme is already well established in Israel (Bar-Anan, 1966).

CHAPTER 4

Genotype–Environment Interactions

4.1 INTRODUCTION

It is widely accepted that the environment has a considerable effect upon the visible expression of many characters. But the fact that particular breeds or the offspring of a particular sire perform better in one environment than in another is not, in itself, evidence of genotype–environment interaction, nor does it seriously affect breeding operations. However, a problem does arise if certain environments have different effects upon specific genotypes, such that the order of merit in terms of performance is dependent upon the environment in which the breeds or offspring are maintained. Under such circumstances, the most suitable breed or sire for one environment may be quite unsuitable in another. Selection of breeding stock is then complicated by the need to undertake it in the specific environment wherein the animals or their progeny will be used.

Dickerson (1962) listed the environmental factors which could affect phenotypic expression or evaluation of genetic differences as:

(1) External physical influences: temperature, humidity, light, housing, feed, drugs, disease, etc.
(2) "Background" genotype: strictly this involves gene interactions rather than genotype–environment interactions, but it can be included on the grounds that the environmental effect is still there, albeit internal rather than external in origin.
(3) Maternal effects: non-chromosomal effects of the dam on her progeny either as a foetus or during lactation.
(4) Social environment: genetic constitution of the population and the physical environment.
(5) Economic forces: e.g. market differences may make a higher level of carcass fatness acceptable in one area and thus one type of animal more suitable there than elsewhere.

The extent to which genotype–environment interactions are deemed important will vary with circumstances. In some respects those concerned with economic forces may be said to be the most important of all since they affect the profitability of any given enterprise. Clearly a country seeking to export meat to each of two markets might find that bull meat is desired in one and brings a lower financial return in another. The exporter will thus have to fatten steers or bulls according to the market. Although this type of interaction can be grouped in Dickerson's (1962) definition, it is largely an artificial type of interaction and one which is readily resolvable without recourse to breeding programmes. Of greater relevance to us in this chapter is the effect of different climates or feeding and management systems upon animal performance in so far as they lead to interaction. If, for example, steers are to be fattened on high-roughage diets, must we undertake selection of their sires under the same type of feeding conditions, or can we select under a quite different set of circumstances such as all-concentrate feeding?

In 1947 Hammond ventured the opinion that animals should be selected under optimal environmental conditions since this would enable full expression of genetic potential. This theory, of course, assumed that the animal would continue to express its superiority in a poorer environment, a contradiction which was first commented on by Falconer and Latyzewski (1952a). They pointed out that if an animal failed to express its superiority in a poor environment for purposes of selection, it would also fail to do so for purposes of production and there would thus be little benefit from selection. These same workers (1952b) also showed that, in selecting mice for 6 week weight on *ad libitum* or restricted diets, performance was better on the former. However, interchange of animals (from the environment in which they were selected to the other environment) revealed that those selected on the restricted diet performed better on it than did animals selected on the *ad libitum* diet. On the *ad libitum* diet, however, both selected groups performed equally well. In a later study, Falconer (1960a) selected mice for high or low gain in good or bad environments with similar results. He favoured selection in the environment under which animals would be used for production, a conclusion later supported by Korkman (1961) working with mice and Hansen *et al.* (1961) with rats. Korkman (1957) had earlier shown that a genotype which encouraged growth in one sex might do so to a much lesser extent in the other, so that sex itself became an environment affecting genotypic expression. In a selection study for 70 day weight in rats fed either an all-concentrate or a 35% roughage diet, Bailey and Weeth (1963) obtained inconclusive results. When compared on the concentrate diet those selected on roughage were inferior. When comparisons were made on the roughage diet, females selected on this diet were superior to those selected on concentrates, but the reverse was true in the case of males. Subsequently Dalton (1967) found no evidence of genotype–environment interactions in mice selected for high or low growth rate on each of two diets. In a study over 17 generations of rats Hansen (1967) selected for gain on *ad libitum* or restricted feeding followed by reciprocal transfer. The results showed that selection was essentially for the same genes, but realized heritability was significantly higher on the higher plane. When comparisons were made between diets differing in quantity and quality (% protein), selection was for different genes and interactions occurred. However, selection on low-quality diets produced animals which on any diet were the fattest; this is not a desirable trait in beef cattle.

There is sufficient evidence from plant breeding and from studies with laboratory animals to demonstrate the inaccuracy of Hammond's theory for widespread application. But to what extent can such laboratory work be applied to larger animals? This is particularly important when one realizes that mice trials are usually carried out under much more standard conditions than are possible with larger animals. Even the "low" diet used by Falconer (1960a) was standardized in that the animals were fed a concentrate in which 20% of the mix was indigestible, whereas "low" environments for beef cattle (e.g. unsupplemented range feeding) are not only difficult to measure accurately but impossible to reproduce from year to year.

The situation becomes even more complicated when, in addition to genotype–nutrition interactions, one is faced with the problem of genotype–climate interactions. These may involve relatively limited changes, such as those between animals housed on slatted floors or kept in open yards or on pasture, to the more violent changes such as might be encountered in a country like Australia where the same breeds of cattle might be expected to perform on lush pasture in one state and on arid range in another.

Neither type of interaction has been widely studied. In 1958 McBride considered that little reliable data existed on genotype–environment interactions in large animals and the situation has altered little although opinions both well- and ill-informed abound. The ensuing discussion deals with nutritional and climatic interactions as separate entities, but it must be remembered that in many cases the two are closely interwoven.

4.2 NUTRITIONAL ASPECTS

4.2.1 Evidence from other species

In 1960 Fowler and Ensminger published the results of a genotype–environment study involving 1705 pigs selected over nine generations for rate of gain on both high (*ad libitum*) and low (restricted) feeding levels. In absolute terms response to selection was greater on the former, although in terms of percentage improvement it was greater on the low level. Interchange of environments after six generations showed that in both cases pigs performed better in their own environment than did pigs selected in the other environment. Selection differentials were similar but heritability estimates were greater at the high level (0.52 against 0.49). The workers agreed with the previously discussed findings of other investigators and concluded that, on the low level of nutrition, selection for growth was actually commensurate with selection for better feed utilization, whereas at the high level it was for a more complex structure.

Using "nutrition" in a wide sense, further evidence of genotype–nutrition interactions for growth rate has been found in pigs by Kristjansson (1957), Salmela *et al.* (1960) and Omtvedt *et al.* (1962), and in sheep by King and Young (1955) and Morley (1956). On the other hand, Dunlop (1963) and Osman and Bradford (1967) considered that genotype–environment interactions in economic traits of sheep were generally small and were not a major source of variation in performance, even under a wide range of nutritional conditions.

In dairy cattle, Bonnier *et al.* (1948) claimed such interactions with monozygous twins, but Robertson *et al.* (1960) in the UK and Van Vleck (1963) in the US effectively proved that the use of contemporary comparisons in ranking dairy bulls for milk yield was unaffected by the management level of the herds in which their daughters were milked. Accordingly, almost all dairy cattle testing is based on the non-existence of such interactions (see review by Willis, 1966).

4.2.2 The evidence in beef cattle

The existence of interactions in other species of domestic animal leads one to suppose that they may well occur in beef cattle. In the US, Warwick *et al.* (1964) did find some evidence of interactions for growth rate on high or low concentrate diets, but like Bonnier and his colleagues used monozygous twins. Such animals are completely atypical, and however valuable they may be from an academic point of view can hardly serve as material from which general conclusions can be drawn. Maltos *et al.* (1961), in Costa Rica, produced some evidence of interaction in growth rate when cattle were fattened in drylots or on pasture. However, there was serious confounding in their data. Significant sire × year interactions have been observed by Warwick and Cartwright (1955) in Texas while Dillard *et al.* (1964) in North Carolina found a significant effect on one carcass trait (% lean in 9th–10th–11th rib section) from various sire × location (mountain, piedmont or coastal plain) interactions. Temple *et al.* (1961) found, in an analysis of various crossbreeds, that the breed of the sire ranked differently for different years when the trait considered was birth weight. This may well have been due to the use of different sires in each year, in which event it is not a true genotype–environment interaction.

On the other hand, Lagos and Cartwright (1963) found no evidence of important interactions in an experiment involving Santa Gertrudis heifers fed concentrates in drylot or as supplementation on pasture. A second experiment involving 66 or 33% concentrates in relation to roughage also had little effect upon the ranking of sires. Of 9 Hereford sires three pairs changed one place, while of 15 sires with crossbred progeny only two changed ranking substantially (three places). They concluded that selection on either diet would be effective for the other. Brown and Gacula (1962) found no evidence of interaction of sire with management, location, season or sex for Hereford and Angus sires in Arkansas. In a study involving 205 Hereford steers by 23 sires, Urick *et al.* (1957) found that the rates of growth on a moderate fattening ration, on summer pasture, on mountain range and on a final fattening ration were all highly correlated. They suggested that selection on any one system would result in genetic gain on the others. They did, however, consider that improvement would be maximized (on a generation basis) if selection was undertaken in the environment where progeny would be used. Klosterman *et al.* (1965a) found no genotype–environment interactions with Charolais and Hereford sires in Ohio, although year × management effects were important. In Europe, Skjervold and Gravir (1961) compared bulls and steers of each of 4 breeds fed on improved lowland pasture or under mountain conditions. They found differences between breeds and pastures but no evidence of interaction for rate of gain.

According to Stobbs (1966a), genotype–nutrition interactions were important in a herd of East African Zebu in Uganda, and the selection programme was changed accordingly. The evidence for this adoption of the Falconer thesis was based on the fact that one particular sire, which at 3 years of age was 40% heavier than his contemporaries, had progeny which were considered to be below average under grassland conditions. However, examinations of the highly subjective discussion showed that the bull in question was, in fact, given supplementary feed, hence his higher rate of gain. Had all sires been given supplementary feed, Stobbs's opinion might have been of value. Since this was not the case, the "evidence" for genotype–environment interactions is totally invalid.

In a similar manner the data of Reynolds *et al.* (1967b), relating to the wintering of Angus and Brahman heifers and their crosses on two nutritional levels, must be treated cautiously. On both nutritional planes the ranking of breeds for growth rate during the winter period was the same although, not unnaturally, differences were more pronounced in absolute terms on the high plane. Summer gains were of a completely different order, not only between breeds but also between wintering levels. At first sight this appears to be evidence for interaction but a much more likely explanation is that of compensatory growth. Animals or breeds which suffered in the winter from a low nutritional plane compensated in the summer.

The complicated nature of interactions is demonstrated in the interim results of a study in which Herefords raised for many generations in Florida and Montana were interchanged. According to Koger (1968) female offspring grew less well in the new environment than those from cows native to the region; this interaction was evident up to 18 months of age. In marked contrast there was no evidence of any interaction in males fattened under drylot conditions.

It is perhaps in connection with the Brahman and other *Bos indicus* types that most misunderstanding exists. Much of this relates to climatic effects and is discussed in § 4.3, but it is also believed that *B. indicus* cattle have a different digestive efficiency than *B. taurus* animals. Howes *et al.* (1963) have, in fact, shown that on low protein diets the Brahman digested more protein and consumed more DM than the Hereford, but to what extent this was related to performance was not indicated. The belief that it might lead to better growth capacity on high roughage diets is certainly not substantiated by the data which we have accumulated in Cuba (Table 4.1).

The four experiments detailed in Table 4.1 were all undertaken at the same station but under a wide variety of conditions ranging from all-concentrate feeding from 90 days to forage with molasses supplementation. The comparisons related only to the Brahman and Brown Swiss × Brahman breeds, since these were the only two represented in all trials. It is clearly evident that at all management levels the crossbred animals were superior, although the extent of this superiority was greater with the higher nutritional planes. Although sires and ages were accurately known only in the case of the performance-tested cattle, these differences are unlikely to be due to sires within breeds since cattle were collected from all over the island and must have come from a very large number of sires.

4.3 CLIMATIC ASPECTS

4.3.1 Some generalizations

We have shown that, with regard to genotype–nutrition interactions, there is both a paucity of accurate data and considerable confusion as to what constitutes interaction. The situation is even more equivocal with regard to climate. In part this arises because in many countries the range of climatic variation at a fixed point of time is small. Thus interpretations and opinions are invariably confounded through being based on the performance of breeds in different countries. There is no guarantee that a given breed has the same genetic makeup in different countries, in fact there is evidence to the contrary in dairy cattle; the Holstein/Friesian of Canada, the UK and Holland are quite distinct in their genetic potential for milk yield and milk-fat percentage (Willis, 1962).

There are, however, several countries which have a wide enough range of climatic conditions (e.g. Australia, the US, Kenya) to allow expression of genotype–climate

TABLE 4.1 THE PERFORMANCE OF BRAHMAN AND BROWN SWISS × BRAHMAN BULLS UNDER DIFFERENT ENVIRONMENTAL CONDITIONS

No. of bulls	Housing system[a]	Diet[b]	Daily gain		Conversion		Excess fat		Authors
			Brahman (kg)	Brown Swiss × Brahman (%[c])	Brahman	Brown Swiss × Brahman (%[c])	Brahman (%)	Brown Swiss × Brahman (%[d])	
32	Groups of 3	71:29[e]	0.60	—3	36.5[f]	4	8.0	16	Preston *et al.*, 1969a
138	Groups of 10	52:48[g]	0.48	13			7.5	15	Quintana, 1968
33	Groups of 3	71:29[h]	0.94	27	21.0[f]	16	10.4	38	Preston *et al.*, 1969a
64	Individual	100:0	0.88	32	7.58[i]	22	11.9	18	Willis & Preston, 1969c

[a] All on slatted floors.
[b] Concentrate roughage (as ME).
[c] % improvement over Brahman.
[d] Reduction in excess fat.
[e] Molasses/urea diet with poultry waste as protein supplement.
[f] ME per kg of gain.
[g] Molasses per urea and forage only.
[h] Molasses per urea diet with fishmeal as protein supplement.
[i] kg air dry feed per kg of gain.

interactions should they exist. Despite this, most data on breed differences in response to temperature and humidity relate to experiments in climatic chambers and to traits not directly related to productive performance. Even with respect to field studies, investigators seem to have been more concerned with evidence for climatic stress rather than productivity in terms of growth, efficiency and reproductive rate. Few authors seem to have realized that the importance of climate varies with the nature of the productive process. The beef cow is (and will continue to be for some considerable time) maintained in the *actual* climate. The fattening animal, on the other hand, is mostly taken out of the natural environment (and submitted to a less severe micro-climate) for economic and nutritional reasons related to scale and efficiency of operation independent of climatic factors.

Since the major economic effect of climate is on feed intake it is vitally important to consider reproduction separately from fattening. Only in the latter is intake related to productivity and hence profitability.

There is a complete absence of data on genotype–environment effects involving low temperature, but this is not so serious an omission as it may at first appear, since in this case the primary effect of climate is on food supply. The areas of future livestock development are mostly in tropical and subtropical regions, thus our primary interest is in effects of high temperature and humidity rather than cold.

With a few notable exceptions, the tropical and subtropical regions are only now developing an animal agriculture, and cultural/technical problems still dominate. Speaking of such countries, Lee (1953) considered that even "when full allowances are made for all these cultural and indirect climatic effects an important portion of the fall in production still seems to be attributable to the direct action of hot climates upon the animal". That this philosophy is widely accepted is typified by the statement of French and Ledger (1957) that, in relation to East Africa, it would be unwise to select for improved genetic types on a plane of feeding and management superior to that which they are likely to receive in African ownership, and that genetic studies ought to be carried out on a maintenance level of feeding. Many other workers appear to have accepted the existence and importance of genotype–climate interaction in hot countries. Thus Bonsma *et al.* (1953) suggested that climates with mean average temperatures in excess of 18°C were not suitable for British and European breeds of cattle, that the Africander was the most suitable for hot, dry environments and the N'guni best for hot, wet areas. Yeates (1965) put forward an elaborate classification scheme for allocation of specific breeds to the distinct climatic regions of Northern Australia, albeit without specifying the type of production he had in mind. It would seem that some of the breeds put forward are characterized only by their ability to survive. This same author cites Betts (1963) as advocating a similar classification of beef breeds in Kenya, according to altitude and temperature. Faulkner and Brown (1953) expressed considerable doubt about the use of European breeds in tropical conditions, while Williamson and Payne (1959) stated that ". . . cattle of the improved breeds cannot thrive under tropical conditions and their potential productivity may be of no account". The height of absurdity in this field was reached by Webster and Wilson (1966) who classified the tropics into six different regions, giving for each the most suitable proportions of *B. taurus* and *B. indicus*. While this appears at first sight to be a scientific approach, there is in fact no evidence whatsoever to justify such a stratification.

The aim of the ensuing discussion is to review breed interaction with respect to climatological factors and productive rates. Some aspects of the physiological mechanisms by which animals maintain their normal body temperature are discussed in Chapter 10.

4.3.2 Physiological aspects

4.3.2.1 Sweating. Although in 1953 Worstell and Brody considered that cattle lost heat only by evaporation from the mouth, tongue and upper respiratory tract, Dowling (1958) reported that sweating did occur; while Goshi *et al.* (1968) showed that in Zebu cattle under heat stress surface evaporative loss from the skin came mainly from the sweat glands. The structure and function of sweat glands was reviewed by Nay (1959), Weiner and Hellmann (1960) and Yeates (1965). According to Nay there are distinct differences between *B. indicus* and *B. taurus* cattle, the former having a large baggy type of sweat gland while the latter had tubular coiled glands of small diameter; crosses between the species tended to have an intermediate shape in that they were baggy at the lower part and narrow and coiled towards the upper end. Although these differences imply a clear differentiation between breeds, Barker and Nay (1964) subsequently found that even within a breed, sweat gland type and size was very variable.

Nay (1959) inferred that gland volume could be a good index of heat tolerance, but the fact that man has smaller sweat glands but secretes at a relatively much higher rate (Brook and Short, 1960) suggests that sweat gland size *per se* is not the most important factor. This is supported by the finding of Walker (1960) that within 14 breeds of *B. indicus* cattle heat tolerance was closely related to rate of sweat secretion.

It may be that the activity of sweat glands depends more upon their blood supply than upon their size since it is known that vascular development is high in man but sparse in cattle (Goodall and Yang, 1954). There appears to be no information on breed differences with respect to blood supply, although there are indications from the work of Brown and Motasem (1965) that it may be more developed in cattle of European origin. Holsteins lost 592 g moisture/m^2/hr compared with 563 and 551 for Jerseys and Jersey × Brahman. As ambient temperature increased from 22.7 to 28.2°C, evaporation rates increased by 6.8, 1.2 and 1.0% for the 3 breeds respectively; salts also accumulated more rapidly on the skin of the Holsteins.

It may be argued that Zebu cattle have a greater surface area per unit of weight which would compensate for any reduced evaporation rate per unit area. But it is by no means certain that the Zebu has in fact a greater surface area, and the work of McDowell (1958) showed that in any event this was not an important factor. Removal of the hump and dewlap and reducing the size of the ears of Red Sindhi bulls appeared to have no effect on their heat tolerance or their ability to lose heat by surface evaporation.

Yeck and Kibler (1958) attempted to predict heat tolerance of 6 breeds in terms of their relative vaporization rates at temperatures of 26.6 and 10°C. At 5 months of age the ratio ranged from 2.75 in Brahmans to 1.35 in Shorthorns, however at 12 months of age, Brown Swiss were as tolerant as Brahmans; moreover, the *B. indicus* breeds with a high ratio at 5 months declined at one year while European breeds (Brown Swiss, Jersey, Holstein and Shorthorn) showed marked increases. The above data tend to indicate that there are no consistent differences between *B. indicus* and *B. taurus* species.

4.3.2.2 Coat type. The other aspect is heat loss by convection and radiation and, equally important, heat absorption. In this respect coat characteristics, such as colour of skin and colour and length of hair, may well be important. Bonsma (1949) found that animals which failed to shed their hair and which had woolly coats had lower productivity than those with smooth coats. Coat type was also correlated with heat tolerance in that cattle with woolly coats had higher rectal temperatures and greater respiration rates. Turner and Schleger (1960) also reported that coat type was related to productive characteristics and was of high heritability ($h^2 = 0.63$). In fact, coat score accounted for only 16% of the variation in live weight gain and this during the period of 16–28 months of age. Their conclusion that coat type was a better indicator of live weight gain potential in the second year of life than live weight gain in the first year has relevance neither to the practice of intensive beef production, nor to genetic improvement of cattle for tropical conditions.

While accepting the obvious fact that a long or woolly coat must be a disadvantage in a tropical climate, we are extremely sceptical of its value as a selection tool. It is perhaps significant that Bonsma (1949), Yeates (1965) and other enthusiasts for the importance of coat type have worked almost exclusively with Shorthorns, relating the undesirable coat type of this breed with its inferior performance. It does not appear to have occurred to them that for beef production the Shorthorn is the most inferior breed for almost all traits, as has been demonstrated throughout this book. There appears to be no evidence that woolly coats are a problem in other important breeds, European or otherwise. We also prefer to concur with Webster and Wilson (1966) that poor coat type is more likely to be a reflection of unthriftiness than the reverse.

It is our opinion that selection for live weight gain or efficiency in tropical conditions will both improve performance in these traits and lead to the development of cattle with short coats. Selection for short coat, on the other hand, will not necessarily improve performance.

4.3.2.3 Coat and skin colour. Early South African work (Riemerschmid and Elder, 1945; Bonsma, 1949) showed that solar heat absorption at the coat surface was greater for black than white cattle, brown coats being intermediate. This is to be expected, but it has yet to be shown to be a sufficiently important factor to affect productivity. Our own data (Willis and Preston, 1969a) relating to the almost completely black Holstein × Brahman and the whitish-grey Brahman reveal the former to be superior under both indoor and outdoor conditions of management.

There are specific instances when colour is of major importance, as, for example, the incidence of cancer eye in the Hereford which is associated with white pigmentation of the eyelid (Anderson, 1960; Anderson and Skinner, 1961; Vogt *et al.*, 1963).

4.3.2.4 Heat production. It would appear that too much attention has been given to mechanisms of heat loss in tropical cattle in view of the findings of Johnston *et al.* (1958) that the superior heat tolerance of Red Sindhi × Holstein, in comparison with Jerseys and Holsteins, was essentially due to a lower heat production both in absolute terms and per unit body surface area. Under thermal stress *B. indicus* cattle had lower body temperatures and respiration rates but due to a lower heat production rather than superior heat exchange mechanisms.

It is well established that there are breed differences with respect to physiological expressions of heat stress. Thus Angus cattle had higher rectal temperatures than Herefords (Van Arsdel and Bogart, 1962) and Brahmans lower than either (Haines and Koger, 1964). Brahmans had lower values than a variety of breeds including the Santa Gertrudis, Holstein and Jersey (De Alba and Couto, 1957). It has also been demonstrated that Brahmans have lower metabolic rates than European type cattle (Worstell and Brody, 1953; Johnston *et al.*, 1958), but, in spite of this, required just as much feed energy to maintain weight as Herefords or Holsteins (Garrett, 1965b). Of greater importance are the findings of Bianca (1959a, b), Johnson *et al.* (1961), Kibler (1962) and Berman *et al.* (1963), that lower metabolic rates may develop, even in European breeds, through prolonged exposure to high experimental temperatures. Adaptation has also been demonstrated in high producing animals in terms of their ability to withstand higher than normal rectal temperatures (Berman and Kibler, 1959) and in having lower heat increments of lactation (Berman *et al.*, 1963).

4.3.3 Effects on production traits

4.3.3.1 Growth and efficiency. As far back as 1955 Cartwright considered that animal resistance to heat stress as measured by rectal temperature in climatic chambers was not necessarily an indication of their potential to grow in hot weather. De Alba and Couto (1957) found that even in climatic chambers Santa Gertrudis out-gained Brahmans despite having higher respiration rate and rectal temperature. Vernon *et al.* (1959), in a study of Brahmans, Angus, Santa Gertrudis, Africander–Angus and Brangus, also reported that heat tolerance was not related to productivity, as measured by the cow's weight and that of her progeny. This study encompassed nine years of data in Louisiana and in view of the results obtained *the use of heat tolerance rating as an aid to selection was discontinued.* These workers considered that the ability to maintain normal body temperature and a low respiration rate under adverse conditions was only one of the traits necessary for good performance.

Gutierrez *et al.* (1968) found that feed intake of Brahmans and Herefords decreased as temperature rose from 21 to 32°C but no breed interactions occurred. These same workers (Cowley *et al.*, 1968) found no evidence of differences in thyroid activity between the breeds at either of the two temperatures.

Some evidence for genotype–climate interaction was put forward by Johnson *et al.* (1959) in that efficiency of weight gain in Brown Swiss was greater at 10° than at 26.6°C, while the reverse was true of Holsteins and Jerseys. On the other hand, Hartman *et al.* (1956) reported that, while at 10°C Zebu, Santa Gertrudis and Dairy Shorthorn heifers all grew at the same rate, the Dairy Shorthorns were some 90 kg lighter at 12 months when the temperature was 26.6°C. It is perhaps important to note that this trial was undertaken with the animals continually in climatic chambers, and that the Shorthorns did not shed their hair as did those maintained out of doors.

4.3.3.2 Reproduction. There is general agreement that high ambient temperatures adversely affect semen quality (see Johnston *et al.*, 1963; Gutierrez *et al.*, 1968), and a suggestion (Johnston *et al.*, 1963) that the effect was more noticeable in European breeds than in their crosses with *B. indicus*. No one has yet demonstrated a significant genotype–climate interaction regarding semen quality.

In females the situation is even less clear. Dale *et al.* (1959), in a study with Brahman, Santa Gertrudis and Shorthorn heifers maintained in climatic rooms at 10° or 26.6°C, found the Brahman to be seasonally monoestrus. The higher temperature delayed the outset of puberty in Shorthorns although having little effect in the Santa Gertrudis. Even so both breeds reached puberty earlier than the Brahman. Under field conditions in Queensland, Lampkin and Kennedy (1965) found British cattle (Hereford and Shorthorn) were unable to maintain body weight under the stress of pregnancies in two successive years and produced only 56.0% live calves compared with 77.3% from Africander and 73.8% from Brahman. However, this may have been an acclimatization problem and is certainly not a general phenomenon, since in Florida these same breeds were greatly superior to the Brahman (Meade *et al.*, 1959b; Cobb *et al.*, 1964; Warnick *et al.*, 1967). In a 4 year period in Cuba (semi-humid tropics) the proportion of live calves born to Charolais (81%) was higher than to Brahman (72%), Criollo (71%) or Santa Gertrudis (64%) (Willis and Preston, 1969d). The Charolais were acclimatized, the foundation stock having been imported from France some 40 years previously, thereafter being subjected to natural selection.

Bond *et al.* (1960) lend support to the importance of acclimatization in that they observed that Shorthorn heifers exposed to a temperature of 32°C and a relative humidity of 60% ceased oestrous cycles within 5 weeks, shed their coats and began recycling after 21 weeks. Johnson (1964) also found that the depressing effect of high temperature on feed intake was greater for animals reared at 15.5 as compared to 26.6°C. Similar results were recorded in India by Sharmar (1968), adapted animals having higher feed and water intakes in an adverse environment than those recently brought into the area. Kibler *et al.* (1965) also observed evidence of acclimatization in Holstein cows exposed to temperature of 29°C.

4.3.4 Conclusions

In so far as climate is concerned the crux of the problem is the extent to which high performing *B. taurus* breeds can be used in the adverse environments normally inhabited by *B. indicus*. The data are fragmentary, but it can be concluded that with respect to the physiological indices of response to heat stress, the Brahman and similar *B. indicus* types are superior. The evidence, however, indicates that this superiority results less from their facility to dissipate heat as from a lower heat production. This latter arises partially from their being adapted to the climatic conditions, as a result of natural selection for survival, and partly from their intrinsically lower productivity. In its extreme form this effect can be seen in a comparison of Hereford cattle and Elands undertaken by Taylor and Lyman (1967) in Kenya. They showed that the Eland was both behaviourally and physiologically better adapted to marginal arid regions, but less efficient in the production of meat.

Johnston *et al.* (1958) considered that high producing strains of tropically adapted species (*B. indicus*) would be under nearly as much stress as high producing European breeds. It would seem to us both easier and more certain to adapt high producing *B. taurus* to the conditions than to make *B. indicus* high producing.

If one accepts the negative philosophy put forward by those tropical specialists whose work was reviewed in § 4.3.1, then effectively vast areas of the world are consigned to levels of animal productivity far inferior to those currently enjoyed in the developed temperate regions. To pursue this to its logical conclusion is to imply that there is no point in seeking to bring about improvements in animal production in tropical areas.

We do not ascribe to these sentiments. On the contrary, we believe that the tropics can support a more intensive animal production than the temperate regions in view of their great potential for the production of readily available carbohydrates suitable for animal feed (Preston and Willis, 1969). We also consider that climate has been overemphasized and overstressed, and that it is much less of an obstacle than is the technical development of a country and its people. That Israel with an adverse hot and dry climate should have a national average milk production of over 4500 kg per cow (recorded and unrecorded), and with specific examples of herd yields exceeding 6000 kg in ambient temperatures of over 34°C with European cattle (Holsteins), is proof of the superiority of technology versus nature, and of optimism over pessimism. On a smaller scale we have demonstrated in Cuba that European beef breeds weaned at 3 months can reach 400 kg live weight at 8½ months of age by providing no more than shade and an adequate plane of nutrition (Willis and Preston, 1967, 1968a).

4.4 DISEASE

4.4.1 Pathogenic disease

With a few notable exceptions, there is little evidence for the existence of genotype disease effects in beef cattle. The evidence that the Zebu and other *B. indicus* types are more resistant to parasites and particularly tick-borne diseases is somewhat equivocal. Ross *et al.* (1960) have suggested that in Nigeria resistance to helminthiasis was associated with ability to produce a specific antibody. Similarly, Ashton *et al.* (1968) claimed that the serum amylase phenotype was associated with tick (*Boophilus microplus*) infestation in Australia. Animals with category C phenotype were said to carry fewer ticks. Specific claims of resistance to tick infestations in particular breeds with *Bos indicus* blood have been put forward by Francis and Little (1964) and Francis (1966). The former workers found fewer ticks on Droughtmasters than British breeds and considered this to be due to hypersensitive skin reaction.

We believe this is an oversimplication of the problem and that their finding of reduced incidence of babesiosis in Droughtmasters than in Herefords is more likely to represent acquired rather than genetic resistance. Thus Hewetson and Nolan (1968) found that susceptible Zebu cattle became more resistant with successive infestations up to the fourth.

In Uganda, Stobbs (1966b) reported that Boran cattle introduced from Kenya had a 74% calf mortality due largely to East Coast fever compared with only 23% for indigenous Zebu. No resistance to the disease was found in any of 5 sires. Resistance to this specific disease is wholly acquired (Stobbs, 1967), necessitating exposure early in life. It is probable that other tick-borne diseases are of a similar nature. Our own experience in Cuba with a variety of breeds does not suggest that *B. indicus* types are any less susceptible than the others to anaplasmosis. The development of this disease in European cattle (imported or native-born), which has given rise to the belief that these are more susceptible, mainly reflects management procedures. Calves of these breeds are usually reared artificially and hence not exposed to the disease until about 6 months, at which age they are particularly susceptible. In 4 years of work with a breeding herd of over 600 cows no calf has been lost from anaplasmosis when it has been left with its dam on natural pasture until at least 3 months of age. On the other hand, in a dairy herd of 120 animals where artificial rearing is practised exclusively, both cows and bulls have been lost from this disease (Willis and Preston, 1969a).

4.4.2 Metabolic and other diseases

The problem of cancer eye in Herefords discovered by Guilbert *et al.* (1948) and subsequently studied by Anderson and his co-workers (see Vogt *et al.*, 1963) is an example of an interaction of major economic importance in countries with intense sunlight.

A relatively high incidence of vaginal prolapse was observed in a Hereford herd by Holland and Knox (1967). The condition occurred only in animals maintained on irrigated pasture and not in animals of similar genotype kept under ranch conditions on semi-desert. The heritability of the susceptibility scores was 0.57 (paternal half-sib) and 0.14 (daughter–dam).

We have observed hoof abnormalities in Brahmans undergoing performance tests on high energy diets (Willis and Preston, 1968a). The condition has not appeared on low energy diets. A similar abnormality was reported in Herefords by Brown *et al.* (1967a).

With respect to intensive beef production, the diseases causing most economic loss are *Escherichia coli* in calves destined for dairy-beef, shipping-fever and bloat in fattening cattle, and amongst breeding cows in the tropics tick-borne diseases. There is no real evidence of genotype-disease interactions for any of these conditions other than feedlot bloat which is not a problem on high roughage diets (other than fresh alfalfa) but is more prevalent in particular breeds (Miller and Frederick, 1966; Willis and Preston, 1968a) when high energy diets are used. Since bloating animals invariably grow more slowly, they are automatically selected against in any performance test where high energy diets are used. Beyond this there seems little point in taking account of genotype-disease interactions in testing programmes, although a more intensive study of breed differences with respect to acclimatization, adaptation and acquired immunity is urgently needed.

Fredeen (1965) has tentatively suggested the incorporation of disease resistance into selection programmes particularly with regard to *E. coli* infections. Although this is a laudable idea it is difficult to see how it could be accomplished in practice.

4.5 BREEDING FOR THE ENVIRONMENT

In summarizing the evidence presented in this chapter we consider that there is no economic justification for taking account of genotype-environment interactions in so far as these relate to climate and disease. With respect to nutrition and management the picture is not completely clear and there is still need for more research in this field. One cannot reject entirely the existence of important interactions under specific conditions. As Young (1953) pointed out, there are so many possible genotypes and environments that any evaluation of their interactions must be limited in its application. Their non-existence in one study does not preclude their presence in another. The problem is how to take account of these effects in a selection programme.

In beef cattle, as in dairy cattle, we are rarely faced with a situation in which all the progeny of a bull are kept in the same environment, particularly if such a bull is stationed in AI. Some progeny may be found on open range or pasture, others in feedlots from weaning and yet others on all-concentrate feeding from birth. Even if it were established that genotype–environment interactions did exist, how does one incorporate these into a performance-testing programme when one cannot test a bull simultaneously in all possible environments in which his progeny may one day be used?

Roberts (1965) tentatively suggested that animals might be tested in the least favourable environment likely to be faced by their progeny. Taking an extreme example it is doubtful if there is a much less favourable environment than unsupplemented tropical pasture, but Maltos *et al.* (1961) rejected such testing on the grounds of poor repeatability. Even if this were overcome, one is still faced with the problem of slow growth under these feeding systems such that bulls might well need 3–4 years to reach a required test weight. Testing would then involve long generation intervals and rate of genetic gain per year would be reduced. This same criticism would apply to an even greater extent to any plan involving progeny testing for growth in several different environments.

This economic aspect is a major omission from the reasoning of most theorists in the field. In any trait we are concerned with progress per year rather than per generation, and if we accept that in the case of growth or feed efficiency, testing is best done to a constant weight, it follows that animals must reach this weight as rapidly as possible in order to reduce generation interval. In our own testing in Cuba we have been able to select Charolais bulls as early as 252 days of age and have progeny long before the sire is 2 years old. Selection for the same traits on pasture could not hope to compete with such a turnover in generations.

Considering progress on this basis, the findings of Fowler and Ensminger (1960) are open to a completely different interpretation.

In the actual experiment the investigators mated their pigs at a fixed age thus negating any advantage of faster growth in the high line. In practice, however, a breeder mates his pigs at a fixed weight. Assuming this to be 110 kg and that weaning weights at 56 days are the same for both lines (18 kg) it can be shown that the respective generation intervals would be 344 and 418 days for the high and low lines respectively. On being transferred to the low plane, animals selected on the high plane were approximately 7% inferior to those selected on the low plane over the same number of generations. However, to accomplish 9 generations on low plane testing would require 3700 days which is time for 10.8 generations on high plane testing. The net progress per year in daily gain on the low plane testing would then be 0.0121 compared with 0.0135 kg (i.e. 11% better) if testing were undertaken on the high plane and the pigs subsequently used on the low plane.

Falconer (1960b) reasoned that if the genetic correlation between two characters (e.g. growth rate on a high or on a low plane) is high the two can be regarded as the same trait for all practical purposes. Provided selection intensity and heritability are unaffected, selection in either environment would be equally effective. If genetic correlation is low, Falconer suggested that selection would be best undertaken in the environment in which the animal will be used "unless the heritability or selection intensity in the other environment is very apparently higher".

In annual terms this theory is unacceptable although on a generation basis it is perfectly valid. There are, however, certain other factors which influence judgement. Fowler and Ensminger (1960) showed that heritability was higher on the high plane of nutrition. This phenomenon of higher heritabilities with higher nutritional planes has been observed by Wagnon and Rollins (1959) for long yearling weight in beef cattle, which was higher in a supplemented herd than in non-supplemented range cattle. Bogart *et al.* (1963b) also found several production traits to have higher heritabilities in supplemented beef cattle than in non-supplemented animals, while Lagos and Cartwright (1963) found additive genetic variance higher on high concentrate rations. Mason and Robertson (1956) reported higher heritability estimates for milk yields and butterfat percentage in high-yielding dairy herds than in low-yielding herds in Denmark. This was confirmed by Van Vleck (1963) in the US although such phenomena were not observed by Robertson *et al.* (1960) or by Van Vleck and Bradford (1964), the latter obtaining inconclusive results. In sheep, Osman and Bradford (1965) found some evidence of higher heritabilities in 120 day weight with higher nutritional levels. Increase in variance with increasing nutritional level has been observed for various traits in dairy cattle by Johansson (1953), Korkman (1953), Mitchell *et al.* (1961), Legates (1962), Touchberry (1963) and Van Vleck and Bradford (1964) although the percentage genetic variance did not increase in all cases.

While we are of the opinion that selection is best undertaken on high nutritional planes, our reasons for this are based on shorter generation intervals and possibly higher heritabilities rather than the non-existence of interaction. There are, of course, limitations to such a philosophy, and it cannot be carried to extremes. We would not, for example, suggest testing bulls in the UK and then using them under range conditions in the tropics, since they would almost certainly succumb to disease.

If it is necessary to import exotic blood from temperate countries to the tropics this is best done with semen. If bulls are imported they should be kept protected from disease in an AI station. Their progeny out of the local adapted cattle, if raised on their dams under natural conditions for at least 3 months, will generally acquire the necessary immunity for use in natural service. In specific cases the progeny of some bulls will succumb in early life in which case the bulls should be destroyed.

CHAPTER 5

Physiology of Digestion and Feed Utilization

5.1 INTRODUCTION

The direct effects of feeds on the economic traits in the live animal and its carcass are the subject of Chapters 2 and 9. The intention here is not to provide a complete treatize on theoretical aspects of cattle nutrition, but rather to discuss those features of the animal's physiology and metabolism which are related to feed utilization. We have in the main concentrated our attention on the more recent developments in nutrition since the background information is amply documented in the standard texts of Annison and Lewis (1959), Maynard and Loosli (1962), Blaxter (1966), and MacDonald *et al.* (1966). In keeping with the general objective of this book discussion is deliberately restricted to the conditions of high energy intake.

5.2 PHYSIOLOGY OF DIGESTION

5.2.1 Anatomical development of the digestive tract

5.2.1.1 SIZE AND CAPACITY OF THE STOMACH. Although the calf begins life with its stomach already divided into the four compartments characteristic of the adult ruminant, the relative sizes of these are quite different from those in the mature animal. If the diet is restricted to liquid milk, natural or artificial, all the stomach compartments grow in weight and size at the same rate as that of the whole body (Warner *et al.*, 1956). Under these conditions only the abomasum is functional since liquid feeds bypass the other stomach compartments by means of the oesophageal groove.

When dry feeds are introduced into the diet the pattern of development is quite different since these pass first into the rumen, where they may stay for no more than a few minutes or as much as one or two days depending on their physical and chemical composition. On this type of feeding, the abomasum continues to develop at the same rate as when only milk is given, but the other compartments grow much more rapidly (Warner *et al.*, 1956). When concentrates, hay, or concentrates and hay together were given with whole milk, these same workers found that while the increase in weight of the different stomach compartments was the same relative to body weight, volume was greatest on the hay diet and least on concentrates. Blaxter *et al.* (1952) also considered that roughage increased the volume of the reticulo-rumen and omasum by stretching the walls of these compartments without increasing the actual weight of tissue. According to Lagerlof (1929) the rumen reached the size and position characteristic of the mature animal, in relation to the other stomach compartments, at about 8–9 months of age. However, Grossman (1949) stated that final size and weight relative to adult body size was not reached until 18 months of age, although at 4–6 months the four stomachs approached adult proportions. In calves raised on pasture, Godfrey (1961a) reported that while at 17 weeks the weight of the reticulo-rumen was still increasing relative to live weight, its development relative to the other stomach compartments was at its maximum by 8 weeks of age. Roy (1958) considered that at birth the abomasum represented some 70% of total stomach capacity whereas in the adult ruminant it accounted for only 8%.

Under natural nursing it is generally considered that milk continues to pass into the abomasum by the oesophageal groove until the calf is weaned. However, evidence for the existence of this mechanism in older animals is lacking. Wester (1930) showed that oesophageal groove closure was stimulated by the soluble proteins and milk salts, while Riek (1954) found that 60 ml of a 10% solution of sodium bicarbonate was also effective; glucose stimulated closure but not in all animals. Watson (1944) considered that groove closure was a reflex action elicited, in part, by the suckling mechanism and not for reasons of thirst since water was not as effective as milk.

In general, the mechanics of oesophageal groove closure have received little attention from research workers since there are few economic advantages and many more disadvantages from extending the length of liquid feeding in the case of artificially reared dairy calves. Raven and Robinson (1961) showed that feeding the concentrate part of the diet of ruminating calves in the form of a liquid suspension enabled it to bypass the rumen, bringing about more efficient use of both energy and protein. Attempts to develop the idea into a practical system were less successful (Forbes *et al.*, 1965, 1966; Accardi, 1966). However, the development of molasses feeding systems (§ 9.3.3) reopens the possibility of economic feeding of liquids since the sucrose in molasses is easily inverted to its component monosaccharides (glucose and fructose) which are then available to the calf without the need for enzyme digestion.

The more efficient groove closure claimed to operate with suckling as opposed to drinking from a bucket, has led several workers to advocate giving milk from teats or nipple pails. But it has yet to be demonstrated that weight gains and efficiency of feed conversion are superior with these systems (see Wise and La Master, 1968).

The factors which determine how long feeds stay in the rumen are complex and differ as between concentrates and roughages. Nevertheless, they are extremely important since efficiency of utilization is quite different when digestion takes place in the rumen as compared to the abomasum and intestine.

In the rumen, feeds are exposed to fermentation by micro-organisms which become established there within a few hours of birth and subsequently develop in character and number according to the type of dry feed given. Micro-organisms mostly break down feeds into simple substances, mainly short-chain VFAs and ammonia, which either (a) are absorbed direct from the rumen, (b) are synthesized to form the bodies of bacteria and protozoa, or (c) pass out of the rumen to be absorbed from the subsequent sections of the digestive tract.

5.2.1.2 RUMEN PAPILLAE. Rumen development is not solely the increase in size of this part of the stomach but also the growth of papillae which, by projecting into the rumen, increase the surface area available for nutrient absorption. According to Flatt *et al.* (1959) growth of this tissue is stimulated only by the products of bacterial fermentation of feeds, while milk and fibrous materials *per se* have no effect. Greatest papillary development was brought about by diets low in fibre and high in readily available carbohydrates (Flatt *et al.*, 1958; Bleichner and Ellis, 1968), and by solutions of salts of VFAs (Flatt *et al.*, 1958). Plastic sponges, administered through a fistula to simulate the fibrousness of roughages, enhanced the effect of the VFA on papillary development but were ineffective when given alone. Brownlee (1956) considered that while the rumen epithelium of calves receiving milk and concentrates was heavier than in those given milk and roughage, it was less muscular and more easily damaged. If this is true it could account for our findings (Willis and Preston, 1968a) that calves weaned early on to an all-concentrate diet and thereafter given a similar diet (3.0 Mcal ME/kg DM) to slaughter exhibited the characteristic liver abscesses associated with all-concentrate feeding, whereas these were absent in calves pasture-raised with their mothers to 3 months and given the same high energy diet from 90 days of age to slaughter as those reared artificially.

It appears that papillary development is a function of the metabolism taking place in the rumen wall since sodium butyrate and sodium propionate were effective in inducing development of papillae whereas sodium acetate, sodium chloride and glucose (not metabolized by rumen epithelium) were only slightly so (Sander *et al.*, 1959).

Despite the marked influence which different diets have on papillary development, there appears to be no subsequent effect on efficiency of feed utilization in adult life. Thus Stobo (1961) found that calves reared on high roughage diets for their first 3 months (and which had large reticulo-rumens with poor papillary development) were just as efficient in their subsequent utilization of concentrates as calves reared initially on a high concentrate diet which induced good papillary development but small rumens. The main effect of roughage in the calf diet seems to be to extend the size of the intestinal tract and delay the flow of ingesta through it. The relationship between the diet and the weight of gut contents has been calculated by Stobo and Roy (1963) as

$$Y = 0.20X_1 - 3.33X_3 + 0.40X_2 + 2.90,$$

where Y is the weight of the contents of the alimentary tract (kg), X_1 live weight (kg), X_2 daily concentrate consumption (kg) and X_3 daily hay consumption (kg).

The labile nature of rumen epithilial tissue and its responsiveness to dietary change is demonstrated by the work of Stobo and Roy (1964) and Harrison *et al.* (1957). The former found that rapid changes occurred in rumen epithelial tissue within 3 weeks of the transition from hay to concentrates or vice versa, while the latter showed that the reticulo-rumen and omasum of weaned calves regressed rapidly to an undeveloped state, similar to that of a milk-fed animal, when the diet of hay and grain was replaced by milk alone.

5.2.2 Physiological development of digestive capacity—liquid feeds

5.2.2.1 General considerations. Apart from the anatomical distinctions which exist between the various compartments of the stomach, there are very considerable differences in the way in which they function. The abomasum, which the calf is using almost exclusively in its early days, is like the stomach of a non-ruminant in that digestion is brought about by enzymes in the gastric juices secreted from glands leading into the abomasum and intestine. The reticulo-rumen, on the other hand, is little more than a large fermentation vat inhabited by a mixed population of bacteria and protozoa. These bring about digestion of the solid feeds which always pass first to this compartment. Thus, efficient utilization of a liquid food depends on whether the animal possesses the appropriate enzymes while utilization of hay and concentrates is mainly determined by the degree of development of the rumen and its microflora. The only constituent of the diet in early life is cow's milk and the normal calf must therefore possess enzymes capable of digesting casein, lactose and milk fat. It appears that capacity to utilize other feeds is limited particularly during the first 4 weeks of life.

5.2.2.2 Carbohydrates. It has been known since 1918 (Shaw *et al.*,) that week-old calves are able to digest only small amounts of maize starch, while in 1949 Converse found that dextrinized starch was also an unsatisfactory energy source. Flipse *et al.* (1950a, b) reported that weight gains were less for a synthetic milk which contained starch rather than lactose, and that the incidence of diarrhoea was also much greater. The explanation for these findings came from the work of Dollar and Porter (1957) who showed that whereas the oral administration of lactose and glucose led to a rapid rise in blood glucose, maltose and sucrose had only a small effect and starch and dextrin none. These authors considered that the effects were due to a high lactase activity at birth, which decreased with age, and a correspondingly low amylase/maltase activity increasing with age. In 3-month-old calves given various carbohydrates at a 10% concentration in milk, digestibility was much less for sucrose (57%) than for maltose (97%) or amylopectin (89%) (Huber *et al.*, 1961c). Siddons (1968) later showed that sucrase could not be detected at any age up to 4 months; that lactase and cellobiase activities (as mg/g of protein) were highest in young calves and decreased with age; and that maltase and trehalase activities did not change with age, but were always lower than the lactase activity even in the oldest calf. According to Manunta and Nuvole (1966) no sucrase activity could be found in sheep even up to 3 years of age although both amylase and maltase were present. There is also a quantitative limitation even for use of glucose and lactose since it has been shown (Rojas *et al.*, 1948; Blaxter and Wood, 1953) that diarrhoea and poor performance result if daily intake of either of these sugars exceeds some 250 g per 50 kg live weight.

5.2.2.3 Fat. Some fat is essential in the diet as a source of the polyunsaturated fatty acids such as linoleic and arachidonic acids which the preruminant calf is unable to synthesize (Lambert *et al.*, 1954).

Exact requirements are not known, but there is evidence that they increase in proportion to the total amount of fat in the diet. Fat is more important, however, as a source of highly concentrated energy, and in this respect requirements depend on the intended rate of growth. For slow or moderate rates of gain, fat is not necessary other than to supply the essential fatty acids, as the calf can obtain all the required energy from milk carbohydrates. Thus Converse (1949) was able to grow calves satisfactorily on a diet composed solely of skim milk and fat-soluble vitamins. If more rapid gains are required (>600 g/day), then fat must be added to the milk replacer since, as indicated previously, the maximum amount of carbohydrate that can be fed daily is no more than 200–300 g. When fat is added it should be emulsified and homogenized so as to reduce globule size to less than 2 μ diameter (Kastelic *et al.*, 1950). In very young calves, enzyme hydrolysis of fat occurs to only a limited extent, and much of it must be absorbed directly through the lymphatic system. Even when enzyme activity develops, the process is more efficient if the fat globules are small thus presenting a larger surface area to the digesting enzymes.

The digestibility of fat is also affected by the length of the chain as was found in other species by Lloyd and Crampton (1957). Raven and Robinson (1958) showed that the digestibility of hydrogenated palm oil was less than that of butterfat, while Roy (1964) reported that at 4 weeks of age digestibility of beef tallow was less (85%) than that of margarine (97%), refined lard (93%) and milk fat (97%). The differences were less at 10 weeks, ranging from 89% for tallow to 97% for milk fat. The nutritive value of fat also is affected by its condition and freshness. Crude fats are undesirable because of the impurities they contain and the destructive effects these have on essential vitamins, particularly E. The same is also true of fats or oils which are highly unsaturated, for fatty acids with double bonds are much less stable and easily give rise to breakdown products which destroy vitamin E. Muscular dystrophy, caused by deficiency of vitamin E, has been associated with the feeding of highly unsaturated fatty acids present in marine oils (see Blaxter and McGill, 1955). Spoilage of fat which occurs on storage can be much reduced by the inclusion of antioxidants (e.g. butylated hydroxytoluol and ethoxyquin) which, if added to the fat during its preparation and refining, help to retard breakdown.

5.2.2.4 PROTEIN. The exact mechanism by which the young calf digests protein is still not completely understood. Certainly the enzyme system pepsin/hydrochloric acid is not developed at birth for when a synthetic milk (not coagulated by renin) was fed to 2-day-old calves, they all died, whereas the same milk supported adequate growth at one week of age (Kastelic *et al.*, 1950). It is not known at what point pepsin takes over from renin as the main agent in protein digestion. For example, Henschel *et al.* (1961) investigated proteolytic enzymes in young calves and found that whereas all of the calves produced renin during the first 4 weeks of life not all of them produced pepsin although, in some, secretions of this enzyme could be detected at one week. At 6–8 weeks all calves were secreting pepsin. Renin acts specifically on casein and is much less effective with other proteins, whereas pepsin has a much wider range of activity. Moreover, as the pH of the digesting medium rises, the efficiency with which pepsin breaks down milk protein is considerably greater than the efficiency with which it attacks other proteins such as soya. Since the pH in the stomach of young calves is relatively high in early life and becomes lower as they get older (Pierce, 1962), the implication is that proteins other than casein will only play an appreciable role when the calf reaches at least 3–4 weeks of age. This was confirmed by Bruggeman and Barth (1959) who fed 7-day-old calves with milk replacers containing 50, 60, 70 or 100% dry milk powder in the diet, the difference being made up by fish meal and cereals. The apparent digestibility of the protein at 15 days of age was 80, 84, 88 and 95 on the respective diets and only with increasing age was there a significant rise in the protein digestibility of the diet containing the least amount of milk powder. Rate of growth showed a similar trend to protein digestibility. Thus for the first 4 weeks of life it is almost obligatory to rely on milk products as the source of protein. This is particularly true when high growth rates are required, and hence the level of feeding is at the point where enzyme capacity is being stretched to the limit. But, even when reliance is put only on milk protein, results may still be disappointing unless care is taken with the source of milk powder as regards possible heat damage to the non-casein protein fraction (§ 7.4.2.4).

For the slightly older calf and particularly when only moderate rates of growth are required, newer methods of processing vegetable proteins may allow at least some substitution of the protein fraction. Thus Gorrill and Thomas (1967) reported similar rates of growth for calves given a milk replacer in which the protein was supplied by a 70% crude protein soybean meal as for controls given whole milk. They considered that some of the poor results obtained previously with 50% crude protein soybean meals were due, in part, to trypsin inhibiters.

5.2.2.5 Enzyme adaptation. Although it has been implied that the young calf's ability to digest carbohydrates, fats and proteins is a direct function of its enzyme status at any particular age, this is an oversimplification. Tests of digestibility of nutrients not normally found in fresh milk, on the one hand, and determinations of enzyme activities, on the other, have invariably been made within a few days of introducing the test diet. In view of the known phenomenon of enzyme adaptation to substrate, it is likely that the situation would be different if the calf were given a small quantity of the test feed included in the normal diet immediately after colostrum feeding. Although Huber *et al.* (1961a) found no evidence of such adaptation in calves which from 3 days of age had been given milk containing 2.5% sucrose and 0.5% maize starch, Zerebcov and Seryh (1962) reported 10 times more proteolytic activity and twice as much amylolytic activity per unit of live weight in calves given plant food for the first time at 3 weeks of age compared with not introducing it until 7 weeks. Moreover, in 1962, Huber *et al.* demonstrated increasing lactase activity in the small intestine, in response to rising levels of dietary lactose, while Clary *et al.* (1967a) also reported greater amylase activity of the secreted protein in bile and pancreatic juices in sheep in response to higher levels of maize in the diet.

5.2.3 Physiological development of digestive capacity—solid feeds

5.2.3.1 Rumen microflora. From the first days of life small quantities of milk pass into the rumen, and on this substrate micro-organisms immediately begin to develop (Ziolecki and Briggs, 1961). On a diet of milk alone the bacterial count remains at a low level (Lengemann and Allen, 1959). Introduction of solid feeds greatly increases the number of bacteria but has no effect on the establishment of protozoa unless there is opportunity for direct contact with older calves (Bryant and Small, 1956). Even if protozoa do develop on milk feeding, their subsequent proliferation is entirely dependent on the type of dry feed that is offered. Thus Eadie (1962) reported the presence of protozoa in the second week of life in calves given milk and roughages, although they disappeared immediately the calf had free access to concentrates. In an earlier study, Eadie *et al.* (1959) showed that a mixed fauna of bacteria and ciliates developed in calves maintained on a diet of three parts roughage and one part concentrate, while in others with free access to concentrates and roughages the ciliates were absent until the calves reached 17 weeks of age. Lactobacilli were present in large numbers on both systems prior to weaning and remained at a high level when the diet was *ad libitum* concentrates; on the roughage diet, on the other hand, their numbers diminished rapidly after weaning. There was thus an inverse relationship between ciliates and lactobacilli, the latter being encouraged by diets high in concentrates and the former by roughages. The determining factor for these distinct types of microflora appears to be the rumen pH (Eadie *et al.*, 1967) which is much lower (pH 5 to 6) in calves with free access to concentrates as opposed to those given large amounts of roughages (pH > 6).

Pounden and Hibbs (1948a, b), had earlier demonstrated similar effects in calves weaned at 8–10 weeks, and argued a case for high roughage diets on the basis that they helped to establish micro-organisms characteristic of those found in adult ruminants. This hypothesis presupposes that it is an advantage later in life to have developed at the calf stage a varied microflora including ciliates. Present evidence, in fact, indicates that efficiency of digestion of forage diets by the adult is the same irrespective of whether the rearing diet is high roughage or high concentrate. A distinct disadvantage is that the kind of diet which supports a mixed microflora (including ciliates) is of lower energy concentration, because of its high roughage content, and hence supports slower growth than when there is free access to concentrates (Hibbs *et al.*, 1956).

5.2.3.2 Rumen inoculation. Although one might expect that inoculation of the rumen of the young calf with rumen contents from an adult should be beneficial, this is not supported by the bulk of the evidence from experiments of this type (see Preston, 1963b). The exception to this general rule may well occur with very high urea diets (greater than 50% of the total nitrogen), made possible by the use of molasses as the main energy source. Under such conditions there is evidence that ciliates play a positive role in increasing protein synthesis by utilization of ammonia from urea breakdown (Elías and Preston, 1969c). Since inoculation is essential for the development of protozoa (Bryant and Small, 1956), the technique may well prove useful in such feeding systems.

5.2.3.3 Fermentation. The typical products of fermentation associated with the adult ruminant are also observed in the rumen of young calves although the pattern tends to be different. On milk feeding, rumen ammonia is usually very high (50–100 m-equiv./l) and the VFA concentration low (Dinda, 1960). Lengemann and Allen (1955) reported that lactic-acid concentration was higher at 4 weeks than at later stages; similar findings were reported by Mann *et al.* (1954). On the introduction of concentrates to the diet the pattern of rumen fermentation changes markedly in that pH values fall to a very low level (about pH 5) as does rumen ammonia concentration, while there is a rapid rise in concentration of VFA (Dinda, 1960; Eadie *et al.*, 1967). Within 1 week of weaning at 4 weeks of age, Dinda (1960) reported a VFA concentration of 120 m-equiv./l which is comparable with that of rumen liquor from adults. Flatt *et al.* (1959), Lengemann and Allen (1955) and McCarthy and Kesler (1956) also reported increasing VFA concentration with age, but their maximum values were not reached until 8 weeks compared to 4 weeks in the experiment reported by Dinda (1960). This was probably an effect of the different weaning ages which were 6–8 weeks in the case of the earlier investigators.

For calves raised on pasture, Godfiey (1961b) reported that VFAs reached constant levels at 5 weeks of age, whereas pH tended to rise steadily until 17 weeks. Dinda (1960) found that the lowest values for pH were within 1 week of offering concentrates and thereafter there was also a lineal increase with age. Eadie *et al.* (1967) showed that rumen pH in calves weaned onto concentrates was lowest soon after weaning, thereafter rising steadily until an age of about 60 days. Since pH and VFA are normally inversely related (Briggs *et al.*, 1957), the implication is that either there are considerable quantities of lactic acid in the rumen of the young calf—since this has a greater influence on pH than has the VFA—or the salivary secretions, which are primarily responsible for neutralizing the rumen VFA, are imperfectly developed in the young animal. Evidence for the existence of lactic acid in the rumen of the young calf is equivocal (see Preston, 1963b) and the more likely explanation is that the production of saliva increases with age (see review by Kay, 1966). It seems that salivary gland development is not related to rumen development since lambs receiving a purified diet which encouraged the latter had only slightly more salivary gland development than lambs on a milk diet. In contrast those allowed to eat wood shavings had the same salivary gland development as lambs grazing or receiving hay (Wilson, 1963).

The proportions of the individual VFAs in the developing rumen of calves fed mainly concentrates are similar to those observed in adults given the same diets. However, there was some evidence of high concentrations of butyric acid at the expense of propionic according to Hibbs *et al.* (1954) and Flatt *et al.* (1959). There was more propionic acid in calves weaned early rather than late (Steger *et al.*, 1966).

Although the calf's ability to digest cellulose appears to be poorly developed in early life, thereafter increasing steadily (Lengemann and Allen, 1955; McCarthy and Kesler, 1956; Flatt *et al.*, 1959), there is conclusive evidence that the DM digestibility of a high-quality diet such as young grass (Preston *et al.*, 1957; Godfrey, 1961b) or concentrates (Preston and Whitelaw, 1962) is as high at 3–5 weeks of age as at 12–14 weeks.

Since the 4-week-old calf is digesting dry feed by microbial fermentation it is to be expected that the end products (VFA) are absorbed and utilized as sources of energy. VFA have been detected in the blood of week-old calves (McCarthy and Kesler, 1956) and that they are used efficiently as sources of energy was demonstrated by Martin *et al.* (1959). These latter workers fed 2-week-old calves on either whole milk, a mixture of casein, starch, glucose, hay, oil and mineral and vitamin supplements or this latter diet with the hay and starch replaced by the sodium salts of VFA in the proportions found in normally functioning ruminants. Daily gains were 0.64, 0.37 and 0.45 kg respectively, indicating that the VFA were used slightly more efficiently than starch and hay.

5.3 UTILIZATION OF ENERGY

5.3.1 General principles

There are three generalizations which tend to dominate current thinking on the nutrition of ruminants. These are:

(a) By far the greater part of the digestible DM of a particular feed disappears in the rumen leaving only some 15–30% to be hydrolysed in the abomasum and intestine by the animal's own enzymes.

(b) Ruminal fermentation releases almost all the energy-yielding components of the diet, chiefly as VFA; and that post-ruminal digestion is important only with respect to the amino-acid yielding fraction, namely bacterial protoplasm and unattacked fragments of feed protein.

(c) All dietary nitrogen sources are hydrolysed to varying degrees by bacterial enzymes in the rumen and are subsequently resynthesized into bacterial and protozoal protein prior to intestinal hydrolysis to amino acids; thus biological value of the protein has little or no significance.

We propose to examine these three hypotheses in some detail since they have considerable bearing on the formulation of feeds for intensive beef-production systems.

A special characteristic of the ruminant is the amount of energy absorbed, and therefore metabolized, in the form of VFA. The work of Blaxter and Armstrong (see Blaxter, 1966) has shown that mixtures of VFA are used with different efficiencies according to their composition (i.e. the relative proportions of acetic, propionic and butyric acids) and the productive state of the animal (maintenance, fattening, pregnancy, etc.). The lowest efficiencies (about 25%) were for fattening on feeds producing ruminal fatty acid mixtures with 70% acetic acid, and the highest (about 85%) for maintenance on feeds giving rise to proportions of less than 30% of acetic acid in rumen liquor. By comparison, glucose absorbed from the abomasum was used with 100% efficiency for maintenance and, at the worst, 71.5% for fattening.

It is thus clear that, from the practical standpoint, there are obvious advantages (a) from using diets which, on fermentation, yield the minimum amount of acetic acid; and (b) if the diet contains *soluble* carbohydrate for which the animal possesses the appropriate enzymes, to ensure that as much of this as possible passes through to the abomasum largely unfermented.

There are two major stages in feed utilization. The first of these concerns the losses in faeces, in urine, as methane and as heat, before energy-yielding components reach the tissues. The value of a feed to this point is termed its metabolizable energy (ME). The second stage concerns the efficiency of utilization of this ME for productive processes; losses at this point are manifested as heat (heat increment) and the energy either synthesized into animal tissues or secretions, or used to maintain essential metabolic processes, is termed net energy (NE).

The various factors which influence either or both these stages are (a) the level and method of feeding, (b) the chemical and physical nature of the feed, (c) the nature of the productive processes (muscle growth, fat deposition, foetal development, etc.) and (d) the age and body composition of the animal.

5.3.2 Digestion

5.3.2.1 Ruminal digestion. The soluble carbohydrates, i.e. starch and sugars, are fermented mainly to propionic acid, some lactic acid may be formed and also acids higher than C_4. Lactic acid itself is almost immediately converted to propionic acid. The more complex carbohydrates, including cellulose and hemicellulose, yield predominately acetic acid, no lactic acid and, rarely, acids higher than C_4.

Fermentation of protein gives rise to peptides, amino acids, ammonia, VFA and carbon dioxide; in particular there is production of branched-chain acids (El Shazly, 1952a, b). Synthesis of microbial protein takes place concomitantly with hydrolysis of the feed protein.

Fats are first hydrolysed to glycerol and their constituent fatty acids. The glycerol is fermented to propionic acid while unsaturated fatty acids may be hydrogenated. There is probably little degradation of the fatty-acid chains while in the rumen and absorption is thought to take place mostly from the intestine. Roberts and McKirdy (1964) reported that digestibility of sunflower seed oil (which is highly unsaturated) was significantly less than either animal tallow or rapeseed oils. Faecal soap excretion was highest with sunflower and least with tallow, indicating that glycerides containing large quantities of unsaturated fatty acids were preferentially complexed as soaps and thus rendered relatively unavailable for absorption.

5.3.2.2 Post-ruminal digestion. The inability of the very young calf to digest starch and even disacharides, other then lactose, has already been pointed out (§ 5.2.2.2). Dollar and Porter (1957) considered that this was due to an almost complete lack of sucrase, maltase and amylase in early life, but that there was evidence for development of these enzymes in calves that were 10–12 weeks old. An earlier study by Larsen *et al.* (1956) with calves of 9–12 months of age implied that while maltose was readily hydrolysed and absorbed there was no evidence for digestion of starch or maize carbohydrate; the experiment was, however, carried out under somewhat abnormal physiological conditions since the various carbohydrates were administered as slurries directly into the omasoabomasal orifice and there was profuse diarrhoea throughout the 2 days when the test diets were given. These authors also showed that, while post-ruminal administration of glucose and maltose gave rise to significant increases in the levels of blood sugar, there were no such effects from giving starch; similar findings were reported by Huber *et al.* (1961b).

These latter workers (Huber *et al.*, 1967) subsequently were able to detect increases in blood glucose in 8-month-old steers as a result of feeding starch by a nipple pail, although the extent of the response and the average growth rate of the calves was much less than when lactose was given as the carbohydrate source. Overall starch digestibility (dietary starch intake was 0.84 kg per 100 kg live weight daily) was 60%. The significance of change in blood glucose as an indicator of post-ruminal carbohydrate digestion was questioned by Wright *et al.* (1966) who found that sheep could utilize 0.5 g of glucose per kg live weight per hour, (1.2 kg per 100 kg live weight per day), from post-ruminal degradation and absorption of carbohydrate, without a rise in blood glucose. It was left to Henschel *et al.* (1963), estimating directly the enzyme activity of the mucosa lining the intestine, to prove conclusively that starch digestion does take place in the small intestine of ruminants.

All these investigations relating to post-ruminal utilization of carbohydrate were initiated with the major objective of simplifying the formulation of milk replacers for young ruminants being fed on liquid diets. However, there has been a revival of interest in the subject as a result of the development of all-concentrate feeding systems in which it is quite customary for 60% of the diet to be present in the form of starch. With high level feeding, particularly in the absence of long roughage, considerable quantities of starch can escape from the rumen without fermentation and hence the degree and efficiency of carbohydrate utilization in the intestinal tract posterior to the rumen becomes of considerable significance.

The most important work in this area has been carried out by a group of workers at the University of Kentucky. The importance of efficient intestinal digestion of starch was pointed out by Karr *et al.* (1966). They fed steers of 360 kg live weight with 5 kg daily of rations containing 20, 40, 60 or 80% of ground maize and found that the proportion of the dietary starch digested in the rumen rose from 64 to 73 as the maize content increased from 20 to 40% thereafter decreasing to 67 and 63% when the maize supplied 60 and then 80% of the total diet. The amount of starch digested and absorbed from the small intestine rose accordingly from 331 to 463, 609 and 624 g; digestion in the large intestine was 14, 62, 129 and 296 g respectively. In another experiment with the same diets the percentage of starch digested in the rumen fell progressively from 84% to 72, 64 and 62 as the dietary maize content was increased. It can be computed from these data that up to 30% of dietary starch reached the small intestine, thus emphasizing the need for information on factors which affect post-ruminal digestion of this carbohydrate.

The fact that the above authors recorded a reduced efficiency of starch digestion in the small intestine at the highest level of intake led them to suggest that amylolytic activity in this part of the gut might be inadequate. Clary *et al.* (1966) therefore studied the enzyme activity of pancreatic homogenates from 113 steers given three different rations. Amylase activity, expressed as amount of starch digested per unit of enzyme protein, was 588 $\pm$ 53 for steers on unsupplemented pasture compared with 827 $\pm$ 61 for similar animals given an all-concentrate diet. These workers also examined the variation in enzyme activity on diets of varying maize content (Clary *et al.*, 1967a), and found that the relative amylase activity increased as the amount of starch in the diet rose and there were commensurate changes in the glucose concentration of jugular blood. They were not able to determine accurately the time required for complete adaptation to a high grain diet, but considered that it was longer than had been reported for rats.

The amylases from cattle and swine had similar overall effects on starch from potatoes, maize, rice and protozoa; however, there was a suggestion that ruminant amylases were more effective than those of swine in breaking down starch fragments, although less so in attacking intact starch molecules (Clary *et al.*, 1967b). Similar findings were observed in sheep by Tucker *et al.* (1966) regarding passage of starch from the rumen and its subsequent digestion in the intestine.

In contrast with these US findings, work at the University of Newcastle (Armstrong *et al.*, 1967) showed that while in sheep post-ruminal digestion accounted for 21 rising to 30% of the total DE for diets of all-hay and hay plus barley (34:66), only 7–9% of the dietary starch passed through to the abomasum. Topps *et al.* (1968) also found that only 5% of the starch from an all-concentrate barley diet given to 6-month-old steers passed through to the abomasum. The reasons for the discrepancies between these various groups of workers are not known but may be related to the type of carbohydrate used, i.e. maize as opposed to barley or, alternatively, the method of feeding.

It seems to us that the logical extension of these experiments is to investigate the effect of *ad libitum* feeding of an all-concentrate diet, for it is known that under these conditions the amount of material passing from the rumen unfermented is greater than when a restricted pattern of twice daily feeding is employed (Blaxter, 1966).

Although the available evidence would suggest that the intestinal enzymes digest starch less efficiently when they are presented with large rather than small quantities, there is no doubt that the total amount utilized by this route increases with the amount of starch consumed daily (Little *et al.*, 1968b); moreover, what cannot be digested in the small intestine appears to be almost completely utilized subsequently (probably by fermentation) in the large intestine so that the overall starch digestibility from mouth to rectum is effectively 100% (Karr *et al.*, 1966).

Thus the overall effect of presenting the animal with increasing quantities of starch, at least in a solid diet, is a net gain in terms of the amount of energy passing into the tissues as glucose. In contrast the work of Huber *et al.* (1967) indicates that such a high utilization may not be possible when the starch is given in a liquid diet at fairly high levels (0.8 kg per 100 kg live weight). They found the overall digestibility to be about 60% as did Little *et al.* (1968b) when they also bypassed the rumen by infusing starch (0.16 kg per 100 kg live weight) directly into the abomasum. It is thus possible that subjecting the starch to some degree of fermentative action in the rumen is a prerequisite to its efficient digestion in the intestine. Evidence for this effect is discussed in more detail in § 5.3.6.

5.3.3 Factors affecting metabolizable energy

5.3.3.1 Nature of the feed. The amount of energy lost in the faeces is probably the most important factor determining the nutritive value of feeds. The loss is almost a direct function of the content of structural carbohydrates—lignin, cellulose and hemicellulose—and the levels of these latter components either singly (Walker and Hepburn, 1955) or in composite form as crude fibre have been shown to be reasonably good indices of apparent digestibility.

As would be expected, diets deficient in essential nutrients are less well digested than those properly balanced, although this applies, in the main, to diets high in structural carbohydrates where digestion depends on rumen microbial fermentation. Thus, adding urea to a poor quality barley–straw diet encouraged greater microbial activity and hence greater digestibility (Balch and Campling, 1962). Similar mechanisms, operating in a reverse direction, account for the depressing effect on digestibility of certain fats and oils (Swift *et al.*, 1947), although, as with nitrogen, the effect is most pronounced with diets high in forages. According to Bohman and Lesperance (1962) the major effect of fat was to depress the digestibility of fibre while the digestibility of ether extract and the soluble carbohydrates fraction was actually increased. This suggests that fat should only be used in high concentrate rations.

The depressing effect of soluble carbohydrates on cellulose digestibility is well established (El Shazly *et al.*, 1961), but according to McCullough (1968) both the source of roughage and of carbohydrate are important factors. Thus hay was superior to maize silage and beet pulp better than flaked maize for maintaining cellulose digestibility.

According to Perkins and Luther (1967) rumen protozoa are important for maximum digestibility on high concentrate diets but less so on high forage diets. They reported an 8% increase in DM digestibility on the former compared with only 5% on the low energy diets, due to the presence of protozoa. For protein the figures were 7 and 4% respectively.

Although in forage-based diets energy losses as methane tend to increase slightly with increase in apparent digestibility, this is not true with diets high in concentrates for which methane losses are minimal (Blaxter, 1966). The addition to the diet of certain unsaturated fatty acids has also been shown to considerably reduce losses of energy by this route (Czerkawski *et al.*, 1966) and offers promise as a positive means of increasing efficiency of energy utilization.

The major feed ingredient which affects loss of energy in urine is protein and there is a direct relation between the nitrogen content of the diet and ensuing energy loss (Martin and Blaxter, 1961), due mainly to the need to excrete the excess nitrogen, usually as energy-containing urea. Urine energy also decreases with reducing dietary roughage (Blaxter, 1966).

Heat losses due to the process of digestion are inevitably greater in ruminants than in simple stomached animals due to the added cost of microbial fermentation. It is also likely that losses are greater when more fibrous feeds are given, particularly if these are in the long state. It is obvious that the more of the soluble carbohydrate that passes undigested from the rumen, the less will be the heat loss of fermentation.

5.3.3.2 Level and method of feeding. Faecal losses are least at the maintenance level of feeding and increase with the amount of feed given above maintenance (Flatt *et al.*, 1967; Van Es and Nijkamp, 1967); the increased loss with feeding level is also relatively greater for feeds of low as opposed to high digestibility (Blaxter, 1961). In contrast, methane losses decline with increase in feeding level (Blaxter, 1961; Van Es and Nijkamp, 1967) as do, although to a smaller extent, losses of energy in urine (Reid, 1956; Armstrong, 1964; Flatt *et al.*, 1967). The combined effects of feeding level on ME have been summarized as

$$Y = 9.5 - 0.11X,$$

where Y is the percentage depression of ME on increasing feed intake fiom maintenance to twice maintenance, and X is ME as a percentage of gross energy at maintenance (ARC, 1965). This equation shows that the depression of ME due to feeding level is only considerable with feeds of poor quality. Blaxter (1966) has reasoned that the depression with poor quality (*ipso facto* fibrous) feeds is a result of their passing too quickly out of the rumen (due to the stimulus of greater feed intake) before microbial digestion has been completed. For although some fibre digestion occurs in the large intestine, the efficiency of the process in that part of the tract is only some 50% of what is achieved in the rumen (Putnam and Davis, 1965). This effect has much less significance in diets of high quality due to their greater content of soluble carbohydrates which can be hydrolysed by intestinal enzymes.

5.3.4 Use of ME for productive processes

5.3.4.1 General considerations. The importance to the ruminant of the energy-yielding products of microbial fermentation (the VFA) has been known since the

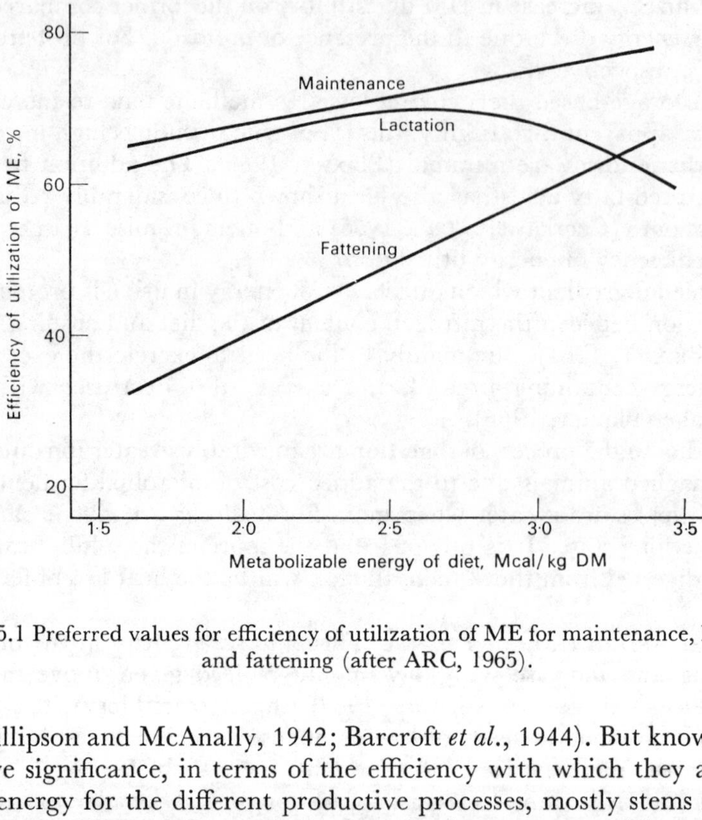

Fig. 5.1 Preferred values for efficiency of utilization of ME for maintenance, lactation and fattening (after ARC, 1965).

1940's (Phillipson and McAnally, 1942; Barcroft *et al.*, 1944). But knowledge of their quantitative significance, in terms of the efficiency with which they are utilized as sources of energy for the different productive processes, mostly stems from research carried out at the Hannah Research Institute by Armstrong and Blaxter (see Blaxter, 1966). Unfortunately the vast amount of work carried out in this area has tended to overshadow consideration of the energetic contribution which can be made by products of abomasal and intestinal digestion; on certain diets this may not be inconsiderable.

The ME of high concentrate diets is always used more efficiently than the ME of poor-quality diets, but the order of the difference varies with the nature of the productive process (Fig. 5.1). For maintenance the relative superiority of high (3.4 Mcal ME/kg DM) over low (1.6 Mcal ME/kg DM) energy feeds is only some 18% compared with 100% when the need is for fat deposition. This fact alone justifies the stratification of natural resources, whereby poor quality feeds are used for beef cows (which are fed at maintenance or sub-maintenance most of their lives and thus differentiate only slightly between high and low energy feeds), while those of high quality are reserved for growth and fattening where the resultant improvement in efficiency is so much greater.

5.3.4.2 Maintenance, pregnancy and lactation. It has already been pointed out that the efficiency of utilization of the ME of the diet for maintenance increases with the metabolizability of the diet. The equation relating these two variables was

$$Y = 66.2 + 0.31X,$$

where Y is the efficiency of utilization of ME at maintenance (%) and X the percentage of the gross energy metabolized (Blaxter and Wainman, 1964).

The fasting heat production of pregnant cows is higher than in non-pregnant animals of the same weight (Ritzman and Benedict, 1938). Van Es (1961) has also shown that heat production in late pregnancy rises at a greater rate than expected for a non-pregnant animal retaining the same amount of energy. As proposed by ARC (1965) it is most unlikely that the greater heat production represents a reduced efficiency for the synthesis of new tissues within the uterus, and that an increased maternal maintenance cost is a more likely explanation. Neville and McCullough (1968) have also calculated that the maintenance requirement of a lactating cow is 36–58% higher than in a dry cow of the same live weight. This hypothesis of a maintenance cost which varies with the nature of the productive process has been discussed by Preston *et al.* (1969c) and is of considerable significance particularly in formulation of energy requirements.

The efficiency of ME utilization for lactation is relatively high at about 70%. Lower values are only obtained in the case of extreme diets such as poor quality roughage or all-concentrates.

5.3.4.3 Exercise and maintenance of body temperature. It is considered that the efficiency with which ME is used for muscular work is the same as for maintenance (ARC, 1965) and that ME is used with an efficiency of 100% for maintaining body temperature (Graham *et al.*, 1959a).

5.3.4.4 Growth and fattening. Almost all the work carried out on energy utilization for growth has been specifically with respect to fat synthesis. This has shown conclusively that increasing the amount of concentrate in the diet increases the efficiency of ME utilization. Since high concentrate diets also give rise to a rumen fermentation characterized by low proportions of acetic acid, this has been taken to corroborate acid infusion studies which showed that mixtures low in acetic acid induced a smaller heat increment than mixtures high in this acid. There is, however, the possibility that some of the increased efficiency results from increased amounts of energy being presented to the animal as glucose rather than as fatty acid, for calorimetric studies do not differentiate between the relative contributions of the two.

The high efficiency with which glucose absorbed from the abomasum is used for fattening has already been mentioned. It is therefore to be expected that the efficiency with which dietary ME is used by young calves given liquid diets should be high. Values quoted for the efficiency of utilization of the ME in whole milk were 85%

(Blaxter, 1952) and 77 and 82% (González-Jiménez and Blaxter, 1962); for milk replacers based on dried skim-milk powder and fat, Van Es and Nijkamp (1967) found the efficiency for gain to be 69%.

There appear to be no data on the efficiency of growth in weaned calves that are laying down tissues high in protein content. Moreover, it has not so far been possible to estimate the efficiency with which ME is used for protein synthesis since lipogenesis occurs simultaneously. Thus the fat content of body-weight gain in veal calves was found to be between 60 and 75% and only fell to 50% when the level of feeding was reduced from 2.5 to 1.5 times the maintenance requirement (Van Es and Nijkamp, 1967).

There is some evidence that even when ME intake is the same, diets which on fermentation give rise to VFA mixtures high in propionic acid support a lower rate of nitrogen retention than diets which produce more acetic acid. This is shown circumstantially by the fact that at the same live weight there is more fat and less protein in the body of animals fed diets of high rather than low energy content. Thus Weiss *et al.* (1967) gave either 100% alfalfa (daily DE intake 22.6 Mcal) or 57.6% alfalfa plus maize, soybean meal and urea (daily DE intake 22.1 Mcal) to fattening steers starting at 327 and finishing at 452 kg live weight. The acetic propionic ratios were 3.4:1 and 2.8:1 and the protein contents of the carcass 16.1 and 15.7% respectively. Rook *et al.* (1963) also observed that infusing acetic acid into the rumen of growing heifers promoted a greater nitrogen retention than did the infusion of propionic acid.

A close examination of the work involving direct administration of fatty acids or their salts shows that the marked differences between acetic and propionic acids were based on VFA infusions as a result of which ruminal acetic acid concentration was either some 75 or 25% of the total VFA. Such situations represent the extremes of the normal range and are rarely encountered with mixed diets. For example, on all-roughage diets, acetic acid accounted for 65% of total VFA (Weiss *et al.*, 1967) and 66–73% (Cook and Miller, 1965; Balch and Rowland, 1957). There are few comparative studies on the effect of VFA infusions when the variation in molar concentration of acetic acid in rumen liquor was within the more normal range of 45–65%.

The results from feeding trials are equivocal. Different ratios of VFA salts were fed to lambs by Essig *et al.* (1959) without apparent effects on rate of gain, while Ørskov and Allen (1966b) found no significant differences in the efficiency with which acetic, propionic or butyric acids, added singly as the calcium and sodium salts to a hay diet, promoted gains in live weight, empty body weight and carcass weight. There appeared to be equal efficiency of utilization of the gross energy of the VFA and of the ME of a concentrate feed mixture used as control. Significant responses in carcass weight gain were observed by Hovell (1964) when he supplemented the basal diet of lambs with 377 kcal of the calcium salt of either acetate or proprionate, but there were no differences between them.

Johnson *et al.* (1965) made an extensive analysis of rumen VFA ratios in 78 animals given diets of different ME content and considered that differences in proportions of rumen fermentation end products did not account for differences in animal performance. According to Kromann and Meyer (1966)—who varied dietary energy content, physical form and buffers—animal response was related to energy intake and not to differences in rumen metabolism. Hayer *et al.* (1961) also observed that the rate of live weight gain and feed efficiency were the same on all-concentrate diets based on dry-rolled barley or steam-rolled barley even though the proportion of propionic acid to acetic acid was higher on the dry-rolled diet.

In contrast to the effect that level of feeding has on the metabolizability of the diet, it appears that it does not affect the efficiency with which ME is used for energy retention (Blaxter and Wainman, 1961b; Nehring *et al.*, 1961). Animal age also seems to be unimportant since Blaxter *et al.* (1966) showed that there were no differences between calves of 15 and 81 weeks of age in the efficiency with which ME was used for lipogenesis. Not unnaturally, nitrogen retention was more efficient in the younger animals.

From the above evidence it is clear that the composition of the diet has a profound effect on the efficiency with which ME is used to synthesize protein and fatty tissue. Desirable factors are clearly those which lead to the rapid passage out of the rumen (prior to being fermented) of those soluble carbohydrates for which the animal already possesses the appropriate enzymes. The evidence for encouraging a type of rumen fermentation which gives the narrowest possible ratio of acetic to propionic acid is, however, equivocal. One difficulty is with the units in which efficiency is measured. If the prime interest is the conversion of dietary ME into meat protein it is probable that the required conditions are different from those favouring conversion of ME into carcass calories *per se*. Certainly fatty-acid mixtures rich in propionic acid promote the most efficient fattening; but it may be that if lean carcasses are desired then the rumen fermentation should be characterized by having greater quantities of acetic acid provided this can be achieved without reduction in the overall metabolizability of the diet.

In any event it is of considerable importance to understand the dietary effects which determine the relative proportions of VFA likely to be produced as well as the extent of ruminal as opposed to post-ruminal digestion.

5.3.5 Factors affecting VFA ratios

5.3.5.1 PROTEIN. When protein passes into the rumen it is fermented to an extent which depends on the composition of the basic diet and the level of feeding. At maintenance most is probably fermented. Thus Martin and Blaxter (1961) found the efficiency which with the ME of casein was used for this purpose was some 5% less than for the VFA. For fattening, casein was used with an efficiency of 50%—more than would be expected from the rumen VFA pattern (% acetic acid was 60) which was considered to be due to the beneficial effects of amino acids among the absorbed products of digestion, particularly as efficiency was even higher (65%) when the casein was infused directly into the abomasum.

The heat increment response to increasing levels of dietary protein was found by Cock *et al.* (1967) in sheep to be curvilinear with the highest values at around 16% crude protein in DM. With urea diets the heat increment was significantly lower for the same nitrogen content. This is in agreement with the earlier findings of Colobos *et al.* (1965).

5.3.5.2 FAT. Early work in Maryland (Ensor *et al.*, 1959; Shaw *et al.*, 1960) first demonstrated the beneficial effect of linseed oil and specifically linolenic acid on both the pattern of rumen fermentation (supplementation led to a narrower acetic propionic ratio) and better overall efficiency of feed utilization. Addition of cod-liver oil to mixed diets was also found to increase propionic at the expense of acetic acid (Broster *et al.*, 1965). Comprehensive studies of the effects of a wide range of aliphatic compounds showed that saturated as well as unsaturated long-chain fatty acids depressed methane production. There was a tendency with the saturated acids for the depression of methane production (up to 67.5 kcal reduction per 100 kcal of added acid) to be negated by a reduced overall digestibility of the diet (Blaxter and Czerkawski, 1966).

5.3.5.3 Concentrates/roughage ratio. It is established that increasing the proportion of concentrates (chiefly cereal grains) in the diet results in a narrowing of the acetic/propionic ratio (Balch and Rowland, 1957; Woods and Rhodes, 1962; Donefer *et al.*, 1963; Weiss *et al.*, 1967). There are, however, exceptions to this general rule since Topps *et al.* (1966) found no significant differences in VFA composition when the roughage varied from 0 to 30% of a maize diet. There was, in fact, a tendency for propionic acid to increase with roughage content up to 20%. The addition of low quantities (3%) of roughage (either oyster shell or hay) had no effect on VFA ratios according to Larson *et al.* (1968b), and at least 10% of hay was needed to bring about any significant alteration.

5.3.5.4 Miscellaneous effects. Inoculating lambs on a 50 concentrate/50 roughage diet with protozoa led to a reduction in rumen pH and a narrower acetic/propionic ratio (Christiansen *et al.*, 1965). Similar results were obtained by Luther *et al.* (1966) for both high and low roughage diets; conversely, defaunation led to widening of the ratio (Perkins and Luther, 1967) although only on high energy diets. These effects of protozoa were also manifested *in vitro* (Yoder *et al.*, 1966).

Frequent feeding led to narrower acetic propionic ratios than did twice daily feeding of mixed diets (Knox and Ward, 1961) and also to higher concentrations of protozoa (Putnam *et al.*, 1961).

Animals maintained in psychrometric chambers for 12 weeks at 32°C were found by Weldy *et al.* (1962) to have narrower acetic/propionic ratios than comparable animals kept at 21°C.

5.3.6 Feed processing

5.3.6.1 Pelleting. The effect of pelleting on rumen fermentation appears to depend on the kind of ration being used. On all-roughage diets the main effect is to reduce the retention time in the rumen (Blaxter, 1966). However there appears to be little or no change in the pattern of fermentation *per se*; when concentrates are combined with the roughage, pelleting leads to a narrowing of the acetic/propionic ratio (Woods and Luther, 1962; Luther and Trenkle, 1967). According to the latter workers, rumen micro-organisms do not distinguish the effects of pelleting but only respond to changes in the proportion of soluble carbohydrates. Thus the reduced acetic/propionic ratio through pelleting a mixed diet may well result from a more rapid passage of the roughage fraction (due to reduced particle size) which would effectively raise the concentrate/roughage ratio in the rumen. The heat generated in the pelleting process may also increase the susceptibility of the concentrate fraction to microbial attack. Of greater interest in the context of intensive beef production is the effect of moist heat treatment and ensiling.

5.3.6.2 MOIST HEAT TREATMENT. The stimulation for the considerable amount of research carried out in this area in the 1960's arose from observations by workers in Arizona that animal performance was almost always superior on barley than on sorghum despite the former's higher fibre content and lower apparent ME value as determined by proximate analysis. This difference was found to be due primarily to lower digestibility of the sorghum. Thus, in comparative trials with the two cereals, barley was found to have a significantly higher digestibility of DM, crude protein, NFE and starch (Saba *et al.*, 1964); the difference in starch digestibility was 10% in favour of barley while TDN values were calculated from the digestibility coefficients to be 75 and 85 for sorghum and barley respectively.

The procedure of moist heat cooking followed by flat flaking, developed by Hale and his associates in Arizona to improve the feeding value of sorghum, is described in § 9.4.4. Here we are concerned with the causal factors of the significant improvement in feed utilization efficiency which is generally credited to the moist heat-flaking technique.

It was shown by Hale *et al.* (1965) that a major effect of the steam-processing procedure was to raise digestibility coefficients for DM, NFE and GE as compared with dry rolling, while Husted *et al.* (1966) subsequently reported that both the flaking and the moist heat treatment contributed towards the improvement in utilization. They compared dry rolling, steam processing followed by flaking or cutting with a decorticator, and simple soaking in water followed by cutting. The steam processing was moist steam for 20 min and the cutting was done in such a way as to break the grain into 6–10 pieces with a minimum of pressure. Digestible energy was 75.5 with steam processing and flaking and only 63–65 for the remaining treatments; in particular, digestibility of the NFE component was 84 for steaming and flaking compared with only 73 for steaming followed by cutting which latter was, in fact, slightly worse than the value (75) obtained with simple soaking in water and cutting. These results showed that the flaking process was the major factor in securing a higher digestibility but that soaking with water could also lead to some improvement in utilization. That the commercially developed system of pressure cooking (steam under a pressure of about 1.0 kg/cm^2 for 1–2 min) had essentially the same effects as the low pressure/extended time method was shown by comparative data for the two systems. Thus DM digestibilities were 69, 76 and 75 for sorghum which had been dry-rolled, steam-treated at atmospheric pressure for 30 min or pressure-cooked (Mehen *et al.*, 1966). Fine grinding also appeared to raise digestibility slightly compared with dry rolling; however, this is not a desirable method under actual conditions of feedlot fattening (§ 9.3.1).

It must be stressed that steam cooking can also have deleterious effects. Thus in almost all reports, protein digestibility was reduced, e.g. from 59 to 56 with the low pressure system and to 53 with pressure cooking (Mehen *et al.*, 1966). Similar results were previously reported by Trei *et al.* (1964). Depressions of this order are not serious and are more than compensated for by improved energy availability. On the other hand, if the degree of heat treatment is excessive the net result on animal performance can be negative (Riley *et al.*, 1965). According to Ward and Morrill (1966), protein digestibility was reduced by half when sorghum grain was processed by a combination of heat, moisture and pressure to the point of complete gelatinization of the starch; under these conditions there was also a reduction in the digestibility of the GE and no improvement in NFE digestibility which is the fraction usually most enhanced by processing. Similar effects were obtained in maize by Perry and Mudd (1967) when digestibility fell from 81 to 74 as the degree of gelatinization rose from 0 to 100%.

In vitro techniques have also contributed valuable information with respect to differences between barley and sorghum and the effect of processing. Starch digestion *in vitro*, using 0.05% pancreatin as enzyme, was 18.2 ± 1.6 for 11 samples of sorghum and 24.3 ± 2.0 for 8 of barley. Pressure cooking (2.8 kg/cm² for 1 min) or low pressure steam for 30 min—without rolling—significantly decreased *in vitro* starch digestibility of both grains. Increasing the pressure brought about significant improvement; e.g. 1.4 kg/cm² gave 14.9, 2.8 kg/cm² 17.3, 4.2 kg/cm² 24.7 and 5.6 kg/cm² 32.1. Comparable values for untreated and low pressure steam were 18.0 and 13.8 respectively (Osman *et al.*, 1966). These workers also reported that flaking after steaming or pressure cooking significantly increased *in vitro* digestion and that the rise was proportional to the flatness of the flake; values were 17.8 for untreated, 16 for steam processing with poor rolling and 45.6 when rolling was carried out with little tolerance so that an extremely flat flake was produced.

The importance of flaking was further demonstrated in a series of studies in which *in vitro* digestibilities with and without flaking were 10 and 51, 29 and 52, 38 and 57, and 45 and 60 for cooking at pressures of 2.8, 4.2, 5.6 and 7.0 kg/cm² respectively. Similar results were obtained with barley (Frederick *et al.*, 1968). These studies, together with those of Trei *et al.* (1966) and Theurer *et al.* (1967), show that heat, moisture and pressure are all involved in increasing the susceptibility of cereal starch to enzyme attack.

Information regarding effects of moist heat and pressure treatment of grains on rumen fermentation is equivocal. It has been considered that such processing tends to narrow acetic/propionic ratios (Erwin, 1966) and certainly, when the degree of gelatinization of maize starch exceeded 60%, there was an increase in propionic acid and also in lactic acid in one study (Wilson and Woods, 1967). On the other hand, Theurer *et al.* (1967) found that molar percentages of the VFA were not markedly affected by steam processing and flaking while Johnson *et al.* (1968) reported that acetic/propionic ratios were extremely variable and not related to processing method, the range of values being from 1.9 to 2.5.

The experiment carried out by Johnson *et al.* (1968) has probably been the most valuable in terms of understanding the significance of the various factors contributing to improved feed efficiency from steam processing. They prepared flaked maize by steaming the grain for approximately 12 min at a chamber temperature of 93°C so that moisture content increased from 12.5 to 17.5%; the hot wet maize was then dropped onto spring tensioned rollers set at near zero tolerance. A 5% increase in DM digestibility was reported as a result of this technique, but a more important observation was that the mean retention time in the digestive tract was only 29 hr for the flaked maize compared with 38 hr when the grain was merely cracked in the absence of heat treatment; steam processing also decreased the amount of energy lost as methane.

It is clear that effects on digestibility did not account for all the increased feed efficiency since the estimated increase in energy retention due to processing was some 6–10% compared with an improvement in digestibility of only 4–6%. As there were no consistent changes in the VFA pattern, our interpretation is that at least a part of the improved utilization arose through more of the starch being digested enzymically in the intestine, as a result of the 30% greater rate of passage (§ 5.3.2.2). Johnson *et al.* (1968) considered that the derangement of the molecules within the starch granules brought about by heat treatment was probably responsible for the observed increase in water uptake, the resulting lower specific gravity and, in turn, more rapid rate of passage of digesta. They did not observe these effects in maize exposed to the same treatment, but cracked rather than rolled, and therefore concluded that the derangement must have occurred when the hot wet maize was flattened by the rollers.

Although the above study was carried out with maize it seems to us very likely that the better feed utilization obtained by steam processing and flaking of sorghum also results from a combination of improved overall digestibility together with a greater utilization of starch posterior to the rumen with attendant increases in efficiency of utilization of absorbed energy as has been described earlier.

5.3.6.3 Ensiling of high moisture grain. It is known that the ensiling of grain, harvested early at a high moisture content or after reconstitution to a moisture content of some 30%, brings about improvements in animal performance commensurate with, if not slightly greater than, those obtained as a result of steam processing and flaking (§ 9.4.5). It appears that the overall effects of both processes are similar. Thus Hale *et al.* (1963) and Michelena and Preston (1968) noted that ensiling reconstituted sorghum for 21 days in sealed towers brought about an improvement in *in vivo* digestibility by the nylon-bag technique, while McGinty *et al.* (1967) reported DM digestibilities of 54.5 and 83.1 for dry and ensiled reconstituted sorghum respectively. In contrast to steam processing, ensiling does not lead to a reduction in protein digestibility; in fact in the data of McGinty *et al.* (1967) the digestibility coefficients for protein were 44.5 and 61.7 for the dry and reconstituted products respectively. Buchanan-Smith *et al.* (1968) and McLaren and Matsushima (1968) also found that DM and GE digestibilities were significantly increased in reconstituted as opposed to dry grain; this was equally true in maize and sorghum. Evidence for derangement of the molecules in the starch granule as a result of this method of processing was given by Florence *et al.* (1968). They noted non-distinct poorly defined cell walls in starch granules which they considered to be evidence of breakdown of the proteinaceous matrix normally surrounding the starch granule. Although specific data are lacking with respect to rate-of-passage studies on ensiled high moisture grain, it seems very likely that the same combination of factors is responsible for its better utilization as was suggested in the case of grain processed by moisture, heat and pressure.

5.4 FACTORS CONTROLLING FEED INTAKE

Experimental models describing the pattern of feed intake in ruminants and the major ration parameters which determine them have been described by Montgomery and Baumgardt (1965), Conrad (1966) and Waldo (1967). All these workers arrived at the same conclusion that improvements in nutritive value of the diet bring about a linear increase in net energy intake up to a maximum corresponding usually to a diet of some 70% digestibility. Beyond this point further increases in dietary digestibility (due to declining roughage content) progressively reduce DM intake while net energy consumption, by virtue of the increasing nutritive value of the ration, tends to remain relatively constant. The typical model proposed by Montgomery and Baumgardt (1965) is shown in Fig. 5.2.

It is established that voluntary intake during the first phase (high roughage diets) is mainly determined by the rate of passage of digesta from the rumen (Blaxter *et al.*,

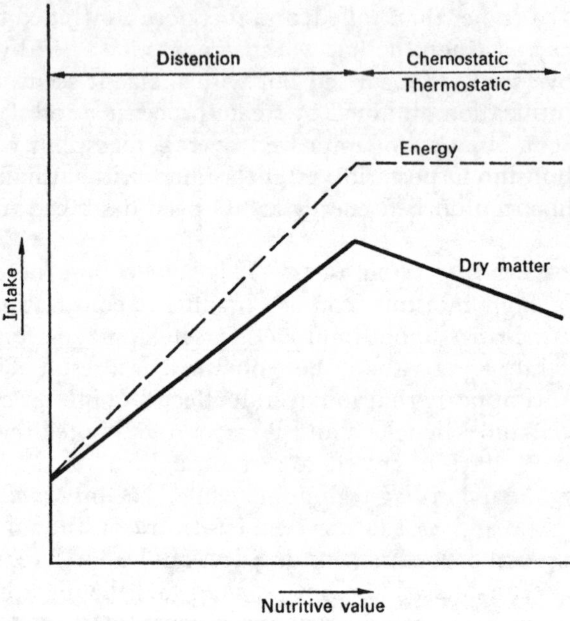

FIG. 5.2 Proposed relationships in the regulation of feed intake in ruminants (from Montgomery and Baumgard, 1965).

1961; Campling *et al.*, 1961) and by factors which limit the distension of that organ such as fat deposits (Tayler, 1959) or the presence of a foetus (Reid, 1961). Beyond the point of inflection the factors determining satiety are considered to be thermostatic or chemostatic in origin and hence a function of the physiological state of the animal. Thus increases in voluntary intake (of the same diet) were noted in sheep which changed from nursing one lamb to nursing two lambs (Davies, 1962), while cows ate more in early than in late lactation due to the more rapid removal of energy from the body (as milk) and the animal's attempt to maintain energy equilibrium (Aitken and Preston, 1964). In a similar way, animals which were in lean condition consumed more than fat animals of the same weight (Bowers, 1968).

While the various physical factors determining feed intake on low- to moderate-quality rations have been fairly adequately defined (see Balch and Campling, 1962), it was only in the mid-1960's that evidence became available concerning feed intake on high concentrate diets. The implication from the often criticized experiment of Dowden and Jacobson (1960), that blood levels of the VFA played a vital role in controlling feed intake on such diets, was an important starting point for a large number of investigations which subsequently studied in more detail the effect of individual VFA as well as associated factors such as rumen pH and buffering capacity. It has since been conclusively shown (Rook *et al.*, 1963; Montgomery *et al.*, 1963; Simkins *et al.*,1965; Ulyatt, 1965; Baile and Pfander, 1966; Egan, 1966) that infusions of acetic acid at physiological levels cause depressions of feed intake. Propionic acid and butyric acid have also been observed to exert similar effects although usually not until somewhat abnormally high levels were used (Ulyatt, 1965). Egan (1966) also found that propionic acid depressed intake less than did acetic acid. The findings of Ulyatt substantiate the pivotal role of acetic acid in that the intake depressions caused by its infusion was greater on a poor- than a high-quality diet. He pointed out that since acetate metabolism is more rapid in animals on a high than a low plane of nutrition (Annison *et al.*, 1963), effects of infusion would be expected to be less pronounced on the former. Ulyatt's other finding, that infusion of low levels of propionic acid in sheep on a poor-quality diet led to an actual increase in feed intake, is also consistent with the above hypothesis, as in such a situation the effect would be to increase the rate of metabolism and hence removal of the circulating acetic acid. Although Montgomery *et al.* (1963) could find no effect of acid infusion on blood constituents, particularly pH and total carbon dioxide, the intake-restricting action of acetate is undoubtedly linked to its behaviour as a free acid, since infusion of sodium acetate, or partially neutralized acetic acid, had no significant effect on intake, and the small depression caused was much less than had been obtained previously with acetic acid (Montgomery *et al.*, 1963).

In contrast to the situation with high roughage diets, physical factors such as dietary density and presence of inert bulky material had little or no effect on ME intake when highly digestible rations were given (Carr and Jacobson, 1962; Bolin *et al.*, 1967).

The indirect role of rumen pH in intake control has been discussed by Bhattacharya and Warner (1968). They had earlier shown that lowering rumen pH by infusion of inorganic acids was equally as effective as administering acetic acid (Battacharya and Warner, 1967). In their 1968 paper they reported that administering alkalis (sodium carbonate and bicarbonate and calcium hydroxide) raised rumen pH which in turn led to increases in feed intake. They postulated that the observed reductions in blood VFA concentration were responsible for the greater intakes and that this situation arose through the well known effect of increased rumen pH acting to reduce the rate of VFA absorption from the rumen (Stevens and Stettler, 1966). The implication was not that overall absorption of VFA was reduced by feeding alkali; on the contrary, rumen concentrations and almost certainly rates of production were higher, but that absorption was over a more extended period. The fact that increasing frequency of feeding leads to greater intake is another manifestation of the same effect (§ 10.3.3).

The exact mechanism by which the blood level of VFA regulates feed intake has not been elucidated. The ultimate control centre is now known to reside in the ventromedial area of the hypothalamus (Baile *et al.*, 1967a), and in this respect simulates the situation in monogastric animals (Mayer, 1966). The fact that intake falls with increase in ambient temperature (§ 10.2.1) and that there is a high heat increment of feeding in ruminants, suggests that temperature of the hypothalamus might be one of the determining factors in intake regulation. But this has now been disproved by Baile *et al.* (1967b) who showed that in goats, contrary to what might have been expected, hypothalamic temperature decreased following eating.

5.5 NITROGEN UTILIZATION

5.5.1 Introduction

Nitrogen metabolism in the ruminant has been the subject of a continuing series of reviews, the most recent of which have been by McLaren (1964), Phillipson (1964), Blackburn (1965), Hungate (1966), Chalupa (1968), Waldo (1968) and Kay (1969). The aim in this section is to highlight those aspects of the subject considered to have most relevance to the problems of intensive beef production.

In general terms there can be said to be four sets of factors which determine nitrogen utilization in the ruminant. The first concerns the conditions which lead to maximum growth rate of the rumen microflora. Secondly, there is the capacity of the rumen mucosa to convert ammonia to glutamate which later serves in the liver as an intermediate in transamination reactions. The third factor is the amino-acid composition of the synthesized microbial protein, while the fourth—possibly the most critical of all—is the amount and quality of the feed protein which contributes directly to the amino-acid pool without microbial modification.

5.5.2 Microbial growth

It is often inferred (e.g. Chalupa, 1968) that, because urea hydrolysis can occur much faster than uptake of the liberated ammonia, most attention should be given to reducing the rate of ammonia production. This hypothesis, apart from ignoring the fact that even under optimum conditions the rate of microbial synthesis is insufficient to supply much more than half the animal's requirement (§ 5.5.5), does not equate with the majority of experimental findings. Thus Russell *et al.* (1962) found that, while the rate of ammonia production in the rumen was less for DAP than urea, there were no differences in nitrogen retention between the two sources. Similarly, Oltjen *et al.* (1963) found that animals could withstand twice the amount of DAP than urea before toxicity symptoms developed yet nitrogen retention was better on the latter. Johnson *et al.* (1962) reported that coating urea with wax and various fatty compounds reduced the rate of ammonia release but had no influence on the growth rate of cattle or sheep. They also found that the inclusion of copper sulphate in the urea pellets inhibited urease activity and hence rate of ammonia production but without affecting performance. Pérez *et al.* (1967) studied the use of urea-phosphate, a compound made by combining equimolar amounts of urea and phosphoric acid. Rate of ammonia production from this was much slower than from urea alone when given to lambs in a single dose. In a feeding trial, blood urea was also less with the new compound; however, nitrogen retention was either unchanged or significantly poorer than with urea.

A starch urea product (Starea) has been developed by passing a mixture of urea and grain through a cooker–extruder under conditions that cause the major part of the starch to gelatinize (Bartley *et al.*, 1968). The extravagant claims for this product are justified solely with respect to its reduced toxic properties and greater palatability. The reduced rumen ammonia level (30–45 mg per 100 ml) on Starea was still more than twice what normally obtains when commercial urea/grain mixtures are fed *ad libitum* (10–20 mg per 100 ml: Elías *et al.*, 1967; Preston *et al.*, 1967b); greater microbial growth *in vitro* may have reflected greater starch availability due to gelatinization (§ 5.4.6.2); the increased milk production solely reflected differences in voluntary concentrate intake (efficiency was in fact higher with urea); on the fattening trial differences between Starea (1.23 kg/day) and urea (1.16 kg/day) were not significant and may have been caused by greater intakes, but these were not reported.

The reduced significance of rate of ammonia production is due to the urea recycling mechanism, whereby urea synthesized in the liver is returned to the rumen via saliva and by direct diffusion from the blood into the rumen (McDonald, 1948; Houpt, 1959; Juhasz, 1965). In this way periods of too rapid ammonia production in the rumen are evened out with times of scarcity. This phenomenon is particularly important when dietary nitrogen supplies are poor as is common in semi-arid environments (Schmidt-Nielsen and Osaki, 1958). Clearly if dietary nitrogen supplies are excessive, there will be wastage; nevertheless, the amount lost is more likely to represent the difference between supply and requirements rather than any factor relating to the rate of hydrolysis of the nitrogen source, at least as regards the kind of diets in intensive systems. For grain-based diets, other factors operate to reduce the need to treat NPN sources to make them more slowly hydrolysed. Thus the pH optimum for urease is between 6.4 and 6.9 (Clifford *et al.*, 1967) which is above that found in the rumen on high concentrate feeding. However, even on high molasses/urea diets, for which rumen pH is within the optimum range for urease activity (Elías *et al.*, 1968b), rumen ammonia levels have been exceedingly low (4–5 mg-equiv./l.) despite urea and ammonium salts contributing some 60% of the total dietary nitrogen.

Bryant (1961) found that of 44 strains of rumen bacteria, 80% could be grown with ammonia as the sole nitrogen source, while 26% would not grow unless ammonia was present. Several workers have shown that ammonium salts and urea are more effective for *in vitro* starch digestion than maize protein (Little *et al.*, 1963), or amino acids (Acord *et al.* 1965). There is, however, evidence that for certain amino acids (e.g. phenylalanine, tryptophan, leucine and isoleucine) specific precursors are needed, although the probability is that these are carbon skeletons rather than amino groups. A specific need of certain cellulolytic micro-organisms for the branched-chain fatty acids—isobutyric and isovaleric acid (Allison *et al.*, 1962)—led a number of investigators to determine the extent to which these were limiting factors for microbial utilization of NPN. Hemsley and Moir (1963) recorded significant increases in digestible DM intake when 0.56% of branched-chain acids were added to a 4.6% protein hay supplemented with urea. Cline *et al.* (1966) also showed that isobutyric and isovaleric acids were present in minimal quantities in rumen fluid of lambs given an NPN purified diet; supplementation with these acids both increased nitrogen retention and reduced rumen ammonia. That growth was limited on purified diets which produced low rumen concentrations of branched-chain fatty acids was also reported by Oltjen and Putnam (1966). On the other hand, branched-chain fatty acids have not always improved performance even on purified diets (e.g. Clifford *et al.*, 1967a), and there is no evidence that on natural grain-based diets additional amounts need to be given when supplementary nitrogen has been solely as NPN.

Evidence has also been presented that certain rumen bacteria require the presence of peptides for most efficient growth (Bryant and Robinson, 1962). This almost certainly accounts for the more rapid growth of lambs on purified diets containing casein as the main nitrogen source rather than urea (Matrone *et al.*, 1965) and that addition of 5% alfalfa meal or a mixture of amino acids increased growth on synthetic diets (Bunn *et al.*, 1967). Adding alfalfa to a casein diet had no such effect but markedly improved performance when the nitrogen source was urea (Matrone *et al.*, 1964). Hydrolysed casein also increased nitrogen utilization on a semi-purified diet (McLaren *et al.*, 1962). McLaren *et al.* (1965) reported improvements in nitrogen utilization when some of the urea in a semi-purified diet was replaced with isonitrogenous amounts of methionine and tryptophan. Nevertheless, as with branched-chain fatty acids, it seems that these effects only arise on highly purified diets and that there are no benefits from added amino nitrogen when natural diets containing at least some 20–30% preformed protein are used.

Another important factor limiting rate of microbial growth is the rumen pH. Thus, in *in vitro* studies, Henderickx and Martin (1963) showed that microbial synthesis of protein was limited to the pH range of 6–8 with a maximum at pH 7. An optimum pH of between 6 and 7 for protelytic activity was also found by Blackburn and Hobson (1960) and Borchers (1965), while Christiansen *et al.* (1962) observed that VFA production by protozoa was at a maximum at pH 7 and fell by one half at pH 6. The optimum for urease activity was between pH 6.4 and 6.9 (Clifford *et al.*, 1967a). The fact that the rumen pH on all-concentrate diets is mostly below 6.5 (Eadie *et al.*, 1967 Elías *et al.*, 1967) suggests that this would not be the optimum environment for efficient utilization of NPN. This is confirmed in practice in that on purified and semi-purified diets animal performance has always been superior with preformed protein than urea (Oltjen *et al.*, 1967). The indirect effect of rumen pH is on protozoal population since these are inhibited by acid conditions (Eadie, 1962; Purser and Moir, 1959; Elías *et al.*, 1967). Klopfenstein *et al.* (1966) suggested that the beneficial effect of protozoa was mediated through increased protein degradation to ammonia (available for microbial synthesis), furthermore protein digestibility was enhanced, as was utilization of absorbed amino acids, by the presence of protozoa. Lower plasma amino-acid concentrations in faunated lambs and indications that lysine may be limiting in defaunated animals provide evidence for more efficient utilization of absorbed amino acids in animals containing protozoa (Klopfenstein *et al.*, 1966; Purser *et al.* 1966). Abou Akkada and El-Shazley (1965) also found that nitrogen retention was superior in faunated lambs, and Christiansen *et al.* (1965) reported better gains in the presence of protozoa.

Although workers in West Virginia have put forward considerable data in support of the concept that urea utilization increases with time (Smith *et al.*, 1960; McLaren *et al.*, 1965a, b) the evidence is by no means conclusive. Barth *et al.* (1961) could not detect differences in capacity for protein synthesis in rumen micro-organisms obtained at weekly intervals from animals on all-urea nitrogen supplemented diets. Utilization of infused urea nitrogen was the same whether lambs had previously received urea in the diet or not (Caffrey *et al.*, 1967b). Moreover, there were no differences in nitrogen retention or urea cycling 4, 20 or 41 days of NPN feeding according to Caffrey *et al.* (1967a).

It may well be that when adaptation responses have been observed these have been more the result of changes in energetic constituents, as noted by Elías and Preston (1969d), than in the nitrogen fraction *per se*.

5.5.3 Fixation of ammonia by rumen mucosa

Glutamate synthesis by rumen mucosal homogenates from ammonia and alpha-ketoglutarate was first demonstrated by McLaren *et al.* (1961). Hoshino *et al.* (1966) confirmed these findings and showed that the active enzyme system was also present in mucosa from the reticulum and omasum. These latter workers suggested that this reaction provided a means for storing ammonia for use in tissue synthesis.

5.5.4 Biological value of microbial protein

The amino-acid composition of rumen bacteria was shown to be relatively constant by Purser and Buechler (1966). However, protozoa were considered to have both a higher biological value (Weller, 1957) and a higher digestibility (McNaught *et al.*, 1950). There are, nevertheless, reports that both bacterial and protozoal protein are limiting in the sulphur amino acids (Abdo *et al.*, 1964; Bergen *et al.*, 1968). Although early findings (Weller, 1957) implied that diet had little effect on biological value of microbial protein, later work with all-concentrate diets suggests that these support a microbial protein of higher biological value than do roughages (Little *et al.*, 1965; Abdo *et al.*, 1964). There would thus seem to be advantages in favouring a microbial population with as high a protozoan level as possible and, perhaps, preferring diets of high concentrate content.

5.5.5 Importance of feed protein

The majority of reviewers have either ignored the direct contribution to protein metabolism of feed protein *per se* (e.g. McLaren, 1964; Armstrong and Trinder, 1966) or merely mentioned it in passing (Chalupa, 1968). Nevertheless, on high energy diets the nature of the feed protein is probably the most important determinant of nitrogen utilization. There are reasons for believing that the nature of the feed protein is less important on high roughage diets. Not only are protein requirements less due to the lower growth rates on these diets, but the rumen conditions favour protein degradation and microbial synthesis. Thus there was more rumen nitrogen of microbial origin on roughages than on concentrates (Gausseres and Fauconneau, 1965) while Conrad *et al.* (1967a) found that rumen degradation of feed methionine was only 43% on a high concentrate diet compared with 67% when more roughage was fed.

The first direct evidence that the quality of the feed protein could affect nitrogen utilization was produced in a series of metabolism and feeding trials with early weaned calves at the Rowett Research Institute, where it was demonstrated that the protein in fishmeal was utilized up to 30% more efficiently than that in a poor quality meal such as groundnut (Whitelaw *et al.*, 1961, 1963; Whitelaw and Preston,

1963; Kay *et al.*, 1966b). Soybean meal was never as good as fishmeal but was better than cottonseed meal (Whitelaw *et al.*, 1962) or groundnut meal (Kay *et al.*, 1966b). Generally, the relative value of the protein source in these experiments could be related to its composition in terms of balance of essential amino acids. That this was not the sole factor, however, was shown in a subsequent trial (Whitelaw *et al.*, 1964) in which, within different types of fishmeal, there were differences in utilization which could be attributed to solubility. Thus a highly soluble meal made by a spray-drying process following partial enzymic degradation (some 40% of the nitrogen in the form of free amino acids) gave significantly poorer results than groundnut meal (Whitelaw and Preston, 1963; Whitelaw *et al.*, 1964). Moreover, addition of synthetic L-lysine and DL-methionine to groundnut meal (which is deficient in both) also gave no improvement (Preston *et al.*, 1964). It was further shown that although groundnut meal was much more soluble than normal fishmeal in molar sodium chloride the former had, in fact, a lower solubility when buffered solutions of pHs of 6.7 and 5 were used. The spray-dried fishmeal, on the other hand, maintained its high solubility irrespective of the pH of the extracting medium. These results were interpreted as indicating that when the feed protein was of low solubility, or had a low potential solubility, in the rumen, its nutritive value would depend largely on its amino-acid composition, but that protein hydrolysates and amino acids would be no better used than ammonia. It was proposed that on all-concentrate diets feed proteins of low, or potentially low, solubility would pass out of the rumen without serious degradation to be digested in a manner analogous to that in monogastric animals (Whitelaw and Preston, 1963).

The importance of protein solubility has been amply confirmed by workers at Oklahoma. When cottonseed meal was heated at a pressure of 1.05 kg/cm^2, urinary nitrogen decreased and faecal nitrogen increased with time, best results, in terms of nitrogen retention and performance, being obtained after 60–75 min (Sherrod and Tillman, 1962, 1964; Danke *et al.*, 1966). Similar results were obtained with soybean meal (Totusek and Hall, 1967; Glimp *et al.*, 1967; Hudson *et al.*, 1967). That insolubility should be accompanied by good biological value was emphasized by Ely *et al.* (1967).

Theoretical support for the concept of feed protein contributing directly to the amino-acid pool can be found in the work of Hungate. He pointed out (1966) that the extent of microbial growth depends not only on the amount and nature of dietary constituents which can be transformed into cells, but also on the usable high energy compounds (ATP) that can be derived from the substrate. From theoretical considerations this proportion is likely to be independent of the type of fermentation and to be of the order of some 4–5 ATP per hexose molecule (Hungate, 1965). As this represents only about 10% of the energy available under anaerobic conditions, Hungate (1966) concluded that the maximum rate of nitrogen assimilation by the microflora would be 1.1 g per 100 g of carbohydrate fermented; a slightly higher rate of some 1.8 g microbial N per 100 g of carbohydrate was predicted by Bloomfield *et al.* (1964) on the basis of *in vitro* studies. The practical significance of this can be understood by taking the case of a beef animal of 250 kg live weight, fed *ad libitum* on an all-concentrate diet, and thus consuming some 3.5 kg of starch daily. According to Hungate (1965) this would be sufficient for the synthesis of 240 g crude protein daily, i.e. some 40–50% of its requirement (§ 9.5.1). Using Bloomfield's estimate the figure is

400 g crude protein daily, some 66% of requirements. Thus on high energy diets a minimum of one-third of the host protein requirement and a maximum of some two-thirds probably have to be derived from sources other than microbial cells.

There is now considerable evidence to support this hypothesis. Plasma amino acids were reduced 8% when urea replaced soybean meal in higher energy diets with levels of lysine, isoleucine and methionine being most affected (Little *et al.*, 1966). Similar results were reported by Frietag *et al.* (1966). On a predominantly ear maize diet, Little *et al.* (1968c) recorded that the rate of passage of amino acids into the abomasum was 23% less when urea was the supplementary nitrogen source rather than soybean meal.

Further confirmation is the finding of Schelling and Hatfield (1967) that abomasal infusion of essential amino acids increased nitrogen retention on urea-based purified diets. Infusion of individual amino acids, e.g. methionine alone or methionine and lysine (Schelling *et al.*, 1967), had no effect which suggests that the deficiency was quantitative rather than qualitative. As might be expected, abomasally infused lysine did give an improvement on an ear maize diet supplemented with maize gluten meal (Devlin and Woods, 1964)—a basal ration notably deficient in this amino acid. The report of Poley and Trenkle (1963) that blood and abomasal amino-acid patterns reflected the composition of dietary protein and the finding of Conrad *et al.* (1967b) that in dairy cows 91% of the protein of fish meal passed undegraded from the rumen, all add support to the concept of passage of feed protein into the abomasum.

CHAPTER 6

Beef Calf Production

6.1 INTRODUCTION

The profitability of a beef calf production enterprise depends basically on the reproductive rate of the cow, the subsequent growth rate of the calf to weaning and the overall efficiency of feed utilization. These parameters are themselves subject to a wide range of genetic, nutritional, environmental and management factors. The ways in which these characters can be improved genetically have already been discussed in Chapter 3. Certain fundamental aspects of nutrition as they affect the cow and her calf have also been dealt with (Chapter 5). We are concerned here with those factors which are to a large extent under the producer's control (e.g. choice of breed, method of feeding and management).

6.2 FERTILITY

6.2.1 Parameters

From the producer's point of view, the most efficient measure of the cow's fertility is the number of calves per year of life. The best cows are clearly those which have their first calf at an early age, live a long time, wean heavy calves and have minimum calving intervals. Selection for most of these traits will be unsuccessful since these characters, other than weaning weight, have low heritability. On the other hand, there are genetic differences between breeds and crossbreeds with regard to age at first service, gestation length and calf mortality. There are also very important environmental effects which may interact with breed.

6.2.2 Age at first calving

6.2.2.1 BREED. It is usual practice in beef herds not to calve heifers before they are 3 years old. Under such circumstances, the potential of breeds which reach puberty early is not exploited nor has there been any incentive to look for differences in this trait. Wiltbank *et al.* (1959) reported that Hereford heifers in Nebraska had an average age at puberty of 434 $\pm$ 27 days at which time they weighed 254 $\pm$ 24 kg. These same workers (Kaltenbach and Wiltbank, 1962; Wiltbank *et al.*, 1966) compared Hereford, Shorthorn and Angus heifers and their crosses given either a low or a high plane of nutrition after weaning. Herefords were older and heavier at puberty than the other two breeds while crossbreds were 35–41 days younger and

2–3 kg lighter than purebreds, depending on nutritional plane. The data were considered to be characteristic of the breeds used rather than specific sires within breeds. Data from this experiment and from one undertaken in Montana are set out in Table 6.1.

TABLE 6.1 EFFECT OF BREED ON AGE (DAYS) AND WEIGHT (KG) AT PUBERTY

	Angus	Hereford	Shorthorn	Charolais
Wiltbank *et al.*, 1966				
Low plane				
No.	29	26	30	
Age	396	457	413	
Weight	233	269	226	
High plane				
No.	25	26	25	
Age	337	413	318	
Weight	251	306	243	
Bellows, 1968				
No.	14	16		23
Age	360	386		370
Weight	268	270		320

Under tropical conditions in Cuba, using a policy of hand mating at the first observed heat after 250 kg live weight, Willis and Preston (1969a) found that the average age at calving for Charolais, Santa Gertrudis and Criollo heifers was 26, 28 and 33 months respectively. Brahmans, on the other hand, calved first at an average age of 3 years. A delayed puberty for Brahmans in Florida was also reported by Plasse *et al.* (1968a). In their survey, age at first oestrus ranged from 420 to 780 days with a mean of 580; by comparison Brahman × Shorthorn crosses reached puberty by 510 days and were less variable (450–600 days) for this trait. Age at puberty was negatively related to weaning weight ($r = -0.46$ for Brahman and -0.41 for crosses). In their analysis of Hereford records, Wiltbank *et al.* (1959) found a lower correlation ($r = -0.23$) for these traits.

6.2.2.2 NUTRITION. The data of Wiltbank *et al.* (1966) in Table 6.1 indicate that raising the plane of nutrition accelerates puberty and increases the weight when heat is first manifested. Plasse *et al.* (1965) also found a correlation between weight and onset of puberty ($r = -0.43$). In Ayrshire and Friesian cattle, Crichton *et al.* (1959) recorded first oestrus at 372, 552, 474 and 440 days for high–high, high–low, low–low and low–high levels of feeding, respectively, treatment changes being at 308 days. Corresponding live weights were 256, 248, 238 and 257 kg. This supported earlier work of Eckles (1946), Reid (1953b), Joubert (1954a, b), Wiltbank *et al.* (1957) and Sorenson *et al.* (1959) that restricted feeding of heifers delayed the onset of oestrus.

Both low protein (60% of NRC standards) and low energy (82% of NRC) delayed puberty in Herefords according to Clanton *et al.* (1964). Controls (100% of NRC) reached puberty at a mean of 384 days, and 93% had cycled prior to 15 months. In contrast, animals restricted in either protein or energy required, on average, 66 days longer and only 36% had cycled by 15 months. A specific stimulatory effect of an all-concentrate diet in initiating ovarian activity was claimed by Buchanan-Smith *et al.* (1964).

Attempts to exploit the effect of high plane rearing have not really been undertaken in beef cattle, although we have had some success in Cuba in calving Charolais and Holstein × Brahman as early as 18–20 months of age. In Israel the subject has received intensive study in dairy cattle, and Amir *et al.* (1967) reported average calving ages of 18.0, 19.5 and 21.6 months for a very high nutritional level (milk to 6 months), a high level (concentrates *ad libitum*) and a control treatment, respectively. The earliest calving was at 13 months and 24% of all animals calved at less than 17.5 months. The disadvantage of the procedure is that calf mortality can be high when birth weights are high relative to mature size of the mother. Although this is of less importance in dairy cattle, where milk production is the primary objective, it could completely invalidate an early calving technique in a beef cow enterprise unless combined with a nutritional system which induced less than average birth weights.

6.2.2.3 Effect on lifetime performance. A comprehensive study with some 114,000 records has been made in dairy cattle in East Germany by Weiland (1966). Age at first calving did not significantly affect subsequent calving intervals although it did reduce yield in the first lactation. Results with beef cattle would appear to be similar since Bernard and Laland (1967) in Canada found that calving Shorthorn heifers at 24 as opposed to 36 months had no effect on subsequent performance. Similar results were reported by Bauer (1965) for Herefords in Rhodesia. Pinney *et al.* (1962b) reported the results of a long-term study begun in 1948 with 120 weaned heifers. Those which calved for the first time at 2 years of age survived as long as those calving first at 3 years and had a slightly better calving rate (86.7 vs. 85.2).

6.2.2.4 Environment. Continued exposure to high temperature delays puberty according to Dale *et al.* (1959) (Table 6.2). There was little effect in the Santa Gertrudis breed, although there was a suggestion that superior heat tolerance was associated with delayed puberty. McDowell *et al.* (1959) compared Jersey and Jersey × Red Sindhi in Maryland and Louisiana and found that age of puberty varied more between environments than between breeds. The hotter climate delayed first oestrus by 25%. They also found that increasing the proportion of Zebu blood delayed puberty which supports Dale's conclusions and our own experience in Cuba.

Table 6.2 Effect of Breed and Ambient Temperature (°C) on Age and Weight at Puberty in Missouri (after Dale *et al.*, 1959)

	Brahman			Shorthorn			Santa Gertrudis		
	10°	27°	Outside	10°	27°	Outside	10°	27°	Outside
Number	3	3	3	3	3	4	3	3	5
Age, days	307	463	397	303	440	280	290	290	306
Live weight (kg)	261	357	296	263	267	219	295	269	243

6.2.3 Calving rate

6.2.3.1 Breed. Some data on calving rate (number of live calves born per 100 cows exposed to the bull) are set out in Table 6.3. There is little consistency in the results obtained in different locations. The only tentative conclusion one can draw is that the Brahman appears to be least fertile since its calving rate has always been less than contemporary breeds, notwithstanding the fact that most of the comparisons were made in tropical or sub-tropical climates supposedly favourable to it. Further confirmation of this idea can be found in a survey of cattle in experimental stations in the south-eastern US, which showed a 79% calving rate for all cows and a 73% rate for those containing Brahman blood (Kincaid, 1957). Warnick *et al.* (1960) reported that 79% of cattle of British breeding were diagnosed pregnant following the breeding season compared with only 63% for Brahman. The problem with the Brahman may partly arise from its shorter oestrous period which was first observed as a characteristic of *Bos indicus* cattle by Anderson (1936). De Alba *et al.* (1961) reported a tendency for Brahman and Criollo cattle to have shorter oestrous periods when natural service was used. They considered that the refusal of certain cows to accept more than one service could also affect fertility in herds where bulls had poor semen quality but pronounced libido.

The only exception to the general trend is a report by England *et al.* (1963b) wherein the Brahman was better than other breeds when dry at the time of service. The relevance of this finding is extremely limited in view of the very low overall fertility of the herd in question, a situation which is almost certainly atypical.

There was an indication in the work of Gaines *et al.* (1966) that the Shorthorn was less fertile than the Angus and Hereford; this was not due to bull infertility since Shorthorn bulls performed well when crossed with other breeds. In contrast, Wiltbank *et al.* (1967a) reported little or no differences between these breeds in a similar experiment undertaken in Nebraska.

Calving rate is unlikely to be improved by the use of any specific breed, and in general terms one can say that breeds differ little from one to another in this trait. The sole exception appears to be the Brahman which is almost certain to give lower calving rates than most others. Plasse *et al.* (1968c) considered that selection for reproductive performance during a short breeding season would decrease average calving interval and thus improve overall reproductive performance. Since they found repeatability of this trait to be only from 0.03 to 0.08 it is somewhat difficult to understand the basis for such a statement.

There appears to be little published information on calving interval in beef breeds. Some comparative results are given in Table 6.4.

Individual sire effects may well have considerable influence upon overall calving rate but actual sire management can be as important. Thus Bellows (1967), in an analysis of 19 single sire Montana herds (28.2 cows per bull) found calf crop to be 87%. In contrast in 77 multiple sire herds, calf crop was only 81.3% despite a reduced number of cows (18.7) per bull. The lower fertility was attributed to intensive competition and hence more fighting than mating.

6.2.3.2 Age and lactation status. The more important effects are shown in the

TABLE 6.3 EFFECT OF BREED ON CALVING RATE (LIVE CALVES PER 100 COWS PUT TO THE BULL)

Location	Angus	Africander	Brahman	Brangus	Charolais	Hereford	Shorthorn	Other *B. taurus*	Santa Gertrudis	Authors
SW Africa	81	84				76	71	70[a] 69[b] 72[c]		Anon., 1956
Louisiana	75		68	74		67				Chapman & England, 1965
Florida	86		65	73		81			65	Cobb *et al.*, 1964
Louisiana[d]	82		80							De Rouen *et al.*, 1963
Louisiana[e]	74		57							De Rouen *et al.*, 1963
Louisiana[f]	48		78	62		48				England *et al.*, 1963b
Louisiana[g]	63		63	71		56				England *et al.*, 1963b
Virginia	90					90	76			Gaines *et al.*, 1966
Florida[e]	76		50					58[h]		Kidder *et al.*, 1964
Australia						67	54			Lampkin & Kennedy, 1965
Florida	73[i]		57	65					57	Meade *et al.*, 1959b
Louisiana[f]		81		77						Reynolds *et al.*, 1963
Louisiana	60	69	49	53						Reynolds *et al.*, 1966
Missouri	78				74	92				Sagebiel *et al.*, 1967a
Louisiana	63		67	64		63				Turner *et al.*, 1968
Florida	83		69	81		81			68	Warnick *et al.*, 1967
Cuba			72		81			71[j]	64	Willis & Preston, 1969[d]
Virginia[e]	77					75	65			Wiltbank *et al.*, 1961
Louisiana		71	59	60						Wiltbank *et al.*, 1961
Nebraska	86					83	83			Wiltbank *et al.*, 1967a

[a] Red Poll. [b] South Devon. [c] Brown Swiss. [d] Conception rate. [e] Reared to weaning. [f] Dry cows. [g] Lactating cows. [h] Devon.
[i] British breeds. [j] Criollo.

TABLE 6.4 EFFECT OF BREED ON CALVING INTERVAL

Location	Angus	Brahman	Charolais	Criollo	Hereford	Sta. Gertrudis	Authors
Georgia	387				400[a]	433	Warren *et al.*, 1965b
Florida		410					Plasse *et al.*, 1968c
Colorado					381		Fagerlin *et al.*, 1968
Cuba		427[b]	420	489		440	Willis & Preston, 1969[d]
US	420						Brown *et al.*, 1954

[a] 386 for grade Herefords. [b] 488 for grade Brahmans.

data in Table 6.5 which are based on work undertaken in Louisiana. The 2-year-old heifers appeared to be more fertile than those calving for the first time at 3 years while cow fertility rose up to about 10 years of age after which there was a decline. More important than age was the effect of nursing which, on average, reduced calving rate by 20%. Similar deleterious effects on conception due to nursing were reported by Meade *et al.* (1959b) in records of 10,170 beef cows from eighteen stations in Florida over a 5-year period. Wiltbank and Cook (1958) found that Dairy Shorthorns nursing calves required 1.8 services per conception compared with only 1.54 for those milked daily; only 57% of nursing cows conceived at first service compared with 71% of those being milked. Similar findings were reported by De Alba (1960) in Costa Rica. In a study of 3994 beef cattle in Florida (Koger *et al.*, 1962b), lactation status had the greatest influence on calving rate in that, of cows dry at time of service, 84% calved compared with only 63% of those that were lactating. Quite different findings were reported by Temple *et al.* (1964) in a survey based on records from four southern states of the US in the period 1957–60. They noted that cows of the British breeds bred when nursing had a larger subsequent calf crop than if they were dry at the time of breeding. The reverse was found to be the case with Brahmans. The problem is not of lactation *per se* since Saiduddin *et al.* (1967) showed conclusively that allowing calves to suckle Holstein dams increased the mean interval from calving to first oestrus by 50% as compared with those milked by machine.

TABLE 6.5 EFFECT OF AGE AND LACTATION STATUS ON CALVING RATE (AFTER WILTBANK AND HARVEY, 1963)

Cow age	Brahman–Angus[a]		Africander–Angus[b]	
	Dry	Lactating	Dry	Lactating
2 year heifers	75		79	
3 year heifers	63		65	
3–4 year cows	80	58	83	50
5–10 year cows	82	73	94	78
> 10 year cows	77	63	73	76

[a] 1955 records. [b] 570 records.

From a study of 3606 gestation records in an AI-bred Hereford herd in Oklahoma, Lindley *et al.* (1958) reported that cows served within 60 days of calving required more services per conception than those served subsequently. The deleterious effect of a short service period upon fertility has also been demonstrated by Vandemark and Salisbury (1950), Shannon *et al.* (1952) and Trimberger (1954) in dairy cows, and by Lasley and Bogart (1943) in beef cows.

Lindley *et al.* (1958) found a curvilinear effect of age of cow on reproduction in that performance improved up to 10 years of age, thereafter declining. A 53 year study on the reproductive performance of a Holstein herd (Davis, 1951) also supports this age effect, as do the data of Warnick *et al.* (1967) in Brahman, Hereford and Shorthorn breeds. These latter workers found no effect in Angus and Brangus although this may have been due to insufficient numbers. In Florida, Burns *et al.* (1959) and Warnick *et al.* (1960) demonstrated that young lactating cows became pregnant less readily than older ones. Lasley and Bogart (1943) found a calving rate of 66% in 2-year-old Herefords compared to 86% in 5- to 6-year-old cows, while according to Stonaker (1958), the peak calf production in Herefords was at 6–7 years of age.

According to Koger *et al.* (1962b), calving rate was lowest in 2- to 3-year-old heifers, increasing to a maximum at 6 or 7 years of age after which dry animals remained nearly constant while lactating cows declined slightly. On the other hand, later work in an AI-bred beef herd in Michigan (Pani *et al.*, 1967) implied that neither age of dam, service period, nor lactation status had any effect on calving performance, which was most affected by the sire used. There is support for this opinion in the data of Wiltbank *et al.* (1956), where services per conception ranged from 1.28 to 4.62 depending on the bull used. Also out of line with the general trend are the findings of England *et al.* (1963b) in which there was no consistent difference in calving rate between cows which were dry or lactating at the time of service. Reynolds *et al.* (1966) also found that young animals were more difficult to get pregnant, particularly those calving late in the season. The calving interval of Brahmans in Venezuela (Linares and Plasse, 1966) rose from 448 days in 3-year-olds to an average of 475 days in 5- to 6-year olds, thereafter declining to some 430 days.

6.2.3.3 Nutrition. In an extensive study of beef herds in Florida, Meade *et al.* (1959b) reported that pregnancy rate varied from 59 to 74% in the years 1953–7 and from 42 to 83% among the eighteen locations. Poor nutrition in a climatically bad year also adversely affected reproductive performance in a Santa Gertrudis herd in Texas according to Dickey and Cartwright (1966). It is obvious from this that management and nutrition play a vital role in securing high calf crops. There is a large amount of published data to support the contention that a rising plane of nutrition during the breeding season is probably the most important single factor involved. In Florida, Koger *et al.* (1962b) found that cattle on an unimproved range had a 64% calf crop compared to 78% with improved pasture and supplementary feeding; while Pinney *et al.* (1963) in Oklahoma confirmed that a low nutritional plane during the winter reduced calf crop and also delayed the date of calving. McClure (1965) found that Jerseys in New Zealand, given supplementary hay from calving to 3 weeks after service, had a 62% conception to first service compared to only 13% for unsupplemented animals.

Zimmerman *et al.* (1961a) fed Hereford heifers different levels of protein and energy according to a 2 × 2 factorial design. They found that the interval from calving to first heat was not influenced by restricted protein feeding whereas the average on high energy feeding was 53 days compared with 145 days for the low energy diets. The conception rate was not given for those on the low energy diet but 83% of those on high energy/high protein feeding conceived to first service compared to only 38% for those on high energy/low protein. This effect of protein on conception rate was confirmed by Wallace and Raleigh (1967) in Oregon where the winter feeding of 20% more crude protein than NRC standards increased the calf crop compared with animals given 20% less protein than NRC standards. Jones *et al.* (1966) also reported that increasing the energy intake of cows decreased the time between calving and conception; the effect was less consistent with heifers. The situation is summarized by the results of Dunn *et al.* (1964) and Wiltbank *et al.* (1964) which are given in Tables 6.6 and 6.7.

Christenson *et al.* (1967) fed beef heifers high or low energy diets for 140 days prior to calving and found that those on the former exhibited oestrus earlier. Although this particular effect was also noted by Wiltbank *et al.* (1962), Dunn *et al.* (1964) and

TABLE 6.6 EFFECT OF POST-PARTUM ENERGY LEVEL ON FERTILITY (69 HEREFORD COWS) (AFTER WILTBANK *et al.*, 1964)

	Energy level (kg TDN/day)				
	5.68	7.50	11.36	3.86[a]/7.50	3.86[a]/11.36
Calving to conception (days)	80	67	75	86	87
Conception to first service (%)	54	31	83	46	87
Pregnant (%)	71	78	92	69	100

[a] For 28 days then higher level.

TABLE 6.7 EFFECT OF ENERGY LEVEL (kg TDN PER DAY), PRE- (140 DAYS) AND POST- (120 DAYS) CALVING ON REPRODUCTIVE PERFORMANCE (AFTER DUNN *et al.*, 1964)

Pre-calving level:	3.68			1.95		
Post-calving level:	10.4	5.90	3.10	10.4		5.90
No. of heifers	48	48	48	48		48
Precalving weight (kg)		414			338	
Weight gained after calving[a]	88	36	−24	120		62
Days to first oestrus	56	50	44	63		64
Conception to first service (%)	62	62	43	73		49
Anoestrus (%)	0	0	19	0		7
Pregnancy rate (%)	81	70	64	90		73

[a] During 120 days.

Bellows (1967), it is not necessarily an index of subsequent fertility. The more important factor would appear to be the plane of nutrition at the time of breeding as was noted by King (1968) (Table 6.8) and Kail *et al.* (1968) in dairy cattle. Supporting evidence in beef cattle is evident in the data of Wiltbank *et al.* (1962, 1964), Dunn *et al.* (1964) and Bellows (1967).

TABLE 6.8 EFFECT OF CHANGE IN BODY WEIGHT ON FERTILITY OF DAIRY COWS (AFTER KING, 1968)

No. of cows	Gain in weight over 4 week period including service (kg)	Conception rate (%)
13	0.0	76.0
51	0.4 to 12.3	70.6
30	12.4 to 25.0	76.7
10	25.1 to 37.7	100.0
42	−0.5 to −12.3	28.6
35	−12.4 to −25.5	8.6
9	−25.6 to −37.7	0.0

Nutrition during the breeding season was studied by Witt *et al.* (1958). Pregnancy rate was drastically reduced in cows and heifers when the total weight loss from calving to the end of the breeding season (168 days) was of the order of 78 kg compared with 10 kg in animals fed on a higher level. If the nutritional level during breeding is particularly poor, the effect of supplementary feeding on conception rate may be very dramatic. In Rhodesia, Bauer (1965) gave supplementary feeding to 66 3-year-old Herefords of which 83% calved compared with only 13% of 70 animals not supplemented.

Warnick *et al.* (1967) showed that the weight change of Brahman and Santa Gertrudis cows during the breeding season significantly affected pregnancy rate. Early calvers had a higher pregnancy rate than late calvers, a finding previously reported by Burris and Priode (1958) and Wiltbank and Harvey (1963). This effect is almost certainly a manifestation of the cow's nutritional status since the breeding season of early calvers is more likely to coincide with the period of optimum pasture growth. In Brangus and Africander–Angus calving for the first time at 2 years of age, those which had had the highest weaning weights had a higher calving rate (Reynolds *et al.*, 1963). When weaning weight exceeded 180 kg the subsequent calving percentage was 80 compared with 66 for animals weighing less than 180 kg at weaning. Results may be different with cows, for Hawkins *et al.* (1965) found that Hereford cows in Ohio which were heaviest pre-calving had fewer calves subsequently.

Parker *et al.* (1966) and Robinson and Marion (1966) failed to observe any effect of nutrition (good or bad grazing with different levels of supplementation) upon percentage calf crop. In both cases, however, the overall fertility was very high (87–96%), which indicates the adequacy of even the poorest treatment.

The dangers of over-feeding are demonstrated by the work of Arnett and

Totusek (1963) who fed twin heifers in drylot for three lactations on high or moderate energy levels. The average number of services per conception was 1.43 for the moderate compared with 1.70 for the high energy diet. All 12 of the moderate group completed three lactations whereas 4 of the high energy animals died. Calving difficulties and calf mortality were also higher on high energy feeding. A further argument in favour of not giving too high a plane of nutrition prior to calving is presented in the data of Pinney *et al.* (1962b). They supplemented 120 females on natural pasture during the winter period with 0.45, or 1.03 kg/day of cottonseed meal or the latter plus 1.36 kg of oats. The low level, which was considered equivalent to 60% of the NRC protein requirement, delayed maturity and reduced mature size among heifers calving as 2-year-olds (but not as 3-year-olds). Although animals on this treatment always calved later in the year, the percentage calf crop weaned was 90 compared with 84 for the higher levels. Length of productive life also favoured the low plane treatment, being 12.7, 11.6 and 10.7 years per cow for the increasing levels of supplementation. There was no effect on birth or weaning weight.

That specific vitamin deficiencies at a sub-clinical level can reduce the calf crop is implied by the work of Bradfield and Behrens (1968) which is summarized in Table 6.9. The experiment was undertaken on nine Nevada ranches and involved 2417 cow/years. Injecting 6 million IU vitamin A in the autumn and spring had a marked beneficial effect in Florida (Burns *et al.*, 1968). Pregnancy rate of 2-year-old heifers was 81% compared with 65% for untreated controls, but no significant effect was observed in older cows. Lane (1964) injected 1 million IU vitamin A into yearling heifers prior to the breeding season and increased calf crop by 11%.

TABLE 6.9 EFFECT OF VITAMIN INJECTIONS ON CONCEPTION RATE (AFTER BRADFIELD AND BEHRENS, 1968)

Year	Control	Vitamin injected[a]
1964	77.4	88.0
1965	80.0	92.2
1966	54.8	74.4
1967	71.2	82.2
Overall	70.8	84.2

[a] A combined injection of vitamins A, D, and E was given 14–30 days prior to the breeding season.

6.2.3.4 ENVIRONMENT. Bonsma (1949) claimed that there is a relationship between coat character, heat tolerance and the productivity (fertility) of cattle in tropical and sub-tropical environments. Yeates (1965) has supported this opinion albeit without presenting scientific evidence in justification. While we are prepared to agree that animals with long coats are more likely to suffer heat stress than those with short coats, there is no evidence of a reliable nature to relate this to fertility *per se*. Our own data from Cuba clearly demonstrate the superior fertility of Charolais over Santa Gertrudis, Brahman and Criollo. Of these 4 breeds the Charolais is noticeably longer-coated thus providing contradictory results to those of Bonsma. We have previously laid down methods for the selection of beet cattle in the tropics (Chapters 3 and 4) and can only reiterate here that any breeder seeking to improve his stock by selecting for such affectations as coat length is not likely to make progress in productivity.

The suggestion of Yeates (1965) that Bonsma (1949) in South Africa and Turner and Schleger in Australia (1960) have, by selection, produced short-coated strains of cattle, is open to severe criticism since it takes no account of adaptation. It is probable that natural selection alone will lead to the development of shorter coats in European cattle in the tropics. Until conclusive evidence is presented to show that shorter coats have been directly responsible for increased fertility, the whole subject must be regarded as nothing more than "breeding lore".

6.2.4 Gestation length

6.2.4.1 Breed. There are breed differences in gestation length, and it is known that both the Angus and the Holstein are carried for a shorter time than most other beef breeds (Table 6.10). The Brahman and animals of like origin usually have the longest gestation period (>290 days). The effect of *B. indicus* "blood" on gestation length is emphasized by the results of McDowell *et al.* (1959) with Jersey × Red Sindhi in that for each 25% of Red Sindhi blood gestation length was increased by three days.

It may be that sire effects within breeds are as great as differences between breeds. Van Graan and Joubert (1961) studied the gestation period of 4 Africander sires and found that their progeny means ranged from 289.8 (87 daughters) to 293.8 (115 daughters). In a Belgian study of 4113 pregnancies by 21 bulls, Hansett (1966) found the mean gestation length of progeny groups to range from 279.2 to 284.1 days. Jafar *et al.* (1950), Tandon (1951), Buch *et al.* (1959) and Crockett and Kidder (1967) all confirmed the importance of sire effects as did Anderson and Plum (1965) in their review of the subject.

6.2.4.2 Sex. Female calves are generally carried for a shorter time than males (Table 6.10), although not all workers found significant differences (see Buiatti and Polidou, 1962; Sagebiel *et al.*, 1967a). Kortstee (1963) analysed the records of over 9000 MRY and Friesian cattle in Holland and found that twins were carried 4–5 days less than single calves. This effect has been confirmed in other breeds by Guerreiro (1964), Butaje (1965), Bordi *et al.* (1966) and Hansett (1966), although the magnitude of the effect varied with breed. An interesting observation by Hansett was that double-muscled calves were carried 2.2 days longer than normal ones.

6.2.4.3 Age of dam. Several workers (e.g. Jafar *et al.*, 1950; Tandon, 1951; Buch *et al.*, 1959; Lasley *et al.*, 1961) considered that age of dam was positively correlated with gestation length, but this was not so in the results of Reynolds *et al.* (1965a). Van Graan and Joubert (1961) found that gestation length in Africanders increased with age only up to 7 years.

6.2.4.4 Nutrition. From 1600 records of MRY cows in Holland, Bannerjee-Schotsman (1965) showed that gestation length was affected by season, being least for August calvings, but that there was no year effect. Butaje (1965) also reported shorter

TABLE 6.10 EFFECT OF BREED AND SEX ON GESTATION LENGTH[a]

	Angus	Brahman	Charolais	Here ord	Holstein[b]	MRY	Shorthorn	Other *B. taurus*	Other *B. indicus*	Authors
Holland						278.6 (0.57)				Bannerjee-Schotsman, 1965
Italy								298.4 (0.9)[c]		Bordi *et al.*, 1966
		292								Briquet & DeAbreu, 1949
Italy								296.0 (0.0)[c]		Buiatti & Polidou, 1962
Nebraska	286			282			284			Burris & Blunn, 1952
Holland								286.2 (1.4)[d]		Butaye, 1965
					283.8 (2.0)					Dessouky & Rakha, 1961
Michigan					279.5 (0.9)					Everett & Magee, 1965
Portugal					276.5					Guerreiro, 1964
Honduras		293.6 (1.5)[e]								Haines, 1961
Venezuela								288		Hernandez, 1965
Canada							282.3 (2.5)			Hidiroglou *et al.*, 1966
UK								287.6 (1.0)[g]		Joubert, 1957
S. Africa					277.5					Joubert, 1961
USA							280.8			Knapp *et al.*, 1940
Holland					279.1 (1.4)	280.4 (1.4)				Kortstee, 1963
Belgium								284.9 (2.6)[d]		Lampo & Willems, 1965
Arizona				287.4 (0.8)						Lasley *et al.*, 1961
Oklahoma				285.7						Lindley *et al.*, 1958
W. Virginia	283			285	278					Livesay & Bee, 1945
USA					281.2 (1.3)					Norton, 1956
Hungary					280.8			286.9[h]		Obracevic, 1956
Hungary								286.2[h]		Petrovic, 1952
Florida		293.7 (1.7)								Plasse *et al.*, 1968b
Louisiana	280	291							288[i]	Reynolds *et al.*, 1965a
Louisiana									286[j]	
Missouri	280.0 (2.0)		282.0 (0.0)	285.0 (0.0)						Sagebiel *et al.*, 1967a
S. Africa				289.4 (1.8)					296.5 (1.8)[i]	Skinner & Joubert, 1963
S. Africa									292.2 (1.8)[j]	
USSR					280.9 (12.6)					Skvorcov & Zilov, 1966
USSR								83[k]		Tezebaev, 1967
Virginia	279.5			287.2			283			Thornton & Wiltbank, 1959
S. Africa									291.5 (0.7)[l]	Van Graan & Joubert, 1961
S. Africa		291.4								Veiga *et al.*, 1946
Argentine			287							Vianna *et al.*, 1964b
Cuba		290	288		279			289[l]		Willis & Preston, 1968a
Poland					278.6 (1.5)					Zurkowska, 1962

[a] Data refer to male births; numbers in brackets indicate fewer days for female births. When only one number given it is the mean for both sexes.
[b] Includes Black Pied Lowland. [c] Chiana. [d] East Flemish Red Pied. [e] Zebu. [f] Brown Swiss. [g] South Devon. [h] Simmental. [i] Afrikander. [j] Santa Gertrudis. [k] Galloway. [l] Criollo.

gestations in May and September with the longest being during the period November to February. In the US, on the other hand. Lasley *et al.* (1961) showed that date of birth was not related to gestation length in Herefords; a similar result was obtained with Chiani in Italy (Buiatti and Polidou, 1962). Reynolds *et al.* (1965a) found that cow live weight in a Hereford herd also had no effect on gestation length. In contrast, there is a suggestion in the report of O'Connor *et al.* (1968) that there were longer gestations in Friesians in locations where cow live weight was greatest. Edwards *et al.* (1966) also noted this location effect on gestation length in dairy cows mated to Charolais, Hereford or sires of their own breed.

It is perhaps significant that season and location effects on gestation length have only been observed in dairy cattle. This may well reflect some nutritional factor as feeding levels during gestation are invariably higher when cows are kept to produce milk rather than calves only, the implication then being that high levels of feeding (energy) tend to prolong gestation.

6.3 ARTIFICIAL METHODS OF AUGMENTING FERTILITY

6.3.1 Introduction

The maximum natural fertility of cattle can be considered to be the production of one calf per year. In reality this figure is rarely achieved and reasons for this have been discussed in the previous sections. Although the application of genetic and nutritional knowledge can do much to correct existing deficiencies, these disciplines offer little hope of the major breakthrough which is necessary if the efficiency of reproduction is to approach that of growth and fattening. The problem lies not with the male, for AI bulls are capable of carrying out thousands of successful inseminations in a single year. The limiting factor is the female. Very little can be gained by breeding for a reduced gestation period, for despite its quite high heritability (0.40), the extent of any improvement will be only a matter of a few days.

It is difficult to get cows to conceive within 60 days of calving (§ 6.2.3.2) in view of the time required for the uterus to involute and for oestrous cycling to resume. That the normal balance is disturbed in this period is indicated by the findings of Kidder *et al.* (1952) that silent heats were more prevalent in the first 60 days *post-partum* than subsequently. Nevertheless, a considerable improvement in fertility will be brought about by having cows become pregnant as soon as possible after this 60 day period and to this end improvement in AI techniques, as well as an ascending plane of nutrition for the cows at the time of service (§ 6.2.3.3), could contribute materially to reaching this objective. The only real possibility, however, for an increase in reproductive rate is by means of multiple births.

The natural twinning rate is between 1 and 3%, and there is no evidence at the moment that this can be improved by selection (§ 3.4.5.4). The other approach, and fortunately one which promises much for the future, is the use of hormones.

6.3.2 The role of hormones in reproduction

Before discussing the various ways in which synthetic hormones can be used to augment fertility, it is desirable to explain briefly the respective roles in reproduction of the natural hormones.

Hormones implicated in the reproductive process are produced from the pituitary gland, the gonads, the adenals and—in pregnant animals—the placenta. Of these sites the most important is the pituitary since this is the co-ordinating centre for the whole process. Hormones produced by the pituitary are collectively referred as to gonadotrophic hormones and are water-soluble proteins of, as yet, unknown chemical structure. Three of them which are directly involved in reproduction are follicle-stimulating hormone (FSH), luteinizing hormone (LH) and prolactin. The gonadal or sex hormones are produced by the ovaries, adrenals and the placenta. They all have a steroid structure, the two distinct types being oestrogen (oestradiol, oestrone, and oestriol) and progesterone.

FSH is responsible for inducing follicle growth in the ovary while LH causes these follicles to rupture and thus release the ova. This latter hormone also permits the growth of the corpus luteum in the vacated cavity. Prolactin, on the other hand, acts on the corpus luteum causing the luteal cells to produce progesterone. It is also involved in lactation.

The primary physiological role of oestrogens is to develop the accessory reproductive organs—oviducts, uterus, vagina and mammary glands—and to induce oestrus. It is now well established that oestrogens are secreted by the follicle cells under the simultaneous influence of FSH and low levels of LH. In pregnancy, oestrogens are produced mainly from the placenta, reaching their highest level at parturition and falling rapidly immediately after birth.

The action of progesterone is to prepare the uterus for the reception and implantation of the fertilized ovum; it also promotes development of placental tissue. Since progesterone is formed by the corpus luteum, and this body persists throughout the whole gestation period, progesterone prevents the maturation of further follicles and thus suppresses oestrogen secretion from the ovary. The mode of action is believed to be through a suppression of the production of LH from the pituitary. Progesterone is essential for the maintenance of pregnancy, and thus a corpus luteum is equally important. In cattle it has been shown by McDonald *et al.* (1952) that a functional corpus luteum is necessary for the first 200 days of gestation.

Cyclic reproductive behaviour in females is generally considered to be due to alternating inhibition of pituitary gonadotrophic secretions by gonadal steroids followed by reinstatement of secretion as the level of steroid falls. Thus, immediately prior to oestrus (when circulating levels of both oestrogen and progesterone are at their lowest), the stimulus of FSH from the pituitary causes the growth of one or more follicles in the ovary. The growth of the follicles in turn brings about a rapid increase in secretion of oestrogen which is responsible for the outward manifestations of oestrus. At some stage during oestrus, pituitary LH causes the follicles to rupture, releasing ova and developing in their place one or more corpus lutea, depending on the number of ova produced. The corpus luteum persists into pregnancy if fertilization is successful and, if not, rapidly regresses with the growth of new follicles.

Increasing fecundity necessitates the production of more than one ovum. In view of the determinant role of gonadotrophic hormones in the maturation and rupturing of follicles, it is to be expected that injection of these would lead to superovulation and the possibility of multiple births. Although FSH and LH are not available in synthetic form, it is known that pregnant mare serum (PMS) contains gonadotrophins which closely resemble the FSH and LH hormones produced by the pituitary. Moreover, the proportions in which the active substances are found are such that the biological activity of PMS is comparable with that produced by the normal pituitary hormones. Since gonadotrophic hormones are only effective when the blood levels of the steroid hormones—oestrogen and progesterone—are low, an essential adjunct of almost all experimental work to augment fertility has involved a study of methods that would permit synchronization of the oestrous cycle.

6.3.3 Synchronization of oestrus

Quite apart from being a necessary component in techniques for promoting multiple births, heat synchronization has an important role to play in the application of AI to beef cattle breeding. In fact, in the US most of the work done so far on synchronization has had this objective in mind.

Early investigators used crystalline progesterone, either as a single injection of 500–1000 mg or repeated injections of 50–100 mg spread over a period of up to 20 days. An effective synchronization was invariably achieved by these methods, but fertility was usually low (Ulberg *et al.*, 1951; Trimberger and Hansel, 1955; Nellor and Cole, 1956; Ulberg and Lindley, 1960; Hansel *et al.*, 1961; Ray *et al.*, 1961). According to Ulberg and Lindley (1960), oestrus and ovulation could be inhibited by as little as 12.5 mg/day of progesterone, oestrus occurring within 2.5–9 days after withdrawal of the hormone. Loy *et al.* (1960) considered that hormone injection caused an imbalance between ovarian and pituitary hormones and that this led to the reduced fertility. Support for this view was subsequently given by Ray *et al.* (1961) who found that pituitary FSH and LH production was lower in animals treated with progesterone than in controls.

An attempt to investigate the effect of giving different proportions of progesterone and oestrogen was undertaken by Wiltbank *et al.* (1965). In common with all workers in this field they obtained very effective synchronization. However, although fertility was relatively high on some treatments the results were variable, ranging from a low of 30% to a maximum of 80%. There was no apparent correlation between treatment and fertility, and although the authors claimed good results from a combination of 40 mg progesterone and 80 mcg of oestradiol, the numbers of animal per group (20) were really too small to justify this conclusion. This is shown by the fact that in a second trial, involving 104 heifers injected with either 20 or 40 mg progesterone and either 80 or 160 mcg of oestradiol, the fertility was lower than in the controls.

From the early 1960's several new products, mainly derivatives of progesterone, have been investigated. They include Delalutin (17-α-hydroxyprogesterone-n-Caproate), CAP (6-chloro-Δ^6-17-acetoxyprogesterone), MAP (6-α-methyl-17-α-acetoxyprogesterone) and MGA (melengestrol acetate). Results with some of these hormones are set out in Table 6.11.

The new products appear to be equally effective as progesterone in synchronizing oestrus, but there are indications of higher fertility which, in the case of MAP, was almost comparable to control animals. The dose level appeared to bear relation to the time between the end of hormone treatment and the onset of oestrus as well as the efficiency of synchronization. Wagner *et al.* (1963) treated 112 Angus heifers with doses ranging from 1 to 25 mg CAP daily for 18 days. All except the 1 mg dose were effective in producing 90–100% synchronization within 4 days; at the higher dose

TABLE 6.11 HORMONE SYNCHRONIZATION OF OESTRUS AND FERTILITY

Hormone used and no. of animals treated	Dose level[a] (mg)	Duration of treatment (days)	Days to oestrus after withdrawal of treatment	Improvement in conception[b] 1st service (%)	Improvement in conception[b] all services (%)	Authors
Progesterone						
10	50[c]	14–24[d]	29[d]	25	−45	Saiduddin *et al.*, 1968
10	50	5–15[d]	22[d]	0	−36	Saiduddin *et al.*, 1968
10	50[c]	23–33[d]	43[d]	0	−24	Saiduddin *et al.*, 1968
18	50*[c]	5–15[d]	34	−10	−22	Saiduddin *et al.*, 1968
20	50[c]	12–23[d]	27[d]		−16	Foote & Hunter, 1964
20	50[c]	12–23[d]	41[d]		−14	Foote & Hunter, 1964
18	50*	5–15[d]	45	−10	3	Saiduddin *et al.*, 1968
10	50*	18–33[d]	44	−43	9	Saiduddin *et al.*, 1968
10	50*[c]	18–33[d]	39	−86	9	Saiduddin *et al.*, 1968
53	100*	2–9		62		Johnson *et al.*, 1958
Oestradiol						
20	10†	25	27		−16	Foote & Hunter, 1964
18	10†	17[d]	29	−40	−13	Saiduddin *et al.*, 1968
10	10†	35[d]	41	−43	11	Saiduddin *et al.*, 1968
Delalutin						
27	100*	42[e]	70		1	Fosgate *et al.*, 1962
17	500*	2nd day	77		83	Johnson *et al.*, 1958
CAP						
97	10[f]	19	−(80%)	5	−3	Brunner *et al.*, 1964
98	10	18	−(90%)	8	0	Brunner *et al.*, 1964
30	10	18	6(90%)	50[g]	70[g]	Veenhuizen & Wagner, 1964

MAP							
	100	180	18	3(75%)	−30	−22	Sorensen & Foster, 1963
	10	150	20	4	−17	0	Anderson *et al.*, 1962
	16	180	18	4(81%)	132	6	Dhindsa *et al.*, 1967
	31	180	18	3.5(87%)	105	6	Dhindsa *et al.*, 1964
	15	90 + 90	18	4(93%)	74	6	Dhindsa *et al.*, 1967
	10	210	20	3	0	13	Anderson *et al.*, 1962
	49	90 + 90	18	4(49%)	−23	14	Dhindsa *et al.*, 1967
	100	180	18	3.5(55%)	−30	19	Dhindsa *et al.*, 1964
	50	180	18	4(60%)	−35	25	Dhindsa *et al.*, 1967
	32	968 + 500	10 + 10	3–4(50%)	25[g]		Hansel *et al.*, 1961
DHPA							
	100	400[h]	9	3(80%)		16	Wiltbank *et al.*, 1967b
	50	500	20	3(96%)		42	Wiltbank *et al.*, 1967b
	46	400[h]	9	3(74%)	−25		Wiltbank & Kasson, 1968
	44	75[h]	9	3(77%)	−29		Wiltbank & Kasson, 1968
	174	125[h]	9	5(66%)	34[k]		Absher *et al.*, 1968
	163	135			−31	89[g]	Zimbelman, 1963
NE							
	10	0.462*	11th[i]	13	−29	11	Anderson *et al.*, 1962
	10	0.462*	1st[i]	14	−71	33	Anderson *et al.*, 1962
MGA							
	15	0.4	0–84[j]		0	8	O'Brien & Arndt, 1968
	15	0.4	64–84[j]		0	250	O'Brien & Arndt, 1968
	15	0.4	0–63[j]			560	O'Brien & Arndt, 1968

[a] Oral unless marked * injection.
[b] Difference from controls.
[c] Plus 10 mg oestradiol 2 days after withdrawal of progesterone.
[d] *Post-partum.*
[e] Alternate days.
[f] Plus 9 mg thyro-protein.
[g] Actual conception rate (no control).
[h] Plus 5 mg oestradiol valerate.
[i] Of oestrus.
[j] From start of 84 day trial.
[k] Pregnant during 28 day breeding period following withdrawal of treatment.

levels a greater time elapsed between end of treatment and onset of oestrus. These workers also found that 5 or 10 mg of CAP plus 10 mg of oestrogen, or 10 mg of CAP plus 20 mg of oestrogen, resulted in a conception to first service of 42–50% and of 75–100% to two services. According to Zimbelman (1963), the minimum dose of MAP for complete suppression of oestrus was 135 mg/day. Rey (1968) found that pessaries impregnated with 90 mg of fluorogestone acetate completely suppressed oestrus when inserted for 14–17 days. Oestrus was synchronized within 83 hr of removal; fertility to first service was only 20% but was 100% at the subsequent heat (21 cows). An injection of 750 IU PMS 1 day before pessary removal synchronized oestrus within 27 hr, but fertility was only 36 and 54% to first and second services respectively.

The minimum dose of MGA to secure complete suppression of oestrus appears to be 0.4 mg/day (Young *et al.*, 1967). There was no suppression with only 0.24 mg/day (O'Brien and Baumgardner, 1967). The results of O'Brien and Arndt (1968) show that while the feeding of this product at 0.4 mg/day gave good synchronization, best fertility came from mating at the second and third oestrus after withdrawal.

Norethandrolone has been investigated by Curl *et al.* (1968a). Different levels were implanted subcutaneously and removed after 16 days. Although they considered that dose levels of 153.7 and 168 mg were the most effective, the experiment was invalidated by the fact that only 4–7 cows were used per treatment group. Efficient heat synchronization with norethisterone (17-α-ethinyl-19-nortestosterone) was reported by Astrom (1968), but conception rate was extremely variable. More critical experiments are necessary before evaluation of these products is possible.

The importance of the rate of involution of the uterus, in determining when cows can be bred after parturition, has already been mentioned. One possible role of progesterone and like compounds is in reducing the time and hence allowing earlier mating. Encouraging results were reported by Foote *et al.* (1965) in that a 50 mg injection of progesterone on each of 10 days reduced involution time from 50 to 30 days. The treatment was less effective when given with oestradiol. In an earlier experiment (Foote and Hunter, 1964), there was no difference in the effect of progesterone alone or with oestrogen and the improvement over controls was much less (30 vs. 47 days to involution). Days to conception, similarly, were not significantly different. Using Delalutin, Fosgate *et al.* (1962) reported an increase in involution time due to treatment of 42 days versus 27.5 for controls; however, conception rates were identical.

6.3.4 Multiple births

Despite the possibilities of hormone-induced multiple births as a means of increasing the efficiency of beef calf production, only limited research has been undertaken.

In 1962 Gordon *et al.* published the results of a trial in which 416 cattle in the UK were treated with from 800 to 2000 IU of PMS. Although the report ran to 56 pages of text and 84 tables, there was no statistical analysis of the data and the authors' conclusions must therefore be treated with reservation. The mean ovulation rate was 2.4 and appeared to be related to the PMS dose level. Although the conception rate of 76% to first service was extremely satisfactory, embryonic loss was such that only 191 of the 416 cows actually calved. From these there were 35 sets of twins, 8 triplets and 1 set of quintuplets. Ten per cent of twin calves and 54% of those born as triplets were born dead, and by 2 weeks of age only 84% of twin calves and 29% born as triplets still survived.

Better results were obtained by Turman *et al.* (1968) in Oklahoma. Eighty-one cows were treated with two subcutaneous injections of PMS, the dose levels being 1500 IU on the 4th, 5th or 6th day of the cycle, and 2000 IU on the 16th, 17th or 18th day. At oestrus, 2500 IU of chorionic gonadotropin were injected intravenously. Overall conception rate was 87.7%, but only 48 cows (59%) calved to service at the first post-treatment oestrus. The distribution of births was 25 singles, 12 twins, 8 triplets, 2 quadruplets and 1 quintuplet. All the twins and 24 of the singles were alive at birth, but of the remainder 54% were stillbirths. Although the live birth rate of some 107% of cows mated is encouraging, more vital data concerns survival to weaning. Since many of the multiple births weighed considerably less than 20 kg, their viability might well have been poor.

6.4. BIRTH WEIGHT

6.4.1 Breed

It is well established that there are breed differences in birth weight; nevertheless, few comparative trials have been carried out. The existing data, summarized in Table 6.12, indicate that the Charolais, Holstein and Brown Swiss (limited observations) are considerably larger at birth than the overall average. The Hereford is around the average, while the Brahman and Angus occupy the lowest place in the list of breeds studied with birth weights well below average. The superiority of Herefords over Angus has been shown in every comparative trial reported in Table 6.12 and also by Meiske *et al.* (1964).

The data of Franke *et al.* (1965), taken from an experiment in Louisiana with 1081 calvings by 6 sire breeds and a variety of dams, confirm the general findings. The differences (kg) from the overall adjusted mean birth weight were −2.8 (Angus), −1.4 (Brangus), −0.9 (Shorthorn), −0.2 (Hereford), 1.8 (Brahman) and 3.4 (Charolais). In this trial breed of dam was the most important factor affecting birth weight accounting for 7.4% of total variance.

Some of the specific factors contributing to variance in birth weight within breeds are summarized in Table 6.13.

6.4.2 Sex

Males are heavier at birth than females (Table 6.12). The superiority is obvious in all comparisons as well as in the work of Reynolds *et al.* (1959, 1965a), Lasley *et al.* (1961), Taylor *et al.* (1960a), Loganathan *et al.* (1965), Bannerjee-Schotsman (1965) and Koonce and Dillard (1967). It is generally accepted that twins are smaller than singles (Matassino and Marati, 1964) but, as with the effect of sex, this is confounded with differences in gestation length.

6.4.3 Gestation length

The factors which affect gestation length have been discussed previously (§ 6.2.4), but this parameter itself has a pronounced effect upon birth weight. Lampo and

TABLE 6.12 EFFECT OF BREED AND SEX* ON BIRTH WEIGHT

Location	Angus	Brahman	Charolais	Hereford	Holstein	Shorthorn	Other *B. taurus*	Other *B. indicus*	Authors
Belgium							39.7[a]		Abelein & Ritter, 1959
Kenya								22.3 (3.2)[b]	Ayre-Smith, 1956
Hungary							40.7 (5.4)[c]		Belic, 1965
Kentucky				31.4					Bradley *et al.*, 1966a
Montana				36.0 (2.3)					Brinks *et al.*, 1961
Montana				35.0					Brinks *et al.*, 1964c
Texas	28.0	29.7	40.3	33.0				32.2[d] 40.3[e]	Brown *et al.*, 1967c
Italy							45.3[f]		Bujatti, 1956
Florida	25.5	26.8		29.1				28.6[g] 30.0[d]	Cobb *et al.*, 1964
Ruanda								26.4 (2.1)[h]	Compére, 1965
Wisconsin				32.7 (1.8)					Christian *et al.*, 1965b
France			45.8 (3.1)						De Vree, 1961
Brazil			42.0 (1.0)						Dom ngues, 1961
France			50.2 (4.3)						Dumont *et al.*, 1959
Texas		28.3		32.1					Ellis *et al.*, 1965
New Zealand	30.7 (1.1)				38.5 (–)				Everitt, 1967
Michigan					44.6 (0.6)				Everett & Magee, 1965
Hungary							39.0[l]		Florschutz, 1967
Canada					45.0 (–)				Forrest, 1964
Nebraska	30.6 (2.4)			36.3 (1.8)		33.7 (2.0)			Gregory *et al.*, 1965
Virginia	28.6			32.9		32.5			Gaines *et al.*, 1968
Uruguay	32.0			35.6		31.5		32.5[r]	Granizo, *et al.*, 1968
Honduras		27.7 (1.7)							Haines, 1961
Pennsylvania	26.3 (2.3)			31.7 (1.9)					Hallman, 1966
S. Africa							46.2[j]		Joubert, 1957
S. Africa					32.2	27.6		29[k]	Joubert & Bonsma, 1957
Ohio			39.0	31.0					Klosterman *et al.*, 1965a
New Jersey					44.8 (3.7)				Lal *et al.*, 1966
Belgium							52.1 (3.1)[p]		Lampo & Willem, 1965
Arizona				33.3 (1.2)					Lasley *et al.*, 1961
Canada					32.3			28.9[q]	Lawson & Peters, 1964
Argentina	29.8			34.5		31.7			Lopez Saubidet *et al.*, 1963
New Zealand	29.6 (1.6)			34.4 (2.8)					MacDonald, 1954
Italy							46.1 (2.3)[l]		Matassino & Marati, 1964
Mississippi	28.0			30.2					Meade *et al.*, 1959a
Costa Rica		27.5					29.1[m]	32.5[d]	Muñoz & Martin, 1968
Oregon	28.7 (2.6)			32.7 (1.2)					Nelms & Bogart, 1956
Arizona				37.2 (1.0)			46.3 (3.6)[l]		Pahnish *et al.*, 1964
Hungary									Petrovic, 1952
Venezuela		27.0					25.0[m]		Plasse, 1968
Venezuela								33.7[d]	Plasse & Koger, 1967
S. Africa					38.5 (3.3)				Reyneke & Penzhorn, 1964
Louisiana	27	27						29[g] 31[k]	Reynolds *et al.*, 1965a
Missouri	28.8 (1.4)		38.1 (2.4)	32.9 (2.2)					Sagebiel *et al.*, 1967a
Australia				31.8		31.2			Seifert & Kennedy, 1966
S. Africa				33.2				33.6[d] 31.9[k]	Skinner & Joubert, 1963
Holland					38.5 (2.3)				Stegenga, 1961
Ohio				33.6 (1.8)					Swiger *et al.*, 1961a
Virginia	29.2 (2.1)			31.9 (2.3)		32.1 (1.8)			Taylor *et al.*, 1960a
UK				36.4 (3.1)					Taylor, 1967
USSR							27.0[n]		Tezebaev, 1967
Rhodesia								20.0 (1.8)[o]	Walker, 1964
Cuba		28.4 (0.3)	36.7 (1.7)				33.3 (3.0)[m]	34.4 (0.4)[d]	Willis & Preston, 1968a

* Figure in brackets is the reduction for females, otherwise mean value for both sexes is given.
[a] Fleckvieh. [b] Boron. [c] Red Pied Lowland. [d] Santa Gertrudis. [e] Charbray. [f] Chiana. [g] Brangus. [h] Ankole. [i] Simmental. [j] South Devon. [k] Africander. [l] Marchi. [m] Criollo.
[n] Galloway. [o] Angoni. [p] MRY. [q] Highland. [r] Limousin.

TABLE 6.13 MAJOR FACTORS CONTRIBUTING TO VARIATION IN BIRTH WEIGHT (AFTER BROWN AND GALVEZ, 1968)

Source of variation	Percentage of total variance	
	Angus[a]	Hereford[b]
Sire	9.5	20.0
Year	3.4	0.1
Individual cow	9.3	17.6
Age of cow	5.7	5.9

[a] 932 calves from 325 cows by 60 sires.
[b] 789 calves from 245 cows by 46 sires.

Willem (1965) found that there were correlations of 0.42 and 0.27 between gestation length and birth weight in male and female calves of the East Flemish Red Pied breed. In the Red Dane, Andersen (1962) found these correlations to be 0.42 and 0.41, while Skinner and Joubert (1963) noted the correlation to be 0.35 and 0.24 in various pure and crossbred beef cattle in South Africa. DeFries *et al.* (1959) observed that for 5 dairy breeds in Illinois each additional 1 day in gestation length increased birth weight by 0.45 kg. This is more than twice as high as the figures obtained by Burris and Blunn (1952) for US beef breeds and by O'Connor *et al.* (1968) for Friesians in the UK. The latter estimate, however, agrees with that of Reynolds *et al.* (1965a) who found a regression of 0.29 kg per day of gestation and Edwards *et al.* (1966) who obtained 0.30 in pure and crossbred dairy cattle. The difference in birth weight between sexes is thus, in part, a reflection of a greater gestation length for males. For example, O'Connor *et al.* (1968) found that males were carried 1.6 days longer than females, but the difference in birth weight was 4.1 kg. The relation between gestation and birth weight has been reviewed by Anderson and Plum (1965).

6.4.4 Age of dam

Most published work supports the view that age of dam, in terms of parity, has an effect on birth weight. Lampo and Willem (1965) found correlations of 0.28 and 0.47 between age of dam and birth weight in male and female calves. The correlations between parity and birth weight were identical with those for age. Reynolds *et al* (1959) with a mixed population of Brahmans and crosses noted that birth weight was at a maximum with cows aged 5–10 years, while 2-, 3- and 4-year-old cows produced calves which were 2.5, 1.5 and 1.0 kg lighter than the average. Everett and Magee (1965) showed that 2-year-old heifers had calves 1.8–3.2 kg lighter than 8-year-old cows. In a closed population of Holstein–Zebu crosses, Wilson and Horton (1962) reported that heifers had calves 1.1 kg lighter than older cows. Age effects have also been discussed by Lasley *et al.* (1961), Christian *et al.* (1965), Ellis *et al.* (1965), Reynolds *et al.* (1965a) and Loganathan *et al.* (1965). Koonce and Dillard (1967) reported a quadratic effect of age on birth weight from 3 to 12 years of age. The low weights were at 3 and 4 years, the average was at 5–7 years and from 8 to 11 years birth weight was above average and thereafter declined. Walker (1964) found no effect of parity in Angoni cattle in Rhodesia, but birth weights were abnormally low (20 kg).

6.4.5 Nutrition

In general, cow live-weight is directly related to birth weight. Lampo and Willem (1965) obtained correlations of 0.55 and 0.43 between pre-calving weight and the birth weights of male and female calves respectively. Similarly, O'Connor *et al.* (1968), analysing the data of Ridler *et al.* (1963), reported a regression coefficient of calf birth-weight (kg) upon dams' post-calving weight (kg) of 0.034. Vaccaro and Dillard (1966) recorded that the heaviest cows 90 days before calving also had the heaviest calves; each kilogram increase in cow weight at this time raised birth weight by 0.025 kg. According to Marchello *et al.* (1960), the 18 month weight of heifers was poorly correlated ($r = 0.27$) with the birth weight of their first calf.

In Oklahoma, Smithson *et al.* (1966) studied the birth weight of 7 calf crops from 45 animals which in their first winter were fed to make no gain, 0.23 kg/day or 0.45 kg/day, and in succeeding winters to lose a total of 20, 10 and 5% of autumn weight respectively. Birth weights were positively correlated to winter nutrition for the first 3 calf crops, but thereafter were not affected. This same group also studied the effect of a low (25% loss of autumn weight) or high plane of nutrition (7% loss of autumn weight) prior to calving. Birth weight was significantly depressed by the former treatment being 28.4 kg versus 34.8 kg (Renbarger *et al.*, 1964). Wilcox (1967) found a high plane of nutrition during the winter for heifers calving at 3 years to result in birth weights of 38 compared with 35.4 kg from heifers on a low plane. Age of calving was more important in that calving at 2 years gave 31.4 kg birth weight even if feeding was at a high level. Differences were not significant in the second crop, the birth weights being 33.7, 33.7 and 34.6.

That energy rather than protein is the determining factor is implied in the data of Clanton *et al.* (1961) set out in Table 6.14 and by Bond *et al.* (1964). Furr and Nelson (1964) fed 1.0–1.3 kg of cottonseed meal alone or plus 2 kg of sorghum during the winter and found no significant effect upon birth weight irrespective of whether the cow was on pasture or in drylot. Christenson *et al.* (1967) fed Hereford heifers for 140 days pre-calving on either 196 or 127 kcal DE/$W^{0.75}$ and obtained birth weights of 29.9 and 26.6 kg respectively.

TABLE 6.14 EFFECT OF DAM NUTRITION ON BIRTH WEIGHT OF CALVES FROM HEIFERS (AFTER CLANTON *et al.*, 1961)

	Nutrition during winter (140 days)[a]			
DCP (%):	2.3	5.4	2.9	5.6
ME kcal/kg:	304	324	392	416
Winter weight loss of cow in 140 days (kg)	−4.5	+9.1	+27.7	+52.7
Birth weight (kg)	27.9	29.3	29.5	31.4
Weaning weight at 180 days (kg)	133.6	147.3	140.0	132.7

[a] Identical feeding in summer.

6.5 WEANING WEIGHT

6.5.1 Breed

Although weaning weight has been studied intensively, particularly in the US, few breed comparisons have been made. From the data that exist (Table 6.15) there appears to be little to choose between the British breeds Angus, Hereford and Shorthorn. There are few observations on the Charolais breed, but in every comparison it has outperformed its rivals. The Brahman has been variable and usually inferior to other breeds developed from it such as the Brangus and Santa Gertrudis.

Sire effects within breeds are probably more important than overall breed differences as they more truly reflect genetic differences for growth and are not confounded with milk yield. Important sire effects have been noted by Nelms and Bogart (1956) and Brown (1960).

6.5.2 Sex

Without exception, live weights at weaning (when this has been at 180 days or more) have been higher for males than for females (Table 6.15). But our data (Willis and Preston, 1969a) for calves out of Brahman dams by 6 different sire breeds show no such effects, presumably because weaning was at 90 days before sex hormone influences begin to be manifested. Creek and Nestel (1964), working in Jamaica, found no sex effect on 210 day weaning weight, but in their case the effect was attributed to a low nutritional plane. In an analysis of 28,500 Angus, Hereford and Santa Gertrudis weaning records in Georgia over a 6 year period, Warren *et al.* (1965a) found bulls to be 12 kg heavier than steers which were 7.7 kg heavier than heifers.

Brown (1960) studied calf weights at 60, 120, 180 and 240 days of age in one Hereford and two Angus herds and found that the difference between sires increased with age, but while it was linear in one herd it was curvilinear in the other two. This supports the suggestion of Koch *et al.* (1959b) that the shape of the growth curve, as well as the magnitude of the gain, would affect observed differences between sexes. Thus sex correction factors would be of value only for the environment in which they were developed. In general, multiplicative correction factors are more appropriate than additive factors in so far as sex effects are concerned since coefficients of variation are equal according to Cundiff *et al.* (1966c, d). Koger *et al.* (1962c) and Linton *et al.* (1968) had the same opinion on this matter.

6.5.3 Age of weaning

It is axiomatic that weaning weight increases with weaning age, and fairly typical results are shown in Table 6.16. The linear regression of weight (kg) on age (days) was 0.55 which compares with 0.63 (Koger and Knox, 1945), 0.65 (Botkin and Whatley, 1953), 0.64 (Hamann *et al.*, 1963), 0.68 for Herefords and 0.76 for Angus (Cunningham and Henderson, 1965a) and 0.77 and 0.55 for two inbred lines of Shorthorn (Gottlieb *et al.*, 1962). Johnson and Dinkel (1951) found that the growth rate of calves on range was virtually linear from birth to 155 days of age, thereafter decreasing progressively.

TABLE 6.15 EFFECT OF BREED AND SEX* ON WEANING WEIGHT (kg)

Location	Weaning age (days)	Angus	Brahman	Charolais	Hereford	Shorthorn	Santa Gertrudis	Other *B. taurus*	Other *B. indicus*	Authors
Hungary								131 (2)[a]		Belic, 1965
Kentucky	275				237					Bradley *et al.*, 1966
Montana	180				182 (11)					Brinks *et al.*, 1961
Montana	230				180					Brinks *et al.*, 1964b
Canada	243				263 (–)					Burgess & Bowman, 1965
Florida	215	168	178			168	210		188[b]	Cobb *et al.*, 1964
Louisiana	240	175	170		189				197[b]	Damon *et al.*, 1959a
Virginia		188			176	190				Gaines *et al.*, 1966
Nebraska	200	198 (22)			193 (17)	195 (19)				Gregory *et al.*, 1966a, b
Colorado	200				181 (10)					Harwin *et al.*, 1966
UK	180							158 (10)[c]		Joubert, 1957
Florida	205	147	150					159[d]		Kidder *et al.*, 1964
Ohio	260			279	206					Klosterman *et al.*, 1965a
Arizona	210				170 (12)					Lasley *et al.*, 1961
Canada					163			154[e]		Lawson & Peters, 1964
Hawaii	240				210 (17)					Mahmud & Cobb , 1963
Mississippi	205	188 (11)			175 (10)					Meade *et al.*, 1959a
Costa Rica			194				210	209[f]		Muñoz *et al.*,1964
Arizona	230				218 (16)					Pahnish *et al.*, 1964
Florida			168			140				Peacock *et al.*, 1960
Venezuela	205		152					139[f]		Plasse, 1968
Venezuela	205						175 (10)			Plasse & Koger, 1967
California	240				198					Rollins & Wagnon, 1956a
Missouri	205	154		189	153					Sagebiel *et al.*, 1967b
Ohio					206 (21)					Swiger *et al.*, 1961a
UK	200				231 (40)					Taylor, 1967
Texas	205				183					Tovar *et al.*, 1966
Rhodesia	200								128 (6)[g]	Walker, 1964
Cuba	90		101 (6)	120 (6)			113 (3)	118 (14)[f]		Willis & Preston, 1968a

* Figure in brackets is reduction in weight of females, otherwise a single figure relates to the mean of both sexes.
[a] Red Pied Lowland. [b] Brangus. [c] South Devon. [d] Devon. [e] Highland. [f] Criollo. [g] Angoni.

TABLE 6.16 EFFECT OF AGE OF CALF ON WEANING WEIGHT[a] (AFTER MINYARD AND DINKEL, 1965a)

Calf age (days)	No. of animals	Weaning weight (kg)
80–99	7	137.7
100–119	21	138.2
120–139	55	136.8
140–159	144	171.4
160–179	312	182.7
180–199	525	200.5
200–219	577	214.5
220–239	406	215.0
240–259	214	228.6
260–279	63	235.0
280–299	22	244.5
> 300	5	262.7

[a] Hereford and Angus calves from 20 herds in South Dakota (1951–7).

6.5.4 Age and size of dam

Numerous investigators have drawn attention to the importance of age of dam and the effect this has on weaning weight. The most comprehensive studies are summarized in Table 6.17 and show that maximum weaning weight was obtained when the dams were some 6 years or more of age. Jamison *et al.* (1965), Cundiff *et al.*

TABLE 6.17 EFFECT OF SEX OF CALF AND

Location	Weaning age (days)	No. of records	Overall mean (kg)	Sex effect					
				B	S	H	2	3	4
Colorado	—			6	−3	−4	−7	2	2
Florida	180		151	6		−6	−16	−5	−2
Arkansas	180	267	170	8		−8	−17	−17	−6
Arkansas	180	309	166	8		−8	−6	−6	−1
Arkansas	180	252	160	9		−9	−29	−29	−16
Virginia	203	1987	183	11	−5	−8	−24	−10	−1
Florida	205	999		7		−7	10	10	−3
Ohio	230	748	196	10		−10	−26	−8	−6
Kansas	—	}265	170	14		−14	−43	−6	−10
Kansas	—		158	4		−4	−25	−13	−2
Hawaii	240	1306	204	12		−12		−14	−10
Louisiana	180	1400	166	11	0	−8	−11	−11	−1
Canada	243	1372	266	All males			−16	−6	1
S. Dakota	190	2351	189	8		−8	−25	−9	−2
Colorado	200	1627	176	2		−2	−6	−6	2
Oklahoma	205	13937	189	15	−5	−10	−12	−12	0
UK	200	2516	212	20		−20	−20	−15	−15
Mississippi	205		202	6		−6	−18	−18	−10
Kansas	238	1861	242		9	−9	−44	−25	−15
Georgia	205	28493	183	10	0	−7	−31	−22	−13

[a] Values show difference (kg) from overall mean except for age of dam effect in the final three papers

(1966b) and Smith and Fitzhugh (1968) have emphasized that age is more important in the first 4 years while Cundiff *et al.* (1966b) considered that adjustment factors over this period should be made for each 3–5 months of age difference of dams rather than on the normal yearly basis. In support of their proposal they pointed out that in the Mid-West and other high rainfall areas (see Botkin and Whatley, 1953; Brown, 1958, 1960; Marlowe and Gaines, 1958; Kieffer, 1959; Swiger, 1961; Koger *et al.*, 1962c; Marlowe, 1962; Hamann *et al.*, 1963; Thrift, 1964; Cunningham and Henderson, 1965a; Marlowe *et al.*, 1965) there was not the pronounced decline in calf weaning-weight from cows of over 8 years, such as was observed in more arid regions by Knapp *et al.* (1942), Knox and Koger (1945) and Koch and Clark (1955a).

The difficulty with any study of the effect of dam age is that selection inevitably biases the results in favour of older animals. This was first pointed out by Lush and Shrode (1950) and subsequently studied in beef cattle by Koch and Clark (1955a) and Marlowe *et al.* (1965). The former suggested that correction factors tended to under-correct the data for older cows, while Marlowe *et al.* (1965), using 15,436 calves, found that selection for cow productivity was either not practised or not effective. Cundiff *et al.* (1966c, d) suggested that as standard deviations for weaning weights for different ages of dam were fairly constant, additive correction factors were the most suitable. This is in agreement with the work of O'Mary and Ament (1961) who found that the correlation between calf weaning-weight and dam age was 0.93 (unadjusted), 0.61 (adjusted on a multiplicative basis) and −0.004 (adjusted on an additive basis); the last-named method was the most effective in reducing variation due to age of dam. Linton *et al.* (1968) dissent from the majority opinion in preferring multiplicative correction factors.

Koger *et al.* (1962c) found that weaning weights of Brahmans were less affected by

Age of Dam on Weaning Weight

Age of dam (years) effect											Authors
5	6	7	8	9	10	11	12	13	14	15	
2	10	10	10	−5	−5	−5	−5	−5	−5	−5	Burgess *et al.*, 1954
0	0	0	0	0	0	−1	−4	−8	−16	−24	Clum *et al.*, 1956
0	1	0	1	−1	−1						Brown, 1960
4	3	0	5	15	4						Brown, 1960
−6	−10	0	5	0	−8						Brown, 1960
5	11	5	5	0	0	−5	−13	2	−8		Lehmann *et al.*, 1961
0	2	5	6	2	1	−1	−4	−2	−4	11	Meade *et al.*, 1961
16	16	16	20	20	20	20	20	12	12	12	Swiger, 1961
2	3	16	27	12	−3	−5	0	9			Gottlieb *et al.*, 1962
−2	4	9	4	16	−3	0		14			Gottlieb *et al.*, 1962
−5	−2	0	0	0							Mahmud & Cobb, 1963
6	6	6	6	6	6	6	6	6	6	6	Vernon *et al.*, 1964
3	1	2	1	7	7	6	6	6	6	6	Burgess & Bowman, 1965
2	10	11	12	8	5	1	−6	−7	−7	−7	Minyard & Dinkel, 1965
2	5	5	5	5	2						Harwin *et al.*, 1966
3	6	7	8	8	7	7	6	7	4	−2	Cundiff *et al.*, 1966c
−5	2	3	9	6	6	6	6	6	6	6	Taylor, 1967
0	0	0	0	0	0	−3	2				Meade *et al.*, 1959a
−13	−4	−2	0	0	0	0	0	0	0	0	Hamann *et al.*, 1963
−7	−7	−5	0	0	0	0	−6				Warren *et al.*, 1965a

which show difference from highest value.

age of dam than were those of other breeds, and our own findings in Cuba tend to confirm this, albeit with weaning at 90 days of age. We would agree with these Florida workers that the indiscriminate use of correction factors may lead to more serious errors than exist in the unadjusted data.

O'Mary *et al.* (1959a) found that of 15 body measurements on dams, only 3—rump length, forearm circumference and length of foreshank—were significantly correlated ($r = 0.46$–0.48) with 180 day weaning weight of the calf. A multiple correlation of these three measurements accounted for 82% of the variation in weaning weight while cow weight alone had a correlation with weaning weight of 0.51. A lower correlation of 0.34 for these latter traits was found by Tanner *et al.* (1965) who used a larger sample of cows. The relationship was said to be linear in Angus and curvilinear in Herefords which suggests an effect of the greater milking ability of the former. The increase in calf weaning-weight per 100 kg of cow weight was 8.5 and 4.9 kg in Angus and Hereford respectively.

According to Ewing *et al.* (1967), the regression coefficient for Herefords was 9.78 kg of calf weaning-weight per 100 kg cow weight; however, they worked with an inadequate sample. In a more extensive study (1616 calves) by Nelson and Cartwright (1967), pre-weaning gain was best for Angus dams weighing 570 kg and Herefords at 600 kg. The most fertile cows tended to wean lighter calves probably because their own live weights were less than those of less fertile animals. Weight at 18 months was poorly correlated ($r = 0.20$) with progeny performance to 18 months (Sawyer *et al.*, 1963) or to weaning ($r = 0.24$) (Marchello *et al.*, 1960). A preliminary report on the effect of the cow's condition (fat-depth) on calf performance suggests this is not an important factor (Sanders, 1968).

6.5.5 Effect of birth weight

The phenotypic and genetic correlations between birth weight and weaning weight have been discussed in Chapter 3. Birth weight has a significant effect on weaning weight but the relationship is not close. Vaccaro and Dillard (1966) observed that each kilogram increase in birth weight increased total gain to 180 days by 1.9 kg, while Nelms and Bogart (1956) found that each kilogram increase in birth weight increased average daily gain to weaning by 0.012 kg.

6.5.6 Milk production

6.5.6.1 BREED. Surprisingly, few workers have compared the milk production of different beef breeds. There are grounds for believing that the Shorthorn is capable of relatively high milk production although the mean yield of 8 kg/day in a 252 day lactation quoted by Dawson *et al.* (1960) come from a highly selected herd and the original data were collected in the 1930's and thus may not be relevant today. Charolais cows appeared to be better milkers (4.5 kg/day) than Angus (3.8) which in turn were better than Herefords (3.3) (Melton *et al.*, 1967c). These workers used a 175 day lactation, but the Angus yield was in good agreement with that obtained by Cole and Johansson (1933) and Bond *et al.* (1964). Hereford data have been reported by Gifford *et al.* (1953), Furr and Nelson (1964), and Christian *et al.* (1965b), the means ranging from 2.7 to 4.3 kg/day. The poor yields recorded for Brahmans by

Reynolds *et al.* (1967a) are supported by unpublished data from Cuba, where Brahman cows managed as dairy animals averaged only some 2 kg/day in 7-month lactations (Wollner, 1968). According to Wistrand and Riggs (1966), the Santa Gertrudis has more milk potential in that yield averaged 6.8 kg daily in a 205 lactation. An interesting although numerically small experiment was made in South Africa by Reyneke and Bonsma (1964) in which Hereford and Bonsmara calves were left with their dams or changed to a dam of the other breed. Calves reared on Bonsmara dams were heavier at weaning than those reared on Herefords, independent of their breed. They concluded that the Hereford did not have sufficient milk to produce high weaning-weights although it was perfectly adaptable to subtropical conditions.

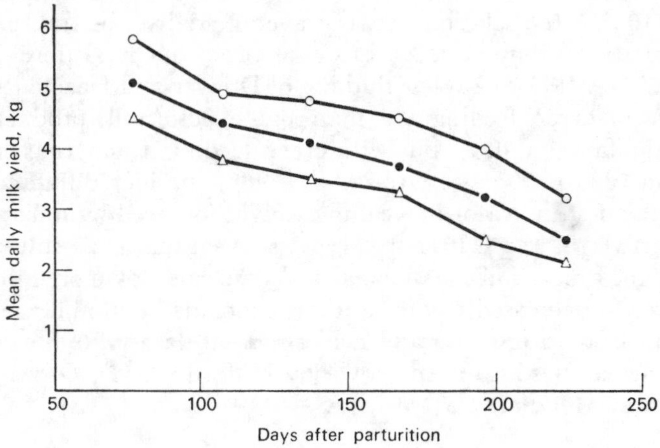

FIG. 6.1 Relative milk yields of Charolais ○, Angus ●, and Hereford △ breeds—15 animals per breed (after Melton *et al.*, 1967c).

6.5.6.2 AGE AND SIZE. It is well established that dairy cows give more milk as they become older, and such evidence as is available suggests a similar relation in beef cattle. Gifford (1949, 1953) considered that maximum milk production in Herefords was reached at 6 years of age, while Drewry *et al.* (1959), Dawson *et al.* (1960), Christian *et al.* (1965b) and Melton *et al.* (1967c) all found that older cows gave more milk. The correlation of body size and milk production in dairy cows is of the order of 0.4 (e.g. Harville and Henderson, 1964). Such relationships have not been worked out with beef cattle; however, the higher milk production of the Charolais, according to Melton *et al.* (1967b), may be a reflection of its greater size (522–707 kg) compared with Herefords (476–624 kg). The data of Nelson *et al.* (1967) suggest that *post-partum* weights of Angus and Hereford cows are similar, although the milk yield of the Angus tends to be higher (Fig. 6.1). Among cows of Angus × Holstein breeding (Gillooly *et al.*, 1967) and in a mixed herd of purebreds and crosses (Todd *et al.*, 1968), there was no relation between cow size and milk production, but the samples were not large.

6.5.6.3 NUTRITION. It is to be expected that the plane of nutrition of the dam should affect milk production. Bond *et al.* (1964) compared different energy and protein levels after calving and found that only the former had a significant effect on yield. Furr and Nelson (1964) studied different protein supplements given in drylot and on range and found no differences in average milk yield although there was a tendency for better results in drylot; poorest yields were with low protein on range. Schake *et al.* (1966) fed Herefords a grain/silage ration at 100, 130 or 70% of their non-pregnant maintenance requirement for 3 months before calving and during lactation, the latter two levels being interchanged at calving. There was a suggestion that the 130/70 treatment produced least milk.

6.5.6.4 Effect on weaning weight. Table 6.18 suggests that milk yield can account for between 16 and 62% of the variation in weaning weight. According to Melton *et al.* (1967b) the relation between average daily gain and milk production declined as lactation progressed, a feature reported on by Gifford (1953), Howes *et al.* (1958) and Neville (1962). The findings of Drewry and Hazel (1966) imply that in the absence of creep feeding the maternal effect (milk production?) is most important in the first 100 days, but with creep feeding a maternal effect was more noticeable from 100 to 200 days. Kress *et al.* (1968) considered feed consumption by the calf to be the best indicator of weaning weight followed by milk production.

Work by Cartwright and Carpenter (1961) showed that male calves suckled more frequently and took more milk than females. As the calf took more milk from its dam her own live weight decreased and the authors concluded that milk yield was affected by the genotype of both the dam and her calf. That dams of bull calves yield more than dams of heifers has also been shown by Gifford (1953), Drewry *et al.* (1959), Heyns (1960) and Melton *et al.* (1967b).

Table 6.18 Correlations between Milk Production and Weaning Weight

<table>
<tr><th colspan="6">Month of lactation</th><th rowspan="2">Total</th><th rowspan="2">Authors</th></tr>
<tr><th>1</th><th>2</th><th>3</th><th>4</th><th>5</th><th>6</th></tr>
<tr><td colspan="2">0.46</td><td colspan="4">0.48[a]</td><td></td><td>Christian *et al.*, 1965b</td></tr>
<tr><td>0.12[c]</td><td></td><td>0.43[c]</td><td></td><td></td><td>0.46[c]</td><td></td><td>Drewry *et al.*, 1959</td></tr>
<tr><td></td><td></td><td></td><td></td><td></td><td></td><td>0.75–0.91[b]</td><td>Furr & Nelson, 1964</td></tr>
<tr><td></td><td></td><td></td><td></td><td></td><td></td><td>0.60[b]</td><td>Gifford, 1953</td></tr>
<tr><td>0.67[b]</td><td>0.83[b]</td><td>0.50[b]</td><td>0.45[b]</td><td></td><td></td><td></td><td>Howes *et al.*, 1958</td></tr>
<tr><td></td><td></td><td></td><td></td><td></td><td></td><td>0.52[b]</td><td>Knapp & Black, 1941</td></tr>
<tr><td></td><td></td><td>0.64[c]</td><td></td><td></td><td>0.60[c]</td><td></td><td>Lampkin & Lampkin, 1960</td></tr>
<tr><td>0.58</td><td>0.38</td><td>0.01</td><td>0.19</td><td>0.27</td><td>0.03</td><td>0.40</td><td>Melton *et al.*, 1967c</td></tr>
<tr><td colspan="2">0.74[b]</td><td colspan="2">0.63[b]</td><td colspan="2">0.59[b]</td><td>0.69–0.81</td><td>Neville, 1962</td></tr>
<tr><td>0.29[b]</td><td></td><td></td><td></td><td></td><td></td><td></td><td>Schwulst *et al.*, 1966</td></tr>
<tr><td></td><td></td><td></td><td></td><td></td><td></td><td>0.14</td><td>Todd *et al.*, 1968</td></tr>
<tr><td></td><td></td><td></td><td></td><td></td><td></td><td>0.46[d]</td><td>Wilson *et al.*, 1968</td></tr>
<tr><td></td><td></td><td></td><td>0.68[c]</td><td></td><td></td><td></td><td>Wistrand & Riggs, 1966</td></tr>
</table>

[a] 60–240 days. [b] With mean daily gain. [c] Between calf weight and milk production to this point. [d] 72–200 days.

The greater birth weight of bulls is not the only stimulating factor since Melton *et al.* (1967b) reported greater milk yield by dams of Angus bulls even though in this case they were only 0.1 kg heavier than heifers. The implication is that bull calves suckle more frequently as was reported above.

Drewry *et al.* (1959) found that average daily milk production and birth weight of the calf were correlated 0.43, 0.29 and 0.12 for the first, third and sixth month of lactation. This suggests that lighter calves compensate by taking more milk, which is consistent with the findings of Gifford (1949, 1953) that milk production of the dam was limited to the capacity of its calf to consume the milk. Melton *et al.* (1967b) support this with their findings that the amount of milk given by dams of bull calves in excess of that given by dams of heifer calves diminished with advancing lactation. The dissentient report on this subject is that of Christian *et al.* (1965b) who found correlations between birth weight and milk production at 60 days and from 60 to 240 days to be 0.19 and 0.11 respectively.

6.5.6.5 Milk utilization efficiency. According to Anthony *et al.* (1965), the gross energy content of milk from Angus and Hereford cows is 770 $\pm$ 5.7 kcal/kg which is higher than values obtained for milk from Holsteins. It is difficult to reconcile this with the relatively low milk fats ($<3.7\%$) reported by Melton *et al.* (1967b) and Christian *et al.* (1965b). Both these groups of workers, however, used sampling techniques while Cole and Johansson (1933), and Dawson *et al.* (1960), who quoted a milk fat content of about 4%, actually milked the cows as though they were dairy animals. It is almost certain that analysis of a small sample of milk drawn from the udder underestimates the fat content.

Christian *et al.* (1965b) obtained significant partial regressions of 0.44 for weaning weight and average daily gain to weaning on the milk fat production in the first 60 days, but not thereafter. They concluded that milk fat may be more important than milk volume in this early period, whereas after 60 days the availability of creep feed reduces the influence of the dam's milk production. On the other hand, Melton *et al.* (1967b) found correlations in the region of 0.40 between total gain to weaning and weight of fat and other constituents.

Several authors have measured milk utilization efficiency as calf growth per unit of milk consumed. Drewry *et al.* (1959) concluded that it required 12.5, 10.8 and 6.3 kg of milk to achieve 1 kg of gain in the first, third and sixth months respectively. Melton *et al.* (1967b) considered that over the whole weaning period 5.7, 5.2 and 4.7 kg of milk per kg of gain were needed for Angus, Charolais, and Hereford calves respectively. The efficiency figure during the first 8 weeks of life was put at 8.1 by Montsma (1960) while Neville (1962) obtained values of 12.5 and 23.5 depending on the nutritional plane of the dam. The data of Drewry and his co-workers are similar to those reported by Willard (1948) with Holsteins and imply that forage consumption is small in the first 3 months of life. Some of the conversion figures, particularly those of Neville (1962), are abnormally high and may be due to faulty methodology.

6.5.7 Creep feeding

6.5.7.1 Effect on weaning weight. American workers are in unanimous agreement that giving supplementary feed to suckling calves increases their weaning weight (Furr and Nelson, 1959; Hammes *et al.*, 1959; Kuhlman *et al.*, 1961; Burns and Koger, 1963; Wilson *et al.*, 1966; Hunsley *et al.*, 1967a; Smith *et al.*, 1967b).

Response to creep feeding depends on dam nutrition since Furr and Nelson (1959) increased weaning weights by 40 kg as a result of creep feeding when cows had a low wintering level compared with only 24 kg when the dams had been on a high plane. Contrary results were obtained by Anthony and Starling (1968) in that creep feeding gave greater calf gains when the dams were also supplemented. A more important aspect of this work was that supplementation of the cow increased her gain but not that of the calf, while creep feeding without supplementation of the dam increased both calf and cow weight gain.

There may also be a year effect (nutrition and environment) since Temple and Robertson (1961) found that calves creep-fed from 150 to 234 days of age gained 16 kg more than controls in 1959, but less than the controls in 1960. The authors

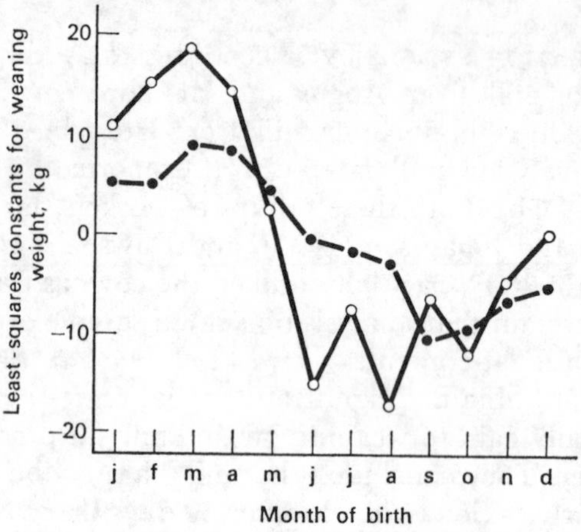

FIG. 6.2 Influence of month of birth on weight at weaning of creep-fed ● and non-creep-fed ○ calves (after Cundiff *et al.*, 1966).

claimed that conditions and management were identical for both groups, but this is hard to believe as this is the only report in the literature of a negative response to creep feeding. Smith *et al.* (1964) did not obtain a significant effect from creep feeding in Alabama, but in each of 3 years the supplemented animals had higher weaning weights and their market values were $6.92 per head higher. At a second station, average daily gains of creep-fed calves were 0.73 against 0.52 kg and weaning weights were 12.3 kg greater.

In an extensive study of factors affecting weaning weight, involving nearly 14,000 Hereford and Angus calves in Oklahoma, Cundiff *et al.* (1966b) found that creep feeding improved 205 day weaning weight by 12.8 kg. They noted that creep feeding reduced the seasonal effect on weaning weight (Fig. 6.2) in that deviations from the mean were less than when there was no creep feeding. The advantage was greater for calves born in summer and autumn.

6.5.7.2 ECONOMICAL ASPECTS. From the producer's point of view the important issue is not whether creep feeding improves weaning weight but what are the economic consequences of the practice. In a 4 year study with 314 calves which were creep-fed from about 3 months to almost 8 months, according to a limited (0.9 kg/day maximum), free choice or nil basis, Hunsley *et al.* (1967a) found creep feeding to be economic. At a sale price of 25 cents/kg, creep-fed calves returned from $3.91 to $28.38 more than the cost of the supplementary feed. On the other hand, limited creep feeding gave more consistent gains at only half the cost of the free-choice system. Wilson *et al.* (1966) also considered creep feeding to be economic. They early-weaned calves on to 4.7 kg of 50/50 concentrate/hay diet or creep-fed them for 140 days with 2.27 kg concentrates and 1.41 kg hay/day or gave them no supplement. Dams of the early weaned calves were fed at maintenance and the others at 76% of the energy requirements of a lactating beef cow. Average daily gains were 0.69, 0.87 and 0.50 kg for the three groups respectively; cow and calf feed costs per kilogram of calf gain were least for creep feeding and highest for controls. Similar results in favour of creep-feeding grain were obtained by Hammes *et al.* (1959) in Virginia (Tables 6.19 and 6.20).

TABLE 6.19 EFFECT OF CREEP FEEDING AND RESTRICTED FEEDING OF THE DAM ON LIVE WEIGHT CHANGES IN THE COW AND CALF[a] (AFTER HAMMES *et al.*, 1959)

kg DM fed to dam:	7.0 (50)[b]		8.2 (75)[b]		10.9 (100)[b]	
Cattle supplement:	Forage	Forage and grain	Forage	Forage and grain	Forage	Forage and grain
Daily gain of dam (kg)	−0.19	−0.15	−0.04	−0.18	0.25	0.21
Daily gain of calf[c] (kg)	0.82	0.95	0.75	0.99	0.80	0.97
Calf weaning-weight (kg)	209	220	203	224	206	222
Daily DM per calf (kg)	3.14	3.86	3.05	3.95	3.05	3.86
Daily TDN per calf (kg)	1.91	2.73	1.86	2.82	1.86	2.73

[a] Averages from three calf crops.
[b] 100 = amount of feed dams consume free choice in 2 hr feeds morning and evening.
[c] Initial weight 132 kg.

It is significant that Wilson *et al.* and Hammes *et al.* kept their animals in drylot, for under pasture conditions Furr and Nelson (1959) found that neither creep feeding nor high wintering of the cows was profitable. A similar conclusion can almost certainly be drawn from the data of Burns and Koger (1963) who creep-fed on a free choice basis Angus, Brangus, Hereford and Santa Gertrudis calves for 57 days immediately prior to weaning. The consumptions were 1.99, 1.32, 2.37 and 0.80 kg per day for the respective breeds while the additional weaning weight over controls was only 10.9, 5.0, 15.0 and 6.8 kg respectively. Rather surprisingly, Brahman calves refused to eat any creep feed, a situation which is quite atypical to judge from our own results in Cuba.

The high cost of creep feeding under pasture conditions is best illustrated by the work of Kuhlman *et al.* (1961) in Oklahoma. Creep-feeding calves of mature cows from 2 to 8.5 months of age increased weaning weight by 32 kg, but the calves con-

TABLE 6.20 EFFECT OF TYPE OF CREEP FEED ON WEIGHT CHANGES OF DAM AND CALF PERFORMANCE[a] (AFTER HAMMES *et al.*, 1959)

	Type of creep feed			
	Dam's milk only	Plus forage	Plus forage and grain	Plus grain
No. of calves	11	11	11	11
Daily gain of dam (kg)	0.16	0.22	0.16	0.15
Initial weight of calf (kg)	133	145	144	137
Daily gain of calf (kg)	0.15	0.82	1.00	1.00
Calf weaning-weight (kg)	146	220	235	228
Daily DM per calf (kg)				
Maize silage		1.32	0.59	—
Hay		2.09	1.55	—
Grain		—	2.09	2.59
Total		3.41	4.23	2.59
Daily TDN per calf (kg)		2.05	2.95	2.09

[a] Dams were fed to appetite; data for two calf crops.

sumed 399 kg of concentrates per head. Calves from young cows on the same regime gained 45 kg but ate 429 kg of concentrates. It was even less efficient giving concentrates to the cow since 429 kg fed to young cows only increased calf weaning-weight by 27 kg. In other experiments these investigators improved efficiency by removing the creep feed in April rather than mid-July; this reduced concentrate consumption by 227 kg/head and only reduced gains by 16 kg. Data pertaining to this investigation are given in Table 6.21. The uneconomic nature of this type of supplementary feeding is apparent when it is remembered that feed conversions during final fattening in the feedlot are much less (6–8) than the values for creep feeding in this experiment (7–19).

In areas where pasture land has a relatively high value, creep feeding can be economic if full account is taken of savings in pasture rental, since creep-fed calves reach a specified weight much earlier. A great deal would appear to depend on the growth potential of the animal. Thus Almquist (1968) found creep feeding to be uneconomic with heifers (where the growth improvement was only 8%), unless pasture savings were included, as feed costs were higher than the value of the extra weight obtained. With steers, on the other hand, the growth response to creep feeding was 24% and was economic on the basis of feed conversion alone which represented a 60% gross margin over creep feed consumed.

6.5.7.3 EARLY WEANING. Another factor which could well influence the response to creep feeding is the age at weaning. Both Wallace and Raleigh (1961) and Wilson *et al.* (1966) observed that early weaning on to concentrate/hay mixtures gave better results than leaving calves with their dams without creep feeding. The earlier workers weaned calves at 177 days of age in September and found that in the next 37 days, until the controls were weaned, those weaned early gained 0.38 kg/day compared

TABLE 6.21 EFFECT OF CREEP FEEDING ON CALF GAINS (AFTER KUHLMAN *et al.*, 1961)

	Type of creep feed					
	Nil	Basal[a] to weaning	Basal[a] to spring	Basal[a] (pelleted) to spring	Alfalfa hay to spring	Alfalfa hay (pelleted) to spring
Calf gain (kg)						
Dec.–April	55.9	73.6	78.2	68.2	66.8	67.3
April–July	72.3	88.2	66.4	68.6	68.6	69.1
Total	128.2	161.8	144.6	136.8	135.4	136.4
Feed consumed (kg)	0	419	115	88	140	102
Supplementary feed per kg additional gain (kg)	—	12.5	7.0	10.2	19.4	12.4

[a] Basal = 55% rolled sorghum, 33% whole oats, 10% cottonseed meal, 5% molasses.

with 0.19 kg for calves still suckling. Neither of these studies incorporated creep feeding before early weaning and the diets post-weaning were not high energy. An important aspect for the success of early weaning would seem to be the diet used, for weaning at 4 months on to a diet based on maize silage gave poorer calf gains and feed utilization than conventional nursing (Hammes *et al.*, 1968a). In contrast, when the nutritional plane of the early weaned calves was improved, and the feeding plane of the dry cows reduced, there was an overall advantage for early weaning (Hammes *et al.*, 1968b).

It may be that creep feeding offers most possibilities as a means of conditioning animals to the high energy diets they will subsequently receive in the feedlot. Hunsley *et al.* (1967a) found that creep-fed calves put immediately into the feedlot after weaning reached slaughter weight faster and had a significantly better carcass weight for age than their non-creep-fed counterparts. In this instance weaning was at the customary age of 7–8 months. We believe that the feeding regimes of the future will necessitate early weaning at 3–4 months directly on to a high energy diet. Under such circumstances creep feeding of a concentrate mixture is justified as a means of preconditioning the calves to the diet they will subsequently receive in the feedlot. An essential adjunct of this procedure is maintenance feeding of the cows, throughout their life, except for short periods of time immediately prior to service. In Virginia, Hammes *et al.* (1965) have advocated weaning at 4 months, coupled with a winter feeding level for dry cows of 2.5 kg TDN daily. They considered that this system resulted in the most efficient use of feed per unit of calf gain.

6.5.8 Effect of hormones

Implants of 12 mg DES were given to non-creep-fed nursing calves in three trials by Essig and Williams (1962). Implanted calves gained faster in all three trials which ranged from 110 to 140 days duration. The overall improvement due to treatment was 12%. In this experiment calves of both sexes were used whereas subsequent work by Patton and Ralston (1968) related specifically to bull calves. Implantation (12 mg) at birth induced significantly faster gains to 3 months of age and there was still a slight weight advantage for treated animals at weaning. Treatment at birth, or at 3 months, or at both ages delayed development of such secondary sex characteristics as crest and shoulder development.

The possibilities of utilizing thyroxine implants to improve milk production was investigated in Wyoming by Asplund *et al.* (1963). A 48 mg implant given 4–6 weeks after calving significantly increased weaning weight by 4%. No information was given regarding effects on cow weight.

6.5.9 Repeatability of weaning weight

The degree to which the weaning weight of a calf can serve as a guide to the weight of subsequent half-sibs is unlikely to be high. Hoover *et al.* (1956) found the repeatability of 210 day weight in 1110 calves from 303 cows to be 0.32. In the report of Drewry and Hazel (1966), weight at 100 days was less repeatable with creep feeding ($r = 0.38$) than without ($r = 0.50$) which is to be expected. At weaning, however, values were similar ($r = 0.43$ and 0.44) and in good agreement with the figure of 0.48 derived by Cunningham and Henderson (1965b) from 4838 records in New York State. A study of similar scale carried out by Hohenboken and Brinks (1968) in Colorado gave repeatability of only 0.25.

6.6. CALF MORTALITY

6.6.1 Causes

In beef herds the statistic "calf mortality" has little meaning except with respect to the specific conditions pertaining to the individual herd. In many areas the extensive methods of beef cow management, often involving no more than an annual "round up", preclude the recording of death prior to weaning. The importance of mortality in a particular herd is illustrated by the analysis of data from a Colorado Hereford herd in the period 1930–67 (Fagerlin *et al.*, 1968). In 24,710 calvings by 4531 cows, 35% of cows produced at least one dead calf during their lifetime, while 6% aborted at least once. On average they each produced 5.4 calves and lived for 8.2 years.

Generally, under US or European conditions disease is not a major factor. For example, Anderson and Bellows (1967), in a survey of 3049 Hereford calvings in Montana during 1956–61, found that 4.7% of calves died, of which 86% were born dead or died within 24 hr, the remainder being lost in the first 30 days of life. Of those lost at birth, 79% were physically normal and death was due to injury following a difficult or delayed calving; the remaining 21% had skeletal or organic abnormalities. Non-functional lungs were found in 70.5% of calves born dead. Pneumonia, and to a lesser extent injury, were the major causes of loss between birth and 30 days of age.

The significance of embryonic mortality as a factor influencing calf crop is illustrated by the finding of Laing (1949) that, in 48 heifers slaughtered 25 days post-insemination, the incidence of loss from this cause was 25%. In records relating to

1475 births from four different breeds of cattle in Louisiana, DeRouen *et al.* (1967) found that of total calf deaths up to 72 hr, 42% were stillborn, 48% died within the first 24 hr, 5% on the second day and the remainder between 48 and 72 hr. Forty-four per cent of the losses within 24 hr of birth were due to drowning in amniotic fluid. There appeared to be a close relationship between low temperature, high rainfall and observed mortality. Koger *et al.* (1967) investigated calf mortality in 3408 calvings from several breeds over 5 years. Abortions accounted for 6.2% of total deaths, 50.8% died within 24 hr, 12% died between 24 and 72 hr and the remaining 31% of deaths occurred prior to weaning. Hurst and Godley (1965) reported a 76% live calf crop, a 74% weaning crop and a stillbirth rate of 9% in a South Carolina beef herd.

Stillbirths are an important problem not only because this represents a lower calf crop, but also because subsequent cow fertility may be reduced. Thus in the MRY breed in Holland, Van Dieten (1966) reported that conception rate was 13–14% lower after stillbirths. This is probably due, in part, to retained placentas which were 10% more frequent following stillbirths. An analysis in Switzerland (Friedli, 1965) revealed that the longer the interval between first loss of amniotic fluid and the expulsion of the foetus, the greater the risk of stillbirths.

6.6.2 Breed effects

Available data on calf mortality in different beef breeds are given in Table 6.22. There is much confounding due to location and system of management. Probably the only valid conclusion is that in the Americas the Brahman is inferior to other breeds. Some of the difficulties in Brahmans may well be associated with the tendency of some cows to fail to nurse. This phenomenon has been reported on by Reynolds *et al.* (1967a) and we have also observed some 10% losses mainly due to this cause among Brahman calves in Cuba. Chagas *et al.* (1966) reported on the low vigour immediately *post-partum* of Brahman calves despite the fact that they were heavier than the calves of other breeds in the comparison. It may be that this low vigour is not so much a characteristic of the calf but rather the failure of its mother to supply it with sufficient milk. DeRouen *et al.* (1963) also showed that 6% of Red Sindhi cows refused their calves at birth.

The possibility of sire effects on calf losses was first raised by Hurst and Godley (1965) and was confirmed by the results of an extensive analysis of AI data in Israeli Friesians (Heiman, 1968). Selection of sires led to a 30% reduction in stillbirths and dystokia problems.

In areas where disease is enzootic, mortality can assume massive proportions, and genetically conferred resistance or acquired resistance becomes a major factor. This is discussed in § 4.4.

6.6.3 Age of dam

The data of Anderson and Bellows (1967) show a clear effect of dam age on calf mortality in that 9.5% were lost from 3-year-old cows, 4.3% from 4-year-olds and only 2.4% from mature cows. Koger *et al.* (1967), on the other hand, observed that calf survival rate was remarkably constant up to 10 years but declined rapidly in aged cows of over 11 years.

TABLE 6.22 EFFECT OF BREED ON CALF MORTALITY

Location	Angus	Afr. Angus	Brahman	Brangus	Charolais	Hereford	Others	Authors
Montana						4.1[a]		Bellows, 1968
Italy							1.1[bc]	Bordi *et al.*, 1966
Texas			23.5			4.3		Chagas *et al.*, 1966
Colorado						3.4[b] 6.0[a]		Clark *et al.*, 1963
Louisiana	5.0[d]	6.0[d]	19.0[d]	9.0[d]				DeRouen *et al.*, 1967
France					13			De Vree, 1961
Colorado						8.1[b]		Fagerlin *et al.*, 1968
Virginia	8.9[a]					13.3[a]	7.9[ai]	Gaines *et al.*, 1966
Florida			14.2[a]					Koger *et al.*, 1967
Ceylon			16[af]					Ranatunga, 1965
S. Africa		1.0[a]				16.2[a]	5.8[g]	Reilly, 1957
Missouri	11.4[h]				5.6[h]	0.0[h]		Sagebiel *et al.*, 1967a
Louisiana	2.8[b] 7.4[a]		0.9[b] 8.0[a]	2.8[b] 7.6[a]		4.0[b] 9.0[a]		Turner *et al.*, 1968
Virginia	9.0[b]					7.8[b]	13.0[bi]	Wiltbank *et al.*, 1961
Virginia	13.0[a]					10.3[a]	19.2[ai]	Wiltbank *et al.*, 1961
Louisiana		10.4[a]	23.0[a]	16.0[a]				Wiltbank *et al.*, 1961
Nebraska	6.0[a]					8.0[a]	9.0[ai]	Wiltbank *et al.* ,1967a
Montana						3.6[b]		Woodward & Clark, 1959
Cuba			21.6[a]		10.6[a]		11.5[aj] 12.9[ak]	Willis & Preston, 1968a

[a] To weaning. [b] Stillbirths. [c] Chiani. [d] To 72 hr *post-partum*. [e] Other breeds 3.8–7.5%. [f] Zebu. [g] Bonsmara. [h] Embryonic.
[i] Shorthorn. [j] Criollo. [k] Santa Gertrudis.

Van Loen and Van Dieten (1962) reported that in dairy herds in Holland there was a gradual decline in stillbirths from first calvers, from 15.9% in 1956 to 9.2% in 1960. Fifty per cent of Hereford heifers in Oklahoma needed assistance at calving, according to Moore *et al.* (1956). Fifteen per cent of calves and 5% of their dams died at parturition. Subsequently Bellows (1968) blamed calving difficulties and delay for 57% of total losses.

The data in Table 6.23 show that age effects are not due to abnormal presentations or to particularly large calves in absolute terms, but are more probably due to the smaller pelvic size of the dam and the size of the calf relative to dam weight.

TABLE 6.23 EFFECT OF AGE ON CALVING DIFFICULTIES (AFTER BELLOWS, 1968)

Age and lactation status of dam	No. of calvings	Calvings requiring assistance		Birth weight of calf
		Normal presentations (%)	Abnormal presentations (%)	(kg)
Cows over 4 years	465	0.8	2.2	37.6
Heifers				
3 years	158	15.8	6.3	35.4
2 years	287	43.2	2.8	32.7

6.6.4 Sex and size of calf

In their analysis of Hereford cattle in Montana, Woodward and Clark (1959) reported that 62% of stillbirths were males although total male births were only 51%. In this herd, 52% of deaths from birth to weaning were females, thus sex ratio at weaning was similar to that at birth (Clark *et al.*, 1963). Anderson and Bellows (1967) also found that 60.5% of calves born dead were males; stillborn males weighed 34.4 while females were only 26.5 kg. In the East Flemish Red Pied, 78% of calving difficulties were with males which Vandeplassche *et al.* (1965) considered to be due to their greater breadth rather than weight. Woodward and Clark (1959) thought that heavy birth weights were not the sole cause of deaths since stillborn calves ranged from 8 to 57 kg compared with 12–51 kg for live births. Koger *et al.* (1967) also found that birth weight showed a quadratic relation with survival, more calves being lost at the extremes of the birth weight ranges.

In a report of Charolais crossbreeding trials in the UK, Edwards *et al.* (1966) found a marked sex effect on mortality as well as a breed effect, in that males and Charolais crosses were more likely to die than females or Hereford crosses or the pure dairy breeds. These findings almost certainly reflected the greater size of males compared with females and Charolais crossbreds versus the other breeds. An earlier report on this same data (Wood, 1965) indicated that calving difficulties and associated calf mortality were related to birth weight, but that the weight at which difficulties began was lower for female calves than for males. Amir *et al.* (1967) considered calf size to be a major cause of calf death in very early calving Friesian heifers, as difficulties only occurred with calves weighing more than 35 kg. They concluded that calf size relative to maternal size was more important than birth weight *per se*. Schultze (1965) and Vandeplassche *et al.* (1965) stressed this same point in concluding that dystokia was more prevalent when birth weight exceeded 8–9% of dam weight. According to Friedli (1965), 37% of 894 cases of dystokia were caused by oversize, and 20% by abnormal presentation.

In this connection it is perhaps necessary to comment upon calving difficulties alleged to be associated with the Charolais. Evidence from the UK (Anon., 1963a; Edwards *et al.*, 1966) illustrates the higher proportion of calving difficulties attendant upon the use of bulls of this breed, although it must be pointed out that advance publicity on the Charolais importations had emphasized this aspect with the result that some of the reported problems may have been more imaginary than real. This is borne out by the sharp decline in incidence of calving problems in the second year of births. A similar study in Ireland (Crowley, 1965), confirmed that there were more dystokia cases with Charolais sires than with other breeds (Dairy Shorthorn, Hereford and Friesian). Dystokia incidence was 29.6 versus 11.7%; however, calf losses were no different, e.g. 1.6% for Charolais sires compared with 1.7% for other breeds. Charolais cross calves were carried longer but no clear link could be determined between gestation period and dystokia. Nevertheless, such crosses weighed more than 39 kg in 66% of births compared with only 26.7% for other breeds. Ekman-Bjaresten (1965) found that calving difficulties in Swedish polled cattle increased from 5.6 to 22.2% when Charolais sires were used. In contrast, when Charolais were used on Jersey cattle in Denmark, relatively few problems were encountered (Hansen, 1965, 1966).

Work by Reyneke and Penzhorn (1964) in South Africa revealed 30.4% dystokia cases when Charolais were mated with Friesland cows. Higher birth weight was a major contributing factor and problems were most severe in young dams. In a specific study of dystokia in reciprocal crosses of Angus, Charolais and Hereford, Sagebiel *et al.* (1968) considered the Charolais to be one of the main causes of this condition. Sire breeds did not differ significantly in causing dystokia in Hereford or Charolais cows but Angus cows crossed with Charolais and Hereford had 39 and 29% more dystokia than when bred pure. Greater dystokia in Zebu when they were mated to Charolais was reported in Brazil by Vianna *et al.* (1964b), although it was not highly correlated with birth weight.

When the Charolais is bred pure, dystokia appears to be no more of a problem with this breed than with any other, for Creek and Nestel (1962), using animals of fifteen-sixteenths Charolais breeding, obtained only 5 dystokia cases in 467 births. Neuvy and Vissac (1962) also reported only 2% dystokia (1.5% stillbirths) in 440 double-muscled (Cullard) cows; rearing losses were 3%. Our own observations in Cuba support these findings in that there were no dystokia cases in over 150 births even though calves occasionally exceeded 50 kg in weight, while heifers have calved as early as 20 months of age. In crosses with Brahman dams, however, some cases of dystokia occurred. De Vree (1961) studied French Charolais records and observed that 75% of cows reared calves to weaning at 8 months with some 3% abortions and 12% stillbirths or barrenness. He did not mention dystokia problems even though birth weights of males averaged more than 45 kg. Jobst (1963) quoted French data on 898 Charolais calvings of which 86% were normal. Of 218 heifer calvings only 70% were normal. In a more extensive survey of over 10,000 cows in the Nevers region of France, Chatre *et al.* (1967) reported that 82% of calvings were normal, 10% required assistance and 8% veterinary assistance. Most dystokia occurred in the winter when cows were housed. The greater incidence of calving difficulties in purebred herds in France is almost certainly a reflection of a higher nutritional plane since it is known that this leads to greater dystokia (Dickey and Cartwright, 1966).

6.6.5 Nutrition

Nutritional effects on calf liveability are implied in the work of Hawkins *et al.* (1965) for the heaviest cows pre-calving weaned fewer and lighter calves. That this may be related to calving difficulties is suggested by the work of Anscher and Hobbs (1968) who fed cows and heifers 3.24, 3.99 or 4.16 kg TDN/day prior to calving. Scores for calving difficulties were 1.09, 1.23 and 1.75 respectively, the scale being 1–4 in ascending order of severity. The percentages of animals requiring assistance at calving were 38, 50 and 65 for the low, medium and high nutritional levels. Under range conditions, moderate supplementary feeding of Herefords did not increase abortions, stillbirths or other deaths which were 2.0, 3.2 and 4 to 7% respectively (Wagnon *et al.*, 1959). More specific data are those of Speth *et al.* (1962) who reported significantly higher calf mortality when cows were fed a commercial protein supplement in contrast to the use of barley, alfalfa or no supplement; the losses were 16.7, 0.0, 1.7 and 3.3% respectively. These cattle were Herefords on semi-desert range in Nevada. Knox and Watkins (1958) in New Mexico and Olsen (1959) in Utah also reported high calf losses when cows were fed protein supplements. This should not be construed as indicating that supplementary feeding of beef cows with protein is always deleterious. The problem is certainly not a direct consequence of giving protein, on the contrary very severe restriction of dietary protein during gestation and lactation has been shown in rats to cause permanent stunting of the progeny such that they never reached normal adult weight and their feed conversion was less efficient due to nitrogen wastage (Chow, 1968). According to this author, growth hormone injections reversed the stunting process which implies that damage in the foetal stage was to the pituitary gland.

The observations of Bohman *et al.* (1962), that plasma carotene and liver vitamin A of beef cows were lower when supplementary protein was fed, suggest that the deleterious effect of protein supplementation is in fact a secondary one, and that vitamin A deficiency is the real cause. Significantly, Speth *et al.* (1962) reported that protein supplementation decreased plasma carotene and vitamin A while barley increased it. Although Wheeler *et al.* (1957) considered that pregnant cows could obtain sufficient vitamin A from spring grazing to cover their needs in the subsequent winter, this is not universally accepted. Thus, during a 4 year period with year-round calving we have observed a notably higher incidence of stillbirths at the end of the Cuban dry season (February–April). These losses were not related to breed, size at birth or gestation period. The condition occurred most frequently in heifers calving early at low live-weights, a situation certain to aggravate possible vitamin deficiencies.

A specific benefit from giving daily 16,000 rising to 40,000 IU vitamin A during mid and late gestation (November to April) was implied in the data of Meacham *et al.* (1964). Treated cows had 6.6% stillbirths and 8.1% post-natal mortality compared with 8.8 and 16.5% for untreated controls. Burns *et al.* (1968) found that vitamin A injections (3 million IU to calves and 6 million IU to cows in the autumn and spring) did not affect calf survival rate in Florida; nevertheless calves from injected cows were significantly heavier at birth. For effects of vitamin A on reproduction see § 6.2.3.3.

A specific vitamin A deficiency was probably responsible for abortions and stillbirths, as well as retained placentas, in beef cows maintained on all-concentrate diets based on barley (Nicholson and Cunningham, 1965). The data are sparse, but in three trials there were 21 retained placentas and 9 dead calves from 43 cows not given vitamin A and only one retained placenta and no deaths from 27 cows given control diets or barley plus vitamin A. Neither vitamin E nor selenium had any beneficial effect.

Increased calf mortality due to feeding beef cows in late gestation on rations of straw and roots was shown by Blaxter and Sharman (1953) to be due to muscular dystrophy caused by dietary lack of vitamin E.

In East Africa, Stobbs (1967) managed indigenous Zebu stock under different systems, namely hand milking with bucket feeding of calves, milking half the udder and letting the calf suckle the other two quarters and natural suckling on open range. Calf mortality (1947–51) was 14.3, 11.1 and 7.7% respectively. The author ascribed the high losses, when the cows were milked by hand, to the calf receiving insufficient milk. From 1952 to 1956 an additional treatment, namely milking once daily—the calves subsequently having access to the cow for 12 hr—was introduced. Mortality with this procedure was 19.1% whereas in the same period losses on bucket feeding had risen to 23.8%.

6.7 BEEF COW NUTRITION

6.7.1 Nutrient requirements

Various estimates of the maintenance requirement of a dry non-pregnant cow weighing 500 kg are given in Table 6.24. There is fairly good agreement as regards energy needs and a value of some 11 Mcal ME/day would seem to be a safe estimate. Although Elliott *et al.* (1964) found a 15% difference existed between two breeds of *B. indicus*, few animals were used and the differences may well not have been significant. Klosterman *et al.* (1968) observed that Charolais and Hereford had the same requirements on a metabolic body weight basis which is in agreement with the findings of Van Es (1961) that between animal variation in the energy requirements for maintenance was only 5%.

The situation with respect to protein needs is much less clear. The estimate of Elliott and Topps (1963a) is by far the lowest. However, this should be qualified by the fact that it was obtained with a 50% concentrate diet which is known to improve efficiency of nitrogen utilization (§ 5.5). The NRC estimate is clearly excessive and we consider that for the type of situation normally encountered by the beef cow, i.e. high roughage feeding, a value of about 400 g daily would seem most satisfactory. This is in agreement with the findings of Winchester and Harvey (1966).

Both the ARC and the NRC propose a considerable increase (50–80%) in the energy allowance during the two final months of pregnancy, and this is supported by

TABLE 6.24 DAILY CRUDE PROTEIN AND ME REQUIRED TO MAINTAIN WEIGHT IN A 500 kg BEEF COW[a]

ME (Mcal)	Crude protein (g)	Authors
11.3	370	ARC, 1965
13.8	560	NRC, 1963
—	475	Bond *et al.*, 1962
—	234	Elliott & Topps, 1963a
9.3	—	Elliott *et al.*, 1964
11.8	—	Garrett *et al.*, 1959b
11.0	414	Klosterman *et al.*, 1968
13.0	—	Neville & McCullough, 1968
11.5	—	Van Es & Nijkamp, 1967

[a] Requirements for other weights can be calculated by converting to metabolic body weight ($W^{0.75}$).

the finding of Van Es (1961) that heat production increases in late pregnancy at a rate greater than would be expected for non-pregnant animals gaining the same amount of weight.

6.7.2 Range feeding

Specific nutrient requirements have little value in the general context of a ranching operation. The overall aim must be to carry as many cows as possible without reducing fertility and calf performance. As conditions vary immensely, carrying capacity can only be evaluated by experience. However, it must be realised that the only criterion is the weaned calf crop and not the condition of the cows. To this end grazing management and supplementation should be directed towards improving cow fertility and calf liveability and growth. It has already been established that an increasing plane of nutrition at the time of mating will improve conception rate (§ 6.2.3.3); on the other hand, high energy feeding in late pregnancy will tend to increase calving difficulties (§ 6.6.5). We therefore consider that, contrary to usual recommendations, feed allowances should not be raised in late pregnancy, but rather in the breeding season. Since this latter coincides with early lactation an increased nutritional plane at this time will also improve calf performance. We believe that at all other stages of her productive life the beef cow should be kept at the minimum live weight and condition consistent with survival. Moreover, there are grounds for believing that cows adapt to low energy feeding (Elliott *et al.*, 1966) and thus lean cows may well have lower lifetime requirements than those kept in good condition.

There is no reason to believe that keeping cows in a poor body condition need reduce calf crop and Texas workers (Mathis and Kothmann, 1968) have shown that while a heavy stocking density resulted in lighter cows, the percentage calf crop was not affected. In some cases this may result in lighter calves at weaning, but a rancher is likely to benefit more by carrying a greater number of cows, and hence weaning more calves although of slightly lower weight. Under an early weaning system the advantages for greater carrying capacities will be even more marked.

While grazing management should aim to conserve feed supplies for the breeding season this may not always be possible and it might be more convenient to rely on supplementation with grain, molasses or other available energy sources. That some degree of supplementation is necessary is apparent from the data of Waldrip and Marion (1963) where no supplementation resulted in an 84% calf crop, whereas winter supplementation with 0.68 kg of cottonseed meal increased calf crop to 90%. Doubling the supplementary allowance had no further beneficial effect upon fertility.

In contrast to results in the feedlot (§ 9.5.2.2) there is almost unanimous agreement that nitrogen-containing supplements based on urea do not promote the same level of performance, particularly weaning weight, as true protein sources such as cottonseed meal (Nelson *et al.*, 1957; Nelson and Waller, 1962; Williams *et al.*, 1968b). This is not unexpected (§ 5.5).

6.7.3 Drylot feeding

The justification for maintaining single-purpose beef herds is that the breeding cows can exist on land unsuitable for cultivation. In Europe where all land is in short supply such specialist operations represent a comparatively small proportion of total cattle numbers. It is only in the extensive continents of America, Africa and Australia that beef herds predominate.

Population growth and rising living standards both result in increasing encroachment on land hitherto given over to natural grasslands. Some of this development represents land lost to agriculture and, in any event, the overall effect is one of forcing greater intensification on all branches of the industry.

Of all agricultural enterprises beef breeding has so far been the most resistant to change, but in the early 1960's reports began to appear, particularly from the US, regarding the feasability of keeping beef cows under drylot conditions. Much of the incentive for this development undoubtedly stems from the increasing cost of labour and the inherent difficulties of replacing men with machines in extensive ranch operations. Diminishing profit margins have also focused attention on the need to raise productivity, in terms of percentage calf crop; unfortunately, the remedies for this are themselves costly in labour and thus can only be justified where cows are kept intensively.

The most extensive data on drylot versus pasture management for beef cows were obtained by Marion *et al.* (1962, 1964, 1968) from an experiment begun in Texas in 1959. The results for seven calf crops showed that both groups of cows weaned on average an 88% crop with a fractional advantage in weaning weight (2%) in favour of cows kept in drylot. Possible dangers inherent in the system were revealed in the eighth calf crop when all the drylot cows calved but weaned only 71% of calves at a mean weight of 205 kg; in contrast, the controls weaned 88% of calves at an average weight of 241 kg. Marion *et al.* (1968) considered that this was due to cumulative mineral and vitamin deficiencies since supplementation had not been consistent. On the credit side was the fact that after 9 years, 86% of the original 36 drylot cows still remained compared with only 69% of controls.

Greater animal losses on pasture rather than in drylot were also noted by Goodrich and Meiske (1967) in their report of a similar experiment which began in Minnesota in 1963. In this trial, mean calf crops were 85% on pasture and 86% in drylot and there appeared to be no differences between the systems in regard to reproductive capacity. The birth and weaning weights of the drylot calves were somewhat less despite higher consumption of creep feed, and it was considered that milk production was slightly lower under such a system.

The results of Reynolds *et al.* (1964b) in Louisiana confirm the findings of the Texas work (Marion *et al.*, 1964) that level of nutrition was more important than management system (drylot versus pasture) with respect to reproductive performance.

Some indication of the feed requirements for a confinement feeding operation were given by Brown *et al.* (1968). The average yearly consumption over a 3 year period was 11,400 kg of silage and 202 kg of cottonseed meal per cow and 588 kg of grain creep-fed to the calf (89% weaned calf crop at 240 kg). Giving Coastal Bermuda grass hay and only 0.45 kg of cottonseed meal daily reduced calf crop to 73% and weaning weight to 222 kg, despite only a 4% reduction in consumption of creep feed.

There is some suggestion in the data of Neville and McCullough (1968) that group-fed cows gained 10% less than those fed individually on the same amount of feed. If this is corroborated it would imply that drylot feeding might benefit from being arranged on a cafeteria system such as is frequently done with pigs, cows being left in groups but receiving their feed individually.

6.8 CONDITIONING CATTLE FOR THE FEEDLOT

6.8.1 Introduction

It was considered by Herrick (1968) that under US feedlot conditions the financial loss occasioned by the changeover from pasture to intensive fattening amounted to between $10 and $20 per animal entering the feedlot. Estimates of loss associated with the introduction of calves and cattle into dairy beef programmes in Europe are not available but are likely to be of similar magnitude.

Certain problems are common to both systems, namely, deaths in transit and subsequent respiratory disease on arrival. Others are specific to the particular management system. Thus acidosis can be a serious factor if the change from pasture to all-concentrate feeding is made too rapidly (§ 11.3.1), while potassium poisoning can occur when the fattening diet is based on molasses (§ 11.3.6).

Specific "conditioning" procedures to adapt cattle for transit and their subsequent fattening have been developed with a view to reducing losses and improving feedlot performance. Such preconditioning has two basic components—that aimed at combating diseases associated with transit and metabolic upsets and that which seeks to adapt the animal to the eventual fattening diet. In the main, measures against disease must be initiated by the calf producer while nutritional adaptation is usually better undertaken at the actual feedlot.

6.8.2 Transit stress

6.8.2.1 TRANQUILLIZERS. Early attempts to alleviate stress factors in transit and to minimize shrinkage involved the use of tranquillizer drugs. Luther *et al.* (1959)

injected different levels of perphenazine 17–20 hr prior to transporting cattle for distances of up to 480 km. Although the drug was effective in inducing mild sedation, it had no appreciable effect on transit shrink or subsequent performance. A similar lack of effectiveness with respect to the drug tetrahydrozoline was reported by England and Taylor (1960). Slightly more encouraging findings were observed by Haines and Chapman (1962) using a commercial product based on reserpine. Low levels (0.88–1.4 mg per 100 kg live weight) reduced transit shrink, but higher doses induced detrimental side effects including death.

6.8.2.2 Management factors. Males *et al.* (1968) studied the effect of various management procedures upon the incidence of stress and sickness. One hundred and thirty steer and heifer calves of 120 kg were used. On average each had to be treated 4.27 times for sickness. Transporting them directly from farm to feedlot produced fewer problems (2.5 treatments) than when they passed through an auction market (5.1 treatments). Weaning the calf immediately prior to transit, or one month earlier, was not an important factor. Similarly, vaccination 2 weeks prior to transit was of no advantage compared with vaccination on arrival at the feedlot. Daily gain for the month prior to transit averaged 0.48 and fell to 0.21 kg for the first month in the feedlot. None of the six treatments affected daily gain over the whole 2 month period.

Data from Iowa, quoted at a conference on preconditioning in Wyoming (Bristol, 1968), reinforce the above findings that the major effect of transit stress is upon health and not subsequent gain. Of cattle in transit for up to 24 hr, 4.2% became sick and of these 14.2% died; corresponding figures for transit times in excess of 24 hr were 9.4 and 17.0%. Although animals in the 130–200 kg weight range had 3 times as much respiratory disease as heavier animals, the mortality rate tended to be greater with the latter.

6.8.2.3 Measures to be taken by the producer. During 1967 and 1968 considerable controversy existed in the US regarding the advantages and disadvantages of various preconditioning programmes, aimed primarily at reducing disease incidence in cattle arriving at the feedlot. Typical recommendations made by Drake (1967) in Nevada included: (a) vaccination at branding and 3 weeks prior to weaning to give immunity against blackleg and malignant oedoema, redwater fever, leptospirosis, shipping fever, bovine virus diarrhoea and in some cases anthrax and anaplasmosis; (b) weaning 30 days prior to transit and being accustomed to hay and grain; and (c) castration and dehorning at an early age and treatment for parasites.

While none of these measures is harmful, they are not always beneficial and some are positively difficult for the rancher to execute. They certainly cost money—up to $10.00–$14.50 per head according to Herrick (1967)—and no rancher would embark on them without the expectation of receiving a better price for his product. However, the feedlot operator will be unlikely to pay more for preconditioned cattle unless he can recover his investment through reduced disease incidence and/or better subsequent gains and efficiency. At the moment no concrete evidence exists as to what degree of improvement, if any, can be expected as a result of preconditioning. For example, Sudweeks and Smith (1968) preconditioned 6-month-old steers on alfalfa hay alone or with either grain or a commercial weaning ration plus antibiotics. During the 22 days following weaning there were no significant differences in daily gain, but the first treatment was the most economic costing 11 and 46% less, respectively, than the other two.

With respect to the transport of dairy beef calves (from 1 to 12 weeks of age), our unpublished observations suggest that it is beneficial (in terms of reduced sickness) to avoid overcrowding and to employ an independent ventilation system when the transport is stationary. But, as with preconditioning, it is difficult to assess the value of these measures in economic terms.

6.8.2.4 Preventive measures at the feedlot. Jensen and Mackey (1965) advocated giving high roughage feeds for a week after arrival at the feedlot, although there is no experimental evidence to indicate that this in any way helps to prevent disease. Concentrates *per se* are not the problem since in dairy beef production artificially reared calves, already receiving all-concentrate diets, are as subject to transit fever when moved to the feedlot as animals previously raised on roughage.

Concrete evidence that the major problem is diminished resistance to disease challenge, as a result of transit and other stress factors, was put forward by Drain *et al.* (1966). In four trails with cattle previously subjected to stress, they observed that 350 mg/head daily of chlortetracycline improved weight gain by 14% over controls in the first 4 weeks in the feedlot; sulphamethazine fed at the same rate improved gains by 7%; while the two drugs combined gave a 22% response. There were related improvements in feed conversion although of a lower magnitude. In a similar experiment, Furr *et al.* (1968d) obtained growth improvements of the order of 20% by use of chlortetracycline alone or combined with sulphamethazine. The latter given alone was somewhat less effective (11%). Confirmatory results with respect to the use of these two drugs in combination were given by Beeson (1968).

The same treatments were also applied by Kercher and Paules (1968a) to Hereford calves during a 28 day period after transit. The combined treatment gave fastest gains during the conditioning period although the effect had largely disappeared 56 days later. In a second trial when only chlortetracycline was used, the improved gains were not significantly different from controls.

Wieser *et al.* (1966) fed chlortetracycline at the rate of 20 mg/kg of an all-concentrate diet for dairy beef calves from arrival at the feedlot, and reported significantly greater live weight gains during the first 2 months for the treated stock compared with controls. The growth response due to antibiotic treatment was negatively related to the performance of the controls which implied that the better growth of the treated animals reflected, in part, a control of sub-clinical disease. Calves are most resistant in the early weeks of life while they still possess passive immunity from their dam's colostrum. Thus, in an integrated operation where artificially reared diary calves from different sources are to be fattened intensively it would be advantageous for them to be mixed together as early in life as possible so that they could gain immunity while under the protection of maternal antibodies.

Antibiotic treatment of animals on arrival at the feedlot is often more effectively done by medication of the water supply since new arrivals are more certain to drink than to eat.

6.8.3 Adaptation to diet

6.8.3.1 High concentrate systems. Durham *et al.* (1967b) inoculated cattle 6 days after starting on an all-concentrate diet, using rumen ingesta from an animal previously fed on the same ration. Over a 53 day period, 23 inoculated steers gained 1.06 kg with a feed conversion of 7.38 compared with 0.84 and 8.54 respectively for a similar number of controls. Values for 26 heifers given the same treatment were 1.21 and 5.82 for inoculated against 1.03 and 6.52 for controls. The authors considered that inoculation helped to speed up adaptation to the new diet.

A procedure developed by UK workers (Preston, 1963a; RRI, 1964) made use of a special high fibre pelleted diet in the intermediate stage when cattle were changed from pasture to all-concentrate feeding. The mixture was 25% undecorticated cotton-seed meal, 25% oat husks, 20% rolled oats, 28% rolled barley and minerals and vitamins. Other diets, for example 50% ground maize cobs and 50% ground ear maize, or 25% bagasse pith and 75% ground maize, have also been used successfully by us in Cuba. The recommended feeding plan is to give the changeover diet *ad libitum* from a self-feeder for the first 7 days after cattle come from grass or forage. The all-concentrate diet is then substituted gradually over the next 7–10 days so that at least 14 days elapse before cattle are maintained solely on all-concentrate feed.

6.8.3.2 High molasses systems. The research and development work connected with this system of feeding is described in § 9.3.3 and the specific disease problems associated with these diets are outlined in § 11.3.6.

With weaned calves raised on pasture to at least 120 kg live weight there appear to be no real difficulties provided the changeover is made gradually over a 14 day period. A suitable procedure is to give the full quantity of protein supplement from the start but not to introduce molasses until the end of the first week during which time fresh forage is fed at the rate of about 10 kg per head daily. The molasses/urea solution is then introduced and gradually increased in quantity until after a further 7 days it is available *ad libitum*. During this time the forage is gradually reduced to the desired level of 1.5 kg (0.3 kg DM) per 100 kg live weight.

There is evidence that it is much safer to give the molasses/urea in dilute form (14–35° Brix) during the first 2 months of the fattening period since this reduces the risk of over-consumption at a time when the animals are most susceptible to molasses toxicity (Preston *et al.*, 1968a). In heavily parasitized cattle the period of changeover may have to be extended beyond 14 days as this class of animal appears most prone to toxicity problems.

Specific difficulties have arisen with dairy beef calves which have been raised artificially by early weaning on all-concentrate diets. The limiting factor appears to be rumen pH which is always low in such calves and must be raised by giving only forage for a minimum of one week (Elías and Preston, 1969d). As protozoa also play an integral role in the utilization of the urea in these diets, rumen inoculation with ingesta from adult animals is practised as a safeguard, although its efficiency has yet to be demonstrated experimentally. In pasture-raised cattle, already possessing microflora rich in protozoa, such inoculations have proved to be of no benefit (Elías *et al.*, 1968a).

CHAPTER 7

Dairy Calf Production

7.1 INTRODUCTION

The dairy industry supplies a high proportion of the beef (and veal) consumed in Europe and is becoming increasingly important as a source of calves in the US which hitherto has relied almost exclusively on a specialized beef industry. Barfield (1966) showed that 75% of the beef consumed in the UK had its origin in dairy herds. A proportion of this meat comes from cows at the end of their milk-producing life and, as such, does not affect the intensive meat producer other than as a form of competition in the meat market. What is important to the intensive beef producer is the supply of male, and to a lesser extent female, calves which are not needed as sires or dairy herd replacements and are thus available for fattening. Beef from the dairy herd is a European concept, largely because the population density is such that there is not enough land for milk and beef production to be undertaken as separate entities.

It is not our intention to discuss in detail the pre-natal factors of dairy calf production since these are exclusively the province of the dairy farmer. We are concerned with the genetic makeup of the dairy calf (§ 3.6) and its growth and survival after birth, the former being important to the feedlot operator while the latter has a direct effect on the profitability of specialist dairybeef rearing units.

7.2 BREED SUITABILITY

In the UK there are six specialized dairy breeds and eight so-called dual-purpose breeds. The make-up of the National dairy herd is given in Table 7.1 and insemination data in Tables 7.2a and·b.

The most notable feature in Table 7.2 is the precipitous decline of the Dairy Shorthorn. One is tempted to conclude that this reflects a "lack of purpose", this breed apparently being considered by commercial farmers to be inefficient both for milk and beef production. On the other hand, the rapid increase in Friesian numbers reflects not only a potential high efficiency for milk production but also an eminent suitability for intensive beef production (Magruder and Nelson, 1964; Preston, 1964; Natz, 1968). The declining popularity of the Ayrshire and Channel Island breeds may not have arisen solely because of failing as milk producers but rather through their inferiority to the Friesian as producers of meat (MacLeod *et al.*, 1968). The so-called dual-purpose breeds might have fared better had their breeders concentrated exclusively on meat production, since the South Devon, for example,

TABLE 7.1 COMPOSITION OF THE NATIONAL HERD (%) (ENGLAND AND WALES)

Breed	1908	1955	1960	1965
Dairy breeds	1.8	56.8	65.5	74.2
Ayrshire	—	15.6	15.7	13.0
Friesian	—	34.5	41.9	53.0
Guernsey } Jersey }	1.8	{ 4.5	5.1	4.7
		{ 2.2	2.7	3.5
Dual purpose breeds	83.6	28.2	16.5	8.3
Dairy Shorthorn	70.8	21.5	11.9	5.2
Red Poll	0.5	0.9	0.6	0.3
South Devon	—	1.3	1.1	0.7
Welsh Black	4.3	0.6	0.4	0.2
Others	8.0	3.9	2.5	1.9
Beef breeds	14.6	15.0	18.0	17.5
Total population ('000)	5730[a]	2913[b]	3113[b]	3209[b]
Source	MMB (1955)	MMB (1955)	MMB (1960a)	MMB (1965)

[a] Total cattle. [b] Cows and heifers in milk and cows in calf.

TABLE 7.2A FIRST INSEMINATIONS IN GREAT BRITAIN ('000) ACCORDING TO BREED

	1947–8	1956–7	1966–7[a]
Friesian	55.0	685.0	1141.5
Ayrshire	12.5	203.5	80.1
Channel Island	23.0	181.5	170.9
Dairy	90.5	1070.0	1392.5
Dairy Shorthorn	60.0	223.5	18.5
Other dual-purpose	10.5	52.5	30.9
Dual purpose	70.5	276.0	49.7
Hereford	4.0	200.0	402.8
Angus	—	163.0	159.9
Shorthorn	—	3.5	0.4
Devon	1.2	60.0	31.6
Charolais .	—	—	92.8
Other beef	—	20.0	9.1
Beef	5.2	446.5	696.6
Total	166.2	1792.5	2138.8

[a] Excludes Scotland, which had a total of 149,000 inseminations (mainly Ayrshire and Angus).

TABLE 7.2B FIRST INSEMINATIONS IN UK: BULLS USED ACCORDING TO BREED OF COW, 1967–8 (AFTER MMB, 1968)

Breed of cow	Percentage bred to bulls of			
	Same breed	Dairy breeds	Dual-purpose breeds	Beef breeds
Ayrshire	27	41	1	31
Friesian	70	2	0	28
Channel Island	62	12	1	25
Dairy Shorthorn	15	36	1	48
Angus	27	26	0	47
Hereford	69	13	3	15
Others	55	12	3	30
Total	62	9	0	29

has the largest mature size of all British breeds and has comparable merit to the Holstein for intensive beef production yet only produces about 3100 litres per lactation (MMB, 1967). Other parts of Europe are better endowed with genuine dual-purpose breeds as, for example, the Meuse–Rhine–Yssel, Brown Swiss, Fleckvieh and, to a lesser extent, the Normandie.

The alleged deficiencies of dairy breeds as meat producers are often given as excuses for large-scale crossing by purebred beef bulls. Thus it is common practise in many countries for dairy farmers to mate a proportion of their herd with bulls of the Angus, Hereford and, more recently, Charolais breeds. Crossing of Friesian heifers with Angus bulls has the primary objective of reducing calf size and hence calving difficulties, which in one survey were 3.9% for crossbred foetuses compared with 8.8% in Friesian heifers bred pure (MMB, 1960c).

While it may be true that crossing Ayrshire, Jersey and Guernsey with Charolais and Hereford will improve their growth potential, there is no justification in crossing Friesians with Angus (Preston *et al.*, 1963c) or Hereford (McDonald and Kay, 1967), although there may well be with breeds such as the Charolais (Edwards *et al.*, 1966). Moreover, in a dairy industry committed to increasing the efficiency of milk production by means of organized progeny testing through AI, such a crossing programme is misguided to say the least. The individual farmer who follows such a procedure is able to exert much less selection, while from a national point of view the losses of records from dairy sires is not recompensed since there is no gain in meat production except when Charolais sires are used.

7.3 CALF PROCUREMENT

7.3.1 Marketing

According to the MMB (1967) some 3 million calves were born in England and Wales in 1966–7 and of these about 1 million were sold through auction markets.

The seasonal trend of sales followed that of calvings with peaks in January and September–October and lowest values in May and June. Results of sample surveys involving over 18,000 rearing calves (67% males) from 15 selected markets are shown in Table 7.3. In addition to those sold for rearing, the survey covered 4000 "bobby" calves disposed of for manufacturing meat. It is difficult to extrapolate from a survey of this type particularly since some of the best calves (e.g. Charolais crosses) may be sold privately or retained by the breeder. Nevertheless, the declining popularity of Angus and Shorthorn crosses, purebred Herefords and Hereford crosses other than on the Friesian is obvious. The failure of the Friesian to increase was attributable to an increase in the number of such calves sold for slaughter soon after birth.

TABLE 7.3 BREED MAKEUP OF CALVES SOLD FOR REARING IN THE UK (AFTER MMB, 1967)

Breed type	1965–6 (%)	1966–7 (%)	Change from 1965–6 (%)
Friesian	37	38	1
Hereford/Friesian	33	37	11
Hereford	5	4	−22
Other Hereford crosses	10	9	−15
Angus crosses	7	5	−27
Charolais crosses	1	2	81
Shorthorn crosses	2	1	−66
Others	5	4	−9
Total in sample	18,810	18,525	−1

There are no data in this survey concerning calf age, but most of them were probably less than 1 week old, since markets are held weekly and the expected increase in price with age rarely compensates for the liquid milk consumed—the major concern of the dairyman. If 3 million calves are born, then approximately 1 million are needed to replace 25% of the National herd (about 4 million), a million find their way to market, which leaves almost 1 million being reared on the farms where they were born or being sold privately. This degree of calf movement has important consequences in any study of calf mortality and methods of rearing. It is clear that the greater proportion of calves intended for beef production are reared on farms other than where they were born. In the short term this results in undesirable side effects as mortality among bought-in calves is greater than among home-reared ones according to an MMB survey of 36,000 herds (Sellers *et al.*, 1968). But looking to the future it is preferable that rearing be centralized, for this allows economies of scale and the development of specialized management procedures, while the intensive beef producer benefits from being able to obtain his requirements from fewer sources.

7.3.2 Siting of calf-rearing units

The major dairying regions in England are located in the west and south-west, whereas the fattening units (the destination of the reared calf) tend to be situated either near the large centres of population or the main sources of feed (in this case barley grain), i.e. in the east. The accurate siting of large calf-rearing units has an important bearing on their profitability. One cannot generalize, and the most precise results will be obtained by use of linear programming techniques taking into account all the variables and costs involved. It is, however, safe to conclude that such rearing units should generally be sited close to the fattening units.

The major inputs to calf rearing are the live calf (about 40 kg in weight), milk replacers (15–20 kg/head) and concentrates (150 kg/calf), while the output is a reared calf about 3 months old and weighing from 80 to 100 kg. The cost of milk replacers and concentrates varies little in different regions of the country, while the advantage of transporting the calf soon after birth is not solely due to its lighter weight but also the fact that its conferred immunity renders it less susceptible to new infections than the 3-month-old animal (Loosmore, 1964).

7.4 MORTALITY AND DISEASE

7.4.1 Pre-natal losses

Some data on calf mortality in dairy herds are summarized in Table 7.4. There is good agreement that deaths due to stillbirths are in the region of 4–6%. The high incidence of abortions noted by Lovell and Hill (1940) was before widespread vaccination with S19. As in beef cattle, perinatal deaths are more prevalent in heifers than cows, a feature noted by many of the workers quoted in the table. Moreover, it is known that crossbreeding can reduce losses (see Chapter 3).

At first sight it appears surprising that pre-natal mortality should be as high in dairy as in beef calves since the dams of the former are better fed and there is almost always attendance at calving. However, calves from Holstein or MRY cows are much bigger relative to mature body size of the dam than calves of the majority of beef breeds. As Schultze (1965) and Amir *et al.* (1967) have pointed out, calving difficulties and associated calf deaths are due to large calf weight in relation to size of dam (greater than 9%). It may be that the better feeding of dairy cows, particularly the practice of steaming-up prior to calving, is, on the whole, disadvantageous to calf health. We are of the opinion that if it is necessary to have cows in good body condition at calving then the extra feeding to achieve this may be more opportunely given during early pregnancy (i.e. mid-lactation) than at a later stage when the foetus is more responsive to an increased nutritional plane and thus more likely to develop to an excessive size (Wallace, 1948; Jakobsen, 1957). Problems of specific nutrient deficiencies, as are occasionally met with in beef cows under range conditions, are not normally encountered in dairy herds for obvious reasons.

7.4.2 Post-natal losses

7.4.2.1 SEASONAL EFFECTS. As with beef herds, statistics on post-natal mortality in dairy calves have little meaning since they represent averages about which variation is as great as the number of management systems employed. In our own Holstein herd in Cuba the average losses from birth to 3 months, from all causes, were about

TABLE 7.4 MORTALITY IN DAIRY HERDS

Location	Breed	Embryonic	Abortions	Stillbirths	Postnatal	Total	Authors
Florida	Jersey			4.9			Arnold & Becker, 1953
UK	Dairy Shorthorn		5.1	6.3	4.8		Braude & Walker, 1949
Nebraska	Dairy					9.0[a]	Davis, 1952
Mozambique	Dairy					20.3[b]	De Pinho, 1962
England	Dairy					4.8[c]	Donald, 1963
Germany	BPL[d]	18.7					Jahn, 1963
England	Dairy		5.5	4.7	5.5		Lovell & Hill, 1940
Scotland	Dairy		5.2	2.9	11.4		Lovell & Hill, 1940
Ceylon	European/Zebu			4.9	4.8[b]	4.8[b]	Ranatunga, 1965
Poland	BPL[d]			4.8			Rosochowicz, 1965
UK	Dairy					5.0	Sellars *et al.*, 1968
Holland	MRY			6.1			Van Dieton, 1964
UK			1.2	5.3			Withers, 1953

[a] At birth. [b] Includes post natal. [c] Perinatal. [d] Black Pied Lowland.

8%. On the other hand, a survey of six farms (a total of over 2000 cows) during 1965–6 showed average mortality to be 25% with one farm as high as 50% (Willis and Preston, 1968b). In the UK, Withers (1952) reported a post-natal mortality of 8% and while this is generally considered acceptable by many dairy farmers the specialist calf rearer must aim to reduce this to no more than 1–2%.

Various authors (Withers, 1952; Roy, 1959; Sellers *et al.*, 1968) have reported that mortality in the UK is seasonal with most losses occurring in spring and least in autumn as is indicated in Fig. 7.1. Attempts to associate the higher spring losses with the carotene and vitamin A content of the *pre-partum* diet (Walker, 1948; Payne, 1949) have not so far been substantiated and, certainly, specific attempts to combat scouring (the most common cause of mortality) by feeding vitamin A to the calf were

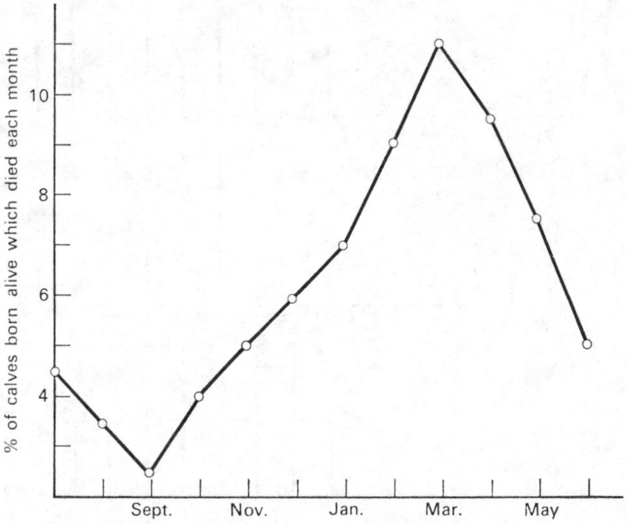

FIG. 7.1 Relation between calf mortality and time of year (after Roy, 1959).

not successful (Aschaffenburg *et al.*, 1953). The explanation of Roy *et al.* (1955) was that infection in a calf house reaches a peak in early spring because such units are effectively rested in summer—when few calves are born—and then, in winter, subjected to continuous use following the peak period of births in October–November. These workers showed that, in each of 5 years in a house where calves were introduced every one to two days, each successive calf gained less weight than its predecessor and scouring increased gradually until deaths from *Escherichia coli* intestinal infection began to occur. An example of this effect is given in Fig. 7.2.

7.4.2.2 IMPORTANCE OF COLOSTRUM. Colostrum is a rich source of carotenoids and the fat soluble vitamins A, D and E, all of which are deficient in the newly born calf. Its more important role, however, is as a supplier of immune globulins which provide the calf with protection against septicaemia due to *E. coli*. Only a small amount is needed to prevent septicaemia but it must be given within 36 hr of birth since during this time the intestine rapidly becomes impermeable to the transfer of antibodies. According to Roy (1964) no benefit accrues from feeding colostrum once the intestine is impermeable if none was given originally. He noted, however, that additional colostrum after 3 days of age could reduce mortality and scouring. This is emphasized by the results of an experiment carried out by Schoenaers and Kaeckenbeerk (1960). Of 40 calves given colostrum from cows immunized against a particular strain of *E. coli*, only 4 died when challenged orally with the same strain. In contrast 19 out of 24 died when colostrum was not given. Walker (1950) reported that, with natural nursing, the daily consumption of colostrum was of the order of 9–30 kg,

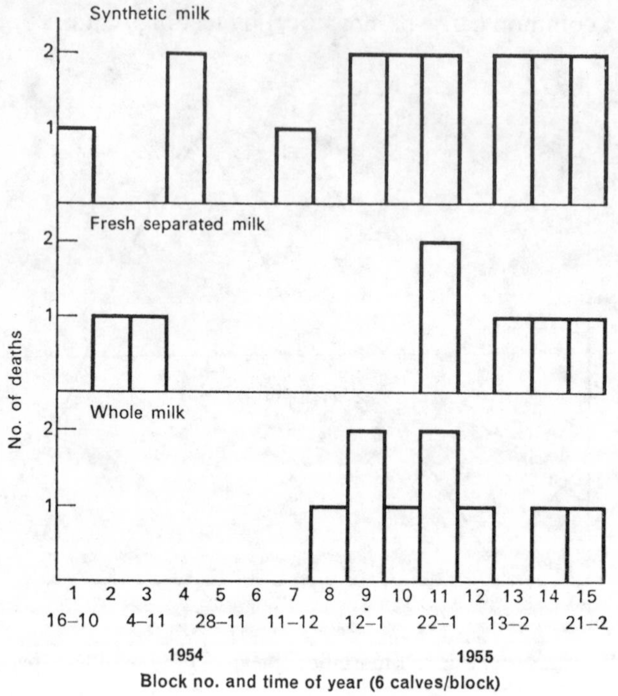

FIG. 7.2 Distribution of mortality according to type of milk diet throughout the course of an experiment (after Shillam *et al.*, 1962).

while Weiland and Klose (1962) showed that with bucket feeding, voluntary intake was only 13 kg in 3 days. These differences in consumption probably account for the findings of Smith *et al.*, (1967a) that immune globulins were higher in the serum of calves which had received colostrum by suckling rather than from a bucket. This, together with Roy's observations, might explain Wither's (1952, 1953) earlier conclusion that mortality was less in calves which suckled than in those which drank colostrum from a bucket. The significance of the protein fraction of colostrum does not appear to be a function of its nutritive value *per se*, since though quickly absorbed, it is rapidly excreted in the urine (Deutsch and Smith, 1957; Bangham *et al.*, 1958). A more positive role was ascribed to it by Balfour and Comline (1962) who noted that there was a protein fraction in the whey, not coagulable by heating, which had a marked influence on the absorption of γ-globulins.

Plates 1 and 2: The interior of two "barley-beef" units in Scotland: note the high stocking density made possible by the slatted floors.

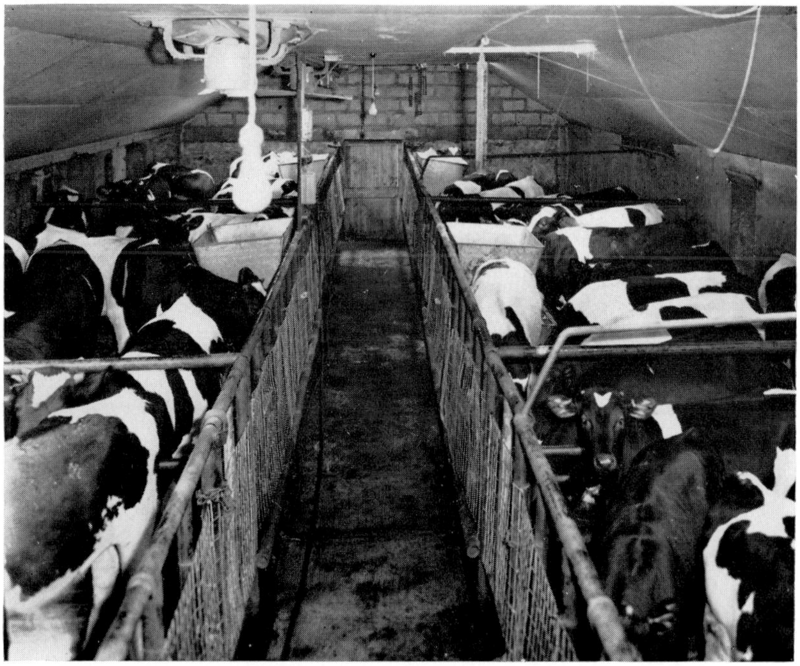

PLATE 3: A recently completed "barley-beef" unit in Scotland showing arrangement of slatted floors and self feeders.

PLATE 4: Intensive beef unit in Cuba designed for fattening 240 cattle on high forage diets and converted for molasses feeding.

PLATE 5: A typical US feedlot in Arizona for 30,000 head. Note the feed mill in the background and the economical shades.

PLATE 6: An intensive fattening unit in Cuba for 1,000 head on high molasses/urea diets. The bulls are Brown Swiss × Zebu.

PLATES 7 and 8: Intensive beef production on molasses/urea. Note the shade over the molasses trough to prevent solar heating of the molasses. The bulls in plate 7 are Holstein × Zebu and in plate 8 Brown Swiss × Zebu.

PLATES 9 and 10: Molasses/urea tanker recharging the feeding troughs. The absence of shade over the molasses in the pens shown in plate 10 led to reduced performance and more bloat problems than in pens where shade was provided.

Plate 11: Examples of "complete" early-weaning diets for dairy-beef calves. On the left a coarse mixture based on flaked maize and rolled oats. On the right a pelleted diet made from cracked maize and whole oats.

PLATE 12: "Complete" fattening diets for barley-beef cattle. On the left is rolled barley with pelleted supplement; on the right is pelleted rolled barley and supplement.

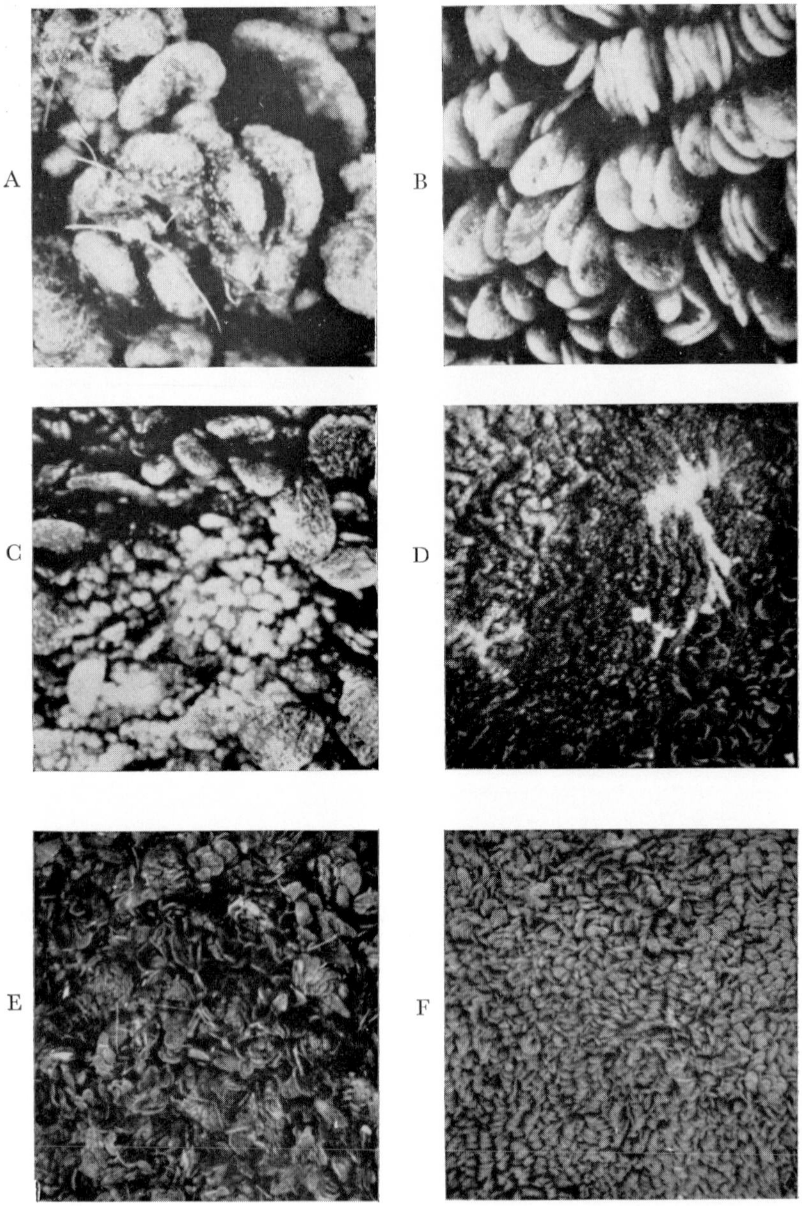

PLATE 13: Rumenitis in barley-beef cattle. A, Clump of villi bound by exudate, food material and hair (anterior dorsal sac); notice flattened and hyperkeratinised villi compared with normal villi shown in B. B, Normal villi (anterior dorsal sac). C, Chronic rumenitis, devillation with epithelial nodule hyperplasia (anterior ventral sac). D, Chronic rumenitis, devillation and depigmentation together with well-defined scar (anterior ventral sac). E, Clumping of villi (anterior ventral sac). F, Normal rumen wall (anterior ventral sac).

PLATE 14: One of five performance test buildings (each housing 48 bulls) at the Institute of Animal Science, Cuba. Note the intensive housing and self feeding hoppers. The pens measure 2 × 2.5m and have concrete slatted floors. The bulls are a variety of pure breeds and some two- and three-breed crosses.

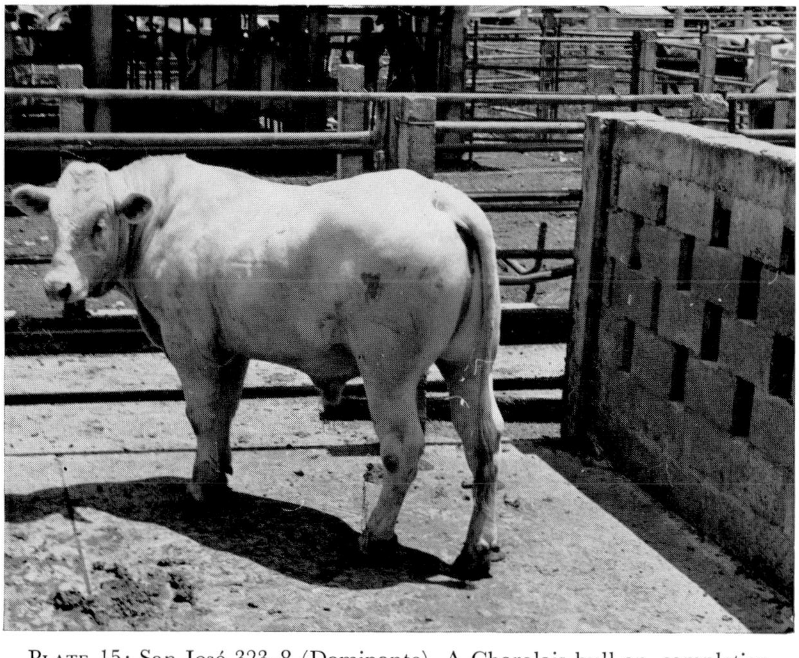

PLATE 15: San José 323–8 (Dominante). A Charolais bull on completion of test at 400 kg and 273 days of age. Daily gain on test from 90 days of age was 1.44 kg and feed conversion 5.05. The facilities described in plate 14 are now used exclusively for testing Charolais bulls.

7.4.2.3 *Escherichia coli* INFECTION. As Roy (1959) has pointed out, infection with *E. coli* follows one of two pathways. The first invariably occurs in calves not given colostrum and which die from septicaemia in the first few days. The second he referred to as a localized intestinal infection wherein *E. coli* organisms—normal inhabitants of the gastrointestinal tract (Smith, 1965)—multiply to such an extent as to cause excessive scouring. They do not, however, invade the tissues and the calf generally dies of dehydration. Ingram (1962) provided confirmatory evidence on the build-up of *E. coli* in animals scouring severely until death. Smith (1962), on the other hand, found no differences in *E. coli* counts between healthy and severely scouring animals, which Roy (1964) attributed to differences in the severity of infection. Another explanation is that derived from the experiments of Blaxter and Wood (1951), wherein they showed that overfeeding could lead to the passage of undigested food material into the colon thereby provoking a non-specific bacterial fermentation. The resultant increase in osmotic pressure within the gut caused water to enter and thus diarrhoea to develop.

The dangers from *E. coli* infection are intimately linked with the type of nutrition. Coliform contamination of colostrum or cows' milk does not appear to be a contributory factor (Roy, 1964). This is borne out by the work of Fey (1962) who found that infection could be induced by this method only in calves which had not received colostrum, or which, having had colostrum, nevertheless had a very low level of γ-globulins. There is, however, evidence that *E. coli* septicaemia can be induced experimentally (see review by Roy, 1964).

In their studies on the relationship of nutrition to *E. coli* infection, the Shinfield workers (Shillam *et al.*, 1962a) observed that the rate of build-up of *E. coli* infection was always faster with milk substitutes than with cows' milk. This observation led to an intensive study of the factors in milk substitutes which were predisposing to *E. coli* infection.

7.4.2.4 MILK PROCESSING. Milk substitutes are based almost entirely on skim-milk powders and are made by a variety of methods according to the conditions under which the original liquid milk is pasteurized and dried, i.e. by a spray or roller drying process. In a series of experiments, Shillam and his co-workers found that calf performance was directly related to the previous heat treatment of the skim milk employed (Shillam *et al.*, 1960, 1962a, b, c; Shillam and Roy, 1963a). Milks which had been treated by ultra high temperature sterilization (135°C for 1–3 sec), roller drying (110°C) or pasteurization for 30 min at 74°C followed by spray drying were all associated with poor calf performance. The only suitable milks were those which had been subjected to less intense heating procedures (i.e. 77°C for only 15 sec or 63°C for 30 min) followed by spray drying. The effects of these different milks on calf performance are summarized in Table 7.5.

It appears that excessive heating of the milk brings about denaturation of the whey proteins; associated with this is a reduction of ionizable calcium, poor clotting ability by rennet and reduced digestibility. The specific relation with *E. coli* infection is implicated by the fact that overall biological value of the milk protein is not affected, damage being restricted to the non-casein nitrogen fraction. Confirmation of this hypothesis can be seen in the data of McCoy *et al.* (1967), where mortality was significantly higher on milk diets with 1.50 mg whey N/g milk powder compared with levels

TABLE 7.5 PERFORMANCE OF CALVES IN RELATION TO DEGREE OF HEAT TREATMENT OF THE MILK (AFTER SHILLAM *et al.*, 1962b)

	Heat treatment			
	77°C 15 sec	74°C 30 min	74°C 30 min	135°C 1–3 sec
Non-casein protein Nitrogen as % of total Nitrogen	15.4	8.4	a	6.9
Daily gain (kg)	0.22	0.12	0.30	0.17

[a] Plus whey from milk heated at 77°C for 15 sec.

in excess of 4.7 mg/g. Reduced calf performance probably comes about through impairment of the rennet-clotting capacity of the milk, predisposing the calf to *E. coli* infection. Kannan and Jenness (1961) showed that the denaturing of whey proteins increased the rennet-clotting time of casein, and this was confirmed by Shillam *et al.* (1962c) who found that only the addition of undermatured whey proteins would improve rennet-clotting time and hence calf performance on a diet containing severely heat-treated milk. Additional calcium was not beneficial (Shillam and Roy, 1963b). The importance of clotting time, and hence the dangers of using overheated skim milks, existed only in the first 2–3 weeks of life. The reason for this is explained by the findings of Henschel *et al.* (1961) that whereas all calves up to 4 weeks of age produced renin, few produced pepsin. Furthermore, the pH of the abomasum in the first 2 weeks is not sufficiently low for pepsin proteolysis to occur according to Pierce (1962).

7.4.2.5 SALMONELLOSIS. This disease, caused by either *Salmonella dublin* or *S. typhinurium*, has increased in incidence in most developed countries as a result of intensive calf-rearing methods involving the movement of animals from one region to another. The organisms are highly infectious, are carried by rodents and can live for long periods outside the animal body. They have an additional importance in that they are infectious to man, and in some countries the disease is notifiable to the civil authorities.

Symptoms are rarely manifested before 3 weeks of age. They include diarrhoea, a dry hair coat, and often severe respiratory distress which can be confused with pneumonia. The basis of prevention is strict isolation of infected calves and complete sterilization of transport vehicles and rearing units between successive batches. A considerable step forward in control measures is promised by the availability of specific vaccines to confer immunity during the early weeks of life when the calf is most susceptible to the disease.

7.5 NUTRITION*

7.5.1 Introduction

There are innumerable methods of feeding dairy calves. In many underdeveloped countries it is common practice to leave the calf with its dam during part or all of the

* A revised version of the material in the first two paragraphs of this section is given in Appendix I.

lactation. The procedure has arisen largely through lack of any other method of raising the calf until it is able to exist on natural pasture and the mistaken belief that presence of the calf is essential for milk letdown. A common method is to give the calf access to the cow for half the day, milking her once before the calf is introduced. Another procedure allows the calf access to the cow only after milking and then for a limited period, usually about one hour. There is no real justification for either practice, since all breeds can be induced to letdown their milk by suitable management procedures, the most important of which is to separate the calf from the cow at birth.

There is a slightly better case for multiple suckling, since it is less wasteful of milk. Enthusiasts for the system (Williams and Edgar, 1966) have claimed economic advantages from its use under specific conditions. But in less skilful hands it poses considerable management problems, particularly with respect to the need to have cows and calves available at the right time of year, and it is only really applicable on the large, mixed dairy farm. The system has failed to impress the specialist calf rearer who, without exception, prefers to employ completely artificial systems of rearing.

Artificial rearing of dairy calves for intensive beef production is usually in the hands of two kinds of operator. Some dairymen obtain an additional source of income from the rearing of surplus calves which are sold subsequently to feedlots at about 3–4 months of age. The more important enterprise, however, is that of the specialist calf rearer who obtains calves at about 1 week of age, thereafter rearing them for sale to the feedlot at whatever stage is most economical under the specific circumstances. It is a fundamental instinct of young calves to suckle, and while they are easily taught to drink milk from a pail they rarely show an interest in consuming dry feed before 2 weeks of age. Colostrum and, thereafter, some form of liquid diet must therefore be given for a minimum period of 1–6 weeks.

The decisions facing calf rearers are therefore: (a) what kind of liquid feed to give; (b) when should the calves be weaned from liquids; and (c) what kind of diet should succeed the liquid feeding? The dairyman has available some colostrum (in excess of that needed for the maximum health of individual calves) and usually some milk from cows with mastitis or some such problem. However, this is never sufficient and he must therefore decide whether to continue on cows' milk (a saleable commodity) or on some form of liquid milk replacer. Post-weaning, he usually has available concentrates and conserved forages or pasture. The specialist rearer, on the other hand, usually has to purchase all his feed requirements since he rarely has either cows or pasture. Such enterprises therefore tend to be based on the use of milk replacers and concentrates.

For the dairyman it may be convenient to use only cows' milk until weaning, particularly when one bears in mind that the disease risk is somewhat less than with milk replacers (§ 7.4.2.4); however, since milk is saleable his primary concern must be to feed as little of it as possible and thus to wean at the earliest age. If, on the other hand, he decides to use a milk replacer, then weaning age becomes slightly less critical and almost certainly has to be extended slightly in order to overcome the check which occurs when calves are changed from whole milk to any kind of substitute.

The specialist rearer is mainly concerned with what is the best type of milk replacer to use, what age to wean and what kind of feeding system to employ after weaning. These decisions depend on the economic situation with regard to the relative prices of milk replacers and dry feeds and the restraints imposed by the physiological development of the digestive system of the ruminant (§ 5.2).

7.5.2 Milk replacers

7.5.2.1 Level and composition. The composition of a milk replacer is determined primarily by the rate of gain required and the age and weight of the calf. In contrast with the situation in beef calves, maximum gain is not necessarily the objective of the rearer of dairy calves. This arises through the need to give a liquid diet during the

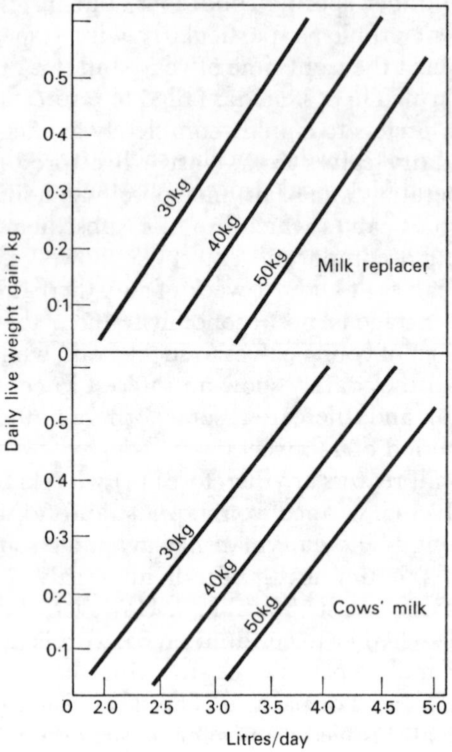

Fig. 7.3 Requirements of calves for different rates of gain at live weights of 30, 40 and 50 kg in terms of cows' milk and a milk replacer of comparable energy content (GE = 0.7 Mcal/l) (after Roy *et al.*, 1958).

first weeks of life, the energy of which is always more expensive than in dry feeds. Rationing of liquid diets is therefore standard practice, and for this reason the rearer needs to know the relationship between milk consumption and growth.

The most comprehensive study of the milk requirements of dairy calves was made by Roy *et al.* (1958). These workers used covariance analysis techniques on growth and consumption data from 324 calves in 12 experiments. Their recommendations for both whole and synthetic milk diets are summarized in Fig. 7.3.

In order to support maximum rate of gain and feed efficiency, it is necessary to have (a) maximum energy concentration with optimum proportions of other nutrients, and (b) a high feed intake. A milk replacer must therefore be composed of highly digestible ingredients so as to reduce the risk of undigested feed forming a substrate for pathogenic bacteria in the colon and giving rise to diarrhoea and possibly fatal infections. Stobo *et al.* (1967d) have shown that there is no benefit to be gained in growth rate or nitrogen retention by raising the fat content of the milk replacer from 19 to 28% of DM. The carcasses (slaughter live weight 115 kg) were fatter at the higher level of dietary fat, but this would be beneficial only for veal production. Growth was significantly poorer on a 27% fat diet when the protein content was reduced from 26 to 19%. Unfortunately the experimental design did not include a diet with 19% fat and 19% protein, although as there were no differences in growth rate or nitrogen retention between the two fat levels one can assume that 19% protein would also have been inferior at the lower fat level. Brisson *et al.* (1957) also found that nitrogen retention and growth were highest on a fat-containing milk replacer when the protein content was between 22 and 30% of the DM.

The choice of type of milk powder and fat should take into account the various limitations imposed by physiological aspects relating to their utilization (§ 5.2.2). Since, at the present state of knowledge, only milk protein should be used, a protein level of 27% permits only the use of skim-milk powder and added fat. The fat soluble vitamins (A, D and E) must be added to milk replacers intended for feeding at high levels. Unless the diet of the pregnant cow has deliberately been supplemented with vitamin A, the reserves in the liver of the calf at birth are extremely small (Walker *et al.*, 1949). Although the daily requirement for vitamin A by the young calf is put at about 2000–3000 IU (ARC, 1965), the majority of workers (see Anon., 1961) consider that there are advantages, particularly in terms of health, from giving very much larger amounts (15,000–20,000 IU daily). This is equivalent to the addition of about 20 million IU/t of milk replacer powder.

7.5.2.2 MANAGEMENT FACTORS. Although disease risk would seem to be less if the calf takes its colostrum directly from the dam rather than from a bucket (§ 7.4.2.2), there appear to be no growth advantages later from simulating the suckling mechanism by the use of nipple pails (Wise and La Master, 1968). Nevertheless, the fact that suckling has been found to stimulate the secretion of renin and other proteolytic enzymes leads us to believe that it may be beneficial in circumstances where disease risk is high. The real disadvantage of nipple pails and similar devices is the management problem occasioned by their use. These difficulties are likely to be lessened or eliminated by the use of machines which reconstitute milk replacer automatically and dispense it in measured quantities at prescribed intervals. Unfortunately the units currently on sale are designed for group feeding systems. Under such circumstances it is (a) difficult to control individual intake, and (b) there is the hazard of cross-infection when calves are not housed individually. In a study of two such machines Hodgson (1967) found that increasing group size from 20 to 30 calves slightly reduced the individual variation in milk consumption but increased variation in weight gain. Future development would seem to lie in the adaptation of such machines to enable individual housing and feeding (at least during the critical first 3 weeks of life) without losing the advantages of automation. Prototypes are in commercial operation in the US and also undergoing experimental trials at Shinfield.

Normal practice with bucket feeding is to give the required quantity of milk in two feeds. Owen *et al.* (1965) have reported that when restricted feeding was practised (3.2 l daily) there was no effect on growth by giving this in one or two feeds. This experiment was undertaken with whole milk, but similar results were obtained with milk replacer by Burt (1968).

7.5.3 Age of weaning

As a general rule the energy in dry concentrates (mainly cereal grains) is less expensive than in whole milk or milk replacers as currently constituted. It is also well established that the utilization of dry feeds requires no period of adaptation such that digestibility of concentrates or forages can be as high in the 3-week-old calf as in the adult (§ 5.2.3). The problem of early weaning is how to encourage the very young calf to eat sufficient dry feed to satisfy its requirements for maintenance and gain when its natural instinct is to prefer liquids.

Prior to the 1950's, the standard weaning age for dairy calves was of the order of 7–10 weeks (see Norton and Eaton, 1946). Canadian workers (Whiting and Clark, 1955) found that this could be reduced to 4 weeks, while British investigations led to weaning at 21–24 days (Preston, 1956b; Quayle, 1958). The latter workers based their diets on flaked maize with added molasses, which is more palatable than the oat/wheat mixture used by the Canadians. Mochrie and Murley (1957) were able to rear calves successfully on a dry feed (albeit of milk solids) after only 8 days of liquid feeding; however, this is an isolated report and unpublished data (Preston, 1956a; Quayle, 1956) suggest that it is too problematical to attempt weaning earlier than 21 days under commercial conditions.

Calves weaned at between 3 and 6 weeks almost always suffer some setback in growth in the immediate post-weaning period, but in comparison with conventional late-weaning procedures performance has been the same to 14 weeks (Castle and Watson, 1959), 18 weeks (Randel, 1966) or slaughter at about 12 months (Aitken *et al.*, 1963).

Several studies have been undertaken to determine whether early weaning should be done abruptly or gradually. The results are unanimous that the method of weaning has no bearing on performance of mortality (Preston, 1956b; Quayle, 1958; Clark and Whiting, 1961), and this is true even under tropical conditions (Quiñones and Preston, 1968).

7.5.4 Dry feeds

7.5.4.1 Energy intake. The major factor limiting the utilization of dry feeds by the young calf is their acceptability, and factors which increase voluntary intake have considerable priority.

Most important is the need to have free access to water from the moment that solid feeds are on offer, since Mäkelä (1958) found that dry feed consumption was increased by from 10 to 30% when water was freely available. Although forage is the natural diet of the ruminant, calves given access to concentrates or hay show a marked preference for the former, consuming up to 90% of total DM intake in this form (Preston, 1960). Stobo *et al.* (1966) also found that the intake of hay by early weaned calves decreased as the maximum daily allowance of concentrates increased. At the highest concentrate level (2.27 kg/day), hay contributed only 4% of the total dry feed intake. Ottersby and Rust (1965) gave early weaned calves access to concentrate and hay and found that total DM intake and, to a greater extent, energy intake, was higher when the calves only had access to concentrates; daily gains were also some 50% greater when no hay was given. Poorer growth when calves were given access to hay as well as concentrates was also reported by Noller and Dickson (1953). It is perhaps noteworthy that a reduced DM intake, through giving access to roughages, is the reverse of the situation encountered in older cattle (§ 9.1.3) possibly because rumen volume is more of a limiting factor in the young animal. This tends to be supported by the finding of Brundage and Sweetman (1963) that calves weaned at 25 or 60 days of age were 12% lighter at 180 days when the roughage source was silage rather than hay.

In view of the importance of stimulating high voluntary intakes of dry feed it might be expected that sweetening agents and specific flavouring ingredients would have a beneficial effect on feed intake. The importance of the former was indicated in a report by Norton and Eaton (1946) that concentrate consumption was significantly greater when the molasses content of the feed was raised from 5 to 12.5%, while Preston (1956c) found that replacing linseed cake meal in an early weaning diet with dry skim-milk powder increased consumption and hence growth rate. In a subsequent experiment (Preston, 1958), the addition of 15% of a mixture of 75% molasses and 24% sphagnum moss significantly increased concentrate consumption up to 56 days of age. The increased intake on the molasses containing diet led to greater growth rates in the period from 3 to 31 days of age, thus confirming the importance of encouraging dry feed intake in this early period. Inclusion of 15% of sugar was found to increase feed intake by Piatkowski and Steger (1967).

There were no benefits to be gained from the inclusion of flavours such as aniseed and peppermint (Preston, 1960), and poor results from the use of anise oil were reported by Miller *et al.* (1958). The latter was in fact found to depress DM intake.

7.5.4.2 Importance of roughage. It is established that roughage is not necessary for the development of rumen function in terms of the calf's ability to absorb and metabolize volatile fatty acids (§ 5.2.3). Nevertheless, it has been the opinion of many investigators (NRC, 1963) that ruminant diets should contain a certain amount of coarse roughage such as stemmy material or leaves with rough surfaces in order to promote normal physiological activity of the gastrointestinal tract. The implication is that digestive upsets and bloat will develop when this stimulatory material is absent. Preston and Whitelaw (1962) found that there were no differences in growth rates of early weaned calves given concentrates only, and bedded on sawdust or straw, or given concentrates and hay to appetite; however, the diet contained 35% of rolled oats. Whitaker *et al.* (1957) observed no differences in rate of gain to 8 or 16 weeks of age in Holstein and Jersey calves given concentrates which contained 5, 9 or 13% of fibre coming from maize cobs or alfalfa meal. The calves also had access to alfalfa hay. There were positive correlations between daily gain and concentrate consumption and negative correlations between daily gain and hay consumption, which supports earlier statements that better performance will be obtained in early weaned calves by not allowing access to hay. In the tropics, Quiñones and Preston (1968) observed that Holstein calves weaned at 5 or 6 weeks were slower to reach 90 kg of live weight when the concentrate diet, based on ground maize, was supplemented with 5% of coarsely ground alfalfa hay. Hibbs *et al.* (1953) advocated the use of a complete feed for weaned calves containing 60% of alfalfa hay, claiming that with this system the rumen microflora was more diverse and more typical of that encountered in the adult, while blood components also changed more rapidly to those characteristic of the mature ruminant (Hibbs *et al.*, 1956). However, they presented no evidence to show whether such calves grew faster than those given smaller proportions of roughage.

It is our opinion that in diets based on cereal grains there is no advantage, from the point of view of growth and feed conversion, in giving additional roughage.

The situation with regard to purified diets is different. In the main, these have been developed to study mineral and vitamin requirements and there has been less interest in performance, which has generally been poorer (see Miller and Miller, 1960; Ott *et al.*, 1965) than with natural feeds. In a diet based on starch, glucose, soybean, protein, minerals and vitamins, Smith *et al.* (1966) reported much improved growth rates when 25% of ground cellulose was included although this additional fibre gave no improvement when the complete diet was pelleted.

In concluding that there is no benefit from giving supplemental roughage to the young calf, it must be remembered that the pattern of rumen fermentation which develops on any specific rearing system has certain characteristics which can affect the animal's subsequent performance. If it is the intention to continue on high cereal or all-concentrate diets to slaughter, rearing without roughage may be desirable. There is, however, some suggestion that this method may predispose the animal to rumen damage and, as a result, more liver abcesses than when the calf is raised on a diet of lower energy content (e.g. milk, creep feed and pasture) even if feeding from 3 months of age is identical in both cases (Willis and Preston, 1968a). The other aspect, and this is of particular significance in situations where proteins are in short supply, is that calves raised on concentrates to 3 months—and, having as a result more poorly developed salivary glands (Kay, 1966), a more acid rumen and a specialized microflora (Eadie *et al.*, 1967)—may be less able to utilize high urea-containing diets when they reach the age of 3 months, than animals reared on pasture (Elías and Preston, 1969b).

7.5.4.3 Source of energy. Since energy is the main limiting factor to rate of gain, it is essential not only to obtain the maximum intake of feed DM but also to choose energy sources which are as concentrated as possible, due account being taken of palatability. Preston (1958) provided some evidence that a concentrate containing 40% of cooked flaked maize was more palatable as well as having more ME than one based on rolled oats, and supported significantly higher rates of gain (0.63 vs, 0.49 kg/day) from birth to 3 months. Steam flaking of sorgum compared with steam rolling significantly improved feed conversion in calves weaned at 6 weeks (Lima *et al.*, 1968), although weight gains were not affected. Both flaked and rolled barley were also better than steam-rolled sorghum.

The use of fat would appear to be an obvious way of increasing energy consumption, and Johnson *et al.* (1956) found that growth rate was some 5–6% greater in calves given concentrates containing from 2.5 to 10% inedible stabilized tallow; there were no differences between levels. Greater increases in body size from birth to

3 months of age, as a result of adding 5% of stabilized tallow to the concentrate mixture, were noted by Preston *et al.* (1960c); while Gardner (1968) reported a 12% increase in daily gain and 8% better feed conversion from adding 5% animal fat to an 80% concentrate diet given to Holstein calves from 69 to 112 kg.

It is nevertheless doubtful if the improvement in performance is sufficient to warrant the additional problems of mixing fat into meal diets.

7.5.4.4 PROTEIN LEVEL AND QUALITY. In intensive calf rearing the aim is usually to encourage maximum consumption of dry feed, thus the rearer is rarely interested in energy requirements *per se.* With regard to other nutrients, however, the situation is reversed, the aim being to give as little as possible without reducing growth rate or efficiency of energy utilization. Animal health must not be ignored although a reduction in performance is usually the first sign of impending sickness.

After energy, protein is the major nutrient and more expensive than the micronutrients such as vitamins and minerals. Both quality and quantity of protein are important to the young calf, for although it has been stated that the biological value of protein has no significance in the functioning ruminant, due to microbial modification of ingested nitrogen (Johnson *et al.*, 1942; Blaxter, 1958), this is now known to be much too simple an explanation (§ 5.5). Brown *et al.* (1956b) found that calves weaned at 7 weeks grew as well on 15% protein diets containing 3% urea or the equivalent amount of linseed oil meal but the diets had different amounts of crude fibre. Subsequently Kay *et al.* (1967) and Stobo *et al.* (1967c) recorded that calves weaned at 3 and 5 weeks grew slower and had a significantly poorer feed conversion between 50 and 90 kg live weight when urea replaced from 20 to 40% of the total dietary nitrogen; controls had fish meal and soybean meal. Similar results were reported by Nelson *et al.* (1966) and Oltjen *et al.* (1967) in comparisons between soybean meal and urea.

Admittedly urea, on the one hand, and soybean and fish meal, on the other, represent extremes in protein quality; nevertheless, differences have been shown to exist within different sources of true protein.

For example, Whitelaw *et al.* (1963) fed diets containing groundnut meal or fish meal to Friesian calves weaned at 3 weeks. Over the live weight range 55–90 kg those given fish meal gained 20% faster with a 16% better feed conversion. When the diets were given on a restricted basis (8% of $W^{0.74}$) the superiority of the fish meal was 13% for gain and 11% for conversion.

Piatkowski (1966) found similar advantages for fish meal as compared to groundnut meal, while, among different meat meals, Leibholz and Moss (1967) found that growth rates were negatively related to their content of keratin, a protein of poor nutritive value. Leibholz (1967) also found that meat meal promoted significantly better live weight gains than dried skim-milk, the factor presumably being the higher solubility of the latter. Comparisons of fish meal and soybean meal have not been made under feeding trial conditions, but the indications from metabolism studies (§ 5.5) are that the latter occupies an intermediate position between fish meal and groundnut meal.

It appears that for the early weaned calf up to some 3 months of age, the relative value of a nitrogen source depends on its amino-acid makeup and solubility. Knowledge exists as to the relative ranking of the more common nitrogen sources, but there is, as yet, insufficient data to assign a precise value to each so as to enable quantification in, for example, linear programmes.

7.5.4.5 PROTEIN LEVELS. The factorial system of partitioning nitrogen requirements according to separate body needs and then applying a biological value for the protein used helps to set a minimum value on which feeding trial studies can be planned. But, as with fattening cattle (§ 9.5.1), the factorial system underestimates animal needs for maximum performance (Preston, 1963b). The available data do not allow calculation of response curves for rate of growth and feed conversion as a function of the amount of protein offered. The results of experiments in which different ratios of protein to energy were given to early weaned calves, and the response measured in terms of rate of live weight gain or nitrogen retention, are set out in Table 7.6.

In calves weaned early and given free access to concentrates and hay, consumption of the latter is very low, and energy intakes are comparable to those on complete all-concentrate diets; moreover, there is not the problem of compensatory growth which affects voluntary intake in older cattle. As a result, voluntary intake of ME in calves of about 80 kg live weight is fairly constant, being of the order of 80 to 85 kcal/kg live weight. From the work of Stobo *et al.* (1967a, b, c) it seems that the optimum protein energy ratio lies between 50 and 80 g protein/Mcal ME. Unfortunately, these workers studied protein/energy ratios at the extreme ends of the likely range, although their findings in one trial where an intermediate level was used, together with the data of Preston *et al.* (1965c), suggest that the optimum protein/energy ratio is of the order of 60–65 g protein/Mcal ME. The lower ratio (48) suggested by Gardner (1968) is associated with the lowest recorded rate of live weight gain, considerably less than is normally obtained with early weaned calves at this age. The suggested ratio of 60–65 g protein/Mcal ME (equivalent to approximately 19% crude protein in the DM of a diet of 2.9 Mcal ME/kg DM) is also supported by the early work of Brown *et al.* (1958) and by the findings of Piatkowski (1966). It should be remembered, too, that the proposed ratio only applies when at least one-third of the protein is supplied in the form of fish meal; a higher ratio is likely to be needed if poorer quality proteins are used.

7.5.4.6 MINERALS. Estimates of dietary requirements of the major elements were calculated by the ARC (1965) using the factorial system. By this procedure estimated quantities are given in grams per day for different rates of gain at specific live weights. In this form, the estimates are of limited practical value since the calf rearer is invariably concerned with the formulation of a diet to cover requirements from weaning to about 90 kg live weight. We have therefore transformed the data (Table 7.7) to apply to Holstein calves which after weaning at 3–5 weeks can be expected to gain at about 1 kg/day for a mean daily DM intake of 2.25 kg (Whitelaw *et al.*, 1963).

Few feeding trials have been undertaken to determine the effect of different levels of the respective minerals on growth and feed conversion of early weaned calves. Guegen and Mathieu (1965) studied levels of calcium and phosphorus ranging from 0.8 to 1.6% (of DM) and from 0.55 to 1.15% respectively. They reported that mineralization of the skeleton was better at the higher levels but that growth rate was unaffected. These data confirm that phosphorus levels need not be higher than

TABLE 7.6 EFFECT OF PROTEIN/ENERGY RATIO IN HIGH-ENERGY DIETS ON THE PERFORMANCE OF CALVES

Mean live weight	ME in DM	ME intake/ live weight	Nitrogen × 6.25/ME Diets				Daily gain Diet 1	Improvement over diet 1			Nitrogen × 6.25/ live weight[a]	Authors
			1	2	3	4		2	3	4		
(kg)	(Mcal/kg)	(kcal/kg)	(6.25 g/Mcal)				(kg)	(%)	(%)	(%)	(g/kg)	
60–66	2.87	78–80	47	80			0.58	12*			6.2	Stobo *et al.*, 1967c
63–67	2.87	85–80	51	86			0.72	6*			6.9	Stobo *et al.*, 1967a
66	2.66	73	48	58	70		0.57*	0	−2		3.5	Gardner, 1968
77–80	2.87	72–75[b]	47	80			0.68	13*			6.0	Stobo *et al.*, 1967a
78	2.9	80–83	52	58	67	75	27[c]	15	30*	26	5.6	Preston *et al.*, 1965c
82–87	2.87	89–86	50	85			0.93*	0			4.5	Stobo *et al.*, 1967a
86	2.87	83–85	49	62	81		0.91	7*	9		5.3	Stobo *et al.*, 1967b

[a] Preferred value based on growth and conversion (* selected diet).
[b] Maximum concentrate intake of 2 kg per day.
[c] Nitrogen retained (g per day).

TABLE 7.7 MINERAL AND VITAMIN REQUIREMENT OF EARLY WEANED CALVES[a] OVER THE WEIGHT RANGE 55–90kg

Mineral	Dietary concentration		Vitamin	Dietary concentration	
	ARC (1965)[b]	Our estimate[c]		ARC (1965)[b]	Our estimate
	(% in DM)			(IU/kg DM)	
Calcium	1.00	0.80	A	1530	6000
Phosphorus	0.54		D	130	1200
Magnesium	0.55		E	3.5	20
Potassium	0.63				
Sodium	0.12				
Chlorine	0.13				
	mg/kg DM				
Iron	30				
Copper	10				
Zinc	50				
Manganese	40				
Cobalt	0.10				
Iodine	0.12				

[a] Expected mean gain 1.0 kg per day; expected mean DM intake 2.25 kg per day.
[b] Derived from ARC (1965).
[c] Disagreement only in case of calcium.

the ARC standards; on the other hand, it would seem that the calcium standard is higher than necessary. We suggest that for this element a dietary concentration of 0.8% is satisfactory.

The effect of reducing the copper content of the diet from 10.8 to 4.2 mg/kg DM was studied by Engel *et al.* (1964). There were no differences in growth rate of male calves to 20 weeks of age nor in subsequent reproductive performance of heifers maintained on similar copper levels to 42 months of age. Although this implies that 5 mg copper/kg of diet DM is adequate, the feeding system did not allow full expression of the calves' growth potential. In the absence of any evidence to the contrary, the ARC (1965) standards for all minerals, other than calcium, are the most reliable guide to feed formulation.

7.5.4.7 VITAMINS. The vitamin A standards proposed by ARC (1965) (see Table 7.7) bear no relation to the amounts used in commercial practice which range from 4000 IU/kg DM (Preston, 1967) to 10,000 (Foll, 1964). Although there is no direct experimental evidence to justify these high levels in calf diets, it is established that these quantities are needed in high energy diets for older dairy-beef cattle (§ 9.7). It has been shown that the need for such levels is a function of the diet rather than the animal, thus it seems logical to assume that requirements for early weaned calves will be of a similar order.

Very little is known about vitamin D requirements on high energy diets. However, in view of the fact that an inbalance of vitamins A and D can lead to rickets (Grant, 1955), it seems wise to maintain vitamin D in the commercially accepted proportions of some 20–25% of the amount of vitamin A.

TABLE 7.8 THE EFFECT OF ANTIBIOTICS ON GROWTH AND FEED CONVERSION IN THE EARLY WEANED CALF

Antibiotic level (mg/kg diet)	Feeding period (weeks)	Daily gain		Feed conversion		Authors
		Control (kg)	Improvement with antibiotic (%)	Control	Improvement with antibiotic (%)	
Tetracyclines						
18/o	6–12	0.79	19	3.16	11	Whitelaw *et al.*, 1963
30/c	1–12	0.56	21	2.5	12	Quayle, 1958
40/c	0–12	0.44	37	2.25	21	Landagora *et al.*, 1957
20/c	4–12	0.44	40	3.36	17	Preston *et al.*, 1959
20–80/c	0–7	0.31	48	2.40	20	Hogue *et al.*, 1957
Bacitracin/penicillin 20–80	0–7	0.31	16	2.40	10	Hogue *et al.*, 1957
Streptomycin 20–80	0–7	0.31	31	2.40	13	Hogue *et al.*, 1957

c = chlortetracycline. o = oxytetracycline.

Vitamin E appears to behave similarly to vitamin A in that requirements are a function of the kind of diet used. We consider a safe level in an early weaning diet to be of the order of 20 IU/kg DM.

7.5.4.8 Antibiotics. In a comprehensive review of the subject, Lassiter (1955) concluded that the inclusion of tetracyclines in the diet led to a 10–30% increase in growth rate and a commensurate improvement in feed conversion. It is now known (see Preston, 1962a) that both the mode of action and the degree of response differ according to whether early or late weaning systems are used.

Results of some experiments in which antibiotics were fed to early weaned calves are given in Table 7.8. All the data were published subsequent to Lassiter's review, and it is interesting to note that the mean response in gain is towards the upper end of the range put forward by this author. This would appear to confirm that the response is determined largely by age of weaning. Moreover, both Landagora *et al.* (1957) and Whitelaw *et al.* (1963) provided evidence which strongly suggests that the degree of response is not related either to disease level or previous antibiotic usage. There is then no question but that it is economical to feed antibiotics—particularly the tetracyclines—to this class of animal.

Part III. The Production

CHAPTER 8

Growth and Efficiency: Breed, Sex and Hormones

8.1. GROWTH MECHANISMS

Up to this point discussion has centred around the raw materials available to the intensive beef producer and the factors affecting their use. The nature of the product has also been examined, particularly from the viewpoint of what the modern market needs and the restraints this puts upon the product. The purpose of this and the subsequent two chapters is to examine the ways in which, within any given production system, the various inputs can be combined so that growth and efficiency are maximized.

The rate at which an animal grows is determined by two sets of factors. The potential limits are set by hormonal relationships which are basically under genetic control, while realization of this potential depends upon the environment (particularly the nutritional component) and its interaction with genotype.

All animals grow most rapidly when young. As they approach physical maturity growth rate decreases until a stage is reached where there is no further increase of bone or muscle. Gains in weight beyond this point (chemical maturity) are almost exclusively due to fat deposition. Since the markets mainly require lean meat the producer is primarily concerned with the growth phase prior to both physical and chemical maturity. It is often expedient to slaughter cattle well before physical maturity; it will rarely be economic to do so later.

The multiplication of cells which brings about protein synthesis and hence muscle growth, is mainly controlled by a protein (somatotrophic hormone) secreted by the acidophilic cells of the anterior lobe of the pituitary gland. There is some evidence (Andik *et al.*, 1966) that in rats this hormone has a direct stimulating effect upon feed intake. On the other hand, Bogart *et al.* (1963a) found that rapidly growing cattle did not necessarily eat more food per unit of live weight than slow growers but utilized it more efficiently. It is well established that somatotrophin acts upon the skeleton, particularly the long bones, to cause new bone formation; at the same time it affects the retention rate of ingested nitrogen, thus controlling the formation of the protein-containing tissues of the body (see review by Nalbandov, 1963). Tepperman and Tepperman (1960) have shown that somatotrophin achieves these effects by making cell walls permeable to amino acids and by activating the enzyme systems of the microsomes, thus allowing the latter to form the proteins typical of the tissues to which they belong. These effects occur at a rate proportional to the amount of somatotrophin available. Bogart *et al.* (1963a) found that rapidly growing cattle withdrew amino acids from the blood at a faster rate than their slower-growing contemporaries. There was also a suggestion that rate of growth was related to enzyme activity.

It is the availability of growth hormone which appears to be under genetic control, and Baird *et al.* (1952) have shown that in pigs selected for fast or slow rates of growth the amount of somatotrophin per unit of pituitary gland tissue was greater in the faster growing line at all ages. These workers considered that the amount of available somatotrophin declined as the animal approached physical maturity; and that although the hormone continued to be secreted in physically mature animals there was only sufficient to replace and repair worn-out and damaged tissue.

In cattle it has been demonstrated by Armstrong and Hansel (1956) and Curl *et al.* (1968b) that the concentration of growth hormone expressed either per unit of body size or gland weight was greatest in early life and declined with age. The former workers reported a positive correlation between rate of growth in Holstein heifers and the growth hormone content per gram of pituitary tissue. Brumby (1959) induced faster growth in 12-week-old calves by daily injections of growth hormone (0.1 mg/kg live weight). This, together with the work of Simpson *et al.* (1950), who caused mature rats to begin growing again following somatotrophin injections, lends support to the belief that vigorous growth depends upon the amount of circulating somatotrophin per unit of body weight.

The other hormones concerned with growth are the steroids produced by the gonads and the adrenals. It is well known that males acquire a larger muscle mass at a faster rate than do females, and that castration, by elimination of the gonads, reduces this. That castrated males still out-grow females implies that adrenal steroids are also implicated in protein anabolic processes. As might be expected, gonadal androgens only begin to affect growth beyond puberty. For instance, Palsson and Verges (1952a, b) showed that the growth curve of male and female lambs began to diverge at about 4 weeks of age (18 kg live weight) while bulls only began to out-gain steers beyond a live weight of 250 kg (Preston *et al.*, 1968b). The role of adrenal steroids is less well understood, but the increased adrenal size in castrates treated with synthetic oestrogens suggests that they may have a compensatory function (Preston *et al.*, 1960b).

As with somatotrophin, the secretion rate of the endogenous steroid hormones is basically under genetic control. Under normal circumstances the only non-genetic means of changing the animal's growth potential is by the administration of exogenous synthetic hormones (§ 8.4). There is some evidence that severe undernutrition in pre- and immediate post-natal life can have an irreversible effect upon subsequent growth (Chow, 1968; Gunthrie and Brown, 1968). The action appears to be upon brain size and brain DNA and cannot apparently be induced in the post-weaning period. So far these effects have only been demonstrated in laboratory animals, and it is doubtful if the nutritional plane in practice is ever sufficiently low to induce similar problems in cattle.

The growth cycle was classified by Hafez (1963) into pre- and post-natal stages, the latter being further subdivided into pre- and post-weaning periods. Pre-natal and pre-weaning phases have been discussed in Chapter 6. In chapters 8, 9 and 10 we are concerned with factors influencing growth post-weaning, i.e. at the stage of intensification of the fattening operation. For the purposes of discussion we consider these to be (a) breed, sex and exogenous hormones—which determine the potential for growth, and (b) nutrition (Chapter 9), environment and management (Chapter 10) —which are the factors governing realization of the growth potential.

8.2 BREED

The genetics of growth and the ways in which potentially more productive cattle can be developed have been discussed in Chapter 3. The aim of this section is to describe the differences existing between specific breeds under particular environmental conditions. The breeds of cattle in existence are legion, and it is not our intention to categorize them, even less to describe their colours, horn shapes, conformation or distribution. Those interested in such data should read Mason (1957), Philips (1961) or French (1966). What we seek to provide are comparative statistics which will allow the intensive producer to select, from within the breeds and cross breeds available, those likely to perform best on his own particular feeding and management system.

Although a great deal of beef cattle research has been conducted in the US, meaningful comparisons among the different pure breeds are scarce. On the other hand, much work has been carried out in Europe, particularly in Russia, but with so little statistical control and in such poorly organized trials that few worthwhile conclusions can be drawn. The more reliable data available are set out in Tables 8.1 and 8.2 for pure breeds and crossbreeds respectively. It is abundantly clear that the Angus and the Shorthorn, both as pure breeds and as crossing sires, are inferior to most others. On the few occasions when the Angus has had better feed conversions than contemporary breeds (e.g. Burgi, 1964), the comparisons have been confounded with respect to the live-weight ranges studied.

The outstanding breed is the Charolais since it has been superior in almost all the comparisons reported. It performed badly in East Africa (Pagot, 1951–2) when crossed with N'dama cattle, but this may well have been due to inadequate feeding (Pagot, 1967). It has given good results in Britain (Edwards *et al.*, 1966), Scandinavia (Westbye and Naess, 1967), Hungary (Barczy *et al.*, 1965), Russia (Calaja, 1965), Portugal (Carrilho, 1964), Canada (Hidiroglou *et al.*, 1964, 1966), Cuba (Willis and Preston, 1968a) and Latin America (López Saubidet *et al.*, 1963). Although Dodsworth *et al.* (1966) concluded that Charolais × Ayrshire steers required 7–8 weeks longer than Shorthorn × Ayrshires to reach the same degree of finish, the former at this stage were 64 kg heavier, which makes such comparisons irrelevant.

Kidwell and McCormick (1956) and Anon. (1966a) claimed that the Holstein was faster growing than the Hereford, while the former suggested as a general thesis that inherent rate of growth is directly related to mature body size. Better performance from Friesians than from Angus or Hereford as crossing sires on Dairy Shorthorns was reported in Ireland by Harte and Conniffe (1967).

It is interesting to note that the breeds (Angus and Shorthorn), which in the UK decreased most in mature size from 1913 to the late 1950's (Mason, 1961), are those with the poorest growth rates and feed conversions.

TABLE 8.1 PERFORMANCE[a] OF DIFFERENT PURE BREEDS

Angus	Brahman	Charolais	Hereford	Holstein	Shorthorn	Sta. Gertrudis	Others	Authors
0.60/12.5			0.60/12.5	0.90/11.1				Bond *et al.*, 1967
1.02/10.4			1.08/9.5					Butler *et al.*, 1962
	0.86/9.29		0.98/8.43					Carroll *et al.*, 1955
0.79	0.55		0.83					Damon *et al.*, 1959a
0.76	0.73							De Rouen *et al.*, 1961
0.75/6.2			0.86/5.3		0.79/5.8			Gregory *et al.*, 1966b
		0.89	0.71					Klosterman *et al.*, 1965a
	0.68/6.6				0.62/7.0			Koger *et al.*, 1962a
				1.15/5.23			1.02/5.83[b]	MacLeod *et al.*, 1968
1.00/8.4			1.11/7.4					Melton *et al.*, 1967a
	0.50					0.49	0.47[c]	Muñoz *et al.*, 1964
0.84/8.5		0.98/8.5	0.90/8.4					Sagebiel *et al.*, 1967b
				1.17			1.18[d]	Vilstrup, 1964
0.97			1.05		1.00			Vogt *et al.*, 1967
	0.86/8.1	1.20/5.2		1.18/5.6		1.16/6.0	1.06/6.4[c]	Willis & Preston, 1968a

[a] Daily gain/feed conversion. [b] Ayrshire. [c] Criollo. [d] Brown Swiss.

TABLE 8.2 PERFORMANCE[a] OF DIFFERENT CROSSBREEDS

Maternal breed	Paternal breed								Authors
	Angus	Brahman	Charolais	Hereford	Holstein	Shorthorn	Sta. Gertrudis	Others	
Ayrshire			0.81			0.77			Broadbent *et al.*, 1967
Simmental	0.83		0.87					0.84[b]	Burgi, 1964
Angus	0.79	0.89	0.88	0.77		0.82		0.73[c]	Damon *et al.*, 1959a
Brahman	0.78	0.55	0.70	0.82		0.77		0.69[c]	Damon *et al.*, 1959a
Brangus	0.76	0.68	0.77	0.76		0.91		0.71[c]	Damon *et al.*, 1959a
Hereford	0.81	0.93	0.92	0.83		0.81		0.87[c]	Damon *et al.*, 1959a
Ayrshire			0.76			0.73			Dodsworth *et al.*, 1966
Dairy			0.76	0.69	0.72				Edwards *et al.*, 1966
Angus	0.75/6.2			0.81/5.6		0.73/6.4			Gregory *et al.*, 1966b
Hereford	0.84/5.4			0.86/5.3		0.80/5.6			Gregory *et al.*, 1966b
Shorthorn	0.78/5.8			0.83/5.6		0.79/5.8			Gregory *et al.*, 1966b
Shorthorn	0.63		0.71	0.67		0.58			Hidiroglou *et al.*, 1964
Shorthorn		0.72/6.4				0.62/7.0			Koger *et al.*, 1962a
Brahman		0.50					0.59	0.61[d]	Muñoz *et al.*, 1964
Criollo		0.56					0.48	0.47[d]	Muñoz *et al.*, 1964
Sta. Gertrudis		0.57					0.49	0.50[d]	Muñoz *et al.*, 1964
Friesian					1.08			1.09[e]	Raimondi, 1965
Holstein			0.76		0.73				Smirnov, 1965
Brahman		0.94/7.1	1.16/5.7		1.07/5.8			0.96/6.8[d]	Willis & Preston, 1969c
								1.16/5.9[f]	Willis & Preston, 1969c

[a] Daily gain/feed conversion. [b] Simmental. [c] Brangus. [d] Criollo. [e] Piedmont. [f] Brown Swiss.

8.3 SEX

8.3.1 Males

In almost all the major beef-producing countries males not required for breeding are castrated. The advantages claimed are that castrates deposit fat more quickly and their meat has better texture and is less strongly flavoured than that of bulls. Castration does prevent such undesirable secondary sex characteristics as excessive crest development, aggressive temperament and sexual activity; thus steers can be housed with heifers and are generally more easily managed than entire males. Some of these reasons are valid enough when feeding systems are based on low energy feeds and the meat market is predicated towards "well-finished" carcasses from animals of 2 years and over. However, the advent of intensive, higher energy feeding systems and the increasing desire for leaner meat on the part of the housewife has led to a reappraisal of the role of the male sex hormones (androgens) as growth promoters rather than determinants of secondary sex characters.

The relative growth rates and feed conversions of bulls, steers and heifers, fed intensively or semi-intensively, are set out in Table 8.3. The data show conclusively that bulls are superior to steers in gain and feed conversion. When account is also taken of the higher lean meat content of bull carcasses (§ 2.3), the equivocal nature of reported differences in tenderness and flavour (§ 2.5) and the fact that management of young bulls represents not real difficulties (Robertson and Laing, 1965; Dalton *et al.*, 1967), it is difficult to understand why castration is still universally practised. Consumer studies (e.g. Field *et al.*, 1964c) imply that the problem lies not with the housewife but with the prejudices of butchers and wholesale meat buyers. It is true that skilful butchers can, by careful examination, distinguish between bull and steer carcasses. However, there is no evidence to relate secondary sex characters to eating quality, particularly in young animals. Melton *et al.* (1967a) have obtained a relationship between weight of forequarter and secondary sex characteristics, but this is more than compensated for by bulls having a higher proportion of first-quality edible meat and a lower fat content (§ 2.3.4.4).

It is worth noting than in non-English speaking areas of the world such "sexual" prejudices are absent with the result that the entire male is the animal of choice for intensive feeding. That Yugoslavia has been successful in selling bull meat to the traditional English market demonstrates that the real barrier to the much wider use of bulls in the UK is the Ministry of Agriculture and their insistence on the licensing of all males at 10 months of age or their castration. The British farmer is thus compelled to use less efficient animals in his beef enterprise. In the US, on the other hand, although licensing does not exist, the grading system and associated premiums for fat carcasses have a similar discouraging effect on the use of bulls. However, there is hope that the increasing number of scientific papers denigrating both the grading system and the performance of steers relative to bulls will lead to a reappraisal at least on the part of American cattle feeders.

During the late 1950's attempts were made to combine the advantages of bulls and steers by employing the partial castration technique developed in Russia by Baiburtcjan and which consisted of removing only the parenchyma of the testis. The advantages claimed for this method were reviewed by Turton (1962) and by Baiburtcjan (1963). Critical experiments in the UK showed that this procedure did

TABLE 8.3 EFFECT OF SEX ON GROWTH AND FEED CONVERSION (NON-IMPLANTED ANIMALS)

Initial weight (kg)	Final live weight (kg)			Daily gain (kg)			Feed conversion			Authors
	Bulls	Steers	Heifers	Bulls	Steers	Heifers	Bulls	Steers	Heifers	
280	453	446		1.24	1.06		8.33	9.43		Bailey *et al.*, 1966a
183	414	407		1.19	1.06		6.54	7.09		Bailey *et al.*, 1966a
		479	431		1.01	0.86				Bradley *et al.*, 1966a
							5.44	5.92		Brannang, 1966a
84		510	447		0.80	0.74				Broadbent *et al.*, 1967
70		444	390		0.77	0.69				Broadbent *et al.*, 1967
				1.27	1.04		6.12	7.14		Champagne *et al.*, 1964
					1.00[a]			7.37[a]		Champagne *et al.*, 1964
	474	468		0.86	0.81		4.22	4.55		Cobic, 1968
68	405	400		1.08	0.95		3.61	3.83		Forbes *et al.*, 1966
100	461	430		0.92	0.84		3.52	3.90		Harte & Curran, 1967
105	461	443		0.77	0.73		Pasture			Harte & Curran, 1967
113	377	347		0.69	0.61		6.29	7.08		Harte *et al.*, 1965
					1.07	0.93				Hawkins *et al.*, 1967a
					1.12	0.97		7.38	7.88	Hawkins *et al.*, 1967b
165	424	393		1.20	1.07		6.25	6.94		Isakov, 1961
	535	505		1.06	0.95					Ivanov & Zahariev, 1964
82				0.98	0.94	0.93				McGinty & Marion, 1965
	370	370		1.07	0.95		3.81	4.11		Nichols *et al.*, 1964
	490	490		1.05	0.98		4.31	4.73		Nichols *et al.*, 1964
				0.99	0.94					Pilkington *et al.*, 1959
40	433	400		1.06	0.97		3.34	3.63		Preston *et al.*, 1968b
40	414	411		0.98	0.88		3.31	3.75		Preston *et al.*, 1968b
160	410	398		1.26	1.07		5.36	6.06		Preston *et al.*, 1968b
				1.07	0.98		4.09	4.49		Raimondi, 1955
				1.26	1.02					Richter *et al.*, 1960
				1.33	1.01	0.93	7.49	8.76	9.00	Warner *et al.*, 1965
				1.00	0.85	0.74	7.29	8.63	9.61	Williams *et al.*, 1965
		437	408		0.99	0.92				Wilson *et al.*, 1967
				1.11		0.82	6.53		7.74	Zeremski & Koljajic, 1966

[a] Late castrates

little more than render the animal infertile, while secondary sex characters still developed. Since in several experiments growth rates of partial castrates were less than those of entire males (e.g. Robertson and Laing, 1965), there seems little justification for the widespread use of the technique, particularly as considerable skill is needed to carry out the operation successfully.

8.3.2 Females

A proportion of heifers not required for herd replacements are available for fattening. Although less experimental work has been done with heifers (Table 8.3) it is well established that their growth rates are inferior to males. Feed conversion is also much worse.

A poorer performance from females is to be expected from their sex hormone balance since the predominating secretion of oestrogens from the ovaries has a depressing effect on growth (Albert, 1942; Mathews *et al.*, 1942). It is commonly believed that the expression of oestrus causes behavioural disturbances, particularly in group-fed animals, and that these have a further deleterious effect on performance. Spaying (i.e. removal of the ovaries) has been investigated in the hope that it would lead to improved growth and efficiency (Dinusson *et al.*, 1950; Clegg and Caroll, 1956; Kercher *et al.*, 1958) but results were inconclusive, possibly because the ovaries are not the only site of oestrogen production. The stress of the operation may also have militated in part against better performance. Certainly the practice has not been accepted in commercial feedlots nor is it ever likely to be because of the inconvenience of the operation. A more hopeful solution to the heifer problem lies in the neutralization of the endogenous oestrogen by synthetic hormones (§ 8.4.3).

In biological terms it is perfectly clear that efficiency of lean meat production is greatest in bulls and least in heifers. The decision as to which sex to use in a particular fattening operation will depend on the relative price of bull, steer and heifer calves, and the value of their respective carcasses. In certain circumstances these factors, separately or in combination, may nullify differences in biological efficiency. Account must also be taken of the availability of synthetic hormones and the regulations governing their use. For, although oestrogen-treated steers can have comparable growth and feed conversion to bulls, in some countries (e.g. Denmark, France, Italy and Sweden) the use of hormones is prohibited.

8.4 HORMONES

8.4.1 Introduction

The synthesis of the steroid hormones—diethylstilbestrol (DES) and hexoestrol and the demonstration that their properties resemble those of natural oestrogens have been well documented (Burrows, 1949; Pincus and Thimann, 1955). Their use to stimulate growth in castrated male cattle was first reported by Andrews *et al.* (1950) and, as it was later developed by Burroughs *et al.* (1954, 1955), this technique ranks as one of the major advances in the field of beef cattle production. The success of its application is illustrated by the fact that at the present time almost all steers in the US are treated with steroid hormones.

The literature on this topic, particularly between 1955 and 1963, is voluminous, but the mode of action is still imperfectly understood. Administration of exogenous hormones obviously affects the balance of natural hormones, but whether it leads to an increased production of androgens from the adrenals, in an attempt to compensate for added oestrogens (Clegg and Cole, 1954; Preston and Gee, 1957; Preston *et al.*, 1960b), or the anterior pituitary is stimulated so as to produce more somatotrophin (Martin and Lamming, 1958; Struempler and Burroughs, 1959) is still open to question.

The chronological development of hormone administration to cattle was first with steers, which have been investigated the most intensively, followed by heifers and bulls. They will be discussed here in the same order.

8.4.2 Steers

8.4.2.1 NATURE OF THE EFFECT. Tables 8.4–8.7 summarize the results of some experiments on the administration of oestrogens to steers under drylot conditions. Effects on pasture have been summarized by Alder *et al.* (1964).

Although the data encompass a variety of ages, breeds, feeding systems and locations, in only a small proportion of the trials reported here and by Alder *et al.* (1964) was there no positive effect. In the majority of cases voluntary feed intake was unchanged, thus improvement in rate of weight gain has always resulted in better feed conversion—when this has been measured. The effect of steroid hormones on carcass characteristics has been discussed in Chapter 2. Essentially, the changes brought about in the carcass are commensurate with the hypothesis that, in hormone-treated animals, absorbed nutrients are diverted to bone and muscle synthesis at the expense of fat deposition. The overall energy of the gain in carcass weight remains the same (Preston and Gee, 1957) but, as calorific content of the tissues is less in hormone-treated animals, there is a greater total weight gain and a better efficiency in terms of weight of product per unit of feed intake. Calorific efficiency is unchanged (Gee and Preston, 1957; Ogilvie *et al.*, 1960; Garrett, 1965a), but efficiency of converting feed protein into carcass protein is considerably enhanced (Gee and Preston, 1957; Ogilvie *et al.*, 1960).

There are minor disadvantages to hormone treatment caused by the secondary sex effects which include increased sexual activity (Clegg and Cole, 1954), raising of the tail head or depression of the loin due to loosening of the muscles (O'Mary *et al.*, 1956; Good *et al.*, 1957) and slight mammary development (Beeson *et al.*, 1956b; Good *et al.*, 1957; Perry *et al.*, 1958; Ray and McBride, 1961). O'Mary *et al.* (1956) noted that depression of the loin occurred some 65–85 days after treatment and although Andrews *et al.* (1954) believed that the condition returned to normal with time, O'Mary *et al.* found it still existed, in some cases, at 182 days. In the carcass only the elevated tail head may be apparent whereas, in the live animal, side effects are more easily noticed. Thus in a study involving 168 animals, half of which had been treated, it was reported that 86% of implanted steers were correctly identified by eye appraisal (Ray and McBride, 1961). This can lead to buyer discrimination in some markets. The severity of side effects is directly related to the amount of hormone administered although, in the case of implantation, there is a tendency for these effects to regress with increasing time after treatment (Perry *et al.*, 1958).

TABLE 8.4 EFFECT OF DIETHYLSTILBOESTROL ON DAILY GAIN OF STEERS

Total no. of steers	Daily gain of control	Percentage improvement obtained by DES							Authors
		Oral (mg/day)			Implantation (mg)				
		10	Other levels	< 24	24	30/36	45/48	⩾60	
14	0.83			−8[a]					Meiske *et al.*, 1960
16	0.99	0							Homb, 1959
18	0.92			2[a]					Meiske *et al.*, 1960
	1.10					4			McGinty & Marion, 1965
14	0.81	5							Stothers & Stringham, 1956
20	0.88	5							O'Mary *et al.*, 1959b
	0.94					6			McGinty & Marion, 1965
56	0.87					7			Klosterman *et al.*, 1959
38	0.30					7	4		Folman & Volcani, 1960
80	1.43					8			Furr *et al.*, 1968a
32	0.93					8			Bradley *et al.*, 1959
16	1.04							8	Clegg & Carroll, 1957
18	1.06	8							Wallentine *et al.*, 1961
65	1.10	8						6	Clegg & Carroll, 1957
24	0.78					9			Bradley *et al.*, 1959
40	0.97	4		−1[a]	9				O'Mary *et al.*, 1959b
200	1.22					9			Clegg & Carroll, 1957
109	1.28	9							Woods, 1962
20	1.19					10			Clegg & Carroll, 1957
80	1.32	4				10			Furr *et al.*, 1968a
69	1.45	−4		10[b]					Clegg & Carroll, 1957
	0.89				11				Wipf *et al.*, 1964
	0.90	17				12			Klosterman *et al.*, 1959
66	0.93					12		11	Thomas *et al.*, 1957
40	0.96				12				Frederick *et al.*, 1962
24	0.97					12			Sherman *et al.*, 1959
160	1.05	12							Matsushima *et al.*, 1959
18	1.07	12							Beeson *et al.*, 1956a
152	0.95						13[c]		Wilson *et al.*, 1963a
30	1.06		13[d]						Smith *et al.*, 1956

36	1.06	13				11			Thomas *et al.*, 1958
23	1.10					13			Burgess & Lamming, 1960
32	1.11	4	13[e]						Ogilvie *et al.*, 1960
216	1.38			13[a]	12	6			Ralston, 1965
120	0.80			14[a]	10	13			Thomas *et al.*, 1957
32	0.96	14							Kolari *et al.*, 1960
24	0.96	14		12[b]					Clegg & Carroll, 1957
28	1.05	14							Deans *et al.*, 1956
32	1.07							14[f]	Hawkins *et al.*, 1967a
69	1.09	9			14				Thomas *et al.*, 1958
16	1.09	14							Homb, 1959
18	1.05					14	14		Folman & Volcani, 1960
24	1.10					14			Hale *et al.*, 1959
116	1.12	14							Woods, 1962
200	0.85	15							Clegg & Carroll, 1957
60	0.94				15				Dilley *et al.*, 1959
125	1.05	12				15			Clegg & Carroll, 1957
40	1.06				15				Frederick *et al.*, 1962
16	0.80	16							Kastelic *et al.*, 1956
24	0.99	16							Heinemann & Fanelli, 1963
31	1.10					16			Garrett, 1965a
75	1.12	2		3[a]				16	Clegg & Carroll, 1957
8	0.77	17							Burgess & Lamming, 1960
40	0.79	17							Perry *et al.*, 1960
	0.84				17				Wipf *et al.*, 1964
36	1.02	15				17			Perry *et al.*, 1958
20	1.02	17							Marion *et al*, 1960b
	1.09					17			Marion, 1959
144	0.80						16	18	England & Taylor, 1959
20	0.93					18			Clegg & Carroll, 1957
38	0.93	11						18	Clegg & Carroll, 1957
404	0.95	18						13	Clegg & Carroll, 1957
36	1.00	15		5[g]	7	18	12		Perry *et al.*, 1958
18	1.02	18							Homb, 1959
41	1.06				18				Bailey *et al.*, 1966a
	1.23	−6			14	18			Beeson *et al.*, 1957b
18	1.02					19			Marion *et al.*, 1960a
24	0.90					20			Shermann *et al.*, 1959
17	0.95	20							Andrews *et al.*, 1956

TABLE 8.4 (cont.)

Total no. of steers	Daily gain of control	Percentage improvement obtained by DES							Authors
		Oral (mg/day)		Implantation (mg)					
		10	Other levels	< 24	24	30/36	45/48	≥ 60	
20	0.95	20							Koch *et al.*, 1959c
48	1.00	−5			13	20			Beeson *et al.*, 1956b
36	1.04			14[h]	7	20	15		Beeson *et al.*, 1956b
	1.23	10						21	Good *et al.*, 1957
20	1.02	22							Marion, 1960
50	0.75					23[i]			O'Mary *et al.*, 1956
120	0.77	23							Heinemann & Kyd, 1956
	1.02	20				23			Aunan *et al.*, 1956
40	1.15						23		Wipf *et al.*, 1964
29	1.07	8	9[d]	24[j]					Kastelic *et al.*, 1956
40	0.73				25				Fletcher *et al.*, 1957
90	0.98	22		21[b]		25		16	Clegg & Carroll, 1957
72	0.75				27				Goodwin, 1958
149	1.04	28							Clegg & Carroll, 1957
88	0.58			17[a]	29	16			Thomas *et al.*, 1957
224	0.99	29		14[b]		20	10	19	Clegg & Carroll, 1957
49	0.61					30		30[k]	O'Mary *et al.*, 1956
144	1.01			19[b]		33	26		Clegg & Carroll, 1957
54	1.06		17[d]					35	Clegg & Carroll, 1957
16	1.13			21[b]		39	37	36	Clegg & Carroll, 1957
125	0.97			21[b]		39	37	38	Clegg & Carroll, 1957
30	0.60					25		40	Folman & Volcani, 1960
38	0.56				36	54			Burgess & Lamming, 1960
14	0.55							64	Burgess & Lamming, 1960
Median values		14	13	12	14	16	16	18	
Overall		14		16					

[a] 12 mg. [b] 15 mg. [c] 24 + 24 mg in two implants. [d] 5 mg. [e] 30 mg. [f] 24 + 36 mg in two implants. [g] 11 mg. [h] 10 mg. [i] 12 + 24 mg in two implants. [j] 20 mg. [k] 36 + 36 in two implants

TABLE 8.5 EFFECT OF DIETHYLSTILBOESTROL ON FEED CONVERSION IN STEERS

Total no. of steers	Control	Improvement due to different doses of DES (mg): Oral	Implantation			Authors
		10	< 30	30/36	> 36	
404	10.4	−17			−21[a]	Clegg & Carroll, 1957
16	5.5	0				Homb, 1959
56	5.4			2		Klosterman *et al.*, 1956
69	9.6	−2	2[b]			Clegg & Carroll, 1957
	8.7			3		McGinty & Marion, 1965
28	5.2	4				Homb, 1959
24	8.4	4				Hentges *et al.*, 1960
80	6.7	4		1		Furr *et al.*, 1968a
109	8.8	4				Woods, 1962
30	18.4		5			Smith *et al.*, 1956
16	11.2				7[a]	Clegg & Carroll, 1957
14	9.0	7				Stothers & Stringham, 1956
24	11.0			8		Sherman *et al.*, 1959
36		8		7		Beeson *et al.*, 1956b
41	9.4		9[c]			Bailey *et al.*, 1966a
36		9		7		Perry *et al.*, 1958
32	6.1	4/9[d]				Ogilvie *et al.*, 1960
166	9.7	10				Woods, 1962
60	10.4		11[c]			Dilley *et al.*, 1959
16	4.6	11				Homb, 1959
24	11.6			12		Sherman *et al.*, 1959
8	5.4	13				Burgess & Lamming, 1960
125	9.3	12		13		Clegg & Carroll, 1957
18				14		Marion *et al.*, 1960b
31	7.1			14		Garrett, 1965a
200	12.1			18		Clegg & Carroll, 1957
149	12.5	19				Clegg & Carroll, 1957
54	12.0	11			20[a]	Clegg & Carroll, 1957
16	11.6				22[a]	Clegg & Carroll, 1957
144	10.7		15[b]	24	20[e]	Clegg & Carroll, 1957
Median values		7	10			

[a] 60 mg. [b] 15 mg. [c] 24 mg. [d] 30 mg. [e] 45 mg.

8.4.2.2 TYPE OF HORMONE. The most commonly used hormones have been DES and hexoestrol, the former being developed in the US and the latter in Great Britain. They differ only slightly in structure and are generally considered to be equally effective (Perry *et al.*, 1955). Andrews *et al.* (1956) and Burgess and Lamming (1960) obtained slightly better results from DES, but Thurber *et al.* (1959) claimed from results with 1326 animals in 11 trials that hexoestrol was superior to all others.

TABLE 8.6 EFFECT OF HEXOESTROL ON GAIN AND FEED CONVERSION IN STEERS

Total no. of steers	Daily gain of control (kg)	Improvement with hexoestrol		Feed conversion of control	Improvement with hexoestrol (%)	Authors
		Oral (%)	Implantation (%)			
17	0.95		8.4[a]			Andrews *et al.*, 1956
175	1.09		20.2[b]			RRI, 1964
—	1.27	22.0[a]				Dyer *et al.*, 1956
20	0.92	23.9[c]		21.7	15.7	Beeson *et al.*, 1957b
—	1.14	27.2[a]				Dyer *et al.*, 1956
10	0.73		35.6[d]	9.1	27.5	Aitken & Crichton, 1956
18	0.65		43.1[d]	13.4	28.4	Dodsworth, 1959
33	0.56		46.4[e]			Burgess & Lamming, 1960
24	0.53		54.7[b]			Dodsworth, 1959

[a] 10 mg. [b] 60 mg. [c] 20 mg. [d] 120 mg. [e] 30 mg.

Other hormones have been investigated primarily in the hope of finding a product or combination of products which would have the same growth-promoting potential as DES or hexoestrol but less oestrogenic activity and hence reduced side effects. One such product is a diphenyl hexane derivative (3,3′ diallyl hexoestrol) which has approximately 0.2 to 2% of the oestrogenic activity of DES (Dyer *et al.*, 1960). Diallyl stilboestrol is similar (Kercher, 1960b). They appear to have the same growth-promoting properties but have never been evaluated alongside DES or hexoestrol. It is necessary to comment at this stage upon the claim of Stob in the official NAS–NRC publication on hormones (1966) that hexoestrol and diallyl hexoestrol are not as effective as DES. In fact, (a) the latter has not been compared with DES, (b) in many of the experiments cited by Stob hexoestrol was used alone; and (c) the extensive data quoted in this chapter, if anything, support the conclusion of Thurber *et al.* (1959) that hexoestrol is superior.

There have been claims that the natural oestrogen oestradriol benzoate coupled with progesterone helped to reduce side effects, but the evidence is not conclusive. The greater cost of this product has not enabled it to compete with the synthetic steroids DES and hexoestrol which are the hormones of choice in almost all commercial fattening units. The natural androgenic hormone testosterone is less efficient than DES (Dinusson *et al.*, 1950), requires too frequent administration (Burris *et al.*, 1953) and has the definite disadvantage of being more expensive. Combinations of hormones have been used occasionally, but there is no evidence that they are in any way better than a single product (Thurber *et al.*, 1959).

8.4.2.3 METHOD OF ADMINISTRATION. The first experiments at Purdue University on the use of synthetic oestrogens employed implantation techniques (Andrews *et al.*, 1950, 1951); however, emphasis shifted rapidly to oral administration when it was claimed that side effects with this method were less (Burroughs *et al.*, 1954). It was

TABLE 8.7 EFFECT OF HORMONES OTHER THAN DES OR HEXOESTROL ON STEER PERFORMANCE

No. of steers	Hormone used	Dose level (mg)	Daily gain Control (kg)	Daily gain Improvement (%)	Authors
32	Diallylstilboestrol	24[a]	1.10	−2	Kercher, 1960a
30	Diallylhexoestrol	38[a]	0.66	18	Dyer *et al.*, 1960
30	Diallylhexoestrol	19[a]	0.66	24	Dyer *et al.*, 1960
18	Dienoestrol	10[b]	0.95	11	Andrews *et al.*, 1956
38	Melengestrol acetate	1.74[b]	0.98	−9	Bloss *et al.*, 1966
38	Melengestrol acetate	0.35[b]	0.98	−4	Bloss *et al.*, 1966
32	Melengestrol acetate	0.35[b]	1.07	1	Hawkins *et al.*, 1967a
32	Melengestrol acetate[c]	0.35[b]	1.07	14	Hawkins *et al.*, 1967a
144	Oestradiol[d]	24[a]	1.08	5	Koch *et al.*, 1959c
40	Oestradiol[e]	20[a]	1.15	5	Webb *et al.*, 1957
24	Oestradiol[f]	20[a]	1.06	9	Thomas *et al.*, 1958
84	Oestradiol[f]	20[a]	0.80	9	Ray & McBride, 1961
144	Oestradiol[f]	20[a]	1.08	11	Koch *et al.*, 1959
32	Oestradiol[f]	20[a]	0.93	13	Bradley *et al.*, 1959
84	Oestradiol[f]	20[a]	0.86	15	Ray & McBride, 1961
24	Oestradiol[f]	20[a]	0.78	18	Bradley *et al.*, 1959
28	Oestradiol[g]	50[a]	1.05	31	Deans *et al.*, 1956
1345	PSP[h]	250–500[a]	1.23	11	Algeo & Gassner, 1966
18	Testosterone[i]	175[b]	1.07	4	Beeson *et al.*, 1956a
36	Testosterone[j]	450[a]	0.80	10	England & Taylor, 1959
18	Testosterone[k]	175[b]	1.07	11	Beeson *et al.*, 1956a
36	Testosterone[l]	450[a]	0.80	15	England & Taylor, 1959
8	Testosterone		0.67	19	Burgess & Lamming, 1960

[a] Implantation. [b] Oral. [c] Plus 60 mg DES implanted. [d] Plus 60 mg progesterone caproate & 60 mg testosterone ethanate. [e] Plus 1.0 g progesterone. [f] Plus 200 mg progesterone. [g] Plus 1.5 g progesterone. [h] Polydiethylstilboestrol phosphate. [i] Plus 15 mg DES. [j] Plus 30 mg DES. [k] Plus 5 mg DES. [l] Plus 45 mg DES.

subsequently found that the doses used in the early implantation trials were unnecessarily high (up to 120 mg) and that equal growth stimulation—but fewer side effects—could be obtained with as little as 25–36 mg (e.g. O'Mary *et al.*, 1956; Perry *et al.*, 1958). Even at these lower levels, implantation has given slightly higher gains than feeding (see Table 8.4), while side effects have been the same for both procedures (Aunan *et al.*, 1956; Beeson *et al.*, 1956b; Good *et al.*, 1957; Perry *et al.*, 1958). O'Mary *et al.* (1959b) considered that for feeding periods of 120–150 days a 24 mg implant was more effective than either 12 mg implanted or 10 mg fed daily. Implantation obviously requires less hormone than oral administration and thus is a cheaper procedure. The only disadvantage is that handling facilities must be available, and in large-scale operations it is often more convenient to administer the hormone orally. On the other hand, there is a risk of feed contamination in mixing plants when the hormone has to be included in the ration.

8.4.2.4 Dose level. There is a dearth of information regarding the optimum dose level for oral administration. The general practice has been to accept 10 mg daily, and although this has invariably given a response, it is worth noting that Ogilvie *et al.* (1960) found that 10 mg did not stimulate gain or feed efficiency, but that there was a significant response with 30 mg. Kastelic *et al.* (1956) reported increases in gain with as little as 5 mg per head per day, but the response improved with up to 20 mg daily (his highest level). Much more work has been done on the effect of different doses by implantation. It is fairly certain that levels of 10–12 mg are too low and 24–36 mg are more satisfactory. Thus Blair *et al.* (1958) used implants of 6, 12, 18 and 30 mg DES and found the latter two to be significantly better than the others. They reported that the response curve was of a quadratic type. In one experiment, 48 mg gave no better response than 36 mg (Perry *et al.*, 1958). In British work, on the other hand, with all-concentrate feeding of Holsteins to slaughter at under one year, 60 mg of hexoestrol was always superior to 30 mg (RRI, 1964).

8.4.2.5 Reimplantation. When synthetic oestrogens are administered orally it is reasonable to expect that daily blood levels, and hence stimulatory effect on gain, will be constant throughout the feeding period. From the work of Mitchell *et al.* (1956) and Melampy *et al.* (1959) it would seem that about 2 mg of DES are absorbed daily when the oral dose is 10 mg. On the other hand, with the implantation route, absorption rate is primarily a function of the surface area of the pellet (Hale *et al.*, 1959). These latter workers found that approximately 25 mg were absorbed from a 36 mg implantation over a 112 day period, i.e. an average of 0.2 mg/day. In theory one would expect the amounts absorbed to decrease with time after implantation, according to a first degree polynomial, and hence the growth response to gradually diminish and this was observed in practice (RRI, 1964). One would thus imagine that there would be a strong argument in favour of reimplantation after a period of 80–120 days. Hale *et al.* (1959), when testing three distinct pellet formulations, found that rate of absorption was highest in the first 56 days; nevertheless, with one of the formulations they showed that while the growth response to the hormone was fairly uniform throughout the first 112 days, it decreased thereafter although still maintaining a positive effect through to 175 days.

In practice few animals, at least in US feedlots, remain on full feed for much longer than 4 months, thus there is little incentive for reimplantation. Most interest in reimplantation therefore has centred round the effects of an initial implant treatment to cattle on range/pasture followed by additional hormone treatment in the feedlot. Thompson and Kercher (1959) studied the response of 119 steers kept on summer pasture for 142 days and fed in drylot for a further 120 days. The pasture treatments were nothing (control) or implants of 24 mg DES or Synovex-S. On entering the feedlot, half the treated animals were reimplanted with the same hormone, while control animals were given either nothing or one of the two implant treatments. In the feedlot, highest gains were registered by those given implants at the beginning of this period. Those which only received implantation on pasture performed no better in the feedlot than those which had never been implanted. Over the whole 262 day period the trends were the same as in the feedlot. These data indicate that there is no advantage from early implantation on pasture and that only implants in the feedlot give significant results. Similar findings were reported by Newman and Oaks (1961) for animals implanted with 36 mg DES on entering the feedlot, having previously being given nothing or a 24 mg DES implant while on pasture. Feeding periods were 233 days on pasture and 140 in the feedlot. Although implanted steers grew faster on pasture they subsequently gained less after reimplantation in the feedlot than those given only a single implant for the fattening period. Overall gains were identical for the two systems. O'Mary *et al.* (1959b) observed that feedlot gains were 1.15, 1.01, 0.96 and 0.85 for steers implanted for the first time in the feedlot, implanted on pasture and in feedlot, not implanted at all and implanted on pasture, respectively. Albert and Neumann (1956) found that DES-fed cattle on pasture grew 13% faster than controls while on the pasture but 7% slower in the subsequent feedlot stage.

In contrast to these data, Koch *et al.* (1959c), Nelson and Pope (1959), Roubicek *et al.* (1960) and Woods (1962) all reported that implantation on pasture improved gains (or reduced winter loss) and that implanted animals responded equally to controls when reimplanted or fed DES in the feedlot. Some of Wood's results are summarized in Table 8.8. The data suggest that a 12 mg implant on pasture followed by 10 mg orally in the feedlot is a better combination than 24 mg on pasture followed by 10 mg orally. On pasture the former was superior to the control yet both responded equally to DES in the feedlot; in contrast, the 24 mg treatment, although superior on pasture, was slightly inferior when DES was supplied in the feedlot. It should be noted that feed conversion in the feedlot always favoured animals not previously implanted, and while part of this may have been due to their lighter weight at the start, the degree of difference suggests that other mechanisms, possibly compensatory growth, were operating to their advantage. It can be concluded that pasture implantation is justified for the rancher who raises calves for the feedlot provided he obtains the same price per unit of weight for implanted and non-

TABLE 8.8 EFFECT OF REIMPLANTATION WITH DIETHYLSTILBOESTROL ON GROWTH AND PERFORMANCE IN HEREFORD STEERS (AFTER WOODS, 1962)

Pasture treatment (mg)	Control		12 mg		Control		12 mg	
Feedlot treatment (mg)	0	12	0	12	0	24	0	24
Pasture[a]								
No. of steers	84		87		55		54	
Daily gain (kg)	0.71		0.84		0.67		0.77	
Feedlot[b]								
No. of steers	38	46	38	44	27	28	27	27
Daily gain (kg)	1.10	1.26	1.14	1.29	1.30	1.44	1.27	1.37
Final weight (kg)	500	532	527	554	529	547	532	546
Conversion	9.8	8.7	9.7	8.9	8.7	8.1	8.8	8.7

[a] 134 days. [b] 139 days.

implanted animals. The fattener, on the other hand, who intends to use steroid hormones in his feeding programme would be well advised to pay slightly less for such implanted cattle—if he can identify them.

Some studies on reimplantation of cattle while they were still in the feedlot have shown that, when the initial implantation was at the normally recommended level of 30–36 mg, a second treatment after 42 days was of no advantage (O'Mary *et al.*, 1956). When reimplantation was after 56 days it was advantageous only if the initial implantation was low (12 mg). In contrast RRI (1964) data with hexoestrol showed that reimplantation (30 mg) 56 days after an initial implant of 30 mg gave the same results as a single 60 mg implant given at the start and better results than a single 30 mg implant at the start. England and Taylor (1959) found that the time of reimplantation (92 or 182 days after the start), appeared to be of no consequence when the feeding period was 255 days. Their data do not enable conclusions to be drawn as to the efficacy of reimplantation *per se*.

8.4.2.6 Nutritional plane. Since exogenous oestrogens act in the same way as growth hormones or androgens one would expect the degree of response to increase with nutritional plane. That this is the case, in general terms, is shown by the fact that the mean response in carcass weight in experiments with grass-fed cattle was only some 4% (Alder *et al.*, 1964) which compares unfavourably with the median response of 16% in live weight gain for the mainly grain-fed cattle in Table 8.4. Webb *et al.* (1957) increased the energy value of the diet by replacing hay with maize and found that the response to DES implantation (48 mg) increased from zero on the 45% maize diet to 21%, and 47% for diets with 55% and 65% of maize respectively. A greater response to DES on high-energy diets was also reported by Klosterman *et al.* (1959).

One might expect that the protein level would be an even more critical factor in view of the greater muscle growth in hormone-treated animals. However, although Reynolds *et al.* (1956) and Klosterman *et al.* (1959) showed that maximum response to DES was dependent on there being adequate crude protein in the diet, the feeding of additional protein over and above normal requirements was not beneficial in the experiments carried out by Goodwin (1958), Dodsworth (1959) and Klosterman *et al.* (1959). Nevertheless, neither of the first two reports can be considered critical since Dodsworth (1959) worked with early maturing beef steers weighing 425 kg at the start (whose protein needs are minimal) and Goodwin fed his protein supplement on pasture and hence had little control over what was actually eaten. R. L. Preston and Burroughs (1958) found that response to DES in lambs increased with energy level irrespective of protein but that protein only increased response to the hormone when dietary energy was high. Jones *et al.* (1958) found no interaction between DES and protein and energy levels which were each set at 90 or 120% of the minimum recommendations.

It is surprising, in view of the mass of work undertaken with hormones, that so little attention has been given to their interaction with dietary energy and protein level. One can safely assume that response to DES will increase proportionately with energy intake, but no firm conclusions can be drawn with regard to protein except that its role is probably more critical on high energy diets.

8.4.2.7 Hormone residues in meat. The administration of natural or synthetic oestrogens to beef cattle has important implications from the standpoint of human health should oestrogenic activity remain in the carcass. Domestic carnivors (e.g. mink and dogs) would also be affected since the tissues inedible to man are fed to these animals. It has been established that there are oestrogenic residues in certain poultry tissues (Gowe, 1949; Swift, 1954), and reproductive disorders in mink given offal from treated birds have been reported. However, in poultry the dose rate relative to body size is some 100 times greater than in cattle, and one would not therefore expect similar hazards in the latter species. A further important factor is the hormone used, thus oestrogenic activity was some 10 times less for hexoestrol than DES (Stob, 1956).

Perry *et al.* (1955) found no oestrogenic residues in steers fed DES, and R. L. Preston *et al.* (1956) also concluded that there were no detectable residues in the lean, fat, liver, heart, kidney or offals when 2.75–12 mg DES were fed daily. These workers used a technique with a sensitivity of 2 μg/kg fresh tissue. Turner (1956) employed the same procedure and reported residues only in the kidney (4 μg/kg) and lungs (10–12 μg/kg). Wiberg and Stephenson (1957) and Unberger *et al.* (1959) also observed no oestrogenic activity in body tissues even though the latter workers gave up to 60 mg DES daily in the diet over a 180 day period.

The dissenting reports are those of Gossett *et al.* (1956) and Stob *et al.* (1956). The former gave 200 mg DES orally per day while the latter continued to administer the hormone up to the time of slaughter. Stob *et al.* (1956) found oestrogenic activity in muscles, kidney, fat, intestines and liver. When dinoestrol was fed there were residues in all the tissues except muscles, while in the case of hexoestrol there were only residues in kidney and kidney fat. Using tritium-labelled DES and giving it up to 24 hr prior to slaughter, Mitchell *et al.* (1956) obtained levels of 9.1 μg/kg in the liver and 4.2 in the kidney, negligible amounts in lean meat and fat and none in the heart. It is significant that both Mitchell *et al.* and Stob *et al.* continued administering the hormone up to the last day of life, whereas those workers who found no residues withdrew the hormone 2 days prior to slaughter as is recommended practice.

One can reasonably conclude that provided hormones are withdrawn from the feed at least 2 days prior to slaughter, there is no health hazard. Although all the experimental work has been done with oral administration, the same conclusion must apply to implantation except for the actual site of implantation (usually the ear) which is discarded.

There are other aspects to the subject of hormone residues, namely that oestrogens eliminated in faeces and urine might be taken up by pasture or crops and thereby constitute a potential reproductive hazard to animals or humans. Mellampy *et al.* (1959) have shown that cows fed 10 mg DES daily excreted 55–84% of this in faeces and urine. When given 100 mg daily there was no appreciable change in the proportion excreted (42–76%). According to Story *et al.* (1957) some 80% of the oestrogen administered to lambs was recoverable in the faeces and urine. Faeces and urine from hormone-treated animals are clearly a potent source of oestrogens. There is at least one case on record when manure from hormone-fed steers was used to seal a silage clamp and, through contamination of the silage, induced abortions in heifers (Rankin, 1959). The activity in the manure persisted some 9–12 months.

The hazard from such materials will also depend (a) on whether or not the oestrogens are broken down by soil micro-organisms, and (b) the extent to which they can be absorbed by plants. Glascock and Jones (1961) found that there was no loss of hexoestrol from the soil by leeching or evaporation, but they also failed to detect significant quantities of hexoestrol in grass, clover or turnips grown on affected soil. In a later paper (Glascock and Hewitt, 1963) it was found that a small amount was taken up, but also that the hormone was transformed in sandy soils. There is evidence (Anon., 1960) that certain micro-organisms widely found in soils are capable of metabolizing hexoestrol. A Gram-negative stumpy rod organism was isolated from pasture soil, the washed cells of which grew in media containing 0.001% hexoestrol and caused the hormone to disappear within 5 weeks. More recently Hacker *et al.* (1967), using faeces containing DES, have shown that a variety of plants (lettuce, onions, wheat, raddishes, beans, fruit) did take up oestrogen from the soil but that only lettuce roots and raddish leaves (neither of which are normally consumed) had any uterotropic activity. These workers agreed with their British counterparts in concluding that no hazard existed to human or animal health from application to the soil of excreta from oestrogen-treated animals.

8.4.3 Heifers

Oestrogens and androgens are produced by both sexes, males and females being characterized by the preponderence of one over the other. One would therefore expect the response to exogenous hormones to be different in heifers.

Fewer trials have been undertaken with heifers (Tables 8.9 and 8.10), and the evidence indicates that the response to oestrogen is both much less and more variable (Klosterman *et al.*, 1958; Thurber *et al.*, 1959). Side effects are definitely more pronounced than with steers. In some experiments there were reports of vaginal prolapse (Clegg and Cole, 1954; Neumann *et al.*, 1956), and slackness and oedoema around the vulva (Clegg and Carroll, 1956) while Fletcher *et al.* (1957) reported excessive mucuous secretion and prolonged oestrus without any indication of vaginal prolapse. Increased mammary development is more serious than in steers and gives the carcass the appearance of a pregnant animal. Spaying lessened the effect of synthetic oestrogens on the vaginal musculature; on the other hand, mammary development was increased even more (Clegg and Carroll, 1956). Growth stimulation without side effects was reported in an experiment with 172 heifers treated with testosterone (Klosterman *et al.*, 1958), however the cost of this hormone has mitigated against its widespread use.

The disadvantages to the use of oestrogens for heifers led to investigations aimed at retarding or reducing the growth depressing action of the natural oestrogens. Spaying was not a solution, but the advent of synthetic progesterones, originally developed to prevent ovulation in the human female, reopened the possibility of having growth promotion in heifers without side effects. One such product known as melengesterol acetate (developed by the Upjohn Co., Michigan, USA) has been evaluated by several American university experimental stations with extremely encouraging results as can be seen from Table 8.10. Not only does this steroid avoid the side effects associated with the use of DES, but there is the added advantage accruing from the elimination of oestrus (Newland and Henderson, 1966; Ralston *et al.*, 1968).

The method of administering hormones is more critical in heifers than in steers, since the side effects from excessive absorption are more serious. For this reason,

TABLE 8.9 EFFECT OF DIETHYLSTILBOESTROL ON GROWTH AND FEED CONVERSION IN HEIFERS

No. of heifers	Daily gain (kg) of control	Gain improvement (%) by different doses (mg)				Improvement (%) in conversion	Authors
		Oral	Implantation				
		10	< 15	15–30	⩾ 30		
40	0.89	−6					Newland & Henderson, 1966
20	0.93			0			McGinty & Marion, 1965
20	0.94	8					Thomas *et al.*, 1959
16	0.93	8					Hawkins *et al.*, 1967a
31	0.99	9					Kolari *et al.*, 1960
32	0.80	11				11	Canto *et al.*, 1968
15	0.94	7/12					Kastelic *et al.*, 1956
14	0.85				16	5	Clegg & Carroll, 1956
33	0.68	20					Hentges *et al.*, 1960
14[a]	0.81				21	5	Clegg & Carroll, 1956
90[a]	0.38		11/42	50/40	26		Thomas *et al.*, 1957
33	0.63			32			Fletcher *et al.*, 1957
40	0.94	6[b]–12[b]					Thomas *et al.*, 1959

[a] Spayed. [b] Diallylstilboestrol.

TABLE 8.10 EFFECT OF MELENGESTROL ACETATE ON GROWTH AND FEED CONVERSION IN HEIFERS

No. of heifers	Control	Daily gain			Conversion			Authors
		Improvement over control with different doses (mg/day) orally						
		< 0.30	0.3–0.4	> 0.4	< 0.3	0.3–0.4	> 0.4	
	kg		%			%		
40	1.09			−8			8	Bloss *et al.*, 1966
36	1.11			−1		0		Bloss *et al.*, 1966
657[a]	1.21		1			3		Matsushima, 1968b
40	0.85	3	1	−1				Young *et al.*, 1967
400[a]	1.10		3			1		Matsushima, 1968b
2106	1.05[b]		5			7		Matsushima, 1968b
63	0.97		7			11		Perry *et al.*, 1968c
48	—		8			5		Davis & Truesdale, 1968
586[a]	1.06		8			5		Matsushima, 1968b
72	1.15	7		9/2[c]	4		6/1[c]	Bloss *et al.*, 1966
80	0.92		11					Smart & Drake, 1968
32	0.90		11			3		O'Brien *et al.*, 1968
24	0.93		12					Hawkins *et al.*, 1967a
433[a]	0.78		14			15		Matsushima, 1968b
80			15			9		Burroughs *et al.*, 1966
134	0.92		15			10		Perry *et al.*, 1968c
24	0.93		17					Hawkins *et al.*, 1967a
24	0.70		18			15		Canto *et al.*, 1968
56	0.85	3	19	9	5	9	7	Bloss *et al.*, 1966
40	0.89		26/29					Newland & Hendson, 1966
31	0.80		37			18		O'Brien *et al.*, 1968
Median values			11			8		

[a] Spayed. [b] 10 mg per day oral DES. [c] 0.85 mg per day MGA.

and particularly with synthetic oestrogens, oral administration is preferable to implantation. Dose levels are usually the same as in steers (i.e. 10 mg daily) but, in the case of MGA, much lower levels are used (0.2–0.5 mg). Although the optimum level of MGA has still to be established, it has been shown that while growth promotion can be induced with 0.24 mg daily, supression of oestrus requires at least 0.45 mg (§ 6.3.3). Little work seems to have been undertaken on reimplantation of the synthetic oestrogens, almost certainly in the belief that this would inevitably produce side effects.

In heifers one is concerned also with the long-term effects of hormone treatment on subsequent reproduction, since animals destined originally for slaughter are often retained for breeding. There is also the possibility of stimulating gains during the growing period. In Mississippi, Williams and Baker (1961) found that a 24 mg implant for grazing heifers had no harmful effects on subsequent reproductive performance; however, repeated implants of 20 mg every month for 196 days led to severe physiological disturbances (Neumann *et al.*, 1956).

8.4.4 Bulls

Little is known about the response of bulls to hormone treatment. With the exception of such early publications as those by Klosterman *et al.* (1955) and Pope *et al.* (1960), the hormone treatment of bulls only became a serious subject of study in the late 1960's. Such production data as is available (Table 8.11) is favourable to oestrogen treatment particularly when considered with the suggestion of improved carcass quality (Chapter 2) and absence of serious side effects other than slightly raised tail heads (Cahill *et al.*, 1956).

Although the data in Table 8.11 suggest an increasing growth response with higher dose levels of DES, this was not the case in the trials reported by Folman and

TABLE 8.11 EFFECT OF DIETHYLSTILBOESTROL TREATMENT ON GROWTH AND FEED CONVERSION IN BULLS

Total bulls	Treatment[a] (mg)	Control gain (kg/day)	Improvement due to DES		Authors
			Gain (%)	Feed conversion (%)	
20	36	1.00	−4		Pilkington *et al.*, 1959
24	24	1.16	1		Wipf *et al.*, 1964
12	24	1.11	1		Wipf *et al.*, 1964
39	60	1.24	5	3.2	Bailey *et al.*, 1966a
40	36	1.52	8		Obracevic *et al.*, 1961
20	57[b]	0.99	11		McGinty & Marion, 1965
40	36	—	11	4.7	Sljivovacki *et al.*, 1966
42	60	1.29	12		Bailey *et al.*, 1966a
48	72	0.91	15		Casas & Raun, 1964
48	96	0.53	70	8.1	Casas & Raun, 1964

[a] All implanted.
[b] 12 mg at 6 weeks; 15 mg at 16 weeks; 30 mg at 36 weeks.

Volcani (1960). Their results (Table 8.12) demonstrated no extra response beyond an implant of 36 mg.

TABLE 8.12 EFFECT OF DIFFERENT DES IMPLANTS ON GROWTH OF ISRAELI FRIESIAN BULLS (AFTER FOLMAN AND VOLCANI, 1960)

Trial no.	Days on trial	No. of bulls	Dose level (mg)			
			0	36	72	108
1	70	54	1.03	1.32	1.13	1.12
1[a]	154	35	1.05	1.20	1.11	1.14
2	49	14	1.09	1.42		

[a] Continuation of trial 1, 19 bulls having been sold with equal representation by treatment; data refers to time from the start.

CHAPTER 9

Growth and Efficiency: Nutrition

9.1 ENERGY INTAKE

9.1.1 Introduction

As a general rule animals which eat more will produce more—be it milk, wool, muscle or fat. It also follows that as productivity increases while the overheads (maintenance) remain either constant, or increase only slightly, efficiency also increases. R. L. Preston (1968) has drawn attention to the fact that different species vary widely in their voluntary energy intake expressed as a function of metabolic body size, and that, furthermore, the relative efficiency of converting feed protein to edible protein is in direct relation to voluntary intake (Table 9.1).

TABLE 9.1 VOLUNTARY ENERGY INTAKE AND EFFICIENCY IN DIFFERENT SPECIES (FROM R. L. PRESTON, 1968)

Species	Voluntary energy intake		Efficiency
	$DE/W^{0.75}$	Level of feeding (Intake/maintenance)	$\left(100 \times \frac{\text{Edible protein}}{\text{Protein consumed}}\right)$
Dairy cows (36 kg milk/day)	608	4.3	28
Pigs (4.5–102 kg)	430	3.1	17
Broilers			26
Laying hens			23
Beef cattle (growing-finishing)	320	2.3	8

The various genetic, nutritional and management factors which determine voluntary feed intake are discussed in chapters 3, 5 and 10. In the short term, considerable improvements can be made in feed intake by manipulation of the diet and by attention to various aspects of management, but long-term progress toward improved efficiency in beef cattle necessitates a radical change in the genetic makeup of our beef animals.

In general, voluntary DM intake (expressed as a function of live weight) falls exponentially as fattening progresses (Figs. 9.1 and 9.2). On all-concentrate diets (§ 9.2.2) the drop is from a maximum of some 2.9% for a weaned dairy beef animal of 100 kg to a minimum of 1.8–2.0% at the point of slaughter (400 kg) (Fig. 9.1). Late-weaned beef animals on restricted feeding programmes prior to entering the feedlot at some 200 kg live weight also begin eating at the rate of 2.8–3.0% at the start of fattening, although in their case intake declines even more rapidly to reach the same minimum level of 1.8–2.0% at 400–450 kg live weight (Fig. 9.2). The data on which these graphs are based were taken from a study with over 100 Holstein steers fed pelleted whole barley and protein supplement (Bowers, 1968). Similar results can be expected with other cereals, high molasses diets, and other breeds. The provisos to be

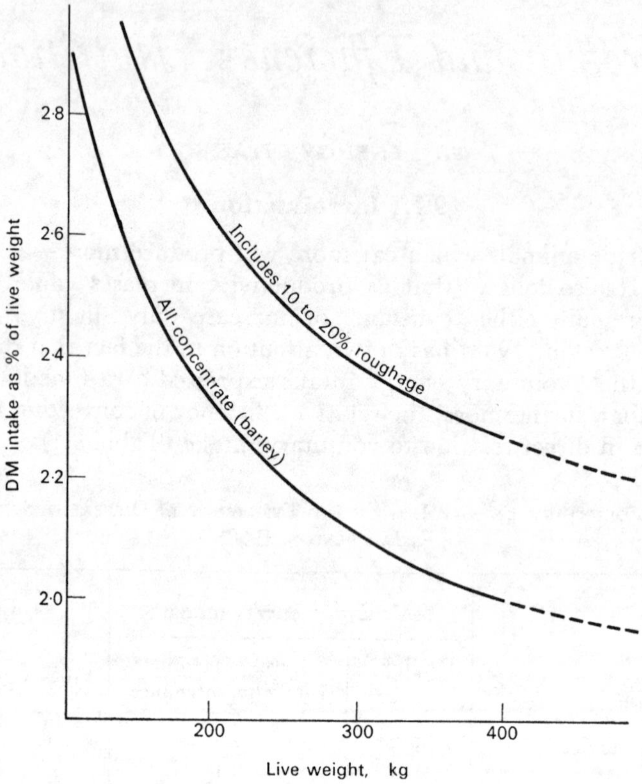

FIG. 9.1 DM intake as a function of live weight in intensive dairy beef steers fed all-concentrate or 10–20% roughage diets.

borne in mind are that cattle will consume slightly less of cereals of higher digestibility (e.g. maize) or which have been heat-treated (§ 9.4.4) or ensiled (§ 9.4.5), while breeds inherently fatter than the Holstein will also consume less at any given live weight. Similarly, the addition of 10–20% roughage (§ 9.2.2.2) brings about a general increase in voluntary intake of some 13% (Figs. 9.1 and 9.2).

9.1.2 Compensatory growth

Most beef cattle spend a period of time in which their growth rate is not maximum relative to their genetic potential. In the case of single-suckled beef calves, creep-fed with concentrates and fattened from weaning on all-concentrate diets, the degree of restriction is minimal. Faster gains are undoubtedly made by beef calves which also have access to foster mothers, particularly Holsteins. This system is practised by pedigree bull breeders, particularly in the UK, and has economic justification when the resultant calves are sold for very high prices. These systems have no bearing whatsoever on commercial beef production or on the genetic improvement of cattle. In many countries, and this is particularly true in the tropics, traditional methods of raising beef cattle can lead to very severe growth restriction. This most frequently occurs in the 6 months following weaning, a period which usually coincides with winter (the dry season in tropical regions) when natural feed supplies are scarce.

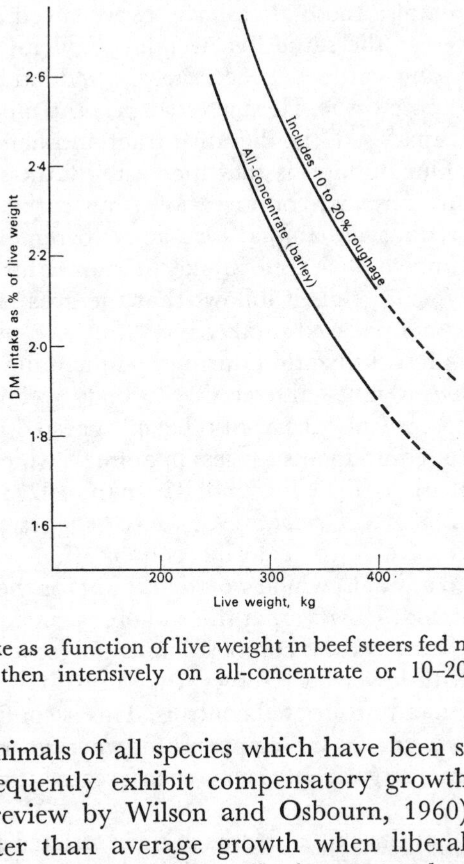

FIG. 9.2 DM intake as a function of live weight in beef steers fed moderately to 250 kg live weight and then intensively on all-concentrate or 10–20% roughage diets.

It is known that animals of all species which have been subjected to a period of under-nutrition subsequently exhibit compensatory growth during the period of realimentation (see review by Wilson and Osbourn, 1960). This phenomenon is characterized by faster than average growth when liberal feed supplies become available, although the exact reasons why it comes about are not established. McMeekan (1940a, b, c) considered that in pigs the faster gains of realimentated animals could be entirely accounted for by increased gut contents. However, the work of Winchester and Howe (1955) and Tayler *et al.* (1957) showed that while part of the increased gain could be ascribed to gut contents, cattle exhibiting compensatory growth also laid down tissue at a faster rate than unrestricted controls. It is established (Sheehy and Senior, 1942; Winchester and Howe, 1955) that animals previously underfed have greater feed intakes during the period of realimentation than unrestricted animals of the same live weight. Wilson and Osbourn (1960) proposed that this greater appetite could be attributed to a greater capacity of the digestive system since these tissues were only slightly retarded by undernutrition (see Palsson, 1955). Although the digestive tract of realimentated animals may well be larger, relative to body size, than is the case with unrestricted animals it is unlikely that this could explain greater feed intake other than in the specific case of animals realimentated on pasture. In fact, in the majority of experiments on the subject, realimentation has been invariably brought about on high energy diets, the voluntary intake of which is determined not by size of the digestive tract but by the end products of the fermentation of the diet (§ 5.4).

One effect of submaintenance feeding is to deplenish body reserves so that, compared with well-fed animals, those that have experienced retarded growth also possess lower fat reserves at the same live weight. Tayler (1959) demonstrated a negative relation in grazing cattle between faecal production (a measure of DM intake) and weight of adipose tissue. He suggested that the physical presence of these fat deposits limited the capacity of the digestive tract and hence the animal's ability to consume more feed. Our opinion is that increasing fatness steadily reduces feed intake not because of any physical considerations, but rather because the effect of increasing fatness is to reduce the animal's capacity to remove from the blood the circulating VFA. It is known that feed intake in ruminants can be depressed by administration of VFA (§ 5.4), thus it follows that the greater the depression of fat reserves the higher the potential feed intake.

Improved efficiency of feed utilization during realimentation is an obvious consequence of the greater live weight gain relative to body weight in these animals as compared to unrestricted controls; it has also been suggested that, even at the same live weight, maintenance requirements are less in animals which have been subjected to a period of undernutrition (Benedict and Ritzman, 1927; Hogan, 1929). Some workers (Steensberg, 1947; Reid *et al.*, 1955) have suggested that realimentated animals lay down tissue of a lower calorific content (i.e. with less fat and more muscle) than unrestricted animals, which would account for their greater efficiency of feed utilization in this period. However, at the end of realimentation such cattle have been shown to have the same carcass composition as unrestricted animals (§ 2.3.3.2) and, since they began with lower fat reserves, they must have laid down tissue of a higher calorific content than unrestricted controls. This is confirmed by the results of Meyer *et al.* (1965). Thus during the compensatory period, realimentated animals show an improvement in energetic efficiency even greater than that manifested for feed conversion.

It is logical to expect that the causal factors of the restricted growth must influence the subsequent compensation. Winchester and Howe (1955) and Winchester *et al.* (1957) found that animals could recover from restriction of either energy or protein to the extent that feed conversion on a lifetime basis was unaffected. However, even their most severely undernourished animals made some growth during retardation, in contrast to those of Sheehy and Senior (1942) which lost weight during restriction. These latter, when realimentated, were found to have consumed more total food than unrestricted controls.

The effect of the stage in development at which restriction is imposed is not well established. Hammond (1932) considered that the effect of uterine and immediate *post-partum* restriction, as, for example, between twins and singles, was maintained up to 2 years of age in sheep. Similarly, Black *et al.* (1940) and Bohman (1955) showed that calves given the poorer nutrition in their first winter were unable to compensate during the following spring and summer, and it took one further winter before differences between them and controls were eliminated. Joubert (1954a) reported similar findings and considered it to be due to the older animals' greater ability to withstand a period of undernutrition. It is probable that all these effects can be explained, in the greater part, by inadequate programmes of realimentation. Ralston *et al.* (1966) found that the rate of compensatory growth was inversely related to the rate of gain during restriction, while Bohman (1955) and Heinemann and Van Keuren (1956) have shown that the plane of nutrition during realimentation is the major determinant of the rate of compensatory growth. With this in mind, Wilson and Osbourn (1960) suggested that the period of restriction should be subdivided into short phases of underfeeding each followed by realimentation. These workers reported encouraging results from this procedure in chickens but the idea has yet to be evaluated in cattle.

From the foregoing discussion it is obvious that the feedlot operator can expect to profit from buying retarded cattle, since their growth and efficiency in the feedlot will be above average. The economics of raising such cattle is, however, a more debatable matter due to the lower live weight and resultingly poorer price. The practice is frequently defended in areas where grazing land is cheap and unlimited, but a closer analysis of such situations usually reveals that it would be more economic to wean calves early, and hence in better physical condition, and to increase the size of the breeding herd.

The economic benefits from compensatory growth during realimentation at the feedlot stage are accepted. Our concern here is to examine the overall efficiency of the process in terms of the effect of restriction and subsequent realimentation on feed efficiency from birth to slaughter. For integrated rearing and fattening operations, and certainly from a national point of view, the only justification for compensatory growth would be a lifetime net gain in terms of feed required per unit of meat produced. The effect of compensatory growth on carcass characteristics has been discussed in Chapter 2 and appears to be negligible. The other two important factors are the time required to reach slaughter weight and feed efficiency. With respect to time the evidence is quite conclusive. In experiments where animals were continued to the same live weight those restricted in early life took longer (Winchester *et al.*, 1957; Connolly *et al.*, 1967; Stuedemann, 1968), while in those trials where slaughter was at the same age restricted animals were always lighter (Pinney *et al.*, 1962a; Carroll *et al.*, 1963a, 1964; Harte, 1967).

With regard to effects on feed efficiency, few of the published experiments have been designed to produce definite conclusions. Experiments such as those of Bohman and Torell (1956), Carroll *et al.* (1963a), Connolly *et al.* (1967) and Dodsworth *et al.* (1967) are valueless in this respect since the animals spent part of their lives on pasture and intakes were not recorded. Similarly, Bond and Lehman (1967) compared restricted feeding followed by *ad libitum* feeding with what was in effect a constant restricted growth pattern. Where lifetime feed intakes were recorded (Winchester *et al.*, 1957; Winchester and Ellis, 1957; Carroll *et al.*, 1964) feed efficiency was the same for both treatments. The only report of greater lifetime efficiency for restricted animals is that of Harte (1967). He used eleven pairs of Holstein twins, one member of which was restricted during the first 6 months and then realimentated, its twin being fed *ad libitum* throughout life. Although growth rates were similar, restricted animals were significantly more efficient in converting feed into live weight gain and into lean meat. It is, however, impossible to accept that the results for the *ad libitum* animals were typical since, despite the use of an all-concentrate diet from 3 months of age, it required 669 days to reach a slaughter live weight of 447 kg. The norm for this breed–diet–weight range would be of the order of 380–400 (Preston, 1964).

The most comprehensive published experiment was a 3 year study by Meyer *et al.* (1965) involving 258 steers. They found that compensatory growth occurred in each period following a stage of low energy intake. Some of the data are given in Table 9.2 from which it is clear that high plane feeding throughout was the most efficient in terms of time and overall feed conversion (ME intake per unit of live weight gain or calorific gain). Nevertheless, where pasture or forage are much cheaper than concentrates there may be economic advantages from a period of restricted growth, although it would seem that this should not be too severe.

The findings of Connolly *et al.* (1967) show that if the period of restriction is to be on pasture then supplements during this stage are undesirable. They found that animals fed only on all-concentrate diets consumed less concentrates in their life than those given a period of restriction on pasture, but with supplementary concentrates. This latter group not only ate more concentrates but they took as long to reach slaughter weight as those animals given a period of pasture restriction without supplementation; both groups took 113 days longer to reach slaughter weight than animals fed on high plane throughout.

9.2 ENERGY CONCENTRATION

9.2.1 Concentrate–roughage ratio

Early workers in this field (Black *et al.*, 1943; Keith *et al.*, 1955; Pahnish *et al.*, 1956; Pope *et al.*, 1957) considered that the concentrate/roughage ratio had no great effect on performance although there was a tendency for better gains with more concentrates. At that time cattle were considerably older on entering the final period of intensive fattening than is current practice, and one would expect the feeding of roughages would give quite good results in this class of animal. Both compensatory growth and age would result in a large voluntary intake relative to body weight which is the important factor if efficient use is to be made of roughages. Cattle intended for slaughter before 18 months of age have less opportunity for compensatory growth. Moreover they are less able to consume large quantities of roughage. Thus, in young cattle, roughage plays a more critical role. A considerable amount of work was carried out during the 1960's regarding the effect of concentrate/roughage ratios upon performance. Data from ten experiments are given in Table 9.3.

Interpretation of these results is made difficult by the wide variety of diets used, the different types and sources of cattle and the different management techniques employed. Nevertheless, broad trends can be established. It is apparent that when concentrates replace roughages, at least up to the point of contributing 80–85% of the diet, there is an improvement in daily gain and a marked increase in efficiency of feed utilization. Moreover, decreasing the roughage content of the diet also leads to

TABLE 9.2 EFFECTS OF PERIODS OF UNDERNUTRITION ON LIFETIME PERFORMANCE (AFTER MEYER *et al.*, 1965)

Level of feeding: Period 1 Period 2 Period 3	High — —	Medium High —	Medium Liberal High	Medium Medium High	Medium Low High	Low High —	Low Liberal High	Low Medium High	Low Low High
Total days	222	296	358	367	367	321	388	397	398
No. of animals	20	12	6	6	9	12	6	6	9
Final weight (kg)	436	440	471	472	459	413	455	455	459
Final empty weight (kg)	419	428	440	439	423	401	421	422	426
Carcass weight (kg)	268	274	281	281	270	255	269	269	272
Daily gain (kg)	1.05	0.87	0.83	0.80	0.77	0.71	0.75	0.71	0.69
Intake of DM (kg)									
Concentrates	1123	687	371	449	445	830	580	652	682
Roughage	481	1530	2412	2290	2082	1153	2063	1895	1800
Total	1604	2217	2783	2739	2527	1983	2643	2547	2482
Conversion (kg DM/kg gain)	6.88	8.61	9.37	9.33	8.94	8.70	9.08	9.04	9.04

TABLE 9.3 EFFECT OF CONCENTRATE/ROUGHAGE RATIO ON GROWTH AND FEED CONVERSION IN FATTENING CATTLE

Concentrate roughage	Daily gain (kg)	Feed conversion	Authors
70:30	1.35	8.9	Beardsley *et al.*, 1959
55:45	1.23	10.1	
40:60	1.12	10.6	
50:50	1.04	8.00	Garrett *et al.*, 1961
0:100	0.91	9.60	
60:40	1.22	8.28	
0:100	0.93	12.00	
80:20	1.00	9.20	McCroskey *et al.*, 1961
20:80	0.94	11.90	
84:16	1.15	9.50	Richardson *et al.*, 1961
75:25	0.93	10.50	
50:50	0.89	11.90	
50 → 84:50 → 16	0.93	10.70	
95:5	1.48	8.40	Bucy & Bennion, 1962
85:15	1.45		
70:30	1.27	10.1	
30:60	1.21	9.4	Woods & Scholl, 1962
25:75	1.10	10.1	
20:80	1.02	10.6	
10:90	0.90	11.7	
5:95	0.75	12.8	
0:100	0.61	15.6	
75:25	1.04	8.4	Clanton & Woods, 1966
50:50	0.85	10.4	
25:75	0.83	10.2	
0:100	0.62	16.5	
100:0	1.30	6.5	Lamming *et al.*, 1966
90:10	1.33	6.5	
80:20	1.30	6.5	
70:30	1.27	6.9	
80:20	1.34	7.0	
70:30	1.32	6.9	
60:40	1.20	8.1	
50:50	1.26	7.7	
83:17	1.09	7.0	Weiss *et al.*, 1967
42:58	0.85	9.20	
0:100	0.89	10.70	
91:9	1.16	7.0	Miller *et al.*, 1967
26:74	1.07	8.0	

a reduction in gut contents (Stobo *et al.*, 1966) and hence a higher killing out percentage (§ 2.2.2).

The economics of selecting a particular concentrate/roughage ratio will depend upon the relative cost of these two major ingredients together with the cost of processing. The other aspect is the relationship between the concentrate roughage ratio and the type of carcass required. It has been shown (§ 2.3.3.1) that increasing the proportion of concentrates in the diet leads to a greater deposition of fat. There is also an interaction between diet and breed. Animals of high growth potential but late maturity (e.g. Holstein, Brown Swiss and Charolais) will tend to produce very lean carcasses if given too much roughage in the diet; thus for these, high energy—and hence high concentrate—feeding is almost essential. On the other hand, very early maturing breeds such as Angus and Shorthorn may produce carcasses which are excessively fat if fed from weaning on very high concentrate diets; for these a higher proportion of roughage may be desirable.

9.2.2 All-concentrate diets

9.2.2.1 Historical development. The previous section dealt with the use of roughage as a source of energy. In many circumstances, however, the cattle-fattening operation would show economic benefit if roughage could be eliminated. The question then arises as to whether cattle can be fattened satisfactorily on an all-concentrate diet or whether some form of roughage is necessary for health.

The interest in feeding animals without roughage is no innovation. Davenport in 1897 and later McCandlish (1923) tried unsuccessfully to raise calves without hay. In 1928 Huffman considered that there was some unknown factor in hay essential for animal health, but by 1931 Mead and Reagan were able to raise calves satisfactorily to 19 months of age on a diet of barley, oats, wheat bran and linseed oil meal. They considered that the previous failures had been due to a deficiency of vitamin A.

The first successful attempt to use an all-concentrate diet in the fattening of beef cattle was reported by Geurin *et al.* (1956); the ration was crimped oats and protein supplement plus vitamin A and trace minerals. Daily gains of 1.13 kg were 0.09 kg better than on a control ration of rolled barley, protein supplement and alfalfa hay. Oats is not, however, a very important grain, and the major stimulus to the economic possibilities of all-concentrate feeding came when these same workers (Geurin *et al.*, 1959) reported satisfactory results with a diet of rolled barley and a supplement containing protein, minerals and vitamins A and D. No bloat was observed, and they ascribed the success of the diet to the rolling of the barley which preserved the roughage-like nature of the husks. These results were obtained under typical US feedlot conditions in which high energy feeding is only introduced during the last 90–120 days of fattening after 12–18 months spent on pasture. The application of this method of feeding to UK conditions, where barley is the major cereal grain, was taken up by Preston and his co-workers at the Rowett Institute. Their objective was somewhat different to that of US workers since in Britain dairy steers are a major source of beef; they therefore used artificially reared Friesian calves and gave rolled barley and protein supplement from a starting age of 3–4 months through to slaughter at 10–14 months. The fact that this was an integrated system starting with young animals of high growth potential accounts for the extremely low conversion rates of less than 5 kg concentrate/kg gain (Preston *et al.*, 1963a).

In the UK, all-concentrate feeding came to be known as "barley beef" since it was based almost exclusively on this cereal. But, in the US, all concentrate systems developed on a variety of energy sources. Thus Beeson *et al.* (1957a) successfully used ground ear maize while ground maize without the cob formed the basis of the diets developed by Gordon and Erwin (1960) and Wise *et al.* (1961). All-concentrate feeding on cracked sorghum was reported by Durham *et al.* (1963), while systems using wheat were first put forward by Wood (1962) in Canada.

The successful commercial application of such systems has firmly established that cattle can be fattened on all-concentrate diets without supplementary roughage. An indication of the degree of response that can be expected is shown by the results given in Table 9.4.

9.2.2.2 THE EFFECT OF ADDED ROUGHAGE. The results of numerous experiments involving the addition of many kinds of roughage to otherwise all-concentrate diets are given in Table 9.5. One cannot generalize on the overall value of small additions of roughage since response depends in part on the type of grain used (9.3) and the processing method (9.4).

In the experiments summarized in Table 9.5 there has been an increase in daily gain in about 60% of the cases where small amounts (up to 20%) of roughage have been added; improvement due to roughage appears to occur more frequently with maize grain than with ear maize or other cereals. Invariably feed intake is increased by the addition of roughage, and in some cases this probably accounts for a proportion of the greater daily gain. When roughage has exceeded 20% of the diet there was no further increase in feed intake or daily gain, and beyond 40% both were reduced.

With respect to feed conversion rate there is almost complete unanimity that increasing use of forage leads to deterioration in efficiency, whether this is considered as DM or ME per unit of gain. It is interesting that a number of workers (Harper *et al.*, 1962; Whetzel *et al.*, 1962; Wise *et al.*, 1965) found that the addition of small quantities of roughages to all-concentrate diets did not reduce the amount of concentrates used per unit of live weight gain.

9.2.2.3 TYPE OF ROUGHAGE. Although in high forage diets, type and quality is of paramount importance, the same is not necessarily true when roughage is given in small amounts. For example, when sorghum grain contributed 90% of the DM of a fattening diet for Herefords, Morris *et al.* (1967) found that there was little to choose between wheat straw, sorghum silage or lucerne hay as regards both daily gain and feed conversion. A similar lack of difference between effects of various fibrous by-products (e.g. rice and cottonseed husks), as supplements to all-concentrate diets, is apparent from a study of Table 9.5. We also observed no significant differences between napier and maize (Martin *et al.*, 1968b) or these two forages compared with sorghum and alfalfa (Martin *et al.*, 1968a) when these roughages supplied some 10% of the DM of a fattening diet based on molasses. Encouraging results with 2.5% of hardwood sawdust in a maize diet were reported by Anthony and Cunningham (1968); however, the use of other roughage substitutes (oyster shell, polyethylene and cotton wood) has always led to poorer performance (Table 9.5).

Although it has been implied that few differences exist between types of natural roughage, this is true only with regard to growth and feed conversion. Differences do exist in the effect that forage can have upon health. With certain cereals, particularly those lacking "built-in" roughage, small amounts of forage can help to alleviate such metabolic disorders as bloat and liver abscesses. On the other hand, alfalfa, both as hay and fresh forage, can lead to a higher bloat incidence and even death as compared with other forages (Morris *et al.*, 1967; Martin *et al.*, 1968a). Oyster shell has

TABLE 9.4 PERFORMANCE OF STEERS GIVEN ALL-CONCENTRATE DIETS WITHOUT ADDED ROUGHAGE

Cereal	Processing	Initial weight (kg)	Final weight (kg)	Daily gain (kg)	Feed conversion (kg/kg)	Authors
Barley	Rolled	—	—	0.89	8.89	Goodrich *et al.*, 1962
	Rolled	96	464	0.90	6.44	Rice & Paules, 1965
	Rolled	—	—	1.00	8.20	Frederick *et al.*, 1962
	Ground	84	380	1.05	4.54	McCullough & Chestnut, 1965
	Rolled	160	398	1.07	6.06	Preston *et al.*, 1968b
	Steam-rolled	382	533	1.08	8.75	Thomas & Myers, 1961
	HM-rolled	—	—	1.14	7.95	Frederick *et al.*, 1962
	Rolled	104	405	1.18	4.76	Preston *et al.*, 1963a
	Ground	180	360	1.23	4.80	Borini, 1963
	Rolled	115	360	1.23	4.92	Wieser *et al.*, 1966
	Rolled[a]	159	410	1.26	5.36	Preston *et al.*, 1968b
	Rolled	—	386	1.31	6.73	Lofgreen, 1961
	Rolled	—	—	1.34	7.08	Geurin *et al.*, 1959
	Rolled	—	386	1.38	7.10	Lofgreen, 1961
	Ground	—	—	1.38	6.96	Kercher *et al.*, 1966
	Rolled	—	—	1.39	6.07	McCartor *et al.*, 1964
	Rolled	297	470	1.56	6.03	Nicholson *et al.*, 1963
Beet pulp	Dried	—	—	1.15	8.28	Kercher *et al.*, 1966
	Dried	140	475	1.28	5.69	Buysse & Boucque, 1967
Ear maize	Ground[a]	111	400	0.86	8.08	Willis & Preston, 1968a
	Ground	—	—	0.91	11.10	Goodrich *et al.*, 1962
	Ground	—	—	0.95	8.87	Brown *et al.*, 1964a
	Ground	—	—	0.96	7.03	Goodrich & Meiske, 1966
	Ground	290	520	1.18	8.62	Beeson *et al.*, 1957a
	Ground	—	—	1.20	8.65	Geurin *et al.*, 1959
	Ground[a]	135	400	1.20	5.17	Willis & Preston, 1968a
	Ground	110	421	1.44	5.74	Isakov & Ognjanovick, 1964
Maize	Ground	180	343	0.73	7.09	Wise *et al.*, 1965
	Ground	240	318	0.88	5.80	Wise *et al.*, 1961
	Cracked	—	—	0.88	7.44	Gordon & Erwin, 1960

TABLE 9.4 (cont.)

Cereal	Processing	Initial weight (kg)	Final weight (kg)	Daily gain (kg)	Feed conversion (kg/kg)	Authors
	Cracked	280	400	0.95	7.20	Oltjen, 1965
	Ground	229	407	1.14	5.21	Wise *et al.*, 1965
	Ground	195	330	1.14	5.00	Wise *et al.*, 1961
	Ground	—	—	1.17	5.17	Thrasher *et al.*, 1967
	Ground	—	—	1.23	6.97	Kercher *et al.*, 1966
	Ground	99	409	1.27	—[b]	Preston *et al.*, 1963a
	Ground	305	492	1.27	6.59	Wise *et al.*, 1965
	Ground	230	456	1.34	5.62	Wise *et al.*, 1965
	Cracked	355	492	1.40	6.40	Oltjen *et al.*, 1966
Oats	Crimped	—	—	1.14	8.50	Geurin *et al.*, 1956
Sorghum	Flaked	—	—	1.12	—	Durham *et al.*, 1967a
	50% cracked / 50% popped	228	359	1.17	5.67	Ellis & Carpenter, 1966
	Cracked	228	364	1.22	6.80	Ellis & Carpenter, 1966
	Popped	—	—	1.23	—	Durham *et al.*, 1967a
	Cracked	238	411	1.26	6.33	Albin & Durham, 1967
	Cracked	—	—	1.27	—	Durham *et al.*, 1967a
	Rolled	—	386	1.28	7.92	Lofgreen, 1961
	Cracked	263	422	1.32	6.97	Durham & Pruett, 1966
	Rolled	—	—	1.45	6.59	McCartor *et al.*, 1964
Wheat	Cracked	360	478	1.20	7.80	Oltjen *et al.*, 1966
Wheat/maize	Cracked 60/30	359	467	1.10	8.10	Oltjen *et al.*, 1966
	Cracked 30/60	364	491	1.30	7.10	Oltjen *et al.*, 1966

[a] Bulls.
[b] 25% mortality due to bloat.

given rise to both bloat and severe rumen damage and, possibly as a consequence of the latter, a higher incidence of abscessed livers (§ 11.3.5). These effects must be borne in mind when decisions are made as to which forage is to be fed or whether it is to be included at all.

9.3 ENERGY SOURCE

9.3.1 Cereals

9.3.1.1 Barley. The most widely used cereal for intensive beef production io Europe is barley. Of all grains it is the most suited for all-concentrate diets since it contains sufficient "roughage" in the husk to allow optimum performance in terms nf rate of gain and feed conversion as well as freedom from digestive upsets such as bloat. For best results it should normally be rolled at a moisture content of some 16%. This is somewhat inconvenient in that for safe storage the moisture content of barley should be reduced to 12–14%. Experience indicates that the best method of processing dry barley is to use a crimper. Dry barley can also be processed by pelleting the whole grain (without previous grinding) using a die aperture of approximately 1 cm (Williamson *et al.*, 1961; RRI, 1964). The other approach is to add sufficient water prior to rolling to raise the moisture content to 16–18%; to be successful this requires that the barley and added water are in contact for a period of at least 24 hr before rolling. Yet another possibility is to inject steam immediately before rolling with the sole objective of moistening the grain. Deliberate heat treatment to improve nutritive value is another matter which is discussed subsequently (§ 9.4.4). High moisture barley stored anaerobically is probably the best form of all in terms of permitting efficient rolling of the grain with minimal damage to the husk.

The objective of all these processing techniques is to retain sufficient of the roughage characteristics of the grain husk to permit maximum intake and utilization with the minimum of digestive upsets. None of these methods affects the nutritive value of the grain (Preston *et al.*, 1963b, 1965a; Kay *et al.*, 1966).

Grinding is not a satisfactory method of preparation in that it destroys the greater part of the physical structure of the husk, thus increasing the likelihood of bloat. Pelleting of ground barley is even more dangerous since the overall effect is further to reduce particle size, and, quite apart from increasing bloat incidence, there is some evidence that growth rate is also reduced (RRI, 1964). For a discussion of the effect of processing on bloat, see § 11.3.2.

9.3.1.2 Maize. Two possibilities exist with this cereal. One is to use the complete ear including grain and cob but excluding the husk. The other is the use of the grain alone. Ear maize was the basis of one of the earliest all-concentrate diets (Beeson *et al.*, 1957a). It supports satisfactory growth rates and, in view of the built-in roughage of the cob, does not require the addition of any fibrous supplement nor does it appear to need special processing other than coarse grinding. Bloat does not normally occur on ear maize although we have reported it in the Santa Gertrudis and to a lesser extent the Holstein breed (Willis and Preston, 1968a).

Under US feedlot conditions, expected daily gains are of the order of 1 kg with feed conversion in the range of 8. Isakov and Ognjanovic (1964) and Willis and Preston (1967a) have reported gains of 1.44 and 1.20 kg/day with feed conversions

TABLE 9.5 EFFECT OF ADDING ROUGHAGE TO ALL-CONCENTRATE DIETS ON GROWTH AND FEED CONVERSION IN FATTENING CATTLE

Cereal	Added roughage[a] (kg/day)	Daily gain		Feed conversion		Authors
		All-concentrate (kg)	Change due to roughage (%)	All-concentrate (feed/gain)	Deterioration due to roughage (%)	
Barley	0.3 hay	1.05	16	4.54	4	McCullough & Chestnutt, 1965
	ad lib. hay	1.00	8	8.20	5	Frederick *et al.*, 1962
	0.9 hay	1.08	6	8.75	6	Thomas & Myers, 1961
	50% hay	0.90	—2	6.44	8	Rice & Paules, 1965
	ad lib. hay	1.14	—9	7.95	13	Frederick *et al.*, 1962
	2.7 hay	1.08	—9	8.75	31	Thomas & Myers, 1961
Ear maize	2.5% oyster shell	1.24	−8	6.90	−4	Perry *et al.*, 1968b
	15% CSH[b]	0.97	2	8.82	—4	Brown *et al.*, 1964a
	15% CSH[c]	0.95	1	8.87	−2	Brown *et al.*, 1964a
	14% cottonwood	1.29	−9	9.70	5	Vara *et al.*, 1968
	0.3 oyster shell	1.02	−8	8.63	6	Williams *et al.*, 1968a
	1.79 hay	0.96	18	7.03	7	Goodrich & Meiske, 1966
	28% cottonwood	1.27	—9	9.7	15	Vara *et al.*, 1968
Maize	1.8 long hay	0.91	26	8.46	−7	Thompson *et al.*, 1965
	3% oyster shell	1.30	15	6.79	−6	Larson *et al.*, 1968a
	1.8 ground hay	0.91	36	8.40	−4	Thompson *et al.*, 1965
	2.5% oyster shell	1.31	−2	6.43	−2	Goodrich *et al.*, 1968
	10.0% oyster shell	1.30	17	6.79	0	Larson *et al.*, 1968a
	5% RH whole	1.17	4	6.00	0	Harvey *et al.*, 1968
	3% oyster shell	1.30	1	6.79	2	Larson *et al.*, 1968a
	7.5% oyster shell	1.31	10	6.43	4	Goodrich *et al.*, 1968
	5% RH ground	1.17	−3	6.00	5	Harvey *et al.*, 1968
	1.36 hay	1.17	2	6.00	5	Harvey *et al.*, 1968
	2.5% oyster shell[d]	1.31	7	6.43	6	Goodrich *et al.*, 1968
	20.0% osyter shell	1.30	15	6.79	10	Larson *et al.*, 1968a
	0.23 kg oyster shell	0.91	−20	8.15	13	Williams *et al.*, 1968a
	15% oyster shell	1.31	7	6.43	15	Goodrich *et al.*, 1968

	30% hay	0.99	−4	6.60	15	Gordon & Erwin, 1960
	20% grass pellets	1.17	−8	5.17	18	Thrasher *et al.*, 1967
	1.1 ground hay	1.13	4	5.00	20	Wise *et al.*, 1961
	1.36 hay	1.33	−2	5.62	20	Wise *et al.*, 1962
	1.1 long hay	1.13	0	5.00	24	Wise *et al.*, 1961
	20% CSH	1.40	−5	6.21	25	Thrasher *et al.*, 1964a
	30% hay[e]	0.88	−16	7.44	25	Gordon & Erwin, 1960
	20% CSH	0.99	1	5.30	28	Thrasher *et al.*, 1964b
	30% hay	0.96	16	7.75	30	Anthony *et al.*, 1961b
	2.42 hay	1.33	3	5.62	32	Wise *et al.*, 1962
	22% CSH	1.12	2	5.17	46	Thrasher *et al.*, 1964a
Sorghum	8% CSH	1.45	−2	6.59	7	McCartor *et al.*, 1964
	10% RH	1.50	−5	3.09	8	McCartor & Hefley, 1965
	10% RH	1.08	3	6.78	8	Conrad *et al.*, 1965
	10% sorghum silage	1.43	1	5.60	9	Morris, 1966
	10% CSH	1.50	−5	3.09	10	McCartor & Hefley, 1965
	20% RH	1.08	4	6.78	10	Conrad *et al.*, 1965
	10% flax shives	1.08	0	6.78	10	Conrad *et al.*, 1965
	10% maize silage	1.45	1	6.59	11	McCartor *et al.*, 1964
	20% flax shives	1.08	−17	6.78	14	Conrad *et al.*, 1965
	20% RH	0.98	4	6.60	15	White & Reynolds, 1968
	10% CSH	1.08	5	6.78	16	Conrad *et al.*, 1965
	20% CSH	1.08	6	6.78	18	Conrad *et al.*, 1965
	20% rice straw	0.98	25	6.60	21	White & Reynolds, 1968
	30% RH	1.08	−19	6.78	22	Conrad *et al.*, 1965
	20% hay	0.98	−6	6.60	24	White & Reynolds, 1968
	30% CSH	1.08	8	6.78	28	Conrad *et al.*, 1965
	30% flax shives	1.08	−26	6.78	29	Conrad *et al.*, 1965
	40% hay	0.98	0	6.60	29	White & Reynolds, 1968
	20% sorghum silage	1.43	−15	5.60	30	Morris, 1966
	40% grass pellets	0.98	8	6.60	38	White & Reynolds, 1968
	40% rice straw	0.98	11	6.60	44	White & Reynolds, 1968
	20% polythene	0.98	−15	6.60	48	White & Reynolds, 1968

[a] Coarsely ground alfalfa hay unless stated otherwise. [b] 15% molasses in diet.
[c] 10% molasses in diet. [d] Plus 7.5% hay. [e] 7.5% fat in the diet. CSH = cottonseed husks. RH = rice husks.

of 5.74 and 5.16 respectively. However, these trials involved animals starting at approximately 3 months of age and slaughtered at some 400 kg; moreover they were animals (Simmental and Charolais) with a superior genetic potential for growth than the British breeds traditionally employed in the US. Ear maize is essentially a feed for use in the area where it is grown due to the high transport costs associated with its bulky nature. Moreover, the changing pattern of harvesting, wherein combines are gradually replacing pickers, means that less of this feed will be available in the future.

Although all-concentrate diets based on ground or cracked maize have featured in many experiments (see Table 9.4), they have found little application in commercial feedlot practice. This does not stem from any inferior performance in terms of daily gain (about 1.1 kg) or conversion (about 6) but rather from management problems, since the incidence of bloat can be very high. Thus in one trial Preston *et al.* (1963a) reported 33% deaths from bloat on ground maize, although in this case the presence of 2.5% of sodium bicarbonate in the diet might have contributed to the problem. Maize is very low in fibre and hence, by comparison with grains such as barley, has virtually no roughage characteristics. That this was the main limiting factor in the use of maize was implied by results of further trials in which the addition of 25% of rolled oats effectively eliminated the bloat risk (RRI, 1964). The work of Cooley and Burroughs (1962) gives further support to the suggestion that an all-concentrate diet based on ground maize is lacking in abrasive properties, since the addition of 2% of sand slightly improved performance. The workers considered this effect to be purely a physical one as there was no similar response on high roughage diets and there was no evidence of absorption. Preston and his co-workers (RRI, 1964) also found no benefit from the addition of 2% of sand to an all-concentrate diet based on rolled barley.

9.3.1.3 OATS. Since the work of Geurin *et al.* (1956) with this cereal marked the beginning of economic investigations into the possibilities of all-concentrate feeding, it is surprising that no subsequent work with this grain has been reported. It is very likely that the reluctance to use oats on a large scale arose from its too-fibrous nature. Thus it has been used as a diluent for cereals which have themselves insufficient roughage characteristics (e.g. maize) and this is probably its more useful role.

9.3.1.4 SORGHUM. The interest in the use of sorghum as the cereal component of all-concentrate diets stems from the work of Durham and his colleagues in Texas. Growth performance on this cereal appears to have been slightly better than that on maize, but conversions have tended to be fractionally poorer. There are theoretical reasons for such differences (§ 5.3.6.2). It appears that bloat is less of a problem with sorghum than with maize, and this, too, can be explained by the fact that rate of fermentation on the former proceeds at an even slower rate than on barley (Trei *et al.*, 1966).

Although in energy terms there appears to be little to choose between barley and sorghum as components of all-concentrate diets, there is evidence that, with some additional roughage present, results are better with barley than with sorghum. Thus in a series of six trials undertaken in Arizona with a total of 374 steers, Hale *et al.* (1962) found that in every instance conversion was better on barley than on sorghum, and that in all but one trial live weight gain was also superior. The proportion of grain in the diets ranged from 49 to 55% and the overall average daily gains were 1.19 and 1.24 kg with feed conversions of 8.74 and 8.00 for sorghum and barley respectively. Hale and his associates considered that some of the response could be accounted for by the slightly higher protein content of the barley (9.4 vs. 8.9%); moreover, in rations with 66% of grain the protein in barley was more digestible than that in sorghum (66.4 vs. 60.2%). Rumen *in vivo* bag techniques showed that after 7 hr, 42% of the DM of the barley had disappeared compared with only 14% of the sorghum. On the other hand, Ralston *et al.* (1963) used diets with 20% added roughage and found that there were no significant differences in overall daily gain and feed conversion when the remainder of the diet comprised 85% sorghum and 15% beet pulp compared with 55% sorghum, 30% barley and 15% beet pulp or 35% sorghum, 50% barley and 15% beet pulp.

9.3.1.5 Wheat. This was one of the last cereals to be investigated as a basis for all-concentrate feeding. Early work in British Colombia (Wood, 1962) demonstrated its possibilities, particularly in the feeding of Holsteins for dairy beef production. Subsequently, Oltjen *et al.* (1966) found that daily gains were lower for all-concentrate diets with 90% wheat, or 60% wheat and 30% maize, than for diets with maize only or 60% maize and 30% of wheat. Group feeding and lack of replication did not permit a statistical analysis of feed conversion data although there was a suggestion that this was best on the all-maize diet. In view of the high initial weight (360 kg) this is not an experiment from which firm conclusions can be drawn. It is, however, interesting to note that liver abcesses were greater on the wheat-containing diets than on maize alone (42 vs. 10%).

In rations containing 30–35% added roughage it was reported by Dyer and Weaver (1955) that ground wheat caused frequent digestive disturbances, slow gains and lower grade carcasses. On the other hand, Baker and Baker (1960) concluded that wheat could be used to replace 50% of the maize in conventional fattening diets. Good results from wheat in roughage-containing diets were also reported by Bris *et al.* (1966); results were poorer with barley. Thomas and Geissler (1968) found wheat and barley to be equal in value when hay was available *ad libitum*, while Clary *et al.* (1968) showed that wheat was similar to maize and superior to sorghum as regards both gain and efficiency in diets which also contained roughage.

9.3.1.6 Rice. There is a preliminary report from Guayana (Anon., 1966b) on the use of rolled paddy rice (i.e. with the husk) as the cereal component of an all-concentrate diet. Reported daily gains ranged from 0.68 to 0.91 kg, but there appeared to have been inadequate vitamin supplementation as there were reports of blindness. There would appear to be no obvious reason why this cereal cannot be used for cattle fattening in rice-growing areas, particularly in view of its ever-increasing yields.

9.3.2 Sugar-beet

9.3.2.1 Beet pulp. There appears to be only one report on the use of beet pulp as the major energy source in an all-concentrate diet. This experiment, undertaken in

Wyoming with 110 Hereford steers, is detailed in Table 9.6 and shows conclusively that replacing either ground barley or ground maize with beet pulp led to steady deterioration in feed efficiency. There was a similar reduction in rate of daily gain which approached significance.

TABLE 9.6 USE OF BEET PULP IN ALL-CONCENTRATE DIETS (AFTER KERCHER *et al.*, 1966)

	Percentage of cereal replaced by beet pulp[a]			
	0	33.3	66.7	100
Days on test				
Barley	147	157	165	176
Maize	157	170	164	
Daily gain (kg)				
Barley	1.38	1.30	1.18	1.15
Maize	1.23	1.21	1.24	
Feed conversion (kg feed/kg gain)				
Barley	6.96	7.30	7.87	8.28
Maize	6.97	7.49	7.72	

[a] 7% of the diet made up by a protein, mineral, stilboestrol and chlortetracycline supplement.

An earlier study (Kercher and Bishop, 1963) compared beet pulp with steam-rolled barley, oats or sorgum in diets which also contained 12.5% dehydrated alfalfa pellets. Daily gains and feed conversion were poorest for the beet pulp.

As part of a larger study on compensatory growth, Connolly *et al.* (1967) included comparisons of maize, barley and beet pulp given *ad libitum* to housed Friesian steer calves from 2 weeks of age to slaughter at about 380 kg. Although there was little difference in rate of gain between the different energy sources, feed conversion was some 20% poorer with beet pulp than with barley and even worse when compared with maize (Table 9.7). The effect of the moisture content of beet pulp was studied by Boucque *et al.* (1967a). They compared ordinary ensiled pulp (11.7% DM), ensiled pressed pulp (16.9% DM) and dried pulp (90.1% DM) given *ad libitum* together with 2.5 kg of a 30% protein supplement. Daily gains of dairy beef bulls from 200 to 510 kg were 1.17, 1.18 and 1.29 kg respectively; corresponding feed conversions were 4.8, 5.1 and 5.2 kg DM/kg gain.

9.3.2.2 WHOLE BEET. Investigations in Denmark (Larsen, 1966) and Belgium (Boucque *et al.*, 1967b) showed that fodder beet could replace 50% of the concentrates in high energy diets for dairy beef bulls without reduction in live weight gain. In the Danish work, daily gains were 1.07 kg from calfhood (40 kg) to 530 kg, while the corresponding Belgian data were 1.15 kg from 226 to 525 kg.

9.3.3 Sugar cane*

9.3.3.1 INTRODUCTION. In almost all developed countries the intensification of beef cattle production has been by the feeding of increasing quantities of cereal grain. There are agronomic reasons for this procedure since cereal production has, possibly to a greater extent than almost all other crops, been subjected to increasing mechanization and the application of genetic and management techniques to raise yields. Furthermore, from the feedlot operators' point of view, grains are easily transported and stored, besides being readily adaptable to mechanized feeding practices.

What distinguishes the developing countries, and particularly those in tropical and sub-tropical regions, is the scarcity of feed grains. Apart from rice (which is grown entirely for human consumption), there has been little or no development of modern, intensive grain production. This situation has led most tropical advisers to try to develop livestock enterprises on the basis of pasture and forages, with the inevitable result that animal production in these regions has been characterized by low levels of productivity and efficiency.

The excessive preoccupation with the *problems* of the tropics, particularly the difficulty of producing conventional animal feed supplies, has been unfortunate. For, in fact, the tropics are potentially richer than any temperate region; the important difference is that their wealth lies not so much in pasture and certainly not in grain, but rather in crops such as sugar cane, cassava and even bananas. These are typically food crops, and have been grown for centuries, both as a staple of the local human diet and for export. Sugar cane in particular has enormous potential for capturing solar energy. In fact, it is known that, along with certain other tropical grasses, sugar cane possesses an additional enzyme system not found in temperate type grasses or cereals, and which provides it with this faculty for efficient transfer of solar energy into carbohydrate (Hatch and Slack, 1966). To the traditional sugar technologist it may appear heretical to suggest the growing of sugar cane for animals rather than humans. But there are convincing reasons to justify such a change of emphasis.

There are two approaches to the use of sugar cane as the basis of intensive cattle fattening in the tropics. One is to utilize the by-products, which arise in the normal course of sugar manufacture, principally final (blackstrap) molasses and bagasse (Table 9.7); the other is to use sugar cane directly, after removal of the indigestible

TABLE 9.7 BY-PRODUCTS FOR ANIMAL FEEDING WHICH ARISE DURING NORMAL SUGAR PRODUCTION

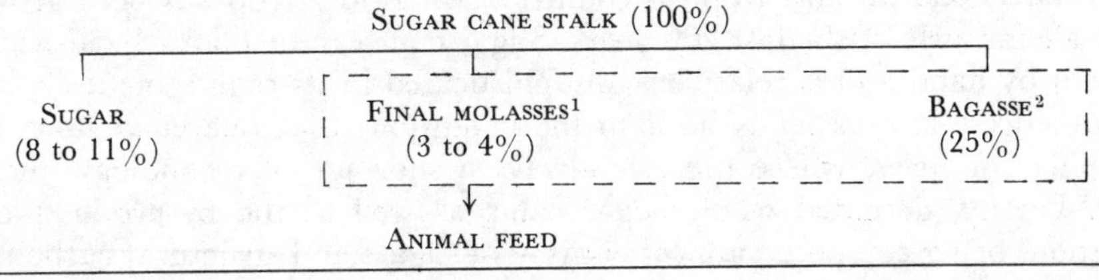

[1] Contains 20% moisture.
[2] Contains 50% moisture.

* See supplementary list of references.

rind (Table 9.8). The technology for this latter process was developed by Miller and Tilby in Canada (Dion, 1973). They invented a machine which splits the sugar cane stalk, scoops out and grinds the pith containing the sugars and discards the two strips of rind. The coarsely ground pith is a creamy white palatable feed with the consistency of wet sawdust. It is readily eaten by cattle and is an excellent energy source for intensive beef production (Table 9.9).

TABLE 9.8 DERINDING OF SUGAR CANE FOR ANIMAL FEEDING (FROM PIGDEN, 1972)

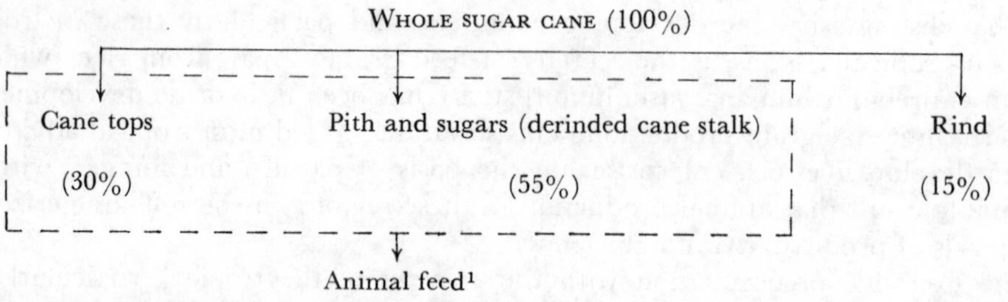

[1] Both components combined can supply total diet needs for readily fermentable carbohydrate and roughage.

TABLE 9.9 AVERAGE VALUES (AND RANGE) FOR COMPOSITION OF DERINDED CANE STALK ALONE AND WITH THE TOPS INCLUDED (FROM PIGDEN, 1972)

	Derinded cane stalk	Derinded cane stalk plus tops
Dry matter (DM), %	30 (27–31)	32 (30–33)
Composition of DM, %		
N × 6.25	1.9 (1–2.5)	3.0 (1.8–4.2)
Cellulose	18 (15–20)	24 (21–38)
Total Sugars	50 (40–63)	43 (40–48)
Digestibility of DM, %	70 (68–73)	69 (68–71)

The great advantage of using sugar cane and its by-products for animal feeding in the tropics lies in the high yield potential. Moreover, sugar cane technology is widely understood in most tropical countries, where the crop has been grown on a large scale for at least the last 200 years. Sugar cane can be planted, cultivated, and harvested by hand and is relatively unsophisticated in its requirement for management practices. It thus lends itself to the conditions that one encounters in most developing countries, where there is always a shortage of technology and skilled labour. Finally, derinded whole sugar cane, as well as the by-products of sugar production, being composed almost entirely of sugars and structural carbohydrates, are ideal substrates for the utilization of non-protein nitrogen through the medium of the microorganisms in the digestive tract of ruminants, thus leading to the direct synthesis of animal protein from chemical nitrogen. Such a system can exist symbiotically with the needs of the human population, since the two do not compete for raw materials—as is the case with pig and poultry production in the tropics, for these species must consume cereal grain and vegetable and animal proteins—themselves the staple of the human diet in these regions, and almost always in short supply.

The yields per hectare in several tropical countries of the by-products from sugar production and of derinded sugar cane combined with cane tops are set out in Table 9.10; for comparison, yields of certain cereal grains and of cassava tubers are also included.

TABLE 9.10 YIELDS OF TOTAL DIGESTIBLE NUTRIENTS (TDN) FROM CARBOHYDRATE CROPS IN SELECTED TROPICAL COUNTRIES (FROM DATA IN FAO 1969, AND PIGDEN, 1972)

	Maize grain	Sorghum grain	Cassava tubers	Derinded whole sugar cane	Final molasses	Dry bagasse
	Total digestible nutrients, t/ha				t/ha	
Peru	1.28	1.36	2.07	21.8	3.62	12.8
Ethiopia	0.88	0.56		21.6	3.59	12.7
Uganda	0.88	0.88	0.66	13.8	2.29	8.13
Taiwan	1.82	1.28	2.88	11.0	1.83	6.48
Ecuador	0.40			10.4	1.73	6.13
Jamaica	0.96		0.40	10.4	1.73	6.13
Mexico	0.96	2.00		9.4	1.56	5.54
India	0.80	0.40	2.35	7.2	1.20	4.24
Kenya	3.44	0.64	1.17	7.0	1.16	4.12

It is immediately obvious the enormous potential that sugar cane has as a basis for intensive beef production in the humid tropics. No other crop can approach its potential for yielding up to 20 tons/ha of digestible nutrients; moreover, it has a high nutritive value midway between maize silage and maize grain, which makes it eminently suitable as a basis for intensive feeding.

Comparable per hectare yields can be obtained from many grasses, but this is always at the expense of feed value, the final product being of only moderate digestibility which will barely support maintenance when used as the sole energy component in the ration.

Even after extraction of sugar, the yield per hectare of only one of the by-products, namely final molasses, is greater than present average yields of cereal grains in the tropics.

9.3.3.2 FINAL MOLASSES. Final molasses has been fed to beef cattle for many years, mainly as an additive to increase palatability or to improve pelleting characteristics in conventional dry mixed rations. It has also been used as a vehicle for various types of proprietary liquid feeds used as supplements for range cattle; in these cases the other components have been mainly urea and phosphoric acid (or other soluble sources of phosphorus) and occasionally other minerals and vitamins. These mixes were not designed for fattening cattle, since it was generally considered that the intake of molasses should be restricted to relatively low levels for fear of digestive disturbances and laxative effects.

The mixing of liquid molasses in dry feeds at the farm level is difficult without special machinery, and several attempts have been made to produce a "dry" molasses feed by combining it with a highly absorbent inert base such as bagasse pith. In such "dry" mixes the molasses level can be as high as 70 to 75%. These formulae have been used commercially in South Africa (Cleasby, 1963) and to some extent in the United States (Brown, 1962). The idea has not found widespread application, partly due to the poor handling qualities of the mixes, but more so to the cost and difficulties of the mixing operation, which requires special machinery. Considering the circumstances of the developing world/humid tropics, which is the origin of the greater part of the cane molasses that is produced, the question of specialized machinery and advanced technology presents particularly serious constraints. Moreover, another characteristic of the humid tropics is the ready availability of poor quality roughage; thus it makes little economic sense to expend energy and money in mixing and transporting poor quality roughage as a component of a molasses-based feed. Finally, in the sugar factories where it is produced, molasses is always handled in liquid form, and there would appear to be advantages in keeping it liquid in order to utilize these same factories as points of storage and distribution.

This was the reasoning behind the decision, in initiating the development programme in Cuba on the use of molasses, to accept from the start that the molasses should be mixed, transported and fed as a liquid.

The composition of final molasses is given in Tables 9.11 and 9.12. It appears to be reasonably homogeneous in composition from country to country, except with

TABLE 9.11 COMPOSITION DATA FOR FINAL MOLASSES

	Mauritius[1]	Rhodesia[2]	USA[3]	Cuba[4]
Dry matter	80.4	80.0	74.5	76.9
Sucrose	33.6	29.6	52.2 (sucrose + reducing sugars)	35.0
Reducing sugars	13.5	17.0		17.0
N × 6.25	5.06	4.0	4.30	3.40
Minerals	9–10	7.8	8.10	5.54
Potassium	3.42	3.54	2.38	2.00
Calcium	1.11	0.66	0.89	0.71
Phosphorus	0.10	0.07	0.08	0.06
Magnesium	0.60	0.34	0.35	0.45
Sodium		0.13	0.17	

[1] MSIRI, 1961. [2] Fincham, 1966. [3] NRC, 1956.
[4] Institute of Animal Science, Havana, Cuba, unpublished data.

respect to its potassium content, which probably reflects fertilizer practices and soil composition in the original cane lands. With respect to its suitability as the major component in an intensive fattening ration, attention should be directed to these factors:

TABLE 9.12 MINERAL COMPOSITION OF MOLASSES FROM FOUR DIFFERENT SUGAR FACTORIES IN MAURITIUS (SANSOUCY, 1973, UNPUBLISHED DATA)

Sample	Ash %	Calcium %	Phosphorus %	Potassium %	Sodium %	Magnesium %	Zinc mg/kg	Iron mg/kg	Manganese mg/kg	Copper mg/kg
1	11.1	1.16	0.08	3.20	0.060	0.45	13	180	59	11
2	9.9	0.96	0.05	2.80	0.039	0.46	14	142	36	22
3	10.7	0.93	0.06	3.10	0.054	0.45	10	106	17	6
4	11.3	0.85	0.06	3.45	0.036	0.53	12	120	21	5
Average	10.9	0.94	0.06	3.175	0.046	0.47	12.25	137	33.2	11.0

1. It has no "roughage" characteristics, in contrast to other high carbohydrate feeds such as cereal grains.
2. It contains very little nitrogenous material (less than 5% of N × 6.25) in the dry matter, and of this only one-third is considered to be in the form of amino-acids, and furthermore these appear to be in highly soluble form (Anon., 1970). At best, then, the existing nitrogenous material in molasses cannot be considered as other than a source of N for microbial growth.
3. It is a good source of all the major and minor mineral elements, with the exception of phosphorus—in which it is highly deficient in relation to animal requirements even for fattening—and sodium, the need for which is enhanced due to the presence of so much potassium; in certain circumstances there may also be a need for additional manganese, copper, cobalt, zinc and selenium, one or all of which have been detected in low concentrations in molasses arising from specific regions.
4. The form of the readily available carbohydrate in molasses is entirely as highly soluble sugars—mainly sucrose and the reducing sugars glucose and fructose—which has important consequences in relation to the pattern of rumen fermentation associated with high levels of molasses feeding.

The successful utilization of high levels of molasses in the fattening of cattle requires an understanding of the above four factors, particularly the need for, and the effect of, specific supplements, namely roughage, protein, minerals and non-sugar carbohydrates. In discussing these various factors it is assumed that, except where stated otherwise (e.g. in the section on urea/protein), the molasses in the experiments referred to contains 2 to 3% of urea).

Roughage: Although molasses is generally considered to be highly palatable to cattle, in fact this is not true over the whole range of feed intake. The data in Table 9.12a refer to experiments in which Zebu bulls had free access to molasses/urea

TABLE 9.12A PERFORMANCE OF ZEBU BULLS GIVEN *ad libitum* MOLASSES WITH 3% UREA AND EITHER GROUND SORGHUM GRAIN OR FRESHLY-CUT ELEPHANT GRASS (FROM PRESTON AND WILLIS, 1969)

	Molasses-urea and	
	Grain	Forage
Number of bulls	80	246
Initial weight, kg	194	218
Final weight, kg	368	398
Daily gain, kg	0.97	0.59
Daily feed intake, kg		
Molasses	1.0	5.3
Grain	6.1	
Forage		56
Percent of total ME consumed in form of molasses	11	58
Feed conversion, Mcal ME/kg gain	18.8	43

and either ground sorghum grain or elephant grass forage. When the alternative food was grain, the bulls ate only 11% of the total diet ME in the form of molasses; when freshly cut forage was the alternative feed, then more molasses was consumed (58% of diet ME); however, animal performance was considerably inferior. Restricting the intake of forage to a level of 1.5% of animal live weight per day (Table 9.12b)

TABLE 9.12B PERFORMANCE OF ZEBU BULLS GIVEN *ad libitum* MOLASSES WITH 3% UREA AND EITHER *ad libitum* OR RESTRICTED MAIZE FORAGE (1.5% OF LIVE WEIGHT) AND CONCENTRATE SUPPLEMENT (MARTIN *et al.*, 1968)

	Forage *ad libitum*	Forage restricted
Number of bulls	24	23
Initial weight, kg	220	210
Final weight, kg	385	390
Daily gain, kg	0.63	0.76
Feed intake, kg		
Molasses	3.36	5.6
Forage	30.6	4.3
Consumption of ME in form of molasses, %	33	72
Feed conversion, Mcal/kg gain	32.8	20.6
Killing out %	51.7	52.3

brought about a marked increase in the consumption of molasses as a proportion of the diet (72% of total ME); individual animal performance was also considerably improved as compared with *ad libitum* forage. A rate of 1.5% of live weight implies an average forage intake of approximately 15% of total diet DM. Figure 9.2a shows

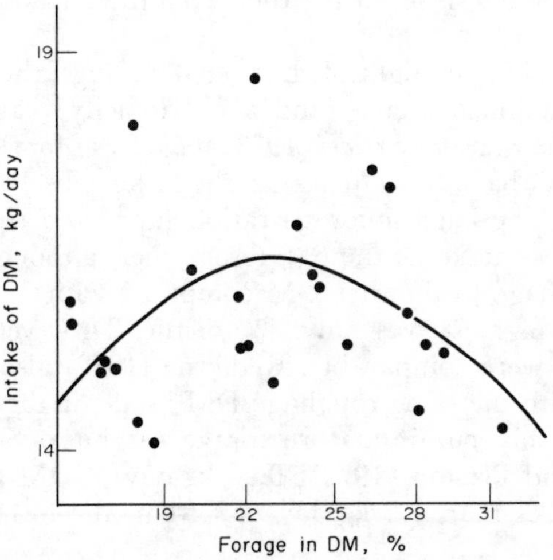

FIG. 9.2a Effect of forage content of a molasses-based diet on voluntary intake of DM by milking cows $Y = 1.767 + 1.27\ X - 0.027\ X^2$ (Clark, 1971).

that total DM intake is at a maximum for forage concentrations between 20 and 28% of diet DM; however, above or below this range intake falls rapidly. At increasing forage concentrations the reduction in dry matter intake is understandable as a dilution effect, due to decreasing digestibility. But at the low forage levels some metabolic and/or physiological mechanism is presumably involved. The results of experiments carried out by Perón and Preston (1971) and by Losada and Preston (1972) suggest that the principal effect is physiological, probably due to the stimulatory effect of "roughage" on rumen motility and hence on rumen turnover time and finally on voluntary intake. The former authors supplemented molasses/urea with fresh forage (1.5% of live weight), plastic simulated roughage, or no roughage; intake of molasses was highest with fresh forage, lowest with no forage and intermediate with the plastic (Table 9.12c). Losada and Preston gave fresh

TABLE 9.12C EFFECT OF ARTIFICIAL ROUGHAGE, OR NONE, ON VOLUNTARY INTAKE OF MOLASSES AND TOTAL DIET BY YOUNG BULLS (BASAL DIET WAS *ad libitum* MOLASSES, PROTEIN SUPPLEMENT AND THE RESPECTIVE FORAGE SOURCES)

	No forage	Plastic roughage	Fresh forage	Dried ground forage
Perón and Preston (1971)				
Molasses, kg DM/day	2.32	3.17	4.92	
Total diet DM, kg/day	2.68	3.53	5.64	
Losada and Preston (1972)				
Molasses, kg DM/day	1.53		1.91	1.32
Total diet DM, kg/day	1.81		2.38	2.04

forage, ground dehydrated forage or none, and reported declining molasses intakes in the same order. There was also increased incidence of molasses toxicity with declining roughage characteristics of the diet, even though absolute molasses intakes on these diets were lower.

As would be expected in the light of the above findings, the absolute amounts of forage required to maximize intake (and avoid toxicity) varies according to the nature of the roughage. Sansoucy *et al.* (1973) gave fresh forage (elephant grass) at 3% of live weight, fresh bagasse *ad libitum* or the latter plus 1% live weight as fresh forage (Table 9.12d). The bagasse/forage ration supported equal growth rate and slightly higher molasses intake as the 3% forage diet, although the former contributed only 15% roughage to the diet DM compared with 27% for the latter. On bagasse alone, total roughage was only 7% of diet DM, yet molasses intakes as percent of live weight were comparable. Redferne (1972) also found that molasses intakes were higher with the same roughage DM intake in the form of wheat straw, as compared with freshly cut immature forage sorghum. Similar findings were reported by Martin and Preston (1972); 0.96 kg/day of DM as bagasse supported higher total DM intakes than 1.2 kg/day of DM in the form of rice husks (7.32 vs. 6.08).

In all these reports the low quality dry roughages were fed *ad libitum* and the cattle voluntarily restricted themselves to much lower intakes of roughage DM than

TABLE 9.12D EFFECT OF TYPE OF ROUGHAGE ON FEED INTAKE AND PERFORMANCE OF ZEBU BULLS FED MOLASSES/UREA BASED DIETS IN MAURITIUS (SANSOUCY *et al.*, 1973)

	Forage 3% of LW	Forage 1% LW Bagasse *ad lib.*	Bagasse *ad lib.*
Molasses intake			
kg/day	6.21	6.48	5.84
% of live wt	2.23	2.33	2.30
% of total DM	68	78.6	86.2
Roughage intake, kg DM/day			
Bagasse		0.31	0.38
Forage	1.41	0.50	—
Total	1.41	0.81	0.38
Total as % of diet DM	26.6	15.2	6.9
Average daily gain, kg	0.53	0.52	0.37

when fresh forage was given *ad libitum*. This has some relevance to construction of feedlots, since reduced trough feeding space is required (and therefore construction costs are less) when feeding is *ad libitum*.

The above discussion relates entirely to conditions of drylot feeding where forage is transported to the cattle. Similar results are obtainable, in terms of animal performance and molasses intakes, when cattle are allowed to harvest their own roughage, the restriction being applied by limiting the number of hours spent grazing, usually to 3 to 4 hours daily—preferably in two periods, morning and evening of 1 to 2 hours each. Results for this system are compared with those for the conventional drylot in Tables 9.12i and 9.12j.

In conclusion, it would appear that for molasses fattening, the roughage input is critical as a means of maximizing animal performance. Wherever possible it is preferable to use a type of forage that supplies maximum "roughage" characteristics, i.e. contains long fibres that will induce adequate stimulation of the rumen wall, and yet is sufficiently palatable to be eaten in the minimum required amount—probably about some 10% of total DM, in the case of a roughage of optimum physical consistency such as wheat or rice straw. The use of restricted grazing as a roughage source, in conjunction with simple fenced enclosures for confining the animals and giving the molasses, is particularly attractive as a low investment system which is particularly suited to dry season fattening; accumulation of mud and difficulties in transporting molasses tankers restrict the use of this system in the wet rainy season.

Urea/protein: In designing the nitrogen component of a molasses-based ration, it is important to appreciate that the constraints which apply to this aspect of the diet formulation are quite different from those which apply to a grain or forage-based diet.

All of the soluble sugars present in molasses are fermented in the rumen and none reaches the abomasum and duodenum (Geerken and Sutherland, 1969; Kowalczyk *et al.*, 1969; Ramírez and Kowalczyk, 1971). First, then, one must satisfy the nitrogen needs of the microorganisms so that these grow as fast, and as efficiently, as possible, so as to maximize rate of production of microbial cells which will be the major supplier of protein to the animal. The work of Hume *et al.* (1970) shows that microbial growth is maximized when ammonia nitrogen is approximately 2.5% of the carbohydrate fermentable in the rumen; in terms of 80° Brix molasses this is equivalent to a level of about 1.5%. Assuming the nitrogen in the molasses is about 0.5%, of which half is available to microorganisms, then the need for supplementary nitrogen is 1.25% which can be supplied most economically and conveniently by fertilizer grade urea (46% nitrogen) added at the level of 2.5% of the molasses (80° Brix).

Theoretical considerations lead us to expect that microbial growth in the rumen is not a sufficiently efficient process to cover the entire protein needs of the fast growing ruminant, since the latter is physiologically unable to consume the required amounts of fermentable carbohydrate. With an average molasses intake of some 2.5% of live weight, the diet carbohydrate that is fermentable in the rumen will be sufficient to supply some 60% of total protein requirements as microbial protein, according to the theoretical conversion rates for this process in a molasses-based diet, estimated *in vivo* by Ramírez and Kowalczyk (1971). Supplementary dietary protein would therefore need to be supplied to the extent of 40% of total needs; moreover, this should be as "protected" or insoluble protein to avoid it being degraded in passage through the rumen. Confirmation of this hypothesis is provided by the data given in Fig. 9.2b. The experiment was carried out with a typical molasses fattening ration

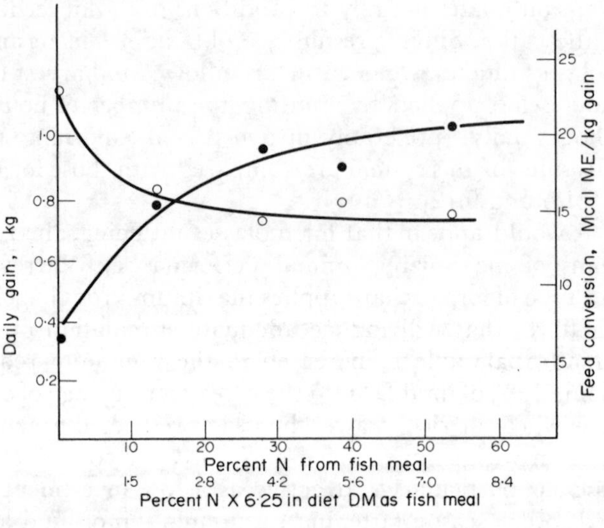

FIG. 9.2b Effect of replacing urea N with fish meal N on growth rate and feed conversion in Holstein × Brahman bulls fattened on a molasses-based diet ● = Daily gain, ○ = feed conversion (Preston and Martin, 1972).

except that the composition of the nitrogen fraction, over and above that present in the forage and molasses, was varied between 100% urea N and 100% fish meal N, the latter being considered as a naturally insoluble protein due to the heat treatment received in its manufacture. The response to the fish meal protein was curvilinear with the biological optimum at some 40% of fish meal N in the diet. In view of the much greater cost of fish meal compared to urea nitrogen, the economic optimum is closer to 20% fish meal N, i.e. the equivalent of some 4% of fish meal in the diet

DM. A similar trial was carried out with yeast protein (*Torulopsis candida*) by Preston and Muñoz (1971). The nature of the response curve (Fig. 9.2c) was broadly similar to that with fish meal, the only difference being that a greater total amount of protein was needed to reach maximum animal performance, a finding possibly related to the lower level of sulphur aminoacids in this particular protein source.

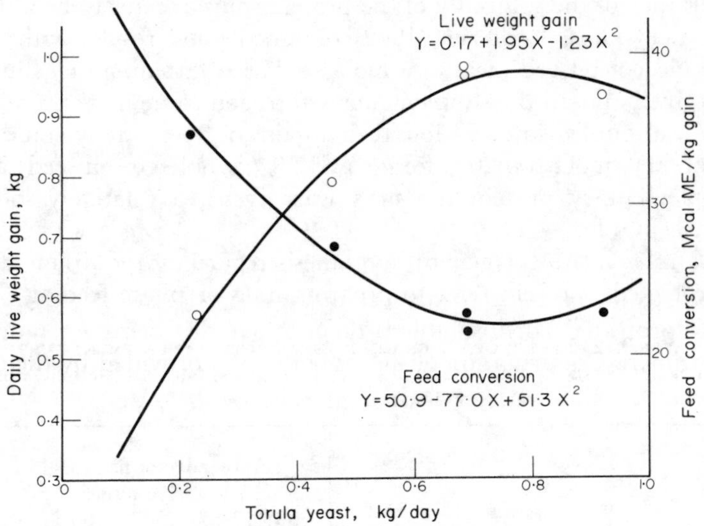

FIG. 9.2c Effect of yeast protein on performance of bulls fed a molasses/urea based ration (from Preston and Muñoz, 1971).

The importance of the insolubility of the supplementary protein is emphasized by results (Table 9.12e) from an experiment where the supplementary protein for a molasses/urea diet was supplied by either solvent-extracted rapeseed meal, fish meal, or a mixture of the two (Preston and Molina, 1972).

Animal performance on the rapeseed ration was no better than that expected from urea alone and less than half that recorded on the fish meal diet. The rapeseed

TABLE 9.12E RAPESEED MEAL AS A SUPPLEMENT TO MOLASSES-UREA DIETS FOR CROSS-BRED BRAHAM BULLS (PRESTON AND MOLINA, 1972)

	Fish meal[1]	Fish meal and rapeseed (50:50)[2]	Rapeseed meal[3]
Initial weight, kg	135.6	133.6	134.8
Final weight, kg	208.4[a]	184.6[b]	166.0[c]
Daily gain, kg	0.85[a]	0.59[b]	0.36[c]
Conversion, Mcal ME/kg gain	11.4[c]	13.8[b]	20.8[a]

a,b,c, Means without letter in common differ at $p < 0.05$.

[1] Basal diet of *ad libitum* molasses (with 2% urea), fresh forage (1.5% of LW daily) and minerals, plus 450 g fish meal daily.

[2] Basal plus 200 g fish meal and 392 g rapeseed meal.

[3] Basal plus 785 g rapeseed meal.

meal was found to be 80% "soluble" in rumen fluid, and therefore likely to be degraded rapidly by rumen organisms. Subsequent trials have shown that "expeller" rapeseed meal, which is less soluble due to the heating received in the extraction process, is much more suitable as a protein supplement for molasses/urea diets (Donefer, 1973, personal communication).

The importance of the solubility of the protein source seems to be a function of its level in the diet. Thus, Redferne (1972) obtained good results with a mixture of maize germ and cottonseed meal in a molasses-based fattening diet, but in this case no urea was given and all the supplementary nitrogen came from protein. Similarly, Preston (1973, unpublished data) found that gains of 0.9 kg daily could be obtained from a diet of 60% molasses, 20% forage and 20% whole cotton seed; again, at this level of supplementary protein (no urea was given), a relatively soluble protein source was acceptable.

Other data relevant to the general hypothesis regarding requirements for supplementary "protected" protein refer to programming or phase feeding (Table 9.12f)

TABLE 9.12F EFFECT OF PROGRAMMING THE PROTEIN SUPPLEMENT SUPPLY FOR HOLSTEIN × BRAHAM BULLS GIVEN *ad libitum* MOLASSES-UREA AND RESTRICTED GRAZING (MORCIEGO *et al.*, 1972)

	Allowance of fish meal in successive months, g	
	300:172:57:57	400:57:57:57
Number of bulls	700	700
Live weight, kg		
Initial	270	262
Final	345	330
Daily gain	0.581	0.641
Conversion, kg/kg gain		
Molasses	9.64	8.80
Fish meal	0.275	0.231
Mean daily intake of fish meal, kg	0.160	0.148

supplying the protein at higher levels during the first month, supported better animal performance and more efficient use of both the molasses and the protein. In some respects, such findings could be interpreted as indicating a period of adaptation to urea utilization (section 5.5.2); however, we prefer to agree with Burroughs *et al.* (1970) that the implied adaptation is more likely to be related to the energetic components of the diet, for which there is adequate documentation (Turner and Hodgetts, 1955; Marty and Sutherland, 1970), and that this in turn affects microbial growth, in view of the energy limiting nature of this process (section 5.5.5).

Feed intake always increased after the transition period, thus providing for greater microbial synthesis, and hence reduced requirement for supplementary protein. There is also the fact that protein requirement relative to energy, decreases with time on feed, because of the changing composition of the tissue being laid down.

Non-sugar carbohydrate: It has been shown that the pattern of rumen fermentation on molasses-based diets is characterized by abnormally high levels of butyrate and low levels of propionate (see Table 9.12g). Such a situation could lead to low voluntary intakes (section 5.4) and to decreased efficiency of energy utilization for fattening (section 5.3.4.4). Addition of a source of starch to a molasses-based ration theoretically would be expected to increase propionate levels and, in fact, this hypothesis has been proved experimentally in dairy cows (see Table 9.12h). While conclusive data are lacking for such effects on the rumen fermentation pattern in fattening bulls there is evidence that supplementary starch has a non-additive (i.e. stimulatory) effect on animal performance. A linear improvement in voluntary feed intake, live weight gain and feed conversion to added maize grain was reported by

TABLE 9.12G MOLAR COMPOSITION OF THE VFA IN RUMEN LIQUOR FROM CATTLE GIVEN HIGH LEVELS OF MOLASSES COMPARED WITH VALUES FROM THE LITERATURE FOR MORE CONVENTIONAL DIETS (MARTY AND PRESTON, 1970)

Class and number of animals	Diet	Total VFA (m-equiv/litre)	Molar proportions, %			
			acetic	propionic	butyric	others
Dairy cows						
2	Pasture	131–148	65–67	18–19	11–12	3–4
—	High-grain	148	58	20–21	15–16	4–5
8	High-molasses	114	36	24	29	10
Fattening cattle						
2	Alfalfa hay	107	74	18–19	7–8	
5	High-grain	115	39	40	21	
8	High-molasses	143	31	19	41	9
Weaned calves						
4	High-grain	115	50	37	13	
8	High-molasses	96	28	20	37	14

TABLE 9.12H EFFECT ON RUMEN FERMENTATION OF SUBSTITUTING MAIZE WITH MOLASSES IN A LOW-FORAGE DIET GIVEN TO DAIRY COWS (CLARK, 1971)

	Maize: molasses (as % of diet DM)			
	63.8	42.25	20.45	0.61
VFA, molar %				
Acetic	57.4	56.8	55.8	51.9
Propionic	29.3	23.9	19.9	18.0
Butyric	10.7	17.4	21.1	25.8
Valeric	0.6	1.2	2.6	3.7
Blood ketone bodies, mg/100 ml	4.6	3.9	4.9	7.0

Preston *et al.* (1973) for Zebu bulls fattened on a molasses-based ration in Mauritius (see Fig. 9.2d). A curvilinear response to increments of maize bran (including the germ) in a molasses ration was observed by Redferne (1972) in Kenya (Fig. 9.2e).

Since, in the early phase of supplementation with cereal grain, the response appears to be in excess of the substitution value of the ME of the starch source (there is also an increase in voluntary intake), it will usually be economic to include some cereal grain (or grain by-product) at low levels in a molasses-based ration—despite the higher price of the energy in cereal grain or by-product relative to that in molasses. There is also the added advantage that inclusion of some grain product appears to give protection against molasses toxicity—since this syndrome also seems to be caused by low levels of propionate production (Losada *et al.*, 1971).

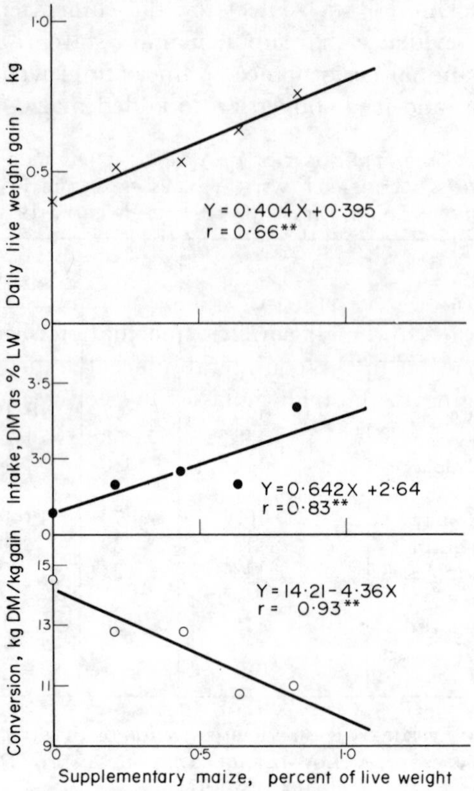

FIG. 9.2d Effect of supplementary maize grain on performance of Zebu bulls fed a diet based on molasses/urea (Preston *et al.*, 1973).

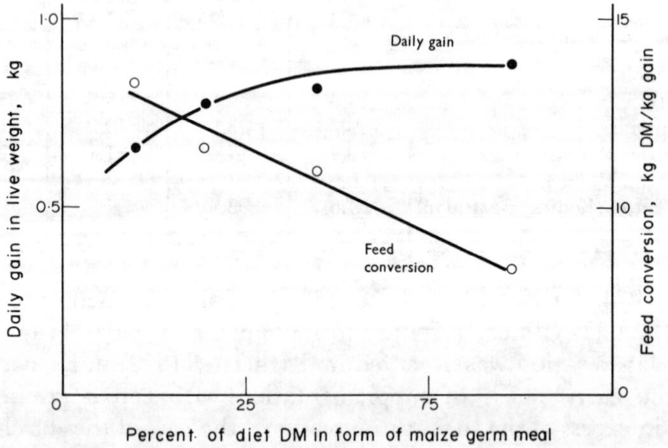

FIG. 9.2e Effect of adding increasing amounts of maize germ meal on performance of Zebu steers fed a molasses-based diet (Redferne, 1972, unpublished data).

Input–output data for molasses fattening: There can be no one formula, or combination of ingredients, applicable to all the varied situations where molasses is produced. For each particular region, input–output studies must be carried out in order to determine the most economic combination of inputs. The information given in the preceding part of this section aims to provide a guide line as to the nature of the responses to be expected, but it can be no substitute for experimental data using the actual raw materials available.

In 1970/71 the molasses fattening programme in Cuba was based on fish meal as the only supplement to the basal diet of molasses/urea and minerals and forage. The data in Tables 9.12i and 9.12j refer to the input–output relationships obtained with these ingredients in a commercial 10,000 head feedlot, and in a series of dry-season fattening units employing the restricted grazing system. For the feedlot, comparative figures are given for the previous year when a more conventional feeding system was in operation, based on *ad libitum* forage supplemented with smaller quantities of concentrates and molasses. The information is self-explanatory, but it is relevant to draw attention to the considerably greater throughput which was one consequence of changing to the high molasses–low forage programme. This simply reflects the considerable logistics problem involved in trying to cut and transport large amounts of green forage; and how much easier it is to move liquid molasses. The high mortality and emergency slaughter figures in the first year of the molasses programme also merit some explanation. In part, they reflect management difficulties which are bound to arise when making a radical change in feeding systems. Nevertheless, it should also be pointed out that despite the greater losses, the overall economics of high molasses feeding remained attractive, as in terms of all the major

TABLE 9.12I INPUT–OUTPUT DATA (JANUARY TO JUNE INCLUSIVE) FOR FATTENING BULLS ON MOLASSES-BASED (1970 AND 1971) COMPARED WITH FORAGE-BASED (1969) DIETS IN A 10,000 HEAD CAPACITY FEED-LOT (FROM MUÑOZ *et al.*, 1970; MUÑOZ, UNPUBLISHED DATA, 1971)

	Forage-based, 1969	Molasses-based	
		1970	1971
Total daily LW gain (kg) in the feed-lot	3274	8295	13,797
Daily LW gain (kg) per:			
Bull	0.43	0.88	0.89
Worker	14.3	51.8	82.2
Tractor	85.6	420	282
Conversion, kg/kg LW gain			
Forage	34.7	11.9	10.3
Molasses	3.10	10	9.62
Urea	0.23	0.32	0.31
Concentrates	3.84		
Fish meal		0.41	0.41
Minerals		0.13	0.10
DM	15.4	10.8	9.82
Mortality, %	0.1	1	0.21
Emergency slaughter, %	0.4	3.04	1.31

TABLE 9.12j INPUT–OUTPUT DATA FOR FATTENING BULLS GIVEN *ad libitum* MOLASSES–UREA AND RESTRICTED GRAZING AND FISH MEAL SUPPLEMENTATION (FROM MORCIEGO *et al.*, 1970) (3500 BULLS IN 11 UNITS)[1]

	Best unit	Mean of all units	Worst unit
Daily live weight gain, kg	1.04	0.83	0.74
Conversion, kg feed/kg gain			
Molasses	5.9	9.1	14.7
Fish meal	0.32	0.45	0.54
Urea	0.19	0.29	0.47
Mortality, %	0.0	0.38	1.33
Emergency slaughter, %	0.0	0.44	1.33

[1] Mean initial and final weights were 313 and 403 kg; breeds were Brahman and Holstein × Brahman.

inputs, i.e. animals, labour, machinery, feed–output was considerably increased, inclusive of the losses.

There were no important differences in input–output relationships between the restricted grazing and the feedlot system; in fact, health problems were considerably reduced on the former, probably reflecting a better control over the forage input, since the animal under conditions of free grazing can select more effectively this portion of its diet.

9.3.3.3 DERINDED SUGAR CANE. In contrast to the high molasses fattening system, there are only limited animal data available on the use of derinded sugar cane. The development work has been carried out exclusively in Barbados, and mainly with Holstein steers, by-products from the local dairy industry. The scope of the research facilities available did not allow comprehensive evaluation of the different inputs associated with this feeding method; nevertheless, certain dietary variables have been studied and in general the results obtained indicate that in most respects similar constraints apply to derinded sugar cane as to final molasses, when it is used as the major component in a fattening programme.

Forage: Although derinded cane obviously has better "roughage" characteristics than liquid molasses, animal performance seems to be improved by incorporating additional forage in the form of the cane tops (Table 9.12k). As with molasses, supplementary forage seems to exert its major effect in increasing voluntary intake, and as a result rate of live weight gain, but with slight deterioration in efficiency of feed conversion. The ratio of tops to derinded cane was fixed at that normally found in whole sugar cane; it is not known if slightly narrower ratios, i.e. a lower proportion of tops might not be more beneficial.

Cereal grain: Two carbohydrate supplements, maize grain and molasses, were added to rations based on derinded whole sugar cane (Table 9.12l). Both supplements, which were supplied at the rate of 1% of live weight daily, brought about consistent increases in voluntary intake and in live weight gain. Gain was increased over 25% by maize, and there was also an important improvement in feed conversion (11% on average). Molasses increased gain by a lesser amount (about 9%) and caused a deterioration in feed conversion. Data are not available on the rumen

TABLE 9.12K DERINDED SUGAR CANE AS THE BASIS FOR INTENSIVE FEEDING OF HOLSTEIN STEERS (JAMES, 1973)

	Derinded cane stalk		Improvement due to cane tops (%)
	Alone	Plus tops	
Number of calves	12	13	
Live weight, kg			
Initial	105	102	
Final	257	271	
Daily gain	0.59	0.66	12
Feed intake, kg/day			
Derinded cane stalk	12.8	10.9	
Cane tops		4.3	
Derinded whole cane	12.8	15.2	19
Protein supplement	1.1	1.1	
Total DM	4.72	5.63	19
Conversion, kg DM/kg gain	8.0	8.5	−6

[1] It was considered that in this trial the live weight gains were lower than would normally be expected, due to use of immature cane and effect of flooding on cane quality.

fermentation on derinded sugar cane, but it is probable that it will show the same constraints as on molasses, i.e. propionate production will be limiting, since the beneficial effects of added maize grain are of the same magnitude on both feeds.

The level of maize supplementation in these trials was high (32% of the diet DM), and in most cases would not be economic. It is probable that smaller amounts would be more appropriate, since it can be expected that the response curve to maize supplementation will be curvilinear, with the greatest effect being observed in the early phase of substitution.

Protein: In all the trials reported with derinded cane, urea was added to supply from 50 to 60% of the total N requirements; however, the absolute quantities of protein/nitrogen in the diet were higher than in the Cuba work with molasses. This might account for the apparent absence of response to fish meal in comparison with the more soluble rapeseed meal (Table 9.12m). Further trials are needed with more critical levels of protein, before definitive conclusions can be made on this aspect.

Ensiling: One disadvantage of using derinded sugar cane as animal feed is that because of its high moisture and sugar content it ferments quickly–necessitating that it be produced and fed daily. A similar problem exists with the feeding of whole crop maize, and which has been solved by ensiling the material; in this form maize stores easily and is well accepted by cattle. Unfortunately, the ensiling process appears to be much less suitable for derinded cane. The data in Table 9.12n show that there is a serious fall off in animal performance, specifically gain and feed conversion, when fresh derinded cane is replaced by the ensiled material; the effect can be related in greater part to depression in voluntary intake of the ensiled material and to reduced efficiency of its utilization. Both these effects can be corrected by addition of either molasses or maize. Rate of gain on ensiled derinded cane plus energy supplement was comparable with that on fresh unsupplemented material. Nevertheless, both gain and intake remained below the levels reached when these energy supplements were added to fresh derinded cane.

Input–output data for a feedlot using derinded sugar cane: Available data are summarized in Table 9.12o. Caution must be used in interpreting this information, since only limited numbers of animals were involved, and the same group did not

TABLE 9.12L EFFECT OF ADDED (1% OF LW) MAIZE OR FINAL MOLASSES ON PERFORMANCE OF HOLSTEIN STEERS FATTENED ON A BASAL DIET OF DERINDED SUGAR CANE (FROM JAMES, 1973)

		Improvement over control, %	
	Control[1]	Molasses	Maize
Initial wt, kg			
Trial 1	308		
Trial 2	322		
Trial 3	380		
Final wt, kg			
Trial 1	459		
Trial 2	407		
Trial 3	426		
Mean daily gain, kg			
Trial 1	0.99	9	27
Trial 2	0.95	13	24
Trial 3	1.02	3	32
DM intake, % live wt			
Trial 1	2.40	29	17
Trial 2	2.47	14	11
Trial 3	2.47	7	4
Feed conversion, kg DM/kg gain			
Trial 1	9.1	−16	8
Trial 2	10.1	0.0	11
Trial 3	9.9	−15	15

[1] Control diet was (% DM basis): derinded cane stalk 52, cane tops 28, protein/min/vit. supplement 20.

TABLE 9.12M EFFECT OF THE TYPE OF PROTEIN SUPPLEMENT ON THE PERFORMANCE OF HOLSTEIN STEERS FED A BASAL DIET OF DERINDED SUGAR CANE (FROM JAMES, 1973)[1]

	Fish meal	Fish meal/ rapeseed	Rapeseed
Live weight, kg			
Initial	146	148	147
Final	303	308	309
Daily gain	0.90	0.91	0.91
Feed conversion, DM intake/gain	8.3	8.5	8.7

[1] The diets were (DM basis, %): 60 derinded cane plus tops, 12 protein supplement, and 27 maize grain or molasses, for the fish meal diet; and 54 derinded cane plus tops, 19 protein supplement, and 27 maize or molasses for rapeseed meal; the mixed protein diet was intermediate in proportions of the two protein sources.

continue throughout the full feeding period. The overall level of performance is similar to that recorded on molasses-based rations. It should be remembered that the breed used was Canadian Holstein; limited observations on Zebu steers (James, 1973) indicated that average gains on similar rations were some 18% poorer than for the Holstein.

TABLE 9.12N EFFECT OF ENSILING DERINDED WHOLE SUGAR CANE ON PERFORMANCE OF HOLSTEIN STEERS (FROM JAMES, 1973)

	Derinded whole sugar cane					
	No supp.	Molasses	Maize	No supp.	Molasses	Maize
	Fresh			Ensiled		
Number of steers	8	8	8	8	7	8
Number of days	95	95	95	42	95	95
Live weight, kg						
Initial	322	310	336	290	325	325
Final	407	405	440	304	408	415
Daily gain	0.89	1.00	1.09	0.31	0.87	0.94
Feed intake, kg DM/day						
Derinded whole cane	7.45	5.86	5.31	4.45	4.45	3.22
Protein supplement	1.54	1.54	1.59	1.45	1.54	1.54
Energy supplement	—	2.81	3.09	—	2.86	3.04
Conversion, kg DM/kg gain	10.1	10.1	9.1	18.8	10.1	8.2

TABLE 9.12O INPUT–OUTPUT DATA FOR FATTENING HOLSTEIN STEERS GIVEN DIETS BASED ON DERINDED WHOLE SUGAR CANE[1]

Days in feedlot	446		
Live weight, kg			
Initial	102		
Final	459		
Daily gain	0.80		
Feed intake, kg		As fed	Dry matter
Derinded cane stalk		5620	1713
Cane tops		2300	854
Protein supplement		676	598
Total			3165
Conversion rate, kg DM/kg gain			8.87

[1] These relationships are calculated from data in Tables 9.12k and 9.12l. The information relates to 13 animals over the first part of the growth curve, to 271 kg; and only 6 animals from 308 to 459 kg. Performance from 271 to 308 kg was assumed to be at the average rate for the range 308 to 459 kg.

9.3.4 Fat

It is common practice in the larger US feedlots to include a certain amount of fat in the diet. One reason for doing this is to reduce dust problems associated with the inclusion of ground dry forages and to this end the fat is usually incorporated immediately prior to chopping and grinding. Of greater importance is its value as a concentrated source of energy.

Large quantities of fat came onto the market in the late 1950's as a result of the increased production of synthetic detergents, but it is still a relatively expensive resource. In underdeveloped countries fats tend to be in very short supply, and such as are available are used for direct human consumption.

The economics of including fat will clearly depend upon the relationships between its price, the price of the basic energy ingredient it is replacing, and the degree of response that can be expected from its incorporation. Table 9.13 summarizes the results of over 20 experiments in which dietary fat additions varying from 2–10% were studied. There are only three reports of depressed performance as a result of including fat and, of these, the poor results noted by Dyer *et al.* (1957) can be safely ignored on the grounds that only three animals per treatment were used and one on the fat treatment died. It is clear that an improvement of about 9% can be expected in gain and feed conversion from adding 4–5% of fat to an all-concentrate or a high energy diet.

The report of Bradley *et al.* (1966b) of a 7% reduction through including 5% of tallow was not a valid comparison of the use of fat, in that the diets were made isocaloric by including greater quantities of roughage in the fat diet. Thus it cannot be ascertained whether the depression was due to the inclusion of roughage (with possible effects on VFA ratios) or the effects of the fat *per se*. In the main, the addition of fat appears to have little or no effect on voluntary feed intake.

Although animal tallow has been the choice in most experiments, results seem to be equally good with the use of vegetable oils. Incorporating a whole oil seed, such as cottonseed, seems to have been particularly beneficial (e.g. Durham *et al.*, 1964; McGinty *et al.*, 1966a, b). Quite apart from the fact that it is more convenient to use natural oils rather than the hydrogenated product, the use of the latter is contraindicated in view of the findings of Ellis *et al.* (1962) that 5% hydrogenated cottonseed oil led to an undesirable flavour in the meat.

There is evidence (§ 9.5.2.3) that there are problems associated with the combined use of fat and urea. These reports all stem from the University of Kentucky, and although they have not yet been corroborated elsewhere this combination of ingredients should perhaps be avoided until further evidence becomes available.

Northern Ireland workers gave Friesian steers a high fat concentrate (20% expanded maize, 18.8% tallow and 1.2% soya lecithin plus skim-milk powder and fish meal) as a liquid suspension in an attempt to bypass the rumen. Fed with hay only (Forbes *et al.*, 1965, 1966) the results were poor (about 0.75 kg daily gain) and even when fed with *ad libitum* rolled barley performance was inferior (4% for gain and 6% for conversion) as compared with the standard all-concentrate diet based on rolled barley (Forbes *et al.*, 1966).

9.4 GRAIN PROCESSING

9.4.1 Introduction

Reference has already been made to grain processing (§ 9.3.1) and the effect this has in maintaining the roughage characteristics of the grain husk. Processing also has a more positive role in that it can be used to improve nutritive value.

TABLE 9.13 EFFECT OF DIETARY FAT ON GROWTH AND FEED CONVERSION IN FATTENING CATTLE

Proportion of concentrates in the diet (%)	Level of fat[a] (%)	Feed intake		Daily gain		Feed conversion		Authors
		Control (kg/day)	Change with fat (%)	Control (kg)	Change with fat (%)	Control	Improvement with fat (%)	
80	7	7.0	−1	0.79	−10	8.90	−10	Dyer *et al.*, 1957
100	5[b]	7.8	−10	0.93	−19	8.7	−8	Putnam *et al.*, 1967b
100	2	7.3	0	1.18	−6	6.18	−6	Wise *et al.*, 1963
81	2	9.7	−2	1.24	−4	7.92	−1	Taylor *et al.*, 1964
70	4	7.6	0	1.07	0	8.16	0	Esplin *et al.*, 1963
100	2.3[c]	—	—	—	—	7.15	5	Durham *et al.*, 1964
80	4	10.3	1	1.39	9	7.42	7	Taylor *et al.*, 1964
90	5	9.2	−2	1.01	6	9.15	7	Robets & Mckirdy, 1964
55	4	8.1	−15	1.20	10	9.71	8	Hubbert *et al.*, 1961
55	4[d]	8.1	−15	1.20	8	9.71	8	Hubbert *et al.*, 1961
81	4	9.7	1	1.24	8	7.92	8	Taylor *et al.*, 1964
80	5[e]	—	less	—	less	—	9	Ellis *et al.*, 1962
90	5[f]	9.2	0	1.01	10	9.15	9	Roberts & Mckirdy, 1964
80	4[g]	9.8	0	1.12	9	8.70	9	Taylor *et al.*, 1964
55	4	—	less	—	0	10.34	10	Hubbert *et al.*, 1961
100	7.25	6.5	−1	0.88	12	7.44	11	Gordon & Erwin, 1960
90	5[h]	9.2	7	1.01	19	9.15	11	Roberts & Mckirdy, 1964
80	4	9.8	−1	1.12	11	8.70	11	Taylor *et al.*, 1964
100	3.5[c]	8.5	1	1.14	14	7.43	11	McGinty *et al.*, 1966a
80	4	9.6	0	1.19	14	8.12	13	Taylor *et al.*, 1964
100	2.3[c]	9.9	−4	1.31	15	7.55	15	McGinty *et al.*, 1966b
80	7	5.3	−11	0.61	21	8.60	16	Dyer *et al.*, 1957
50	10	10.8	−5	0.91	13	11.80	17	Bohman *et al.*, 1957
70	7.25	6.9	5	0.74	28	9.31	18	Gordon & Erwin, 1960
50	5	10.8	−2	0.91	28	11.80	24	Bohman *et al.*, 1957

[a] Animal tallow unless stated otherwise.
[b] Soybean oil.
[c] Cottonseed oil.
[d] Plus 1% dicalcium phosphate.
[e] Mean for diets containing 5% of either yellow grease, hydrogenated cottonseed oil or crude cottonseed oil.
[f] Rape oil.
[g] Hydrolysed animal and vegetable fat.
[h] Sunflower oil.

9.4.2 Grinding and rolling

Some data relating to these two methods of processing are set out in Table 9.14. It must be stressed that the results relate to trials in which additional roughage was fed even though the diets were of high energy. The results have no application to situations in which cereals are fed with protein supplement as the sole component of the diet. Under these conditions the effect of grinding or rolling is quite marked as has been discussed in § 9.2.2.

TABLE 9.14 EFFECT OF VARIOUS PROCESSING METHODS COMPARED WITH COARSE GRINDING UPON GROWTH AND FEED CONVERSION OF FATTENING CATTLE

Cereal and treatment used for comparison	Daily gain		Feed conversion		Authors
	Coarse grinding (kg)	Change due to treatment (%)	Coarse grinding (feed/gain)	Improvement due to treatment (%)	
Barley/sorghum					
Fine-ground	1.44	−13	6.97	−5	Ralston *et al.*, 1963
Steam-rolled	1.10	−11	7.70	−1	Garrett, 1965a
Steam-rolled	1.16	3	6.50	0	Garrett, 1965a
Maize					
Cracked	1.50	−9	8.30	−8	Hentges *et al.*, 1961
Cracked	1.51	1	6.51	−3	Hentges *et al.*, 1962
Sorghum					
Cracked	1.06[a]	−21	9.01[a]	−31	Hale, 1965
Rolled	1.24	11	8.80	−3	Phar, 1968
Fine-ground	1.15[b]	8[b]	9.45[b]	−3[b]	Hale, 1965
Rolled	1.20[a]	13	7.96[a]	3	Hale, 1965
Rolled	0.98	2	9.17	3	Hale, 1965
Fine-ground	0.98	6	9.17	7	Hale, 1965
Fine-ground	1.14	4	9.52	8	Hale, 1965
Fine-ground	1.11	3	7.92	8	Matsushima, 1968b

[a] Fine-ground. [b] Steam-treated.

The general implication from the limited information available is that procedures which tend to give a finer particle size result in better performance, particularly with respect to feed efficiency on maize and sorghum. This opinion is supported by the findings of Pope *et al.* (1959a, b). However, despite the tendency for better feed efficiency with fine grinding, this technique is not widely used under commercial feedlot conditions. Hubbert *et al.* (1962b) have shown that feed consumption is often reduced if the particle size is too small and, in high concentrate diets, there is the added problem of digestive upsets and bloat known to be associated with a lack of coarse material. On the other hand, Hinds *et al.* (1956) found that if ear maize was too coarsely ground, animals tended to select against the cob fraction. With barley there is no evidence of any significant differences between grinding and steam rolling (Thomas and Myers, 1961; Ralston *et al.*, 1963). In a mixed diet containing 61% barley and 22% alfalfa plus protein supplement, Putnam and Davis (1964) found that when the hay was finely ground (0.38 cm screen) gains were better on rolled barley, but when the hay was coarsely ground (3.8 cm) gains were better with ground barley. Earlier, Cox and Smith (1952) and Smith and Parrish (1953) found no difference between rolling or grinding of sorghum grain when long roughage was also given.

9.4.3 Pelleting

The effect of pelleting on high concentrate diets is complicated in that the nature of the response depends partly on the amount of roughage in the diet and whether pelleting is of the complete diet or only of the concentrate or roughage portions. Table 9.15 relates to the effect of pelleting complete diets with different concentrate roughage ratios. With regard to live weight gain the evidence is quite conclusive. In high concentrate diets (i.e. less than 30% roughage), pellets are the same or inferior to meal and as the proportion of concentrate decreases pellets become increasingly superior to a diet prepared in meal form. With respect to feed conversion, pelleting is invariably superior to the use of meal, this advantage increasing steadily as the proportion of roughage in the diet increases.

TABLE 9.15 EFFECT OF PELLETING COMPLETE DIETS WITH DIFFERENT CONCENTRATE/ROUGHAGE RATIOS

Concentrate	Roughage	Daily gain (kg)		Feed conversion		Authors
		Meal	Pellets	Meal	Pellets	
Snapped maize	Grass hay					
70	30	1.35	1.18	8.9	8.5	Beardsley *et al.*, 1959
55	45	1.23	1.22	10.1	9.1	Beardsley *et al.*, 1959
40	60	1.12	1.27	10.6	9.3	Beardsley *et al.*, 1959
Sorghum	Alfalfa + CSH					
80	20	1.01	0.87	8.5	8.4	McCroskey *et al.*, 1961
80	20	1.09	1.11	10.6	9.4	McCroskey *et al.*, 1961
20	80	0.84	1.04	10.7	9.9	McCroskey *et al.*, 1961
20	80	0.86	1.14	14.2	13.9	Williamson *et al.*, 1961
Whole barley		1.12	1.15	8.17	7.43	Williamson *et al.*, 1961

CSH = cottonseed hulls.

There is little information on the effect of pellet size other than the work of Garrett *et al.* (1961). They used 40:60 or 50:50 concentrate/roughage ratios and found that a 0.63 cm pellet gave better gains and feed conversion than 0.25 cm. Split wafers (10 cm) tended to give gains equal to, or better than, the smaller pellets but feed conversion was poorer.

Table 9.16 shows the effect of pelleting either the concentrate or roughage components of the diet. With a 70:30 ratio, performance was poorest when both components were pelleted; the effect was slightly less pronounced when the ratio was 65:35. Clanton *et al.* (1959) also found that gains and feed efficiency were poorest when a 70:30 diet had the forage pelleted and the concentrate in ground form. There appears to be no consistent effect of pelleting the concentrate portion when it is given

TABLE 9.16 EFFECT OF PELLETING (P) OR GRINDING (G) THE CONCENTRATE OR ROUGHAGE PORTION OF THE DIET

Roughage:	Long/chopped		Ground		Pelleted		Authors
Concentrate:	G	P	G	P	G	P	
Concentrate/ roughage	Daily live weight gain (kg)						
65:35	0.83	0.88			0.95	0.87	Kolari *et al.*, 1961
65:35	0.83	0.94			0.90	0.83	
70:30	1.10		1.15			0.99	Cullison, 1961
70:30	0.95		0.92			0.74	
70:30			1.03[a]			1.02[a]	
70:30	1.36	1.18	1.35	1.29			Clanton & Woods, 1966
65:35			1.06	0.94	1.04	0.85	
	Feed conversion (kg feed/kg gain)						
65:35	11.1	10.2			10.1	10.1	Kolari *et al.*, 1961
65:35	8.70	8.30			8.40	9.10	
70:30	8.18		7.76			7.75	Cullison, 1961
70:30	8.16		7.62			8.26	
			8.25[a]			8.25[a]	
70:30	7.69	7.79	7.63	7.54			Clanton & Woods, 1966
65:35			8.10	8.60	8.40	9.20	

[a] Plus long straw.

in conjunction with long roughage. The pelleting of sorghum, or of wheat, in comparison to dry rolling, was found by Anon. (1962b) and Bris *et al.* (1966) to give better efficiency provided roughage was also fed. There is evidence (Preston, 1962b) that for whole barley without supplemental roughage, pellet size is critical: diameters of 0.60 to 1.00 cm were generally found to be superior since at smaller diameters the roughage of the barley husk was destroyed completely, while with larger pellets there was insufficient breakdown to give maximum digestibility.

The relationship between pelleting and parakeratosis of the rumen is described in § 11.3.5.

9.4.4 Heat treatment

The increasingly competitive nature of the cattle fattening operations in the US has stimulated interest in methods whereby the utilization of the concentrate part of the diet (which frequently accounts for some 90% of the total energy) might be increased. Another factor has been the greater availability of sorghum grain and the realization that, with conventional methods of processing (i.e. dry rolling or coarse grinding), this grain tended to support poorer performance than barley, despite the fact that proximate analysis indicated both to have the same potential nutritive value (Hale *et al.*, 1962). There are suggestions that very fine grinding of sorghum improves performance (Ralston *et al.*, 1963; Matsushima, 1968b), but in high concentrate diets this practice is undesirable since loss of the roughage-like properties of the grain husk increases susceptibility to bloat and other digestive upsets.

TABLE 9.17 EFFECT OF STEAM PROCESSING OF CEREAL GRAINS ON GROWTH AND FEED CONVERSION IN FATTENING CATTLE

Cereal	Processing: Control	Processing: Treated	Daily gain: Control (kg)	Daily gain: Change due to treatment (%)	Feed conversion: Contol (feed/grain)	Feed conversion: Improvement due to treatment(%)	Authors
Barley	Dry-rolled	Flaked[a]	1.31	8	7.22	−1	Hale *et al.*, 1966
	Dry-rolled	Flaked[h]	1.43	8	6.82	6	Garrett *et al.*, 1966
Maize	Cracked	Cracked[b]	1.19	−5	8.06	−8	Matsushima, 1966
	Ground	Thick flakes[c]	1.20	3	6.88	3	Matsushima, 1967
	Rolled	Gelatinized	1.22	12	6.10	3	Perry & Mudd, 1967
	Ground	Flaked[e]	1.07	4	8.24	3	Thompson *et al.*, 1965
	Cracked	Flaked[b]	1.19	−3	8.06	4	Matsushima, 1966
	Rolled	Flaked[h]	1.38	11	6.70	6	Garrett *et al.*, 1966
	Cracked	Flaked[b]	1.25	0	8.04	6	Matsushima & Stenquist, 1967
	Rolled	Flaked[c]	1.12	0	9.02	6	Matsushima, 1968b
	Ground	Flaked[c]	1.50	0	8.30	10	Hentges *et al.*, 1961
	Cracked	Flaked[c]	0.96	2	8.40	10	Erwin, 1967
	Ground	Flaked[c]	1.51	8	6.51	11	Hentges *et al.*, 1962
	Ground	Thin flakes[c]	1.20	7	6.88	11	Matsushima, 1967
	Ground	Flaked[c]	0.93	25	3.99	17	Ensor *et al.*, 1959
	Ground	Crumbed[d]	0.78	5	9.01	17	Newland *et al.*, 1962
Sorghum	Ground	25% gelatinized[e]	1.28	−4	8.87	−7	Drake *et al.*, 1967
	Ground	50% gelatinized[e]	1.28	−2	8.87	−1	Drake *et al.*, 1967
	Ground	Gelatinized ground	1.14	−10	6.69	−1	Hale, 1967
	Ground	75% gelatinized[e]	1.28	−4	8.87	3	Drake *et al.*, 1967
	Ground	Flaked[a]	1.11	7	7.92	4	Totusek *et al.*, 1967
	Rolled	Flaked[a]	1.28	10	8.00	5	Hale, 1967
	Rolled	Flaked[a]	1.28	11	8.30	5	Hale *et al.*, 1966
	Rolled	Flaked[a]	1.32	5	7.51	6	Hale *et al.*, 1966
	Ground	Rolled[f]	1.11	−1	7.92	7	Totusek *et al.*, 1967
	Rolled	Flaked[h]	1.41	14	6.71	10	Garrett *et al.*, 1966
	Cracked	50% popped[c]	1.22	−4	6.80	12	Ellis & Carpenter, 1966
Sorghum/barley	Rolled	Flaked	1.17	0	7.90	−6	Riley *et al.*, 1965

[a] Low pressure steam 99°C for 25 min.
[b] 94°C for 12 min.
[c] Steam cooked (no details).
[d] 121°C for 30 min, flaked, pelleted then rolled into crumbles.
[e] 149°C extruded.
[f] Reconstituted and ensiled, then steamed at atmospheric pressure for 10 min before rolling.
[g] 1.2 kg/cm² for 30 min.
[h] 1.4 kg/cm² for 1.5 min.

Workers at the University of Arizona (see Hale, 1967) have been at the forefront in developing processing methods involving moist heat treatment of grains, particularly sorghum, with a view to improving their nutritive value and thus increasing animal response. The two most successful methods have been that developed by Hale and his colleagues and the pressure cooking technique designed by commercial companies and described by Erwin (1967). Hale's procedure involves subjecting the grain to low pressure, high moisture steam for 20–30 min until the temperature reaches about 95–98°C. The grain, which should then have about 16% moisture in the case of sorghum (15% for barley), is rolled flat with a 0.05 cm tolerance between the rollers. The resultant flake should have a density approximately half that of the original untreated grain (Husted *et al.*, 1966). Steaming at these low pressures for only 3–5 min does not induce a sufficiently high temperature (rarely above 80°C) and has no beneficial effect compared with dry rolling (Hale, 1965).

The commercially designed method employs a continuous pressure cooker in which the grain is subjected to moist steam at a pressure of some 3.5 kg/cm^2 for approximately one minute (3.5 ± 0.7 kg/cm$_2$ and 1.5 ± 0.5 min); the heated grain is then flaked, while still hot, at a temperature of approximately 95–100°C. Although the technique was developed specifically for sorghum, it has also been applied to other cereals. In the pressure-cooking system, as one might expect, timing is critical, for if the grain is overcooked to the point of gelatinization, performance can be startlingly reduced.

Results of the heat treatment of different grains are set out in Table 9.17. Although there is no consistent effect on rate of live weight gain, there is a pronounced improvement in feed conversion. It is by no means established that this process has any positive effect on the nutritive value of barley and the advantages appear to be confined to maize and sorghum, with an apparently slightly greater effect in the former. Results are somewhat confounded in that, in most of the quoted experiments with maize, the processing was pressure cooking, while the majority of reports on sorghum were obtained with the low pressure steam system. Erwin (1967) claimed that under feedlot conditions pressure cooking of sorghum gave from 5 to 7% better response than steaming at atmospheric pressure for 15 min. In support of this he presented data on some 159,000 cattle from a large commercial feedlot. This unit began to use pressure cooking in August 1965, but, during a period of 3 months, when the cooker was being overhauled, reverted to steam rolling. Data collected prior to and after the period when steam rolling was used showed an 11% improvement in feed conversion through pressure cooking (see Table 9.18).

TABLE 9.18 EFFECT OF STEAM-PROCESSING THE GRAIN ON FEED CONVERSION IN A COMMERCIAL FEEDLOT IN ARIZONA (FROM ERWIN, 1967)

Diet	Period	No. of cattle	Feed Conversion
Steam-rolled barley/sorghum	Jan.–Dec. 1962	70,995	8.64
Pressure-processed sorghum	Aug. 1965–Feb. 1966	35,967	7.49
Steam-rolled sorghum	Feb.–April 1966	34,500	8.38
Pressure-processed sorghum	May–July 1966	17,811	7.42

Improvement due to pressure-processing of sorghum = 11.0%

TABLE 9.19 EFFECT OF PRESSURE-COOKING GRAINS ON GROWTH AND FEED CONVERSION IN FATTENING STEERS[a] (FROM GARRETT *et al.*, CITED BY MATSUSHIMA, 1966)

	Dry-rolled	Processing method		
		8 min 0 kg/cm²	1.5 min 1.4 kg/cm²	1.5 min 4.2 kg/cm²
Daily gain (kg)				
Barley	1.43	1.36	1.54	1.42
Maize	1.37	1.50	1.52	1.42
Sorghum	1.41	1.41	1.60	1.36
Feed intake (kg DM)				
Barley	9.30	9.25	9.35	9.10
Maize	9.15	9.85	9.50	9.00
Sorghum	9.42	10.00	9.65	8.70
Feed conversion (kg DM/kg gain)				
Barley	6.52	6.82	6.11	6.52
Maize	6.70	6.54	6.33	6.29
Sorghum	6.71	7.12	6.04	6.41

[a] 9 steers per treatment group.

The effect of over-cooking sorghum is clearly seen in the data in Table 9.19, and similar deleterious effects from the gelatinization of maize have been reported by DeBie and Woods (1964), Drake *et al.* (1967) and Woods and Wilson (1967).

Popped or exploded sorghum is produced by high pressure cooking followed by sudden reduction to atmospheric pressure which leads to rapid expansion of the grain. According to Durham *et al.* (1967a) and Algeo *et al.* (1968), this process is as good as, or better than, steam processing and flaking.

9.4.5 Ensiling of high moisture grain

The ensiling of high moisture grain developed as an agronomic technique with the objective of reducing field losses. The procedure has particular application in tropical countries where insect damage is considerable in the later stages of ripening (ICA, 1967). As such early harvested grain can have a moisture content of up to 36% it is not economic to dry it artificially to the 14% moisture content required for safe aerobic storage. It is now established that such grain can be stored in sealed silos, or even in pits lined with polythene. A slight fermentation takes place, but overall losses are negligible provided the grain is maintained under anaerobic conditions.

The technique was first used with ear maize in 1958 but did not become popular until the mid-1960's when a large number of reports were published on a variety of cereals. Results of some experiments are set out in Table 9.20.

The technique of reconstituting dry grain to about 30% moisture (by adding water then ensiling for a period of 2 weeks or more) came about when it was found that the feeding value of high moisture grain tended to be higher than that of dry grain. The ensiling of grain thus became a processing technique in its own right as distinct to the original purpose which was to simplify harvesting.

TABLE 9.20 ENSILED HIGH MOISTURE GRAIN VERSUS DRY GRAIN ON GROWTH AND FEED CONVERSION IN FATTENING CATTLE

Grain and processing used before feeding	Processing used before ensiling	Daily gain		Feed conversion		Authors
		Control (kg)	Change due to treatment (%)	Control	Improvement due to treatment (%)	
Barley						
Rolled	EH/W	1.09	8	8.17	3	Frederick *et al.*, 1962
Rolled	EH/W	0.96	14	8.13	4	Frederick *et al.*, 1962
Rolled	EH/W	0.93	5	7.25	4	Dinusson *et al.*, 1964
Rolled	EH/W	1.11	−2	7.35	11	Dinusson *et al.*, 1964
Ear maize						
Ground	EH/G	0.99	−2	9.27	7	Beeson & Perry, 1958
Ground	EH/G	1.06	8	11.3	13	Beeson & Perry, 1958
Maize						
Ground	EH/W	0.86	−20	10.5	−13	Heuberger *et al.*, 1959
Ground	R/W	1.25	−6	8.04	−1	Matsushima & Stenquist, 1967
Ground	EH/G	1.13	−7	8.84	0	Matsushima, 1968a
Ground	EH/W	0.86	0	10.5	1	Heuberger *et al.*, 1959
Ground	EH/W	0.86	1	10.5	1	Heuberger *et al.*, 1959
Ground	EH/G	1.25	−6	8.04	2	Matsushima & Stenquist, 1967
Rolled	R/–	1.26	6	7.94	3	Larson *et al.*, 1966
Rolled	EH/W	1.12	−5	9.02	6	Matsushima, 1968a
Rolled	EH/–	1.25	−5	8.04	6	Matsushima & Stenquist, 1967
Rolled	EH/G	1.13	17	10.6	12	Baker, 1967b

Sorghum						
Ground	R/G	1.20	−6	7.62	−7	McGinty *et al.*, 1968
Ground	R/G	1.27	−6	6.57	−5	McGinty, *et al.*, 1968
	EH/–	1.03	2	8.10	0	Parrett *et al.*, 1966
Ground	R/W	1.20	2	7.62	2	McGinty *et al.*, 1968
Rolled	R/W	1.11	0	7.92	5	Totusek *et al.*, 1967
Ground	EH/–	1.24	2	8.80	6	Phar, 1968
	EH/–	0.73	3	10.8	9	Riggs, 1965
	EH/–	0.98	−3	9.15	9	Riggs, 1965
	R/–	1.10	1	4.40	9	Totusek, *et al.* 1967
	EH/W	1.47	−5	9.15	10	Phar, 1968
Ground	EH/–	1.24	2	8.80	10	Phar, 1968
Ground	R/W	1.27	0	6.57	11	McGinty *et al.*, 1968
	EH/–	1.19	3	11.3	12	Brethour, 1961
	EH/–	1.08	2	13.3	13	Riggs, 1965
Ground	EH/G	1.47	−6	9.15	14	Phar, 1968
	R/–	1.03	8	8.10	15	Parrett *et al.*, 1966
	EH/–	0.89	−1	11.7	15	Riggs, 1965
	EH/–	0.80	5	11.7	15	Ripp, 1959
Ground	R/G	1.03	0	2.77	17	McGinty & Riggs, 1967
Ground	EH/G	0.93	2	2.47	18	McGinty & Riggs, 1967
Ground	R/W	1.00	23	6.79	24	McGinty *et al.*, 1968

EH = Early-harvested, high moisture.
R = Reconstituted by adding water to dry grain.
W = Ensiled whole.
G = Ensiled ground.

As with other methods of processing there is little consistent response in live weight gain. On the other hand, response in feed conversion, particularly with barley and sorghum, appears to be better than with any other processing technique currently available. Thus for sorghum the *median* value is equivalent to an 11% improvement in comparison with approximately 6–7% for moist heat treatment techniques. With barley there is no evidence that other techniques give any response.

Although Parrett and Riggs (1967) claimed fractionally better gains on 15% less DM intake with reconstituted sorghum as opposed to high moisture sorghum, the balance of the evidence indicates that there is no difference between the two methods. Of greater importance appears to be whether or not the grain is ensiled whole or ground. Phar (1968) found that grinding before ensiling, in comparison with ensiling whole grain and grinding prior to feeding, improved gain by 15% and feed conversion by 11%. In a second trial there was virtually no effect on gain but feed efficiency was some 5% better. Brethour and Duitsman (1962) considered that for gain there was little difference between grinding prior to ensiling and rolled dry grain, but that feed efficiency was better on the former. Grain ensiled whole was less palatable and produced inferior gains and feed conversions than grain ensiled after grinding. Riggs (1965) compared ensiled sorghum fed whole or ground and found the latter gave 30% better gains and 31% better feed conversion. He also studied the effect of ensiling the whole head (37% moisture; approximately 70% grain) and found that conversion was better than with dry ground grain. That ensiling *per se* is an essential component of this procedure is demonstrated by the results of Matsushima (1968a). He compared dry maize and maize reconstituted to 30% moisture at the time of feeding and found slightly poorer gains and conversion on the reconstituted, non-ensiled grain.

It is commonly believed that digestive upsets are less on all-concentrate diets based on high moisture grain than on dry grain. This is supported by the findings of Heuberger *et al.* (1959) that cattle started on feed more quickly and with fewer problems when high-moisture grain rather than dry grain was used.

Some disadvantages exist with high moisture or reconstituted ensiled grains. Fermentation begins immediately on exposure to the air so that diets based on high moisture grain are less suitable for giving in self-feeding hoppers. There are also dangers of moulds developing which may lead to feed refusals and digestive upsets. There are fewer difficulties when feeding is several times a day in open troughs as is practised in US feedlots. A problem we experienced in Cuba with high moisture sorghum (to which the only balancer had been urea, minerals and vitamins) was a rapid release of ammonia leading to reduced feed intakes and poorer performance. This is likely to be less serious when the urea is incorporated into a pelleted supplement along with other materials such as alfalfa meal or some ground cereal or protein.

A technique which promises to overcome most of these difficulties is the mixing of propionic acid into the high moisture grain immediately after it has been harvested. This technique was developed by BP Chemicals (UK) Ltd. and consists of adding the acid at a level of approximately 1% of the wet grain. Subsequent storage can be aerobic without danger of mould formation or fermentation, thus the investment of sealed storage is avoided. In one trial with 36 steers given an all-concentrate diet based on high moisture barley, daily gains were 1.20 and 1.18 and conversions 4.70 and 4.86 (DM basis) for propionic acid-treated and ensiled grain respectively (Walker, 1968).

A further factor affecting the use of high moisture grain is that it is only economical within a restricted distance of where it is grown, since transport charges and the risk of fermentation prohibit moving it long distances. For this reason, together with the fact that the investment in capital equipment is very much less than for a pressure cooker, the technique is most applicable to smaller fattening units situated in close proximity to the grain growing areas. In feedlots of 20,000 head or more, pressure cooking has so far been the method of choice; however, reconstitution of dry grain and ensiling it for a short period would appear to give as good and perhaps better results than steam cooking, and, as it employs dry grain, should be equally applicable to the needs of the large-scale feedlot operator.

9.5 PROTEIN

9.5.1 Protein level

The feedlot operator can estimate the genetic potential of his animals for growth and feed conversion from a knowledge of their breed, sex, size, previous history and whether or not they are, or are to be, implanted with synthetic hormones. Provided feeding is *ad libitum*, the evidence so far presented indicates that the use of any of the common cereal grains, either in all-concentrate diets or with a maximum of 10–15% added roughage, will permit realization of the animals' potential for growth. The determining factor with respect to choice of cereal-method of processing and whether or not to include roughage will be the cost of the diet in relation to expected feed conversion ratio.

Although energy is the major feature of a fattening diet, other ingredients essential to the normal functioning of the animal must be considered. All these latter components (protein, minerals, vitamins, etc.) are more expensive per unit of weight than the basic energy source. Moreover most of them act directly upon rate of live weight gain and only indirectly upon feed conversion, hence the objective must be to give the minimum amounts compatible with the achievement of the required rate of growth while maintaining the health of the animal. There may be situations in which maximum growth rate does not equate with maximum profitability. This would arise when the savings in feed cost, brought about by giving less than the optimum amount of protein (or other nutrient), more than offset the effect of reduction in rate of gain.

Of the nutrients needed in addition to energy, the contribution made by protein is greatest in both dietary and economic terms. Given a specific diet and animals of known potential the feedlot operator needs to ascertain (a) the minimum level of protein consistent with normal growth and health; (b) the amount of protein needed to maximize gain; and (c) the effect on gain of varying the protein between these lower and upper limits. This kind of information is not yet available in comprehensive form in the literature. The standard texts on protein requirements of ruminants are those developed by the National Research Council of the US (NRC, 1963) and the Agricultural Research Council of the UK (ARC, 1965). These latter are based on the use of a factorial method which is claimed to estimate the minimum protein requirements for any specific live weight and rate of growth. The NRC standards, on the other hand, are more empirical, being based on the results of feeding trials in which the amounts of protein fed were equated with the growth responses obtained. Although both these standards set out to describe minimum protein requirements, there is wide divergence between them to the extent that at a weight of 400 kg the factorial estimate is only some 50% of that advocated by the NRC.

In discussing these differences the ARC report does mention the practical estimates based on the data of Preston (1963c) and Richter (1963). These latter values agree well with each other and are only slightly higher than NRC figures although they were specifically designed for conditions of all-concentrate feeding of dairy beef cattle exceeding 1 kg/day in gain. With respect to the discrepancies between the practical and factorial estimates the ARC (1965) claims that they "... may be more apparent than real and could arise from the circumstance that with the feeding stuffs more usually available in temperate climates it may be desirable to supply more than the minimum level of protein in daily rations ...". In support of this statement the report quotes the work of Elliott and Topps (1963a, b) and Elliott *et al.* (1964) which are referred to as "recent practical trials under tropical conditions", and which are interpretated as suggesting that the current practical standards of protein requirements for growing cattle are much too high. It should be pointed out that the first two of these papers referred to nitrogen balance trials involving 1- to 3-year-old animals and set out to determine maintenance requirements. The work of Elliott *et al.* (1964) was with 2-year-old steers which, during the experiment, had live weight gains ranging from −0.14 kg to 0.42 kg/day. Under no circumstances can these papers be considered as having application to the practical feeding of fattening cattle in the tropics or elsewhere. That the ARC report is seeking to defend the indefensible is borne out by a study of literature relating specifically to the effect of protein levels on fattening cattle fed according to intensive methods (Table 9.21).

The most common methods for describing protein requirements make use of the term "percentage protein in the DM of the diet" or some similar measure of protein/energy ratio. This is clearly an over simplification. Much of the current difficulties have arisen since the advent of high energy and all-concentrate feeding. In traditional high roughage diets, increasing the ME concentration by adding concentrates generally leads to an increase in voluntary DM intake. In contrast, with high energy diets using little or no roughage, voluntary DM tends to be inversely related to the ME concentration. The same is true when comparing ground or rolled maize or sorghum with the same grains steam-processed or ensiled at high moisture content; intakes of DM are almost always less on the latter treatments. Thus, increasing the ME concentration in high roughage diets gives rise to higher rates of gain while the associated increase in DM intake means that at any fixed protein:energy ratio more protein is consumed. At the other end of the scale, increasing the ME concentration of a high energy diet, without altering the protein/energy ratio, can lead to a reduced protein intake. R. L. Preston (1966) considered that the three variables determining protein requirements were body weight, rate of live weight gain and the protein digestibility. We agree with this statement as it relates to a specific type of diet, however, in comparing diets with different energy sources and/or processed in different ways a further variable, namely voluntary intake (Mcal ME/kg live weight) must be added. The necessity for this is clearly demonstrated by comparing Figs. 9.3 and 9.4. In the former there is a positive relationship ($P < 0.01$) between live weight

TABLE 9.21 EFFECT OF PROTEIN LEVEL ON PERFORMANCE OF STEERS GIVEN HIGH-ENERGY DIETS

Mean live weight[a] (kg)	ME in DM (Mcal/kg)	ME intake/ live weight (kcal/kg)	Protein/energy ratio[b] diets (g/Mcal)				Diet	Daily gain improvement (%)			N × 6.25/ live weight[a] (g/kg)	Authors
			1	2	3	4	1 (kg)	2	3	4		
200	3.0	58–70	37	47	57		0.92	22*	17		3.25	Kay *et al.*, 1968
244	3.1	73	41	46			1.09	4*			3.22	Thrasher *et al.*, 1967
254		60–55	32	52			0.60	47*			2.86	Thompson *et al.*, 1962
259		42	41	67			0.57	16*			2.82	Thompson *et al.*, 1961
280		55–53	30	49			0.73	19*			2.60	Thompson *et al.*, 1961
300	3.0	60–66	37	47	57		1.20*	3	−5		2.16	Kay *et al.*, 1968
307[c]	3.0	60–75	30	38	44	44	0.64	39	47	50*	3.07	Preston *et al.*, 1967b
323	2.9	72	40	50			1.18*	−3			2.85	Morris *et al.*, 1967
326	2.8	67	47	56			1.05	16*			3.76	Morris *et al.*, 1967
328	2.9	75–82	42	50			1.13	10*			4.10	Morris *et al.*, 1967
330	2.6	62–64	40	49			0.84	11*			3.10	Zimmerman *et al.*, 1961b
332	2.9	65–66	40	49			0.84	13*			3.18	Zimmerman *et al.*, 1961b
347	3.3	58–59	37	47			1.05	6*			2.74	Haskins *et al.*, 1967
350	3.0	63–67	37	44	44		1.08	4*	5		2.74	McGinty *et al.*, 1966b
353	3.3	58–59	37	47			1.06	7*			2.77	Haskins *et al.*, 1967
359	2.8	70	32	41			1.21	9*			2.88	Blaylock *et al.*, 1965
362[d]	3.0	73	46	49	52	55	1.36	3*	4	3	3.66	Furr & Carpenter, 1967a
364	3.0	72–75	47	50	51		1.36*	0	−4		3.46	McGinty *et al.*, 1966a
366	3.4	74–75	36	63			1.15*	−4			2.42	Erwin *et al.*, 1963
367	3.0	69–72	41	71			1.16*	−4			2.58	Erwin *et al.*, 1963
378	2.8	64–65	44	56			1.14	9*			3.64	Hale *et al.*, 1964a
390[e]	3.0	65–66	41	52			1.26*	2			2.66	Woods *et al.*, 1961
396	2.8	65–67	44	56			1.36	6*			3.70	Hale *et al.*, 1964a
400[d]	2.6	88	43	55			1.46	6*			4.85	Hubbert *et al.*, 1961

[a] For selected diet*.
[b] N × 6.25/ME.
[c] Bulls.
[d] Estimated.
[e] Heifers.

gain Y in kg/day and the daily protein consumption X in g/kg live weight. The regression equation is:

$$Y = 0.2241\,X + 0.4351 \pm 0.062.$$

By contrast the relationship between daily gain Y and protein/energy ratio X (Fig. 9.4) is negative ($P < 0.10$) largely due to the confounding effect of voluntary feed intake.

The data used to prepare Figs. 9.3 and 9.4 and Table 9.21 are our calculations based on the original input/output information given by the various authors. In calculating the regressions, the data of Woods *et al.* (1961) were omitted on the grounds that these referred to heifers. Similarly, the results in the paper of Kay *et al.*

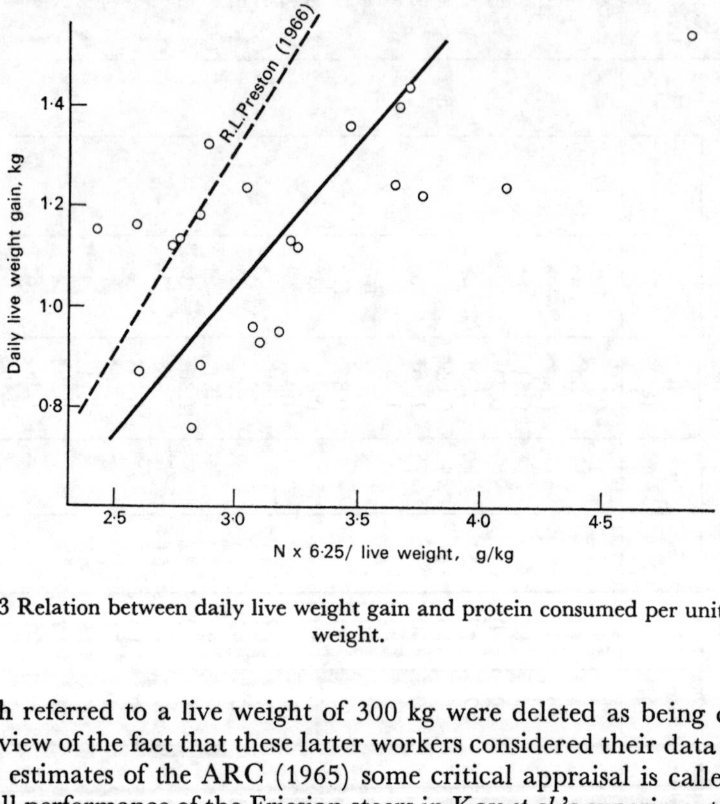

FIG. 9.3 Relation between daily live weight gain and protein consumed per unit live weight.

(1968) which referred to a live weight of 300 kg were deleted as being completely atypical. In view of the fact that these latter workers considered their data to support the factorial estimates of the ARC (1965) some critical appraisal is called for.

The overall performance of the Friesian steers in Kay *et al.*'s experiment (which on the best treatment averaged 1.11 kg/day) does not represent the genetic potential of this breed on this type of diet, since in field trials in the same area the average daily gain of over 500 Friesian steers given similar diets with 16% of protein in DM was 1.23 kg (Macdearmid, 1967). In the experiment reported by Kay *et al.* (1968), animals were tied individually—a system of management which is known to reduce performance (RRI, 1964). Furthermore, the experimental design was such that animals remained on the same protein level throughout the entire experimental period. Up to 250 kg live weight steers on the 11% protein level were deficient in protein and their growth was retarded. Winchester *et al.* (1957) have shown that animals given less than optimum amounts of protein subsequently exhibit compensatory growth when realimentated with an adequate diet. Although the diet used by Kay *et al.* in the second stage was the same as used previously, it is not unlikely that from 250 to 400 kg the animals previously on the deficient diet were exhibiting some compensatory growth.

Support for this is provided by the voluntary feed intakes which on the low protein diet remained constant relative to body weight in both growth periods, but which declined by 9% on the 14% protein diet after 250 kg. This latter effect is typical of intensive fattening from birth (Buysse *et al.*, 1966; Bowers, 1968; Willis and Preston, 1969a); while the former is an indication of compensatory growth (§ 9.12). The correct interpretation of the results of Kay *et al.* (1968) is not only that 11% was

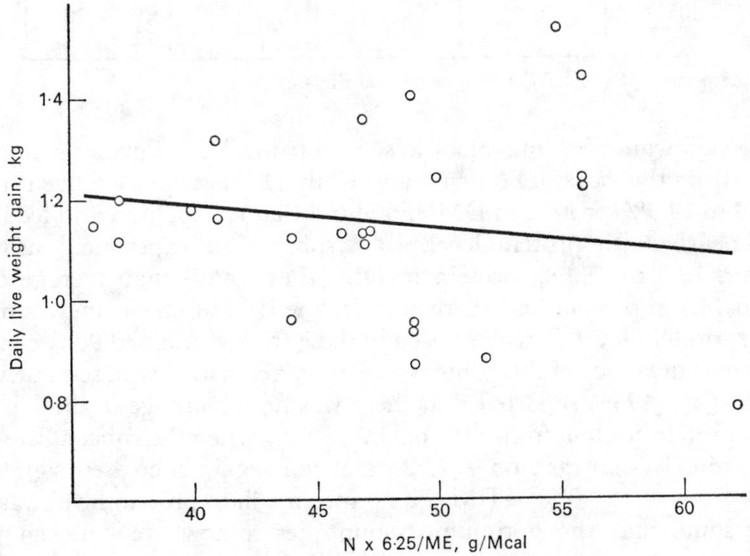

FIG. 9.4 Relation between daily live weight gain and protein/energy ratio.

inadequate up to 250 kg, but that subsequent to this weight the data on this treatment are unreliable. Thus from 250 kg one can only conclude that 17% was too high and the optimum level was 14% or less. The claim of Kay and his co-workers that above 250 kg their figures were in good agreement with the ARC (1965) factorial estimates is also without justification as a reappraisal of their data (Table 9.22) shows that the best agreement over the whole period is between the 14% level fed and the NRC (1963) recommendations. It is totally untenable to claim good agreement with ARC recommendations when at the highest live weight, even the low protein diet provided 20% more digestible crude protein than ARC (1965) actually recommended.

Our analysis (Fig. 9.3) of the valid experiments given in Table 9.21 is confounded, in part, by the range of body weights involved, nevertheless in the area of most concern to the feedlot operator, namely 0.90–1.25 kg/day gain and a live weight of around 300 kg, there is good agreement with values predicted from the regression of R. L. Preston (1966). In an all-concentrate diet the protein requirement according

TABLE 9.22 RE-EVALUATION OF THE DATA OF KAY *et al.* (1968) REGARDING ACTUAL PROTEIN FED AND RECOMMENDED ALLOWANCES

Mean live weight (kg)	Digestible crude protein fed (g/day)		Differences between amounts fed (=100) and accepted standards (%)			
			NRC (1963)		ARC (1965)	
	11%[a]	14%[a]	11%[a]	14%[a]	11%[a]	14%[a]
140	205	315	81	18	51	0
175	240	390	86	14	31	−14
225	300	500	75	5	13	−28
275	395	570	52	6	−7	−33
325	435	674	50	−5	−11	−40
375	505	700	37	−1	−20	−40

[a] Crude protein content (% DM) of experimental diets.

to our regression would be equivalent to some 14% in DM. Further support for this value comes from the work of Fontenot and Kelly (1963) who used five rations varying from 9.9 to 14.3% protein in DM and found that rate of gain and feed efficiency increased linearly with protein level. In a subsequent experiment using rations ranging from 10.9 to 19.0% protein in DM, they found that average daily gain increased to 14.7% protein and thereafter declined. Feed efficiency was maximized at the 14.7% protein level. The diets used in these trials contained 90% concentrates. Similar findings in favour of this protein level were reported by these same workers in 1967. Keith *et al.* (1965) reported that there was no advantage in daily gain by increasing the protein content from 11% of DM to 15% when the concentrate/roughage ratio was 50:50. In contrast, on a 75:25 diet daily gain increased significantly as protein rose from 11 to 20% in DM. As no intermediate protein level was used one can only assume that the optimum amount lies somewhere between these two extremes.

One is obliged to conclude that as presently constituted the ARC (1965) factorial system is totally misleading as regards the needs of growing and fattening cattle. The intensive producer, seeking to make a profit from his operations, is advised to use the standards given in Table 9.23, which are based on NRC (1963) proposals, due allowance having being made for differences in voluntary feed intake on the major types of diet used in practice.

9.5.2 Protein source

9.5.2.1 TRUE PROTEIN. Although a certain amount of work has been done on the effect of different protein sources on growth and feed conversion in early weaned calves (§ 7.5.4.4), very little data exist for older and heavier animals. It has been established that dairy calves reared by early weaning systems in which concentrates are available on a free choice basis possess, by the age of 3 months, a rumen fermentation characterized by a relatively low pH (Eadie *et al.*, 1967; Elías and Preston, 1969b), a relatively high concentration of VFA and an almost complete absence of protozoa. By comparison, calves raised with their dams on pasture have, at weaning,

TABLE 9.23 RECOMMENDED PROTEIN (N × 6.25) ALLOWANCES FOR FATTENING CATTLE GAINING AT 1.25 KG/DAY

Live weight (kg)	Protein required[a] (g/kg LW/day)	DM intake[b] (kg/100 kg LW)	Our estimate of requirements (% of DM)	
			All-concentrate[c]	With 10–20% roughage
100	3.96	2.93	13.5	12.0
150	3.57	2.52	14.2	12.6
200	3.30	2.32	14.2	12.6
250	3.18	2.19	14.5	12.9
300	3.03	2.11	14.4	12.8
350	2.92	2.04	14.6	12.9
400	2.80	2.01	13.9	12.4
450	2.74	1.97	13.9	12.4

[a] Calculated from R. L. Preston (1966).
[b] On all-concentrate diet; with 10–20% roughage intake is 20% higher.
[c] Includes high molasses/urea diets (§ 9.3.3).

a rumen fermentation pattern much more akin to that in the adult; rumen pH is higher, the VFA concentration lower and the microflora more varied, with large quantities of protozoa (Elías and Preston, 1969b). The rumen condition in early weaned calves has a considerable influence on protein utilization (§ 5.5) as a result of which biological value is likely to be of much more significance in these animals than in beef calves raised on pasture. Thus, Buysse *et al.* (1966) found that East Flemish early weaned calves, given concentrate *ad libitum* until slaughter at approximately 12 months of age, exhibited 1.3% faster growth and 3.4% better feed conversion when soybean meal was the protein source rather than a mixture of groundnut meal and cotton seed meal. In a second experiment bull calves of the same breed fattened from 17 weeks to 460 kg grew faster and had better feed conversion with soybean (1.34 kg/day and 4.65 FU/kg gain) than with groundnut (1.23 and 4.95) or cottonseed (1.30 and 4.98). Ekern (1967) compared herring meal against a mixture of ground nut, soybean and sunflower meals and found the former supported from 6 to 15% better gain (5 trials) with a 10% reduction in feed intake. Some evidence exists (Bowers *et al.*, 1965) for better nitrogen retention in Friesian steers given free access to rolled barley diets when the protein source was fish meal or cottonseed meal as compared with groundnut meal. Results with soybean meal were intermediate between the other two.

There is a paucity of data on the effect of protein source under US style feedlot conditions. Herd *et al.* (1966) found that maize gluten meal gave poorer gains and feed efficiency than soybean meal or distiller solubles when given to cattle with an initial weight of 336 kg (the complete diet used was based on ground ear maize). In Peru, frozen anchovies were compared with cottonseed meal and cottonseed meal and fish meal combinations (Mendoza *et al.*, 1968). Performance was significantly worse (0.50 kg/day and 8.7 conversion ratio) when the anchovies were the sole source of protein supplement although a mixture of cottonseed meal and anchovies was almost as good (0.90 and 5.3) as cottonseed meal and standard fish meal (0.97

and 5.0). Encouraging results with guar meal in comparison with cottonseed meal were reported by Harris (1968). At a dietary level of 10%, gain was identical (1.18 kg/day) and conversion slightly better on the former (7.67 vs. 8.03). In general terms, one would not expect protein quality to be an important factor when cattle enter the feedlot at relative high weights and are fed for comparatively short periods of time.

9.5.2.2 Urea. The use of urea in cattle feeding was extensively reviewed by Reid (1953a) who concluded that it could satisfactorily replace up to 25% of the total dietary nitrogen; however, there was evidence that growth of young animals was slightly poorer on such diets than with conventional protein. Palatability was often reduced when urea exceeded 1% of the ration, but this could be counteracted with molasses. It is logical that there will only be a growth response from added NPN if the basal diet provides insufficient crude protein to permit a maximum utilization of the available energy. The issue thus hinges upon what are the protein requirements for fattening cattle. According to the ARC (1965) "... comparison of the factorial requirements for protein with results of practical feeding experiments has suggested that with the exception of poorer quality roughages protein is not likely to be limiting in many diets available to growing ruminants in temperate countries". Assuming that these factorial requirements are correct, they then go on to conclude "that few experiments on the utilization of NPN have been conducted with sufficiently critical attention to interrelationships between dietary energy and protein". We have already shown (§ 9.5.1) that the addition of protein to diets adequate according to the factorial system has led to significant responses in growth rate. There are also specific instances where the addition of urea to diets already adequate (according to the factorial system) has brought about significant responses in both daily gain and feed conversion. Thus, in Australia, Morris (1966) increased gains of steers on a high energy diet containing 10.2% crude protein in DM by adding urea. Similarly, Thrasher *et al.* (1967) in Louisiana used an all-concentrate or an 80:20 concentrate/roughage diet and obtained better gains by using urea to raise the protein level from 11 to 12.5% in DM. Similar responses were obtained with soybean meal and there was no interaction between level, source of protein and type of diet. In Cuba we gave fattening bulls a basal diet of *ad libitum* grain and molasses (the latter supplying up to 18% of total ME) with 9.2% protein in DM (Preston *et al.*, 1967b). Adding urea to raise the effective protein content to 11.6% crude protein in DM increased gains and feed efficiency by 39 and 5% respectively. Increasing the protein to 13% in DM increased gains by 50% over the control and feed conversion ratio by 19%. It is true that all of these experiments were undertaken in the tropical or sub-tropical zones; however, this is largely irrelevant since the feeds used were typical of those employed in cattle fattening operations in both the US and Europe. Moreover, the findings are in agreement with the work of Blaylock *et al.* (1965) in Minnesota and Kercher and Pauls (1968b) in Wyoming who improved both gain and efficiency by adding urea to high grain rations containing 9.8 and 11% crude protein in DM respectively.

Urea clearly has an important role to play in intensive fattening of beef cattle, and this is borne out by the fact that the volume of urea-containing feeds and supplements used in the US rose by 20% from 1963 to 1965. Urea usage was 210,000 tons in 1963 and was expected to rise to 275,000 by 1970 (Anon., 1965c). In 1966 one-third of all feedlots and 58% of all cattle on feed were using urea, while of those feedlots with more than 300 head some 75% were employing urea (Anon., 1968b). The possibilities for urea usage are even greater in those developing countries where proteins are in short supply and the economic incentive to use synthetic forms of nitrogen is that much greater (Preston and Willis, 1969). The decision to replace protein with urea is, for the feedlot operator, purely an economic one. The grain portion of an all-concentrate diet generally supplies about 30 to 33 g protein/Mcal ME, and since the requirement on such diets is of the order of 45 g protein/Mcal ME, the maximum proportion of nitrogen that can be furnished by urea is about 30%. The feedlot

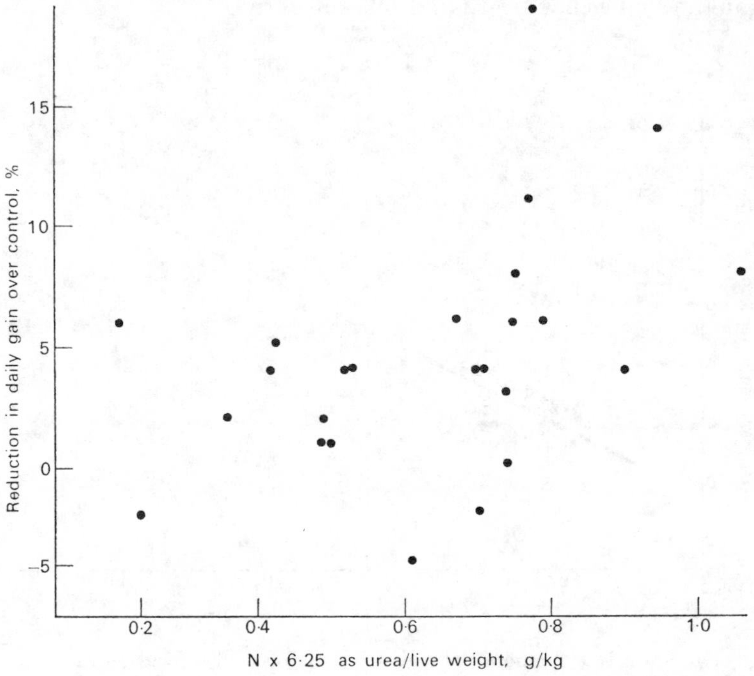

FIG. 9.5 Effect of amount of urea fed daily on rate of live weight gain.

operator therefore requires to know the effect on both live weight gain and feed conversion of including urea at up to approximately one-third of the total protein requirement. The cost of a mixture of grain and urea is always less than the equivalent amount of true protein but the economics of replacement depend upon whether performance is reduced by so doing, and if so, to what extent.

In seeking to answer these questions we have set out in Table 9.24 the data from several experiments in which urea was used to replace protein and in which the protein/energy ratio employed was critical in terms of expected requirements (Table 9.23). All the diets were of high energy as shown by the fact that daily gains of controls ranged from 0.95 to 1.33 kg. There is a definite trend in the data towards reduced performance in both gain and conversion with increasing rate of replacement of protein nitrogen by urea. The data are shown graphically in Figs. 9.5 and 9.6. The calculated linear regressions are significant ($P < 0.01$), but care must be taken in interpretation in that the original data relate to a wide range of conditions. For instance, Colenbrander *et al.* (1968) found no difference between urea and soybean meal as sole nitrogen supplements to maize and hay given free choice. Similarly, Furr *et al.* (1968b) found urea alone, or with cottonseed meal, to be as good in terms of daily gain and slightly better in efficiency when compared with a cottonseed meal control. Long *et al.* (1968) actually reported a 17% improvement in gain and 21% better conversion with urea rather than soybean meal. However, only small numbers of animals were used (6 per treatment). In contrast, Piatkowski *et al.* (1967) used 2.0% fish meal to replace part of the urea in an all-concentrate diet (18.6% protein) and improved gain and efficiency by 12 and 6% respectively.

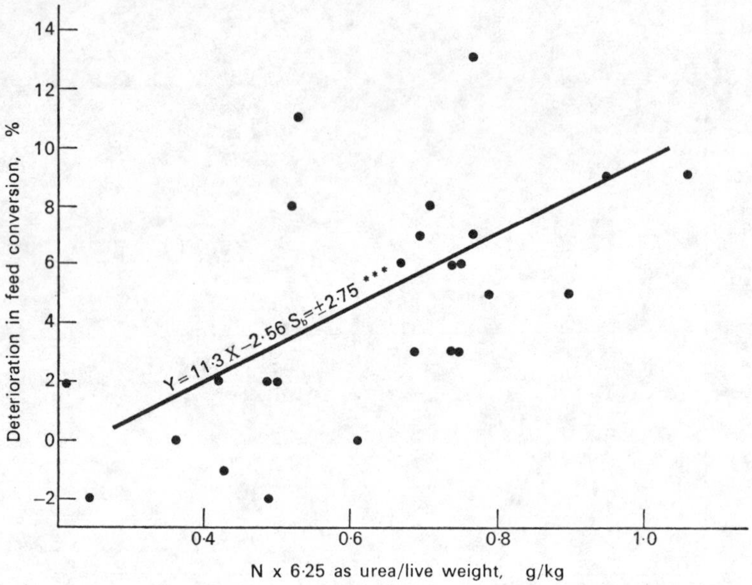

FIG. 9.6 Effect of amount of urea fed daily on feed conversion rate.

It is known that the response to urea is less on high roughage rations and this is confirmed by the data of Perry *et al.* (1967), where the reduction in gain and conversion exceeded 20% when urea supplied approximately 290 g of protein equivalent/day. These data were not included in Figs. 9.5 and 9.6 nor in the regression analysis.

There have been several attempts to improve the value of urea by reducing its rate of hydrolysis in the rumen (§ 5.5.2), but few have resulted in commercially usable products. Oklahoma investigators reduced rumen ureolytic activity by giving subcutaneous injections of jackbean urease to induce immunity to the enzyme. Although encouraging results were obtained with lambs (Glimp and Tillman, 1965) the technique was ineffective in growing calves between 80 and 175 kg (Harbers *et al.*, 1965). Biuret is hydrolysed in the rumen more slowly than urea (Meiske *et al.*, 1955) but, despite this, gains and feed conversion have been no better (Campbell *et al.*, 1963).

The approach used by Kansas workers (Deyoe *et al.*, 1968) was to pass a mixture of finely ground grain and urea through a cooker-extruder under conditions sufficient

Energy source	N × 6.25 as urea (g/day)	Effect of urea on gain		Effect of urea on conversion		N × 6.25 as urea (g/kg LW)	Authors
		Control (kg/day)	Reduction (%)	Control	Deterioration (%)		
Silage[a]	290	0.95	41	7.4	57	1.10	Perry *et al.*, 1967
Silage[b]	290	0.35	32	18.2	43	0.83	Perry *et al.*, 1967
Silage[c]	290	0.50	20	14.2	23	0.83	Perry *et al.*, 1967
Ear maize	290	1.32	19	7.49	13	0.77	Little *et al.*, 1968a
Ear maize	350	1.01	14	9.76	9	0.95	Brown *et al.*, 1967b
Ear maize	290	1.20	11	7.62	7	0.77	Little *et al.*, 1968a
70:30[d]	360	1.33	8	8.30	9	1.06	Lamming *et al.*, 1967
80:20[e]	290	1.29	8	7.60	6	0.75	Perry *et al.*, 1967
Ear maize		0.99	7	7.45	3		Goodrich *et al.*, 1967
80:20[e]	260	1.09	6	8.20	6	0.67	Perry *et al.*, 1967
80:20[e]	290	1.09	6	8.10	5	0.79	Perry *et al.*, 1967
80:20[e]	290	1.29	6	7.60	3	0.75	Perry *et al.*, 1967
	63	1.01	6	7.42	2	0.21	Brown *et al.*, 1966
	162	1.35	5	9.18	−1	0.43	Hale *et al.*, 1964b
	124	1.01	4	7.42	2	0.42	Brown *et al.*, 1966
	340	0.97	4	8.46	5	0.90	Bradley *et al.*, 1966b
80:20[e]	260	1.05	4	8.40	8	0.71	Perry *et al.*, 1967
80:20[e]	270	1.09	4	8.20	7	0.70	Perry *et al.*, 1967
100:0	200	1.12	4	8.06	11	0.53	McCartor *et al.*, 1967
100:0	180	1.15	4	6.06	8	0.52	Hawkins *et al.*, 1967
80:20[e]	290	1.09	3	8.20	6	0.74	Perry *et al.*, 1967
	140	1.02	2	9.40	0	0.36	Herd *et al.*, 1966
100:0	110	1.37	2	5.02	2	0.49	Preston *et al.*, 1965b
100:0	170	1.13	1	7.43	−2	0.49	McGinty *et al.*, 1966a
100:0	44	1.07	1	8.38	0	0.11	McCartor *et al.*, 1967
100:0	170	1.06	1	6.39	2	0.50	Hawkins *et al.*, 1967
100:0	250	0.95	0	7.05	3	0.74	Oltjen *et al.*, 1965
80:20[e]	260	1.16	0	7.80	3	0.69	Perry *et al.*, 1967
90:10	170	1.11	−2			0.70	Thrasher *et al.*, 1967
100:0	90	1.07	−2	8.38	−2	0.24	McCartor *et al.*, 1967
100:0	220	1.31	−4	7.55	0	0.61	McGinty *et al.*, 1966b
		1.16	−4	7.50	−5		Richardson *et al.*, 1966

[a] Maize silage.
[b] Maize stover silage.
[c] Maize silage plus grain.
[d] 70 barley 30 ground straw.
[e] *Ad lib.* ear maize plus 6–8 kg silage.

to cause gelatinization of the starch. This product (Starea) gave slower release of ammonia in the rumen and was claimed to support better performance than urea; daily gains for groups of five animals on soybean meal, Starea and urea were 1.26, 1.24 and 1.16 respectively (Bartley *et al.*, 1968).

Toxicity problems associated with urea feeding are discussed elsewhere (§ 11.3.7).

9.5.2.3 Urea and fat. Some studies have been undertaken at the University of Kentucky (Bradley *et al.*, 1966b, Thompson *et al.*, 1967) which suggest that there is a particularly severe depression in both gain and feed conversion when animal fat (5%), and urea (1.5%) are included in the same diet. It should, however, be noted that these were not strictly higher energy diets in that they contained from 30 to 50% of maize cobs. Bradley *et al.* considered that the added fat might have interfered with utilization of urea and in one experiment gave more protein. This reduced the extent of the depression but did not eliminate it. Addition of lysine or distillers dried grain solubles also did not alleviate the problem. Thompson *et al.* (1967) gave their diets either in meal form or as pellets and, as might be expected with a medium roughage diet, obtained better performance with the latter. There was also an indication that the degree of depression with combined fat and urea was less, particularly with regard to feed conversion.

9.5.2.4 Ammonium phosphate. According to Richardson *et al.* (1966) monoammonium phosphate, diammonium phosphate, or a mixture of the latter with urea, could be fed to steers at levels of up to 204 g/day with no harmful effects. In a feeding trial with 300 kg steers given hay and sorghum grain *ad libitum*, there were no significant differences between supplements containing dehydrated alfalfa meal with soybean meal alone or plus diammonium phosphate or diammonium phosphate and urea. Brown *et al.* (1966) also reported no differences in performance of cattle given ground maize and either cottonseed meal or diammonium phosphate. In contrast, earlier work by Cowman and Thomas (1962) had implied poorer gains and feed conversion when monoammonium phosphate was used in an all-concentrate diet to replace soybean meal. There is insufficient evidence to put a definitive value upon either product as an NPN source although the implication is that results will be similar to those with urea.

Ammonium salts of the VFA were investigated by Walker *et al.* (1968). Friesian steers weighing 130 kg were fed rolled barley and mixed VFA salts of ammonia, calcium, potassium, sodium, zinc and cobalt disolved in the drinking water; the control treatment was soybean meal given as a mixed diet with rolled barley. There were no apparent differences in daily gain and feed conversion between the different treatments.

9.5.2.5 Poultry litter and waste. There have been some attempts to use by-products from the poultry industry as nitrogen sources for beef cattle. Drake *et al.* (1965) compared diets containing 25% of broiler litter, made from either groundnut husks or wood shavings, with a conventional diet of hay, maize and protein supplement. Feed efficiency was worst with groundnut husk litter, daily gains were lower for wood shavings and overall performance was superior on the control treatment. In a second trial, these same workers compared broiler litter made from groundnut husks, ground maize cobs, chopped hay or soybean husks. These made up 25 or 40% of the diets. Performance was better at the lower level of usage but the control treatment was superior to any of those using litter.

Hydrolysed protein waste, which included feathers and excreta, was investigated by Rusnak *et al.* (1966) at the 10% level in an all-concentrate diet with soybean meal as a control. No differences in gain were observed. Unfortuntaely the cattle used had starting weights of 425 kg which does not really allow a critical evaluation of any nitrogen source. The same criticism can be advanced with regard to the work of Drake and his co-workers with cattle of 375 kg starting weight. Lighter cattle (301 kg Angus steers) were used by Long *et al.* (1968); hydrolysed poultry waste appeared to be as good as soybean meal although the dried product was slightly inferior. However, numbers were too small to permit valid conclusions.

Our own results, using laying hen excreta in a high molasses diet to supply 12, 25 or 33% of the total nitrogen at the expense of urea, showed that gains diminished with increasing proportions of excreta in the diet. By comparison, animals given fish meal in similar proportions showed improved performance with increasing contribution of protein from fish meal. Overall results with fish meal were some 25% superior than with poultry excreta (Preston *et al.*, 1969a).

Poorer results with broiler litter as compared with cottonseed meal (Noland *et al.*, 1955; Southwell *et al.*, 1958) lend support to the belief that poultry litter has limited application in an intensive fattening system. For wintering diets, however, where maximum performance is of less consequence, results have been more encouraging (Ray and Child, 1964).

It must be realized that broiler house litter or poultry waste are very variable commodities. Their major disadvantage seems to be that they reduce palatability; there is also the problem of drugs which have been administered to the poultry and which may prove toxic to cattle. Thus Southwell *et al.* (1958) concluded that even at 25% of the price, litter was less economical than cottonseed meal.

9.5.2.6 Ammoniated molasses. Ammoniated industrial products have been investigated by Tillman *et al.* (1957). Poor results were obtained from ammoniated cane molasses and ammoniated furfural residues as compared to cottonseed meal, when used as supplements in high energy rations. Use of ammoniated high test molasses was particularly undesirable since on the second day of feeding, 4 of the 6 animals exhibited an excitement syndrome which led to severe physical injury, the trial having to be abandoned. These products clearly have no value at the present time in intensive fattening operations.

9.5.2.7 Amino acids. In 1961, Gossett and his coworkers at Purdue University claimed that the addition of 10 g daily of lysine to a basal ration of rolled maize, maize silage and a protein supplement containing urea, improved feed efficiency by 6% over controls. Methionine analogue, at the rate of 5 g/day, had no effect on either gain or efficiency, but at 10 g/day depressed both parameters. In a fuller account of the trial, Gosset *et al.* (1962) upheld the claim of improved efficiency due to lysine despite the fact that there was no replication of the various treatments. They considered that lysine was not beneficial in low urea diets. Kolari *et al.* (1961a) and Marion and Jones (1961) also found that there was no benefit from giving lysine together with either linseed oil meal or cottonseed meal.

There are no theoretical reasons why supplemental lysine should be beneficial in cattle diets irrespective of whether these are based on protein or partly on urea, and, more recently, Albin and Ellis (1967) have shown that lysine was ineffective when added to all-concentrate diets in which urea was the only supplementary nitrogen source. There would appear to be no justification for the use of lysine or methionine in cattle fattening.

9.6 MINERALS

9.6.1 Introduction

Most work on mineral nutrition has been concerned with the relationship to disease rather than to the effect on economic criteria such as rate of growth and feed conversion. In part this is understandable since minerals are not expensive resources and comprise only a small part of the diet. There has therefore been little incentive to carry out input/output experiments. Interactions of one mineral with another present problems of interpretation and this is particularly true for the minor elements. The literature relating to the mineral requirements of ruminants up to the early 1960's was reviewed by the ARC (1965), while recommendations have also been put forward by the NRC (1963). In the following sections discussion is confined to these published requirements in relation to the more recent data available. Our conclusions are summarized in Table 9.25.

TABLE 9.25 MINERAL REQUIREMENTS OF FATTENING CATTLE GAINING AT ABOUT 1.00 KG/DAY

	ARC (1965)		NRC (1963)	Our estimate
Live weight range (kg)	100–200	200–400	200–400	200–400
		g/day		% of DM
Calcium	28	30–37	20	0.27
Phosphorus	14	15–29	15–18	0.25
Magnesium	2–5	5–8		0.10
Potassium				0.70[a]
Sodium	4	5–8		0.20
Chlorine	5	6–11		0.20
		mg/kg DM		
Iron	30			30
Copper	10			10
Zinc	50			50
Manganese	40			40
Cobalt	0.1			0.5
Iodine	0.12			0.5

[a] See text re high-molasses diets.

9.6.2 Calcium

For a daily live weight gain of 1 kg, the ARC proposed a dietary requirement of 27 g at 100 kg live weight rising to 37.3 g at 400 kg; by comparison the NRC (1963) requirements remain fairly constant at about 20 g/day over the entire weight range. Bushman *et al.* (1967) studied the effect of calcium concentrations ranging from 0.15 to 0.6% in an all-concentrate diet based on ground maize. The average daily gain and feed conversion were 1.44 kg and 8.71 over the whole range and did not differ significantly between levels. Converting these values to (g) calcium per day gives a range of 11.5–44.0. In feeding trials with normal or high test molasses fed with grain, forage or a combination of the two, Preston *et al.* (1967c) found no relation between calcium level and rate of gain and feed conversion. The calcium intake varied from 14 to 34 g daily. According to the ARC (1965) proposals, only two of the six diets employed in this experiment were adequate yet, in fact, daily gains of 0.99 kg/day were obtained with diets containing 32 or 19 g calcium daily, phosphorus levels being the same on both. It was concluded at the time that the ARC standards for calcium were too high and the findings of Bushman *et al.* (1967) appear to confirm this. The reasons for this apparent overestimation of requirements undoubtedly arises from the use of the factorial system. The net requirement for calcium is actually fairly constant over the entire weight range, and is in good agreement with the NRC (1963) standards. In contrast, on the basis of isotope and balance studies, the ARC concluded that availability of dietary calcium diminished steadily with increasing live weight. Thus by applying this correction factor, dietary requirements inevitably rose with increasing animal size. The error arises from the method of measuring response to increasing calcium intake. The authors of the ARC report chose to measure availability rather than growth or feed efficiency. If dietary requirement remains constant and the amount given is increased in relation to size, it is obvious that availability must fall. It appears to us, however, that there is no justification for then using this availability figure to augment the dietary requirements to what is obviously an artificially high level.

9.6.3 Phosphorus

There is reasonably good agreement between the NRC and ARC proposals for fattening animals up to about 300 kg live weight; thereafter, ARC standards are considerably higher such that a 400 kg animal is alleged to need almost twice as much as one of 200 kg. Both standards are considerably higher than the 6 g/day level (108 kg live weight) above which increasing phosphorus gave no response in the experiment carried out by Wise *et al.* (1958) with calves gaining about 0.5 kg/day. On the other hand, phosphorus excretion was abnormally high on all-concentrate diets which may be related to a subclinical acidosis (Reed *et al.*, 1965). There is evidence from our own work (Preston *et al.*, 1967c) that phosphorus requirements increase with increasing gain, and this is to be expected in view of the important role that phosphorus plays in energy metabolism; there is, however, no practical evidence to justify phosphorus levels in excess of those recommended by NRC (1963).

Perhaps the only proviso is in relation to heavily parasitized animals as it has been shown by Waymack *et al.* (1968) that plasma phosphorus decreased after infection with *Ostertagia* spp. Although the requirements will be higher under these circumstances it would be more satisfactory to eliminate the parasite.

9.6.4 Potassium

Neither of the standard works gives a requirement for potassium and, according to the ARC (1965), there is unlikely to be any deficiency in most conventional diets. Nevertheless, it is difficult in low-roughage diets to separate the need for potassium *per se* and its possible role as a buffering agent. Thus Roberts and Omer (1965) in Canada used levels of 0.27, 0.51, 0.72 and 0.85% potassium in a high energy diet for fattening steers. They found that the corresponding daily gains were 0.09, 0.90, 1.32 and 1.25 kg with feed conversion showing a similar trend. In subsequent experiments with all-concentrate diets based on barley, these workers studied potassium levels ranging from 0.5 to 1.05% and found no significant effect over this range. They concluded that the requirement was between 0.5 and 0.6% of the DM. Subsequently, Devlin (1967) found that, on an all-concentrate diet based on 75% brewers dried grains, animals lost weight with 0.34 potassium while growth increased to 0.61 kg/day at a level of 0.62%; a level of 0.72% increased gains by only a further 0.05 kg. Arizona workers (Anon., 1968a) considered that the potassium requirements might be as high as 0.7% of the diet for maximum gain and feed efficiency on fattening rations based on sorghum; performance was inferior with only 0.5%. These workers suggested that inclusion of molasses in all-concentrate diets was beneficial due to its being an excellent source of potassium, gains and performance being worse when it was withdrawn. On the other hand, in a 148 day feeding trial with 64 steers on a 60% (rising to 90%) concentrate diet, removing molasses led to improvements in both gain and efficiency. However, trace minerals were not included in the molasses diet (they were in the others), and this may have affected the results. There is some evidence from the work of Roberts and Omer (1965) that potassium levels in excess of 0.7% might lead to reduced performance on high energy diets based on grains.

The situation with regard to potassium in high molasses diets is much more complicated. Requirements may well be higher under such circumstances since we have reported satisfactory feed efficiency with potassium levels in excess of 1% of the DM. Growth was admittedly less than optimum in relation to the energy available, but this was confounded with many other factors and it is not possible to ascribe an exact role to potassium at this stage (Preston and Willis, 1969).

For high energy or all-concentrate diets based on grain the evidence would indicate a requirement of the order of 0.7% of the DM; on high molasses diets it is almost certain that higher levels are necessary, but evidence does not yet exist on which a recommendation can be based.

9.6.5 Sodium, chlorine and magnesium

The ARC (1965) recommendations range from 3.1 g/day at 100 kg live weight to 8.2 at 400 kg for sodium and 3.5 to 11.3 for chlorine. These estimates are based on body composition and the assumption that the elements are 100% available. NRC (1963) standards are based on the inclusion of 0.5% of salt in the diet which provides a considerably higher level of supplementation of both sodium and chlorine. No critical experiments have been made in recent years to check the validity of either of these standards. Salt is one of the cheapest dietary ingredients, and it is generally believed that its presence at 0.5% of the diet helps to increase palatability.

The ARC (1965) magnesium requirements of cattle gaining 1 kg/day range from 1.7 to 8.0 g/day over the weight range 100–400 kg; NRC (1963) standards for growth are slightly lower. Discussion of these is somewhat academic since all the major energy sources likely to be used in intensive fattening operations contain a minimum of 0.1% magnesium, which is considerably more than is needed.

9.6.6 Minor elements

9.6.6.1 GENERAL. Supplementation of fattening rations with minor elements was rarely necessary when high-quality roughages formed a considerable part of the diet. It was only subsequent to 1950, when increasing proportions of concentrates began to be fed and greater use was made of poor-quality roughages, that a need was demonstrated for minor element supplementation. Thus Klosterman *et al.* (1953, 1956) and Bentley *et al.* (1954) found that gain was increased when the minor elements were added to a diet of ground ear maize, soybean meal and poor-quality hay. The minor elements supplied were iron, copper, cobalt, manganese and zinc. Bentley *et al.* (1954) thought that cobalt was the element primarily responsible for the improvement. Subsequently, Oltjen *et al.* (1959) found that a mixture of the same minor elements plus iodine gave a significant improvement in performance when ground maize was the basis of the diet but not when sorghum was fed; the relative gains and feed conversions (mean of two experiments) were 1.12 and 8.31 for the control and 1.34 and 7.52 for the diet supplemented with the minor elements. The amounts given (mg/day) were: Mn, 56.3; I, 1.97; Co, 1.25; Fe, 46.1; Cu, 3.65; and Zn 3.42. On an all-concentrate diet based on barley and soybean meal, growth rate was increased with a supplement containing copper, cobalt, iron, iodine, manganese and zinc; cobalt, or cobalt and iron only gave partial improvement (Harper *et al.*, 1962). Minor element supplementation of a high energy diet based on barley and 20% dry beet pulp increased gains from 0.91 to 1.13 kg/day and feed efficiency from 9.59 to 8.59 (Thomas *et al.*, 1964). Giving smaller amounts of the mineral mixture in chelated form gave a slightly smaller response.

Cobalt would seem to be the most important minor element in all-concentrate feeding in view of the report of Raun *et al.* (1965) that this element alone improved gains and feed conversion on an all-barley diet as much as did complex mixtures containing cobalt, copper, iron, zinc, manganese and iodine in various combinations.

9.6.6.2 IRON, COPPER, COBALT AND IODINE. The ARC (1965) recommendations are 30, 10, 0.1 and 0.1 mg/kg of dietary DM for iron, copper, cobalt and iodine respectively; when goitrogens are present in the feed it was suggested that the iodine requirement be raised by a factor of 10. Megown (1967), in a review of some fifty publications on minor elements, proposed corresponding levels of 4–9, 0.2–0.5 and 0.5–1.0 for copper, cobalt and iodine respectively.

9.6.6.3 MANGANESE. The ARC suggested a level of 40 mg/kg of feed DM, while Megown (1967) proposed that the required level was between this figure and 25 mg/kg. Embry *et al.* (1958) obtained no response from adding 30 mg Mn/kg to a basal diet which already contained 15 mg/kg. He used identical twin steers, and his diets had only a moderate energy level (producing daily gains of only some 0.6 kg); thus requirements may well be higher than the 15 mg/kg used in his basal ration. There is a report that giving very high levels of manganese might be deleterious to both microbial digestion of cellulose and absorption of iron; however, this was only noticed with manganese at 1000 mg/kg of diet and there was no effect on gain and feed conversion (Robinson *et al.*, 1960).

9.6.6.4 Zinc. Megown (1967) put the required level at between 25 and 35 mg/kg of air-dry feed in comparison with 50 mg/kg DM proposed by ARC (1965). On the other hand, Beeson (1964) suggested as much as 100 mg. This latter estimate can almost certainly be disregarded in view of the findings of Zurcher and Beeson (1968) that adding 50 mg Zn/kg to an all-concentrate diet already containing 28.8 mg/kg failed to bring about any response. There were also no effects on gain and feed conversion from adding 50 mg Zn/kg to a concentrate diet with 10% groundnut husks which already contained 20.7 mg Zn/kg. In contrast, in a ration containing 20% of dried beet pulp (20.9 mg Zn/kg), daily gains increased from 0.69 to 0.83 kg when 75 mg Zn/kg was added. The peculiarity of rations containing beet pulp was further emphasized by the work of Price and Smith (1968) who found that daily gain was decreased from 0.88 to 0.66 kg by the addition of 100 mg Zn/kg to the basal diet of 48% beet pulp which already contained 15 mg Zn/kg. With 81% beet pulp in the diet (13 mg Zn/kg) the addition of 100 mg Zn/kg increased gain from 0.75 to 0.83 kg. This interaction was significant.

Ott *et al.* (1966) obtained gains of 1.22 kg/day on a 75% concentrate diet containing 100 mg Zn/kg, and this was reduced successively to 1.02, 0.22 and −0.06 kg by the addition of 1, 2 or 3 g Zn/kg of diet. A subsequent experiment defined the toxic level as somewhere between 0.5 and 0.9 g/kg of diet. None of the Purdue work has related to levels between 25 and 100 mg Zn/kg.

Oltjen *et al.* (1965) found no differences in performance between zinc levels of 12.5 or 25 mg/kg in all-maize diets given to animals gaining approximately 1 kg/day. In the UK, Mills *et al.* (1967) confirmed that the effect of zinc deficiency was first manifested by reduced growth rates, and they considered that 8 mg/kg was adequate for normal growth although 10–14 mg/kg was the minimum required to maintain plasma levels of zinc at normal concentrations. Thomas *et al.* (1964), in studies of trace element supplementation of high energy diets, also found that 545 mg Zn/day was less effective than 41 mg.

9.6.6.5 Selenium. This mineral is discussed along with vitamin E in § 9.7.

9.7 VITAMINS

9.7.1 Introduction

It is well established that ruminants can synthesize their needs of vitamin C and of the B complex by virtue of the rumen microflora. Discussion in this section will thus be confined to vitamins A, D, E and K.

The accepted norms with respect to requirements of these vitamins were set up originally on the basis of data pertaining to animals fed on conventional diets high in roughages. It is known, however, that the specific conditions of high energy feeding, wherein the greater part of the diet may be composed of concentrates, leads to the destruction in the digestive tract of both vitamins A and E (Warner *et al.*, 1968; Alderson *et al.*, 1968). It is therefore to be expected that this will increase requirements. Even within intensive feeding systems there are varying circumstances. Thus in typical US practice, high energy diets are given over a period of some 4 months to animals previously raised on pasture. Such cattle have some vitamin reserves at the start of the fattening period; moreover, during the final fattening stage the majority of them are kept in open lots with ready access to sunlight. By contrast, the intensive dairy beef operations in Europe involve the indoor fattening of calves which have been reared artificially, usually on milk replacers and concentrates. Thus at 3 months of age when they enter the intensive feeding stage their reserves of vitamins are invariably low.

9.7.2 Vitamin A

The results of US experiments in which different amounts of vitamin A have been given to cattle receiving high energy diets are set out in Table 9.26. Several trials were undertaken on pasture but as the animals concerned had free access to concentrates and were eating almost 2.5% of their body weight in this form, it can be assumed that the contribution made by roughages was negligible. Such experiments, nevertheless, present difficulties in interpretation since it is impossible to estimate the amount of carotene contributed by pasture. It is also difficult to establish a criterion of vitamin adequacy since individual investigations have not always embraced a sufficient range of levels; moreover, there has been considerable variation in the amounts given to controls. Thus the fact that there is not always a response to additional supplementation does not automatically indicate that the control level was the optimum one. Indeed, there are several experiments in which it is quite obvious that the control level was already excessive. Nevertheless, it can be safely concluded that levels of 20–37 IU vitamin A/kg live weight (i.e. about 10,000 to 13,000 IU/day) are inadequate, since further supplementation has invariably led to a significant growth response. At the other extreme, it seems that levels of 150 IU and above are unnecessarily high.

Our interpretation of the data (Fig. 9.7) is that a level of some 100 IU vitamin A/kg of live weight/day, i.e. about 30,000–35,000 IU/head, will ensure that growth is not limited by this vitamin. Growth is not the sole criterion since vitamin A plays an important role in combating sub-clinical diseases, particularly those affecting vision and the respiratory organs, thus it is probably an advantage to set the requirement slightly on the high side. In practice this presents little economic problem as vitamin A is not expensive. It should also be realized that the majority of the experiments reported in Table 9.26 were carried out with diets based on ear maize. In view of the fact that the destruction of vitamin A in the intestine is greater with increasing proportions of concentrate in the diet, it may well be that for other all-concentrate diets the optimum level will be even higher.

No critical experiments have been carried out to determine the optimum level of vitamin A for intensive dairy beef cattle managed according to the European system. In the development work on "barley beef" in the UK, vitamin A was given at about 100 IU/kg live weight per day (4000 IU/kg diet). Despite this apparent high level of

TABLE 9.26 EFFECT OF SUPPLEMENTARY VITAMIN A ON GROWTH AND FEED CONVERSION IN FATTENING CATTLE

Basal diet	Vitamin A/day (IU/kg live weight) Control	Treated	Daily gain Control (kg)	Improvement due to treatment (%)	Authors
50/50[a]	645	663	0.86	−6	Rice & Paules, 1965
Ear maize	29	251	0.74	−6	German & Adams, 1962
All-conc.[b]	119	137	0.90	−5	Rice & Paules, 1965
Ear maize[c]	70	114[d]	1.19	−5	Perry *et al.*, 1966b
Ear maize[e]	65	312	0.99	0	Beeson *et al.*, 1962
80/20[a]	60	87	1.32	0	Weichenthal *et al.*, 1963
Ear maize[c]	70	97[d]	0.89	0	Perry *et al.*, 1966b
Ear maize[c]	70	63[d]	1.19	0	Perry *et al.*, 1965
80/20[a]	60	87	1.32	1	Weichenthal *et al.*, 1963
Ear maize	29		0.74	1	German & Adams, 1962
Ear maize[c]	70	86[d]	0.98	1	Perry *et al.*, 1966b
Ear maize[c]	70	349[d]	1.19	1	Perry *et al.*, 1966b
All-conc.	11	22	1.09	1	Hansen *et al.*, 1963
Ear maize[e]	65	195	0.99	2	Beeson *et al.*, 1962
Ear maize[e]	65	234	0.99	2	Beeson *et al.*, 1962
Ear maize[c]	70	268[d]	1.19	2	Perry *et al.*, 1965
Ear maize[c]	70	234[d]	1.19	2	Perry *et al.*, 1965
Silage/hay	28	389	0.97	2	Newland *et al.*, 1966
Maize/citrus[c] meal	30	88	1.22	2	Chapman *et al.*, 1964
Ear maize	29	64	0.69	3	Perry *et al.*, 1962
Ear maize[e]	44	79	0.97	3	Perry *et al*, 1968a
All-conc.	14	28	1.10	3	Hansen *et al.*, 1963
All-conc.[b]	119	156	0.90	4	Rice & Paules, 1965
Ear maize[c]	70	171[d]	0.98	4	Perry *et al.*, 1966b
Ear maize	29	37	0.69	5	Perry *et al.*, 1962
50/50[a]	645	681	0.86	7	Rice & Paules, 1965
Ear maize	29	33	0.69	8	Perry *et al.*, 1962
All-conc.	22	44	1.03	8	Embry *et al.*, 1962
All-conc.	22	66	1.03	8	Embry *et al.*, 1962
All-conc.	22	88	1.03	8	Embry *et al.*, 1962
All-conc.	22	110	1.03	8	Embry *et al.*, 1962
All-conc.	14	56	1.10	8	Hansen *et al.*, 1963
Ear maize	37	140	0.99	9	Newland *et al.*, 1966
Ear maize	39		0.80	12	Beeson *et al.*, 1963
Maize/citrus pulp[c]	71	131	1.07	12	Chapman *et al.*, 1964
All-conc.	14	84	1.10	12	Hansen *et al.*, 1963
Ear maize	29	46	0.69	13	Perry *et al.*, 1962
Ear maize[f]	79	109	0.98	13	Perry *et al.*, 1962
Ear maize	39		0.80	14	Beeson *et al.*, 1963
Ear maize[f]	79	168	0.98	14	Perry *et al.*, 1962
Ear maize[f]	79	197	0.98	14	Perry *et al.*, 1962
Ear maize[f]	79	226	0.98	15	Perry *et al.*, 1962
All-conc.	11	44	1.09	15	Hansen *et al.*, 1963
Ear maize	39		0.80	16	Beeson *et al.*, 1963
Ear maize	29	60	0.74	17	German & Adams, 1962
Ear maize[f]	79	138	0.98	17	Perry *et al.*, 1962

Table 9.26 (cont.)

Basal diet	Vitamin A/day (IU/kg live weight) Control	Treated	Daily gain Control (kg)	Improvement due to treatment (%)	Authors
All-conc.	11	88	1.09	17	Hansen *et al.*, 1963
Ear maize	39	100	0.80	18	Beeson *et al.*, 1963
Maize/citrus pulp[c]	72	190	1.07	18	Chapman *et al.*, 1964
Ear maize	29	99	0.69	20	Perry *et al.*, 1962
Ear maize	29	59	0.83	20	Perry *et al.*, 1962
Ear maize	29	118	0.83	21	Perry *et al.*, 1962
Ear maize	28	64	0.78	22	Perry *et al.*, 1968a
Ear maize	41	80	0.77[g]	26	Beeson *et al.*, 1962
Ear maize	29	147	0.83	28	Perry *et al.*, 1962
Ear maize	29	176	0.83	30	Perry *et al.*, 1962
Ear maize	29	88	0.83	31	Perry *et al.*, 1962
Ear maize	41	119	0.77[g]	32	Beeson *et al.*, 1962
Ear maize	41	197	0.77[g]	32	Beeson *et al.*, 1962

[a] Barley/alfalfa hay. [b] Includes 4% dehydrated alfalfa. [c] *Ad libitum* fed on pasture. [d] Additional. [e] 0.22 kg dehydrated alfalfa. [f] Plus 10% alfalfa hay. [g] Clinical signs of deficiency.

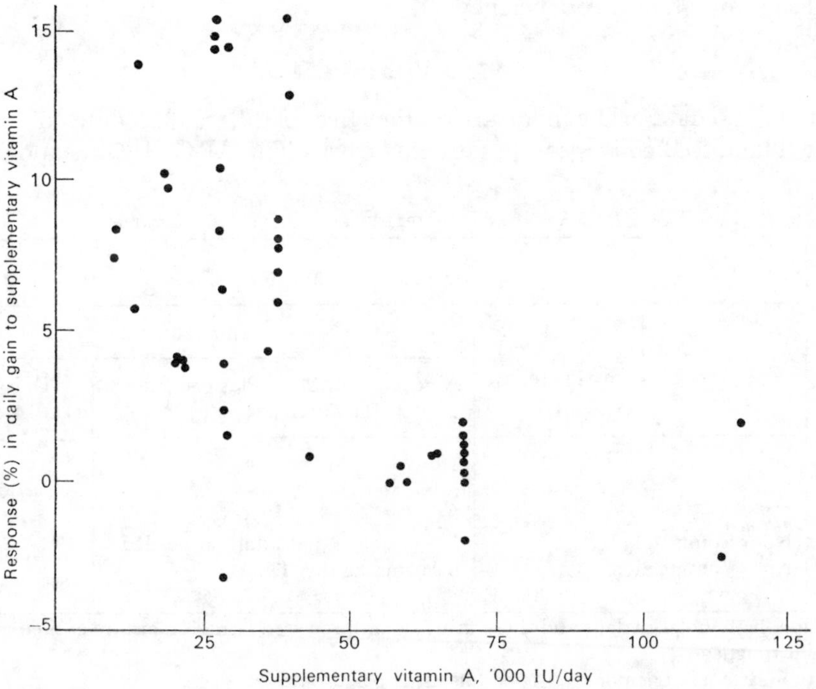

Fig. 9.7 Effect of supplementary vitamin A on daily live weight gain.

usage (adequate for feedlot cattle in the US) there were reports of vitamin A deficiencies varying from loss of skin condition to actual blindness (Foll, 1964; Quarterman and Mills, 1964). When levels were raised to 156 IU vitamin A/kg live weight/day (6000 IU/kg diet), clinical symptoms of deficiency were no longer seen, and adequate levels of vitamin A were found in the liver (Quarterman, 1966). Using this system in Yugoslavia, Obracevic *et al.* (1966) found that even with 36% maize and normally recommended amounts of vitamin A, deficiency symptoms were manifested towards the end of a 207 day fattening trial. In an experiment with 220 "barley beef" animals on eleven farms in the north of Scotland, injections of vitamin A at monthly intervals in addition to 6000 IU/kg of diet did not improve either rate of growth or feed conversion (RRI, 1965). Although Foll (1964) actually recommended 250 IU/kg live weight/day (10,000 IU/kg diet), there is no experimental evidence to justify this very high level, and for the dairy beef animal fattened intensively we consider the optimum to be about 6000 IU/kg diet.

Our recommendations (Table 9.27) both for US feedlot cattle and intensive dairy beef are considerably higher than the standard put forward by the ARC (1965). The ARC criterion for deciding on vitamin requirements was a level "which would ensure freedom from the commonly recognized syndromes of the deficiency stage . . . and also maintain hepatic reserves of the vitamin at least at a measurable level". The level recommended may well be satisfactory for low rates of growth on high-roughage diets, but it is totally inadequate for intensive feeding as is shown by the data of Quarterman and Mills (1964) in which animals given twice the level recommended by ARC (1965) had reserves of vitamin A normally associated with clinical signs of vitamin A deficiency.

9.7.3 Vitamin D

There are no data in the literature on the effect of different amounts of vitamin D on growth and feed conversion in fattening cattle. The ARC (1965) standard of 2.5

TABLE 9.27 VITAMIN REQUIREMENTS IN FATTENING CATTLE

Vitamin	Dietary concentration				
			Our estimate		
	ARC (1965) (IU/kg live weight)	NRC (1963)	All-concentrate[a,b] (IU/kg live weight)	Plus roughage[b]	Dairy-beef[c] (IU/kg diet DM)
A	53	44	100	100	6000
D	2.5	6.6	nil	nil	1500
E	0.1		0.6	0.6	0.6
K	Not recommended		No evidence that addition needed		
Se	Not recommended		0.1[d] (mg/kg diet DM)		

[a] Includes high molasses diets and those using steam-processed or high moisture ensiled grains with or without roughage.

[b] US type system in open or semi-open lots using pasture-raised cattle.

[c] Includes all cattle raised artificially on high energy diets from birth.

[d] High molasses diets only.

IU vitamin D/kg live weight was based on an early experiment carried out in 1936 with heifer calves reared indoors, the results of which are not likely to bear any relation to present conditions of intensive fattening. Cattle under US feedlot conditions with access to sunlight need no supplementation in view of the anti-rachitic properties of ultraviolet radiation. For intensive dairy beef it is customary to give vitamin D at a level of approximately 25% of that of vitamin A (Preston, 1963d), and, in the absence of any experimental evidence to the contrary, coupled with the low cost of this vitamin, we consider this to be a reasonable precaution.

9.7.4 Vitamin E and selenium

The available data on the feeding or injection of vitamin E are set out in Table 9.28. In attempting to interpret this information the following considerations must be borne in mind. There is an interrelation between vitamins A and E (Kohlmeir and Burroughs, 1963). Thus in the experiment carried out by Perry *et al.* (1968a) there were responses to vitamin E levels of 40 and 100 mg/day in the absence of supplementary vitamin A on an ear-maize diet. When supplementary hay was also given, the response to vitamin E was negligible. Similarly, Chapman *et al.* (1964) obtained a slight response in rate of gain from adding 50 mg vitamin E/day, but, in the presence of supplementary A, addition of vitamin E led to depression of gain in one experiment and to a reduced degree of improvement in another. Although Kohlmeir and Burroughs (1963) claimed that vitamin E improved gains and feed conversion irrespective of the level of vitamin A, examination of their data shows that their vitamin A levels were below what we consider to be necessary for optimum performance on ear-maize diets.

The other factor is the proportion of concentrates in the diet since it has been shown by Alderson *et al.* (1968) that the destruction of vitamin E prior to its leaving the rumen increased linearly with increasing grain in the diet. The practical importance of this can be seen in the data of Dyer (1967) wherein replacing alfalfa with wheat led to increasing response from injected vitamin E in the presence of 1 million IU of injected vitamin A; with vitamin A alone there was no improvement in gain other than at the highest level of concentrate usage. We agree with Dyer (1967) that it is no longer "a question as to whether or not vitamin E is beneficial . . . but rather how much should be fed". In the experiments summarized in Table 9.28 the exact amounts of vitamin E in the basal diets were not given. According to Morrison (1956), maize contains, on average, about 24 IU vitamin E/kg, and on this basis the intake of the control animals in the experiments discussed previously would be some 140 mg/day. This is very much higher than the level recommended by the ARC (1965) for calves given diets which do not contain glycerides of the unsaturated fatty acids. The evidence in the table suggests that the required level may well be some 50 mg/day higher, i.e. of the order of 200 IU/day (0.5–0.7 IU vitamin E/kg live weight/day). In the absence of any other information this can be taken as an approximate guide to the amount of vitamin E that should be included in diets composed primarily of cereal grains.

It is now well established that selenium can fulfil many of the functions of vitamin E, although the mode of action and interrelationships of the two are still imperfectly understood. In diets where supplementary vitamin E is required, there is considerable

TABLE 9.28 EFFECT OF VITAMIN E ON GROWTH IN FATTENING CATTLE

Type of diet	Level of E used (IU/day)	Daily gain: Control (kg)	Daily gain: Change due to vitamin E (%)	Supplementary vitamin A (IU/day)	Authors
Ear maize/citrus meal[a]	50	1.25	−10	50,000	Chapman *et al.*, 1964
Ear maize/citrus meal[a]	250	1.25	−9	50,000	Chapman *et al.*, 1964
100% alfalfa	500[b]	0.68	−9	1 million[b]	Dyer, 1967
Ear maize/citrus meal[a]	50	1.19	−7	25,000	Chapman *et al.*, 1964
Ear maize[c]	100[d]	1.18	−7	20,000	Perry *et al.*, 1968a
Ear maize[c]	100	1.18	−4	20,000	Perry *et al.*, 1968a
Ear maize	100	1.11	−4	20,000	Perry *et al.*, 1968a
Ear maize	100[d]	1.11	−3	20,000	Perry *et al.*, 1968a
Ear maize	100[d]	1.20	−1	—	Perry *et al.*, 1965
Ear maize/citrus meal[a]	250	1.19	0	25,000	Chapman *et al.*, 1964
Ear maize	100	1.20	0	—	Perry *et al.*, 1965
Silage/hay	150	0.97	0	—	Newland *et al.*, 1966
Ear maize	200[d]	0.95	0	20,000	Perry *et al.*, 1968a
Ear maize[e]	40	1.00	2	12,500	Perry *et al.*, 1968a
Ear maize	40	0.96	2	12,500	Perry *et al.*, 1968a
Ear maize	200	0.87	2	nil	Perry *et al.*, 1968a
Ear maize	200[d]	0.87	2	nil	Perry *et al.*, 1968a
Ear maize	200	0.96	2	4 million[b]	Perry *et al.*, 1968a
Ear maize	200[d]	0.96	2	4 million[b]	Perry *et al.*, 1968a
Ear maize/citrus meal[a]	50	1.07	3	nil	Chapman *et al.*, 1964
Ear maize/citrus meal[a]	250	1.07	3	nil	Chapman *et al.*, 1964
Silage/hay	150	0.97	4	1 million[f]	Newland *et al.*, 1966
Ear maize	100[d]	1.01	5	nil	Perry *et al.*, 1968a
Ear maize	200[g]	1.27	6	—	Burroughs *et al.*, 1963
20/80	500[b]	0.65	6	1 million[b]	Dyer, 1967
Ear maize[e]	40	0.97	6	nil	Perry *et al.*, 1968a
All-conc.	0.1[h]	0.94	6	—	Thrasher *et al.*, 1965
Ear maize	150	0.99	7	1 million[f]	Newland *et al.*, 1966
Ear maize	200	0.95	7	20,000	Perry *et al.*, 1968a
Ear maize	100	1.01	7	nil	Perry *et al.*, 1968a
Ear maize/citrus meal[a]	50	1.24	8	25,000	Chapman *et al.*, 1966
60/40	500[b]	0.80	8	1 million[b]	Dyer, 1967
Ear maize	40	0.78	8	nil	Perry *et al.*, 1968a
Ear maize	150	0.99	9	—	Newland *et al.*, 1966
Ear maize	200[g]	1.00	10	—	Burroughs *et al.*, 1963
Ear maize/citrus meal[a]	50	1.22	11	nil	Chapman *et al.*, 1964
Ear maize	100[i]	1.37	11	—	Burroughs *et al.*, 1963
Ear maize	0.1[h]	1.23	12	—	Burroughs *et al.*, 1963
Alfal./conc.[j]	500[b]	0.66	15	1 million[b]	Dyer, 1967
40/60	500[b]	0.66	16	1 million[b]	Dyer, 1967
Alfal./con.[j]	500[b]	0.69	27	1 million[b]	Duyer, 1967

[a] *Ad libitum* feeding on pasture. [b] Injected once only. [c] Plus 5% dehydrated alfalfa. [d] Plus 75 mg vitamin K/day. [e] Plus 0.27 kg dehydrated alfalfa. [f] Injected every 28 days. [g] Plus 70 mg vitamin K/day. [h] g/kg diet. [i] Plus 47 mg vitamin K/day. [j] Alfalfa and concentrates.

economic incentive to use selenium in view of the price differential between the two and the fact that 0.1 mg selenium/kg of diet seems to have a similar effect to 100–200 IU vitamin E fed daily. In the US and the UK the use of selenium in animal feeds is prohibited because of the risk of toxicity. This may well need revision in the light of the experimental evidence described here. Moreover, there are specific conditions, as, for example, high molasses diets, in which the natural vitamin E content is undoubtedly low, and in which the use of selenium at the rate of 0.1 mg/kg feed DM has led to economic benefits in terms of better growth rate and feed conversion (Preston *et al.*, 1969b).

9.7.5 Vitamin K

Although vitamin K is synthesized by bacteria in the alimentary tract of the rumen, Burroughs *et al.* (1963) suggested that there might be a need to include it in certain diets. These workers were the first to give vitamin K to fattening cattle, but its effect was confounded with that of vitamin E, and although the two together were beneficial the response clearly could not be ascribed to either. Subsequently, Perry *et al.* (1968a) using basal rations of ground ear maize, fed steers with 75 mg vitamin K daily, either alone or with vitamin E; the diets were or were not supplemented with vitamin A. Although there were significant responses to vitamin A in one experiment and to A and E combined in another, there was no evidence whatsoever of an effect from vitamin K.

9.8 ANTIBIOTICS

The application of antibiotics in the feeding of fattening cattle was first studied in the early 1950's. Since then a large amount of data has accumulated in the US, principally with respect to oxytetracycline and chlortetracycline, and this is summarized in Table 9.29. In so far as these two antibiotics are concerned, their use at levels of approximately 70 mg/day can be expected to bring about an improvement in growth and feed conversion of the order of 5%. Other antibiotics have been studied, but the data do not permit a definitive conclusion as to their efficacy.

Besides their effect on growth and conversion, these antibiotics have a further economic benefit in that they reduce the incidence of liver abscesses, particularly on all-concentrate diets (§ 11.3.5). The implication from this is that the effect of the antibiotic is to reduce sub-clinical disease. In this respect, Wieser *et al.* (1966) showed that the degree of response to chlortetracycline was inversely related to the rate of growth of the control animals. This experiment was carried out in different farms, but all the animals were Friesian steers and the diet was an all-concentrate one composed of rolled barley and protein supplement. Differences between farms could therefore be expected to reflect mainly differences in environmental conditions. The inference that can be drawn is that the effect of antibiotics is likely to be minimal under good management with the greatest response occurring under stress conditions induced by such factors as climate or housing.

The specific use of antibiotics to combat the effect of transit fever and other stress factors at the commencement of fattening is discussed in §§ 6.8.2 and 11.2.8.

It is sometimes considered that the routine use of antibiotics in livestock feeds results in the suppression of susceptible strains of organisms and the emergence of resistant ones. There is evidence for this in dairy calves (Ingram *et al.*, 1956; Smith and Crabb, 1956, a, b; Glantz, 1962) and some suggestion (Gray, 1962) that the routine usage of antibiotics in liquid feeding systems for veal resulted in loss of effectiveness. On the other hand, Whitelaw *et al.* (1963) reported that when antibiotics were routinely added to the concentrate mixture of early weaned calves at the level of 20 mg/kg diet, there was no fall-off in response even after 4 years of such usage. Elliot (1967), in a review of this subject, considered that the dangers of antibiotics were overrated and that there was no evidence that resistant strains were any more or less virulent than their sensitive counterparts. Despite the increasing numbers of resistant strains, isolated disease was no harder to control nor was there any suggestion in the literature for "the development of the existence of health problems in animals or man that have occurred as a result of antibiotic resistance resulting from feed additives".

9.9 OTHER ADDITIVES

9.9.1 Tranquillizers

Research with tranquillizers began in the late 1950's, the object being to see if these products, by causing mild sedation, would give rise to better feedlot performance. In actual fact the levels used were much lower than the clinical dose needed to bring about sedation and as might be expected no such effect was noted. Indeed, Cartwright (1958) reported that the daily feeding of 10 mg of hydroxyzine was associated with greater nervousness. The early reports on giving low levels of hydroxyzine to feedlot cattle were not encouraging in that there were no significant effects on either growth or feed conversion (Cartwright, 1958; Bradley *et al.*, 1959; Burroughs *et al.*, 1959; Matsushima *et al.*, 1959). Similar negative results occurred with trifluomeprazine (Henderson *et al.*, 1959; Bradley *et al.*; Burroughs *et al.*, 1959). Renewed interest in the use of these products was stimulated by the finding of Sherman *et al.* (1959) that both hydroxyzine and reserpine at 2.5 mg/head/day led to improvements of 5–10% in both feed conversion and daily gain. That this finding was somewhat spurious is shown by our summary of published work (Table 9.30). The median value for feed conversion is zero for both hydroxyzine and reserpine. Although the balance of reports suggest a slight improvement in gain for reserpine, on the much larger number of trials with hydroxyzine the median value is again zero. Data on other tranquillizers are limited but give no reason for modifying the conclusion that there are no economic benefits from giving these products to fattening cattle.

9.9.2 Enzymes

Commercial products containing carbohydrate and proteolytic enzymes have been available for some time, and the possibilities of feeding them to fattening cattle were first investigated by Burroughs *et al.* (1960b). Summarizing the data from ten feedlot experiments, these workers concluded that feed efficiency and gain were improved some 6% with the enzyme preparation agrozyme (a combination of amylase, cellulase, hemicellulase, limit-dextrinase and proteinase). Subsequently, Ward *et al.* (1960) found that an amylolytic enzyme, and a combination of this with a

TABLE 9.29 EFFECT OF ANTIBIOTICS ON GROWTH AND FEED CONVERSION IN FATTENING CATTLE

Antibiotic and level used (mg/day)	Level of concentrates in the diet (%)	Daily gain: Control (kg)	Daily gain: Change with antibiotic (%)	Feed conversion: Control (kg/kg)	Feed conversion: Improvement with antibiotic (%)	Authors
Chlortetracycline						
75		1.17	−27		poorer	Staheli *et al.*, 1956
	80	1.32	−7	8.07	−3	Hentges *et al.*, 1960
22[a]	80	0.95	−5	9.15	−2	Hentges *et al.*, 1960
70	100	1.37	0	6.50	−2	Furr *et al.*, 1968b
11[a]	35	0.38	33		0	Erwin *et al.*, 1956
75		0.90	0		0	Staheli *et al.*, 1956
25	20	0.71	4		0	Hentges *et al.*, 1960
75	20	0.71	3		0	Hentges *et al.*, 1960
83	95	1.26	2	5.90	0	Harvey *et al.*, 1968
70	100	1.31	5	6.79	1	Furr *et al.*, 1968b
22[a]	75	0.92	3	7.24	2	Hentges *et al.*, 1960
22[a]	80	0.95	5	9.15	2	Hentges *et al.*, 1960
70	100	1.42	5	6.37	2	Furr *et al.*, 1968c
62		0.84	5	8.69	3	Stothers & Stringham, 1956
80	80	1.10	6	7.86	3	Perry *et al.*, 1958
22[a]	75	0.92	2	7.24	3	Hentges *et al.*, 1960
76	95	1.06	4	6.50	3	Harvey *et al.*, 1968
70	100	1.30	5	6.37	3	Furr & Carpenter, 1967b
20[a]	100	1.23	5	4.92	4	Wieser *et al.*, 1966
70	100	1.23	5	7.41	5	Furr & Carpenter, 1967b
70	50	1.00	6	10.5	6	Bohman *et al.*, 1957
80	80	0.56	9	16.2	7	Perry *et al.*, 1962
75	50	1.07	11		11	Heinemann & Fanelli, 1963
Oxytetracycline						
80	40	1.13	−3		0	Dodsworth & Ball, 1961
75	80	0.90	6	11.6	0	Sherman *et al.*, 1959
80	60	1.11	1	10.4	2	Kolari *et al.*, 1960
80	40	0.67	0	13.8	3	Dodsworth & Ball, 1961

TABLE 9.29 (cont.)

Antibiotic and level used (mg/day)	Level of concentrates in the diet (%)	Daily gain: Control (kg)	Daily gain: Change with antibiotic (%)	Feed conversion: Control (kg/kg)	Feed conversion: Improvement with antibiotic (%)	Authors
75	80	1.05	3	10.4	3	Shermann *et al.*, 1959
70	60	0.95	2	9.51	3	Kolari *et al.*, 1960
70	70	1.04	4	8.97	5	Kolari *et al.*, 1960
22[a]	80	1.30	2	9.18	6	Hale *et al.*, 1964b
80		1.19	8		7	Marion *et al.*, 1960[a]
80	40	1.03	11	11.1	9	Kolari *et al.*, 1960
	80	0.76	23	6.70	12	Dyer *et al.*, 1957
80	80	1.21	19	9.82	15	Reynolds *et al.*, 1958
Erythromycin thiocyanate						
40	100	1.31	0	6.79	1	Furr *et al.*, 1968b
40	100	1.30	4	6.37	2	Furr & Carpenter, 1967b
40	100	1.23	−1	7.41	5	Furr & Carpenter, 1967b
Zinc bacitracin						
70	100	1.32	0	6.97	0	Durham & Pruett, 1966
70[b]	100	1.32	0	6.97	0	Durham & Pruett, 1966
15[a]	100	1.17	6	4.92	4	Macdearmid, 1967
Tylosin						
5[a]	100		0		0	Macdearmid, 1967
35		1.06	7		3	Raun *et al.*, 1963
Penicillin						
32	50	1.07	9		9	Heinemann & Fanelli, 1963
Oleandomycin						
20	80	1.19	0	6.80	2	Perry *et al.*, 1968b
20	80	1.21	40	9.82	27	Reynolds *et al.*, 1958

[a] mg/kg of diet.
[b] 350 mg for 14 days or 500 mg for 10 days or 1000 mg for 5 days (effect is mean for all three) then 70 mg/day for remainder of 120 day trial.

proteolytic enzyme, actually caused a 6% reduction in feed efficiency as well as reducing gain. Perry *et al.* (1966a) published the results of four trials in which four different commercial enzyme preparations were used. There were more negative than positive effects with regard to feed efficiency, the range being −10 to + 2%, while for gain the situation was equivocal with a range of −18 to + 5%. It would seem that, on balance, enzyme supplements are likely to be more deleterious than beneficial.

9.9.3 Goitrogens, strychnine and cortisone

The possibility that thyroid depressants might be utilized in fattening cattle was investigated by Burroughs *et al.* (1958, 1960a), Marion (1960) and Marion *et al.* (1960b). All of these workers used methimazole (1-methyl 2-mercapto Imadazole). Although the Iowa workers obtained a 50% improvement in gain and a 13% improvement in feed efficiency with the use of 600 mg daily of this product, their experiments were run for only short periods of 35–56 days. In contrast, in the Texas experiments there were no effects on feed conversion and a 4–5% decrease in rate of growth when 300 or 600 mg/day were fed during the last 60 days of a 140 day fattening period. Dietary concentrations of 31 and 62 mg/kg feed had no significant effect on steers in an experiment in Arizona (Blair *et al.*, 1958). Promising results with methylthio-uracil (MTU), were obtained with young bulls in Italy (Bonsembiante, 1961). Subsequently, Terblanche (1967) reported an improvement of 25% in daily gain in young steers given this compound, but this was mostly due to increased gut fill. In older animals given 3 g daily of MTU, gain was improved by 30% in one trial and 33% in another, but as in the previous case dressing percentage was much lower for those that were treated. The author concluded that the major effect of MTU was to increase the accumulation of feed in the digestive tract; there were also problems with respect to tissue residues. The overall evidence rather indicates that goitrogens have little or no value in fattening operations.

There have been two isolated reports on the use of other additives. Strychnine sulphate was given to fattening cattle at the rate of 21 mg/kg feed and, according to Cullison and Ward (1961), led to a very slight improvement in performance. Cortisone acetate was given by Carroll *et al.* (1963b) at the rate of 1 g every 3 weeks and although there was an 8% improvement in gain there was a 6% decrease in feed efficiency.

9.9.4 Buffers

Interest in the addition of buffers to ruminant diets stems from the development of all-concentrate feeding systems and the work of Matrone and his colleagues (1957, 1959). They observed that the sodium and potassium salts of the VFA's, or of bicarbonate, led to significant increases in feed intake and growth in lambs given purified diets which contained no fibre and large amounts of starch. The buffers most commonly used in commercial practice have been sodium and potassium bicarbonate and calcium carbonate and, to a lesser extent, sodium acetate and magnesium carbonate. The experimental work was mostly done in the early 1960's and is summarized in Table 9.31.

All-concentrate diets ranging from rolled barley to ground maize were used and

TABLE 9.30 EFFECT OF TRANQUILLIZERS ON GROWTH AND FEED CONVERSION IN FATTENING CATTLE

Tranquillizer and level used (mg/day)	Level of concentrate in diet (%)	Daily gain		Feed conversion		Authors
		Control (kg)	Change due to tranquillizer (%)	Control (kg/kg)	Improvement due to tranquillizer (%)	
Hydroxyzine						
2.5	40	0.70	−7	13.1	−8	Dodsworth & Ball, 1961
2.5	40	1.19	−3	10.8	−4	Perry *et al.*, 1960
2.5	50	0.90	−8	10.2	−3	Kolari *et al.*, 1959
8.4		1.01	−5	7.66	−3	Clark *et al.*, 1961
1.25	50	0.89	0	9.50	−1	Perry *et al.*, 1960
5.0	50	0.89	0	9.50	−1	Perry *et al.*, 1960
312.5			0		0	Ralston & Dyer, 1959
2.5		1.36	18		0	Koch *et al.*, 1959a
2.5		1.21	−2		0	Marion *et al.*, 1960a
2.5	50	0.87	3	8.57	0	Kolari *et al.*, 1961b
50.0		1.15	3	8.50	0	Clark *et al.*, 1961
2.5	50	0.89	7	9.50	1	Perry *et al.*, 1960
2.5			Increase		Improved	Ralston & Dyer, 1959
12.5			Increase		Improved	Ralston & Dyer, 1959
62.5			0		Improved	Ralston & Dyer, 1959
2.5		0.79	8		Improved	Koch *et al.*, 1959a
10.0	80	0.90	9	11.6	4	Shermann *et al.*, 1959
2.5	50	1.08	3	12.9	4	Perry *et al.*, 1960
2.5		1.15	4	8.50	4	Clark *et al.*, 1961
2.4	80	1.30	10	8.57	5	Shermann *et al.*, 1959
1.25	80	0.90	11	11.6	6	Shermann *et al.*, 1959

2.4	80	1.03	6	10.5	6	Shermann *et al.*, 1959
5.0	30	1.02	13	6.77	12	Preston *et al.*, 1960a
2.4	50	1.55	3			Obracevic *et al.*, 1961
5.0		1.18	3			Marion, 1959
2.5		1.15	8			Marion, 1959
Reserpine						
1.0	40	1.19	−7	10.8	−8	Perry *et al.*, 1960
2.0	40	1.19	−7	10.8	−7	Perry *et al.*, 1960
0.06[a]	50	0.89	2	9.50	−2	Perry *et al.*, 1960
0.06	50	0.89	3	9.50	0	Perry *et al.*, 1960
0.06[a]	80	1.03	3	10.5	1	Shermann *et al.*, 1959
1.0	50	1.08	3	12.9	2	Perry *et al.*, 1960
2.0	50	1.08	3	12.9	3	Perry *et al.*, 1960
0.06[a]	80	1.30	13	8.57	4	Shermann *et al.*, 1959
0.06	80	1.01	8	10.6	6	Shermann *et al.*, 1959
Trifluomeprazine						
5.0	40	1.19	−8	10.8	−7	Perry *et al.*, 1960
10.0	40	1.19	−5	10.8	−6	Perry *et al.*, 1960
5.0	50	1.08	−2	12.9	−1	Perry *et al.*, 1960
2.5	50	1.08	0	12.9	1	Perry *et al.*, 1960
5.0		1.04	−3			Koch *et al.*, 1959a
2.5		1.04	5			Koch *et al.*, 1959a
Paxital						
75.0		0.79	8		Improved	Koch *et al.*, 1959a
Tranimal						
30	80		0		0	Beeson *et al.*, 1963

[a] As Rauwolfia vomitoria (0.24% reserpine equivalent).

TABLE 9.31 EFFECT OF DIETARY BUFFERS ON THE PERFORMANCE OF CATTLE FED ALL-CONCENTRATE DIETS

Buffer and level used (%)	Effect of buffer on feed intake	Daily gain		Feed conversion		Authors
		Control (kg)	Change due to buffer	Control (kg/kg)	Improvement due to buffer (%)	
$NaHCO_3$						
5.0	Increased	1.14	7	5.24	−11	Wise *et al.*, 1962
3	Increased	1.17	3	5.11	−10	Godsell & Preston, 1963
2.0	Increased	1.17	−4	5.11	−8	Godsell & Preston, 1963
3.1	Increased	1.56	6	6.03	−7	Nicholson *et al.*, 1963
1.0	Increased	1.17	1	5.11	−4	Godsell & Preston, 1963
0.5[a]		0.72	26	8.50	5	Cullison & Ward, 1961
0.5[a]		0.88	−14			Cullison & Ward, 1961
0.25[a]		0.68	−7			Cullison & Ward, 1961
0.75[a]		0.68	10			Cullison & Ward, 1961
$NaC_2H_3O_2$						
0.5[a]		0.72	16	8.5	9	Cullison & Ward, 1961
Na_2CO_3						
2.5	Increased	1.14	8	5.24	2	Wise *et al.*, 1962
$CaCO_3$						
0.27[b]	Increased	1.34	−11	5.62	2	Wise *et al.*, 1962
Mixed						
11[c]		0.86	−63	5.80	−46	Wise *et al.*, 1961
6[d]	Increased	1.56	−4	6.03	−13	Nicholson *et al.*, 1963
5[e]		1.14	−12	5.00	−12	Wise *et al.*, 1961
4.6[f]		1.00	−9	7.00	−6	Oltjen & Davis, 1963

[a] In drinking water.
[b] kg/head.
[c] 4% $NaHCO_3$ + 7% $KHCO_3$.
[d] 3% $NaHCO_3$ + 2% $CaCO_3$ + 1% K_2CO_3.
[e] 2% $NaC_2H_3O_2$ + 3% $KC_2H_3O_2$.
[f] 2.1% K_2CO_3, 2% $CaCO_3$ + 0.5% $MgSO_4$.

no additional roughage was given. Most investigators reported increases in feed intake when buffers were added to the feed, and in one instance (Cullison and Ward, 1961), when salts were added to the drinking water, there was an increase in water intake. Despite greater feed consumption, the additional buffers mostly had a deleterious effect on gain and particularly on feed conversion. Coupled with the fact that kidney damage can arise in animals given buffers over extended periods of time (Nicholson *et al.*, 1962, 1963), there is clearly no point in their use under commercial feedlot conditions.

CHAPTER 10

Growth and Efficiency: Climate, Housing and Management

10.1 INTRODUCTION

Cattle are fattened in almost all countries of the world and thus encounter a very wide range of environments. The physical components which determine an environment are the air temperature, the humidity, air movement and solar radiation. Thus in general terms climatic conditions are of four basic types: hot and wet; hot and dry; cold and wet; and cold and dry (Fig. 10.1). We are less concerned with mere survival, for cattle can stay alive in almost all climates except extreme Arctic conditions. Of much greater importance is the extent to which environment affects productivity, for only this knowledge enables decisions to be made as to the degree of modification of an environment which is required to support optimum performance. It must also be emphasized that optimum performance refers to economic optima which are not necessarily synonymous with maximum productivity.

The effects of climate on the animal have two components. The direct effect is on the animal's physiology in terms of its body temperature and respiration rate; this in turn affects feed and/or water intake and thus brings about changes in the animal's productivity. The secondary effect of climate is on the feed supply and health of the animal for, in certain areas, diseases are a serious barrier to efficient production. Furthermore, those countries where environment is at its most severe are frequently in the early stages of development and technical skills tend to be at a low level.

Some theoretical aspects of environmental physiology with particular reference to their interaction with genotype are discussed in Chapter 4. The present chapter is concerned with the direct effects of climate on growth and feed efficiency. Housing and management are also discussed since these represent ways by which an environment can be modified.

Any critical discussion of the subject is made difficult by the paucity of reliable data. Despite the vast amount of work that has been undertaken on the effect of genotype and nutrition on animal performance, very little which is capable of economic interpretation has been carried out on the effect of climate, housing and management. This is well illustrated in Yeates's book on modern aspects of animal production (1965). In the six chapters given over to the influence of climate on the animal, there are virtually no data on the direct effects of this on beef cattle productivity. Most of the studies to do with climate and the animal have been of a fundamental nature concerned with the physiological response to climatological stress and

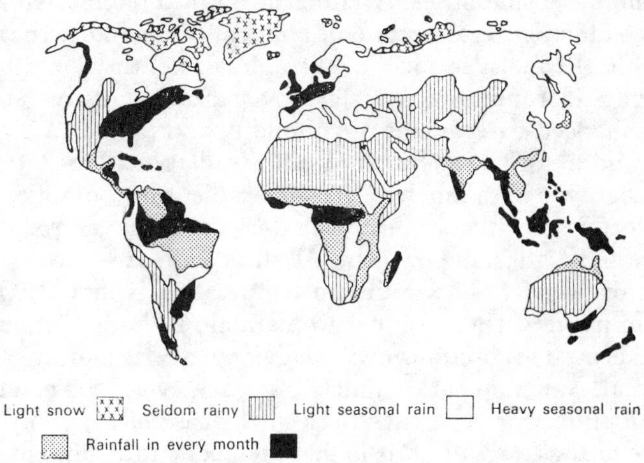

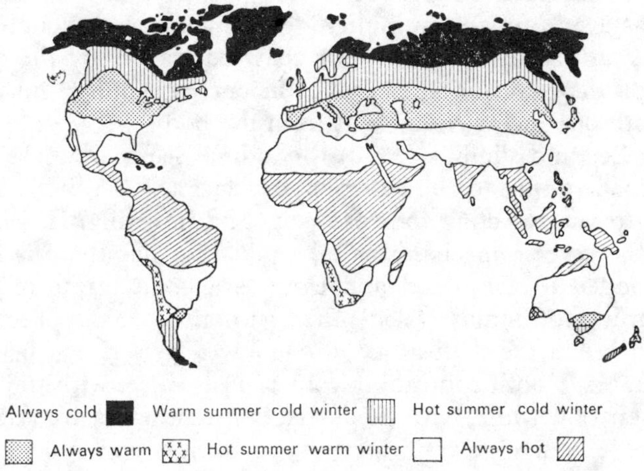

FIG. 10.1 Distribution of climate.

the mechanisms of thermo-regulation. A great deal is known about the nature of the sweat glands of the various breeds, the effects of climate on pulse rate, respiration rate and rectal temperature. In contrast, observations on productivity are conspicuous by their absence and such data as exist have mainly been obtained in climatological chambers with only small numbers of animals. The relevance of much of this information is limited, not merely by the number and atypical nature of the animals used, but also by the fact that, according to Murray (1966), sweat glands may be stimulated more by direct solar radiation than by artificial heat in a laboratory.

10.2 EFFECTS OF CLIMATE

10.2.1 Physiological effects

If there is a difference in temperature between the animal and its environment, heat passes from one to the other by either or all of three mechanisms—radiation, convection or conduction. Irrespective of ambient temperature, heat is also lost by vaporization from the moist surfaces of the animal, i.e. the skin after sweating and from the tongue and respiratory passages by panting. Loss of heat by the latter mechanism is enhanced by reducing air humidity and by increasing air movement. The body can also absorb heat by direct solar radiation. This latter characteristic depends upon coat type in so much as this affects the degree of reflectance (light and glossy coats reflecting much more heat than dark coloured and rough coats) and the insulating properties of the hair coat *per se*. All these traits are considerably modified by factors such as air velocity. The optimum temperature is that at which the animal does not have to use feed energy either to maintain its body temperature or to dissipate excessive heat. This optimum will therefore vary according to the productive state of the animal. At maintenance, much less heat is evolved in metabolism, thus the optimum temperature will be higher than in the case of a rapidly gaining animal producing more heat as a result of its higher metabolic rate. Similarly, a calf obtaining most of its energy supply from its dam's milk has a smaller heat increment (and hence less heat to dissipate) at a given rate of gain than a weaned calf making the same gain on pasture. Rain and humidity also influence heat exchange, not so much by direct effects on insulation of the hair coat, but rather by the cooling effect of water running off the coat during rain and the energy required subsequently to dry out the coat, both of which remove heat from the body.

According to Lee and Phillips (1948) the animal seeks to adjust against cold by reducing the blood supply to the superficial surfaces of the body, removing water from the blood stream, erecting the coat hairs and shivering. In seeking to remove excessive heat the reverse mechanisms take place in that there is increased blood flow, water is added to the blood and there is a greater rate of respiration and sweating. According to Findlay (1950), the first noticeable response to increased air temperature is a rise in the respiratory rate followed by a rise in body temperature. There is adaptation to both continuing cold or heat since, with the former, there is growth of the hair coat while, with the latter, constant levels are attained rapidly in respiration rate (one week), respiratory vaporization and milk production (two weeks), pulse rate (eight weeks); body temperature and hair density continue to decrease after nine weeks (Kibler *et al.*, 1965).

Feed efficiency is affected adversely at both climatic extremes. At temperatures below the optimum, efficiency is reduced since the animal consumes more feed merely to maintain body temperature. In contrast, at elevated ambient temperatures, the animal attempts to lower its heat load by reducing feed intake (Winchester, 1964); this results in a decreased productive rate and hence poorer feed efficiency. Water intake tends to be a function of DM consumption and ambient temperature (Winchester and Morris, 1956). Thus, from −12° to 5°C, water intake tends to be constant thereafter increasing rapidly as the temperature rises to 34°C. According to these workers the slope of the curve varies with species being much steeper for *Bos taurus* cattle than for those of *B. indicus* origin.

Blaxter and Wainman (1961a) considered the lower critical temperature for cattle to be −5°C. In more specific recommendations, Blaxter (1966) proposed that while the critical temperature at maintenance was 7°C, this had fallen to −1°C for a daily gain of 0.50 kg; for gains above 1 kg it is likely that this would be reduced further. Thus it is probable that Sainsbury's (1967) recommendation of −7°C for intensively fed housed beef cattle is acceptable. There are fewer data concerning the upper limit above which feed energy begins to be directed towards heat dissipation. Yeck and Stewart (1959) considered that productive rate would be reduced at ambient temperatures above 25°C, which is considerably greater than the 15°C suggested by Sainsbury. The upper limit is likely to be modified by the relative humidity in that Ragsdale *et al.* (1953) found feed intake to be unaffected at temperatures of 35°C when the relative humidity was low, but began to decline rapidly at 24°C under conditions of high humidity.

Yeck and Stewart (1959) considered that relative humidity had little direct effect on animal productivity except at air temperatures in excess of 25°C. They reported that performance was reduced by 31% when relative humidity was 90% with an air temperature of 44°C. Sainsbury (1967) also thought that humidity *per se* was unlikely to have any direct effect upon productivity within the range of 30–80%. With housed animals he considered that high humidity at normal or subnormal temperatures led to condensation and this is known to play an important role in transmission of disease (Loosmore, 1964). At high air temperature, high humidity increases the difficulty experienced by the animal in dissipating heat by vaporization.

The effect of air velocity is similarly modified by ambient temperature. Thus Blaxter and Wainman (1961a) showed that increasing air speed from 0.87 to 4.05 m^3/min increased heat loss by about 6% when the environmental temperature was 0°C but had no effect at 20°C. In practical terms, this is only likely to be important in animals kept at maintenance and sub-maintenance levels of nutrition. Brody *et al.* (1954) subjected dairy cows to air speeds of from 0.8 to 14.4 km/hr at temperatures ranging from −8° to 35°C with no appreciable effects on milk production, other than a slight tendency to increase feed consumption at the highest temperature and the faster air velocity. In this respect, however, stocking density may well play an important role. Thus Morgan and Parker (1964) considered that the reduction in the efficiency of heat loss as a result of housing beef cattle at a high density (one animal per $2m^2$) could be equivalent to a rise in environmental temperature of about 5°C in comparison with low density housing as used in extensive systems.

10.2.2 Modification of the environment

10.2.2.1 SHADE. Although shade and shelter are sometimes considered synonymous, we prefer to define shade as protection against solar radiation while shelter is protection against rain, wind and snow. In early studies on this subject, McDaniel and Roark (1956) compared the performance of Hereford and Angus cows and calves given access to different types of shade on improved pasture. The shade treatments studied were nil, abundant natural, scanty natural and artificial. In a 4 year study, during which maximum temperatures were of the order of 32°C with relative humidities of about 63%, they found that in the absence of shade cows lost weight, whereas significant gains were made on all the other treatments. The effect on the calves was less severe. There were physiological symptoms of stress on the unshaded pastures and less time spent grazing during daylight hours (6 a.m. to 7 p.m.). Fattening steers in southern Florida responded to shade in terms of better growth rate (Peacock *et al.*, 1965).

Considerable work has been done in the Imperial Valley, California where, during the summer, the climate is characterized by clear skies, effectively no rain, a high maximum (31°C) and a low minimum temperature (12°C), and fairly low relative humidity. Garrett *et al.* (1960) gave 11 m² of shade per head in wire corrals in which each animal had about 33 m² floor area. Daily gains were improved from 0.74 to 1.03 kg and conversions from 9.94 to 8.51. Animals with shade drank slightly more water although this was less when expressed as a function of DM intake. In a subsequent trial with high energy diets fed *ad libitum*, there were no differences in performance attributable to the use of shade, although respiration rate and surface and rectal temperatures were less during the hot part of the day (Garrett *et al.*, 1966). This latter experiment is the more valid because larger numbers of animals were used (16 and 30 per treatment in each of 2 years compared with only 6 in the first experiment). These same workers (Garrett *et al.*, 1962) studied the effect of the amount of shade relative to total space allotment, using 180 head for 3 years in a factorial design. The average daily temperature was 33°C with a range of 24–42° and a relative humidity of 30 to 73%. There were no effects on gain between a shaded area of 2.5 or 4.4 m²/head; similarly, total space allotment of 8.4, 12.5, or 18.5 m²/head did not significantly affect gains although there was a slight tendency to improve feed efficiency with increasing area. There were no interactions between shade and total area, or between these and plane of nutrition.

In Kansas, Boren *et al.* (1960) studied the effect of shade from June to October on the performance of Hereford heifers. The shades were 3.1–3.7 m high and allowed 2.8 m² of shade per animal. The use of shades led to increased gains and better feed conversion. Similar findings were reported from Missouri by Dyer *et al.* (1967). A sheet metal shade was preferred to a slatted (snow fence) arrangement when temperatures exceeded 32°C.

10.2.2.2 Air movement. Ittner *et al.* (1955) considered pen design to be important in that there was 2.1 km/hr greater air velocity in pens made from wire cables as opposed to wooden board fencing. Garrett *et al.* (1960) also appeared to obtain better performance in corrals made of wire rather than wood and this system of construction is in general use in feedlots in the south-western States.

The Californian workers have also studied the effect of increasing air movement by installing fans. Ittner *et al.* (1957) reported the results of 70 day trials carried out between July and September in each of 2 years; air temperature at 2 p.m. was 39°C with 18–20% relative humidity. In both years the greater air movement induced by the fans increased feed intake and daily gains and improved feed conversion. Later however, Garrett *et al.* (1960) found that fans gave no apparent benefit in shaded cable-fenced pens whether used during the day, the night or permanently. Natural air velocity was 3.9 km/hr and was increased to 6.0 by use of fans. In a subsequent trial comparing the use of shade and fans separately or together, respiration rate and rectal and surface temperatures were reduced by fans when there was no shade but were unchanged when shade existed; performance data tended to be better with the use of shade.

In an attempt to study the effect of climate on animal performance under commercial conditions, Riggs (1966) fed 12 Hereford steers in each of six different locations throughout Texas. The ranges were: 976 m of altitude; 889 mm annual rainfall;

16% relative humidity; and 9°C mean temperature; locations varied 885 km east to west and 756 km north to south. There were significant differences between stations with respect to pulse rate, rectal temperature and respiration rate. This latter was correlated with ambient temperature at all locations and with body temperature at the three lower, warmer and more humid stations; wind movement was important at the high, warm locations. Despite these differences in physiological response, gains at the three lower, wetter and warmer stations were almost identical with those at the three higher, drier and cooler locations. Feed intake, water consumption, feed efficiency and carcass traits were similarly unaffected by the variations in climate.

In Alabama, Harris *et al.* (1967) studied the effect of refrigerating the drinking water for steers fed an 80:20 ration for 78 days. Air temperature was 31°C and water temperatures 29°C for controls and 18°C for the treated animals. The results, repeated over three years, indicated no differences in daily gain, feed conversion or carcass traits.

10.2.2.3 SHELTER. Crawford and Butcher (1966) in Utah used individually fed Hereford heifers given 94% concentrate rations to study complete, partial or no shelter for 120 days under feed-lot conditions. Partial shelter involved a roof over the bedded and feeding areas; outside temperature during the trial ranged from −20° to 5°C (mean −2.7°C), while inside temperatures ranged from −10° to 5°C (mean 0.1°C). There were no significant differences in feed intake or daily gain but feed conversion was 6.5 with partial shelter compared with 7.6 for the other two treatments; this difference approached significance. There was some degree of correlation between weekly weight changes and the air temperature but these were also influenced by precipitation (snow and rain); feed intake, on the other hand, varied much less than live weight and did not appear to be related to temperature.

Results of two trials with 234 steers undertaken in Iowa demonstrated a consistent improvement in gain (19 and 17%) and feed conversion (18 and 15%) for shelter (4.4 m^2/head) compared with a 2 m high wooden windbreak (Self *et al.*, 1963). Later, Self (1967) quoted South Dakota and Ohio experiments in which shelter led to slight improvements in performance. These studies, conducted over 2 and 5 years respectively, suggested that provision of shelter led to reduced feed costs such that the additional investment would be repaid within 2 years. In the Ohio trials there were suggestions of improved carcass quality and dressing percentage in animals given access to shelter. Both investigations were carried out under winter conditions but the results of summer trials carried out in Ohio for 4 years were similar to those obtained in winter.

The effect of fattening cattle in sheds as opposed to open yards was studied by Bennett and O'Mary (1965) in Washington State. Outside temperatures ranged from −8.1° to 3°C and during the period of the trial there were 171 mm of rain and 196 mm of snow. Hereford and Shorthorn heifers and Hereford and crossbred steers were compared in each of the two environments. Improvement in daily gain through housing was 13–14% and identical for the different breed sex combinations. Kearl *et al.* (1965) in Utah also found that housing during winter led to significant improvements of 20% in daily gain and 17% in feed conversion. In Illinois, Heuberger (1968) compared open dirt yards with a system whereby animals had access to a shed and a paved open yard. During the winter (November to March) those kept in open yards without shelter grew 12% slower and had a 14% poorer feed conversion; from June to September gains for outside cattle were 7% slower and feed conversion 4% poorer. The open-yard system was particularly inappropriate during the spring rains.

Under cold conditions there may be advantages in warming the drinking water. In Hungary, Illes and Godeny (1967) claimed a 54% increase in winter gain and 75% during summer as a result of giving the drinking water heated to 18°C. However, the trial was with growing heifers and absolute performance was poor.

10.2.2.4 SLATTED FLOORS AND BEDDING. The benefits of paved outside lots reported by Heuberger (1968) are supported by Ohio findings (Self, 1967) that feed conversion was improved 10% when yards were concreted. Labour costs were twice as high for dirt floors and the disparity was even greater under conditions of very wet weather; over a 5 year period there were no differences between the two systems in gain or feed costs, but it took three times as long to clean and maintain the unconcreted yards. Moreover, additional soil had to be brought into the dirt lots to maintain the surface. Previous work in Iowa (Self *et al.*, 1963) was less conclusive although tending to favour complete paving of the feedlot.

Henderson and Newland (1966b) compared a completely roofed installation with a concrete floor and bedding against a system with only the bedded area covered and a third treatment in which all the area was covered and the floor was of earth. There were no effects on average daily gain or feed conversion but straw use was highest with the partially covered system during the winter period; by comparison the completely covered concrete floor required more straw in the summer.

The use of slatted floors as a means of avoiding the need for bedding was pioneered in Scandinavia and introduced in the north of Scotland in the late 1950's and in the US in the early 1960's. Comprehensive surveys of their use in commercial practice in the UK were undertaken by Baxter and Soutar (1964) and Livingston (1965). Although these reports did not include comparisons with other systems the economic advantages of slats is apparent. Thus in the Scottish survey of over 1000 cattle on 12 different farms performance was consistently high (in excess of 1.35 kg per day) and there was almost complete absence of injuries. According to Livingston (1965) cattle performed equally well on various types of slats but "looked better" and commanded better prices at slaughter than cattle kept on bedding.

Klosterman *et al.* (1965b) in the US compared steel slatted floors and straw bedding. They used 24 cattle per treatment and concluded that there were no basic differences in daily gain, feed intake or conversion rate between the two systems; bedded animals required 4 kg of straw per day. In a subsequent comparison on slats versus bedding with or without shelter, Klosterman (1966) reported a tendency for better performance on straw bedding but that animals on slats were fatter. Those on bedding required 3–5 kg of straw per head daily and considerably more man-hours for spreading it. Manure produced under the slatted floors was about 13 kg/head/day compared with 25 kg when straw bedding was used. In Michigan, Henderson and Newland (1966a) fed an 80:20 ration to cattle kept in insulated buildings on either solid concrete or slatted floors; a third treatment was an open-sided building with straw bedding. Daily gains were 0.98, 0.95 and 1.06 kg/day for the three treatments, respectively, with feed conversions of 8.90, 8.88 and 8.29. The latter figure did not include 2.7 kg of bedding straw per kg of gain. In the UK there were no differences between Friesian steers given an all-concentrate diet and kept on concrete slatted floors or on sawdust deep litter (RRI, 1964).

In commercial practice in the UK it has sometimes been reported that slatted floors can be predisposing to feet problems, particularly arthritic conditions. Our own experience in Cuba shows conclusively that this is not a problem in the tropics; however, a factor which must be considered is pen design. The greater stocking density that slatted floors allow tends to restrict air movement, thus it is particularly important that pen divisions and fences be as open as possible. There is some suggestion from our work in Cuba that performance has been reduced when slatted floors have been combined with semi-solid concrete walls.

The evidence under a wide variety of conditions would thus suggest that there are no differences in animal performance whether the cattle are kept on bedding or on slatted floors. Preference for one or other system will hence be determined by factors other than growth and feed conversion. Slatted floors offer distinct advantages in the humid tropics where conventional dry lots are almost uninhabitable during the heavy rains; this is particularly the case when high forage feeds are used.

10.2.2.5 Tied or loose housing. It has been traditional practice in some parts of northern Europe to tie cattle individually during fattening. The system had its origins in the better control of rationing when concentrates were given in limited quantities. For intensive systems of feeding, based on *ad libitum* concentrates, present evidence indicates that results with tied cattle are inferior to those with loose housing. In Yugoslavia, Isakov (1961) compared bulls and steers loose in groups or tied individually and found that while there were no differences between the two systems for bulls, tied steers grew 6% slower and had a 5% poorer feed conversion. Similar results were obtained with steers in experiments with all-concentrate diets in the UK (RRI, 1964). Robertson and Laing (1965) found no differences between yarded and individually tied cattle with respect to growth, but feed efficiency favoured the animals kept loose. It is of interest that bloat and lameness were considerably higher when cattle were tied.

10.2.2.6 Lighting. Although lighting patterns have been extensively studied in the poultry industry, little experimentation has been undertaken with beef cattle. Robertson and Lipper (1963) reported on Kansas work with 250 heifers in which there were slightly higher gains and a 13% reduction in feed costs per kilogram of gain as a result of giving continuous lighting. However, as they pointed out there were differences in the starting times of the control and experimental animals which makes interpretation difficult. The implication is that cattle will eat more under a continuous lighting system, but there is a possibility that after a period of time with the new lighting pattern animals may revert to their previous feeding habits. More work obviously is required before any definitive conclusions on this aspect of management can be made.

10.3 MANAGEMENT PRACTICES

10.3.1 Pen size and building design

As with climatic factors very little experimentation has been undertaken on building design, probably because of the considerable investment required for such research. In the absence of data one can only summarize commercial experience under as wide a variety of conditions as possible.

In the authors' experience of intensive beef units employing slatted floor designs and centred in many different countries, pen size has been determined primarily by the dimensions of the building. General preference has been for groups of between 10 and 15 animals. Baxter and Soutar (1964), in their report on 12 intensive beef units in north-east Scotland, found that the average number of animals per pen was between 10 and 12. On the basis of their survey they recommended a floor area per animal of 1 m^2 at a live weight of 100 kg rising to 2 m^2 as the animal approached slaughter weight (400 kg). Since, in general, long narrow buildings of about 8 m in width facilitate natural air movement a convenient pen figuration is with divisions every 3 m.

In high density intensive beef units, siting is of major importance. As indicated previously buildings should be long and narrow; they should also be orientated in an east–west direction and have sloping roofs. By this means effect of solar radiation is minimized in high temperature regions, while in cooler areas the lower trajectory of the winter sun means that the southern exposure will receive more heat than if siting was in any other direction.

10.3.2 Feeding and watering systems

Experience indicates that self-feeding hoppers should permit a feeding space of some 7.5 cm/head, with a minimum feed capacity of 10 kg/head. They should be sited away from water bowls and gates and have adjustable openings. Baxter and Soutar (1964) found that, on average, one water bowl was installed for every 12–16 animals. In open-sided buildings it is important that these are sited outside the pen to avoid fouling with excrement. In hot climates they should be shaded and, in general, connecting pipes sited underground so as to ensure that drinking water is as cool as possible. When large quantites of forage are given the use of tombstone-type fences reduces waste to a minimum and, in slatted floor installations, helps to prevent forage collecting underneath the floors, a cause of considerable problems if sludge is to be removed by suction.

10.3.3 Feeding patterns

With all-concentrate feeding systems there are considerable labour saving advantages from the use of self-feeding hoppers to which cattle have free access. Under these conditions one might expect specific selection for individual ingredients to occur as was suggested by Baker (1965). However, he offered no evidence to justify his statement, and feed selection is certainly not a problem in large-scale American feedlots where ground mixed diets are preferred practice. Our own experience with *ad libitum* feeding of performance-test bulls has shown that feed selection is not a problem even with animals penned individually. Putnam *et al.* (1967a) offered animals choice of diets containing 25 or 89% roughage given either pelleted or ground. Animals preferred to eat the low roughage pelleted diet and had least preference for the low roughage ground diet but there was no evidence of selection within a diet. In an earlier paper (Putnam and Davis, 1963), using the same rations, feeding time was considerably less with those that were pelleted and diets low in hay.

Techniques of feed rationing are of somewhat academic interest under conditions of commercial practice where almost invariably the aim is to secure the maximum intake. Certain comparisons have been made with respect to frequency of feeding but with conflicting results. Rakes *et al.* (1957) observed significantly better gains in growing heifers on a forage diet given 10 times rather than twice daily. Mohrman *et al.* (1959) fed a 65% concentrate diet either twice or 6 times per day; gains were 20% higher and feed conversions 17% better with greater feeding frequency. In a subsequent trial using a 74% concentrate ration fed twice, 6 times or *ad libitum*, these same workers obtained gains of 0.79, 0.88 and 0.90 kg/day respectively with feed intakes of 8.4, 8.8 and 9.6 kg/day; conversion ratios were 10.6, 10.0 and 10.7. In contrast, Purdue workers (Hillier *et al.*, 1965) claimed that hand feeding (presumably twice daily) a predominantly maize silage ration gave a slight advantage in growth and conversion compared with the same amount given automatically at 4 hr intervals. This report is clearly at variance with the majority of findings. In a review of the subject, Mochrie (1964) also concluded that the greater proportion of experiments showed growth responses to frequent feeding. Energy concentration and level of feeding may be important factors. Most of the work discussed by Mochrie related to low energy diets, and Orskov and Allen (1966a) have shown a differential response according to nutritional plane. There was an advantage to frequent feeding at maintenance but none when the energy allowance was such as to support rapid rates of gain.

Although it is frequently claimed that restricted feeding gives better feed conversions, and this is common practice in UK pig production, the situation is clearly different with cattle. On all-concentrate diets Albin and Durham (1967) found that *ad libitum* feeding gave 14% better gains and 4% better feed conversion than when the animals were restricted to 92% of the consumption of the *ad libitum* group. Moreover, animals fed *ad libitum* had fatter carcasses.

It is normal to feed heifers and steers separately but the findings of Hawkins *et al.* (1967b) indicate that there may be little scientific justification for the practice. There was no effect on economic traits in a 234 day feeding trial when heifers were fed in the same corrals as steers or separately.

CHAPTER 11

Disease

11.1 INTRODUCTION

In this chapter we intend to concern ourselves solely with disease conditions associated with intensive beef production and of these only the most frequently encountered and economically important. We have attempted to be comprehensive in so far as metabolic disturbances are concerned since these generally are specific to feedlot cattle and are intimately linked with management and feeding.

Intensive beef cattle are susceptible to all forms of bovine disease, although, by virtue of their confinement and method of feeding, they are protected from certain nutritional and infectious conditions which frequently affect range and pasture cattle. On the other hand, their very intensification predisposes them to diseases associated with stress conditions. They are often moved great distances from the range or rearing units to the feedlot and again when they go to slaughter; their diet may be changed rapidly from roughages to concentrates; and they are kept in relatively crowded conditions particularly in the dairy beef systems in Europe. On top of all this, they are expected to grow to the limit of their genetic potential, hence, as in any mechanical or biological system which is driven to the maximum, the possibilities of breakdown are that much greater.

11.2 DISEASES CAUSED BY PATHOGENS

11.2.1 Anaplasmosis

This disease is caused by a protozoa *Anaplasma marginale* which is transmitted by cattle ticks of many different kinds. It is common in the tropics and sub-tropics but is rarely encountered in temperate climates. In the US it occurs in the south-eastern states from Texas up to Virginia and on the west coast from California through to Montana. It is found in Central and South America, Africa, Asia and Australia.

According to Oglesby (1962) the losses in the US from this disease amounted to $35 million annually, while Riemenschneider (1962) considered that there were 50,000 deaths per year. To the private individual losses can be catastrophic with up to 28% deaths in affected animals (McDowell *et al.*, 1964).

The disease can occur in all breeds, but in our experience it is likely to be most severe in European cattle imported to tropical areas where the disease is endemic. Young calves up to 6 months of age are highly resistant possibly as a result of maternal immunity coupled with the high plane of nutrition offered by the dam's milk.

Susceptibility increases with age and the most severely affected are mature animals. It is often considered that *Bos indicus* cattle are naturally resistant to the disease, but this is almost certainly an acquired immunity through the calves being exposed to the disease at a stage when they are still highly resistant. Certainly we have found the same resistance in Charolais, Criollo and Santa Gertrudis maintained from birth in the same conditions and exposed to the same risk as Brahmans. Even Holsteins and their crosses appear to be no more susceptible than the so-called resistant breeds provided they are exposed to the disease early in life, however, they succumb very quickly when contacting it for the first time as adults. McDowell *et al.* (1964) also considered there were no differences in resistance to infection among Holstein, Jersey or Red Sindhi crosses maintained as dairy animals.

In calves with natural resistance the disease may pass unnoticed since in the mild form the usual symptoms are loss of appetite and slight fever. In susceptible animals the most striking effect of the disease is a very rapid loss in live weight. The animal becomes anaemic and has a high temperature. Untreated, the disease continues through to emaciation and death.

The pathogen is mainly carried by ticks but mosquitoes and other blood-sucking insects may also be implicated (Roby, 1962). Anaplasmosis is thus most likely to develop when the vector population is most active. If susceptible stock have to be brought into an affected region, this should be done during the winter months and preferably at the earliest possible age. The obvious method of eliminating the disease is to eliminate carrier insects. Under feedlot conditions this is done comparatively easily by routine spraying or dipping. This is particularly important when new batches of animals arrive at the feedlot. In some countries inoculation is practised with blood from infected carrier animals, but this can only safely be done in young stock which still carry natural resistance. Following such an inoculation there is a mild reaction and subsequently the animals become resistant carriers. Under feedlot conditions it is almost certainly more economic to slaughter affected animals rather than attempt to cure them.

11.2.2 Clostridial diseases

11.2.2.1 Enterotoxaemia. This is an acute, infectious, non-contagious disease caused by *Clostridium perfringens* type D (previously called *C. welchii*). Organisms of this strain (of which there are four distinct types A, B, C and D) are more widely known as causal agents of sheep diseases such as lamb dysentery and haemorrhagic enterotoxaemia. The economic importance of disease caused by these pathogens is much less in cattle than in sheep where considerable losses occur unless protective vaccination is adopted. The organisms are normal inhabitants of soil and faeces and usually gain entry to the digestive system through contamination of feed or water.

The disease can occur in feedlot cattle at all stages. Entry of the pathogens into the digestive tract is not necessarily a hazard as they are usually destroyed before reaching the intestine; and even should some pass into the small intestine and produce toxin the condition is not serious when the ration is based on roughages. Danger only seems to arise under conditions of high concentrate feeding when starch also passes into the intestine thereby creating conditions for the rapid multiplication of the pathogen and consequent increased production of toxin to dangerous levels.

Bullen and Scarisbrick (1957) demonstrated that infusion of these organisms directly into the intestine of sheep through a fistula only produced enterotoxaemia when starch (wheat grain) was administered simultaneously.

Usually the first notification of the disease is a dead animal. If observed immediately prior to death the animals may display signs of muscular incoordination. Other symptoms of the disease involve a paralytic stage, the animal rapidly becoming comatose. Infected animals have negligible chances of survival.

One way of preventing the disease would be to use only roughages in the fattening programme, but this is economically pointless if intensive production is sought. Even if an outbreak occurs, there is little to be gained by changing the diet of the remainder, for there is no certainty that other animals will become affected. In fact, there will be greater economic loss from changing the diet than potential benefit from saving one or two animals. Where there is a history of the disease the only effective control is preventative vaccination with attenuated strains of the organism.

11.2.2.2 Quarter ill or blackleg. This is a non-contagious acute disease caused by *C. chauvoei* and related bacteria. It is of low economic importance although infected animals invariably succumb. As with enterotoxaemia, there are some indications that incidence is higher under conditions of all-concentrate feeding (Bowers, 1968). The pathogens gain entry to the tissues through wounds and injuries or even by the digestive tract. Thus surgical castration or dehorning can provoke outbreaks. The disease can occur in animals of all ages or breed, but those in good physical condition and gaining weight rapidly tend to be the more susceptible, since their tissues form a better substrate for the pathogen.

In our experience the first notification of the disease is a dead animal. In temperate climates the incubation period may be from 2 to 4 days before clinical symptoms (loss of appetite, general depression, rapid respiration and oedoematous swellings around the point of infection) are observed; on the other hand, in tropical conditions we have observed that animals injured one day are dead the next and clinical symptoms are non-existent. Dead animals present a typical bloated appearance due to the presence of gas in the muscle tissue.

Since wounds and injuries predispose the animal to infection, care should be taken to minimize handling and to design pens and buildings so that sharp protuberances are avoided. This is particularly important with automatic self-feeding equipment. Where there is a history of the disease the only sure method of prevention is by vaccination with attenuated strains of the organism, as the pathogens are normal inhabitants of the soil, alimentary tract, skin surfaces and faeces.

11.2.2.3 Other conditions. Much of what has been said about Blackleg applies also to Malignant oedema, the causal agents of which are *C. septicum* and related anaerobes. Tetanus (*C. tetani*) has a similar etiology but acts upon the central nervous system. Both diseases are of low economic importance although infected animals invariably die.

Vaccination with attenuated strains of the organisms is the only known method of prevention. Since *perfringens*, *chauvoei*, *septicum* and *tetani* have similar characteristics it is common practice to prepare a polyvalent vaccine so that a single treatment gives protection against all four diseases.

11.2.3 Footrot

This is a chronic contagious disease generally caused by *Spherophorus necrophorus*. According to Jensen and Mackey (1965) this disease is responsible for 40–60% of all foot problems in cattle. It is particularly prevalent in unpaved feedlots during the wet or winter months. The exact etiology is not known, but probably the primary cause is damage to the foot permitting access of *S. necrophorus* which then spreads through the neighbouring tissues. It is very contagious and spreads rapidly from infected to susceptible animals.

Signs of the disease are lameness and swelling of the lower part of the leg. Mortality is negligible, the economic loss resulting from poor performance during the period of the infection.

Most effective prevention is the use of slatted floor buildings which immediately rules out possibilities of infection or reinfection. In the normal US style feedlot useful measures are to concrete the feeding and watering points and to provide adequate drainage. The use of foot baths is often advocated as a means of controlling the disease, but there is no experimental evidence as to their real effectiveness.

11.2.4 Keratitis or pinkeye

This is an acute or chronic contagious disease caused by a variety of agents. Wilcox (1968) considered *Moraxella bovis* to be the major pathogen, but its role is by no means certain. Thus Griffin *et al.* (1965) in Nigeria isolated *M. bovis* in only 6 out of 30 cases. Anon. (1965d) exposed cattle to *M. bovis*, sunlamps or the two combined. The bacteria alone produced only mild keratitis, sunlamps induced eye injury but the two together gave severe keratitis.

The disease appears to be manifested more frequently in young cattle (Farley *et al.*, 1950) and is alleged to be more prevalent in white-faced (non-pigmented) breeds such as the Hereford (Jackson, 1953). Griffin *et al.* (1965) found it more prevalent in Friesians than White Fulani (which have pigmented skins). Our own experience in Cuba confirms a greater incidence among Holstein than a variety of beef breeds.

Mortality is effectively nil, the loss arising through poor performance. Very rarely do animals develop fatal meningitis. However, once established, the infection can spread very rapidly through a herd (Sykes *et al.*, 1964; Spradbrow, 1967). The disease may occur in one or both eyes and affects the conjuntiva producing copious lachrymation. Due to the severe pain the animal tries to keep its eye closed and seeks out darkened areas.

Affected animals should preferably be isolated. A cure is often spontaneous and according to Wilcox (1968) some form of immunity may persist after recovery from attack. Avoidance of excessively dusty feeds and good fly control help to keep disease incidence to a minimum.

11.2.5 Parasites (gastrointestinal)

Intestinal parasites are not usually a serious problem in intensive beef production. In most US feedlots animals are selected for fattening on the basis of their physical condition, thus parasitized animals are indirectly selected against at the very beginning; while, in intensive dairy beef production, parasites have little opportunity to gain access to the animal. However, in certain areas where systems of range management are not well developed, and particularly in developing countries and tropical regions where cattle may be 2 and 3 years old before entering the feedlot, animals are invariably heavily parasitized on arrival. Since there is little possibility of reinfection in a feedlot, the disease rarely increases in severity and mortality is negligible. There is, nevertheless, a considerable economic loss if these animals are not treated since they grow slowly with resultant poor feed conversion. Parasitism is intimately linked with the nutritional status of the animal as was demonstrated by Riedel and Arnold (1956) and Ciordia and Baird (1968).

Vegors *et al.* (1956) found negligible larval numbers in cattle fattened on high concentrate diets in drylot than on pasture (23 vs. 1926), but more adult worms (10,770 vs. 5700). This was largely due to intestinal worms (7500 vs. 3600). Cattle are rarely completely free of parasites but a mild infestation is of little consequence when the nutritional plane is high.

Moderate parasitic infestations are characterized by general unthriftiness and poor rates of growth. Thus Vegors *et al.* (1956) found a negative correlation between total worm load and rate of live weight gain. This was confirmed by Ciordia and Baird (1968). Heavy worm burdens lead to loss of body weight, dry and staring coats, anaemia and diarrhoea, and there is evidence that heavy infestations of *Ostertagia* spp. adversely affect phosphorus utilization in young calves (Waymack *et al.*, 1968). Severely affected animals may die, less from parasitism than from secondary causes likely to be triggered off by stress conditions such as change of diet, transportation or handling. Less severe nematode infestations did not appear to be related to incidence of shipping fever in Illinois (Szanto *et al.*, 1964).

Prevention is usually out of the hands of the feedlot operator. Animals most likely to be parasitized are those coming from poor range at ages between 12 and 18 months. Procured at weaning, most calves will be only mildly infested. This is the best stage at which to purchase animals from regions with a known history of parasite problems.

In view of the large number of adult worms (but not larvae) in drylot cattle, Vegors *et al.* (1956) emphasized the need for antheliminitic treatment at the start of fattening. Treatment is relatively simple as there is a large range of proprietary products available, many of them with a comparatively wide spectrum so that they are effective against most of the species likely to be encountered. Resistance of the parasite may develop and render certain drugs less effective with time (Shelton, 1968). This emphasizes the importance to the feedlot operator of keeping abreast with new developments.

11.2.6 Parasites (external)

11.2.6.1 Ticks. The major ticks found on cattle and the diseases they cause or transmit are set out in Table 11.1. In the main they are of economic significance only in tropical and sub-tropical areas, and Suares (1963) estimated that meat production in the Argentine would be increased by 300,000 tons if ticks could be eradicated. Ticks themselves cause little damage other than anaemia in cases of severe infestation. Their economic significance is as carriers of diseases such as Redwater fever, East Coast fever, anaplasmosis and piraplasmosis. None of these diseases is likely to

TABLE 11.1 CATTLE TICKS AND THE DISEASES THEY TRANSMIT OR PRODUCE

Tick species	Location	Disease transmitted or produced
Amblyoma spp.	Tropics, subtropics	Heart water, Q fever
Boophilus spp.	Subtropics and temperate	Anaplasmosis, piraplasmosis, babesiosis, (red water fever)
Dermacentor spp.	Subtropics and temperate	Anaplasmosis, Q fever, tick paralysis, tularaemia
Ixodes spp.	Tropics, subtropics	Tularaemia, anaplasmosis
Rhipicephalus spp.	Tropics	East coast fever, red water fever

occur in feedlot cattle provided normal precautions are taken at entry, and there is a buffer zone between the outskirts of the feedlot and grazing animals.

An important exception to the general rule is the disease known as tick paralysis which is caused by a neuro-toxin produced by the female tick. This can lead to death from respiratory failure.

11.2.6.2 SCABIES. This is a chronic, contagious dermatitis caused by four types of ectoparasite namely *Psoroptes*, *Sarcoptes*, *Coreoptes* and *Demodex*. The disease has occasionally produced severe losses in cattle feedlots due specifically to loss in body weight (Tobin, 1962). In the US, diseases caused by the first three of these parasites are notifiable and control is then in the hands of the state authorities.

11.2.6.3 FLIES. Most species are a source of annoyance to cattle and if not controlled may impair growth and feed conversion. Major species are stable flies (*Stomoxys calcitrans*), horse flies (*Tabanus* spp.), face flies (*Musca automnalis*), house flies (*M. domestica*) and horn flies (*Hematobia irritans*). In certain countries mosquitoes (*Aedes aegypti*) and the tsetse fly (*Glossina* spp.), which transmits the disease trypanosomiasis, are a serious problem. Most flies breed on faeces and the regular removal of excreta is a means of control. For this reason the use of slatted floors helps to reduce the fly problem.

Warble flies (*Hypoderma lineatum* and *H. bovis*) are serious pests of grazing cattle in temperate climates. The major economic damage is to the hide which in many cases can be rendered valueless by the multiple perforations caused by the emerging larvae. They are not a problem of intensive dairy beef production where calves are housed from birth, and clearly the earlier that range-reared calves are weaned the less the probability of the disease occurring.

Certain drugs administered in the feed can be a highly effective means of control. Thus Cox *et al.* (1964) obtained good control with Co-Ral and Tiguvon although without improving gain and feed conversion. Kohler (1963) reported similar findings for various other drugs.

11.2.6.4 SCREW-WORM. This is caused by the larvae of the fly *Cochliomyia hominivorix* which gains entry through wounds and injuries. Infected tissues are gradually destroyed by the developing larvae, culminating in the eventual death of the host animal. The species is particularly prevalent in South and Central America, the

Caribbean and the south-western United States. Formerly it was found in the south-eastern states but has since been eliminated by biological control.

In the early stages of attack, affected animals appear hyper-nervous due to the pain and very quickly the site of the infection begins to discharge a foul-smelling exudate.

Its elimination from parts of the US and the island of Curacao (ARS, 1962) is a classic example of the application of biological control. The release of male flies rendered sterile by irradiation, and their incorporation into the breeding population of *C. hominivorix* eventually eliminated the insect.

In the absence of such a biological approach any procedure which reduces wounds and injuries will be beneficial.

11.2.7 Ringworm

This disease is usually caused by a fungus *Trichophyton verrucosum* and occasionally by *T. mentagrophytes*. It is most common in young animals and is frequently seen in feedlots because of the crowded conditions which facilitate spread of the infection. It is met with in recently weaned calves and in cattle subjected to stress caused by change in diet, transportation, etc. It is not of great economic significance since animals recover spontaneously once they are on a rising plane of nutrition. There is no simple method of treatment and most procedures are of a high labour nature, usually involving removal of the scar tissue and application of ointments or solutions. In general there is no economic benefit from treatment of this kind.

11.2.8 Respiratory disease

A number of diseases (e.g. shipping or transit fever, viral diarrhoea, pneumonia) can affect the respiratory organs of cattle and the causal agents may be bacteria or viruses (see review by Omar, 1966). In intensive beef production units and feedlots generally such diseases tend to follow a characteristic pattern and arise almost certainly from the interaction of environmental stress and infection by viruses, with bacteria acting as associated or secondary invaders. Because *Pasteurella haemolytica* and *P. multocida* were the most frequently found organisms post mortem (Carter, 1954; Collier *et al.*, 1962; Hoerlein *et al.*, 1961) shipping fever was often referred to as *P. pneumonia* or hemmorrhagic septicaemia, but inoculation of these organisms into healthy cattle invariably failed to reproduce the disease (Carter, 1954; Gale and Smith, 1958). Proof that the active causal agent was a virus was provided by Abinanti and Huebner (1959), Reisinger *et al.* (1959) and Gale and King (1961) who isolated the myxo-virus parainfluenze 3 (SF4) from cattle infected with shipping fever. Less is known about viral diarrhoea.

Viruses do not survive long in the environment, and the degree of infection is generally a function of the number of organisms held in the air in droplets of water and the proximity of animals. Air temperature has little effect on the spread of such disease, but ventilation is paramount since it controls the rate of removal of infectious droplets from the immediate environment of the animal; it also removes irritants such as ammonia and dust which cause coughing and resultant spread of the droplet infection.

Respiratory disease occurs in feedlot cattle in all major cattle-producing countries.

The incidence is greater in autumn and winter and usually developes within 10 days of animals arriving. It is a serious problem in the US and those areas of Europe where cattle are raised on pasture before being introduced to the feedlot. For example in a survey in Montana (Anon., 1963b) there were about 196 cases of shipping fever in 454 ranches, while 7% of cattle examined in Connecticut had neutralizing antibodies to the Oregon C24V mucosal disease agent (Mills and Luginbuhl, 1965).

There is some suggestion (Shope, 1965) that heredity may be involved in viral diarrhoea, since, in one outbreak, the only calves to succumb were by the same sire. Climate also plays a part, for at our station in Cuba we have not so far observed the disease in over 3000 cattle brought in for fattening from all parts of the island. There are no references to the disease in tropical countries. The stress factor of transportation still exists in these regions, but it may be that the higher air temperature, which varies little throughout the year, together with the use of open-sided transport vehicles provides a more favourable environmental situation as compared to conditions in temperate climates.

Respiratory disease is also a serious difficulty in intensive dairy beef production where calves are raised artificially from birth and normally enter the feedlot at 3 months.

In the UK the main causal agent appears to be parainfluenza 3 virus since some 5% of cattle have antibodies to this agent (Loosmore, 1964). The virus is encountered in early life by most calves which thus develop immunity. The failure of some calves to produce neutralizing antibodies against viral diarrhoea was thought by Shope (1965) to be due to destruction of immunologically competing cells by the virus and/or to an excessively slow production, which tend to affirm possible genetic relationships.

Loosmore (1964) has suggested that calves collected from different sources be mixed together as early in life as possible in order to take advantage of maternal immunity. Mixing later, at 4–5 months, is particularly dangerous since maternal immunity begins to wane at this point and may even have ceased to exist (Bogel and Liebelt, 1963).

In general, most types of respiratory disease have similar clinical symptoms. Affected animals stand apart from the group, refuse to eat, have an elevated body temperature and a characteristically dry muzzle and rough coat. At a later stage there is mucous discharge from the nose, profuse lacrimation, rapid respiration, coughing and muscular weakness. Some preventative measures have been discussed earlier (§ 6.8), and while reliance must still be placed on drug therapy, there are now possibilities (Tribe *et al.*, 1968) for the development of effective vaccines. This has not hitherto been considered a reliable means of prophylaxis (Jensen and MacKey, 1965).

11.2.9 Toxins in feeds

Toxicity in calves in the UK caused by feeding Brazilian groundnut meal was first reported by Loosmore and Markson (1961) and subsequently in older cattle by Clegg and Bryson (1962). The causal agent was shown by Sargeant *et al.* (1961b) to be a toxin produced by the fungus *Aspergillus flavus*. Contamination of groundnut usually occurs at around the time of harvest and is not confined to the Brazilian product (Allcroft and Carnaghan, 1963). Careful screening (Sargeant *et al.*, 1961a) of specific batches of groundnuts, irrespective of country of origin, is thus a necessary precaution.

Allcroft and Lewis (1963) and Whitelaw *et al.* (1963) induced fatal poisoning with dietary levels of 18–20% of contaminated groundnut, while Horrocks *et al.* (1965) significantly depressed feed intake and gain in early weaned calves with as little as 4%, even though there were no clinical symptoms. In older cattle given high-roughage diets, 12% of contaminated meal in the concentrate (6% of total diet) had no effect.

Aspergillus moulds can also develop in stored cereals and Aust *et al.* (1963) reported the death of 20 out of 29 cattle fed a diet in which 70% of the maize had been contaminated with the fungus. Mouldy hay may be equally dangerous (Washburn, 1963). There is some evidence that *A. fumigatus*, which develops on mouldy hay or straw, can lead to severe diarrhoea and anorexia such that slaughter is necessary (Starchenkov *et al.*, 1967) while abortions can also occur (Rob and Krpatova, 1967).

11.3 METABOLIC DISTURBANCES

11.3.1 Acidosis

This is a condition of imbalance whereby too much acid is produced in the rumen for the animal to utilize in its blood and tissues. The disease, also referred to as acid or acute indigestion, is associated with both young and old cattle which, coming from forage or pasture feeding, are changed too rapidly to an *ad libitum* high carbohydrate diet usually of cereals. Symptoms of the disease are noted within one or two days of the change and consist of loss of appetite, dullness, posterior incoordination and finally recumbancy and death. The condition was first described in "barley beef" cattle by MacDonald *et al.* (1962) and subsequently by others (e.g. Preston, 1963a; Uhart and Carroll, 1967). Acidosis in dairy cattle has been reported by Broburg (1960), who described similar symptoms in cows suddenly gaining access to cereals. The condition was observed in sheep by Hungate *et al.* as early as 1952.

Broburg (1960) considered acidosis to be characterized by a deficiency of thiamine, which plays an essential role in the enzyme systems involved in VFA metabolism. He obtained rapid recoveries by giving injections of this vitamin to severely affected animals and good results from the same procedure were also noted by Preston (1963a) and Dirksen (1965). Huber (1966) found that administration of thiamine hydrochloride had no effect on clearance rate of lactic acid in sheep made unconscious by lactic acid infusion. This does not necessarily disprove Broburg's thesis since there is no conclusive evidence that lactic acid *per se* is the sole cause of acidosis. Uhart and Carroll (1967) certainly reported increased lactic acid concentration in animals suffering from acidosis and, since total VFA decreased, they considered the effect to be one of lacticacidaemia as reported by Annison (1965), Jensen and Mackey (1965) and Dunlop and Hammond (1965). However, it should be noted that all these reports concerned the use of sheep as experimental animals and it is known (Thomas and Klatte, 1967) that they are much more sensitive to the condition than cattle. Moreover, these latter workers found that levels of blood lactate were the same for cattle regularly consuming high-concentrate diets as in those with an induced acidosis. It may well be that acidosis is not brought about solely by accumulation of lactic acid but rather by increased total acid production, including acetic, propionic and butyric acids. Although Uhart and Carroll (1967) observed that lactic acid concentration increased from 0.10 m-equiv./l in normal animals to 100 in those which had ceased eating, while VFA declined from 149 to 107, the total acid concentration also increased from 149 to 207 m-equiv./l.

All animals are susceptible to acidosis but those with large appetites relative to their size, for example through being in poor body condition, will suffer more. Within this classification, animals which have never received grain are more susceptible than those previously adapted to it (Hyldgaard and Simensen, 1966) even though they may over-eat to the same degree (Allison *et al.*, 1964). The implication from this is that a change in rumen flora in response to change of ration is an important factor influencing tolerance. These same workers showed that giving an inoculum of rumen contents from an animal already adapted to concentrate feeding reduced the severity of the disease in comparison to animals that had not been inoculated.

A method of avoiding acidosis in cattle being introduced to the feedlot is described in § 6.8.3.1.

11.3.2 Bloat

There are two distinct kinds of bloat with the same clinical symptoms but with distinct etiology and methods of treatment. Most common is bloat associated with grazing of legumes, particularly alfalfa, which is generally referred to as frothy or pasture bloat, because gas is dispersed through the rumen contents in a stable form. Feedlot bloat is caused by a pocket of gas and is rarely associated with the presence of foam. Pasture bloat is usually acute, the first indication being the presence of dead animals. Feedlot bloat, on the other hand, is chronic and according to Jensen and Mackey (1965) can lead to secondary complications with diseases such as pneumonia. It is established that pasture bloat responds to treatment with various animal and vegetable oils (see review by Cole and Boda, 1960), whereas in feedlot cattle, soya bean oil, far from having a therapeutic effect can actually increase bloat incidence (Elam *et al.*, 1960; Elam and Davies, 1962).

Bloat is almost certainly the biggest source of economic loss in intensive beef production. There are four distinct sets of factors which appear to be related to the incidence of this disease. These are presence of alfalfa, rumen motility, overeating and exercise.

Experiments were undertaken in Maryland (Lindahl *et al.*, 1957) with a known bloat-inducing diet (61% ground barley, 16% soya bean oil meal, 22% dehydrated alfalfa meal and 1% salt). Replacing the barley with ground maize or the dehydrated alfalfa with alfalfa hay did not alter the bloat-inducing characteristics. In low fibre diets in which molasses supplied 80% of the dietary energy we have also recorded deaths due to bloat when the fibre source was fresh alfalfa as opposed to graminea (Martin *et al.*, 1968a).

In their studies on bloat provoked by alfalfa-containing diets Lindhal *et al.*, (1957) were unable to implicate rumen motility as a causal factor; in fact they reported quite active motility with increasing frequency of contraction as bloating began. In contrast, Daniels and Colvin (1963) decreased rumen motility within 2 weeks of feeding hay ground through a 0.23 cm sieve. Frequent bloating occurred as long as rumen motility was depressed but not when the ground hay was replaced by long hay. With a diet of 85% barley and 15% protein supplement (RRI, 1964) bloat incidence was 33% when barley was ground and increased to 60% when this ground barley ration was pelleted; bloat incidence on rolled barley, pelleted whole barley or rolled barley plus hay was less than 9%. Animals ruminated little on ground barley and scarcely at all on the pelleted ground diets which emphasizes the importance of rumen motility in bloat etiology. Pharr *et al.* (1967) also reported a direct relationship between the fineness of grinding hay and the incidence of bloat.

Over-eating is implicated as a predisposing factor by the findings of Elam *et al.* (1960) that on bloat-inducing diets the observed incidence was 30% when feeding was twice daily compared with 20% when animals were allowed free access to the feed. It was observed that steers fed twice daily ate much more rapidly when feed was placed before them than occurred under conditions of *ad libitum* feeding.

There are indications that when animals were tethered with a chain necktie the incidence of bloat on an all-concentrate diet was greater than when the animals were loose in groups (RRI, 1964; Robertson and Laing, 1965).

The greater incidence of bloat when animals eat rapidly implies that rate of gas production may well contribute to the condition. On all-concentrate diets based upon ground maize, Oltjen and Davis (1965) reported that rumen bicarbonate was higher, and the incidence of bloat significantly greater, when mineral buffers, mainly the carbonate salts of potassium and calcium, were given. A very high incidence of bloat in cattle fed ground maize with 2.5% sodium bicarbonate was also reported by Preston *et al.* (1963a).

Lindahl *et al.* (1957) emphasized the importance of animal variability in the etiology of bloat as did Elam *et al.* (1960). This is probably the most important factor of all in that, while there are certain predisposing factors such as those already outlined, the actual occurrence or non-occurrence of bloat will depend upon the susceptibility of the particular animals involved.

As long ago as 1943, Knapp *et al.* reported a possible inherited susceptibility to bloat. Support for this hypothesis comes from the work of Miller and Frederick (1966) that there were significant differences in bloat incidence between Dairy Shorthorns and Herefords. Similarly, in our own studies in Cuba (Willis and Preston, 1968a, b) bloat was frequently observed in Santa Gertrudis bulls but not in Charolais, Criollo or Brahman reared under identical conditions on *ad libitum* all-concentrate diets based on ground ear maize. Holstein bulls on the same test, despite being accustomed to such diets from birth, also had a measurable bloat incidence. This is not to say that only certain breeds are susceptible to bloat, but simply that susceptibility has a genetic basis.

Monoamine oxidase activity was said to be reduced (Johnson and Dyer, 1965) and the metabolism of tryptophan impaired (Dyer *et al.*, 1963) in chronic bloaters in comparison with normal animals. The origin of this may be genetic.

In view of the confused etiology there can be no hard and fast rules for prevention, nevertheless some guide lines can be laid down. These include: (a) providing some roughage-like material in the diets, either by preserving the husks of the grain (§ 9.3.1) or by adding about 5 to 10% of a high-fibre product such as oat or cotton seed husks, or coarsely-ground roughage; (b) maintaining a fresh feeding face in self-feeders and checking feeders and water bowls regularly to remove dirt and excreta; (c) providing feed *ad libitum*; (d) having cattle loose in groups and not secured in stanchions; and (e) avoiding the feeding of fresh alfalfa along with readily available carbohydrate feeds and using alfalfa hay in preference to young, dehydrated leafy material.

The administration of mineral oils has been shown by Elam and Davies (1962) to reduce feedlot bloat by 40%. Severely bloated animals can be relieved by passing a stomach tube into the rumen. Chronic bloaters should always be slaughtered.

Surface active compounds such as poloxalene may offer more reliable prophylaxis. It is established that this compound can completely prevent frothy bloat (Bartley *et al.*, 1965) and it has also been observed to have some effect against feedlot bloat (Bartley and Meyer, 1967). In two trials the mean bloat score of control animals was 1.64 compared with 0.92 for those given poloxalene in the feed. A level of 22.5 g/head/day appeared to be the most effective. Geissler and Thomas (1966) also recorded fewer cases of bloat in weaned calves fed alfalfa hay and barley and 10 g poloxalene daily.

11.3.3 Excessive hoof growth

Willis and Preston (1968a) reported excessive hoof growth in 7 out of 18 Brahman bulls being performance-tested on an all-concentrate diet. Subsequent observations extending to 48 bulls put the incidence at approximately 18% (Willis and Preston, 1968b). The condition has also been observed in feeding experiments where the diet was composed of maize or sorghum. It is obviously not due to the use of slatted floors since animals have manifested the same symptoms when raised in earth corrals. A high energy diet *per se* is also not implicated, since such problems have never been observed in over 2000 animals fed high energy diets where the carbohydrate was molasses rather than grain. The genetic nature of the problem is apparent from the fact that it has not been observed in Charolais, Criollo, Santa Gertrudis, Holstein or Brown Swiss raised under identical conditions, nor has it been manifested in cross-bred animals out of Brahman dams. Selection against sires producing this condition has markedly reduced the incidence (Willis and Preston, 1969c).

The cause of the condition is not known. Animals usually begin to develop symptoms at about 250 kg live weight and thereafter almost invariably cease growing.

11.3.4 Laminitis

The etiology of this disease is not understood. Jensen and Mackey (1965) consider it a manifestation of acidosis caused by acute indigestion. The blood vessels in the foot dilate and there is also oedema; the combined effect causes swelling and lameness, often to the extent that animals are reduced to walking on their knees.

In the UK the disease has been noticed in Holstein steers fed all-concentrate diets based on barley (MacLean, 1966). We have not observed it in Cuba in over 300 bulls of various breeds performance-tested on all-concentrate diets based on ground ear maize, nor has it occurred in high energy feeding based on molasses diets. On the other hand, Brown *et al.* (1967a) reported 27 cases in 270 related Hereford bulls on performance test over a 14 year period. These authors postulated a genetic basis to the disease since it did not occur in Angus, Shorthorn or other unrelated Herefords under the same testing conditions. Eleven progeny groups showed an incidence varying from 0 to 43%. These same workers (Stallcup *et al.*, 1967) found that affected animals exhibited atrophy of the parathyroids and calcium deposition in the testes, particularly in the seminiferous tubules. These findings were not observed in unaffected animals. There was lower total acid-soluble and inorganic phosphorus and higher calcium in blood serum of affected animals (Brown *et al.*, 1967a).

MacLean (1966) has suggested that laminitis in cattle given high-barley diets may be due to histamine toxicity, but Fell *et al.* (1967) could find no evidence that such diets affected the levels of histamine in the tissues compared to animals fed concentrates and hay.

Animals with laminitis should be slaughtered as the condition tends to deteriorate to the point where economic gains are no longer made. From the long-term point of view it would appear that the disease incidence can be reduced by selecting against sires whose progeny exhibit the condition.

11.3.5 Liver abscesses/ruminitis

There are two types of liver abscesses; acute hepatic necrobacillosis and chronic liver abscesses. Animals infected with the former show depression, occasionally with swelling of the hind limbs; they invariably die and on post mortem exhibit acute peritonitis. This condition has a very low incidence in intensive beef cattle. With chronic liver abscesses, on the other hand, clinical symptoms are rare. Usually the abscess consists of a necrotic core surrounded by pus and connective tissue. The abscesses are often encapsulated. Some are sterile and others appear merely as scar tissue. Affected livers are invariably condemned for human consumption. Since the liver represents approximately 1.5% of the value of the carcass the economic seriousness of this disease is considerable.

Although it has come into prominence with intensive feeding the disease has been known for a considerable time. In 1938, Newsom reported on the presence of liver abscesses, 85% of which were caused by *Spherophorus necrophorus*, 10% by this bacterium in conjunction with others and the remaining 5% by *Corynebacteria*, *Streptococci* and *Staphylococci*. In another study in 1943, Fredrick found that of 2042 cattle with abscessed livers 33% had foreign bodies in their stomachs.

Essentially, abscesses are caused by damage to the rumen wall enabling *Spherophorus necrophorus*, a normal inhabitant of the rumen, to gain access to the portal blood and hence infect the liver. Anything which can damage the rumen wall is thus a potential causal factor of liver abscesses.

Although the earlier reports of abscesses were probably related primarily to presence of foreign bodies in the rumen, the subsequent course of the disease reflected, in much greater part, factors of nutritional origin. According to a USDA survey (1962), 8% of all slaughtered cattle in the US had their livers condemned due to abscesses. In attempting to explain the appearance of *S. necrophorus* in the liver, Smith (1944) and Jensen *et al.* (1954a) examined rumens and livers from a large number of slaughtered cattle and reported significant positive correlations between the occurrence of ruminitis and liver abscesses. Jensen *et al.* (1954b) considered the ruminitis to be a direct result of changing too rapidly from a roughage to a high concentrate diet and of employing, during fattening, rations containing more than a 80:20 ratio of concentrates to roughage. The even greater incidence of liver abscesses with all-concentrate feeding

TABLE 11.2 INCIDENCE OF LIVER ABSCESSES IN STEERS AND ANTIBIOTIC EFFECTS

Energy source	Total no. of animals	Liver abscesses (%)			Authors
		Untreated	Antibiotic		
Ear maize	60[a]	3			Willis & Preston, 1968a
Maize	10	10			Oltjen *et al.*, 1966
Maize	80	18		0[b]	Harvey *et al.*, 1968
Barley	188	23	7[c]		Macdearmid, 1967
50/50[d]	50	25		0[b]	Bohman *et al.*, 1957
Sorghum	90[e]	27	0[f]	3[b]	Furr & Carpenter, 1967b
Barley	271	28	12[g]		Wieser *et al.*, 1966
Sorghum	222	28	10[f]	10[b]	Furr *et al.*, 1968b
Maize	108	34			Bushman *et al.*, 1967
Maize	80	35		5[b]	Harvey *et al.*, 1968
Maize	40	40			Wise *et al.*, 1963
Maize 60, wheat 30	10	40			Oltjen *et al.*, 1966
Maize 30, wheat 60	10	40			Oltjen *et al.*, 1966
Barley	128	41	39[h]		Macdearmid, 1967
Maize	64	44		3[b]	Harvey *et al.*, 1965
Wheat	10	50			Oltjen *et al.*, 1966
Ear maize	63[i]	51	34[j]		Perry *et al.*, 1968b
Sorghum	150	61	16[f]	32[b]	Furr & Carpenter, 1967b
Sorghum	96	67		37[b]	Furr *et al.*, 1968c
Maize	80	72	72[k]		Haskins *et al.*, 1967

[a] Bulls. [b] 70 mg/day chlortetracycline. [c] Tylosin 5 mg/kg diet. [d] 50 alfalfa 50 concentrates (sorghum, barley and beet pulp). [e] Heifers. [f] 40 mg/day erythromycin. [g] Chlortetracycline 20 mg/kg diet. [h] Zinc bacitracin 15 mg/kg diet. [i] Mixed sexes. [j] Oleandomycin 20 mg/day. [k] Zinc bacitracin 10mg /kg diet.

(Table 11.2) supports Jensen's general contention that liver abscesses are increased by concentrate feeding, however, more recent evidence indicates that his conclusions were too sweeping.

Thus the exact ratio of concentrate to roughage appears to be less important than the method of processing. Harris (1965) recorded no rumen parakeratosis on 80:20 diets when long hay was used, but a high incidence on 50:50 diets in which the hay was ground or wafered. Garrett *et al.* (1961) showed that parakeratosis was greatest on finely ground feeds. The condition was alleviated, but not completely eliminated, by giving long hay. On the other hand, fine grinding and pelleting is not the sole factor determining parakeratosis (Vidacs and Ward, 1960; Wieser *et al.*, 1966). While giving long hay can considerably reduce parakeratosis or ruminitis it does not necessarily reduce the incidence of liver abscesses. Wise *et al.* (1963) found no improvement by adding 5% of alfalfa to an otherwise all-maize diet, while Harvey *et al.* (1965) reported that neither hay nor rice hulls had any effect in reducing incidence of liver damage. Increasing the level of rice hulls to 10% of the diet also gave no improvement (McCartor and Hefley, 1965).

More recently, however, Durham (1968) has reported only 36% abscessed livers from animals given diets containing 10% cottonseed hulls compared with 70% on the basal diet of sorghum and cottonseed meal. Set against this benefit was a 10% deterioration in feed conversion.

Far from alleviating the condition, roughage substitutes such as oyster shells have been shown to increase both ruminitis (Perry *et al.*, 1968b) and liver abscesses (Karr and Hodge, 1968; Larsen *et al.*, 1968a; Perry *et al.*, 1968b; Williams *et al.*, 1968a). Oyster shell may act as an irritant since according to Karr and Hodge it became embedded in the rumen wall and could not be washed out. In this connection a number of substances could have similar effects, thus Fell *et al.* (1968) observed that both hair from the animals' coats and vegetable fibres penetrated the rumen epithelium. They suggested that together with the keratinized areas of the epithelium these penetration sites could serve as entry points into the portal blood of pathogenic bacteria involved in liver necrosis and abscess formation. Hair accumulation is likely to be greater on all-concentrate diets which possess no roughage properties and this was demonstrated by Harvey *et al.* (1968). Hair accumulation in the rumen papillae was significantly reduced when 1.36 kg of long hay were fed with a ground maize diet.

The view of Jensen *et al.* (1954b) that a rapid change over from forage to concentrates predisposes animals to liver abscesses is certainly not universally applicable. Dairy beef animals, fed on concentrates from birth, have up to 28% of liver abscesses when slaughtered at 10 to 12 months of age (Wieser *et al.*, 1966). In contrast, 56 beef bulls weaned abruptly at 90 days, having been raised with their mothers on pasture and then changed abruptly to an all-concentrate diet, did not exhibit any liver damage when slaughtered at one year or less (Willis and Preston, 1968a).

Although ruminitis is frequently observed in animals that also show abscessed livers, Wieser *et al.* (1966) could find no relationship between the extent or severity of rumen lesions and liver abscesses, while Wise *et al.* (1963) found that out of 40 animals 16 had liver abscesses but only one showed parakeratosis of the rumen. Evidence that parakeratosis of the rumen does not always lead to liver abscesses was also demonstrated in the work of Beardsley *et al.* (1959). Similarly, Oltjen *et al.* (1966) found that although there was more clumping of rumen papillae on a diet with 90% ground maize than on wheat-based diets, the latter produced more liver abscesses.

While it is clear that high energy diets based on cereals induce a high incidence of liver abscesses it is not necessarily correct that "fermentation of high calorific feeds produces irritating substances of unknown composition which injure the ruminal mucosa", as stated by Jensen and Mackey (1965). High molasses diets of comparable calorific value to those based on cereals have not in our experience produced any liver abscesses nor ruminitis although they have made the rumen wall very dark in colour and in some instances have produced livers of a pale yellowish appearance (Elías *et al.*, 1968b).

There is a slight suggestion in the work of Harbaugh *et al.* (1963) and Furr and Carpenter (1967b) that the incidence of liver abscesses may be less in heifers than steers. Some theoretical justification for this exists in that oestrogens have been shown to have bacteriostatic properties (San Clemente and MacKenzie, 1957). We do not consider that the almost negligible incidence of liver abscesses in bulls encountered by us in our work in Cuba necessarily implies a similar sex effect, since we have not worked with steers in comparable conditions.

While the general evidence indicates that high cereal diets are the main predisposing causes for liver abscesses, prevention by reducing the energy content of the diet makes no economic sense since the reduction that this brings about in rate of gain and feed conversion, and increased labour and other management costs, is much more serious that an average condemnation loss of 30% (approximately $1,00 per animal). This takes no account of any effect of liver abscesses on growth and feed conversion. Little data exist on this aspect although animal performance was not apparently related to either rumen lesions (Oltjen and Davis, 1965) or liver abscesses (Wieser *et al.*, 1966). In an analysis of data from 1190 cattle fed ground sorgum diets, those with abscessed livers (295) were reported poorer in all performance traits, although the difference was significant only in the case of dressing percentage (Powell *et al.*, 1968a).

The most positive approach to prevention was originally suggested by Flint and Jensen (1958) who reported that giving 70 mg daily of chlortetracycline considerably reduced, although did not completely eliminate, the incidence of liver abscesses. This has subsequently been confirmed by Ellis *et al.* (1963) and by other workers (see Table 11.2). According to Wieser *et al.* (1966), antibiotic treatment had no effect on rumen lesions which implies that the beneficial action of the antibiotic is through control of the invading organism. The economics of using antibiotics to control liver abscesses is not solely with respect to reducing incidence of condemned livers since, in general, there is an associated improvement in gain and feed conversion which must also be taken into account (§ 9.8).

Of the antibiotics used chlortetracycline has given the most consistent response. The ineffectiveness of zinc bacitracin apparent in the data in Table 11.2 and the work of Durham and Pruett (1966) is to be expected from its non-systemic action.

11.3.6 Molasses toxicity

This disease was first reported in Cuba and was originally thought to be due to a mineral imbalance caused by an overconsumption of molasses (ICA, 1966). Affected animals show accelerated breathing, reduced body temperature and pronounced muscular weakness. They invariably take up a characteristic stance with their forelegs crossed leaning forward with the shoulders resting against the bars of the corral. They subsequently become comatose and can die within 24 hr. There is little warning of the onset of the condition and animals most frequently affected are those being changed to molasses for the first time or which have been on molasses diets for a short period. In these cases the condition is precipitated by an over-consumption of molasses such as may be caused by a failure in the water supply inducing them to satisfy their water requirements from the molasses.

The condition resembles potassium toxicity as reported by Blaxter (1960). Certainly cane molasses has a high content of this element (Preston and Willis, 1969) and high-test molasses, which contains a much lower concentration of potassium, has never been known to cause the condition. The most effective treatment is to administer a solution rich in phosphorus and sodium and to take the animals off molasses feeding for a few days. To be effective this must be done at the early stages of the disease.

11.3.7 Urea toxicity

Toxic symptoms associated with feeding excessive amounts of urea to cattle have been known for many years. The typical signs of urea poisoning are restlessness, muscular tremors, heavy respiration, lack of coordination, tetany, bloat and copious secretion of saliva. The term urea toxicity is, nevertheless, a misnomer since the condition is, in fact, caused by the inability of the liver to convert all the absorbed ammonia to urea. It was shown by Lewis *et al.* (1957) that, when rumen ammonia levels exceeded 60 m-equiv./l., peripheral blood ammonia increased and toxic symptoms developed once blood ammonia levels reached the critical value of between 1 and 4 mg/100 ml. Lewis (1961) considered that several factors were involved including a direct toxic effect of the ammonium ion, a disturbance of the acid–base status and a change in electrolyte balance.

Toxic levels have usually been established by giving urea as a drench or directly into the rumen through a fistula. Under these circumstances toxicity occurred with amounts of urea equivalent to 30 g per 100 kg live weight (Davis and Roberts, 1959) and 44 g per 100 kg live weight (Word *et al.*, 1968). It is important to note that these toxic levels were somewhat artificially derived since urea is never normally fed in a single dose. Thus in our experiments on high molasses/urea feeding it is a regular occurrence for fattening cattle to consume 75 g urea per 100 kg live weight/day, while as much as 200 g per 100 kg live weight were consumed by dairy cows with no suggestion of toxicity; rumen ammonia levels rarely exceeded 20 m-equiv./l. The only occasions of actual toxicity were when the daily allowance of urea was administered accidentally in a single dose. Another aspect is that, given the opportunity, animals regulate their consumption of urea. Thus with free access to both grain and a molasses/urea mixture even concentrations of 20% urea did not prove harmful as the animals reduced their intake to 500 g of mixture (ICA, 1967). It is obvious that the other ingredients of the ration play a significant role, and that molasses is a particularly effective vehicle for NPN as is proved by the extremely low levels of rumen ammonia which result when this particular combination of ingredients is given (Elias *et al.*, 1968b). Problems can be expected to be more severe on a diet high in structural carbohydrates and deficient in readily available energy, but then there is little purpose in adding urea to such diets. Although Chalupa (1968) concluded that urea should not be given at more than 1% of the total ration there is no physiological or economic basis for such a standard. It is frequently argued that it is extremely difficult to give more than one third of the total dietary nitrogen as urea since most grain and roughages provide the major part of the animal's protein requirement without further supplementation. While this is true with grain-based diets, it is not valid for feeding systems based on molasses. In this case it is perfectly possible (and economic) to supply up to 60% of the animal's total nitrogen requirements in the form of urea; moreover, we have shown that there is no physiological danger from so doing (§ 9.3.3.2).

Treatment of animals suffering from ammonia toxicity necessitates the neutralization of the rumen ammonia. Glutamic acid was considered by Rummler *et al.* (1962) to overcome toxic symptoms, but Oltjen *et al.* (1964) found that acetic acid (the usual treatment) was 3 times more effective. Administration of acetic acid was also found to be a satisfactory therapeutic method by Repp *et al.* (1955) and Davis and

Roberts (1959). It was necessary to undertake the treatment prior to the onset of tetany according to these latter workers.

11.3.8 Urinary calculi

The disease is characterized by the blocking of the urinary tract by calculi composed of a matrix of mucoprotein in which are deposited phosphatic or silaceous salts of ammonia, magnesium and calcium. The economic significance of this disease is that as a result of being unable to urinate either the bladder ruptures, with consequent accumulation of urine in the peritoneal cavity, or the urethra bursts and urine becomes distributed through the subcutaneous tissues of the lower abdomen. In either case, even if the animal is not dead, the carcass is valueless for human consumption. According to Anon. (1963b) it was a major problem in Montana with 911 cases on 559 ranches.

Predisposing conditions are diets which lead to the excretion of mucoproteins (Udall *et al.*, 1958), or an alkaline urine causing the precipitation of phosphates and silicates. This was not true in an experiment carried out by Bailey *et al.* (1963) as incidence of the condition was similar for animals with alkaline or acid urine.

Rice byproducts, which are high in silicates, have been implicated as causal agents by Shirley *et al.* (1964). Riggs and Crookshank (1960) considered that high moisture sorghum was less likely to induce the condition than dry grain although incidence still remained comparatively high. There is evidence that feeding of phosphoric acid or ammonium chloride (Crookshank *et al.*, 1960) or even sodium chloride (Bailey, 1967) will reduce the problem. By contrast, feeding magnesium or calcium carbonate made the condition worse (Jones *et al.*, 1951).

The condition does not appear to arise in bulls or females for even if calculi occur they are more easily eliminated; in contrast the reduced size of the urethra encourages blockages in castrated males.

IV. The Future

CHAPTER 12

Perspectives

12.1 INTRODUCTION

In the preceeding chapters we have attempted to give a comprehensive analysis of the data relating to the different aspects of beef production. From the account we have given it is clear that there are many deficiencies in specific fields. In some cases the literature may exist, but we have not located it. Nevertheless, we believe that most of the deficiencies exist because the relevant research has not yet been undertaken. The intention here is to comment on the more obvious gaps in knowledge and to suggest lines of future investigations.

It is not simply a question of what research to do but also how to do it, who should do it and how the results should be published and commercially exploited. As research is mainly financed by public funds it is necessary to comment on the effectiveness of the organizations involved and to what extent efficient use is made of facilities and personnel. We have also considered it relevant to examine the general philosophy towards applied animal research in the developing countries, particularly as it is necessary that the greatest advances in animal production in the future take place in these areas of the world. The advantage and potential of these regions lies in the almost complete absence of traditional practices, particularly in the field of animal breeding. They are thus in a strong position to apply the results of research undertaken elsewhere without having to overcome the vested interests which exist in some form or other in countries which already have highly sophisticated livestock production systems. On the other hand, developing countries have a disadvantage which could negate the major part of their potential. This is the combination of a lack of technical skill and a desire to be self-sufficient before the necessary abilities have been created.

For easier understanding we have organized this discussion by taking each chapter in turn to highlight both the deficiencies in knowledge and possible lines of investigation that should be pursued.

12.2 CARCASS QUALITY

12.2.1 Carcass evaluation

One of the greatest problems to overcome is the idea that there is one definition of quality, a specific type of carcass which is more desirable than any other and *ipso facto* a superior breed and a superior feeding system. As we stressed earlier (§2.1) there are three basic markets: the luxury trade, the average housewife and the manufacturer. The relative weight given to these respective outlets will depend directly upon the standard of living and customs of the purchasing country. Exporting countries, and producers in general, must therefore organize their production systems, breeding methods and carcass evaluation techniques to take account of the type of market that is likely to be most lucrative for their specific circumstances. Having said this, we consider it an inescapable fact that the major part of the meat market will be accounted for by the supermarket trade and the manufacturer, which means that edible meat yield will be the most important economic trait. Carcass evaluation techniques must therefore be devised to fit in with this type of breakdown.

Content of edible meat will also be a factor in the luxury trade, but eating quality will have a more important role. Moreover, in this market the consumer prefers that the bone be left in and that the degree of fat trim be less pronounced. Evaluation procedures for this type of market should therefore take account of some index of eating quality while assessment of edible meat yield may have to be based on carcass weight and some measurement of fat thickness rather than the boning out and trimming which is fundamental to a supermarket operation.

Certain authorities (e.g. Carroll, 1966) have argued in favour of carcass evaluation based on chemical analysis. While not disputing the fact that this may have biological significance, we are opposed to the notion that it is "commercially meaningful". The same criticism can be directed against complete dissection of individual muscles as practised by the Queensland school (Butterfield, 1964a, b). Here again there is biological significance to the procedure but it is too far removed from the commercial product. We believe that carcass evaluation must be based on the products purchased by the consumer. Furthermore, as future sales will be predicted more and more on trimmed boneless joints, it does not always follow that carcass evaluation must, of necessity, be a costly operation.

Accepting that edible meat yield (which effectively means lean meat) is the most important carcass trait, a great deal more research is needed on the effects of breeds and feeding systems on this criterion. The extensive work on edible meat in the US has been done almost invariably with the traditional British beef breeds. These, under the feeding systems employed, produce carcasses considerably fatter than is the case in most other regions of the world which not only use genetically leaner breeds, but also feeding systems which tend to give less fat deposition. Our own findings (Willis *et al.*, 1968; Martin and Willis, 1969) imply that interrelationships within carcass components are less for "lean" breeds (6–10% excess fat) than is the case in US studies. This is supported by the findings of Abraham *et al.* (1968) where prediction equations applied to Charolais cattle gave different results as when British breeds were used. Although Butterfield (1964b) concluded that there were no differences between breeds in muscle distribution, this is at variance with our own findings using commercial dissection procedures (Table 2.16 (p. 58)). We have shown that the Charolais is consistently superior to other *Bos taurus* and *B. indicus* types and consider it possible that the qualities of this breed (a high proportion of edible meat *per se* and also a higher percentage of this in the more valuable parts of the carcass) are shared by other European breeds such as the Limousin, Simmental and Piedmont. All of these breeds have been conspicuously absent in comparative carcass evaluation studies.

There is another important aspect of breed comparisons, namely the point of slaughter. Carroll (1966) cites and agrees with Taylor (1963) that it may be desirable to slaughter animals at a weight proportional to either mature live weight or, conversely, to birth weight. The assumption that mature live weight is proportional to birth weight has little validity under modern management systems wherein a low birth weight is often obtained as a result of deliberate underfeeding during pregnancy. To slaughter cattle at a point based upon mature live weight necessitates knowledge of the latter (which rarely exists), and in any genetic improvement programme, this will be constantly increasing. The more serious criticism, however, is that acceptance of this philosophy entails comparisons at different carcass weights. Apart from the fact that this calls for considerable biometrical corrections, with resultant errors and loss of precision, there is the all-important factor that such a slaughter point may bear little or no relation to commercial requirements. We are not arguing for one fixed live weight. In fact it should be obvious from our insistence upon the requirements of different markets, that slaughter live weight must vary according to the specific outlet. There is a need to compare breeds for different markets, but between breeds, the comparison can only be on a fixed carcass weight basis.

Any discussion of eating quality tends to be predicated on marbling; indeed, assessment of beef quality in the US is based almost entirely upon this single characteristic. In spite of this its importance is still not well understood. Thus, most US investigations have shown that marbling is poorly related to all aspects of eatability other than juiciness. On the other hand, recent British work (Jones, 1968) strongly implies that in leaner breeds, such as the Charolais, marbling has a definite relationship to both tenderness and flavour as well as juiciness. In view of the preeminent place of the Charolais for edible meat yield, it is of some concern that it may be deficient in meat quality. This emphasizes the importance of (a) establishing the relationship between marbling and eating quality in both lean and fat animals, and (b) determining the extent to which it is related to excess fat. Clearly, if marbling is important in the lean breeds we need to know whether it can be increased by genetic methods without, at the same time, increasing subcutaneous and inter-muscular fat.

Evaluation of eatability suffers from the subjective nature of the methods used. Tenderness is the only characteristic which has so far lent itself to objective measurement, as for example by the Warner–Bratzler shear machine. We are not convinced that the use of trained taste panels is necessarily a good means of assessment since there are some reports in which the relationship between the results obtained by this procedure has agreed only moderately (and sometimes not at all) with consumer preference studies, in the sense that significant differences were detected by the former but not by the latter. While we concede that the trained panel may have a place in the evaluation of meat for the luxury market, there seems to be less justification for it when the aim is to assess meat suitability for the supermarket shopper. As this type of trade obviously extends over a much wider social range the variability is greater. The need, then, is not to refine the method of analysis but rather to extend the coverage. In this respect the consumer acceptance panel, with emphasis on adequate sampling, would appear to have greater relevance.

The use of bulls for meat production presents similar problems. Although their superiority over steers for growth, feed conversion and yield of edible meat is well established under intensive feeding systems, there is evidence of pronounced differences in meat quality primarily, it seems, because of effects of fatness. There is need to study meat quality in bulls and in this respect the role of hormone administration merits particular attention. There also appears to be a considerable deficiency in our knowledge of meat quality in heifers, and there is a particular need to study consumer acceptability of meat from heifers that have produced their first calf.

12.2.2 Organization of research

It is clear from any study of the literature that the major contribution to our knowledge of meat quality has been made by US investigators, the new schools in Australia and, to a lesser extent, by research organizations in Europe. Much of the stimulus for the US development results from the establishment of meat science departments within animal science faculties. Our only criticism is that there has been a tendency to study meat as a separate entity, divorced from the effects of breeding and nutrition. This specialization by discipline has perhaps not had serious consequences up to the present time in view of the breeds and methods of feeding current in the US. But if, as seems highly likely, there is an extension of dairy beef production coupled with the introduction of breeds genetically superior for feed conversion and edible meat yield, there will be an increased need for integrated studies involving geneticists and nutritionists as well as meat scientists.

The creation in the mid-1960's of a meat research institute in the UK was a step in the right direction, for it would not have been economical to have established meat science departments at the agricultural universities. On the other hand, there is a danger of compartmentalization, as has happened with other ARC institutes, such that it could become an isolated entity studying meat *per se* with little or no integration with other disciplines.

Meat research in developing countries would, at first sight, appear to be an unnecessary extravagance since national needs are almost entirely for quantity rather than quality. On the other hand, for many developing countries meat exports represent one of the most promising means of earning foreign exchange, and this is likely to become even more so in the future with the ever-accelerating standards of living in the industrialized nations. As a general rule, the export efforts of many developing countries suffer through inadequate marketing research and attention to quality. This is particularly important for those countries in the tropical and sub-tropical zones whose cattle population is almost entirely made up of *B. indicus* types, of known inferior eatability. There is tremendous scope for genetic improvement programmes, but these should take account of meat quality as well as gain and feed conversion.

12.2.3 Commercial development

The most urgent and long overdue requirement is a complete reappraisal and revision of both marketing and grading systems. Proof of how little development has taken place in the UK is the continued existence of Smithfield Market which has changed little since its original conception. Judged in the context of present-day methods of marketing poultry, Smithfield is an anachronism, increasing the price of meat to the consumer and existing primarily because of inefficient production systems which give rise to a wide range of carcasses whose intrinsic value can only be assessed by the trained eye of a butcher. It is highly significant that most "barley beef" carcasses are able to bypass Smithfield because they represent a standard product of fixed weight and quality which comes about from the use of one breed and a standard diet and system of management. As a result of these restraints, meat quality of "barley beef" is predictable, so that carcasses can be purchased unseen with little commercial risk.

Marketing methods are dictated to a very considerable extent by production systems, and modernization of marketing will be more effectively brought about through standardization of these than by legislation. Government regulations in the UK have played too influential a role by controlling the extent and allocation of price support payments. It is well established that government grading in any country bears no positive relation to commercial carcass merit.

Although US marketing is considerably better organized as a result of the dominant role of feedlots as producers of the nation's beef cattle, it also suffers from an anachronistic grading method together with a purchasing system based almost entirely on live evaluation. It is difficult to understand how, in a country where the major meat outlet is via supermarkets, meat selling should still be based on wholesale cuts rather than on a boneless, trimmed joint. It seems likely that technical progress in US meat marketing will depend upon further integration of producers with large-scale supermarket chains. The spread of dairy beef production, as in California and New York State, should accelerate this development.

The exporting countries face a different type of problem. They do not only have to take account of the specific market requirements of the purchasing countries but they are frequently faced with import tariffs and regulations which are rarely orientated towards efficient marketing. The logical way to export beef from developing countries is in the form of boned-out trimmed wholesale joints, retaining the poor quality meat, the excess fat and bone, all of which find a ready application at home. In reality, tariff systems, such as operate in the UK for example, impose a greater penalty on this type of meat than upon carcass meat. As a result, carcass beef has to be exported at a considerable loss of efficiency, since 15–20% of it finds its way to the garbage bin as bone when it could have been efficiently utilized by the exporting country. Our argument is not against tariffs as such but rather that these should be organized in such a way as to encourage, not discourage, efficient meat marketing.

This section would not be complete without reference to the role of carcass exhibitions and shows. It is our opinion that these serve no useful purpose and frequently mislead both the producer and the consumer. They have helped to perpetuate subjective judging and the continued existence of inefficient breeds and, through the employment of score cards, slide-rule techniques and other pseudo-objective methods, have tended to obscure the real problems of carcass evaluation.

12.3 GENETICS

12.3.1 Research

A vast amount of information has accumulated on the inheritance of growth to weaning, under the conventional 6–9 months system, and of post-weaning growth under US feedlot conditions. Unfortunately, the really important economic traits have received virtually no attention. Thus we know next to nothing about the inheritance of carcass characteristics or their relation to performance; equally, feed conversion has been largely ignored in the mistaken belief that it was so closely related to rate of gain than its separate study was unnecessary. Some attempt is being made to redress the balance in the field of carcass quality (e.g. at the University of Kentucky) but feed conversion remains neglected. It is not just a question of measuring feed conversion rate and calculating heritabilities and genetic correlations. The root of the problem is that almost all performance testing systems evolved in the US and the UK are designed to allow bulls to compensate for environmental differences caused by treatment prior to weaning. As long as such procedures are followed, feed conversion rate will have little or no meaning since it mainly measures not the genetic merit of the bull but compensation to environmental differences prior to arriving at the testing station. Typical of the misguided philosophy in this area is the report of the BRA (1967) in which it was stated that "the whole of the test period should be regarded as an adjustment period during which the bulls' growth rates will compensate for previous levels of management". It is interesting to note that in the testing system we developed in Cuba the relationship between growth rate and feed conversion on test was higher ($r = -0.82$) than other published estimates (Willis and Preston, 1970). Bulls were started on test at 90 days of age and fed a complete concentrate diet. We believe that the high correlation is partly due to the reduction of environmental effects due to early-weaning and to the use of complete all-concentrate diets rather than the feeding of separate components. It is also felt that since feed intake and daily gain are higher relative to mean live weight, than on conventional testing, the proportion of feed going into gain as opposed to maintenance will be higher and this would lead to closer relationships between gain and feed conversion.

The situation regarding feed conversion and its correlation with gain is unlikely to be clarified by the type of investigations sometimes undertaken. Thus in a theoretical discussion (extending to some 15,000 words) of the results of an experiment involving five monozygous and six dizygous twin heifers fed a pelleted diet, Taylor and Young (1966) reached the profound conclusion that "similarly fed animals had similar growth rates and efficiencies and similarly grown animals similar food intakes and efficiencies". It is, indeed, questionable if the use of twin animals for genetic studies, such as have been undertaken at the Animal Breeding Research Organization in Edinburgh since 1949 (see review by Taylor, 1966), is the best means of advancing genetic knowledge of beef cattle. It is significant that such atypical animals hardly figure in US cattle breeding studies which, in the field of beef production, are far in advance of any comparable work elsewhere. The only useful point made by Taylor and Young (1966) was that on restricted feeding variation in growth, feed consumption and efficiency was less than with *ad libitum* feeding, a conclusion which has been accepted in the US for many years. It is a fundamental principle of genetic programmes that variation should exist; it almost goes without saying that *ad libitum* feeding systems are fundamental to performance testing.

More research is needed on methods of performance testing, but with an eye to increasing the precision of the operation rather than the appeasement of breed societies. We believe that starting the test at 90 days has enabled us to select bulls more accurately, but it may be that even earlier weaning is desirable if really meaningful information is to be obtained with respect to feed efficiency. That official performance testing organizations such as the BRA in the UK (Baker, 1965) should continue to emphasize type and conformation to the extent of giving it equal weighting with live weight gain, reflects the preoccupation with breed society politics rather than cattle improvement.

We are not convinced of the need for station progeny testing. The only justification could be to assess carcass quality. However, we believe that the refinement of ultrasonic techniques for measuring fat-depth, coupled with regular greater precision in assessing feed conversion, could provide some information on this trait during the performance test. Admittedly, this will only help with respect to carcass composition and not eatability. But it is unlikely that meaningful information on eatability can be obtained by conventional station tests either, since these rarely incorporate more than ten progeny per bull. Progeny testing for such characteristics would appear to be more sensibly carried out on a feedlot scale using contemporary comparison systems.

There is a wealth of information regarding the improvements in productivity that can accrue from heterosis and the non-existence of such effects in important carcass traits. Future research should be directed less towards heterosis studies *per se* but rather to the determination of the most suitable mating systems for maximizing heterosis on a long term basis. The North Central Regional Project NC1 (Gregory *et al.*, 1966a, b, c) and the Southern Regional Project S10 (Vogt *et al.*, 1967) in the US are excellent examples of how this type of information can be obtained. Our only criticism of the studies so far is that they have been confined to traditional British breeds. The need now is to incorporate the faster-growing lean breeds such as Charolais, Holstein and Brown Swiss and, if possible, other European breeds such as Simmental and Limousin.

Some attention should be given to the combining ability of specific breeds, not necessarily with a view to selecting for this phenomenon, but rather to determine which order of crossing and which combination of breeds is likely to give most heterosis. There is already some evidence (Mueller-Haller *et al.*, 1968; Muñoz and Martin, 1968; Willis and Preston, 1969c) that certain crosses, e.g. Criollo males on Brahman cows, yield little or no heterosis in growth rate and other traits for which heterosis is normally observed.

The area of greatest confusion concerns interactions between genotype and environment. There is too much preoccupation with the existence of interactions *per se* particularly with respect to factors of such an extreme nature as are unlikely to be encountered in commercial practice. For example, the controversy in the tropics regarding possible interactions between breed and intensive or extensive systems of management is somewhat academic if beef cattle production in the future is to be increasingly by intensive methods. Rate of genetic progress is such that programmes designed to produce animals for use 10 years hence need to be started now.

Of greater relevance is the possible existence of interactions within intensive systems as such. Thus we know that ruminal conditions on high molasses/urea feeding are distinct to those on all-concentrate diets; moreover, breeds differ in the type of rumen fermentation which develops even on the same ration (Elías and Preston, 1969a). The ever-increasing economic advantages of replacing crude protein with NPN are also likely to create situations which require a particular rumen environment for most efficient utilization.

Another important area for study, of particular significance in tropical and subtropical regions, is the interaction between disease and genotype. It is commonly supposed that such interactions not only exist but must be taken account of in the development of breeds and crossbreeds for these areas. In actual fact, when a search is made for the evidence to justify these beliefs, data are very difficult to find. The basis for genetically conferred resistance is surprisingly ill-documented and the implication from what does exist is that resistance develops more through acquired immunity than by genetic means. Whatever the true explanation, the fact is that reliable data are urgently needed. At the moment, the almost universal acceptance of a relation between disease resistance and *B. indicus* "blood" is likely to condemn many developing countries to unproductive breeds of livestock for many years to come. For while the relation between disease resistance and genotype may not be well understood, it is established that *B. indicus* are poorer performers with respect to almost all economic traits.

12.3.2 Organization of research

Most agricultural universities have a department of animal genetics. Some of them, such as Cornell, Iowa and Edinburgh, are in the forefront of research and have produced many excellent geneticists. The problem, however, is not one of facilities for fundamental research, since work with *Drosophila* or laboratory animals is comparatively inexpensive. Similarly, in certain fields of applied genetics, e.g. dairy cattle, there are also excellent research facilities, as the major requirement is for records which exist in abundance at organizations such as the MMB in the UK and the DHIA in the US. Unfortunately, comparative facilities do not exist for beef cattle. Even in the US, no university is equipped with sufficient large scale facilities in terms of animals and buildings, while the largest in the UK (North of Scotland College of Agriculture) has relatively few breeding cattle. Two basic difficulties result from this. Firstly, it is impossible to do reliable research on small numbers and, secondly, as the consequence of the first, it is difficult to obtain first-class geneticists. Fredeen (1966) suggested that the problem was even more fundamental. He considered that a top geneticist would not remain interested for long in large-animal breeding programmes. To sustain interest he suggested that it was essential to establish facilities which also included laboratory species. We are not so pessimistic as Fredeen in believing that a top geneticist must perforce work with laboratory species, nor do we feel that the type of researcher who requires this stimulus is the kind likely to be most successful in large-animal breeding programmes. The fundamental difficulty in large-animal genetic research is not a lack of interest because of the species *per se*, but a lack of facilities. We are certain that if facilities existed on a sufficient scale, by which we mean breeding herds of several thousand head, there would be no problem either in finding suitable people or in occupying their time.

How then are facilities to be obtained? In the US one approach to the problem has been via the regional breeding projects, but numbers are still not always sufficient. Similarly, expansion at the experimental station level to take in data from private and institutional herds has the disadvantage that management is not under the researcher's control. Moreover, much of the information collected in this way refers only to weaning—economically the least important stage of the animal's life. It would appear that rationalization of research facilities is the only means of achieving the necessary scale of operation. This is desirable even in the US, but in Europe it is absolutely essential if any progress is to be made. Thus what we hope to see in the future are schools of postgraduate research oriented by species rather than discipline. In this way one of the major criticisms of genetic research, namely its isolation from nutrition and nutrionists, is overcome. Lerner and Donald (1966) have rightly pointed out the need for cross-fertilization among disciplines. But their preference for departmentalization by function rather than by commodity is likely to make applied research even more fragmented than it is at the moment, and lead to the proliferation of academic research for its own sake.

It is difficult to assess what will be the impact of the Meat and Livestock Commission on the Establishment scene in the UK. Colburn (1968) considered it to be an irrelevance likely to be noted only for its high expenditure of public money. While we share much of Colburn's scepticism, we cannot accept his sweeping comments about the negligible animal improvement likely to accrue from the operation of performance testing and like operations. The facts are, as Comstock (1960) pointed out, that genetic progress in performance is both possible and likely to be considerable. Failure to achieve it can be related to inadequate systems of testing rather than intrinsic defects in the procedure as such. As Fredeen (1966) has said, "the failure of our pure breeds to make genetic gains in net merit reflects a plateauing of our breeders and not of our breed populations". Some national organizations such as PIDA and the MMB in the UK, the DHIA in the US and the state-controlled genetic operation in Israel (which has probably been the most successful of all), have made very definite contributions to our knowledge and the genetic merit of pigs and dairy cattle. Poultry have been improved out of all recognition by the application of the results of genetic research. Our concern is thus not with respect to what the Meat and Livestock Commission could do, but rather what we fear it might do. It is ominous that, at the time of writing, the Commission has reported on plans for setting up performance-testing stations and recording schemes for both beef and sheep without having a qualified geneticist on its staff.

Other critics of the Meat and Livestock Commission have been representatives of the commercial meat trade. There is nothing wrong with industry helping to finance research which in the end is of benefit to itself and to the nation. The contributions made to animal production by the wool and meat boards of Australia and New Zealand are examples of what can be achieved with the right kind of organization. The criticism that the Meat and Livestock Commission would cost money is not therefore valid. But concern as to whether or not it will produce anything of value to the meat industry is justifiable. If it follows the line already established by the pioneering work of PIDA the pig industry is certain to continue to benefit. Moreover, the financing of worth-while research projects at universities and other research institutes can be a very positive contribution. The real danger lies in the nature of the operations that the Commission might take upon itself to carry out in the actual field of applied beef cattle genetics.

The general outlook with respect to beef cattle breeding in developed countries is thus not a very hopeful one. The industry is stranded between the restrictive practices of the Establishment, on the one hand, and private breeders and breed societies on the other hand. Commercial producers must also bear some responsibility for this state of affairs by virtue of their general apathy towards this aspect of beef production. There is no doubt that in large countries, such as the US, commercial companies will make progress as a result of sheer economic necessity. Such stimuli rarely operate in countries where production is more fragmented and the producer shielded from the market.

In contrast, the picture in the underdeveloped countries is potentially more encouraging. Not only are facilities, in terms of animal numbers, likely to be larger, but traditional practices have not as yet had time to develop to the point of becoming restrictive. For example, the Serere Research Station in Uganda had in 1966 a breeding herd of some 800 head. Our own Institute in Cuba has, at the time of writing, a breeding herd of 1600 cows together with testing performance facilities for 400 bulls. Even this is nothing compared with some state organizations. Thus the Direccion Nacional de Genética Vacuna-Equino in Cuba had, in 1969, no fewer than nine herds throughout the country, some of which were in excess of 2000 head, together with control of the breeding programme of 100,000 Brahmans. The problem here is not one of animal numbers nor of facilities but simply human talent, since this same organization did not possess a single geneticist. The need in underdeveloped countries is, on the one hand, to recruit first-class applied geneticists, and, on the other, having employed them, to put their knowledge to best use.

12.3.3 Commercial development

Much more serious than all the criticism so far offered regarding research and research services, is the lethargy with which genetic knowledge has been put into commercial practice. In an analysis of 50 years of cattle breeding in the US, Warwick (1958) could find little evidence of genetic improvement in the productive merit of most beef cattle breeds. This is not surprising when account is taken of the relevant effort put into beef cattle breeding as compared with other species. Thus the setting up of the US Range Livestock Research Station in Montana in 1930 was some 25 years after the establishment of dairy-cow-testing in Michigan. The first Beef Cattle Improvement Association in Virginia was founded in 1955, 30 years after the DHIA began its activities. By 1960 a national sire evaluation programme was in operation for dairy cattle in the US, a similar scheme having been initiated 4 years earlier in the UK. As yet nothing comparable exists for beef cattle in either of these countries. By 1964 18% of the national dairy cow herd of the US was involved in DHIA whereas one year later only 1.5% of beef cows were being performance recorded (Baker, 1967a). There is little hope, moreover, of acceleration in the general tempo of progress as long as officials of the breed societies share the attitude of Swaffer (1967) "that conformation and show records are of value to the industry".

There has been some commercial application of beef cattle genetic research in the US, but hardly any sign of development in the UK. The fact that half of the Angus bulls at the Perth sale in 1967 were weight recorded (BRA, 1967) is no index of progress, for such weights reflect more the nutritional skill of the stockmen than the genetic merit of the bull. The very existence of the Perth show and sale, with its almost exclusive preoccupation with conformation and type, is a negation of all one hopes to achieve by recording. Probably the greatest mistake was the reluctance of the MMB to enter the field of beef cattle breeding. Having introduced and developed a system of dairy cattle improvement that became a basic model for many countries and having pioneered such developments as the importation of Charolais, their other activities in the field of beef cattle breeding have been, at best, extremely difficult to understand. Thus the major contribution of their elaborate station progeny testing scheme has been to encourage the mistaken belief that beef cattle improvement schemes must, of necessity, be expensive.

12.4 NUTRITION

12.4.1 Research

In Europe particularly a vast amount of research has been devoted to the nutrition of ruminants, and since the 1940's our knowledge of these species has increased to the extent of creating completely new concepts with respect to the physiology of digestion and metabolism. As is the case with most European basic research, investigations have gone forward with the prime motivation of acquiring knowledge rather than with a view to its subsequent exploitation in applied fields. The disadvantage of this approach is that the information has not been as useful as it might have been. Thus many physiologists and biochemists have been preoccupied with the nature of animal response and have largely ignored changes in commercial feeding practice. Diets on which so many fundamental investigations have been undertaken in Europe have been basically of a high roughage nature, an understandable trend as long as such materials constituted the basis of cattle feeding, but hardly useful for the future. In advanced systems such diets are given only to beef cows, the feedlot operator having long since discarded roughage other than as a possible safeguard to animal health. Major deficiencies in knowledge could have arisen through this separation and only the fact that US basic research has been more commercially orientated has prevented development from being seriously hampered.

Gaps in knowledge mainly relate to the field of all-concentrate and minimum roughage diets. The role of post-ruminal digestion has always been recognized with respect to protein utilization, but it is only now—particularly as a result of the work carried out at the University of Kentucky—that its importance is being understood with respect to carbohydrate metabolism. In this field close collaboration between the basic and the applied nutritionist is essential. For example, the indications are that post-ruminal carbohydrate digestion only becomes significant with *ad libitum* feeding, a procedure rarely adopted by the fundamental researcher as it undoubtedly complicates his investigation. The giving of the greater part of the ruminant diet in liquid form is already a commercial proposition with high molasses/urea systems and its application to the more usual grain-based diets is now being studied in the US. In view of the possibility of liquid feeds evading the rumen, the capacity for digestion in the intestine could easily become a limiting factor. Almost nothing is known about this at the present time.

As a result of the work of Blaxter and his colleagues at the Hannah Research Institute, considerable attention has been given to the relation between the type of rumen fermentation (particularly the relative rates of production of propionic and acetic acids) and efficiency of feed utilization. There is no doubt that a fermentation characterized by a narrow acetic propionic ratio leads to significant changes in carcass composition (increasing fatness), but the information is equivocal as to whether changes in VFA ratio affect efficiency of feed utilization *per se*. The latter invariably improves with increasing proportions of concentrates in the diet and this also has the effect of narrowing the acetic/propionic ratio, but this is not to say that it is the VFA ratios which play the determining role. We believe that the factors which lead to narrowing of the propionic acetic/ratio—such as increasing the amount of concentrates in the diet, moist heat treatment, and pressure processing and pelleting—all tend to increase rate of passage through the rumen and hence the proportion of feed energy available for digestion in the intestine. Such a hypothesis, attractive though it may appear, is nevertheless of little value without supporting data.

R. L. Preston (1968) has rightly stressed the importance of voluntary feed intake in beef cattle production and has suggested that this is the most fertile field for study if a major breakthrough in feed utilization efficiency is to be obtained. The factors determining voluntary feed intake on traditional roughage diets have been known for a considerable time, major contributions in this field having been made by European researchers. On the other hand, it is only since the mid-1960's that the situation on high concentrate diets has begun to be clarified, primarily as the result of US research. While there is now agreement as to the importance of blood levels of acetic acid acting in some way as a satiety signal, the exact mechanisms involved are still largely unknown. Elucidation of this point is of vital importance to the applied worker seeking to bring about improvement in feed efficiency.

Of lesser importance commercially is the discrepancy which appears to exist in the field of energy utilization as between the results of calorimetric studies and feeding trials (Preston *et al.*, 1969c). We believe that there are already sufficient data to cast considerable doubt upon the concept of a fixed maintenance requirement, irrespective of productive rate. Much of the confusion has undoubtedly arisen from relating maintenance requirements to age rather than to production. The fact that this assumption was based on experiments carried out in the 1940's emphasizes our earlier comment that basic research should be brought up to date. We are not questioning the precision with which this early work was undertaken, but make the point that the diets and systems of management then bear little or no relation to modern methods of animal production.

Another important area of ruminant research where data are urgently needed is the utilization of NPN. The commercial implications of replacing preformed protein by chemical nitrogen are obvious. Unfortunately, despite the vast amount of experimentation that has been undertaken on this subject, knowledge has advanced but little. Chalupa (1968) in a comprehensive review had to conclude with essentially the same recommendations which were offered by Rupel *et al.* in 1943. We believe that advances in our knowledge of protein and NPN utilization have been retarded by the preoccupation with what takes place in the rumen. While such an investigational approach at first sight appears logical, since most microbial synthesis takes place in the rumen, information is now becoming available to show that the major factor influencing overall nitrogen utilization is the extent to which unmodified feed protein of high biological value can escape microbial degradation and contribute directly to the amino-acid pool following intestinal digestion. The concept of slowing down the rate of ammonia production as a means of increasing the efficiency of microbial synthesis has been a particular red herring. Again, much of the original work in this area was carried out not only in diets of high roughage content but in some cases (e.g. Chalmers, 1963) with quite excessive levels of dietary protein. In fact, on high energy diets, rumen ammonia levels are determined more by pH than the solubility of the protein or the rate of hydrolysis of the NPN source (Elías and Preston, 1969b). Solubility is certainly an important characteristic, but only for proteins of high biological value (there is little point in encouraging the passage of zein into the intestine). As with energy utilization, it would seem that further work with respect to proteins should also be directed to finding out what happens post-rumen.

In view of the wide discrepancies between the dietary levels of the fat-soluble vitamins used in commercial practice and the theoretical requirements put forward by the ARC (1965) (see § 9.7), investigation in this area is also overdue. The general direction in which this research might be pursued is suggested by the work carried out in Kentucky (§ 9.7) on the destructive effects of high energy diets on these particular nutrients. The exact role of vitamin E and selenium also merit further investigation, while the toxic levels of the latter need reappraisal.

12.4.2 Organization of research

It could be argued that the problem with basic nutritional research is that it is too well organized. Storer (1963) said that "we must expect to find that basic research will become the tail rather than the dog in coming years . . . and we may find it being wagged right off the dog without our being aware of it." In so far as agricultural research is concerned it would probably have been better if basic research had never been the dog in the first place. By this, we do not question the value of academic research. But the problem is one of priorities and small and/or developing countries will less and less be able to afford the luxury of pursuing knowledge for its own sake. Fundamental research on a broad scale, as it has been carried out thus far in the UK, will in the future become more and more the prerogative of the US and the USSR. Elsewhere, basic research will be increasingly called upon to justify its existence which it can only do in the service of applied science.

12.5 BEEF COWS

12.5.1 Research

In a sense all beef cow research is applied and developmental in character. The areas to which greater attention should be devoted in the future are intimately linked with economic studies since rising land values and labour scarcity will force increasing intensification upon the reproductive herd. Means of improving the overall efficiency of the operation are thus paramount. Perhaps the greatest need is for a reappraisal of weaning age and we hope to see more work both on earlier weaning and the effect of this on subsequent feedlot performance. Such developments have the indirect effect of bringing the beef cow herself into the drylot which should stimulate studies on minimum feeding of the cow aimed at determining the optimum time for supplementation to ensure best reproductive performance. For the remainder of the breeding cycle emphasis must be on how little can be given without detriment to overall calf crop percentage. An obvious way of reducing overheads and hence increasing the beef cow's potential productivity is to have earlier calving. In the short term such developments are almost certain to be accompanied by greater calf losses due to stillbirths and dystokia. Nevertheless, this is not inevitable as has been shown in Israel (Heiman, 1968) where early calving of dairy heifers is standard practice and where losses from the above causes have been reduced by a third through genetic selection. The relation of vitamin status to reproduction has been common knowledge for many years, but it is only recently that the economic advantages from timely injections and supplementation are being recognized; earlier calving ought to accelerate developments in this area.

Oestrus synchronization is almost essential in any programme of genetic improvement since it is only in this way that AI can be efficiently utilized. Synchronization presents few problems and many compounds are known to be effective in this respect; unfortunately effects on subsequent fertility have, in the main, been detrimental and this area must be intensively researched.

Studies on multiple births have been conspicuously unsuccessful and this is one field where basic research is the key to securing the necessary breakthrough.

There must also be much more openmindedness as to what constitutes a beef cow. If rotational crossbreeding programmes are followed commercial beef herds will inevitably become more heterogenic to the extent that breed identities will be lost in much the same way as has occurred in the chicken industry. Fundamental to the success of rotational crossbreeding is the need to bring in exotic breeds and in this respect both the Holstein and Brown Swiss, hitherto largely regarded as single-purpose dairy animals, should become more common in beef herds. Already in the US, Angus × Holstein cows are becoming more numerous, while the work of Plum and Harris (1968) suggests that even purebred Holsteins reared as beef animals bring advantages of earlier puberty and earlier calving.

12.5.2 Research organization and development

The most logical way of organizing beef cow research is as an adjunct to genetic investigations. We have already stressed the importance to genetic research of large herds and interdisciplinary collaboration, and it would seem that beef cow research at the same stations is both logical and most economic.

In the US at least there appears to be little reluctance to adopt new management and nutritional techniques, be this in the field of beef calf production or feedlot fattening. It is unfortunate that acceptance of genetic findings is so much slower and the only hope is that it will be forced on the industry as a result of continuing integration. The refusal of some breed societies, both in the UK and the US, to register progeny of AI sires is a restrictive practice which ought to be terminated. Alternatively, since herd books are necessary for recording ancestry, commercial farmers could form their own registration associations.

Increasing land values of themselves will force intensification of beef calf operations and/or integration with the feedlot. There is also considerable scope for the greater utilization of crop residues. The basis can be cereal straw and maize stalks in temperate countries and the fibrous parts of the sugar cane in the tropics. Developments of this kind have the advantage of linking both calf production and growth and fattening with potential benefits in terms of reducing losses from transit stress and increasing the efficiency of the operation.

12.6 DAIRY CALVES

Dairy calf nutrition has been an excellent example of research by commodity rather than by discipline of which European researchers can justifiably be proud since they have made the major contribution. The National Institute for Research in Dairying has been in the forefront of basic research while applied aspects have been most effectively pursued in Holland. The problems which continue to give concern to intensive calf rearers are the interactions between nutrition, stress and disease. The solutions must almost certainly be found on the farms themselves rather than in the laboratory, in much the same way that Dodd and his team at the NIRD have tackled the menace of mastitis.

The greatest scope for development work in dairy calf production is in the tropics. Invariably these areas are short of liquid milk and usually have no milk substitutes. As a result dairy bull calves are either slaughtered at birth or consume inordinate quantities of milk which would be much better directed to a needy population. In some developing countries it is customary for calves to consume up to 500 l. of whole milk and they may consume up to 1500 l. when destined for AI service. Calves can be satisfactorily reared in the tropics on as little as 96 l. of whole milk (§ 7.5.3) while our own observations suggest that milk substitutes can be formulated from molasses and hydrolysed protein products recovered from abattoirs. The problem is mainly of a managerial and organizational nature.

12.7 FEEDLOT FATTENING

12.7.1 Research

Highly sophisticated feeding systems are common in most areas of the US and startling developments are unlikely, the improvement expected from research being of the order of some 2–5%. However, this intense degree of development has taken place mainly in the nutritional field. As we have pointed out earlier (§§ 12.2.1 and 12.3.1), developments in genetics and carcass quality are less advanced.

One of the most important subjects requiring study is compensatory growth. That the phenomenon exists is well known; there is also considerable information as to what happens during realimentation. The deficiency is largely of an economic nature and relates to the need to quantify lifetime efficiency of animals subjected to compensatory growth as opposed to those fattened intensively from birth. There can be no progress if research continues, as it has done thus far, on studies of systems where the period of restriction takes place on pasture. This may be the procedure in practice, but it is impossible to obtain the accurate data on feed intake during this period which is necessary for any comprehensive economic analysis.

Compensatory growth has been to the advantage of the traditional British breeds in that their feedlot performance has been artificially high; conversely, it has acted to the detriment of lean breeds, of known genetic superiority for growth. Whereas the Hereford and Angus tend to lose only fat during restriction (which is regained rapidly and easily in the feedlot), the Holstein, which does not fatten early in life, loses muscle. It is thus more adversely affected during the period of restriction (Kaspar and Willis, 1968) and, as a result, requires a much longer period in the feedlot to recuperate.

The pivotal role of feed intake in determining beef cattle performance has already been mentioned. Much more data is needed on voluntary consumption of different diets by animals of different breeds and varying degrees of body condition on entering the feedlot. In this connection the role of roughage and the effect of cereal processing are still imperfectly understood. Linear programming for the derivation of least cost diets can never be precise without this basic information.

Present information on nutrient requirements is deficient when looked at from an economic point of view where the need is for knowledge of input/output relationships. Despite the relatively high cost of protein supplementation for cattle fattening diets, there is much uncertainty as to both the optimum level and the effect on performance and carcass composition of variation around this. In many ways the situation is confounded by changes in feed intake which can be considerable on the different feeding systems employed in commercial practice.

With the notable exception of "barley beef" production, Europe has developed no feeding system of comparable merit to those of the US. In line with the diverse nature of the feeding systems used, applied research has operated with no apparent objective other than the piecemeal solution of local problems, generally based on low quality feeds. The greatest barrier to progress has been the virtual absence of large-scale commercial fattening operations in which applied research might have been undertaken and in which new findings would certainly have had ready application. Yugoslavia alone has evolved large-scale feeding practices similar to those of the US. But, although enjoying considerable genetic advantages through being able to employ Simmental and Brown Swiss cattle, it has suffered somewhat through a scarcity of highly trained nutritionists. There are encouraging signs of progress in Denmark and Belgium where researchers are engaged in developing intensive feeding systems based upon less conventional, but higher yielding crops, such as sugar beet. Basically the same deficiencies of knowledge exist in Europe as in the US although the problem of compensatory growth is less important.

Such research as has been undertaken in tropical and sub-tropical countries has been largely confined to methods of survival on the one hand and pasture improvement on the other. Neither approach has much aided the countries concerned to increase their meat production. Research in tropical regions must now be aimed at developing intensive production systems based upon carbohydrate-rich crops already available in the country or which show potential for development within the existing climatic and social environment. We have discussed the use of sugar-cane as a basis for such intensification (§ 9.3.3). Attention should also be given to rice together with whatever byproducts are available. The problem is firstly to devise feeding systems and secondly to carry out the necessary investigations to allow the calculation of relevant input/output data.

12.7.2 Research organization

Applied nutrition research, perhaps more than any other discipline, has been characterized by the inadequate training of the scientists undertaking it. The errors have arisen mostly from a lack of appreciation of the importance of experimental design and the use of statistics generally.

Not only does applied nutrition research tend to be a second-rate operation with respect to its personnel, but it is invariably well down the list when it comes to a question of providing facilities. Probably, its greatest disadvantage is that it suffers from a surfeit of advice from experts in every field other than in applied nutrition. A good example of this was the composition of the ARC technical committee charged with the responsibility of setting up feeding standards for farm livestock in 1959. Of the twelve members of the main committee only one can be described as an applied scientist. Their communication on the Nutrient Requirements of Ruminants reflects the makeup of both the technical committee and the working party with specific responsibilities for this publication. For while it is an admirable review of the literature, its attempt to formulate nutrient requirements for commercial animal production has largely failed through extrapolating laboratory data to commercial conditions. As a result, the recommendations with regard to proteins and vitamins, if carried through, would lead to a serious reduction in performance. Animal feeding is not, and can never hope to be, an exact science. It is insufficiently understood and by the very nature of animal variability can never be expected to conform to the exact laws of the physical scientist. The techniques used by modern agricultural economists are more appropriate for the determination of nutrient requirements for commercial livestock production than are relationships based upon physiological and biochemical standards. In the revision of this publication, which is urgently required, it would seem desirable that applied nutritionists should predominate and that there should be a greater representation of agricultural economists together with nutritionists from commercial feed companies.

Scientific research is costly and large-animal investigation the most expensive of all. Thus Loosli (1966), speaking of the financing of US research, considered that the total cost per scientist in terms of salary, assistance, equipment and travel could amount to $45,000 per man/year with an additional $100,000 capital investment. It is obvious from this that considerable care must be exercised both as to what research is to be done and who should do it. Much of what has been said about the means of instigating worth-while genetic research is relevant to applied nutrition investigation. Thus larger breeding herds, as required for a genetic project, would equally benefit the nutritionist, one of whose most serious problems is the difficulty of obtaining sufficient numbers of animals of known history.

This kind of development, while feasible in the US, presents considerable problems in Europe. Here, the most effective compromise and certainly the most rapid in terms of execution would be a greater reliance on co-operative projects carried out on commercial farms. The success of this line of development depends upon the existence of specific and definable beef production systems. This kind of approach was pioneered by the Rowett Research Institute in their studies of nutritional factors of economic significance to "barley beef" production (see, for example, MacDearmid, 1967). Such research can be comparatively inexpensive but it is absolutely dependent upon good public relations, on the part of the investigators, and, enlightened direction which means understanding the farmer's problems and having a sufficient awareness of the subject to be able to suggest the most economic way of overcoming them.

Although industry has played an important role in putting US applied nutrition research in its present preeminent position, the same cannot be said of the situation in Europe. Too often, universities and government-financed research institutes have an ill regard for commerce with the result that very little co-operation exists between the state institutions and commercial companies. This is not to anyone's advantage. What is necessary in the future is a great deal more commercially sponsored research with the understanding that the work that is supported will have practical application.

It might be thought from the above that European applied nutrition research is starved of both men and facilities. In fact, this is not entirely the case. What has happened is a proliferation of research in institutions not always competent to undertake it.

The result has been an unnecessary repetition of low-quality investigations with little or no co-ordination This is particularly true in the UK where applied nutrition research is carried out not only at specific research centres but also at farm institutes, agricultural colleges, National Agricultural Advisory Service experimental husbandry farms and in ill-equipped universities. This is not to say that the work carried out has not been of value, nor that these facilities should not be used. What is required is co-ordination under competent investigators, so that these centres are used in much the same way as the commercial farms in the experiments described by MacDearmid (1967).

An important development in the applied nutrition research field in the US has been the emergence of contract research and consultants. These provide an important service to many companies themselves unable to afford full time research activities, and, by demonstrating that research and development can be a profitable business, they help to remove much of the mystery which only too often surrounds government and university controlled research. As yet, these developments have made little impact in Europe nor are they likely to as long as employees of state-aided research institutions are discouraged, if not prohibited, from acting as consultants or participating in commercially orientated activities.

If research in the developed countries frequently suffers from poor direction, a shortage of the right kind of resources, and considerable confusion about objectives, it is nevertheless active. By comparison the situation in many developing countries is sometimes positively discouraging. Not that no research has been attempted, for nearly all the previously colonized territories have some form of research organization or university. Unfortunately these were established at a time when service abroad was often considered disadvantageous to a scientist's career. Moreover, the excessive preoccupation with disease problems led to organizations staffed, for the most part, by veterinarians. The very nature of the veterinarian's profession makes him ill-suited to developing systems of animal production. A training dedicated to the elimination of disease is the wrong preparation for intensifying animal production which often increases the risk of disease rather than reducing it. In Latin America, veterinarians receive some training in animal husbandry, but the 5 year course of study, as Raun (1968) has pointed out, has been so broad as to be superficial, qualifying the graduate "as neither a professional veterinarian nor an animal husbandry man". It is thus not surprising that research centres in developing countries have so far contributed little to the development of new and economic animal production systems.

The new nations suffer to an even greater extent than the developed countries from poor definition of what should be their objective. This is not entirely the responsibility of the governments concerned but often results from a lack of awareness of the real problems on the part of their advisers. The need for aid to these countries is accepted but, as Schultz (1966) has pointed out, assistance given in the form of food supplies merely reduces the urgency in the importing countries to cope with their own agricultural problems. Examples of successful foreign aid programmes have been those which led to the creation of the International Rice Research Institute (Philippines), the International Maize and Wheat Improvement Centre (Mexico) and the International Agricultural Centre (Colombia). In animal husbandry valuable work is being done by the Instituto Colombiano Agropecuario which was set up by the Government with the aid of various international agencies. According to Raun (1968), the degree of outside financial assistance needed is relatively modest, but to be effective must be "continuing, technologically sound and tailored to the local scene and personnel". It is not without significance that at the second meeting of the Latin American Society for Animal Production in Lima (1968) this organization was the most widely represented and notable for the standard of its contributions. Undoubtedly this stemmed from the presence of competent US scientists on its staff.

By comparison the contribution to agricultural development made by such international agencies as FAO leaves much to be desired. The reason for this is probably related to its advisory rather than executive role, allied to an excessive preoccupation with politics which has often influenced the choice of "experts" to a greater extent than scientific merit or organizational capacity. Advisors are not always what is needed, indeed most developing countries have had more than their fair share of advice. The requirements are for competent scientists to be given executive responsibility and clear terms of reference which should be (a) the production of viable applied research directed towards solving the country's economic problem, and (b) the training of local personnel at a postgraduate level to take over the operation at a predetermined point in time. The FAO does not suffer from any lack of intent or finance nor of a shortage of problems to solve. It does not have a ready supply of scientists of international reputation nor is it likely to have as long as its approach to aid is solely by means of local projects which offer little more than the opportunity of carrying out extension work and give no scope to dedicated researchers. It seems to us that the FAO would do better to set up, in carefully chosen areas, research institutions devoted exclusively to applied animal and crop research for the developing countries. The advantages to the host states are obvious, but there are many others for FAO itself and automatically for those it assists:

(a) Creating good facilities for research automatically attracts better scientists.
(b) Work could be carried out on problems which the developed countries are not interested in solving.
(c) By having its own professional scientists FAO would be in a better position to direct the activities of local projects in aided countries.
(d) Creation of centres dedicated to the development of improved livestock and crop plants would provide reservoirs of superior genetic material which could be made available to countries requiring it.

Another important aspect of aid by the developed countries is with respect to facilities and scholarships. According to the IIE (1966) only 4% of 82,700 foreign students in the US were studying agriculture, despite the fact that the majority came from regions in which agriculture is the mainstay of the economy. As much as anything this reflects the poor status of the agricultural scientist in developing countries and the undoubted fact that more money and prestige are to be gained in the other professions.

The corollary to importing foreign scientists to initiate research and development projects, is the sending out of superior students for higher education at carefully chosen centres, emphasis being placed on instruction in the basic sciences and in biometrics.

12.8 HOUSING

Probably the least understood and certainly the least studied of all branches of beef production is housing. The problems are numerous; unfortunately most of the ways in which solutions can be provided are extremely limited and inordinately expensive. Housing systems have invariably arisen on an empirical basis with major reliance on the experience of private individuals. This approach can be developed by efficient survey techniques such as those undertaken in the UK by the Scottish Farm Buildings Investigation Unit and the Farm Building Unit of the ARC.

It is difficult to see how animal orientated research in this field can be undertaken by conventional methods, since to replicate particular types of farm buildings is clearly a financial impossibility. Some research can be conducted on the value of building materials together with independent reports on equipment and machinery along the lines carried out by the National Institute for Agricultural Engineering in the UK. Beyond this there is little to offer other than learning to avoid other people's mistakes.

The problems in the tropics and in developing countries generally are in some ways easier to solve in that building structures to combat heat are less expensive than those needed to give protection against cold. On the other hand, there are few errors to learn from, although at the rate that some developing countries are using concrete they should rapidly make up the leeway.

For beef cows natural shelter is all that is probably required, and quite simple experiments can be set up to determine the kind of shade that is needed. For fattening beef cattle in the tropics the important factor is not the effect of housing on animal performance but what is the most economical construction from an overall point of view, bearing in mind the limitations of management, investment funds and building materials. In any event, buildings should be as flexible as possible so that modifications dictated by experience can be the more easily incorporated.

12.9 DISEASE

Intensification of cattle production leads almost automatically to an increase in the incidence of certain types of disease. There is thus no place for the philosophy that the first priority is disease elimination. This is particularly important in tropical areas where there has been, and still is, a preoccupation with eradication of tuberculosis, brucellosis, foot-and-mouth disease and the like while animals die by the thousand from malnutrition. This is especially inappropriate when, as is often the case, there is a shortage of experienced veterinarians and ineffective diagnostic services. The application of such policies reflects confusion about economic priorities.

It would be absurd to suggest that disease research is not necessary or that eradication procedures for certain diseases are not desirable. Our concern is solely with the order in which problems should be tackled, and in our experience the most serious disease in the tropics is inadequate nutrition. In certain areas tick-borne diseases are sufficiently virulent completely to inhibit animal production, and there can be no disagreement about the importance of their eradication. But this is far from being a widespread situation.

We believe that disease research should be considered in the same light as basic research (another tail for the dog), playing a supporting role to the primary investigations which would be in nutrition and genetics. In this respect one must question the advisability of setting up research institutes specifically directed to studies of animal diseases or health. Apart from the fact that this is opposed to the principle of research by commodity rather than by discipline, experience suggests that such centres contribute little towards advancing economic disease control measures. This is well illustrated by the history of mastitis research in the UK. None of the animal health research institutes has contributed materially to reducing economic losses from this disease. The real advances at this level have come about almost entirely through the operational type research carried out at the NIRD with the help of commercial companies. We believe this example offers a model of how research into economically important diseases is best carried out. The essentials of such a programme are (a) understanding of the real nature of the problem, (b) large-scale investigation at the level of the commercial producer, and (c) an efficient diagnostic service to help bring the problem to light in the first instance, as well as to evaluate the effectiveness of any control treatments.

12.10 ECONOMIC ASPECTS

12.10.1 General considerations

It is neither desirable nor practicable for us to attempt to define and describe the methods by which the profitability of a beef production enterprise should be assessed, or to be dogmatic about which methods are the most profitable. Because this book is about intensive methods of production it is not to imply that all others must lose money or that all intensive beef producers make a profit. Beef production is like any other enterprise or industrial operation in that some operators are successful while others fail. Methods of beef production are determined to a considerable degree by climate, markets, level of economic development and the available land area per head of population. Political conditions are also extremely important inasmuch as protective measures, price support policies, state ownership, etc., can decisively influence the course of production. The scale of operations and degree of integration necessary for modern intensive beef production systems are not achievable under all circumstances. Apart from suitable economic and political conditions, they require technical and organizational know-how.

It must also be realized that a profitable system today under the specific conditions of a particular location and country will not necessarily be profitable in 5 or 10 years' time. For this reason we consider it more important to examine trends in the progress of beef production rather than analyse the factors operating at any one time.

As we have stressed earlier, beef production divides into two components, namely the raising of the calf and its subsequent fattening. In specialist beef operations almost everywhere the rearing phase is of an extensive nature, whereas in dairy beef operations it is exclusively intensive. In contrast, the fattening operation can take many forms. Thus while dairy beef cattle are, in the main, fattened intensively for slaughter at around 1 year of age, a considerable proportion, as in the UK, spend part of their lives at grass, as a result of which slaughter ages may be anything from $1\frac{1}{2}$ to $2\frac{1}{2}$ years. On the other hand, the fattening of specialist beef cattle depends to a great extent on farming tradition and the stage of economic development. In the underdeveloped countries it is common for steers or bulls to remain with the cow herd, often not reaching slaughter weight until they are 3–5 years of age. While where tradition predominates, as in the UK, beef cattle may be fattened on pasture or under housed conditions but basically on low and medium energy diets for slaughter at 18 months and $2\frac{1}{2}$ years. In the US the final 100–120 days of fattening reaches extreme degrees of sophistication in the large feedlots of the south-west; traditional roughage feeding still persists in the intermediate period between weaning and entering the feedlot, but this is mostly dictated by the unsuitability of the British breeds for intensive fattening from weaning. Possibly the most advanced system of all, in terms of lifetime efficiency and utilization of resources, is the Yugoslavian, in which the great majority of beef cattle enter the feedlot immediately after early weaning and are fattened intensively to reach slaughter weight at around 1 year of age.

This is the present situation. What will it be in 5 or 10 years' time?

We have little doubt that the Yugoslavian type of operation will go from strength to strength. In general terms they possess the right kind of cattle for future market requirements and the system is already efficient in terms of use of natural resources. When to this framework is added the technical expertise (with respect to nutrition, disease control and management) that exists in the US, and when genetic improvement programmes are initiated, that country could become one of the most efficient beef producers in the world in view of its tremendous potential for scale of operation and integration. Nevertheless, because of its relatively small size Yugoslavia can never be other than a minor factor in world beef production.

As the largest beef producer in the world, both in absolute amounts as well as in terms of meat produced per head of cattle, the US must play a dominant role in determining future production systems. Fortunately the general trend in the US is quite clear. In 1967 there were over 200,000 feedlots in the thirty-two major cattle fattening states which marketed a total of 21.7 million head. It is clear from Table 12.1 that since 1962 feedlots have become smaller in number and larger in capacity. Thus feedlots with a capacity of 1000 head and more now account for almost half of all cattle produced, a 77% increase over 1962. The actual number of feedlots in this category increased during the same period by only some 32% which indicates the increasing intensiveness of the operation. Perhaps the most striking feature is that in

1967 there were 13 feedlots with a capacity for 32,000 head or more compared with only 5 in 1962 and that these particular units fattened nearly 1 million cattle. The ranking of the States possessing feedlots with 1000 head capacity or more is significant: Nebraska, 416; California, 300; Texas, 278; Iowa, 140; and Kansas, 100. Of these, only Iowa can be said to produce beef in the traditional way, that is mainly using feeds grown on the farm. Although the national growth rate in cattle fattening was 7% for the 10 years ending 1968, it was only 5% in the traditional corn belt area compared with 11% in the Plains States. According to Hasbargen (1968) the latter obtained better prices for their carcass meat and made more profit primarily by buying so-called "inferior" crossbred cattle instead of "well-bred" Hereford or Angus steers which predominate in the corn belt. More efficient feeds were also used, in that it took 25–30% more energy to produce 1 kg of gain in the corn belt than it did in Colorado and Arizona.

Table 12.1 Feedlots in the 32 Major Cattle-feeding States in the US in 1962 and 1967 (after USDA, 1968)

Size of feedlot (No. of head)	1962		1967	
	No. of feedlots	Total cattle (millions)	No. of feedlots	Total cattle (millions)
< 1000	234,646	—	209,505	11.83
> 1000	1,570	5.57	2,008	9.85
1000–2000	801	0.89	960	1.21
2000–4000	385	0.84	510	1.46
4000–8000	195	1.14	313	1.95
8000–16000	106	1.53	153	2.17
16000–32000	26	0.85	59	2.12
32000	5	0.31	13	0.95
Total	236,216	—	211,513	21.68

Other evidence of increasing intensification comes from a survey of feedlot operators regarding supplies of feeder cattle for the 1968/9 season (Anon., 1968). It was considered that some 42% would be calves, 33% yearlings and only 25.3% between 1 and 2 years old, demonstrating the trend towards the fattening of younger and lighter cattle.

In the light of these statistics, generalized claims such as those of Beeson (1968) that greater profit will accrue from the use of wholecrop feeding programmes and that high roughage systems are more profitable than all-concentrate or very high energy diets are somewhat parochial. Moreover, there is evidence from the work of Beeson's own colleagues (Perry and Mott, cited by Wilkie, 1968) that such claims are not even accurate, since on pasture feeding profitability was found to be directly related to the amount of concentrates given. At the highest profit level, the amount of concentrates eaten was such as to suggest that the animals were using the pasture for little other than exercise.

In contrast to the dynamic development of the feedlot industry in the US ever searching for greater efficiency, the situation in Europe, and particularly in the UK, is stagnant if not retrogressive. Although there was a rapid development of dairy beef production during the 1960's to the extent that some 10% of beef came from this source in 1963–4, it subsequently declined to 6–7% (Barfield, 1966; Campbell, 1968). This decline was not due to lack of efficiency, since in energy terms it is even more efficient than US feedlot fattening; the real reason was the increasing price of calves brought about by the initial popularity of the system. As calf prices rose the intensive producer purchasing both his feed and his cattle was not able to compete with the traditional producer who took his profit as an overall return from stock and land, with price supports and subsidies playing a considerable role.

The barrier to intensification in western Europe is thus not technical but largely political. Europe still uses high fibre feeds rather than grains, and although this results in poor animal efficiency it can be justified economically due to the system of price supports and other economic and fiscal measures current both within the EEC and without. In the long term such a policy is deleterious since it acts as a brake both upon scientific progress and the production of food for an expanding population. The inefficient beef producer survives and while the consumer appears to benefit from the availability of cheap food, the overall cost to a country is in reality very much greater. It is not without significance that the only livestock industry in Europe which has developed standards of technical and economic efficiency comparable with its counterpart in the US has been the meat chicken industry which is almost completely unsubsidized. Similar progress in beef production is unlikely until the present system of subsidies and price supports is revised and economic efficiency becomes more closely related to animal efficiency.

12.10.2 Feedlot operations

12.10.2.1 SCALE. We have already referred to the trend towards larger feedlots which became evident in the US during the 1960's. There are distinct economic advantages from an increase in scale although the effect is not linear. Thus Anon. (1965e) showed that with a throughput of less than 5000 per year the daily non-feed costs per head were 12.7 cents. This fell to 8.7 cents with 7500 cattle and finally to around 7.0 cents when the number fed annually rose to the order of 18,000. Thereafter, non-feed costs remained more or less static, being 7.1 cents at a throughput of 45,000. The reasons for increased economic efficiency with scale of operation are not simply those of spreading fixed investment over a larger number of animals; there are also economies resulting from the better utilization of highly qualified personnel. As Cardon has said, "Purchasing and handling cattle and preparing feeds are highly technical operations and it is economically unsound to collect the necessary human talent in a small unit". On the other hand, there is probably a maximum size beyond which management becomes difficult. One feedlot owner with a unit holding 30,000 preferred to expand by building a completely separate facility some distance away rather than by extending the size of the existing one (Pitman, 1968). It was considered that a 30,000 head unit was as much as one manager and one feedmill could service efficiently.

While there may be good arguments in terms of utilization of machinery and day-to-day management for limiting the capacity of individual feedlots to around 30,000 head, there is no reason why enterprises should be so restricted and, in fact, present developments may well require the creation of larger units although not necessarily at the same site. It may well be that future progress will hinge not upon larger and larger feedlots but rather the integration of fattening with calf procurement, on the one hand, and direct marketing to the consumer, on the other. This is probably the only way to exploit effectively the potential of genetically improved cattle which, although they may be considered lacking in "quality" for the traditional market, are eminently suited to mass outlets such as supermarkets, drive-in restaurants and pre-packed meals for industry. Parker (1968) reported on one such enterprise in the US (annual gross earnings $6.2 million) which, in order to obtain the type of meat it needed for its specific drive-in restaurant operation (i.e. uniform lean red meat), considered it necessary to establish not only an intensive fattening operation but a genetic programme to guarantee the right sort of animal from the beginning.

There has been a rapid development in the application of mathematical methods, such as production functions and linear programming, in the US beef industry. Snyder and Guthrie (1968) have pointed out that simple linear programmes are no longer sufficient to maximize profitability. The need to take account of sales and procurement of feedstuffs as well as their costs and nutritional value means that multi-product formulation programmes may be needed in the future. This again acts as an incentive to increased size of fattening operations.

12.10.2.2 Feed efficiency. It is relatively easy to define the combination of factors necessary to reduce non-feed costs to the minimum. Once this is achieved ultimate profitability depends almost entirely upon feed efficiency. Rate of gain is an important factor in that it determines the length of time needed to fatten a particular group of cattle, and thus the period of time during which facilities are occupied. But the fastest gaining animals are not necessarily the most efficient. Moreover, while rations which promote maximum feed efficiency do not necessarily promote maximum rate of live weight gain, this is largely compensated for by higher killing out percentages due to reduced gut fill. A comprehensive economic analysis of dairy beef production in the north of Scotland was carried out by Clark (1966). The survey covered eleven farms, varying in holding capacity from less than 25 to over 176. In Table 12.2 are shown the net surplus (gross margin minus all other costs), the average number of head at any one time, average daily gain, conversion ratio and mortality. Despite the wide range in size, gain and mortality, these variables appear to have little effect on the profitability of the operation which was found to be highly correlated with the feed conversion ratio. For all practical purposes, therefore, feed conversion can be considered the most important parameter in any feedlot operation.

The usual measurement of feed efficiency is the amount of feed required per unit of live weight gain. This yardstick has been criticized by Ward (1968) who pointed out that (a) feeds vary widely in their energy content, (b) feed intake has little meaning since growth results from energy above maintenance, and (c) weight gains vary greatly in their content of fat, muscle and bone. While these criticisms are theoretically sound, nevertheless feed consumed and rate of live weight gain are the measurements immediately and easily available to the feedlot operator. It is misleading to compare, as Ward (1968) did, conversion rates in animals at different live weights or with widely differing feed intakes. The latter is particularly inappropriate since

TABLE 12.2 RELATION BETWEEN SOME PRODUCTION PARAMETERS AND PROFITABILITY IN DAIRY BEEF ENTERPRISES IN THE NORTH OF SCOTLAND

Farm	Profit/head[a] ($)	No. of head	Feed conversion	Daily gain[b] (kg)	Mortality
4	64	212	4.94	0.91	3.1
1	42	126	4.70	0.91	11.1
6	31	107	4.86	1.00	2.9
12	30	132	5.36	0.84	3.9
11	20	148	5.67	0.78	1.6
3	16	124	5.98	0.83	1.3
2	11	84	6.50	0.96	8.2
5	6	28	5.38	0.92	0.0
13	1	25	6.28	0.79	0.0
7	−6	41	5.06	0.96	1.6
9	−35	30	6.45	0.75	5.1

[a] In $(US) at rate of exchange when report published.

[b] Estimated from total weight gain in 12 months divided by 365 × number of cattle (average gain per animal marketed would be higher).

almost without exception all feedlot cattle are fed *ad libitum* and intake then is a combined function of the animal's genotype and its treatment prior to arriving at the feedlot, as well as the type of diet fed. In practical terms the diet is predetermined by economic factors and the feedlot operator is thus primarily concerned with the response to it by different types or breeds of cattle. In this respect, feed conversion rate expressed as the amount of feed consumed divided by the live weight gain is the most practical index. Better still would be the use of gain in saleable meat in the denominator. This measure may not be feasible at the present time but will undoubtedly become increasingly important once the present systems of selling "on the hoof" or in carcass according to grade are replaced by the more objective criterion of boneless, fat-trimmed, edible meat.

In seeking to maximize feed conversion the feedlot operator must make two kinds of decisions. The first is to select the cheapest ingredients which mixed together will give the desired degree of performance; the second is to choose an animal which, on a given feed, will give best efficiency and still provide the type of carcass the market requires.

12.10.2.3 FEED FORMULATION. It is axiomatic that feed formulation must be by linear programming either in its simple form or the more sophisticated version preferred by Taylor *et al.* (1968) and Snyder and Guthrie (1968). Although increased profitability of up to $3 per ton has been claimed for those techniques, the major source of variability and certainly the greatest weakness in the system is the assignment of feed values to the different dietary ingredients. The minor components—protein, minerals and vitamins—present no serious difficulty. There are some who insist on using digestible rather than crude protein, but as the apparent digestibility of protein is determined as much by its level in the diet as its intrinsic nutritional value, refinements are largely illusory. There is also the problem of how to evaluate urea and other NPN compounds in such a system. We consider that the use of N × 6.25 avoids unnecessary assumptions, is more accurate in terms of analysing individual ingredients and is indoubtedly simpler.

The real difficulty arises with the measurement of energy. Three methods of evaluation are in current use. The simplest from the point of view of feed evaluation is undoubtedly TDN or ME. The most comprehensive in terms of evaluating animal response to widely differing feeds is probably the Californian system of NE for maintenance and production (Lofgreen and Garrett, 1968) and the procedure proposed by ARC (1965) whereby efficiency of ME use for fattening is determined according to the overall metabolizability of the diet. Finally, there is the estimated NE system proposed by Morrison (1968).

The major drawback to the Californian system is that very few feeds have been directly evaluated and the majority of feed values represent calculations based on chemical analysis. Furthermore, it has an intrinsic defect in that it assumes a fixed maintenance requirement. It is biologically improbable that the maintenance cost in an animal gaining 1.5 kg/day will be the same as that in an animal which is merely maintaining or perhaps losing body weight. We have, in fact, shown (Preston *et al.*, 1969c) that the maintenance requirements depends not only on the live weight of the animal but also upon its productive state. Hence the Californian system underestimates the NE for production value of a feed through apportioning too little energy to maintenance. The same criticism applies to the method of feed evaluation proposed by Blaxter (1966). The great contribution of the basic research behind the Californian system and that of Blaxter and his colleagues which preceded it, is that they permit a much better understanding of the reasons why different feeds have widely different values and that this, in turn, depends on the nature of the productive process. In particular it led to the generalization that roughages are most efficiently used for maintenance and concentrates for fattening, which has wide economic implications in terms of how best to use natural feed resources. Unfortunately the very comprehensiveness of the NE approach results in considerable loss of precision when attempts are made to convert the scheme into a system for everyday use. Under practical conditions the feedlot operator is rarely concerned with the nutritive value of roughage *per se*. Firstly, it is only very rarely that the NE in a high-quality roughage such as alfalfa can be purchased as cheaply as energy in cereals, molasses or even fat. Furthermore, the effect of replacing concentrates by roughage is quite different from the effect of replacing one grain with another, for while the latter action has effectively no influence on carcass fatness there is a close relation between fatness and the roughage content of a diet. It is probably true to say that in the great majority of cases roughages find their way into fattening diets primarily as safeguards to health rather than for their nutritive value. In this situation wherein a fixed proportion of roughage in the diet is agreed upon for reasons other than energy value, or in those cases where the feedlot operator prefers an all-concentrate ration, TDN or ME values for all practical purposes will give perfectly acceptable results in least-cost formulations. The advantage of ME or TDN is that the great majority of feeds have been evaluated by experiment rather than by calculation; moreover, the procedure is easy to work with. In specific circumstances, as, for example, in tropical regions where home-grown roughages play an important role in fattening, there may be advantages to the use of some form of NE scale. In this case, however, we would prefer to use Morrison's

(1968) estimated NE system wherein approximate values are given for each ingredient on the understanding that these will be adjusted in the light of local conditions and experience.

We feel that fattening units with throughputs of 20,000 and more per year cannot rely for least-cost formulations on energy values as quoted in the literature. We believe that in these cases the feedlot operator must arrive at his own standards, based upon his own input/output data using a variety of diets which take into account the feed ingredients most likely to be available to him. In such feedlots it would seem necessary to have some small but permanent facilities for development work aimed at evaluating not only local ingredients and available cattle but also the most promising of the new techniques as and when they emerge from commercial, university or government research sources.

12.10.3 Cost of genetic improvement

We have suggested (Chapter 3) that the most effective way of improving a commercial beef cattle population is by means of a rotational crossing programme employing about five pure breeds to provide tested sires. Rotational crossing is considered best to maximize heterosis in a commercial operation and thus secure improvement in percentage calf crop and viability. There may also be a slight bonus in feed conversion, although improvement in this trait through heterosis is unlikely to exceed 5%. The most certain way to guarantee continued improvement in feed conversion ratio is by selecting the crossing sires for this trait following a performance test starting at some 90 days of age and ending at a fixed weight. Such a genetic improvement programme requires a herd of purebred beef cows to supply the bull calves for testing, and a central testing station in which they can be evaluated.

Although genetic improvement plans have been commercially successful in both chickens and pigs, this technique has yet to be applied to beef cattle production. The general opinion is that such programmes cannot be justified because of the expense involved. We do not share this view. In fact, we believe that integration of a genetic improvement scheme into a commercial beef–cattle fattening operation can increase profits considerably.

The following example will give some idea of the scale of the facilities required and the type of calculations that should be carried out. Many assumptions have been made and clearly these cannot be accurate for all circumstances. Nevertheless, they are based on established norms and are unlikely to be in error by more than a small percentage.

Assumptions

(1)	Commercial cattle population	1,000,000
(2)	AI used exclusively	
(3)	Number of first inseminations/bull/year	5,000
(4)	Replacement rate of bulls	25%
(5)	Number of pure breeds for crossing	5
(6)	Heritability of feed conversion	0.35
(7)	Mean feed conversion and standard deviation	6.00 ± 1.00

(8)	Proportion of bulls culled at 250 kg before completing the test (transferred to group feeding for commercial fattening)	50%
(9)	Number of purebred cows in each crossing breed	500
(10)	Calving rate in pure herd	80%
(11)	Calving rate in commercial herd	85%
(12)	Deaths to weaning at 90 days	8%

Calculations

(1)	Number of bulls required per year	50
(2)	Number of bulls available	920
(3)	Selection pressure (approximate)	5%
(4)	Superiority of selected bulls	$2.06 \times 1.00 \times 0.35 = 0.72$
(5)	Annual improvement in commercial fattening operation (a = improvement due to heterosis b = generation interval)	$\frac{0.72 + 0.01^{a}}{2 \times 3.5^{b}} = 0.10$ feed conversion units

This annual improvement is equivalent to a saving of 30 kg of feed per commercial animal fattened, which on the 600,000 cattle from the commercial herd that are fattened annually amounts to 18,000 tons of feed. At $60 per ton this is worth some $1,080,000.

Cost of genetic programme. Of the 920 bulls tested annually, 460 will be culled for group fattening after a period of 4 months in individual pens; the remaining 460 bulls finish the test, which means that on an average they will stay in individual pens for 7 months. The total number of individual pens that should be available is thus 420; in addition, some 12 group pens will be required to provide 230 animal spaces for the culled animals.

We consider that individual pens can be built for some $100 per animal, while group pens will cost approximately $50 per head. The total capital cost is thus $54,000 and if to this is added $15,000 for weighing and sundry facilities, the total capital cost becomes $70,000 for the testing station. With interest at 7% and depreciation over 10 years the annual charge is thus $11,900. The total feed cost for 920 bulls (each consuming 1.8 tons of complete feed at $60 per ton) would be about $100,000. Only 50 bulls would be selected for breeding, the remaining 870 being slaughtered for beef with a value at 400 kg live weight ($182 per bull) of $159,000.

Maintenance of pure herds. There will be 2500 cows and 900 followers which overall is equivalent to some 3000 mature cow equivalents. Assuming these are maintained in a drylot operation, the feed cost is likely to be some 3 tons of grain equivalent per cow plus 0.1 tons of creep feed for each of the 1840 calves. Assuming the grain equivalent cost is some $50 per ton, and the creep feed $60 per ton, the total feed cost would be of the order of $460,000.

Sales of surplus animals would be some 460 heifer calves at weaning at 90 days

(100 kg live weight) with a value of some $25,000. Also available for slaughter would be 460 cows yearly, which at $100 per cow is $46,000.

Thus sales of carcass meat and surplus females would be:

	$
870 bulls	159,000
460 heifers	25,000
460 cows	46,000
	230,000
Major expenses will be:	
Interest and depreciation	11,900
Feed cost for bulls	100,000
Feed cost for cow herd	460,000
	571,900

The net cost of genetic improvement (excluding labour and management) is thus some $341,900. Against this, the feed saving in the commercial fattening unit through genetic improvement of the feed conversion rate is estimated to be $1,080,000. If we assume a profit of $10 a head as an average return of a large-scale commercial fattening operation, genetic improvement offers the possibility of increasing this by some 10% anually.

References

ABDO, K. M., KING, K. W. and ENGEL, R. W. (1964) Protein quality of rumen microorganisms, *J. Anim. Sci.* **23**:734.

ABELEIN, R. and RITTER, H. C. (1959) Relationships between birth weights and weight at one year in heifer calves in a Fleckvieh herd in Grub, *Mitt. bayer. Landesanst. Tierz. Grub.* **7**:145.

ABINANTI, F. R. and HUEBNER, R. J. (1959) Serological relationships of para-influenza 3 virus isolated from humans and cattle with respiratory disease, *Virology* **8**:391.

ABOU AKKADA, A. R. and EL-SHAZLY, K. (1965) Effect of presence or absence of rumen ciliate protozoa on some blood constituents, nitrogen retention and digestibility of food constituents in lambs, *J. Agric. Sci.* **64**:251.

ABRAHAM, H. C., CARPENTER, Z. L., KING, G. T. and BUTLER, O. D. (1968) Relationships of carcass weight, conformation and carcass measurements and their use in predicting beef carcass cutability, *J. Anim. Sci.* **27**:604.

ABSHER, C. W. and HOBBS, C. S. (1968) Pre-calving level of energy in first calf heifers. *J. Anim. Sci.* **27**:1130 Abs.

ABSHER, C. W., HOBBS, C. S. and SMALLING, J. D. (1968) Estrous synchronization in beef cows and heifers, *J. Anim. Sci.* **27**:299 Abs.

ACCARDI, F. (1966) Nutritive utilization of feeds digested in the abomasum and intestine of growing calves, *Aliment. Animale* **10**:613.

ACORD, C. R., MITCHELL, G. E., JR., LITTLE, C. O. and KARR, M. R. (1965) Nitrogen sources for starch digestion by rumen microorganisms, *J. Anim. Sci.* **24**:870 Abs.

ADAMS, C. H. (1964) Factors that influence tenderness of beef and the development of suitable methods for appraising tenderness, *Diss. Abst.* **25**:2435.

ADAMS, C. H. and ARTHAUD, V. H. (1963) Influence of sex and age differences in tenderness of beef, *J. Anim. Sci.* **22**:1112 Abs.

AITKEN, J. N. and CRICHTON, J. A. (1956) The effect of hexoestrol implantation on growth and certain carcass characteristics of fattening steers. *Br. J. Nutr.* **10**:220.

AITKEN, J. N. & PRESTON, T. R. (1964) The self-feeding of complete milled rations to dairy cattle, *Anim. Prod.* **6**:260 Abs.

AITKEN, J. N., PRESTON, T. R., WHITELAW, F. G., MACDEARMID, A. and CHARLESON, E. B. (1963) Intensive beef production. 2: The effect of three, twelve or sixteen week weaning on the performance of Aberdeen–Angus crossbreds, *Anim. Prod.* **5**:53.

ALBAUGH, R. and ELINGS, J. T. (1964) California beef cattle progeny testing programme, *J. Anim. Sci.* **23**:595 Abs.

ALBAUGH, R., STRONG, H. T. and CARROLL, F. D. (1956) Guide to beef cattle improvement program, Calif. Agric. Exp. Sta. Circ. 451.

ALBERT, S. (1942) *Endocrinology* **30**:454.

ALBERT, W. W. and NEUMANN, A. L. (1956) Finishing hormone-fed steers in dry lot and on pasture following self-feeding on legume pasture. *J. Anim. Sci.* **15**:1238 Abs.

ALBIN, R. C. and DURHAM, R. M. (1967) Restricted feeding and use of dehydrated alfalfa meal and beef tallow in an all-concentrate ration for fattening steers, *J. Anim. Sci.* **26**:85.

ALBIN, R. C. and ELLIS, G. F., JR. (1967) Low N and lysine in all-concentrate steer rations, *J. Anim. Sci.* **26**:217 Abs.

ALDER, F. E., TAYLER, J. C. and RUDMAN, J. E. (1964) Hexoestrol implantation of steers fattened at pasture. 2: Effects on empty weight, carcass weight and carcass quality, *Anim. Prod.* **6**:57.

ALDERSON, N. E., MITCHELL, G. E., JR., LITTLE, C. O. and WARNER, R. L. (1968) Pre-intestinal disappearance of vitamin E in steers, *J. Anim. Sci.* **27**:288 Abs.

ALEXANDER, G. I. and BOGART, R. (1961) Effect of inbreeding and selection on performance characteristics of beef cattle, *J. Anim. Sci.* **20**:702.

ALEXANDER, L. M. and CLARK, N. J. (1939) Shrinkage and cooking time of rib roast of beef of different grades as influenced by style of cutting and method of roasting, USDA Tech. Bull. 674.

ALGEO, J. W., BRANNUM, T. P. and HIBBITS, A. G. (1968) An evaluation of the SYRF high pressure grain—exploding process on milo:digestibility (nylon bag), VFA (*in vitro*), steers fattening performance and carcass characteristics, *J. Anim. Sci.* **27**:1159 Abs.

ALGEO, J. W. and GASSNER, F. X. (1966) Effect of polydiethylstilbestrol phosphate (PSP) on the growth of beef cattle. 2: Fattening steers and heifers, *J. Anim. Sci.* **25**:896 Abs.

ALIM, K. A. (1964) Factors affecting birth weight of Kenana calves in the Sudan, *Emp. J. Exp. Agric.* **32**:307.

ALLCROFT, R. and CARNAGHAN, R. B. A. (1963) Toxic products in groundnuts, *Chemy Ind.* **2**:50.

ALLCROFT, R. and LEWIS, G. (1963) Groundnut toxicity in cattle: Experimental poisoning of calves and a report of clinical effects in older cattle, *Vet. Rec.* **75**:487.

ALLEN, D. M., MERKEL, R. A., MAGEE, W. T. and NELSON, R. H. (1968) Variation in some beef carcass compositional characteristics within and between selected weight and fat thickness ranges, *J. Anim. Sci.* **27**:1239.

ALLISON, M. J., BRYANT, M. P. and DOETSCH, R. N. (1962) Studies on the metabolic function of branched-chain volatile fatty acids, growth factors for ruminococci. 1: Incorporation of isovalerate into leucine, *J. Bact.* **83**:523.

ALLISON, M. J., BUCKLIN, J. A. and DOUGHERTY, R. W. (1964) Ruminal changes after overfeeding with wheat and the effect of intraruminal inoculation on adaptation to a ration containing wheat, *J. Anim. Sci.* **23**:1164.

ALMQUIST, H. T. (1968) Supplemental calf feeding trials, *Feedstuffs*, 29 June, p. 18.

ALSMEYER, R. H., PALMER, A. Z., KOGER, M. and KIRK, W. G. (1958) Some genetic aspects of tenderness in beef, *J. Anim. Sci.* **17**:1137 Abs.

ALSMEYER, R. H., PALMER, A. Z., KOGER, M. and KIRK, W. G. (1959) The relative significance of factors influencing and or associated with beef tenderness, Proc. 11th Res. Conf. Am. Meat Inst. Found. Circ. **50**:85.

AMERICAN MEAT INSTITUTE (1960) *Meat Reference Book*, AMI Chicago.

AMIR, S., KALI, R., VOLCANI, R. and PERLMAN, M. (1967) Early breeding of dairy heifers, *Anim. Prod.* **9**:268 Abs.

ANDERSEN, H. (1962) Relationship between the length of gestation and birth weight of the calf, Aarsberetn. Inst. Sterilitetsforskn. K. Vet.-og. Landbokojsh. 115.

ANDERSON, D. C. and BELLOWS, R. A. (1967) Some causes of neonatal and post-natal calf losses, *J. Anim. Sci.* **26**:941 Abs.

ANDERSON, D. E. (1960) Studies on bovine occular squamous carcinoma ("cancer eye"). 5: Genetic aspects, *J. Hered.* **51**:51.

ANDERSON, D. E. and SKINNER, P. E. (1961) Studies on bovine occular squamous carcinoma ("cancer eye"). 11: Effects of sunlight, *J. Anim. Sci.* **20**:474.

ANDERSON, H. and PLUM, M. (1965) Gestation length and birthweight in cattle and buffaloes, *J. Dairy Sci.* **48**:1224.

ANDERSON, J. (1936) Studies in reproduction in cattle. The periodicity and duration of oestrus, *Emp. J. Exp. Agric.* **4**:186.

ANDERSON, L. L., RAY, D. E. and MELAMPY, R. M. (1962) Synchronization of estrus and conception in the beef heifer, *J. Anim. Sci.* **21**:449.

ANDIK, I., SARDI, F. and SCHMIDT, P. (1966) The effect of growth hormone of food intake and food selection, *Acta physiol. hung.* **29**:117.

ANDREWS, F. N., BEESON, W. M. and JOHNSON, F. D. (1950) Effect of hormones on the growth and fattening of yearling steers, Purdue Univ. Agric. Exp. Sta. Mimeo. AH 46.

ANDREWS, F. N., BEESON, W. M. and JOHNSON, F. D. (1951) Effect of hormones on the growth and fattening of yearling steers, Exp. 2, Purdue Univ. Agric. Exp. Sta. Mimeo. AH 60.

ANDREWS, F. N., BEESON, W. M. and JOHNSON, F. D. (1954) The effects of stilbestrol, dienestrol, testosterone and progesterone on the growth and fattening of beef steers, *J. Anim. Sci.* **13**:99.

ANDREWS, F. N., STOB, M., PERRY, M. and BEESON, W. M. (1956) The oral administration of diethystilbestrol, dienestrol and hexestrol for fattening calves, *J. Anim. Sci.* **15**:685.

ANNISON, E. F. (1965) In *Physiology of Digestion in the Ruminant*, Butterworths, London.

ANNISON, E. F., LENG, R. A., LINDSAY, D. B. and WHITE, R. R. (1963) The metabolism of acetic acid, propionic acid and butyric acid in sheep, *Biochem. J.* **88**:248.

ANNISON, E. F. and LEWIS, D. (1959) *Metabolism in the Rumen*, Methuen, London.

ANON. (1956) Cattle compared in SWA trials, *Frms Wkly* (*Bloemfontein*), 5 Sept., p. 59.

ANON. (1958) Advanced registry board for beef cattle, Dep. Agric. Ontario Rep. No. 3.

ANON. (1960) *Report of the Joint ARC/MRC Group on the use of Oestrogens in Farm Livestock Production.*

ANON. (1961) *The Raising and Fattening of Calves with Milk Replacers*, Hoffman La Roche, Basle.

ANON. (1962a) Distinctive flavours from fat, *Agric. Res.* **10**:14.

ANON. (1962b) *Okla. 36th Annual Livestock Feeders Day Rep.*, p. 113.

ANON. (1963a) The Charolais survey carried out by the Veterinary Clinical Observation Unit, *Vet. Rec.* **75**:1045.

ANON. (1963b) *Report to the Montana Livestock Sanitary Board July 1962–June 1963.*

ANON. (1965a) The production of young bulls for meat, *Revue Elev.* **20** (11), 21.

ANON. (1965b) Beef production from young bulls, a report of trials in the United Kingdom, Min. Agric. Fish. Food. Mimeo.

ANON. (1965c) Survey shows growing use of urea in feeds, *Feedstuffs*, 4 Dec. p. 71.

ANON. (1965d) What causes pink eye in cattle?, *Agric. Res. Wash.* **14** (3), 13.

ANON. (1965e) *Cattle Feeding in California*, Bank of America Econ. Res. Dep.

ANON. (1966a) *A Comparison of the Growth of Different Types of Cattle for Beef Production*, Report of Major Beef Res. Project., Royal Smithfield Club, London.

ANON. (1966b) *Annual Report*, Min. Agric., Guyana.

ANON. (1968a) Arizona cattle researchers report new grain processing. *Feedstuffs*, 4 May.

ANON. (1968b) Report in *Feedstuffs*, 20 July, p. 4.

ANTHONY, W. B. and CUNNINGHAM, J. P., JR. (1968) Hardwood sawdust in all concentrate rations for cattle, *J. Anim. Sci.* **27**:1159 Abs.

ANTHONY, W. B., HARRIS, R. R., BROWN, V. L. and STARLING, J. G. (1961a) Influence of winter feeding on milk production of wet beef cows, *J. Anim. Sci.* **20**:399 Abs.

ANTHONY, W. B., HARRIS, R. R. and STARLING, J. G. (1961b) High roughage vs. high energy steer fattening rations, *J. Anim. Sci.* **20**:924 Abs.

ANTHONY, W. B., NIX, R. R., CALDWELL, J. and STARLING, J. G. (1965) Beef cow milk production—energy content, *J. Anim. Sci.* **24**:283 Abs.

ANTHONY, W. B. and STARLING, J. G. (1968) Adequacy of grazed coastal Bermuda grass for cows nursing calves, *J. Anim. Sci.* **27**:289 Abs.

A.R.C. (1965) *Nutrient Requirements of Farm Livestock No. 2 Ruminants*, Agricultural Research Council, London.

ARMSTRONG, D. G. (1964) Evaluation of artificially dried grass as a source of energy for sheep. 2: The energy value of cocksfoot, timothy and two strains of rye-grass at varying stages of maturity, *J. Agric. Sci.* **62**:399.

ARMSTRONG, D. G., SEELEY, R. C. and MACRAE, J. C. (1967) Feed carbohydrates—the contribution of the end products of their digestion to energy supply in the ruminant, *Proc. 4th Energy Symp. Metab. Warsaw.*

ARMSTRONG, D. G. and TRINDER, N. (1966) The use of urea and other NPN substances in rations for ruminants, *J. Univ. Newcastle Agric. Soc.* **20**:3.

ARMSTRONG, D. T. and HANSEL, W. (1956) Effect of age and plane of nutrition on growth hormone and thyrotropic hormone content of pituitary glands of Holstein heifers, *J. Anim. Sci.* **15**:640.

ARMSTRONG, J. B., STONAKER, H. H., SUTHERLAND, T. M. and RIDDLE, K. R. (1965) Selection and genetic change in inbred Herefords, *J. Anim. Sci.* **24**:845 Abs.

ARNETT, D. and TOTUSEK, R. (1963) The influence of moderate vs. very high levels of nutrition on the performance of twin beef females, *J. Anim. Sci.* **22**:239 Abs.

ARNOLD, P. T. D. and BECHER, R. B. (1953) Dairy calves: Their development and survival, Fla. Agric. Exp. Sta. Bull. 529.

ARS (1962) Status of the screwworm in the United States, Agric. Res. Serv. USDA, ARS 22–79. 1.

Aschaffenburg, R., Bartlett, S., Kon, S. K., Roy, J. H. B., Sears, H. J., Thompson, S. Y., Ingram, P. L., Lovell, R. and Wood, P. C. (1953) *Br. J. Nutr.* **7**:275.

Ashton, G. C., Seifert, G. W. and Francis, J. (1968) An association between serum amylase phenotype and tick infestation in cattle, *Aust. J. Biol. Sci.* **21**:308.

Asplund, R. O., Rajender, S. and Nelms, G. E. (1963) The effect of thyroxine implantation of cows on the growth rate of their calves, *J. Anim. Sci.* **22**:853 Abs.

Astrom, G. (1968) Oestrous synchronization of heifers with norethisterone (17-α-ethinyl-19-nortestosterone), *Proc. 6th Congr. Rep. AI Paris*, p. 259.

Aunan, W. J., Harvey, A. L., Lindwall, W. and Burson, P. M. (1956) Should stilbestrol be fed or implanted in fattening steers?, *Proc. Minn. Beef and Grassland Day.*

Auriol, P., Duplan, J. M. and Poirier, P. (1963) Study of performance of the Charolais breed, *CR Acad. Agric. Fr.* **49**:100.

Aust, S. D., Albright, J. L., Olsen, R. E., Byers, J. H. and Broquist, H. P. (1963) Observations on moldy corn toxicosis, *J. Anim. Sci.* **22**:831 Abs.

Averdunk, G. (1968) Genetic aspects of test period length for rate of gain in cattle, *J. Anim. Sci.* **27**:1124 Abs.

Ayre-Smith, R. A. (1956) Beef cattle investigation, *Kenya Frmr*, Sept., p. 38.

Baiburtcjan, A. A. (1963) A new method of increasing the productivity of livestock (by partial castration), *Anim. Breed. Abstr.* **31**:1.

Baile, C. A. and Pfander, W. H. (1966) A possible chemosensitive regulatory mechanism of ovine feed intake, *Am. J. Physiol.* **210**:1243.

Baile, C. A., Mahoney, A. W. and Mayer, J. (1967a) Preliminary report on hypothalmic hyperhagia in ruminants, *J. Dairy Sci.* **50**:1851.

Baile, C. A., Mahoney, A. W. and Mayer, J. (1967b) Preliminary report on feeding activity and hypothalmic temperature in goats, *J. Dairy Sci.* **50**:1854.

Bailey, C. B. (1967) Siliceous urinary calculi in calves: prevention by addition of sodium chloride to the diet, *Science* **155**:696.

Bailey, C. B., Bezeau, L. M. and Lawson, J. E. (1963) Silica urolithiasis in beef cattle. 5: Effect of controlling urine pH on the incidence and composition of urinary calculi in calves, *Can. J. Anim. Sci.* **43**:150.

Bailey, C. M. and Gilbert, F. H. (1962) Factors affecting performance traits of Hereford calves in lines developed in two environments, *J. Anim. Sci.* **21**:661 Abs.

Bailey, C. M., Hunter, J. E. and Torrell, C. R. (1967) Response trends in Hereford lines, *J. Anim. Sci.* **26**:883 Abs.

Bailey, C. M., Probert, L. L. and Bohman, V. R. (1966a) Growth rate, feed utilization and body composition of young bulls and steers, *J. Anim. Sci.* **25**:132.

Bailey, C. M., Probert, L. L., Richardson, P., Bohman, V. R. and Chancerelle, J. (1966b) Quality factors of the longissimus dorsi of young bulls and steers, *J. Anim. Sci.* **25**:504.

Bailey, C. M. and Weeth, H. J. (1963) Selection for 70 day weight in the rat, *J. Anim. Sci.* **22**:815 Abs.

Baird, D. M., Nalbandov, A. V. and Norton, H. W. (1952) Some physiological causes of genetically different rates of growth in swine, *J. Anim. Sci.* **11**:292.

Baker, F. H. (1967a) History and development of beef and dairy performance programmes in the United States, *J. Anim. Sci.* **26**:1261.

Baker, F. S., Jr. (1967b) Univ. Fla. Res. Rep. **12**:5.

Baker, G. N. and Baker, M. L. (1960) Wheat for fattening yearling steers, Nebr. Agric. Exp. Sta. Bull. 454.

Baker, H. K. (1965) The performance and progeny testing of beef bulls, *J. R. Agric. Soc.* **126**:7.

Baker, H. K. (1966) Results from the performance testing of beef cattle, *Proc. 9th Int. Congr. Anim. Prod. Edinburgh*, Abs., p. 20.

Balch, C. C. and Campling, R. C. (1962) Regulation of voluntary food intake in ruminants, *Nutr. Abstr. Rev.* **32**:669.

Balch, C. C. and Rowland, S. J. (1957) Volatile fatty acids and lactic acid in the rumen of dairy cows receiving a variety of diets, *Br. J. Nutr.* **11**:288.

Balfour, W. E. and Comline, R. S. (1962) Acceleration of the absorption of unchanged globulin in the new-born calf by factors in colostrum, *J. Physiol.* **160**:234.

Banerjee-Schotsman, I. (1964) Heritability estimates of gestation period in cattle, *Proc. 5th Int. Congr. Anim. Reprod. AI Trento*, **2**:295.

Banerjee-Schotsman, I. (1965) A biometric study of pregnancy duration in cattle, *Tijdschr. Diergeneesk.* **90**:941.

Bangham, D. R., Ingram, P. L., Roy, J. H. B., Shillam, K. W. G. and Terry, R. J. (1958) The absorption of 131 I-labelled serum and colostral proteins from the gut of the young calf, *Proc. R. Soc.* B, **149**:184.

Bar-Anan, R. (1966) Personal communication.

Bar-Anan, R., Levi, U., Shilo, A. and Soller, M. (1965) Progeny testing Israeli–Friesian AI sires for rate of gain, *Wld Rev. Anim. Prod.* **1**:53.

Barbella, N. G., Tannor, B. and Johnson, T. G. (1939) Relationships of flavour and juiciness of beef to fatness and other factors, *Proc. 32nd Ann. Meeting Am. Soc. Anim. Prod.*, p. 320.

Barcroft, J. M., McAnally, R. A. and Phillipson, A. T. (1944) The production of acetic, propionic and butyric acids in the alimentary canal, *Biochem. J.* **38,** ii, iii, iv.

Barczy, G., Boda, I. and Gondolwics, L. (1965) Comparative fattening of Hungarian Spotted X Charolais and purebred Hungarian Spotted bull and heifer calves, *Kisérl Közl. Álláttenyésztés*, 1963 (1):15.

Barfield, A. (1966) The pattern of beef production in the United Kingdom. In Feeding for beef production, US Feed Grains Council Tech. Publ.

Barker, J. S. F. and Nay, T. (1964) A study of sweat gland characters and their relationship to adaptation in Jersey cattle, *Proc. Aust. Soc. Anim. Prod.* **5**:173.

Bartee, J., Brown, C. J. and Lewis, P. K., (1961) Relationship of test records to eating quality of steaks from beef bulls and steers individually fed on performance tests, *J. Anim. Sci.* **20**:392 Abs.

Barth, K. M., McLaren, G. A. and Anderson, G. C. (1961) Relationship between microbial protein synthesis and the adaptation responses *J. Anim. Sci.* **20**:924 Abs.

Bartley, E. E., Deyoe, C. W., Pfost, H. B., Anstaett, H. B., Boren, F. W., Helmer, L. G., Meyer, R. M., Perry, N. B., Sung, A. C. and Stiles, D. A. (1968) A new urea product for ruminants, *Feedstuffs*, 27 April, p. 9.

Bartley, E. E., Lippke, H., Pfost, H. B., Nijweide, R. J., Jacobson, N. L. and Meyer, R. M. (1965) Bloat in cattle. 10: Efficacy of poloxalene in controlling alfalfa bloat in dairy steers and in lactating cows in commercial dairy herds, *J. Dairy Sci.* **48**:1657.

Bartley, E. E. and Meyer, R. M. (1967) Feedlot bloat prevention with poloxalene, *J. Anim. Sci.* **26**:913.

Barton, R. A. (1958) *Quality Beef Production*, Massey Agric. College, NZ.

Bass, D. D., Jr., Palmer, A. Z., Carpenter, J. W., Hentges, J. F., Jr., Wakeman, D. L., Koger, M. and Murphey, C. E. (1962) Indices of carcass quality and yield grade in feeder steers, *J. Anim. Sci.* **21**:978 Abs.

Bate-Smith, E. C. (1948) The physiology and chemistry of rigor mortis with special reference to the aging of beef, *Adv. Fd Res.* **1**:1.

Batra, T. R. and Desai, R. N. (1962) A genetic study of birth weight in Sahiwal cattle, *Indian J. Vet. Sci.* **32**:188.

Bauer, M. (1965) Five years study of ranch breeding stock 1959–1964, *Rhod. Agric. J.* **62**:28.

Baxter, S. H. and Soutar, D. S. (1964) Slatted floors for intensive beef, *Farmbuildings*, Autumn.

Beardsley, D. W., McCormick, W. C. and Southwell, B. L. (1959) Steer performance on, and rumen effects of, different concentrate/roughage ratios in pelleted and unpelleted mixed fattening rations, *J. Anim. Sci.* **18**:1507 Abs.

Beeson, W. M. (1964) New thinking on trace mineral needs of livestock, *Feedstuffs*, 5 Dec., p. 54.

Beeson, W. M. (1968) Report in *Feedstuffs*, 24 Aug., p. 5.

Beeson, W. M., Andrews, F. N., Stob, M. and Perry, T. W. (1956a) The effects of oral oestrogens and adrogens singly and in combination on yearling steers, *J. Anim. Sci.* **15**:679.

Beeson, W. M. and Perry, T. W. (1958) The comparative feeding value of high moisture corn and low moisture corn with different feed additives for fattening beef cattle, *J. Anim. Sci.* **17**:368.

Beeson, W. M., Perry, T. W., Andrews, F. N., Smith, W. H. and Stob, M. (1956b) The comparative effect of oral and subcutaneous implantation of diethylstilbestrol for fattening steers on drylot and pasture, *J. Anim. Sci.* **15**:1240 Abs.

Beeson, W. M., Perry, T. W. and Mohler, M. (1957a) Self-feeding free choice vs. self-feeding, a complete mixture for fattening steers, *J. Anim. Sci.* **16**:787.

Beeson, W. M., Perry, T. W., Smith, W. H., Andrews, F. N. and Stob, M. (1957b) The comparative effect of oral and subcutaneous implantation of stilbestrol for fattening steers on pasture, Purdue Univ. Agric. Exp. Sta. Mimeo AH 194.

Beeson, W. M., Perry, T. W., Smith, W. H. and Mohler, M. (1962) Effect of vitamin A and E, carotene and dehydrated alfalfa on the performance of steers, *J. Anim. Sci.* **21**:988 Abs.

Beeson, W. M., Perry, T. W., Smith, W. H. and Mohler, M. (1963) Effect of oral vitamin A, injectable vitamin A and tranimal on the performance of steer calves, *J. Anim. Sci.* **22**:1117 Abs.

Belic, M. (1965) The relation between age at first calving and the body weight of the calf at birth and at weaning, *Savremena poljopr.* **13**:47.

Bellows, R. A. (1966) Some effects of breed crossing on reproductive performance, *Beef Cattle Field Day US Range Livestock Exp. Sta. Miles City, Montana*, p. 28.

Bellows, R. A. (1967) Some factors affecting reproductive performance of beef herds bred via natural service, *AI Digest* **15** (3), 6.

Bellows, R. A. (1968) Reproduction and growth in beef heifers, *AI Digest* **16** (1), 2.

Bender, A. E. and Wood, T. (1956) Meat extract—a revaluation, *Fd Manufacture*, June.

Benedict, F. G. and Ritzman, S. (1927) The metabolism of fasting steers, Carnegie Inst. Publ. No. 377.

Bennett, D. D. and O'Mary, C. C. (1965) Effect of housing vs open lots on winter gains of beef calves, *J. Anim. Sci.* **24**:854 Abs.

Bennett, J. A. and Mathews, D. J. (1955) Performance testing studies with beef cattle, Utah Agric. Exp. Sta. Bull. 377.

Bentley, O. G., Moinuddin, M., Hershberger, T. V., Klosterman, E. W. and Moxon, A. L. (1954) The effect of trace minerals on growth performance and vitamin B12 synthesis in steers, *J. Anim. Sci.* **13**:789.

Berg, R. T. and Butterfield, R. M. (1966) Muscle bone ratio and fat percentage as measures of beef carcass composition, *Anim. Prod.* **8**:1.

Berg, R. T. and Butterfield, R. M. (1968) Growth patterns of bovine muscle, fat and bone, *J. Anim. Sci.* **27**:611.

Bergen, W. G., Purser, D. B. and Cline, J. H. (1968) Effect of ration on the nutritive quality of rumen microbial protein, *J. Anim. Sci.* **27**:1497.

Bergström, P. L. (Ed.) (1962) *The Progeny Testing of Bulls on their Beef Production Characteristics*, EAAP, Rome.

Bergström, P. L. (1965) Genetic differences in beef production. *Veeteelt en Zuivelber.* **8**:113.

Berman, A., Amir, S. and Volcani, R. (1963) The relationship between the rate of heat production and the level of milk production in a subtropical climate, *Aust. J. Agric. Res.* **14**:874.

Berman, A. and Kibler, H. H. (1959) Effect of clipping the coat on the thermoregulatory reactions of dairy heifers, *Nature* **183**:606.

Berruecos, J. M. and Robison, O. W. (1968) Preweaning growth in Brahmans, *J. Anim. Sci.* **27**:1124 Abs.

Beuk, J. F., Savick, A. L., Goeser, P. H. and Hogan, J. M. (1959) US Patent No. 2903362.

Bhattacharya, A. N. and Warner, R. G. (1967) Rumen pH as a factor for controlling feed intake in ruminants, *J. Dairy Sci.* **50**:1116.

Bhattacharya, A. N. and Warner, R. G. (1968) Voluntary feed intake of pelleted diets for cattle, sheep and rabbits as affected by different alkali supplements, *J. Anim. Sci.* **27**:1418.

Bianca, W. (1959a) Acclimatization of calves to a hot dry environment, *J. Agric. Sci.* **52**: 296.

Bianca, W. (1959b) Acclimatization of calves to a hot humid environment, *J. Agric. Sci.* **52**:305.

Bidart, J. B., Koch, R. M. and Arthaud, V. H. (1967) Comparative energy use by bulls and steers, *J. Anim. Sci.* **26**:1463 Abs.

Bieber, D. D., Saffle, R. L. and Kamstra, L. D. (1961) Calculation of fat and protein content of beef from specific gravity and moisture, *J. Anim. Sci.* **20**:239.

BIONDINI, P. E., SUTHERLAND, T. M. and HAVERLAND, L. H. (1968) Body composition of mice selected for rapid growth rate, *J. Anim. Sci.* **27**:5.

BIRKETT, R. J., GOOD, D. L. and MACKINTOSH, D. L. (1965) Relationships of various linear measurements and percent yield of trimmed cuts of beef carcasses, *J. Anim. Sci.* **24**:16.

BLACK, W. H., HOWE, P. E., JONES, J. M. and KEATING, F. E. (1943) Fattening steers on milo in the southern great plains, USDA Tech. Bull. 847.

BLACK, W. H., KNAPP, B. and COOK, A. C. (1938) Correlation of body measurements of slaughter steers with rate and efficiency of gain and with certain carcass characteristics, *J. Agric. Res.* **56**:465.

BLACK, W. H., QUESENBERRY, J. R. and BAKER, A. L. (1940) Wintering steers on different planes of nutrition from weaning to 2½ years of age, USDA Tech. Bull. 667.

BLACK, W. H., SEMPLE, A. T. and LUSH, J. L. (1934) Beef production and quality as influenced by crossing Brahmans with Hereford and Shorthorn cattle, USDA Tech. Bull. 417.

BLACKBURN, T. H. (1965) Nitrogen metabolism in the rumen, in *Physiology of Digestion in the Ruminant*, Butterworths, Washington.

BLACKBURN, T. H. and HOBSON, P. N. (1968) Proteolysis in the sheep rumen by whole and fractionated rumen contents, *J. Gen. Microbiol.* **22**:272.

BLACKMON, W. E. (1960) Influence of age on some beef carcass and muscle characteristics, MS. thesis Okla. Univ., Stillwater.

BLACKWELL, R. L., KNOX, J. H., SHELBY, C. E. and CLARK, R. T. (1962) Genetic analysis of economic characteristics of young Hereford cattle, *J. Anim. Sci.* **21**:101.

BLAIR, J. W., ERWIN, E. S. and ROUBICEK, C. B. (1958) Performance of stilbestrol treated steers and lambs as influenced by Tapazole, *J. Anim. Sci.* **17**:851.

BLAXTER, K. L. (1952) The utilization of the energy of whole milk, *Br. J. Nutr.* **6**:12.

BLAXTER, K. L. (1958) *Scientific Principles of Feeding Farm Livestock*, Farmer & Stockbreeder Publ., London.

BLAXTER, K. L. (1960) Personal communication.

BLAXTER, K. L. (1961) The utilization of the energy of food, *Proc. 2nd Symp. Energy Metabol*, EAPP Publ. No. 10, 211.

BLAXTER, K. L. (1966) *The Energy Metabolism of Ruminants*, 2nd edn., Hutchinson, London.

BLAXTER, K. L., CLAPPERTON, J. L. and WAINMAN, F. W. (1966) Utilization of the energy and protein of the same diet by cattle of different ages, *J. Agric. Sci.* **67**:67.

BLAXTER, K. L. and CZERKAWSKI, J. (1966) Modifications of the methane production of the sheep by supplementation of its diet, *J. Sci. Fd Agric.* **17**: 417.

BLAXTER, K. L. HUTCHESON, M. K., ROBERTSON, J. M. and WILSON, A. S. (1952) *Br. J. Nutr.* **6**:i.

BLAXTER, K. L. and MCGILL, R. F. (1955) Muscular dystrophy, *Vet. Rec. Ann.* **1**:91.

BLAXTER, K. L. and SHARMAN, G. A. M. (1953) *Nature* **172**:1006.

BLAXTER, K. L. and WAINMAN, F. W. (1961a) Environmental temperature and the energy metabolism and heat emission of steers, *J. Agric. Sci.* **56**:81.

BLAXTER, K. L. and WAINMAN, F. W. (1961b) The utilization of food by sheep and cattle, *J. Agric. Sci.* **57**:419.

BLAXTER, K. L. and WAINMAN, F. W. (1964) The utilization of the energy of different rations by sheep and cattle for maintenance and for fattening, *J. Agric. Sci.* **63**:113.

BLAXTER, K. L., WAINMAN, F. W. and WILSON, R. S. (1961) The regulation of food intake by sheep, *Anim. Prod.* **3**:51.

BLAXTER, K. L. and WOOD, W. A. (1951) The nutrition of the young Ayrshire calf 4. Some factors affecting the biological value of protein determined by nitrogen balance methods, *Br. J. Nutr.* **5**:55.

BLAXTER, K. L. and WOOD, W. A. 1953, *Vet. Rec.* **65**:889.

BLAYLOCK, L. G., NEAGLE, L. H. and GOIHL, J. H. (1965) Dietary protein and urea levels in beef cattle rations, *J. Anim. Sci.* **24**:874 Abs.

BLEICHNER, K. L. and ELLIS, W. C. (1968) Roughage source and level effects upon rumen papillae size, *J. Anim. Sci.* **27**:1161 Abs.

BLOOMFIELD, R. A., WILSON, R. P. and THOMPSON, G. B. (1964) Influence of energy levels on urea utilization, *J. Anim. Sci.* **23**:868 Abs.

BLOSS, R. E., NORTHAM, J. I., SMITH, L. W. and ZIMBLEMAN, R. G. (1966) Effects of oral melengesterol acetate on the performance of feedlot cattle, *J. Anim. Sci.* **25**:1048.

BLUMER, T. N. (1963) Relationship of marbling to the palatability of beef, *J. Anim. Sci.* **22**:771.

BOCM (1962) *Report on the 4th BOCM Beef Sire Performance Test*, British Oil and Cake Mills, London.

BOCM (1963) *Report on the 5th BOCM Beef Sire Performance Test*, British Oil and Cake Mills, London.

BODWELL, G. E., EVERITT, G. C., HARRINGTON, G. and POMEROY, R. W. (1959a) An investigation of the repeatability of eight measurements of beef carcasses, *Anim. Prod.* **1**:51.

BODWELL, C. E., HARRINGTON, G. and POMEROY, R. W. (1959b) A note on the measurement of eye muscle area in beef carcasses, *Anim. Prod.* **1**:97.

BODWELL, C. E., HARRINGTON, G., POMEROY, R. W. and WILLIAMS, S. D. R. (1959c) Beef carcass measurements in relation to the yields of wholesale and retail cuts: preliminary results, *Proc. 5th Meeting European Research Workers, Paris.*

BOGART, R., AMPY, F. R., ANGLEMIER, A. F. and JOHNSTON, W. K., JR. (1963a) Some physiological studies on growth and feed efficiency of beef cattle, *J. Anim. Sci.* **22**: 993.

BOGART, R. and FRISCHKNECHT, W. D. (1967) Relationships of weights, scores and gains in growing cattle, *J. Anim. Sci.* **26**:883 Abs.

BOGART, R., WALLACE, J. D., RALEIGH, R. J., SAWYER, W. A., BRINKS, J. S. and CLARK, R. T. (1963b) Effect of level of concentrate feeding on heritability of performance traits in cattle, *J. Anim. Sci.* **22**:816 Abs.

BOGEL, K. and LIEBELT, J. (1963) Relationship between maternal antibodies and immunity in calves after vaccination with live para-influenza 3 vaccine, *Zbl. Bakt.* I, **191**:133.

BOGNER, H. (1962) *Züchtungskunde* **34**:424.

BOGNER, H. (1966) Critical evaluation of the Bavarian testing programme for AI bulls particularly in respect of the selection criteria of fattening performance, feed utilization and quantitative carcass value, *Bayer. landw. Jb.* **43**.

BOHMAN, V. R. (1955) Compensatory growth of beef cattle: The effect of hay maturity, *J. Anim. Sci.* **14**:249.

BOHMAN, V. R. and LESPERANCE, A. L. (1962) Effect of dietary fat on the digestion and blood composition in cattle, *J. Anim. Sci.* **21**:658 Abs.

BOHMAN, V. R. and TORELL, C. R. (1956) Compensatory growth of beef cattle: The effect of protein supplements, *J. Anim. Sci.* **15**:1089.

BOHMAN, V. R., WADE, M. A. and HUNTER, J. E. (1957) The effect of chlortetracycline, stilbestrol and animal fat on fattening steers, *J. Anim. Sci.* **16**:833.

BOHMAN, V. R., WADE, M. A. and TORELL, C. R. (1962) Effect of dietary fat and graded level of alfalfa on growth and tissue lipids of the bovine, *J. Anim. Sci.* **21**: 241.

BOLING, J. A., FALTIN, E. C., HOEKSTRA, W. G. and HAUSER, E. R. (1967) Feed intake of cattle in response to dietary dilution with polyethylene, *J. Anim. Sci.* **26**:1385.

BOND, J., EVERSON, D. O., GUTIERREZ, J. and WARWICK, E. J. (1962) Feed intake and gains of beef cattle as affected by source and level of nitrogen in high energy rations, *J. Anim. Sci.* **21**: 728.

BOND, J., HOOVER, N. W., RICHARDSON, G. V. and WARWICK, E. J. (1967) Plane of nutrition: Dairy, dual purpose and beef steers, *J. Anim. Sci.* **26**:218 Abs.

BOND, J. and LEHMANN, R. P. (1967) Compensatory vs continuous growth of steers, *J. Anim. Sci.* **26**: 873.

BOND, J., MCDOWELL, R. E., CURRY, W. A. and WARWICK, E. J. (1960) Reproductive performance of milking Shorthorn heifers as affected by constant high environmental temperatures, *J. Anim. Sci.* **19** 1317 Abs.

BOND, J., WILTBANK, J. N., WARWICK, E. J., LEHMANN, R. P. and KINNEY, T. B. (1964) Feed intake and milk production of beef cows, *J. Anim. Sci.* **23**:901 Abs.

BONNIER, G., HANSSON, A. and SKJERVOLD, H. (1948) Studies on monozygous cattle twins. 9: The interplay of heredity and environment on growth and yield, *Acta agric. suec.* **3**:1.

Bonsembiante, M. (1961) Methylthiouracil for fattening cattle: Experimental contribution, *Riv. Zootec.* **34**: 343.

BONSMA, J. (1949) Breeding cattle for increased adaptability to tropical and sub-tropical environments, *J. Agric. Sci.* **39**:204.

BONSMA, J., VAN MARLE, J. and HOFMEYR, J. H. (1953) Climatological research on animal husbandry and its significance in the beef cattle production in colonial territories, *Emp. J. Exp. Agric.* **21**:154.

BORCHERS, R. (1965) Proteolytic activity of rumen fluid *in vitro*, *J. Anim. Sci.* **24**:1033.

BORDI, A., PROTO, V. and GATTI, L. (1966) A study of some vital statistics of cows of the Chiana breed, *Produz. Anim.* **5**:75.

BOREN, F. W., SMITH, E. F., KOCH, B. A., RICHARDSON, D. and WEARDEN, S. (1960). Effects of shade and estradiol-testosterone implants on the performance and carcass characteristics of summer-fattened heifers, *J. Anim. Sci.* **19**:1250 Abs.

BORINI, P. A. (1963) Beef production from calves of milk breeds, *Produz. Anim.* **2**:1.

BOTKIN, M. P. and WHATLEY, J. A., JR. (1953) Repeatability of production in range beef cows, *J. Anim. Sci.* **12**:552.

BOUCQUE, CH., BUYSSE, F. and COTTYN, B. (1967a) The production of beef from bulls receiving a diet based on sub-products of sugar beet, *Revue. Agric.* **21**:1211.

BOUCQUE, CH., BUYSSE, F. and COTTYN, B. (1967b) The production of beef from diets based on silage and sugar beet. *Revue Agric.* **21**:1229.

BOUTON, P. E., HOWARD, A. and LAWRIE, R. A. (1957) Studies on beef quality. 6. Effects on weight losses and eating quality of further pre-slaughter treatments, DSIR Food Inv. Spec. Rep. No. 66.

BOVARD, K. P., MILLER, R. H. and PRIODE, B. M. (1966) Selection differences in beef calves type and growth, *J. Anim. Sci.* **25**:877 Abs.

BOVARD, K. P., PRIODE, B. M. and HARVEY, W. R. (1963) Estimates of year, sex, age of dam, age and inbreeding effects on beef calf performance to weaning, *J. Anim. Sci.* **22**:244 Abs.

BOWERS, H. B. (1968) Studies on the protein requirements of growing and fattening cattle fed all-concentrate diets, Ph.D. thesis Univ. Aberdeen.

BOWERS, H. B., PRESTON, T. R., MCDONALD, I., MACLEOD, N. A. and PHILIP, E. B. (1965) Intensive beef production. 5. Effect of different sources of protein on nitrogen retention, *Anim. Prod.* **7**:19.

BOWMAN, F., PAGE, E., HAZALEUS, M. H. and STONAKER, H. H. (1958) Factors related to tenderness and juiciness of beef, *J. Anim. Sci.* **17**:1153 Abs.

BOWMAN, J. C. (1957) Selection for heterosis, *Anim. Breed. Abstr.* **27**:261.

BRA (1967) *Third Annual Report*, Beef Recording Assoc. (UK) Ltd., Reading.

BRACKELSBERG, P. O., KLINE, E. A., WILLHAM, R. L. and HAZEL, L. N. (1968) Genetic parameters for some beef carcass traits, *J. Anim. Sci.* **27**:1125 Abs.

BRACKELSBERG, P. O., WILLHAM, R. L. and WALTERS, L. E. (1967) Probing beef cattle to predict carcass fatness, *J. Anim. Sci.* **26**:713.

BRADFIELD, D. and BEHRENS, W. C. (1968) Effects of injectable vitamin on reproductive performance, *J. Anim. Sci.* **27**:1105 Abs.

BRADLEY, N. W., CUNDIFF, L. V., KEMP, J. D. and GREATHOUSE, T. R. (1966a) Effects of sex and sire on performance and carcass traits of Hereford and Hereford–Red Poll calves, *J. Anim. Sci.* **25**:783.

BRADLEY, N. W., CUNDIFF, L. V., KEMP, J. D., OVERFIELD, J. R. and YOUNG, A. W. (1967) Measurement and selection of economically important traits in beef cattle—1966, Ky. Agric. Exp. Sta. Prog. Rep. **170**:66.

BRADLEY, N. W., JONES, B. M. JR., MITCHELL, G. E. and LITTLE, C. O. (1966b) Fat and urea in finishing rations for steers, *J. Anim. Sci.* **25**:480.

BRADLEY, N. W., SUMMERS, L. E. and JONES, B. (1959) Trifluomeprazine and stilbestrol as additives to fattening rations for beef steers, *Ky. Agric. Exp. Sta. Annual Livestock Day*, p.32.

BRADY, D. E. (1937) A study of the factors influencing tenderness and texture of beef, *Proc. Am. Soc. Anim. Prod.*, p. 314.

BRANAMAN, G. A., PEARSON, A. M., MAGEE, W. T., GRISWOLD, R. M. and BROWN, G. A. (1962) Comparison of the cutability and eatability of beef and dairy type cattle, *J. Anim. Sci.* **21**:321.

BRANIFF, D. W., MULLINS, A. M., BOULWARE, R. F. and FIELDER, M. (1961) Meat tenderness: Effect of cooking media on mechanical shear values and organoleptic rating of beef steaks, *J. Anim. Sci.* **20**:395 Abs.

BRÄNNÄNG, E. (1966a) Studies on monozygous cattle twins. 18: The effect of castration and age of castration on the growth rate, feed conversion and carcase traits of Swedish Red and White cattle, *Lantbr. Högsk. Ann.* **32**:329.

BRÄNNÄNG, E. (1966b) Carcass composition of Swedish cattle breeds, *Proc. 9th Int. Congr. Anim. Prod. Edinburgh*, p. 78.

BRANSON, R. E. (1957) The consumer market for beef, Tex. Agric. Esp. Sta. Bull. 856.

BRAUDE, R. and WALKER, D. M. (1949) Mortality and weight and body measurements at birth of Dairy Shorthorn calves, *J. Agric. Sci.* **39**:156.

BRAY, R. W. (1963) Symposium on feed and meat terminology. 4: Quantitative measures of carcass composition and qualitative evaluations. *J. Anim. Sci.* **22**:548.

BREIDENSTEIN, B. C., BREIDENSTEIN, B. B., GRAY, W. J., GARRIGUS, D. S. and NORTON, H. W. (1963) Comparison of carcass characteristics of steers and heifers, *J. Anim. Sci.* **22**: 1113 Abs.

BREIDENSTEIN, B. C., MADAMBA, J. C., ALBERT, W. W., NORTON, H. W. and NEUMANN, A. L. (1965) Influence of type, slaughter weight, energy level and stilbestrol on steer carcasses, *J. Anim. Sci.* **24**:860 Abs.

BRETHOUR, J. R. (1961) Kan. Agric. Exp. Sta. Roundup Rep. 49.

BRETHOUR, J. R. and DUITSMAN, W. W. (1962) Ensiled grain sorghum (whole plant, heads or high moisture grain) in steer fattening trials, *J. Anim. Sci.* **21**:989 Abs.

BREWSTER, J. W. (1968) Personal communication.

BRIGGS, P. K., HOGAN, J. P. and REID, R. L. (1957) The effect of volatile fatty acids, lactic acid and ammonia on rumen pH in sheep, *Aust. J. Agric. Res.* **8**:674.

BRINKS, J. S., CLARK, R. T. and KIEFFER, N. M. (1962a) Relationship of performance and ultrasonic measurements with certain carcass traits, *J. Anim. Sci.* **21**: 664 Abs.

BRINKS, J. S., CLARK, R. T. and KIEFFER, N. M. (1963) Sex differences in response to inbreeding in a line of Hereford cattle, *J. Anim. Sci.* **22**:816 Abs.

BRINKS, J. S., CLARK, R. T., KIEFFER, N. M. and QUESENBERRY, J. R. (1962b) Mature weight in Hereford range cows—heritability, repeatability and relationship to calf performance, *J. Anim. Sci.* **21**:501.

BRINKS, J. S., CLARK, R. T., KIEFFER, N. M. and URICK, J. J. (1964a) Predicting wholesale cuts of beef from linear measurements obtained by photogrammetry, *J. Anim. Sci.* **23**:365.

BRINKS, J. S., CLARK, R. T., KIEFFER, N. M. and URICK, J. J. (1964b) Predicting producing ability in range Hereford cows, *J. Anim. Sci.* **23**:593 Abs.

BRINKS, J. S., CLARK, R. T., KIEFFER, N. M. and URICK, J. J. (1964c) Estimates of genetic, environmental and phenotypic parameters in range Hereford females. *J. Anim. Sci.* **23**:711.

BRINKS, J. S., CLARK, R. T., RICE, F. J. and KIEFFER, N. M. (1961) Adjusting birth weight, weaning weight and preweaning gain for sex of calf in range Hereford cattle, *J. Anim. Sci.* **20**:363.

BRINKS, J. S., URICK, J. J., PAHNISH, O. F., KNAPP, B. W. and RILEY, T. J. (1967) Heterosis in preweaning and weaning traits among lines of Hereford cattle, *J. Amin. Sci.* **26**:278.

BRIQUET, R. and DEABREU, J. (1949) Gestation periods in Zebu breeds, 1, Guzera. Inst. Zootec. (Rio de Jan.) Publ. 4.

BRIS, E. J., DYER, I. A. and HOWES, D. (1966) Wheat as a grain for fattening cattle, *J. Anim. Sci.* **25**: 594 Abs.

BRISKEY, E. J., BRAY, R. W., HOEKSTRA, W. G., PHILLIPS, P. H. and GRUMMER, R. A. (1960) Effect of high protein, high fat and high sucrose rations on the water binding and associated properties or pork muscle, *J. Anim. Sci.* **19**:404.

BRISKEY, E. J. and WISMER-PEDERSEN, J. (1961) *J. Fd. Sci.* **26**:297.

BRISSON, G. J., CUNNINGHAM, M. H. and HASKELL, S. R. (1957) The protein and energy requirements of young dairy calves, *Can. J. Anim. Sci.* **37**:157.

BRISTOL, R. (1968) Report in *Feedstuffs*, 29 June, p. 1.

BROADBENT, R. J. (1967) Individual feeding device for livestock, *Anim. Prod.* **9**:269 Abs.

BROADBENT, P. J., DODSWORTH, T. L., BALL, C. and SAMPFORD, M. R. (1967) A comparison of semi-intensively reared Charolais × Ayrshire and Shorthorn × Ayrshire cattle, *Anim. Prod.* **9**:61.

BROBERG, G. (1960) Acute overeating with cereals in ruminants, Diss. Lovisa Nya Tryckeri-Lovisa, Finland.

BRODY, S. (1945) *Bioenergetics and Growth*, Reinhold, New York.

BRODY, S. A., RAGSDALE, A. C., THOMPSON, H. J. and WORSTELL, D. M. (1954) The effect of wind on milk production, feed and water consumption and body weight in dairy cattle, Mo. Agric. Exp. Sta. Bull. 545.

BROOK, A. H. and SHORT, B. F. (1960) Regulation of body temperature of sheep in a hot environment, *Aust. J. Agric. Res.* **11**:402.

BRØOKES, A. J. and O'BYRNE, M. (1965) The use of cow-heifers in beef production, *J. R. Agric. Soc.* **126**:30.

Brookes, A. J. and Vincent, L. S. (1950) Beef production experiment at Cambridge. *J. R. Agric. Soc.* **111**:110.

Broster, W. H., Sutton, J. D., Tuck, V. J. and Balch, C. C. (1965) The effect of the addition of large amounts of cod-liver oil to the rations of yearling heifers on the rate of live-weight gain, *J. Agric. Sci.* **65**:227.

Brown, C. J. (1958) Heritability of weight and certain body dimensions of beef calves at weaning, Ark. Agric. Exp. Sta. Bull. 597.

Brown, C. J. (1960) Influence of year and season of birth, sex, sire and age of dam on weights of beef calves at 60, 120, 180 and 240 days of age, *J. Anim. Sci.* **19**:1062.

Brown, C. J. (1963) Performance of bulls on Arkansas cooperative beef bull performance test, 1, Rep. Ser. Ark. Agric. Exp. Sta. 124.

Brown, C. J. (1965) Some factors affecting gain of beef bulls, *J. Anim. Sci.* **24**:287 Abs.

Brown, C. J. and Arosemena, J. (1962) Factors affecting appetite of beef bulls for roughage, *J. Anim. Sci.* **21**;385 Abs.

Brown, C. J., Barteem, J. D. and Lewis, P. K., Jr. (1962a) Relationships among performance records, carcass cutout data and eating quality of bulls and steers, Ark. Agric. Exp. Sta. Bull. 655.

Brown, C. J. and Franks, L. (1964) Factors affecting size of young beef cows, *J. Anim. Sci.* **23**:665.

Brown, C. J. and Gacula, M. (1962) Genotype–environment interactions in post-weaning rate of gain of beef cattle, *J. Anim. Sci.* **21**:924.

Brown, C. J. and Gacula, M. (1964) Estimates of heritability of beef cattle performance traits by regression of offspring on sire, *J. Anim. Sci.* **23**:321.

Brown, C. J. and Galvez, V. (1968) Maternal effects on birthweight of beef cattle, *J. Anim. Sci.* **27**: 1125 Abs.

Brown, C. J. and Clifford, W. (1962) Estimates of heritability and genetic correlations among certain traits of performance-tested bulls, Ark. Agric. Exp. Sta. Bull. 653.

Brown, C. J., Hillier, J. C. and Whatley, J. A. (1951) Specific gravity as a measure of the fat content of the pork carcass, *J. Anim. Sci.* **10**:97.

Brown, C. J., Roussel, J. D. and Stallcup, O. T. (1967a) Genetic and other aspects of a hoof anomaly of Hereford bulls, *J. Anim. Sci.* **26**:201 Abs.

Brown, C. J., Warwick, E. J., Smith, H. J., Green, W. W. and Stewart, H. A. (1956a) Relationships between conformation scores and live animal measurements of beef cattle, *J. Anim. Sci.* **15**:911.

Brown, D. L., Mullins, A. M., Boulware, R. F. and Temple, R. S. (1961) Cutability index of crossbred beef carcasses as associated with other traits, *J. Anim. Sci.* **20**:394 Abs.

Brown, D. L., Mullins, A. M., Temple, R. S., Boulware, R. F. and Sullivan, J. S., Jr. (1962b) Relationships between certain carcass characteristics of purebred and crossbred cattle, *J. Anim. Sci.* **21**:388 Abs.

Brown, G. H., Overfield, J. R., Bradley, N. W. and Little, C. O. (1967b) Source of nitrogen for supplementing ground ear corn rations for feedlot cattle—1966, Ky. Agric. Exp. Sta. Prog. Rep. **170**:8.

Brown, J. E., Cartwright, T. C. and Kruse, W. E. (1967c) General and specific combining ability for birthweight in beef cattle, *J. Anim. Sci.* **26**:201 Abs.

Brown, L. D., Lassiter, C. A., Everett, J. P. and Rust, J. W. (1956b) The utilization of urea nitrogen by young dairy calves, *J. Anim. Sci.* **15**:1125.

Brown, L. D., Lassiter, C. A., Everett, J. P., Jr., Seath, D. M. and Rust, J. W. (1958) Effect of protein level in calf starters on the growth rate and metabolism of young calves, *J. Dairy Sci.* **41**:1425.

Brown, L. O., Durham, R. M., Cobb, E. and Knox, J. H. (1954) An analysis of the components of variance in calving intervals in a range herd of beef cattle, *J. Anim. Sci.* **13**:511.

Brown, M. A. and Motasem, M. M. (1965) Comparisons of two techniques for measuring relative rates of moisture evaporation from limited skin areas of dairy cattle, *J. Dairy Sci.* **48**:1643.

Brown, P. B., Hansard, S. L., McCraine, S. E. and Thrasher, D. M. (1964a) Ground ear corn compared with shelled corn in beef steer rations, *J. Anim. Sci.* **23**:305 Abs.

Brown, P. B., Hansard, S. L., Thrasher, D. M. and Robertson, G. L. (1966) Diammonium phosphate and urea in beef cattle rations, *J. Anim. Sci.* **25**:261 Abs.

Brown, V. L., Harris, R. R., Anthony, W. B. and Starling, J. G. (1964b) High roughage vs. high energy mixtures for fattening steers, *J. Anim. Sci.* **23**:304 Abs.

Brown, V. L., Harris, R. R. and Anthony, W. B. (1968) Confinement feeding of beef brood cows, *J. Anim. Sci.* **27**:290 Abs.

Brownlee, A. (1956) *Br. Vet. J.* **112**: 369.

Brüggemann, J. and Barth, K. (1959) Experimental studies on the young calf. 1: The dependence of the digestibility of some nutrients on the age of the calf, *Z. Tierphysiol. Tierernähr. Futtermittelk.* **14**:284.

Brumby, P. J. (1959) The influence of growth hormone on growth in young cattle, *NZ J. Agric. Res.* **2**:683.

Brumby, P. J., Walker, D. K. and Gallagher, R. M. (1962) Growth rate in beef cattle, *Proc. Ruakura Frmrs Conf. Week.*

Brumby, P. J., Walker, D. K. and Gallagher, R. M. (1963) Factors associated with growth in beef cattle, *NZ J. Agric. Res.* **6**:526.

Brundage, A. L. and Sweetman, W. J. (1963) Hay vs. silage for two to six months old dairy calves weaned at 25 or 60 days, *J. Anim. Sci.* **22**:429.

Brungardt, V. H. and Bray, R. W. (1963) Estimate of retail yield of the four major cuts in the beef carcass, *J. Anim. Sci.* **22**: 177.

Brunner, M. A., Hansel, W., Wagner, W. C. and Newman, R. M. (1964) A large scale field trial in estrous cycle synchronization, *J. Anim. Sci.* **23**:902 Abs.

Bryant, M. P. (1961) The nitrogen metabolism of pure cultures or ruminal bacteria, USDA-ARS 44–92.

Bryant, M. P. and Robinson, I. M. (1962) Some nutritional characteristics of predominant culturable ruminal bacteria, *J. Bact.* **84**:605.

Bryant, M. P. and Small, N. (1956) The development of rumen microorganisms in inoculated and isolated calves, *J. Dairy Sci.* **39**:927 Abs.

Buch, N. C., Tyler, W. J. and Casida, L. E. (1959) Variation in some factors affecting length of calving interval, *J. Dairy Sci.* **42**:2.

Buchanan-Smith, J. G., Bannister, W., Durham, R. M. and Curl, S. E. (1964) Effect of all-concentrate fed *ad libitum* versus roughage ration on the occurrence of estrus in beef heifers, *J. Anim. Sci.* **23**:902 Abs.

Buchanan-Smith, J. G., Totusek, R. and Tillman, A. D. (1968) Effect of methods of processing on digestibility and utilization of grain sorghum by cattle and sheep, *J. Anim. Sci.* **27**:525.

Bucy, L. V. and Bennion, L. L. (1962) Concentrate/roughage levels in diets of fattening steers, *J. Anim. Sci.* **21**: 666 Abs.

Bujatti, P. G. (1956) Increase in live weight from birth to 24 months in Chiana heifers, *Riv. Zootec.* **29**:264.

Bujatti, P. G. and Polidou, F. (1962) Investigations on the length of gestation period in cattle in the Val di Chiana, *Riv. Zootec.* **35**:375.

Bull, S., Olsen, F. C. and Longwell, J. H. (1930) Ill. Agric. Exp. Sta. Bull. 355.

Bull, S. and Rusk, H. P. (1942) Effect of exercise on quality of beef, Ill. Agric. Exp. Sta. Bull. 448.

Bullen, J. J. and Scarisbrick, R. (1957) Enterotoxaemia of sheep: Experimental reproduction of the disease, *J. Path. Bact.* **73**:495.

Bunn, C. R., McNeil, J. J. and Matrone, G. (1967) Comparison of amino acid and alfalfa supplementation of purified diets for ruminants, *J. Nutr.* **91**:47.

Bunnell, R. H., Rousseau, J. E., Jr., Eaton, H. P. and Beall, G. (1954) Estimation of vitamin A and carotenoids in calf liver, *J. Dairy Sci.* **37**:1473.

Burgess, J. B., Landblom, N. L. and Stonaker, H. H. (1954) Weaning weights of Hereford calves as affected by inbreeding, sex and age, *J. Anim. Sci.* **13**:843.

Burgess, T. D. and Bowman, G. H. (1965) Environmental factors affecting pre- and post-weaning traits of Hereford bull calves, *Can. J. Anim. Sci.* **45**:189.

Burgess, T. D. and Lamming, G. E. (1960) The effect of diethylstilboestrol, hexoestrol and testosterone on the growth rate and carcass quality of fattening beef steers, *Anim. Prod.* **2**:93.

Burgi, P. (1964) Experiments in crossing Simmental with beef breeds, *Schweiz. landw. Mk.* **42**: 301.

Burns, W. C. and Koger, M. (1963) Response of different breed groups to creep feeding, *J. Anim. Sci.* **22**:244 Abs.

BURNS, W. C., KOGER, M. and KINCAID, C. M. (1958) Feedlot response of steers of different breeds to different rations and hormone treatment, *J. Anim. Sci.* **17**:1143.

BURNS, W. C., KOGER, M., WARNICK, A. C. and KINCAID, C. M. (1959) Beef cattle production data from the West central Florida Experiment Station from 1953–58, Anim. Husb. Nutr. Mimeo. Series No. 60–2.

BURNS, W. C., SHIRLEY, R. L., KOGER, M. CUNHA, T. J., EASLEY, J. F. and CHAPMAN, H. L. (1968) Cow and calf response to injected vitamin A, *J. Anim. Sci.* **27**:290 Abs.

BURRIS, M. J. and BLUNN, C. T. (1952) Some factors affecting gestation length and birth weight of beef cattle, *J. Anim. Sci.* **11**:34.

BURRIS, M. J., BOGART, R. and OLIVER, A. W. (1953) Alteration of daily gain, feed efficiency and carcass characteristics in beef cattle with male hormones, *J. Anim. Sci.* **12**:740.

BURRIS, M. J. and PRIODE, B. M. (1958) Effect of calving date on subsequent calving performance, *J. Anim. Sci.* **17**: 527.

BURROUGHS, W., CULBERTSON, C. C., CHENG, E., HALE, W. H. and HOMEYER, P. (1955) The influence of oral administration of diethylstilbestrol in beef cattle, *J. Anim. Sci.* **14**: 1015.

BURROUGHS, W., CULBERTSON, C. C., KASTELIC, J., CHENG, E. and HALE, W. H. (1954) The effects of trace amounts of diethylstilbestrol in rations of fattening steers, *Science* **120**:66.

BURROUGHS, W., KOHLMEIER, R., BARRINGER, R., KAWASHIMA, R. and TRENKLE, A. (1963) Selenium and vitamin E and K additions to no-hay finishing rations, *J. Anim. Sci.* **22**:929.

BURROUGHS, W., RAUN, A. and CHENG, E. (1958) Effects of methimazole on thyroid and liveweights of cattle, *Science* **128**:147.

BURROUGHS, W., RAUN, A., TRENKEL, A. and RAUN, N. S. (1960a) Further observations upon the effect of methimazole upon feedlot performance and carcass characteristics of fattening beef cattle, *J. Anim. Sci.* **19**:465.

BURROUGHS, W., SUMMERS, L. E., TRENKLE, A. and CULBERTSON, C. C. (1959) Trifluomeprazine additions to supplements for fattening cattle, Ia. State Coll. Anim. Husb. Leaflet 251.

BURROUGHS, W., TRENKLE, A., KAMALU, T. and VETTER, R. L. (1966) Melengesterol acetate as a growth stimulant in heifers and lambs, *J. Anim. Sci.* **25**:1257 Abs.

BURROUGHS, W., WOODS, W., EWING, S. A., GREIG, J. and THEURER, B. (1960b) Enzyme additions to fattening cattle rations, *J. Anim. Sci.* **19**:458.

BURROWS, H. (1949) *Biological Actions of Sex Hormones* 2nd edn.), (Cambridge Univ. Press, Cambridge.

BURT, A. W. A. (1968) A note on the effect of giving milk substitute only once a day to early weaned calves, *Anim. Prod.* **10**:113.

BUSCH, D. A. and DINKEL, C. A. (1967) Heritability estimates for certain beef traits, *J. Anim. Sci.* **26**: 1465 Abs.

BUSCH, D. A., DINKEL, C. A. and MINYARD, J. A. (1966) Live animal prediction of edible portion in beef cattle, *J. Anim. Sci.* **25**:1271 Abs.

BUSCH, D. A., DINKEL, C. A., SCHAEFFER, D. E., TUMA, H. J. and BREIDENSTEIN, B. C. (1968) Predicting edible portion of beef carcasses from rib separation data, *J. Anim. Sci.* **27**:351.

BUSHMAN, D. H., EMBRY, L. B., LUTHER, R. M. and EMERICK, R. J. (1967) Calcium and fat relationships in cattle fed all-concentrate rations, *J. Anim. Sci.* **26**:1486 Abs.

BUTAYE, R. (1965) The duration of pregnancy in the Red Pied cattle of East Flanders, *Vlaams diergeneesk. Tijdschr.* **34**:373.

BUTLER, O. D. (1957) The relation of conformation to carcass traits, *J. Anim. Sci.* **16**: 227.

BUTLER, O. D., CARTWRIGHT, T. C., KUNKLE, L. E., ORTS, F. A., KING, G. T. and LEWTER, D. W. (1962) Comparative feedlot performance and carcass characteristics of Hereford and Angus steers, *J. Anim. Sci.* **21**:298.

BUTLER, O. D., GARBER, M. J. and SMITH, R. L. (1956a) Beef carcass composition and yield of wholesale cuts as estimated from left and right sides, *J. Anim. Sci.* **15**:891.

BUTLER, O. D., REDDISH, R. L., KING, G. T. and SIMMS, R. L. (1956b) Factors contributing to the differences in dressing percentage between Hereford and Brahman × Hereford steers, *J. Anim. Sci.* **15**:523.

BUTLER, O. D., WARWICK, B. L. and CARTWRIGHT, T. C. (1956c) Slaughter and carcass characteristics of short-fed yearling Hereford and Hereford × Brahman steers, *J. Anim. Sci.* **15**:93.

BUTTERFIELD, R. M. (1962) Prediction of muscle content of steer carcasses, *Nature* **195**:193.

BUTTERFIELD, R. M. (1964a) Estimation of carcass composition; the anatomical approach, *Tech. Conf. Carcass Composition and Appraisal of Meat Animals* (ed. D. E. Tribe), CSIRO, Melbourne.
BUTTERFIELD, R. M. (1964b) Relative growth of the musculature of the ox. *Tech. Conf. Carcass Composition and Appraisal of Meat Animals* (ed. D. E. Tribe), CSIRO, Melbourne.
BUTTERFIELD, R. M. (1966) The effect of nutritional stress and recovery on the body composition of cattle, *Res. Vet. Sci.* **7**:168.
BUTTON, J. (1959) The Gallegan cattle of Spain, *Fmrs Wkly* (*Bloemfontein*), 25 Feb., p. 24.
BUYSSE, F. and BOUCQUE, Ch. (1967) Dried pulp as a basis of a feeding system to produce meat intensively, *Revue Agric.* **21**:1029.
BUYSSE, F., BOUCQUE, CH. and EECKHOUT, W. (1966) Intensive beef production (baby beef) principally on concentrates, Min. Agric. Res. Centre (Ghent) Publ. No. 1/1966.

CAB (1968) Nutritive value of sugar cane byproducts for ruminants, Commonwealth Agric. Bureaux (Nutrition) Ann. Bib. 3.
CABRINI, E. J. J. and CAVANDOLI, H. H. (1964) Charolais crosses in Marcos Juarez. Estac. Exp. Agropec. Marcos. Juarez Boln. Tec. 1.
CAFFREY, P. J., HATFIELD, E. E., NORTON, H. W. and GARRIGUS, U.S. (1967a) Nitrogen metabolism in the ovine, 1: Adjustment to a urea-rich diet, *J. Anim. Sci.* **26**:595.
CAFFREY, P. J., SMITH, G. S., NORTON, H. W., HINDS, F. C. and GARRIGUS, U. S. (1967b) Nitrogen metabolism in the ovine. 2: Utilization of blood urea and ammonia, *J. Anim. Sci.* **26**:601.
CAHILL, V. R., KLOSTERMAN, E. W. and OCKERMAN, H. W. (1962) Composition of Charolais beef, *J. Anim. Sci.* **21**:979.
CAHILL, V. R., KUNKLE, L. E., KLOSTERMAN, E. W., DEATHERAGE, F. E. and WIERBICKI, E. (1956) Effect of diethylstilbestrol implantation on carcass composition and the weight of certain endorcine glands of steers and bulls, *J. Anim. Sci.* **15**:701.
CAHILL, V. R., VANSTAVERN, B. D., KUNKLE, L. E. and KLOSTERMAN, E. W. (1959) Evaluation of carcasses sired by long-bodied and short-bodied bulls, *J. Anim. Sci.* **18**:1478 Abs.
CALAJA, A. D. (1965) Crossing Ukrainian Grey cattle with a beef breed, the Charolais, *Zhivotnovodstvo Mosk.* **27**:71.
CALLOW, E. H. (1936) *Ann. Rep. Fd Inv. Board.*
CALLOW, E. H. (1949) Comparative studies of meat. 3: Rates of fattening in relation to the percentage of muscular and fatty tissue in a carcass, *J. Agric. Sci.* **39**:347.
CALLOW, E. H. (1961) Comparative studies of meat. 7: A comparison between Hereford, Dairy Shorthorn and Friesian steers on four levels of nutrition, *J. Agric. Sci.* **56**: 265.
CALLOW, E. H. (1962) The relationship between the weight of a tissue in a single joint and the total weight of tissue in a side of beef, *Anim. Prod.* **4**:37.
CAMPBELL, C. (1968) Report in *Feedstuffs*, 14 Sept., p. 53.
CAMPBELL, E. A. and DODD, H. (1965) Ultrasonic measurement of body components in the live animal, *Aust. Vet. J.* **41**:336.
CAMPBELL, T. C., LOOSLI, J. K., WARNER, R. G. and TASAKI, I. (1963) Utilization of biuret by ruminants, *J. Anim. Sci.* **22**:139.
CAMPLING, R. C., FREER, M. and BALCH, C. C. (1961) Factors affecting the voluntary intake of cows. 2: The relationship between the voluntary intake of roughages, the amount of digesta in the reticulo-rumen and the rate of disappearance of digesta from the alimentary tract, *Br. J. Nutr.* **15**: 531.
CANTO, C. A., WISE, M. B. and BARRICK, E. R. (1968) Melengesterol acetate for finishing heifers, *J. Anim. Sci.* **27**:290 Abs.
CARDON, B. P. (1968) Report in *Feedstuffs*, 20 July, p. 14.
CARMON, J. L., STEWART, H. A., COCKERHAM, C. C. and COMSTOCK, R. E. (1956) Prediction equations for rotational crossbreeding, *J. Anim. Sci.* **15**:930.
CARNEIRO, G. G. and PEREIRA, C. S. (1968) Effect of season of birth and of inheritance on weaning weight of Guzera calves, *Proc. 2nd Reunion ALPA Lima*, p. 76.

CARPENTER, J. W., PALMER, A. Z., KIRK, W. G., PEACOCK, F. M. and KOGER, M. (1955) Slaughter and carcass differences between Brahman and Brahman–Shorthorn crossbred steers, *J. Anim. Sci.* **14**:1228 Abs.

CARPENTER, J. W. and PALMER, A. Z. (1961) Variability of ribeye area and degree of marbling of beef carcasses as influenced by method of ribbing, *J. Anim. Sci.* **20**:915 Abs.

CARPENTER, J. W., PALMER, A. Z., KIRK, W. G., PEACOCK, F. M. and KOGER, M. (1961) Slaughter and carcass characteristics of Brahman and Brahman–Shorthorn crossbred steers, *J. Anim. Sci.* **20**:336.

CARPENTER, Z. L., KAUFFMAN, R. G., BRAY, R. W., BRISKEY, E. J. and WECKEL, K. G. (1963) Factors influencing the quality of pork. 1: Histological observations, *J. Fd Sci.* **28**:467.

CARR, S. B. and JACOBSEN, D. R. (1962) Additional mass placed in the rumen does not reduce voluntary feed intake on an all roughage diet, *J. Anim. Sci.* **21**:989 Abs.

CARRERA, C. and CHÁZARO, S. (1967) Performance and selections of Santa Gertrudis bulls based on their capacity for post-weaning growth, *10th Annual Report Monterey Experimental Station*, p. 11.

CARRILHO, J. A. (1964) Crossbred Charolais × Miranda steers: Cost of production, *Bol. pecuär.* **32** (1), 3.

CARROLL, F. D., ELLSWORTH, D. J. and KROGER, D. (1963) Compensatory carcass growth in steers following protein and energy restriction, *J. Anim. Sci.* **22**:197.

CARROLL, F. D., NELSON, D. D., WOLF, N. H. and PLANGE, G. (1964) Energy utilization in heifers as affected by a low-protein isocaloric diet, *J. Anim. Sci.* **23**:758.

CARROLL, F. D., POWERS, S. B. and CLEGG, M. T. (1963b) Effect of cortisone acetate on steers, *J. Anim. Sci.* **22**:1009.

CARROLL, F. D. and ROLLINS, W. C. (1965) Performance of Charbray and Hereford cattle and crosses between them, *Anim. Prod.* **7**:119.

CARROLL, F. D., ROLLINS, W. C. and ITTNER, N. P. (1955) Brahman–Hereford crossbreds vs. Herefords; gains, carcass yields and carcass differences, *J. Anim. Sci.* **14**: 218.

CARROLL, M. A. (1966) Problems in beef carcass evaluation, *Proc. 9th Int. Congr. Anim. Prod. Edinburgh*, p. 117.

CARTER, R. C. (1954) Observations on the pathology and bacteriology of shipping fever in Canada, *Can. J. Comp. Med.* **18**:359.

CARTER, R. C. and KINCAID, C. M. (1955a) Estimates of genetic and phenotypic parameters in beef cattle. 2: Heritability estimates from parent offspring and half-sib resemblances, *J. Anim. Sci.* **18**:323.

CARTER, R. C. and KINCAID, C. M. (1959d) Estimation of genetic and phenotypic parameters in beef cattle. 3: Genetic and phenotypic correlations among economic characters, *J. Anim. Sci.* **18**:331.

CARTWRIGHT, T. C. (1955) Response of beef cattle to high ambient temperatures, *J. Anim. Sci.* **14**: 350.

CARTWRIGHT, T. C. (1958) Effect of tranquilizers on gain, shrink and temperament of beef cattle, Tex. Agric. Exp. Sta. Prog. Rep. 2049.

CARTWRIGHT, T. C., BUTLER, O. D. and COVER, S. (1958a) The relationship of ration and inheritance to certain production and carcass characteristics of yearling steers, *J. Anim. Sci.* **17**:540.

CARTWRIGHT, T. C., BUTLER, O. D. and COVER, S. (1958b) *Proc. 10th Conf. Am. Meat Inst. Found.*, p. 75.

CARTWRIGHT, T. C. and CARPENTER, J. A., JR. (1961) Effect of nursing habits on calf weights, *J. Anim. Sci.* 20:904 Abs.

CARTWRIGHT, T. C. and DAYHOFF, E. E. (1959) Some factors influencing variation in 28-day gains of feedlot cattle, *J. Anim. Sci.* **18**: 1463 Abs.

CASAS, M. and RAUN, N. S. (1964) Effect of stilbestrol implantation on feedlot bulls, *J. Anim. Sci.* **23**:870 Abs.

CASTLE, M. E. and WATSON, J. N. (1959) A comparison between an early weaning and a more conventional system of rearing dairy calves, *Anim. Prod.* **1**:31.

CAZEMIER, C. H. (1965) Evaluation of the exterior of Dutch Friesian bulls and its importance for the breeding of well-developed cows, *Veeteelt en Zuivelber.* **8**:402.

CHAGAS, E. C., RIGGS, J. K., SMITH, J. C. and COOPER, R. J. (1966) Rotational crossbreeding for beef production, *J. Anim. Sci.* **25**:264 Abs.

CHALMERS, M. I. (1963) The significance of the digestion of protein within the rumen on the nutrition of the animal, in *Progress in Nutrition and Allied Sciences*, Oliver & Boyd, Edinburgh.

CHALUPA, W. (1968) Problems in feeding urea to ruminants. *J. Anim. Sci.* **27**:207.

CHAMPAGNE, J. R., CARPENTER, J. W., HENTGES, J. F., PALMER, A. Z. and CUNHA, T. J. (1964) Effects of age at castration on feedlot performance and carcass characteristics of bulls and steers, *J. Anim. Sci.* **23**:859 Abs.

CHAPMAN, H. D., CARTWRIGHT, T. C. and FITZHUGH, H. A., JR. (1968) Genetic trends in an experimental Hereford herd, *J. Anim. Sci.* **27**:283 Abs.

CHAPMAN, H. D. and ENGLAND, N. (1965) A comparison of the reproductive performance of cows mated to bulls of their own breed vs. that of cows mated to bulls of different breeds, *J. Anim. Sci.* **24**:289 Abs.

CHAPMAN, H. L., SHIRLEY, R. L., PALMER, A. Z., HAINES, C. E., CARPENTER, J. W. and CUNHA, T. J. (1964) Vitamin A and E in steer fattening rations on pasture, *J. Anim. Sci.* **23**:669.

CHARPENTIER, J. (1964) A comparison of various methods of estimating the colour of beef, *Ann. Zootech.* **13**:103.

CHATRE, A., JOUANIN, R., and SOLOGOUB, C. (1967) Some aspects of obstetrics in Charolais breeding, *Bull. meno. Soc. vet. prat. Fr.* **51**:21.

CHOUDHURY, G., LUKTUKE, S. N. and SHARMA, U. D. 1964. Studies on sexual maturity in Hariana heifers, *Proc. 5th Int. Congr. Anim. Reprod. AI Trento*, **7**:516.

CHOW, B. F. (1968) Report in *Feedstuffs*, 11 May, p. 42.

CHRISTENSON, R. R., ZIMMERMAN, D. R., CLANTON, D. C., JONES, L. E., TRIBBLE, R. L. and SOTOMAYOR, R. (1967) Effect of precalving energy levels on performance of beef heifers, *J. Anim. Sci.* **26**:916 Abs.

CHRISTIAN, L. L., HAUSER, E. R. and CHAPMAN, A. B. (1965a) Heritability estimates on beef cattle based on identical and fraternal twins, *J. Anim. Sci.* **24**:643.

CHRISTIAN, L. L., HAUSER, E. R. and CHAPMAN, A. B. (1965b) Association of pre-weaning and post-weaning traits with weaning weight in cattle, *J. Anim. Sci.* **24**:652.

CHRISTIANS, C. J., CHAMBERS, D., WALTERS, L. E., WHITEMAN, J. V. and STEPHENS, D. F. (1962) Heritability estimates of beef characteristics, *J. Anim. Sci.* **21**:387 Abs.

CHRISTIANS, C. J., HENRICKSON, P. L., MORRISON, R. D., CHAMBERS, D. and STEPHENS, D. F. (1961) Some factors affecting tenderness of beef, *J. Anim. Sci.* **20**: 904 Abs.

CHRISTIANSEN, W. C., KAWASHIMA, R. and BURROUGHS, W. (1965) Influence of protozoa upon rumen acid production and liveweight gains in lambs, *J. Anim. Sci.* **24**:730.

CHRISTIANSEN, W. C., QUINN, L. Y. and BURROUGHS, W. (1962) Multiple-tube laboratory technique for studying volatile fatty acid production by rumen protozoa, *J. Anim. Sci.* **21,** 706.

CHURCH, D. C. and RALSTON, A. T. (1963) Comparison of performance of steer calves when fed *ad libitum* vs. twice daily in individual stalls, *J. Anim. Sci.* **22**:708.

CIORDIA, H. and BAIRD, D. M. (1968) Level of parasitism and grazing density of cattle, *J. Anim. Sci.* **27**:291 Abs.

CLANTON, D. C., PEDEN, W. E., JR. and MATSUSHIMA, J. (1959) The digestibility and efficiency of pelleted vs, chopped rations for growing and finishing beef cattle, *J. Amin. Sci.* **18**:1508 Abs.

CLANTON, D. C. and WOODS, W. (1966) Performance of steers and rumen fermentation as influenced by physical form of ingredients and alfalfa: corn ratio, *J. Anim. Sci.* **25**:102.

CLANTON, D. C., ZIMMERMAN, D. R. and ALBIN, R. C. (1964) Effect of protein and energy on growth and pubertal age in beef heifers, *J. Anim. Sci.* **23**:870 Abs.

CLANTON, D. C., ZIMMERMAN, D. R. and MATSUSHIMA, J. (1961) Growth and production in beef heifers as affected by protein and energy intake during gestation, *J. Anim. Sci.* **20**:928 Abs.

CLARK, J. (1966) Economic results from some barley beef units in the North of Scotland 1965/66, N. Scotland Coll. Agric. Econ, Rep. 118.

CLARK, J. D., RALSTON, A. T. and DYER, I. A. (1961) Some effects of hydroxyzine on beef cattle, *J. Anim. Sci.* **20**:669 Abs.

CLARK, R. D. and TOUCHBERRY, R. W. (1962) Effect of body weight and age at calving on milk production in Holstein cattle, *J. Dairy Sci.* **45**:1500.

CLARK, R. D. and WHITING, F. (1961) Further studies on raising dairy calves with limited amounts of milk, *Can. J. Anim. Sci.* **41**:16.

CLARK, R. T., O'MARY, C. C., BRINKS, J. S. and KEIFFER, N. M. (1963) Sex ratios in Hereford range cattle, *J. Anim. Sci.* **22**:817 Abs.

CLARY, F. G., RICHARDSON, D., SMITH, E. F. and BRENT, B. E. (1968) Single and mixed cereal grains for finishing beef cattle, *J. Anim. Sci.* **27**:1162 Abs.

CLARY, J. J., MITCHELL, G. E., JR. and LITTLE, C. O. (1967a) Adaptation of sheep pancreatic secretion to dietary change, *J. Anim. Sci.* **26**:917 Abs.

CLARY, J. J., MITCHELL, G. E., JR. and LITTLE, C. O. (1967b) Action of cattle, sheep and swine amylases on various starches, Ky. Agric. Exp. Sta. Prog. Rep. **170**:24.

CLARY, J. J., MITCHELL, G. E., JR., LITTLE, C. O. and BRADLEY, N. W. (1966) Dietary influence on bovine pancreatic amylase, *J. Anim. Sci.* **25**:899.

CLAUS, A. (1957) Die messung naturlicher grenzflachen in schweinkorper mit ultraschall, *Fleischwirtschaft.* **9**:552.

CLEGG, F. G. and BRYSON, H. (1962) An outbreak of poisoning in store cattle attributed to Brazilian groundnut meal, *Vet. Rec.* **74**:992.

CLEGG, M. T. and CARROLL, F. D. (1956) Further studies in the anabolic effect of stilbestrol in cattle as indicated by carcass composition, *J. Anim. Sci.* **15**:37.

CLEGG, M. T. and CARROLL, F. D. (1957) A comparison of the method of administration of stilbestrol on growth and carcass characteristics of beef steers, *J. Anim. Sci.* **16**:662.

CLEGG, M. T. and COLE, H. H. (1954) The action of stilbestrol on the growth response in ruminants, *J. Anim. Sci.* **13**:108.

CLIFFORD, A. J., BOURDETTE, J. R. and TILLMAN, A. D. (1967a) Studies on ruminal urease activity, *J. Anim. Sci.* **26**:219 Abs.

CLIFFORD, A. J., BOURDETTE, J. R. and TILLMAN, A. D. (1967b) Amino acid supplementation of urea-rich diets for lambs, *J. Anim. Sci.* **26**:917 Abs.

CLINE, T. R., GARRIGUS, U. S. and HATFIELD, E. E. (1966) Addition of branched- and straight-chain volatile fatty acids to purified lamb diets and effects on utilization of certain dietary components, *J. Anim. Sci.* **25**:734.

CLUM, H. V., KIDDER, R. W. and KOGER, M. (1956) Environmental factors affecting weaning weight of calves at the Florida everglades station, *J. Anim. Sci.* **15**:1209 Abs.

CLYBURN, T. M., MCCORMICK, W. C., SAFFLE, R. L. and SOUTHWELL, B. L. (1961) Effects of breed and cross on growth rate and carcass characteristics of beef steers, *J. Anim. Sci.* **20**:392 Abs.

COBB, E. H., BURNS, W. C. and KOGER, M. (1964) Comparative performance of British, Brahman and crossbred foundation cattle, *J. Anim. Sci.* **23**:848 Abs.

COBB, E. H. and OVEJERA, A. (1965) Predicting yield of trimmed retail cuts in beef carcasses, *J. Anim. Sci.* **24**:592 Abs.

COBB, E. H., WALKER, M. and OTAGAKI, K. K. (1961) Correlations among taste panel scores and various other measurements used in beef carcass evaluation, *J. Anim. Sci.* **20**:674 Abs.

COBIC, T. (1968) Castration experiments with Yugoslav Simmental cattle. 1: The effect of castration on growth and live weight gains, *Anim. Prod.* **10**:103.

COCK, L. M., POULTON, R. R., HOOVER, W. H. and KNOWLTON, P. H. (1967) Dietary nitrogen effect on ruminant heat measurement, *J. Anim. Sci.* **26**:845.

COLBURN, O. H. (1968) Letter in *Farmer & Stockbreeder*, 23 July, p. 20.

COLE, H. H. and BODA, J. M. (1960) Continued progress towards controlling bloat: A review, *J. Dairy Sci.* **43**:1585.

COLE, J. W., BACKUS, W. R. and ORME, L. E. (1960a) Specific gravity as an objective measure of beef eating quality, *J. Anim. Sci.* **19**:167.

COLE, J. W., EPLEY, R. H., JR., and ORME, L. E. (1960b) Improving estimates of separable lean in beef carcasses by using combinations of carcass length and longissimus dorsi areas at three locations, *J. Anim. Sci.* **19**:1232 Abs.

COLE, J. W., KINCAID, C. M. and HOBBS, C. S. (1958) Some effects of type and breeds of cattle on basic carcass characteristics, *J. Anim. Sci.* **17**:1153 Abs.

COLE, J. W., ORME, L. E. and KINCAID, C. M. (1960c) Relationship of loin eye area, separable lean of various cuts and carcass measurements to total carcass lean in beef, *J. Anim. Sci.* **19**:89.

COLE, J. W. and RAMSEY, C. B. (1961) Relationship of beef type and breed to offal composition, *J. Anim. Sci.* **20**:915 Abs.

COLE, J. W., RAMSEY, C. B. and EPLEY, R. H., JR. (1962) Simplified method for predicting pounds of lean in beef carcasses, *J. Anim. Sci.* **21**:355.

COLE, J. W., RAMSEY, C. B., HOBBS, C. S. and TEMPLE, R. S. (1963) Effect of type and breed of British, Zebu and dairy cattle on production, palatability and composition. 1: Rate of gain, feed efficiency and factors affecting market value, *J. Amin. Sci.* **22**:702.

Cole, J. W., Ramsey, C. B., Hobbs, C. S. and Temple, R. S. (1964) Effect of type and breed of British, Zebu and dairy cattle on production, palatability and composition. 3: Percent wholesale cuts and yield of edible portion as determined by physical and chemical analysis, *J. Anim. Sci.* **23**:71.

Cole, J. W., Ramsey, C. B. and Odom, L. A. (1960d) Effect of fat content on palatability of boiled ground beef, *J. Anim. Sci.* **19**:1233 Abs.

Cole, L. J. and Johansson, I. (1933) The yield and composition of milk from Aberdeen–Angus cows, *J. Dairy Sci.* **16**:565.

Colenbrander, V. F., Muller, L. D., Martin, D. G. and Carlton, W. W. (1968) Effects of feeding supplemental nitrogen as urea to dairy steers, *J. Dairy Sci.* **51**:979 Abs.

Collier, J. R., Brown, W. W., Jr. and Chow, T. L. (1962) Microbiologic investigations on natural epizootics of shipping fever on cattle, *J. Am. Vet. Med. Assoc.* **140**:807.

Coloris, N. F., Keener, H. A. and Davis, H. A. (1965) Does urea aid fiber utilization of dairy cattle rations?, *Proc. 3rd Symp. Energy Metabol. Troon.*

Compere, R. (1965) The heritability of some economic characters in Ruanda cattle of the Ankole type, *Biométr.-Praxim.* **6**:3.

Comstock, R. E. (1960) Problems and evidence in swine breeding, *J. Anim. Sci.* **19**:75.

Connolly, J. B., Cahill, D., Caffrey, P. J. and Ruane, J. B. (1967) Intensive beef production with and without pasture, *J. Dep. Agric. Eire* **64**:3.

Conrad, B. E., Neal, E. M. and Riggs, J. K. (1965) The influence of kind and level of roughage on beef cattle performance, *Proc 20th Ann. Tex. Nutr. Conf.*, p. 158.

Conrad, H. R. (1966) Symposium on factors influencing the voluntary intake of herbage by ruminants: physiological and physical factors limiting feed intake, *J. Anim. Sci.* **25**:227.

Conrad, H. R., Hibbs, J. W. and Pratt, A. D. (1967a) Effect of plane of nutrition and source of nitrogen on methionine synthesis in cows, *J. Nutr.* **91**:343.

Conrad, H. R., Miles, R. C. and Butdorf, J. (1967b) Estimation of methionine synthesis in intact cows after administering sulphide 35S, *J. Nutr.* **91**:337.

Cook, A. C., Black, W. H., Knapp, B., Jr. and Phillips, R. W. (1942) Relationship of milk production of Milking Shorthorn dams to the carcass quality of their steer progeny, *J. Anim. Sci.* **1**:345 Abs.

Cook, A. C., Kohli, M. L. and Dawson, W. M. (1951) Relationship of five body measurements to slaughter grade, carcass grade and dressing percentage in milking Shorthorn steers, *J. Anim. Sci.* **10**:386.

Cook, C. F. (1964) Techniques for measuring some quality characteristics of meat, *Tech. Conf. Carcass Composition and Appraisal of Meat Animals* (ed. D. E. Tribe), CSIRO, Melbourne.

Cook, R. M. and Miller, L. D. (1965) Utilization of volatile fatty acids in ruminants 1: Removal of them from portal blood by the liver, *J. Dairy Sci.* **48**:1339.

Cooley, J. R. and Burroughs, W. (1962) Sand additions to high-concentrate beef cattle rations, *J. Anim. Sci.* **21**:991 Abs.

Cornforth, V. P., Swanson, V. B. and Sutherland, T. M. (1965) Weaning weights of Herefords, Angus and their reciprocal crosses, *J. Anim. Sci.* **24**:586 Abs.

Converse, H. T. (1949) USDA Circ. 882.

Cover, S. (1959) Scoring for three components of tenderness to characterise differences among beef steaks, *Fd Res.* **24**:564.

Cover, S., Butler, O. D., and Cartwright, T. C. (1956) The relationship of fatness in yearling steers to juiciness and tenderness of broiled and braised steaks, *J. Anim. Sci.* **15**:464.

Cover, S., Cartwright, T. C. and Butler, O. D. (1957) The relationship of ration and inheritance to eating quality of the meat from yearling steers, *J. Anim. Sci.* **16**:946.

Cover, S., King, G. T. and Butler, O. D. (1958) Effect of carcass grades and fatness on tenderness of meat from steers of known history, Tex. Agric. Exp. Sta. Bull. 889.

Cowley, J. J., Warnick, A. C., Gutierrez, J. H. and Hengtes, J. F. (1968) Effect of temperature, breed and sex on thyroid activity in beef cattle, *J. Anim. Sci.* **27**:300 Abs.

Cowman, G. L. and Thomas, O. O. (1962) Diammonium phosphate as a source of nitrogen and phosphorus for beef cattle, *J. Anim. Sci.* **21**:992 Abs.

Cox, D. D., Allen, A. D. and Maurer, E. M. (1964) Feed additives for systemic cattle grub control, *J. Anim. Sci.* **23**:855 Abs.

Cox, R. F. and Smith, E. F. (1952) A comparison of rolled, coarsely ground and finely ground milo grain for fattening steer calves, Kansas Agric. Exp. Sta. Circ. 283.

Craig, H. B., Blumer, T. N. and Barrick, E. R. (1959) Effect of several combinations of grass and grain in the ration of beef steers on the colour characteristics of lean and fat, *J. Anim. Sci.* **18**:241.

Craig, H. B., Blumer, T. N., Smart, W. W. G., Jr. and Wise, M. B. (1966) Evaluation of hemoglobin, myoglobin, blood oxygen content and organoleptic qualities of beef from steers fed grain on pasture or cut forage and grain in drylot, *J. Anim. Sci.* **25**:1128.

Cramer, D. A. (1963) Symposium on feeds and meat terminology, 5: Techniques used in meat flavour research, *J. Anim. Sci.* **22**:555.

Crawford, A. W. and Butcher, J. E. (1966) Effects of weather on feedlot cattle performance, *J. Anim. Sci.* **25**:596 Abs.

Crawford, B. H., Jr., Jones, B. M., Jr., Cundiff, L. V. and Bradley, N. W. (1967) Correlations among performance traits in individually fed bulls, *J. Anim. Sci.* **26**:202 Abs.

Creek, M. J. and Nestel, B. L. (1962) Observations upon the birth weight of crossbred Charolais calves with reference to the absence of difficulty at parturition, *Br. Vet. J.* **118**:382.

Creek, M. J. and Nestel, B. L. (1964) Animal production studies in Jamaica, 3: The effect of dam age upon the 210 day weights of calves and response of male and female calves to different environments, *J. Agric. Sci.* **62**:165.

Crichton, J. A., Aitken, J. N. and Boyne, A. W. (1959) The effect of plane of nutrition during rearing on growth, production, reproduction and health of dairy cattle, 1: Growth to 24 months, *Anim. Prod.* **1**:145.

Crocker, E. C. (1948) Flavor of meat, *Fd Res.* **13**:179.

Crockett, J. R. and Kidder, R. W. (1967) Effect of breed of sire on calving date, *J. Anim. Sci.* **26**:202 Abs.

Crockett, J. R., Koger, M., Chapman, H. L., Jr. and Palmer, A. Z. (1959) Feedlot performance and carcass characteristics of steers of various breeds and crossbreeds, *J. Anim. Sci.* **18**:1474 Abs.

Crookshank, H. R., Keating, F. E., Burnett, E., Jones, J. H. and Davis, R. E. (1960) Effect of chemical and enzymatic agents on the formation of urinary calculi in fattening steers, *J. Anim. Sci.* **19**:595.

Crowley, J. P. (1965) The effect of Charolais bulls on calving performance, *Ir. J. Agric. Res.* **4**:205.

Crown, R. M. and Damon, R. A., Jr. (1960) The value of the 12th rib cut for measuring beef carcass yields and meat quality, *J. Anim. Sci.* **19**:109.

Csomos, Z. (1965) The relation between body weight and lactation yield in Hungarian Spotted cows, *Allattenysztes* **14**:101.

Cullison, A. E. (1961) Effect of physical form of the ration on steer performance and certain rumen phenomena, *J. Anim. Sci.* **20**:478.

Cullison, A. E. and Ward, C. S. (1961) Effect of sodium bicarbonate, sodium acetate and strychnine sulfate on the performance of beef animals receiving a pelleted ration, *J. Anim. Sci.* **20**:930 Abs.

Cundiff, L. V., Bradley, N. W., Kemp, J. D. and Greathouse, T. R. (1966a) Performance and carcass characteristics of Hereford and Hereford × Red Poll steers and heifers, *J. Anim. Sci.* **25**:265 Abs.

Cundiff, L. V., Chambers, D., Stephens, D. F. and Willham, R. L. (1964) Genetic analysis of some growth and carcass traits in beef cattle, *J. Anim. Sci.* **23**:1133.

Cundiff, L. V., Gregory, K. E., Koch, R. M., Breidenstein, B. C. and Dickerson, G. E. (1968) Genetic variation in growth and yield of retail product in beef cattle, *J. Anim. Sci.* **27**:1125 Abs.

Cundiff, L. V., Moody, W. G., Little, J. E., Jr., Jones, B. M., Jr. and Bradley, N. W. (1967) Predicting beef carcass cutability with live animal measurements, *J. Anim. Sci.* **26**:210 Abs.

Cundiff, L. V., Willham, R. L. and Pratt, C. A. (1966b) Effect of certain factors and their two-way interaction on weaning weight in beef cattle, *J. Anim. Sci.* **25**:972.

Cundiff, L. V., Willham, R. L. and Pratt, C. A. (1966c) Additive versus multiplicative correction factors for weaning weight in beef cattle, *J. Anim. Sci.* **25**:983.

Cundiff, L. V., Willham, R. L. and Pratt, C. A. (1966d) Factors to take into account when adjusting weaning weights of calves, Okla. Agric. Exp. Sta. Misc. Publ. 78.

Cunningham, E. P. and Henderson, C. R. (1965a) Estimation of genetic and phenotypic parameters of weaning traits in beef cattle, *J. Anim. Sci.* **24**:182.

CUNNINGHAM, E. P. and HENDERSON, C. R. (1965b) Repeatability of weaning traits in beef cattle, *J. Anim. Sci.* **24**:188.

CURL, S. E., DURFEY, W., PATTERSON, R. and ZINN, D. W. (1968a) Synchronization of estrus in cattle with subcutaneous implants, *J. Anim. Sci.* **27**:1189 Abs.

CURL, S. E., FENNELL, M. A., ZINN, D. W. and ALBIN, R. C. (1968b) Growth and development of the bovine as related to certain endocrine factors, *J. Anim. Sci.* **27**:1011.

CURTO, G. M., GALLARATI, S. G. C. and OLIVETTI, A. (1965) Experimental studies on the quantitative and qualitative characteristics of beef production of young bulls of the Chiana, Red Pied Friuli and Charolais breeds reared in the provine of Siena, *Zootec. Vet.* **20**:104.

CZERKAWSKI, J. W., BLAXTER, K. L. and WAINMAN, F. W. (1966) The metabolism of oeleic, linoleic and linolenic acids by sheep with reference to their effects on methane production, *Br. J. Nutr.* **20**:349.

DAHMEN, J. J. and BOGART, R. (1952) Some factors affecting rate and economy of gain in beef cattle, Oreg. Agric. Exp. Sta. Tech. Bull. 26.

DALE, H. E., RAGSDALE, A. C. and CHENG, C. S. (1959) Effect of constant environmental temperature of 50° and 80°F on appearance of puberty in beef calves, *J. Anim. Sci.* **18**:1363.

DALTON, D. C. (1967) Selection for growth in mice on two diets, *Anim. Prod.* **9**:425.

DALTON, D. C., PEARSON, M. E. and SHEARD, M. (1967) The behaviour of dairy bulls kept in groups, *Anim. Prod.* **9**:1.

DAMON, R. A., JR., CROWN, R. M., SINGLETARY, C. B. and MCCRAINE, S. E. (1960) Carcass characteristics of purebred and crossbred steers in the Gulf Coast region, *J. Anim. Sci.* **19**:820.

DAMON, R. A., JR., HARVEY, W. R., SINGLETARY, C. B., MCCRAINE, S. E. and CROWN, R. M. (1961) Genetic analysis of crossbreeding beef cattle, *J. Anim. Sci.* **20**:849.

DAMON, R. A., JR., MCCRAINE, S. E., CROWN, R. M. and SINGLETARY, C. B. (1959a) Performance of crossbred beef cattle in the Gulf Coast region, *J. Anim. Sci.* **18**:437.

DAMON, R. A., JR., MCCRAINE, S. E., CROWN, R. M. and SINGLETARY, C. B. (1959b) Gains and grades of beef steers in the Gulf Coast region, *J. Anim. Sci.* **18**:1103.

DANIELS, L. B. and COLVIN, H. W. (1963) Rumen motility as effected by the physical form of oat hay, *J. Anim. Sci.* **22**:855 Abs.

DANKE, R. J., SHERROD, L. B., NELSON, E. C. and TILLMAN, A. D. (1966) Effects of autoclaving and steaming of cottonseed meal for different lengths of time on nitrogen solubility and retention in sheep, *J. Anim. Sci.* **25**:181.

DARLOW, A. E. (1958) Fifty years of livestock judging, *J. Anim. Sci.* **17**:1058.

DAVENPORT, E. (1897) On the importance of the physiological requirements of the animal body: Results of an attempt to grow cattle without coarse feed, Ill. Agric. Exp. Sta. Bull. **46**:362.

DAVENPORT, R. L., STONAKER, H. H., RIDDLE, K. R. and SUTHERLAND, T. M. (1965) Heritability of reproductive performance in inbred and linecross beef cows, *J. Anim. Sci.* **24**:434.

DAVIES, H. L. (1962) *Proc. Aust. Soc. Anim. Prod.* **4**:167.

DAVIS, G. K. and ROBERTS, H. F. (1959) Urea toxicity in cattle, Fla. Agric. Exp. Sta. Bull. 611.

DAVIS, H. P. (1951) Reproductive efficiency in a Holstein herd 1897–1950, *J. Dairy Sci.* **34**:495.

DAVIS, H. P. (1952) Dairy calf births and disposals University of Nebraska herd 1904–1948, Nebr. Agric. Exp. Sta. Bull. 411.

DAVIS, J. K., LONG, R. A., SAFFLE, R. L., WARREN, E. P. and CARMON, J. L. (1964) Use of ultrasonics and visual appraisal to estimate total muscling in beef cattle, *J. Anim. Sci.* **23**:638.

DAVIS, J. K., TEMPLE, R. S. and MCCORMICK, W. C. (1966) A comparison of ultrasonic estimates of rib eye area and fat thickness in cattle, *J. Anim. Sci.* **25**:1087.

DAVIS, J. K. and TRUESDALE, R. W. (1968) Effect of melengestrol Acetate on feedlot performance and carcass characteristics of heifers, *J. Anim. Sci.* **27**:1162.

DAVIS, L., EWING, S. A., BURROUGHS, W., HAZEL, L. N., KLINE, E. A. and CARLIN, F. (1963a) Influence of feeding regime on beef carcasses, *J. Anim. Sci.* **22**:1113 Abs.

DAWSON, W. M., COOK, A. C. and KNAPP, B., JR. (1960) Milk production of Beef Shorthorn cows, *J. Anim. Sci.* **19**:502.

Dawson, W. M., Phillips, R. W. and Black, W. H. (1947) Birth weight as a criterion of selection in beef cattle, *J. Anim. Sci.* **6**:247.

Dawson, W. M., Yao, T. S. and Cook, A. C. (1955) Heritability of growth, beef characters and body measurements in milking Shorthorn steers, *J. Anim. Sci.* **14**:208.

De Alba, J. (1960) Milking with the calf and reproductive efficiency of the cow, *Turrialba* **10**:64.

De Alba, J., Villa Corta, E. and Ulloa, G. (1961) Influence of natural service on length of oestrus in the cow, *Anim. Prod.* **3**:327.

Deans, R. J., Van Arsdell, W. J., Reinecke, E. P. and Bratzler, L. J. (1956) The effect of progesterone–estradiol implants and stilbestrol feeding on feedlot performance and carcass characteristics of steers, *J. Anim. Sci.* **15**:1020.

Dearborn, D. and Dinkel, C. A. (1959) Evaluation of final weight in the selection of performance tested bulls, *J. Anim. Sci.* **18**:1464 Abs.

DeBaca, R. C., Bogart, R., Sawyer, W. A. and Hubbert, F., Jr. (1959) The expression of growth compensation for environmental influences affecting gains of steers, *J. Anim. Sci.* **18**:1536 Abs.

DeBie, W. H. and Woods, W. (1964) Rumen fermentation and animal performance as influenced by gelatinized corn and enzyme supplementation, *J. Anim. Sci.* **23**:872 Abs.

Deese, R. E. and Koger, M. (1967a) Maternal effects on preweaning growth rate in cattle, *J. Anim. Sci.* **26**:250.

Deese, R. E. and Koger, M. (1967b) Heritability of fertility in Brahman and crossbred cattle, *J. Anim. Sci.* **26**:984.

DeFries, J. C., Touchberry, R. W. and Hays, R. L. (1959) Heritability of the length of the gestation period in dairy cattle, *J. Dairy Sci.* **42**:598.

De Pinho, F. (1962) Increasing cattle production in Mozambique, *An. Serv. Vet. Mocambique* **8** (1960), 133.

De Rouen, T. M., Reynolds, W. L. and High, J. W., Jr. (1963) Evaluation of the Sindhi breed for beef at the Iberia station, *J. Anim. Sci.* **22**:243 Abs.

DeRouen, T. M., Reynolds, W. L. and Meyerhoeffer, D. C. (1967) Mortality of beef calves in the Gulf Coast region, *J. Anim. Sci.* **26**:202 Abs.

DeRouen, T. M., Reynolds, W. L., Mullins, A. M., Boulware, R. M., High, J. W., Jr., Temple, R. S. and Warwick, E. J. (1964) Relationship of backfat thickness to economic traits in steers, *J. Anim. Sci.* **23**:295 Abs.

DeRouen, T. M., Reynolds, W. L., Mullins, A. M., Boulware, R. F. and Temple, R. S. (1961) Gains and carcass traits of Angus, Zebu and Angus–Zebu steers, *J. Anim. Sci.* **20**:905.

DeRouen, T. M., Reynolds, W. L., Temple, R. S., Kincaid, C. M., Meyerhoeffer, D. C. and Warwick, E. J. (1965) Performance of progeny from Angus and Brahman bulls mated to straightbred and Angus–Zebu cross cows, *J. Anim. Sci.* **24**:287 Abs.

Dessouky, F. I. and Rakha, A. H. (1961) Studies on the gestation period and post partum heat of Friesian cattle in Egypt, *J. Agric. Sci.* **57**:325.

Deutsch, H. F. and Smith, V. R. (1957) Intestinal permeability to proteins in the newborn herbivore, *Am. J. Physiol.* **191**:271.

Devlin, T. J. (1967) Effect of ration potassium level on fattening steers, *J. Anim. Sci.* **26**:1488 Abs.

Devlin, T. J. and Woods, W. (1964) Nitrogen metabolism as influenced by lysine administration in and posterior to the rumen, *J. Anim. Sci.* **23**:872 Abs.

De Vree, J. (1961) Calf production and growth in the Charolais, *Veeteelt en Zuivelber.* **4**:410.

Deyoe, C. W., Bartley, E. E., Pfost, H. B., Boren, F. W., Perry, H. B., Anstaett, F. R., Helmer, L., Stiles, D., Sung, A. C. and Meyer, R. (1968) An improved urea products of ruminants, *J. Anim. Sci.* **27**:1163 Abs.

Dhindsa, D. S., Hoversland, A. S. and Smith, I. P. (1964) Estrus control in beef cattle under ranch conditions, *J. Anim. Sci.* **23**:904 Abs.

Dhindsa, D. S., Hoversland, A. S. and Smith, I. P. (1967) Estrus control and calving performance in beef cattle fed 6-methyl-17-acetoxyprogesterone under ranch conditions, *J. Anim. Sci.* **26**:167.

Dickerson, G. E. (1962) Implications of genetic–environment interaction in animal breeding, *Anim. Prod.* **4**:47.

Dickey, J. R. and Cartwright, T. C. (1966) Reproduction in tropically adapted beef cattle, *J. Anim. Sci.* **25**:251 Abs.

DICKINSON, F. N. and TOUCHBERRY, R. W. (1961) Livability of purebred vs. crossbred dairy cattle, *J. Dairy Sci.* **44**:879.

DIKEMAN, M. E., MERKEL, R. A. and MAGEE, W. T. (1968a) Relationship of beef carcass conformation to fat trim and retail yield, *J. Anim. Sci.* **27**:1139 Abs.

DIKEMAN, M. E., MERKEL, R. A. and MAGEE, W. T. (1968b) Relationship of retail and roast and steak yields of the round, loin, rib and chuck to total side retail cuts, *J. Anim. Sci.* **27**:1139 Abs.

DIKEMAN, M. E., MERKEL, R. A. and MAGEE, W. T. (1968c) Effects of beef-type upon carcass cutability, *J. Anim. Sci.* **27**: 1140 Abs.

DILLARD, E. U., LEGATES, J. E., BLUMER, T. E., PETERSEN, R. G., ROBISON, O. W. and GREGORY, J. H. (1964) Genotype–environment interactions in beef cattle, *J. Anim. Sci.* **23**:848 Abs.

DILLEY, G. W., WISE, M. B., BARRICK, E. R., BLUMER, T. N. and WARWICK, E. J. (1959) Influence of levels of nutrition and stilbestrol on performance and carcass characteristics of growing-finishing beef steers, *J. Anim. Sci.* **18**:1496 Abs.

DINDA, P. K. (1960) Some effects of chlortetracycline on the nutrition of the early weaned calf, Ph.D. thesis, Univ. Aberdeen.

DINKEL, C. A. (1958) Effect of length of feeding period on heritability of post-weaning gain of beef cattle, *J. Anim. Sci.* **17**:1141 Abs.

DINKEL, C. A., BUSCH, D. A., MINYARD, J. A. and TREVELLYAN, W. R. (1968) Effect of inbreeding on growth and conformation of beef cattle, *J. Anim. Sci.* **27**:313.

DINKEL, C. A., WILSON, L. L., TUMA, H. J. and MINYARD, J. A. (1965) Ratios and percents as measures of carcass traits, *J. Anim. Sci.* **24**:425.

DINUSSON, W. E., ANDREWS, F. N. and BEESON, W. M. (1950) The effects of stilbestrol and testosterone, thyroid alteration and spaying on growth and fattening of beef heifers, *J. Anim. Sci.* **9**:321.

DINUSSON, W. E., HAUGSE, C. N., ERICKSON, D. O. and BUCHANAN, M. L. (1964) High-moisture barley in high-energy beef rations, *J. Anim. Sci.* **23**:873 Abs.

DIRKSEN, G. (1965) Rumen acidosis in cattle, *Vet. med. Rev. Leverkusen* **2**:98.

DOBZHANSKY, T. (1952) Nature and origin of heterosis, in *Heterosis* (ed. J. W. Gowen), Iowa State Coll. Press, Ames.

DODSWORTH, T. L. (1957) The use of hexoestrol in beef production, *Agric. Rev.* **1**.

DODSWORTH, T. L. (1959) A report on feeding additional protein to fattening steers implanted with hexoestrol, *Anim. Prod.* **1**:175.

DODSWORTH, T. L. and BALL, C. (1961) A report on the treatment of beef cattle with tranquilizers and antibiotics, *Anim. Prod.* **3**:315.

DODSWORTH, T. L., BALL, C. and BROADBENT, P. J. (1967) The effect of two planes of nutrition in calfhood on the subsequent performance of beef cattle, *Anim. Prod.* **9**:284 Abs.

DODSWORTH, T. L., BALL, C. and RAVELL, J. (1963) Performance and progeny testing of beef bulls at Craibstone, *Scot. Agric.* **42**:194.

DODSWORTH, T. L., RUNCE, K. V., WALKER-LOVE, J., SAMPFORD, M. R., HARKER, A. B. and MACLAREN, N. P. (1966) The Charolais × Ayrshire trials in Scotland 1963–65, *Scot. Agric.* **45**:53.

DOLLER, A. M. and PORTER, J. W. G. (1957) Utilization of carbohydrates by the young calf, *Nature* **179**:1299.

DOMINGUES, O. (1961) *Tropical Cattle*, Inst. Zootec. (R. de Jan). Ser. Mono. 4.

DONALD, H. P. (1963) Perinatal deaths among calves in a crossbred dairy herd, *Anim. Prod.* **5**:87.

DONALD, H. P., RUSSELL, W. S. and TAYLOR, ST. C. S. (1962) Birth weights of reciprocally crossbred calves, *J. Agric. Sci.* **58**:405.

DONALDSON, L. E., RITSON, J. B. and COPEMAN, D. B. (1967) The reproductive efficiency of several North Queensland beef herds. 1: Physiological and management factors and embryonic neonatal losses, *Aust. Vet. J.* **43**:1.

DONEFER, E., LLOYD, L. E. and CRAMPTON, E. M. (1963) Effect of varying alfalfa: barley ratios on energy intake and volatile fatty acid production by sheep, *J. Anim. Sci.* **22**:425.

DONNELLY, T. H., RONGEY, E. H. and BARSUKE, V. J. (1966) Protein composition and functional properties of meat, *J. Agric. Fd Chem.* **14**:196.

DOTY, D. M. and PIERCE, J. C. (1961) Beef muscle characteristics as related to carcass grade, carcass weight and degree of aging, USDA Tech. Bull. 1231.

DOWDEN, D. R. and JACOBSON, D. R. (1960) Inhibition of appetite in dairy cattle by certain intermediate metabolites, *Nature* **188**:148.

Dowling, D. F. (1958) The significance of sweating in heat tolerance of cattle, *Aust. J. Agric. Res.* **9**:579.

Drain, J. J., Zimmer, P. R. and Elliott, R. F. (1966) Effect of combined chlortetracycline–sulfamethazine in starter rations for feeder cattle subjected to weaning, transportation and handling stresses, *J. Anim. Sci.* **25**:1255 Abs.

Drake, C. L., Brent, B. E., Deyoe, C. W. and Pfoot, H. B. (1967) Graded levels of gelatinized sorghum grain in a fattening ration, *J. Anim. Sci.* **26**:917 Abs.

Drake, C. L., McClure, W. H. and Fontenot, J. P. (1965) Effects of level and kind of broiler litter for fattening steers, *J. Anim. Sci.* **24**:879 Abs.

Drake, E. L. (1967) Report in *Feedstuffs*, 2 Dec., p. 46.

Drewry, K. J., Brown, C. J. and Honea, R. S. (1959) Relationships among factors associated with mothering ability in beef cattle, *J. Anim. Sci.* **18**:938.

Drewry, K. J. and Hazel, L. N. (1966) Beef calf weights as indicators of dam producing ability, *J. Anim. Sci.* **25**:878 Abs.

DuBose, L. E. and Cartwright, T. C. (1967) Relationships among production and carcass traits in cattle, *J. Anim. Sci.* **26**:203 Abs.

DuBose, L. E., Cartwright, T. C. and Cooper, R. J. (1967) Predicting steak and roast meat from production and carcass traits, *J. Anim. Sci.* **26**:688.

DuBose, L. E., Laughlin, D. and Holloway, B. (1968) Correlations among production and conformation traits and sale price in a herd of Angus cattle, *J. Anim. Sci.* **27**:1132 Abs.

Duckworth, J. E., Edge, T. M., Harrison, G., Olanijan, D., Holmes, W. and Galazka, H. (1966) Growth efficiency and carcass quality of Pietrains and Landrace pigs, *Anim. Prod.* **8**:356.

Dumont, B. L., Auriol, P. and Duplan, J. M. (1959) Study of the performance of the Charolais. 1: Growth, *CR Acad. Agric. Fr.* **45**:111.

Dumont, B. L., Le Guelte, P. and Arnoux, J. (1961a) Statistical study of beef cattle. 1: Variation in the anatomical composition of the carcasses of Charolais, *Ann. Zootech.* **10**:148.

Dumont, B. L., Le Guelte, P. and Arnoux, J. (1961b) Statistical study of beef cattle. 2: Estimating the weight of muscle in Charolais, *Ann. Zootech.* **10**:321.

Dunlop, A. (1963) Interactions between heredity and environment in Australian Merino. 2: Strain × location interactions in body traits and reproductive performance, *Aust. J. Agric. Res.* **14**:690.

Dunlop, R. H. and Hammond, P. G. (1965) D-lactic acidosis of ruminants, *Ann. NY Acad. Sci.* **119**: 1109.

Dunn, N. K. (1960) Relationship of loin eye area and other beef carcass characteristics with trimmed wholesale cuts and fat trim, MS. thesis, Kansas State Univ., Manhattan.

Dunn, T. G., Wiltbank, J. N., Zimmermann, D. R. and Ingalls, J. E. (1964) Energy level and reproduction in beef females, *J. Anim. Sci.* **23**:594 Abs.

Dunsing, M. (1959) Visual and eating preferences of consumer household panels for beef from animals of different ages, *Fd Tech.* **13**:332.

Durham, R. M. (1968) All concentrate ruminant feeding, *Feedstuffs*, 30 March, p. 26.

Durham, R. M., Elliott, H. and Zinn, D. W. (1961) Technique for marbling beef carcasses, *J. Anim. Sci.* **20**:916 Abs.

Durham, R. M., Ellis, G. F. and Cude, B. (1967a) A comparison of flaked, popped and cracked milo in all-concentrate rations, *J. Anim. Sci.* **26**:220 Abs.

Durham, R. M., Harbaugh, F. G., Stovell, R. and Ellis, G. F. (1963) All-concentrate versus part roughage rations using milo as the grain for fattening cattle, *J. Anim. Sci.* **22**:835 Abs.

Durham, R. M., Lopez, L. and Martin, R. C. (1967b) Specific rumen inoculations in new feeder cattle being fed a specific all-concentrate ration, *J. Anim. Sci.* **26**:917 Abs.

Durham, R. M. and Pruett, J. B. (1966) Effect of early high levels of zinc bacitracin on performance, carcass traits and liver abscesses in steers fed an all-concentrate ration, *J. Anim. Sci.* **25**:594 Abs.

Durham, R. M., Stovell, R., Cude, R. and Powitzhy, E. (1964) Raw soyabeans, whole cottonseed and cottonseed meal as supplements for all-concentrate rations, *J. Anim. Sci.* **23**:873 Abs.

Dyer, A. J., Kennett, A. and Riley, J. G. (1967) Effect of shelter or shade on performance of cattle, *J. Anim. Sci.* **26**:1469 Abs.

Dyer, A. J., Pfander, W. H., Brady, D. E. and Turner, C. W. (1956) Effects of adding hexoestrol and rumen organisms to a cattle fattening ration, *J. Anim. Sci.* **15**:1291 Abs.

DYER, A. J. and WEAVER, L. A. (1955) Corn substitutes for fattening cattle, Mo. Agric. Exp. Sta. Bull. 641.

DYER, I. A. (1967) Vitamin E for beef cattle, *Feedstuffs* 25 March, p. 20.

DYER, I. A., CLARK, J. D. and JOHNSON, R. J. (1963) Serum protein fractions in the normal and bloater bovine, *J. Anim. Sci.* **22**:836. Abs.

DYER, I. A., ENSMINGER, M. E. and BLUE, R. L. (1957) Effects of fat, oxytetracycline and stilbestrol on performance and hepatic stores of carotene and vitamin A in steers, *J. Anim. Sci.* **16**:828.

DYER, I. A., RUPNOW, E. H. and HAM, W. E. (1960) Effects of level of 3,3′-diallylhexestrol on steer performance and carcass characteristics, *J. Anim. Sci.* **19**:1009.

EADIE, J. M. (1962) The development of rumen microbial populations in lambs and calves under various conditions of management, *J. Gen. Microbiol.* **29**:563.

EADIE, J. M., HOBSON, P. N. and MANN, S. O. (1959) A relationship between some bacteria, protozoa and diet in early weaned calves, *Nature* **183**:624.

EADIE, J. M., HOBSON, P. N. and MANN, S. O. (1967) A note on some comparisons between the rumen content of barley fed steers and that of young calves also fed on a high concentrate ration, *Anim. Prod.* **9**:247.

EAST, E. M. (1912) Heterozygosis in evolution and in plant breeding, US Dep. Bull. 243.

ECKLES, C. H. (1946) *Dairy Cattle and Milk Production*, 3rd edn., Macmillan, London.

EDWARDS, J. (1963) Dairy herds and beef supplies (international), Symp. EAAP, Rome, mimeo.

EDWARDS, J., JOBST, D., HODGES, J., LEYBURN, M. H. O'CONNOR, L. K., MACDONALD, A., SMITH, G. F. and WOOD, P. (1966) *The Charolais Report*, MMB, Thames Ditton.

EDWARDS, R. L., TOVER, S. B., BLUMER, T. N. and BARRICK, E. R. (1961) Effects of added dietary fat on fatty acid composition and carcass characteristics of fattening steers, *J. Anim. Sci.* **20**:712.

EFTIMOV, B., KONSTANTINOV, G., VASILEVA, I. and VENEV, I. (1964) Study of conformation, type and some correlations in grey Iskur cattle, *Nauchnii Trud. virsk seklsostop. Inst. Georgi Dimitrov zootekh. Fak.* **15**:187.

EGAN, A. R. (1966) Nutritional status and intake regulation in sheep. 5: Effects of intraruminal infusions of volatile fatty acids upon voluntary intake of roughage by sheep, *Aust. J. Agric. Res.* **17**:741.

EISENHUT, R. C., CASSENS, R. G., BRAY, R. W. and BRISKEY, E. J. (1965) Fiber arrangement and micro-structure of bovine longissimus dorsi muscle, *J. Fd Sci.* **30**:955.

EKERN, A. (1967) Comparisons of herring meal and oil cake meal as protein supplements for young cattle, *Z. Tierphysiol. Tierernahr. Futtermittelk.* **22**:220.

EKMAN-BJARESTEN, I. (1965) Cross breeding experiments with Swedish Polled cattle, *Jord–Gröda–Djur.* **21**:81.

ELAM, C. J. and DAVIS, R. E. (1962) Ruminal characteristics and feedlot bloat incidence in cattle as influenced by vegetable oil, mineral oil and animal fat, *J. Anim. Sci.* **21**:568.

ELAM, C. J., GUTIERREZ, J. and DAVIS, R. E. (1960) Increased feedlot bloat from feeding soyabean oil in a mixed ration for steers, *J. Anim. Sci.* **19**:1089.

ELÍAS, A. and PRESTON, T. R. (1969a) Intensive beef production from sugar cane. 10: The effect of breed and protein supplement on rumen fermentation in bulls given high levels of molasses/urea, *Rev. cubana Cienc. Agric.* (Eng. ed.) **3**:25.

ELÍAS, A. and PRESTON, T. R. (1969b) The effect of high dietary levels of molasses/urea on rumen fermentation in Brahman bulls, *Anim. Prod.* **11**:276 Abs.

ELÍAS, A. and PRESTON, T. R. (1969c) Unpublished data.

ELÍAS, A. and PRESTON, T. R. (1969d) A note on some aspects of rumen fermentation in Holstein calves changed from a high concentrate diet to high levels of molasses/urea and forage, *Anim. Prod.* **11**:565.

ELÍAS, A., PRESTON, T. R. and WILLIS, M. B. (1967) Intensive beef production from sugar cane, 3: Characteristics of rumen contents from bulls given normal or invert molasses as a supplement to forage or concentrates. *Rev. cubana Cienc. Agric.* (Eng. ed.) **2**:49.

ELÍAS, A., PRESTON, T. R. and WILLIS, M. B. (1968a) Intensive beef production from sugar cane, 8:

Effect of rumen inoculation and different levels of forage on the performance of bulls fattened on high levels of molasses/urea, *Rev. cubana Cienc. Agric.* (Eng. ed.), **3**:19.

Elías, A., Preston, T. R., Willis, M. B. and Sutherland, T. M. (1968b) Intensive beef production from sugar cane, 4: Molasses/urea as a substitute for grain in low-fibre diets, *Rev. cubana Cienc. Agric.* (Eng. ed.) **2**:55.

Eller, A. L. and Carter, R. C. (1967) An evaluation of selection based on performance records, *J. Anim. Sci.* **26**:203 Abs.

Elliott, H., Zinn, D. W. and Durham, R. M. (1961) Streamlined hindquarter for cutout in beef cattle, *J. Anim. Sci.* **20**:905 Abs.

Elliott, R. C., Mills, W. R. and Reed, W. D. C. (1966) Survival feeding of Africander cows, *Rhod. Zamb. Mal. J. Agric. Res.* **4**:69.

Elliott, R. C. and Topps, J. H. (1963a) Studies of protein requirements of ruminants, 1: Nitrogen balance trials on two breeds of African cattle given diets adequate in energy and low in protein, *Br. J. Nutr.* **17**:539.

Elliott, R. C. and Topps, J. H. (1963b) Studies of protein requirements of ruminants, 2: Protein requirements for maintenance of three breeds of cattle, *Br. J. Nutr.* **17**:549.

Elliott, R. C., Reed, W. D. C. and Topps, J. H. (1964) Studies of protein requirements of ruminants, 4: Live weight changes of two breeds of African cattle given three levels of dietary protein each with varying amounts of digestible energy, *Br. J. Nutr.* **18**:519.

Elliott, R. F. (1967) Report in *Feedstuffs*, 23 Sept.

Ellis, G. F., Jr. and Carpenter, J. A. (1966) Popped milo in fattening rations for beef cattle, *J. Anim. Sci.* **25**:594 Abs.

Ellis, G. F., Jr. and Cartwright, T. C. (1963) Heterosis in Brahman-Hereford crosses, *J. Anim. Sci.* **22**:817 Abs.

Ellis, G. F., Jr., Cartwright, T. C. and Kruse, W. E. (1965) Heterosis for birth weight in Brahman–Hereford crosses, *J. Anim. Sci.* **24**:93.

Ellis, G. F., Jr., Durham, R. M. and Stovell, R. (1963) *Tex. Tech. Coll. Livestock Feeders Day Rep.*

Ellis, I. J., Jr., Wise, M. B., Blumer, T. N. and Barrick, E. R. (1962) Influence of degree of saturation of fats fed to steers in drylot, *J. Anim. Sci.* **21**:994 Abs.

El-Shazly, K. (1952a) Degradation of protein in the rumen of the sheep, 1: Some volatile fatty acids including branched chain isomers found *in vivo*, *Biochem. J.* **51**:640.

El-Shazly, K. (1952b) Degradation of protein in the rumen of the sheep, 2: The action of rumen microorganisms on amino acids, *Biochem. J.* **51**:647.

El-Shazly, K., Dehority, B. A. and Johnson, R. R. (1961) Effect of starch on the digestion of cellulose *in vitro* and *in vivo* by rumen microorganisms, *J. Anim. Sci.* **20**:268.

Elsley, F. W. H., McDonald, I. and Fowler, V. R. (1964) The effect of plane of nutrition on the carcasses of pigs and lambs when variations in fat content are excluded, *Anim. Prod.* **6**:141.

Ely, D. G., Little, C. O., Woolfolk, P. G. and Mitchell, G. E., Jr. (1967) Estimation of the extent of conversion of dietary zein to microbial protein in the rumen of lambs, *J. Nutr.* **91**:314.

Embry, L. B., Emerick, R. J., Weichenthal, B. A. and Whetzal, F. W. (1962) Vitamin A requirements of fattening cattle, *J. Anim. Sci.* **21**:994 Abs.

Embry, L. B., Gostler, G. F., Ladabaugh, D. V. and Olson, O. E. (1958) Manganese requirements of growing and fattening cattle, *J. Anim. Sci.* **17**:1204 Abs.

Engel, R. W., Hardisone, W. A., Miller, R. F., Price, N. O. and Huber, J. T. (1964) Effect of copper intake on concentration in body tissue and on growth, reproduction and production in dairy cattle, *J. Anim. Sci.* **23**:1160.

England, D. C. (1959) Relationship of inherent growth capacity of beef cattle to response to exogenous stimuli, 1: Response to implanted stilbestrol, *J. Anim. Sci.* **18**:1470 Abs.

England, D. C. and Taylor, N. O. (1959) Effect of implanted testosterone on growth rate of weaner steers with and without previous stilbestrol implantation, *J. Anim. Sci.* **18**:1169 Abs.

England, D. C. and Taylor, N. O. (1960) Effect of an injected tranquilizer on in-transit shrink and feedlot gain of weaner steers, *J. Anim. Sci.* **19**:964 Abs.

England, N., Brinks, J. S., Bogart, R. and Clark, R. T. (1961) Evidence for genetic influence on appetite in beef cattle, *J. Anim. Sci.* **20**:905 Abs.

England, N. and Farthing, B. R. (1964) Comparative performance of reciprocal crosses in beef cattle, *J. Anim. Sci.* **23**:848 Abs.

England, N., Robertson, G. L. and Sullivan, J. S. (1963a) A comparison of four mating systems for beef cattle production, *J. Anim. Sci.* **22**:817 Abs.

England, N., Temple, R. S. and Farthing, B. R. (1963b) The effect of breed of dam and lactation status upon conception rate in beef cattle, *J. Anim. Sci.* **22**:818 Abs.

Ensor, W. L., Shaw, J. C. and Tellechea, H. F. (1959) Special diets for the production of low fat milk and more efficient gains in body weight, *J. Dairy Sci.* **42**:189.

Epley, J., Stringer, W. C., Hedrick, H. B., Schupp, A. R. and White, R. H. (1968). Influence of sire and length of feeding on palatability of beef steaks, *J. Anim. Sci.* **27**:1277.

Erb, R. E. and Ashworth, U. S. (1961) Relationships between age, body weight and yield of dairy cows, *J. Dairy Sci.* **44**:515.

Erwin, E. S. (1966) Personal communication.

Erwin, E. S. (1967) Processing grain for cattle, *Feedstuffs*, 18 Feb., p. 29.

Erwin, E. S., Dyer, I. A. and Ensminger, M. E. (1956) Effects of chlortetracycline, inedible fat, stilbestrol and high and low quality roughage on performance of yearling steers, 1: Feed consumption and rate of gain, *J. Anim. Sci.* **15**:710.

Erwin, E. S., Gordon, R. S. and Algeo, J. W. (1963) Effect of antioxidant, protein and energy on vitamin A and feed utilization in steers, *J. Anim. Sci.* **22**:341.

Esplin, G., Hale, W. H., Hubbert, F. Jr. and Taylor, B. (1963) Effect of animal tallow and hydrolyzed vegetable and animal fat on ration utilization and rumen volatile fatty acid production with fattening steers, *J. Anim. Sci.* **22**:695.

Essig, H. W., Hatfield, E. E. and Johnson, B. C. (1959) Volatile fatty acid for growing lambs, *J. Nutr.* **69**:135.

Essig, H. W. and Williams, L. W. (1962) Diethylstilbestrol implants for nursing calves, *J. Anim. Sci.* **21**:386 Abs.

Everett, R. W. and Magee, W. T. (1965) Maternal ability and genetic ability of birth weight and gestation length, *J. Dairy Sci.* **48**:957.

Everitt, G. C. (1958) Some preferences of butchers for beef cattle, *Bull Inst. Meat* **22**:33.

Everitt, G. C. (1961) A recent development in meat marketing for New Zealand, 3: Edible meat, bone and fat yields of experimental cattle, *Bull. Inst. Meat* **33**:3.

Everitt, G. C. (1964a) Component analysis of meat production using biopsy techniques, *Tech. Conf. Carcass Composition and Appraisal of Meat Animals* (ed. D. E. Tribe), CSIRO, Melbourne.

Everitt, G. C. (1964b) Beef carcass appraisal by jointing, *Tech. Conf. Carcass Composition and Appraisal of Meat Animals* (ed. D. E. Tribe), CSIRO, Melbourne.

Everitt, G. C. (1967) Birth weights of dairy, beef and dairy-beef calves, *Proc. NZ. Soc. Anim. Prod.* **27**:73.

Everitt, G. C. and Carter, A. H. (1961) Growth and muscle development of steers implanted with hexoestrol, *J. Agric. Sci.* **57**:213.

Everitt, G. C. and Carter, A. H. (1963) Field trials on hexoestrol implantation of steers on New Zealand farms, *J. Agric. Sci.* **60**:87.

Everitt, G. C. and Duganzich, D. M. (1965) Implantation of oestrogenic hormones in beef cattle, 5: Boneless beef yield of steers implanted with hexoestrol, *NZ. J. Agric. Res.* **8**:370.

Everitt, G. C. and Jury, K. E. (1964) Implantation of oestrogenic hormones in beef cattle, 4: Effects of oestradiol benzoate plus progesterone on carcass composition and a comparison of methods of carcass evaluation. *NZ. J. Agric. Res.* **7**:158.

Ewing, S. A., Smithson, L. and Stephens, D. (1967) Mature size and energy requirements of producing beef cows, *J. Anim. Sci.* **26**:918 Abs.

Fagerlin, P. T., Brinks, J. S. and Stonaker, H. H. (1968) Environmental effects on calving interval in Herefords, *J. Anim. Sci.* **27**:1103 Abs.

Falconer, D. S. (1960a) Selection of mice of growth on high and low planes of nutrition, *Genet. Res.* **1**:91.

Falconer, D. S. (1960b) *Introduction to Quantitative Genetics*, Oliver & Boyd, Edinburgh.

Falconer, D. S. and Latyszewski, M. (1952a) Selection for size in mice on high and low planes of nutrition, In *Quantitative Inheritance* (eds. E. C. R. Reeve and C. H. Waddington), HMSO, London.

Falconer, D. S. and Latyszewski, M. (1952b) The environment in relation to selection for size in mice, *J. Genet.* **51**:67.

Farley, H., Kliewer, I. O., Pearson, C. C. and Foote, L. E. (1950) *Am. J. Vet. Res.* **22**:17.

Faulkner, D. E. and Brown, J. D. (1953) *The Improvement of Cattle in British Colonial Territories in Africa*, Col. Adv. Course. Agric. Anim. Health & Forestry No. 3, HMSO, London.

Fell, B. F., Boyne, R., Kay, M., Williams, R. B. and MacLeod, N. A. (1967) Effect of feeding barley and other diets on the tissues of the calf, *Vet. Rec.* **79**:593.

Fell, B. F., Kay, M., Whitelaw, F. G. and Boyne, R. (1968) Observations on the development of ruminal lesions in calves fed on barley, *Res. Vet. Sci.* **9**:458.

Fay, H. (1962) *Schweizer Arch. Tierheilk* **104**.

Field, R. A. (1968) Effects of connective tissue characteristics on tenderness, *J. Anim. Sci.* **27**:1140 Abs.

Field, R. A., Nelms, G. E. and Schoonover, C. O. (1966a) Effect of age, marbling and sex on palatability of beef, *J. Anim. Sci.* **25**:360.

Field, R. A. and Schoonover, C. O. (1967) Equations for comparing longissimus dorsi areas in bulls of different weights, *J. Anim. Sci.* **26**:709.

Field, R. A., Schoonover, C. O. and Nelms, G. E. (1964a) Performance data, carcass yield and consumer acceptance of retail cuts from steers and bulls, Wyo. Agric. Exp. Sta. Bull. 417.

Field, R. A., Schoonover, C. O. and Nelms, G. E. (1964b) Carcass characteristics of bulls and steers, *J. Anim. Sci.* **23**:597 Abs.

Field, R. A., Schoonover, C. O. and Nelms, G. E. (1964c) Consumer preferences for retail cuts from bulls and steers, *J. Anim. Sci.* **23**:597 Abs.

Field, R. A., Schoonover, C. O. and Nelms, G. E. (1966b) Relationships between carcass weight and muscle, fat and bone in bull carcasses, *J. Anim. Sci.* **25**:588 Abs.

Findlay, J. D. (1950) *The Effects of Temperature, Humidity, Air Movement and Solar Radiation on the Behaviour and Physiology of Cattle and Other Farm Animals*, Hannah Dairy Res. Inst. Publ.

Fitzhugh, H. A., Jr. (1968) Indicators of pseudo compensation growth, *J. Anim. Sci.* **27**:283 Abs.

Fitzhugh, H. A., Jr., Cartwright, T. C., Kruse, W. E. and Taylor, St. C. S. (1967) Post-weaning gains of cattle fed similar amounts, *J. Anim. Sci.* **26**:203 Abs.

Fitzhugh, H. A., Jr., Cartwright, T. C. and Temple, R. S. (1965a) Effects associated with beef cow weights, *J. Anim. Sci.* **24**:848 Abs.

Fitzhugh, H. A., Jr., King, G. T., Orts, F. A., Carpenter, Z. L. and Butler, O. D. (1965b) Methods of predicting the weight of boneless roast and steak meat from easily obtained beef carcass measurements, *J. Anim. Sci.* **24**:168.

Fitzhugh, H. A., Jr. and Taylor, St. C. S. (1968) Indirect selection for feed efficiency, *J. Anim. Sci.* **27**:1126 Abs.

Flatt, W. P., Moe, P. W., Moore, L. A. and Van Soest, P. J. (1967) Estimation and prediction of the energy value of feeds for ruminants, *Proc. 4th Symp. on Energy Metab. Warsaw.*

Flatt, W. P., Warner, R. G. and Loosli, J. K. (1958) Influence of purified material on the development of the ruminant stomach, *J. Dairy Sci.* **41**:1593.

Flatt, W. P., Warner, R. G. and Loosli, J. K. (1959) Evaluation of several techniques used in the study of developing rumen function, Cornell Agric. Exp. Sta. Mem. 361.

Fleming, H. P., Blumer, T. N. and Craig, H. B. (1960) Quantitative estimation of myoglobin and hemoglobin on beef muscle extracts, *J. Anim. Sci.* **19**:1164.

Fletcher, W. D., Hentges, J. F., Jr. and Cunha, T. J. (1957) Effect of diethylstilbestrol implantation and chlortetracycline on gains and blood components of beef calves and gains and estrus of yearling heifers, *J. Anim. Sci.* **16**:1032 Abs.

Flint, J. C. and Jensen, R. (1958) The effect of chlortetracycline fed continuously during fattening on the incidence of liver abscesses in beef cattle, *Am. J. Vet. Res.* **19**:830.

Flipse, R. J., Huffman, C. F., Duncan, C. W. and Webster, H. D. (1950a) *J. Dairy Sci.* **33**:557.

Flipse, R. J., Huffman, C. F., Webster, H. D. and Duncan, C. W. (1950b) *J. Dairy Sci.* **33**:548.

Flock, D. K., Carter, R. C. and Priode, B. M. (1962) Linear body measurements and other birth observations on beef calves as predictors of preweaning growth rate and weaning type score, *J. Anim. Sci.* **21**:651.

FLORENCE, H. D., JR., RIGGS, J. K. and POTTER, G. D. (1968) Physical characteristics of reconstituted sorghum grain, *J. Anim. Sci.* **27**:1163 Abs.

FLORSCHÜTZ, A. (1967) Comparative study of some reproductive characters of Simmental and Red Pied Lowland cows and their crosses, *Veterinaria Saraj.* **16**:99.

FLOWER, A. E., BRINKS, J. S., URICK, J. J. and WILLSON, F. S. (1963) Comparisons of inbred lines and linecrosses for performance traits in Hereford range cattle, *J. Anim. Sci.* **22**:914.

FLOWER, A. E., BRINKS, J. S., URICK, J. J. and WILLSON, F. S. (1964) Selection intensities and time trends for performance traits in range Hereford cattle under mass and recurrent selection, *J. Anim. Sci.* **23**:189.

FOHRMAN, M. H. and GRAVES, R. R. (1933) Analysis of the advanced registry records of 611 daughters of 51 Ayrshire sires, USDA Tech. Bull. 349.

FOLL, N. J. (1964) Vitamin A requirements of intensive beef steers, *Fert. Feedingstuffs J.*, 27 May.

FOLMAN, Y. and VOLCANI, R. (1960) The influence of diethylstilbestrol (DES) upon growth rate of bull calves and steers, *Ktavim* **10**:179.

FONTENOT, J. P. and KELLY, R. F. (1963) Effects of protein level of steer fattening rations 1. Feedlot performance, nitrogen metabolism and certain blood constituents, *J. Anim. Sci.* **22**:248 Abs.

FONTENOT, J. P. and KELLY, R. F. (1967) Protein and energy levels in steer fattening rations, *J. Anim. Sci.* **26**:918 Abs.

FONTENOT, J. P., KELLY, R. F., WILKINSON, W. S., KINCAID, C. M. and TAYLOR, J. C. (1959) The effect of nutrition and age on the carcass composition of beef steers, *J. Anim. Sci.* **18**:1536 Abs.

FOOTE, W. D. and HUNTER, J. E. (1964) *Post-partum* intervals of beef cows treated with progesterone and estrogen, *J. Anim. Sci.* **23**:517.

FOOTE, W. D., QUEVEDO, M. M. and SAIDUDDIN, S. (1965) Hormone treatment of cows at various stages *post-partum*, *J. Anim. Sci.* **24**:917 Abs.

FORBES, T. J., RAVEN, A. M. and ROBINSON, K. L. (1965) Studies of a concentrate/hay system, a high barley concentrate system and a liquid fed high-fat concentrate/hay system of beef production 1. Growth and feed conversion, *Rec. Agric. Res.* **14** (1), 83.

FORBES, T. J., RAVEN, A. M., ROBINSON, K. L. and IRWIN, J. H. D. (1966) Beef production from bulls and steers, 1: The utilization of experimental high concentrate diets, *Rec. Agric. Res.* **15** (2), 115.

FORREST, R. J. (1966) The production of beef by Holstein–Friesian bulls and steers, *Proc. 9th Int. Congr. Anim. Prod. Edinburgh*, p. 78.

FORREST, R. J. and SATHER, L. A. (1965) The effect of hormones on the rate of gain and feed consumption of Holstein–Freisian steers slaughtered at 340, 522 and 703 kg body weight, *Can. J. Anim. Sci.* **45**:173.

FOSGATE, O. T., CAMERON, N. W. and MCLEOD, R. J. (1962) Influence of 17-α-hydroxyprogesterone-*N*-caproate upon *post-partum* reproductive activity in the bovine, *J. Anim. Sci.* **21**:791.

FOSTER, W. H. (1960) The breeding of White Fulani cattle in Shela, Nigeria. Samura Res, *Bull Min. Agric. North Nigeria* **2**.

FOWLER, S. H. and ENSMINGER, M. E. (1960) Interactions between genotype and plane of nutrition in selection for rate of gain in swine, *J. Anim. Sci.* **19**:434.

FRANCIS, J. (1965) Definition and use of Zebu, Brahman or *Bos indicus* cattle, *Nature* **207**:13.

FRANCIS, J. and LITTLE, D. A. (1964) Resistance of droughtmaster cattle to tick infestation and babesiosis, *Aust. Vet. J.* **40**:247.

FRANKE, D. E. and CARTWRIGHT, T. C. (1968) Estimating individual feed intake of group fed steers, *J. Anim. Sci.* **27**:284 Abs.

FRANKE, D. E., ENGLAND, N. C. and HENDRY, J. E. (1965) Effect of breed of dam and breed of sire on birth weight of beef calves, *J. Anim. Sci.* **24**:281 Abs.

FREDEEN, H. T. (1965) Genetic aspects of disease resistance, *Anim. Breed. Abstr.* **33**:17.

FREDEEN, H. T. (1966) Where should we be going in animal breeding research? *J. Anim. Sci.* **25**:543.

FREDERICK, E. C., REIMER, D., KOLARI, O. E., AUNAN, W. J. and HANSON, L. E. (1962) High moisture ensiled barley for fattening steers, *J. Anim. Sci.* **21**:995 Abs.

FREDERICK, H. M., THEURER, B. and HALE, W. H. (1968) Effect of moisture, heat and pressure on *in vitro* starch digestion of milo and barley, *J. Anim. Sci.* **27**:1110 Abs.

FREDERICK, L. D. (1943) The economic and nutritional importance of bovine hepatic disturbances, *J. Am. Vet. Med. Assoc.* **102**:338.

FREITAG, R. R., SMITH, W. H. and BEESON, W. M. (1966) Comparison of certain metabolites possibly related to nitrogen utilization of urea and soybean meal rations, *J. Anim. Sci.* **25**:901.

FRENCH, M. H. (1966) *European Breeds of Cattle*, Vols. 1 and 2, FAO, Rome.

FRENCH, M. H. and LEDGER, H. P. (1957) Live-weight changes of cattle in East Africa, *Emp. J. Exp. Agric.* **25**:10.

FRIEDLI, K. (1965) Frequency of obstetrical disorders in cows in Switzerland, *Schweizer Arch. Tierheilk.* **107**:497.

FULKENBURG, G. A., RADLOFF, H. D. and RICE, R. W. (1968) Relationship between milk production of Holstein dams and performance of steer progeny, *J. Dairy Sci.* **51**:959.

FURR, R. D. and CARPENTER, J. A. (1967a) Effect of different levels of supplemental protein, copper and cobalt for beef cattle receiving high grain sorghum finishing rations, *J. Anim. Sci.* **26**:221 Abs.

FURR, R. D. and CARPENTER, J. A. (1967b) Comparison of antibiotics in high grain sorghum finishing rations, *J. Anim. Sci.* **26**:919.

FURR, R. D., HANSEN, K. R. and CARPENTER, J. A. (1968a) Different levels of diethylstilbestrol and certain minerals for cattle fed on all-concentrate finishing ration, *J. Anim. Sci.* **27**:1111 Abs.

FURR, R. D., HANSEN, K. R., CARPENTER, J. A. and SHERROD, L. B. (1968b) Effect of different nitrogen sources and antibiotics in all-concentrate finishing rations, *J. Anim. Sci.* **27**:1110 Abs.

FURR, R. D., HANSEN, K. R., CARPENTER, J. A. and SHERROD, L. B. (1968c) Mineral and chlortetracycline supplementation to all-concentrate NPN supplemented feedlot rations, *J. Anim. Sci.* **27**:1111 Abs.

FURR, R. D., SHERROD, L. B., CARPENTER, J. A. and HANSEN, K. R. (1968d) Effect of feeding either chlortetracycline or sulfamethazine or a combination to stressed feeder cattle, *J. Anim. Sci.* **27**:1110 Abs.

FURR, R. D. and NELSON, A. B. (1959) Levels of supplemental winter feeding of beef cows and creep feeding fall calves, *J. Anim. Sci.* **18**:1533 Abs.

FURR, R. D. and NELSON, A. B. (1964) Effect of supplemental winter feed on calf weight and on milk production of fall-calving range beef cows, *J. Anim. Sci.* **23**:775.

GACULA, M. and BROWN, C. J. (1963) Heritability of feedlot performance of beef bulls, *J. Anim. Sci.* **22**:238 Abs.

GAINES, J. A., CARTER, R. C. and KINCAID, C. M. (1958) Heritability of TDN/cwt gain in beef cattle that are full fed, *J. Anim. Sci.* **17**:1143 Abs.

GAINES, J. A., MCCLURE, W. H., VOGT, D. W., CARTER, R. C. and KINCAID, C. M. (1966) Heterosis from crosses among British breeds of beef cattle: fertility and calf performance to weaning, *J. Anim. Sci.* **25**:5.

GAINES, J. A., RICHARDSON, G. V., MCCLURE, W. H., VOGT, D. W. and CARTER, R. C. (1967) Heterosis from crosses among British breeds of beef cattle: carcass characteristics, *J. Anim. Sci.* **26**:1217.

GALE, C. and KING, N. B. (1961) Isolation of a virus from clinical shipping fever in cattle, *J. Am. Vet. Med. Assoc.* **138**:235.

GALE, C. and SMITH, H. R. (1958) Studies on shipping fever of cattle, 1: Experimental exposure of cattle with various cultures of pasturella, *Am. J. Vet. Res.* **19**:815.

GALLAGHER, R. M. (1963) The influence of growth rate selection on some carcass characteristics of beef cattle, *Tech. Conf. Carcass Composition and Appraisal of Meat Animals* (ed. D. E. Tribe), CSIRO, Melbourne.

GARDNER, R. W. (1968) Fat–protein interaction in calf rations, *J. Anim. Sci.* **27**:1111 Abs.

GARRETT, W. N. (1964) Low level of diethylstilbestrol implantation for lambs grazing alfalfa, *J. Anim. Sci.* **23**:430.

GARRETT, W. N. (1965a) Comparative feeding value of steam-rolled or ground barley and milo for feedlot cattle, *J. Anim. Sci.* **24**:726.

GARRETT, W. N. (1965b) Energetic efficiency of three breeds of cattle, *J. Anim. Sci.* **24**:881 Abs.

GARRETT, W. N., BOND, T. E. and KELLY, C. F. (1960) Effect of air velocity on gains and physiological adjustments of Hereford steers in a high temperature environment, *J. Anim. Sci.* **19**:60.

GARRETT, W. N., GIVENS, R., BOND, T. E. and HULL, R. L. (1966) Observations on the need for shade in beef feedlots, *J. Anim. Sci.* **25**:596 Abs.

GARRETT, W. N., KELLY, C. F. and BOND, T. E. (1962) Total and shaded space allotments for beef feedlots as affected by ration in a high temperature environment, *J. Anim. Sci.* **21**:794.

GARRETT, W. N., MEYER, J. H. and LOFGREEN, G. P. (1959a) An evaluation of the antipyrine dilution technique for the determination of total body water in ruminants, *J. Anim. Sci.* **18**:116.

GARRETT, W. N., MEYER, J. H. and LOFGREEN, G. P. (1959b) The comparative energy requirements of sheep and cattle for maintenance and gain, *J. Anim. Sci.* **18**:528.

GARRETT, W. N., MEYER, J. H., LOFGREEN, G. P. and DOBIE, J. B. (1961) Effect of pellet size and composition on feedlot performance, carcass characteristics and rumen parakeratosis of fattening steers, *J. Anim. Sci.* **20**:833.

GAUSSERES, B. and FAUCONNEAU, G. (1965) Quantitative evaluation, with the aid of nucleic acids on the population of microbes in the digestive apparatus of ruminants, 1: Methods of analysis of rumen contents of cattle fed different diets, *Ann. Biol. Anim. Biochem. Biophys.* **5**:5.

GEE, I. and PRESTON, T. R. (1957) The effect of hexoestrol implantation on carcass composition and efficiency of food utilization in fattening lambs, *Br. J. Nutr.* **11**:329.

GEISSLER, B. R. and Thomas, O. O. (1966) Poloxalene as a bloat preventative for wintering calves on barley and alfalfa rations, *J. Anim. Sci.* **25**:589 Abs.

GERLAUGH, P., KUNKLE, L. K. and RIFE, D. C. (1951) Crossbreeding beef cattle: A comparison of the Hereford and Aberdeen–Angus breeds and their reciprocal crosses, Ohio Agric. Exp. Sta. Res. Bull. 703

GERMAN, H. L. and ADAMS, C. R. (1962) Supplemental vitamin A for breeding beef cattle. *J. Anim. Sci.* **21**:996 Abs.

GERRARD, F. (1951) *Meat Technology*, Leonard Hill, London.

GEURIN, H. B., THOMPSON, J. C., WILCKE, H. L. and BETHKE, R. M. (1956) Oats as a cattle fattening feed, *J. Anim. Sci.* **15**:1251 Abs.

GEURIN, H. B., WILLIAMSON, J. L., THOMPSON, J. C., WILCKE, H. L. and BETHKE, R. M. (1959) Rolled common barley serves as both grain and roughage for fattening steers, *J. Anim. Sci.* **18**:1489 Abs.

GIBSON, D. and WATSON, J. H. (1963) A comparison of growth rate in twin cattle of eight breeds and crosses, *Anim. Prod.* **5**:175.

GIFFORD, W. (1949) Importance of high milk production in beef cows over estimated, *J. Anim. Sci.* **8**:605 Abs.

GIFFORD, W. (1953) Records of performance of beef cattle in breeding herds: Milk production of dams and growth of calves, Ark. Agric. Exp. Sta. Bull. 531.

GIL, H., JOHNSON, R. R., KLOSTERMAN, E. W. and CAHILL, V. R. (1968) Estimation of total empty body fat in beef cattle, *J. Anim. Sci.* **27**:1121 Abs.

GILLOOLY, J. E., WILSON, L. L., THOMPSON, C. E., RUGH, M. C., LONG, T. A. and PURDY, H. R. (1967) Effects of energy level and cow size on milk yield and calf gain, *J. Anim. Sci.* **26**:1468 Abs.

GILPIN, G. L., BATCHER, O. M. and GEARY, P. A. (1966) Influence of marbling and final internal temperature on quality characteristics of broiled rib and eye of round steaks, *Fd. Tech.* **19**:152.

GLANTZ, P. J. (1962) *In vitro* sensitivity of *Escherichia coli* to antibiotics and nitrofurans, *Cornell Vet.* **52**:552.

GLASCOCK, R. F. and HEWITT, E. J. (1963) The uptake of hexoestrol by the roots of plants and its retention when applied to the foliage as a spray, *Ann. Appl. Biol.* **52**:163.

GLASCOCK, R. F. and JONES, H. E. H. (1961) The uptake of hexoestrol by plants and its persistence in the soil, *J. Endoocr.* **21**:373.

GLIMP, H. A., KARR, M. R., LITTLE, C. O., WOOLFOLK, P. G., MITCHELL, G. E., JR., and HUDSON, L. W. (1967) Effect of reducing soybean protein solubility by dry heat on the protein utilization of young lambs, *J. Anim. Sci.* **26**:858.

GLIMP, H. A. and TILLMAN, A. D. (1965) Effect of jackbean urease injections on performance, anti-urease production and plasma ammonia and urea levels in sheep, *J. Anim. Sci.* **24**:105.

GODFREY, N. W. (1961a) The functional development of the calf, 1: Growth of the stomach of the calf, *J. Agric. Sci.* **57**:173.

GODFREY, N. W. (1961b) The functional development of the calf, 2: Development of rumen function in the calf, *J. Agric. Sci.* **57**:177.

GODLEY, W. C., GODBEY, E. G., KYZER, E. D. and WHEELER, R. F. (1960) Crossbred and purebred dams for the production of slaughter calves, *J. Anim. Sci.* **19**:203.

GODSELL, T. E. and PRESTON, T. R. (1963) Input–output relationships in beef production, *Proc. Seminar Cooperation between Res. in Agric. Natural Sci. and Agric. Econ. in Production of Input/Output Data*, OECD, Paris.

GOLL, D. E., BRAY, R. W. and HOEKSTRA, W. G. (1963) Age associated changes in muscle composition: The isolation and properties of collagenous residue from bovine muscle, *J. Fd. Sci.* **28**:503.

GOLL, D. E., HAZEL, L. N. and KLINE, E. A. (1961a) Relationship between some beef carcass measurements and yields of wholesale cuts, *J. Anim. Sci.* **20**:264.

GOLL, D. E., HOEKSTRA, W. G. and BRAY, R. W. (1964a) Age associated changes in bovine muscle connective tissue, 1: Rate of hydrolysis by collagenase, *J. Fd. Sci.* **29**:608.

GOLL, D. E., HOEKSTRA, W. G. and BRAY, R. W. (1964b) Age associated changes in bovine muscle connective tissue, 2: Exposure to increasing temperature, *J. Fd. Sci.* **29**:615.

GOLL, D. E., HOEKSTRA, W. G. and BRAY, R. W. (1964c) Age associated changes in bovine muscle connective tissue, 3: Rate of solubilization at 100°C, *J. Fd Sci.* **29**:622.

GOLL, D. E., KLINE, E. A. and HAZEL, L. N. (1961b) Influence of beef carcass grades and weight on yield of wholesale cuts and carcass measurements, *J. Anim. Sci.* **20**: 260.

GONZALEZ-JIMENEZ, E. and BLAXTER, K. L. (1962) The metabolism and thermal regulation of calves in the first month of life, *Br. J. Nutr.* **16**:199.

GOOD, D. L., DAHL, G. M., WEARDEN, S. and WESELI, D. J. (1961) Relationships among live and carcass characteristics of selected slaughter steers, *J. Anim. Sci.* **20**:698.

GOOD, D. L., MACKINTOSH, D. L., SOULE, R. P., COX, R. F. and HARRISON, D. L. (1957) The effect of diethylstilbestrol administered by implantation and by ingestion on growth, fattening and carcass characteristics of beef steers, *Kan. Agric. Exp. Sta. Livestock Feeders Day Rep.*

GOODALL, A. M. and YANG, S. H. (1954) *J. Agric. Sci.* **44**:1.

GOODRICH, R. D., EMBRY, L. B., GASTLER, G. F. and WHETZAL, F. W. (1962) Types of high-concentrate rations for fattening cattle, *J. Anim. Sci.* **21**:996 Abs.

GOODRICH, R. D., JOHNSON, J. H. and MEISKE, J. C. (1967) Supplemental sulfur for ruminants fed urea, *J. Anim. Sci.* **26**:1490 Abs.

GOODRICH, R. D. and MEISKE, J. C. (1966) Value of hay in finishing cattle rations containing ear corn, *J. Anim. Sci.* **25**:1252 Abs.

GOODRICH, R. D. and MEISKE, J. C. (1967) Drylot vs. conventional cow-calf production, *Feedstuffs*, 11 Nov.

GOODRICH, R. D., MEISKE, J. C. and POKORNEY, J. C. (1968) Oyster shells and alfalfa-brome hay levels for yearling steers, *J. Anim. Sci.* **27**:1164 Abs.

GOODWIN, E. E. (1958) Effect of stilbestrol on protein requirements of fattening steers, *J. Anim. Sci.* **17**:1202 Abs.

GORDON, I., WILLIAMS, G. and EDWARDS, J. (1962) The use of serum gonadotrophin (PMS) in the induction of twin pregnancy in the cow, *J. Agric. Sci.* **59**:143.

GORDON, R. S. and ERWIN, E. S. (1960) Effects of energy in steers fed corn-soybean meal rations, *J. Anim. Sci.* **19**:1261 Abs.

GORRILL, A. D. L. and THOMAS, J. W. (1967) Body weight changes, pancreas size and enzyme activity and proteolytic enzyne activity and protein digestion in intestinal contents from calves fed soybean and milk protein diets, *J. Nutr.* **92**:215.

GOSHI, B. C., MCDOWELL, R. E. and SADHU, D. R. (1968) Surface evaporations from the normal body surface and with sweat glands inactivated in Indian cattle, *J. Dairy Sci.* **51**:916.

GOSSETT, F. O., SMITH, F. A. and DOWNING, J. F. (1956) The feeding of high levels of diethylstilbestrol to beef steers, *Symposium on Medicinal Feeds* (eds. H. Welsh and F. Marte-Ibañez), Medical Encyclopedia Inc., New York.

GOSSETT, W. H., BEESON, W. M., PERRY, T. W. and MOHLER, M. T. (1961) Value of supplemental lysine and methionine analog in high urea rations for beef cattle, *J. Anim. Sci.* **20**:933 Abs.

GOSSETT, W. H., PERRY, T. W., MOHLER, M. T., PLUMLEE, M. P. and BEESON, W. M. (1962) Value of supplemental lysine, methionine, methionine analog and trace minerals on high urea fattening rations for beef steers, *J. Anim. Sci.* **21**:248.

GOTHARD, R. H., MULLINS, A. M., HANSARD, S. L. and BOULWARE, R. F. (1966) Relationship between post-morten muscle contraction and tenderness in selected bovine muscles, *J. Anim. Sci.* **25**:256 Abs.

GOTTLIEB, H. A., WHEAT, J. D., SMITH, W. H. and WEARDEN, S. (1962) Factors affecting weaning weight in an inbred Shorthorn herd, *J. Anim. Sci.* **21**:972 Abs.

GOTTSCH, A. H., MERKEL, R. A. and MACKINTOSH, D. E. (1961) Relationship of muscle fat, bone and some physical measurements to beef carcass cutability, *J. Anim. Sci.* **20**:917 Abs.

GOULD, C. M. (1966) Gestation length and growth rate, *Vet. Rec.* **79**:663.

GOWE, R. S. (1949) Residual estrogens in the tissues of fowl treated with dienestrol diacetate, *Poult. Sci.* **28**:666.

GRAHAM, N. McC., WAINMAN, F. W., BLAXTER, K. L. and ARMSTRONG, D. G. (1959a) Environmental temperature, energy metabolism and heat regulation in sheep, 1: Energy metabolism in closely clipped sheep, *J. Agric. Sci.* **52**:13.

GRAHAM, P. P., KELLY, R. F. and FONTENOT, J. P. (1959b) The effect of nutrition and age of beef steers on the cooking and eating characteristics of the meat, *J. Anim. Sci.* **18**: 1475 Abs.

GRANIZO, T., SCARCI, J. C., MALTOS, J. and DE ALBA, J. (1968) Meat production from purebreeds and crosses with Limousin bulls, *Proc. 2nd Reunion ALPA, Lima*, p.83.

GRANT, A. B. (1955) Vitamin A and ovine rickets, *Vet. Rev.* **1**:115.

GRAVERT, H. O. (1962) Investigations on the heritability of meat characters in cattle, 1: Area of longissimus dorsi muscle, water content, water retention and fat content, *Z. Tierzücht. ZüchtBiol.* **78**:43.

GRAVERT, H. O. (1963) Investigations on the heritability of meat characters in cattle, 2: Protein content, pH value, colour, muscle fibre diameter and tenderness, *Z. Tierzucht. ZüchtBiol.* **79**:139.

GRAVERT, H. O. (1965) The heritability of meat characters in young Friesian bulls. *Wld Rev. Anim. Prod.* **1**:37.

GRAVERT, H. O. (1967) Selection for milk, butterfat and beef production in European Friesians, *Proc. 9th Int. Congr. Anim. Prod. Edinburgh*, p. 314.

GRAY, W. V. (1962) Intensive veal production and a hitherto untried nitrofuran. A preliminary trial, *Vet. Rec.* **74**:628.

GREGORY, J. H. and STEWART, H. A. (1962) Relationship of performance of bulls to performance of their progeny, *J. Anim. Sci.* **21**:380 Abs.

GREGORY, K. E. (1965) Symposium on performance testing in beef cattle: evaluating post-weaning performance in beef cattle, *J. Anim. Sci.* **24**:248.

GREGORY, K. E., BLUNN, C. T. and BAKER, M. L. (1950) A study of some of the factors influencing the birth and weaning weights of beef calves, *J. Anim. Sci.* **9**,338.

GREGORY, K. E., SWIGER, L. A., ARTHAUD, V. H., WARREN, R. B., HALLETT, D. K. and KOCH, R. M. (1962) Relationships among certain live and carcass characteristics of beef cattle, *J. Anim. Sci.* **21**:720.

GREGORY, K. E., SWIGER, L. A., BREIDENSTEIN, B. C., ARTHAUD, V. H., WARREN, R. B. and KOCH, R. M. (1964) Subjective live appraisal of beef carcass traits, *J. Anim. Sci.* **23**:1176.

GREGORY, K. E., SWIGER, L. A., KOCH, R. M., SUMPTION, L. J., ROWDEN, W. W. and INGALLS, J. E. (1965) Heterosis in pre-weaning traits of beef cattle, *J. Anim. Sci.* **24**:21.

GREGORY, K. E., SWIGER, L. A., KOCH, R. M., SUMPTION, L. J., INGALLS, J. E., ROWDEN, W. W. and ROTHLISBURGER, J. A. (1966a) Heterosis effects on growth rate of beef heifers, *J. Anim. Sci.* **25**: 290.

GREGORY, K. E., SWIGER, L. A., SUMPTION, L. J., KOCH, R. M., INGALLS, J. E., ROWDEN, W. W. and ROTHLISBURGER, J. A. (1966b) Heterosis effects on growth rate and feed efficiency of beef steers, *J. Anim. Sci.* **25**:299.

GREGORY, K. E., SWIGER, L. A., SUMPTION, L. J., KOCH, R. M., INGALLS, J. E., ROWDEN, W. W. and ROTHLISBURGER, J. A. (1966c) Heterosis effects on carcass traits of beef steers, *J. Anim. Sci.* **25**:311.

GREGORY, P. W., GUILBERT, H. R., SHELBY, C. E. and CLARK, R. T. (1963) Growth of Hereford cows selected and rejected for breeding, *Growth* **27**:205.

GREIMAN, B. and TAYLOR, B. (1964) Project Circle Bar 1962–3, *Ariz. Agric. Exp. Sta. Cattle Feeders Day*, p. 1.

GRIFFIN, R. M., GILEASON, L. N. and SOHEAL, A. S. (1965) Infectious kerato-conjunctivitis in cattle, *Vet. Rec.* **77**:1056.

GROENWALD, H. (1961) Meat production from dairy breeds—a problem of breeding, *Proc. 8th Int. Congr. Anim. Prod. Hamburg*, **2**:16.

GROSSMAN, J. D. (1949) Form, development and topography of the ox, *J. Am. Vet. Med. Assoc.* **114**:416.

GUEGUEN, L. and MATHIEU, C. M. (1965) Utilization of mineral elements in the rations of calves, 2: Influence of the calcium–phosphorus level, *Ann. Zootech.* **14**:231.

GUENTHER, J. J., BUSHMAN, D. H., POPE, L. S. and MORRISON, R. D. (1965) Growth and development of the major carcass tissues in beef calves from weaning to slaughter weight, with reference to the effect of plane of nutrition, *J. Anim. Sci.* **24**: 1184.

GUENTHER, J. J., POPE, L. S., ODELL, G. V. and MORRISON, R. D. (1962) The growth and development of beef calves from weaning to slaughter weight with reference to the effect of plane of nutrition, Okla. Agric. Exp. Sta. Misc. Publ. MP 67.

GUERREIRO, R. T. C. (1964) Length of gestation in Portuguese Friesian cattle, *Proc. 5th Int. Congr. Anim. Reprod. AI Trento* **3**:470.

GUILBERT, H. R., HART, G. H., WAGNON, K. A. and GROSS, H. (1944) The importance of continuous growth in beef cattle, Calif. Agric. Exp. Sta. Bull. 688.

GUILBERT, H. R., WAHID, A., WAGNON, K. A. and GREGORY, P. W. (1948) Observations on pigmentation of eyelids of Hereford cattle in relation to occurrence of ocular squamous epithelismas, *J. Anim. Sci.* **7**:426.

GUNTHRIE, H. A. and BROWN, M. L. (1968) Effect of severe undernutrition in early life on growth, brain size and composition in adult rats, *J. Nutr.* **94**:419.

GUTIERREZ, J. H., WARNICK, A. C., COWLEY, J. J. and HENTGES, J. F., JR. (1968) Temperature, breed and sex effects on physiology in beef cattle, *J. Anim. Sci.* **27**:301 Abs.

HACKER, R. G., CRUEA, D. D., SHIMODA, W. and HOPWOOD, M. L. (1967) Uptake of diethylstilbestrol by edible plants, *J. Anim. Sci.* **26**:1358.

HAFEZ, E. S. E. (1963) Symposium on growth: physio-genetics of prenatal and postnatal growth, *J. Anim. Sci.* **22**:779.

HAINES, C. E. (1961) Gestation periods for a herd of cattle in Honduras, *Ceiba* **9** (2), 81.

HAINES, C. E. and CHAPMAN, H. L., JR. (1962) Observations on the effectiveness of an injectable tranquilizer administered to weaner stocker beef calves, *J. Anim. Sci.* **21**:387 Abs.

HAINES, C. E. and KOGER, M. (1964) Body temperatures of steers in South Florida, *J. Anim. Sci.* **23**: 298 Abs.

HALE, W. H. (1965) The effect of processing on the feeding value of milo for ruminants, *Proc. Texas Nutr. Conf.*

HALE, W. H. (1967) Effect of moist heat treatment of cereal grains on growth, feed utilization by cattle, *Feedstuffs*, 14 March, p. 29.

HALE, W. H., CUITUN, L., SABA, W. J., TAYLOR, B. and THEURER, B. (1966) Effect of steam processing and flaking milo and barley on performance and digestion by steers, *J. Anim. Sci.* **26**:392.

HALE, W. H., HUBBERT, F., JR., CADENA, M. and TAYLOR, B. (1962) Milo-barley studies with fattening steers, *J. Anim. Sci.* **21**:998 Abs.

HALE, W. H., HUBBERT, F., JR., SABA, W. J., STANLEY, E. B. and TAYLOR, B. (1964a) Fat and protein levels with barley and milo fattening rations, *Ariz. Agric. Exp. Sta. Cattle Feeders Day Rep.*, p. 30.

HALE, W. H., HUBBERT, F., JR. and TAYLOR, B. (1964b) Safflower meal, urea and antibiotic in the ration of fattening steers, *Ariz. Agric. Exp. Sta. Cattle Feeders Day Rep.*, p. 6.

HALE, W. H., SABA, W. J., HUBBERT, F., JR. and TAYLOR, B. (1963) Utilization of milo and barley by steers, *J. Anim. Sci.* **22**: 837 Abs.

HALE, W. H., SHERMAN, W. C., WHITE, E. A., KUHN, G., SCHNELL, R. B., REYNOLDS, W. M. and LUTHER, H. G. (1959) Absorption of diethylstilbestrol pellets in steers, *J. Anim. Sci.* **18**:1201.

HALE, W. H., TAYLOR, B., SABA, W. J., CUITIN, L. and THEURER, B. (1965) Effect of steam processing milo and barley on digestion and performance by steers, *J. Anim. Sci.* **24**: 883 Abs.

HALL, J. L., LATSCHAR, S. E. and MACKINTOSH, D. L. (1944) Characteristics of dark cutting beef: Survey and preliminary investigation, Kans. Agric. Exp. Sta. Tech. Bull. 58.

HALLMAN, L. C., JR. (1966) Performance of calves enrolled in the Pennsylvania Beef Cattle Improvement Program, *Diss. Abstr.* **27**:657.

HAMANN, H. K., WEARDEN, S. and SMITH, W. H. (1963) Estimation of genetic and environmental factors affecting weaning weights of creep fed cattle, *J. Anim. Sci.* **22**:316.

HAMM, R. (1964) The water holding capacity of meat, *Tech. Conf. Carcass Composition and Appraisal in Meat Animals* (ed. de Tribe), CSIRO, Melbourne.

HAMMACK, S. P. and BAILEY, C. M. (1968) Carcass composition and energy utilization of young bulls in Hereford lines, *J. Anim. Sci.* **27**:1126 Abs.

HAMMES, R. C., JR., BLASER, R. E., FONTENOT, J. P., BRYANT, H. T. and ENGEL, R. W. (1968a) Relative value of different forages and supplements for nursing and early weaned beef calves, *J. Anim. Sci.* **27**:509.

HAMMES, R. C., JR., BLASER, R. E., KINCAID, C. M., BRYANT, H. T. and ENGEL, R. W. (1959) Effects of full and restricted winter rations on dams and summer dropped suckling calves fed different rations, *J. Anim. Sci.* **18**:21.

HAMMES, R. C., JR., FONTENOT, J. P., BLASER, R. E. and BRYANT, H. T. (1968b) Efficiency and behaviour related to feeding level of cow and separation from calf, *J. Anim. Sci.* **27**:1133 Abs.

HAMMES, R. C., JR., FONTENOT, J. P., BRYANT, H. T. and BLASER, R. E. (1965) Feeding methods and rations for suckling and early weaned summer calves and their dams, *J. Anim. Sci.* **24**:855 Abs.

HAMMOND, J. (1932) *Growth and Development of Mutton Qualities in the Sheep*, Oliver & Boyd, London.

HAMMOND, J. (1944) Physiological factors affecting birth weight, *Proc. Nutr. Soc.* **2**:8.

HAMMOND, J. (1947) Animal breeding in relation to nutrition and environmental conditions, *Biol. Rev.* **22**:195.

HAMMOND, J. (1952a) *Ann. Nutr. Paris* **6**:119.

HAMMOND, J. (1952b) *Farm Animals: Their Breeding, Growth and Inheritance*, Edward Arnold, London.

HAMMOND, J. (1960) *Growth in Living Systems*, Basic Books, New York.

HAMMOND, J. and MANSFIELD, W. S. (1936) Investigations on producing quality in beef, *J. Min. Agric.* **42**:977.

HANKINS, O. G. and ELLIS, N. R. (1939) Fat in relation to quantity and quality factors of meat animal carcasses, *Proc. Am. Soc. Anim. Prod.* **32**:314.

HANKINS, O. G. and HOWE, P. E. (1946) Estimation of the composition of beef carcasses and cuts, USDA Tech. Bull. 926.

HANKINS, O. G., KNAPP, B, JR. and PHILLIPS, R. W. (1943) The muscle–bone ratio as an index of merit in beef and dual-purpose cattle, *J. Anim. Sci.* **2**:42.

HANSEL, W., MALVERN, P. V. and BLACK, O. L. (1961) Estrous cycle regulation in the bovine, *J. Anim. Sci.* **20**:621.

HANSEN, C. T. (1967) The influence of three feeding regimes on the effectiveness of selection for rate of gain from 3 to 9 weeks of age in the albino rat, *Diss. Abstr.* B, **28**:493.

HANSEN, C. T., CHUNG, C. S. and CHAPMAN, A. B. (1961) Effectiveness of selection in different environments, *J. Anim. Sci.* **20**:906 Ans.

HANSEN, K. R. and ZINN, D. W. (1968) Effect of feeding regime on production and carcass traits of light weight calves, *J. Anim. Sci.* **27**:1133 Abs.

HANSEN, L. H. (1965) Parturition and puerperum in dairy cows crossed with Charolais. Arsbetn. Inst. Sterilitetsforsk. K. Vet. og Landbokojsk. 37.

HANSEN, L. H. (1966) The incidence of dystocia and postparturition disorders in Jersey cattle after crossbreeding with Charolais bulls, *Br. Vet. J.* **122**:273.

HANSEN, T. M., EMBRY, L. B., EMERICK, R. J., WHETZAL, F. W. and NYGAARD, L. J. (1963) Vitamin A and carotene requirements of fattening beef cattle, *J. Anim. Sci.* **22**:1121 Abs.

HANSET, R. (1966) Heritability of duration of gestation in Central and Upper Belgian cattle, *Ann. Med. Vet.* **110**:149.

HARBAUGH, F. G., ELLIS, G. F., DURHAM, R. M. and STOVELL, R. (1963) The effect of certain drugs and rations on ulcer formation and liver abscesses in fattening cattle, *J. Anim. Sci.* **22**:860 Abs.

HARBERS, L. H., TILLMAN, A. D., VISEK, W. J. and GLIMP, H. A. (1965) Some effects of jackbean urease immunity in young calves, *J. Anim. Sci.* **24**:102.

HARDY, F. and NOBLE, I. (1945) A comparison of measurements of juiciness in roast pork loin by press-fluid and jury-rating methods, *Fd Res.* **10**:160.

HARGROVE, D. O., KOGER, M., PEACOCK, F. M., CARPENTER, J. W. and WARNICK, A. C. (1961) Expressions of hybrid vigour in beef calves, *J. Anim. Sci.* **20**:906 Abs.

HARGROVE, D. O., KOGER, M., KIRK, W. G., PEACOCK, F. M., WARNICK, A. C. and CUNHA, T. J. (1959) Appetite, growth rate and feed utilization in Brahman, Shorthorn and crossbred calves, *J. Anim. Sci.* **18**:1472 Abs.

HARPER, O. F., POPE, L. S., STEPHENS, D. F. and WALLER, G. R. (1962) Supplements to all-barley rations for fattening steers, *J. Anim. Sci.* **21**:999 Abs.

HARRICHARAN, H., BRATTON, R. W. and HENDERSON, C. R. (1967) Estimates of some genetic parameters of economic importance in Angus cattle, *J. Anim. Sci.* **26**:875 Abs.

HARRINGTON, G. and KING, J. W. B. (1963) A note on the prediction of muscular tissue weight in sides of beef, *Anim. Prod.* **5**:327.

HARRINGTON, G. and POMEROY, R. W. (1959) The yields of wholesale cuts from carcasses of Aberdeen–Angus crosses fattened on grass and in yards, *J. Agric. Sci.* **53**:64.

HARRIS, A. H. (1962) *Vet. Rec.* **74**:434.

HARRIS, B., JR. (1965) Studies on ruminal parakeratosis in dairy calves, *Diss. Abstr.* **26**:1260.

HARRIS, D. L., GRAHAM, P. P., KELLY, R. F. and JUILLERAT, M. E. (1965) An appraisal of beef characteristics that aid in predicting cutability, *J. Anim. Sci.* **24**:862 Abs.

HARRIS, L. A., FAULKNER, L. L. and STONAKER, H. H. (1960) Effect of inbreeding on the estimated breeding soundness of yearling Hereford bulls, *J. Anim. Sci.* **19**:665.

HARRIS, R. R., YATES, H. F. and BARNETT, J. E. (1967) Refrigerated water in fattening steers, *J. Anim. Sci.* **26**:207 Abs.

HARRIS, V. M. (1968) Economics of guar meal in beef finishing rations. *J. Anim. Sci.* **27**:293 Abs.

HARRISON, H. N., WARNER, R. G. and LOOSLI, J. K. (1957) The retrogression of the rumen of dairy calves following the substitution of milk for a hay-grain diet, *J. Anim. Sci.* **16**:1088 Abs.

HARTE, F. J. (1967) The effects of plane of nutrition in the calf stage on growth rate, feed efficiency, carcass yield and composition, *Anim. Prod.* **9**:284 Abs.

HARTE, F. J. and CONNIFFE, D. (1967) Studies on cattle of varying growth potential for beef production, 1: Growth rate, feed conversion efficiency, carcass yield and offals, *Ir. J. Agric. Res.* **6**:137.

HARTE, F. J. and CURRAN, S. (1967) The production of beef from young bulls, 2, *Ir. J. Agric. Res.* **6**:101.

HARTE, F. J., CURRAN, S. and VIAL, V. E. (1965) The production of beef from young bulls, 1, *Ir. J. Agric. Res.* **4**:189.

HARTMAN, D. A., CORNELISON, R., RAGSDALE, A. C. and BRODY, S. (1956) Effect of temperature on the growth and development of Zebu, Milking Shorthorn and Santa Gertrudis heifers, *J. Anim. Sci.* **15**:1219 Abs.

HARVEY, R. W., WISE, M. B. and BARRICK, E. R. (1965) Influence of roughages and an antibiotic on performance, rumen epithelium and liver abscesses of steers fed an all-concentrate ration, *J. Anim. Sci.* **24**:885 Abs.

HARVEY, R. W., WISE, M. B., BLUMER, T. N. and BARRICK, E. R. (1968) Influence of roughage and chloretetracycline to all-concentrate rations for fattening steers, *J. Anim. Sci.* **27**:1438.

HARVILLE, D. A. and HENDERSON, C. R. (1964) Interrelationships between body size and milk production, *J. Anim. Sci.* **23**:849 Abs.

HARWIN, G. O., BRINKS, J. S. and STONAKER, H. H. (1966) Genetic and environmental interactions affecting weaning weights of Hereford calves, *J. Anim. Sci.* **25**:779.

HARWIN, G. O., STONAKER, H. H. and HAZALEUS, M. H. (1961) Factors associated with marbling in yearling beef carcasses, *J. Anim. Sci.* **20**:674 Abs.

HASBARGEN, P. R. (1968) 71st Ann. Meeting Minn. Vet. Med. Assoc.

HASKINS, B. R., WISE, M. B., CRAIG, H. B. and BARRICK, E. R. (1967) Effects of levels of protein, sources of protein and an antibiotic on performance carcass characteristics, rumen environment and liver abscesses of steers fed all-concentrate rations, *J. Anim. Sci.* **26**:430.

HAWK, H. W., TYLER, W. J. and CASIDA, L. E. (1955) Effect of sire and system of mating on estimated embryonic loss, *J. Dairy Sci.* **38**:420.

HAWKINS, D. R., HENDERSON, H. E. and GEASLER, M. R. (1967a) Melengestrol acetate and stilbestrol for finishing steers and heifer calves, *J. Anim. Sci.* **26**:1480 Abs.

HAWKINS, D. R., HENDERSON, H. E. and GEASLER, M. R. (1967b) Effect of sex and concentrate level on feedlot performance, *J. Anim. Sci.* **26**:1481 Abs.

HAWKINS, D. R., PARKER, C. F., KLOSTERMAN, E. W. and HARVEY, W. R. (1965) Body weight as a measure of productivity of Hereford cows, *J. Anim. Sci.* **24**:848 Abs.

HAYER, W. T. (III), TAYLOR, R. E. and HUBBERT, F., JR. (1961) Apparent digestibility and volatile fatty acids studies with all-barley fattening rations for beef steers, *J. Anim. Sci.* **20**:666 Abs.

HAZEL, L. N. (1943) The genetic basis for construction of selection indexes, *Genetics* **28**:476.

HAZEL, L. N. and KLINE, E. A. (1959) Ultrasonic measurement of fatness in swine. *J. Anim. Sci.* **18**:815.

HAZEL, L. N. and LUSH, J. L. (1942) The efficiency of three methods of selection, *J. Hered.* **33**:393.

HECK, M. C., LEWIS, P. K., JR., BROWN, C. J. and STALLCUP, O. T. (1968) Effect of type and storage on beef, *J. Anim. Sci.* **27**:1140 Abs.

HEDRICK, H. B., BOILLOT, J. B., BRADY, D. E. and NAUMANN, H. D. (1959) Miss. Agric. Exp. Sta. Res. Bull. 717.

HEDRICK, H. B., BOILLOT, J. B., DYER, A. J. and NAUMANN, H. D. (1961) Effect of ante-mortem-administration of adrenaline on post-mortem lamb carcass characteristics, *J. Anim. Sci.* **20**:558.

HEDRICK, H. B., MEYER, W. E., ALEXANDER, M. A., ZOBRISKEY, S. E. and NAUMANN, H. D. (1962) Estimation of ribeye area and fat thickness of beef cattle wilh ultrasonics, *J. Anim. Sci.* **21**:362.

HEDRICK, H. B., MILLER, J. C., THOMPSON, G. B. and FREITAG, R. R. (1965) Factors affecting longissimus dorsi area and fat thickness of beef and relation between these measurements and yield, *J. Anim. Sci.* **24**:333.

HEDRICK, H. B., MILLER, J. C., THOMPSON, G. B. and FREITAG, R. R. (1964) Indices of beef carcass cut-out, *J. Anim. Sci.* **23**:860 Abs.

HEDRICK, H. B., STRINGER, W. C., EPLEY, R. J., ALEXANDER, M. A. and KRAUSE, G. F. (1968) Comparison of factors affecting Warner–Bratzler shear values of beef steaks, *J. Anim. Sci.* **27**:628.

HEIDLER, W. (1966) Results of progeny testing for fattening performance and carcass value in cattle, *Arch. Tierz.* **9**:179.

HEIMAN, M. R. (1968) Trends in some biological characters in an AI cattle population, *Proc. 6th Congr. Reprod. AI Paris*, p. 253.

HEINEMANN, W. W. and FANELLI, H. H. (1963) Some effects of feeding stilbestrol chlortetracycline and penicillin with alfalfa soilage on steer performance and carcass quality, *J. Anim. Sci.* **22**:19.

HEINEMANN, W. W. and KYD, C. R. (1956) The use of diethylstilbestrol with alfalfa soilage for fattening yearling steers, *J. Anim. Sci.* **15**:1302 Abs.

HEINEMANN, W. W. and VAN KEUREN, R. W. (1956) The effect of wintering plane of nutrition on subsequent gains of beef yearling steers on irrigated pastures, *J. Anim. Sci.* **15**:1097.

HEIZER, E. E., HARVEY, M. C., BARRETT, G. R. and BRANDT, G. W. (1938) Nicking in dairy cattle, *Proc. Am. Soc. Anim. Prod.* **67**.

HELSER, M. D., NELSON, P. M. and LOWE, B. (1930) Influence of the animals age upon the quality and palatability of beef, Iowa Agric. Exp. Sta. Bull. 272.

HEMSELY, J. A. and MOIR, R. J. (1963) The influence of higher volatile fatty acids on the intake of urea supplemented low quality cereal hay by sheep, *Aust. J. Agric. Res.* **14**:509.

HENDERICKX, H. and MARTIN, J. (1963) *In vitro* study of the nitrogen metabolism in the rumen, IRSA Monog. 31.

HENDERSON, D. W., GOLL, D. E. and KLINE, E. A. (1966a) Relationships of muscling and finish measurements from three different groups of beef carcasses with carcass yield, *J. Anim. Sci.* **25**:323.

HENDERSON, D. W., GOLL, D. E. and KLINE, E. A. (1966b) Measures of carcass yield and tenderness of two muscles in four groups of beef carcasses, *J. Anim. Sci.* **25**:329.

HENDERSON, D. W., GOLL, D. E., STROMER, M. H., WALTER, M. J., KLINE, E. A. and RUST, R. E. (1966c) Effects of different measurement techniques and operators on bovine longissimus dorsi area, *J. Anim. Sci.* **25**:334.

HENDERSON, H. E. and NEWLAND, H. W. (1966a) Controlled atmosphere and slotted floors for feedlot cattle, *J. Anim. Sci.* **25**:1273 Abs.

HENDERSON, H. E. and NEWLAND, H. W. (1966b) Covered vs partially covered housing for beef cattle, *J. Anim. Sci.* **25**:1273 Abs.

HENDERSON, H. E., WHITEHAIR, C. K. and BROWN, W. K. (1959) Tranquilizer addition to beef fattening rations, Mich. Agric. Exp. Sta. Mimeo. AH 38.

HENDRICKSON, R. F. (1962) Some effects of different planes of nutrition on carcass characteristics of fattening steer calves and relationships among various live animal and carcass measurements, Ph.D. thesis, Okla. State Univ., Stillwater.

Henrickson, R. L. and Mjoseth, J. H. (1964) Tenderness variation in two bovine nuscles, *J. Anim. Sci.* **23**:325.

Henschel, M. J., Hill, W. B. and Porter, J. W. G. (1961) Development of proteolytic enzymes in the abomasum of the young calf, *Proc. Nutr. Soc.* **20**:xl Abs.

Henschel, M. J., Hill, W. B. and Porter, J. W. G. (1963) Carbohydrate digestion in the small intestine of the young steer, *Proc. Nutr. Soc.* **22** v.

Hentges, J. F., Jr., Cabezas, M. T., Capote, F. A., Moore, J. E., Palmer, A. Z. and Carpenter, J. W. (1964) Comparative nutritional value of dried citrus meal and corn for fattening cattle, *J. Anim. Sci.* **23**:294 Abs.

Hentges, J. F., Jr., Cabezas, M. T., Bass, D., Palmer, A. Z. and Carpenter, J. W. (1962) Effect of texture of ration on beef cattle response, *J. Anim. Sci.* **21**:1000 Abs.

Hentges, J. F., Jr., Cabezas, M. T., Palmer, A. Z. and Carpenter, J. W. (1961) Effect of physical form of corn on cattle response, *J. Anim. Sci.* **20**:935 Abs.

Hentges, J. F., Jr., Fletcher, W. D., Black, J. A., Tucker, C. A. and Cunha, T. J. (1960) Diethylstilbestrol and aureomycin for fattening beef cattle, Fla. Agric. Exp. Sta. Bull. 627.

Herd, D. B., Bradley, N. W., Little, C. O. and Overfield, J. R. (1966) Utilization of nitrogen from different sources by beef steers fed ground ear corn rations, *J. Anim. Sci.* **25**:260 Abs.

Hernandez, A. (1965) A study of some reproductive characters in purebred and crossbred cows in Venezuela, *Proc. 5th Int. Congr. Anim. Reprod. AI Trento*, **7**:557.

Herrick, J. B. (1967) Report in *Feedstuffs*, 14 Oct., p. 6.

Herrick, J. B. (1968) Report in *Feedstuffs*, 6 Jan., p. 42.

Herring, H. K., Cassens, R. G. and Briskey, E. J. (1965a) Sarcomere length of free and restrained bovine muscles at low temperature as related to tenderness, *J. Sci. Fd Agric.* **16**:379.

Herring, H. K., Cassens, R. G. and Briskey, E. J. (1965b) Further studies on bovine tenderness as influenced by carcass position, sarcomere length and fiber diameter, *J. Fd. Sci.* **30**:1049.

Heuberger, G. L. (1968) Report in *Feedstuffs*, 6 Jan., p. 33.

Heuberger, G. L., Mitchell, G. E., Jr., Albert, W. W. and Neumann, A. L. (1959) The effect of moisture content of field-shelled corn on harvesting and storage losses and on its feeding value for beef cattle, *J. Anim. Sci.* **18**:1527 Abs.

Hewetson, R. W. and Nolan, G. (1968) Resistance of cattle to cattle tick *Boophilus microplus*, 1: The development of resistance to experimental infestation, *Aust. J. Agric. Res.* **19**:323.

Heyns, H. (1960) The growth of the Afrikaner calf in relation to the production and composition of the milk of its dam, 2: The milk production of the dam and growth of the calf, *S. Afr. J. Agric.* **3**:517.

Hibbs, J. W., Conrad, H. R. and Pounden, W. D. (1954) A high roughage system for raising calves based on the early development of rumen function, 5: Some effects of feeding aureomycin with different ratios of hay to grain, *J. Dairy Sci.* **37**:724.

Hibbs, J. W., Conrad, H. R., Pounden, W. D. and Frank, N. (1956) A high roughage system for raising calves based on the early development of rumen function, 4: Influence of hay to grain ratio on calf performance, rumen development and certain blood changes, *J. Dairy Sci.* **39**:171.

Hibbs, J. W., Pounden, W. D. and Conrad, H. R. (1953) A high roughage system for raising calves based on the early development of rumen function. 1. Effect of variations in the ration on growth, feed consumption and utilization, *J. Dairy Sci.* **36**:717.

Hicks, B. J. and Hazel, L. N. (1965) Predicting retail value of beef carcasses from component parts, *J. Anim. Sci.* **24**:863 Abs.

Hidiroglou, M., Carman, G. M., Bernard, L., Jordan, W. A. and Charette, L. A. (1966) Comparative growth rates of Shorthorn and crossbred beef calves from birth to one year of age, *Can. J. Anim. Sci.* **46**:217.

Hidiroglou, M., Charette, L. A. and Patterson, J. S. (1964) A comparison of growth and carcass characteristics of purebred Shorthorn and crossbred beef steers, *Can. J. Anim. Sci.* **44**:249.

High, J. W., Smith, H. J. and Hobbs, C. S. (1959) Relationship of 120-day and weaning daily gains of beef calves, *J. Anim. Sci.* **18**:1149 Abs.

Hill, F. (1966a) Chemical composition of muscles from hexoestrol-treated steers, *Agric. Fd Chem.* **14**: 179.

Hill, F. (1966b) Solubility of intramuscular collagen in meat animals of various ages, *J. Fd Sci.* **31**: 161.

HILL, F. (1967) The chemical composition of muscles from steers which experienced compensatory growth, *J. Sci. Fd Agric.* **18**:164.

HILL, J. R., JR., LEGATES, J. E. and DILLARD, E. U. (1966) Inheritance of maternal effects in beef cattle, *J. Anim. Sci.* **25**:264 Abs.

HILLERS, J., FERYN, R. and BERRY, B. (1968) Comparing three methods of measuring loin–eye area, *J. Anim. Sci.* **27**:1107 Abs.

HILLIER, R. J., PERRY, T. W. and BEESON, W. M. (1965) Timed-interval feeding predominantly corn silage diets to beef steers, *J. Anim. Sci.* **24**:886 Abs.

HINDS, F. C., KLEIS, R. W., ALBERT, W. W. and NEUMANN, A. L. (1956) Comparison of three methods of grinding corn for beef steers, *J. Anim. Sci.* **15**:1237 Abs.

HINER, R. L., ANDERSON, E. E. and FELLERS, C. R. (1955) Amount and character of connective tissue as it relates to tenderness of beef muscle, *Fd Technol.* **9**:80.

HINER, R. L. and HANKINS, O. G. (1950) The tenderness of beef in relation to different muscles and age in the animal, *J. Anim. Sci.* **9**:347.

HINER, R. L., HANKINS, O. G., SLOANE, H. S., FELLERS, C. R. and ANDERSON, E. E. (1953) Fiber diameter in relation to tenderness of beef muscle, *Fd Res.* **18**:364.

HODGES, J. (1960) *Visit to Israel: A Report on Dairying*, MMB, Thames Ditton.

HODGES, J., O'CONNOR, L. K. and HIGGIN, R. (1961) The growth and size of Friesian cattle on commercial farms in England, *Proc. 8th Int. Congr. Anim. Prod. Hamburg* **2**:30.

HODGSON, J. (1967) The effect of group size on the behaviour and performance of calves reared on automatic feeding machines, *Anim. Prod.* **9**: 268 Abs.

HOERLEIN, A. B., SAXENA, S. P. and MANSFIELD, M. E. (1961) Studies on shipping fever of cattle, 2: Prevalence of pasturella species in nasal secretions from normal calves and calves with shipping fever, *Am. J. Vet. Res.* **22**:470.

HOFFMAN, E. W., BOGART, R. and BURRIS, M. J. (1952) Corn, barley and bone-meal for fattening cattle rations, Oreg. Agric. Exp. Sta. Bull. 528.

HOGAN, A. G. (1929) Retarded growth and mature size of beef steers, Mo. Agric. Exp. Sta. Bull. 123.

HOGUE, D. E., WARNER, R. G., LOOSLI, J. K. and GRIPPEN, C. H. (1957) Comparison of antibiotics for dairy calves on two levels of milk feeding, *J. Dairy Sci.* **40**:1072.

HOHENBOKEN, W. D. and BRINKS, J. S. (1968) Effect of environmental corrections on repeatability of weaning weight in Angus, *J. Anim. Sci.* **27**:1126 Abs.

HOLLAND, L. A. and KNOX, J. H. (1967) Vaginal prolapse in Hereford cows, *J. Anim. Sci.* **26**:885 Abs.

HOLTZ, E. W., ERB, R. E. and HODGSON, A. J. (1961) Relationship between rate of gain from birth to six months of age and subsequent yields of dairy cows, *J. Dairy Sci.* **44**:672.

HOMB, T. (1959) Experiments on stilbestrol supplements in feeding young bulls for beef production, *Norges Landbrukskogskole.* **89** (2), 1.

HOORNBEEK, F. K. and BOGART, R. R. (1966) Amount of selection applied and response of traits in four inbred lines of beef cattle, Oreg. Agric. Esp. Sta. Tech. Bull. 96.

HOOVER, C. D., CHAMBERS, D., WHATLEY, J. A., JR. and STEPHENS, D. F. (1956) Productivity of beef cows as appraised by calf weights at 112 or 210 days of age, *J. Anim. Sci.* **15**:1224 Abs.

HORNSTEIN, I. and CROWE, P. F. (1964) Meat flavour—review, *J. Gas. Chromatog.* **2**:128.

HORNSTEIN, I., CROWE, P. F. and SULZBACHER, W. L. (1960) Constituents of meat flavour: beef, *Agric. Fd. Chem.* **8**:65.

HORNSTEIN, I., CROWE, P. F. and SULZBACHER, W. L. (1963) Flavour of beef and whale meat, *Nature* **199**:1252.

HORROCKS, D., BURT, A. W. A., THOMAS, D. C. and LANCASTER, M. C. (1965) Effects of groundnut meal containing aflotoxin in cattle diets, *Anim. Prod.* **7**:253.

HOSHINO, S., SARUMARU, K. and MORIMATO, K. (1966) Ammonia anabolism in ruminants, *J. Dairy Sci.* **49**:1523.

HOSTETLER, E. H., FOSTER, J. E. and HANKINS, O. G. (1936) Production and quality of meat from native and grade yearling cattle, SC Agric. Exp. Sta. Bull. 307.

HOUPT, T. R. (1959) Utilization of blood urea in ruminants, *Am. J. Physiol.* **197**:115.

HOVELL, F. D. (1964) The utilization of acetic and propionic acid salts by growing lambs, *Anim. Prod.* **6**:261.

HOWARD, A. (1964a) The relation between physiological stress and meat quality, *Tech. Conf. Carcass Composition and Appraisal of Meat Animals* (ed. D. E. Tribe) CSIRO, Melbourne.

HOWARD, A. (1964b) The place of the taste panel in quality assessment, *Tech. Conf. Carcass Composition and Appraisal of Meat Animals* (ed. D. E. Tribe), CSIRO, Melbourne.

HOWARD, A. and LAWRIE, R. A. (1957a) Studies on beef quality, IV: The effect of combining blast freezing of hot beef quarters with pre-slaughter injections of magnesium sulphate, DSIR, Food Investig. Special Rep. 64, London.

HOWARD, A. and LAWRIE, R. A. (1957b) Studies on beef quality, V: Further observations on biochemical and physiological responses to preslaughter treatments, DSIR. Food Investig. Special Rep. 65, London.

HOWES, J. R., HENTGES, J. F., JR. and DAVIES, G. K. (1963) Comparative digestive powers of Hereford and Brahman cattle, *J. Anim. Sci.* **22**:22.

HOWES, J. R., HENTGES, J. F., WARNICK, A. C. and CUHNA, T. J. (1958) Yield and composition of milk from Brahman and Hereford heifers fed two levels of protein and the correlated calf growth, *J. Anim. Sci.* **17**:1222 Abs.

HUBBERT, F., JR., HALE, W. H. and TAYLER, B. (1962a) Influence of high levels of vitamin A on performance and carcass characteristics of fattening cattle, *J. Anim. Sci.* **21**:1000 Abs.

HUBBERT, F., JR., HOFFMAN, E. N., SAWYER, W. A., BOGART, R. and OLIVER, A. W. (1955) A comparison of Brahman × Hereford crossbreeds with Herefords, Oreg. Agric. Exp. Sta. Bull. 549.

HUBBERT, F., JR., TAYLER, B., HALE, W. H., CAREY, W. C. and STANLEY, E. B. (1962b) *Ariz. Agric. Exp. Sta. Cattle Feeders Day Rep.*

HUBBERT, F., JR., TAYLER, B., STANLEY, E. B., HALE, W. H. and KUHN, J. (1961) Factors influencing tallow utilization in Arizona feedlot rations, *J. Anim. Sci.* **20**:669 Abs.

HUBER, J. T. (1966) Lactic acid metabolism in sheep, *J. Anim. Sci.* **25**:1276 Abs.

HUBER, J. T., JACOBSON, N. L., ALLEN, R. S. and HARTMAN, P. A. (1961a) Digestive enzyme activities in the young calf, *J. Dairy Sci.* **44**:1494.

HUBER, J. T., JACOBSON, N. L., MCGILLIARD, A. D. and ALLEN, R. S. (1961b) Utilization of carbohydrates introduced directly into the omasalabomasal area of the stomach of cattle of various ages, *J. Dairy Sci.* **44**:321.

HUBER, J. T., JACOBSON, N. L., MCGILLIARD, A. D., MORRILL, J. L. and ALLEN, R. S. (1961c) Digestibilities and diurnal excretion patterns of several carbohydrates fed to calves by nipple pail, *J. Dairy Sci.* **44**:1484.

HUBER, J. T., NATRAJAN, S. and POLAN, C. E. (1967) Adaptation to starch in steers fed by nipple pail, *J. Dairy Sci.* **50**:1161.

HUBER, J. T., RIFKIN, R. J., KEITH, J. M. and GRAF, G. C. (1962) Effect of lactose level on intestinal lactase activity in the young calf *J. Anim. Sci.* **21**:1000 Abs.

HUDSON, L. W., GLIMP, H. A. and LITTLE, C. O. (1967) Effect of level and solubility of protein on young lamb performance, *J. Anim. Sci.* **26**:221, Abs.

HUFFMAN, C. F. (1928) Hay is necessary in rations of dairy cattle; unknown factor present in hay needed to maintain health of dairy cattle, Mich. Exp. Sta. Quart. Bull. **11** (1), 3.

HUFFMAN, D. L., PALMER, A. Z., CARPENTER, J. W. and ALSMEYER, R. H. (1960) Effect of antemortem injection of enzymes on the tenderness of beef cattle, *J. Anim. Sci.* **19**:1236 Abs.

HUFFMAN, D. L., PALMER, A. Z., CARPENTER, J. W., HARGROVE, D. D. and KOGER, M. (1962) Effect of breeding, level of feeding and ante-mortem injection of papain on the tenderness of weanling age calves, *J. Anim. Sci.* **21**:381 Abs.

HUFFMAN, D. L., PALMER, A. Z., CARPENTER, J. W., HARGROVE, D. D. and KOGER, M. (1967a) Effect of breeding, level of feeding and ante-mortem injection of papain on the tenderness of weanling calves, *J. Anim. Sci.* **26**:290.

HUFFMAN, D. L., PALMER, A. Z., CARPENTER, J. W., HENTGES, J. F., JR. and SHIRLEY, R. L. (1967b) Effect of ante-mortem injection of sodium chloride, papain and papain derivatives on the tenderness of beef, *J. Anim. Sci.* **26**:285.

HULL, J. L., MEYER, J. H. and KROMANN, R. (1961) Influences of stocking rate on animal and forage production from irrigated pasture, *J. Anim. Sci.* **20**:46.

HUNGATE, R. E. (1965) Quantitative aspects of the rumen fermentation, in *Physiology of Digestion in the Ruminant* (ed. R. W. Dougherty), Butterworths, Washington.

HUNGATE, R. E. (1966) *The Rumen and its Microbes*, Academic Press, New York.

HUNGATE, R. E., DOUGHERTY, R. W., BRYANT, M. P. and CELLO, R. M. (1952) Microbiological and physiological changes associated with acute indigestion in sheep, *Cornell Vet.* **42**:423.

HUNSLEY, R. (1967) *Iowa State Univ. 49th Ann. Cattle Feeders Day.*

HUNSLEY, R. E., VETTER, R. L. and BURROUGHS, W. (1967a) Effects of creep feeding and diethylstilbestrol implants on pre-weaning performance of male beef calves, *J. Anim. Sci.* **26**:1482 Abs.

HUNSLEY, R. E., VETTER, R. L., KLINE, E. A. and BURROUGHS, W. (1967b) Effects of age and sex on quality, tenderness and collagen content of bovine longissimus dorsi muscle, *J. Anim. Sci.* **26**:1469 Abs.

HUNSLEY, R. E., VETTER, R. L., KLINE, E. A. and BURROUGHS, W. (1967c) Effects of age, sex and diethylstilbestrol on feedlot performance, carcass characteristics and muscle tenderness of male beef cattle, *J. Anim. Sci.* **26**: 1469 Abs.

HUNTER, R. S. (1948) Photo-electric colour difference meter, *J. Optical Soc. Am.* **38**:661.

HURST, V. and GODLEY, W. C. (1965) Reproduction in beef cattle, S. C. Agric. Exp. Sta. Bull. 144.

HUSAINI, S. A., DEATHERAGE, F. E., KUNKLE, L. E. and DROUDT, H. N. (1950a) Studies on meat, 1: The biochemistry of meat as related to tenderness, *Fd Technol.* **4**:313.

HUSAINI, S. A., DEATHERAGE, F. E. and KUNKLE, L. E. (1950b) Studies on meat, 11: Observations on relation of biochemical factors in changes in tenderness, *Fd Technol.* **4**:366.

HUSTED, W. T., HALE, W. H. and THEURER, B. (1966) Effect of various processing methods on milo digestion by steers, *J. Anim. Sci.* **25**:903 Abs.

HUTCHINSON, J. and STEPHENS, A. L. (1959) The planning of a large farm for the Namulonge Cotton Research Station in Uganda: The establishment and improvement of a herd of Nganda cattle, *Emp. Cott. Grow. Rev.* **36**:112.

HYLDGAARD, J. and SIMESEN, M. G. (1966) Overeating of grain in cattle, *Nord Vet. Med.* **18**:73.

ICA (1966) *Informe anual.*, Inst. Cienc. Anim. Havana, Cuba.

ICA (1967) *Annual Report*, Inst. Cienc. Anim. Havana, Cuba.

IIE (*1966*) *Open doors* 1966, Report of International Exchange, Inst. Inter. Education.

ILLÉS, A. and GODÉNY, V. (1967) Effect of warmed drinking water on weight gains in young cattle, *Állattenyésztés* **16**:341.

INSKEEP, E. K., TYLER, W. J. and CASIDA, L. E. (1961) Hereditary variation in conception rate of Holstein Friesian cattle, *J. Dairy Sci.* **44**:1857.

INGRAM, P. L. (1962) Observations on the pathology and parthogenesis of experimental Colibacillosis in calves, Ph.D. thesis, Univ. London.

INGRAM, P. L., LOVELL, R., WOOD, P. C., ASCHAFFENBURG, R., BARTLETT, S., KON, S. K., PALMER, J., ROY, J. H. B. and SHILLAM, K. G. (1956) *Bacterium coli* antibodies in colostrum and their relation to calf survival, *J. Path. Bact.* **72**:561.

ISAKOV, D. (1961) Influence of housing system and castration on gaining ability and feed efficiency in fattening young cattle, *Savremena poljopr.* **1**:1247.

ISAKOV, D. and OGNJANOVIC, A. (1964) Fattening young steers on concentrated pelleted mixture, *Savremena poljopr.* **4**:269.

ITTNER, N. R., BOND, J. E. and KELLY, C. F. (1958) Environment comparison and cattle gains in wood and iron corrals, *J. Anim. Sci.* **14**:818.

ITTNER, N. R., KELLY, C. F. and BOND, J. E. (1957) Cooling cattle by mechanically increasing air movements, *J. Anim. Sci.* **16**:732.

IVANOV, P., VANKOV, K. and ALEKSIEV, A. (1966) Comparative experiment to establish the optimum live weight for intensively fattened bulls and steers, *Zhivor. Nauk* **3**:93.

IVANOV, P. and ZAHARIEV, Z. I. (1964) Intensive fattening of Kula bull calves and steers, *Nauchnii Trud. virsh selskostop. Inst. Georgi Dimitrov. zootech. Fak.* **14**:9.

IWANAGA, I. I. and COBB, E. H. (1963) Relationship between yield of trimmed retail cuts and certain carcass characteristics of beef cattle, *J. Anim. Sci.* **22**:827 Abs.

JACKSON, D. S. and BENTLEY, J. P. (1960) On the significance of the extractable collagens, *J. Biophys. Biochem. Cytol.* **7**:37.

JACKSON, F. C. (1953) *Am. J. Vet. Res.* **14**:19.

JACOBSEN, M. and FENTON, F. (1956) Effects of three levels of nutrition and age of animals on quality of beef, 1: Palatability, cooking data, moisture, fat and nitrogen, *Fd. Res.* **21**:415.

JAFAR, S. M., CHAPMAN, A. B. and CASIDA, L. E. (1950) Causes of variation in length of gestation in dairy cattle, *J. Anim. Sci.* **9**:593.

JAHN, H. (1963) Investigations on oestrous interval in cattle with reference to early embryonic death, Vet. med. Diss. Tierurztl. Hochsch. Hannover.

JAKOBSEN, P. E. (1957) Protein requirements and protein synthesis during growth of the foetus in ruminants, Forsøgslab. Kobenhavn, Beretn. No. 299.

JAMISON, H. M., CHRISTIAN, L. L., TEMPLE, R. S. and BUTTS, W. T., JR. (1965) Factors affecting variations in intra-cow production in beef cattle, *J. Anim. Sci.* **24**:287 Abs.

JENSEN, R., DEANE, H. M., COOPER, L. J., MILLER, V. A. and GRAHAM, W. R. (1954a) The rumenitis-liver abscess complex in beef cattle, *Am. J. Vet. Res.* **15**:202.

JENSEN, R., CONNELL, W. E. and DEEM, A. W. (1954b) Rumenitis and its relation to rate of change of ration and the proportion of concentrates in the ration of cattle, *J. Am. J. Vet. Res.* **15**:425.

JENSEN, R., FLINT, J. C., UDALL, R. H., DEEM, A. W. and SEGAR, C. L. (1958) Parakeratosis of the rumens of lambs fattened on pelleted feed. *Am. J. Vet. Res.* **19**:277.

JENSEN, R. and MACKEY, D. R. (1965) *Diseases of Feedlot Cattle*, Lea & Febiger, Philadelphia.

JILEK, A. F., BURNS, W. C., KOGER, M. and BUTTS, W. T. (1968) Sire by breed of dam interaction in cattle, *J. Anim. Sci.* **27**:1127 Abs.

JOBST, D. (1963) Visit to France, Charolais cattle and beef production, Milk Marketing Board, mimeo.

JOBST, D. (1968) *Farmer & Stockbreeder*, 6th Aug., p. 26.

JOHANSSON, I. (1953) The manifestation and heritability of quantitative characters in dairy cattle under different environmental conditions, *Acta genet. Statist. med.* **4**:221.

JOHANSSON, I. (1964) The relation between body size, conformation and milk yield in dairy cattle, *Anim. Breed Abst.* **32**:421.

JOHNSON, B. C., HAMILTON, T. S., MITCHELL, H. H. and ROBINSON, W. B. (1942) *J. Anim. Sci.* **1**:236.

JOHNSON, D., JR., DOLGE, K. L., ROUSSEAU, J. E., JR., TEICHMAN, R. and EATON, H. D. (1956) Effect of addition of inedible tallow to a calf starter fed to Holstein calves, *J. Dairy Sci.* **39**:1268.

JOHNSON, D. E., MATSUSHIMA, J. K. and KNOX, K. L. (1968) Utilization of flaked vs. cracked corn by steers with observations on starch modification, *J. Anim. Sci.* **27**:1431.

JOHNSON, H. D. (1964) Environmental physiology and shelter engineering with special references to domestic animals, No. 68: Age and temperature effects on TDN water consumption and balance on dairy cows and heifers exposed to environmental temperatures of 35° to 95°F, Mo. Agric. Exp. Sta. Res. Bull. 865.

JOHNSON, H. D., KIBLER, H. H. and RAGSDALE, A. C. (1959) Efficiency of weight gains in dairy cattle during growth at 50° and 80°F, *J. Anim. Sci.* **18**:1561.

JOHNSON, H. D., KIBLER, H. H., RAGSDALE, A. C., BERRY, I. L. and SHANKLIN, M. D. (1961) The role of heat tolerance and production level in responses of lactating Holsteins to different conditions of temperature and humidity, *J. Dairy Sci.* **44**:1191 Abs.

JOHNSON, K. R., ROSS, R. H. and FOURT, D. L. (1958) Effect of progesterone administration on reproductive efficiency, *J. Anim. Sci.* **17**:386.

JOHNSON, L. A., BARTLETT, J. W. and COPELAND, L. (1940) A study of nicking in Jersey cattle, *J. Dairy Sci.* **23**:707.

JOHNSON, L. E. and DINKEL, C. A. (1951) Correction factors for adjusting weaning weights of range calves to the constant age of 196 days, *J. Anim. Sci.* **10**:371.

JOHNSON, L. E., HARSHFIELD, G. S. and MCCONE, W. (1950) Dwarfism, an hereditary defect in cattle, *J. Hered.* **41**:141.

JOHNSON, L. J., JOHNSON, R. R., KLOSTERMAN, E. W. and MCCLURE, K. E. (1963) Digestive functions and individual variation in gain and efficiency of steers, *J. Am. Sci.* **22**:1123 Abs.

JOHNSON, L. J., JOHNSON, R. R., KLOSTERMAN, E. W. and MCCLURE, K. E. (1965) Rumen VFA variability and performance in growing beef cattle, *J. Anim. Sci.* **24**:889 Abs.

JOHNSON, R. J. and DYER, I. A. (1965) Hepatic monoamine oxidase activity of the bloater animal, *J. Anim. Sci.* **24**:889 Abs.

JOHNSON, R. R., BENTLEY, O. G. and HERSHBERGER, T. V. (1962) The effectiveness of coated urea prills and copper treated urea prills as nitrogen sources for rumen micro-organisms, Ohio Agric. Exp. Sta. Res. Bull. **917**.

Johnston, J. E., Hamblin, F. B. and Schrader, G. T. (1958) Factors concerned in the comparative heat tolerance of Jersey, Holstein and Red Sindhi-Holstein F_1 cattle, *J. Anim. Sci.* **17**:473.

Johnston, J. E., Naelapaa, H. and Frye, J. B., Jr (1963) Physiological responses of Holstein, Brown Swiss and Red Sindhi crossbred bulls exposed to high temperatures and humidities, *J. Anim. Sci.* **22**:432.

Jones, B. M., Bradley, N. W. and Grainger, R. B. (1961) Effect of fat and urea in fattening rations for beef steers, *J. Anim. Sci.* **20**:396 Abs.

Jones, E. L. and Francis, A. L. (1963) A performance test of beef bulls *Exp. Husb.* (*Lond.*) **9**:52.

Jones, J. H., Logan, D. S. and Lyerly, P. J. (1955) Unpublished data cited by Butler *et al.*, 1956a.

Jones, J. M., Jones, J. H., Keating, F. E., Ellis, N. R. and Clark, R. T. (1951) The effect of bone-meal and limestone with low and high amounts of cottonseed meal in fattening rations for weanling steer calves, Tex. Agr. Exp. Sta. Rep. 1407.

Jones, J. R., Hogue, D. E. and Hunt, G. L. (1958) Effect of energy level on protein requirements of lambs fattened with or without stilbestrol, *J. Anim. Sci.* **17**:1171 Abs.

Jones, K. B. (1968) Charolais vs. Devon and Hereford for meat quality, *Expt. Husb.* (*Lond.*) **16**:25.

Jones, K. B., Harries, J. M. and Houston, T. W. (1964a) Studies on beef quality, 3: Effects of hexoestrol implantation, *J. Sci. Fd Agric.* **15**:62.

Jones, K. B., Harries, J. M., Robertson, J. and Akers, J. M. (1964b) Studies in beef quality, 4: A comparison of the eating quality of meat from bulls and steers, *J. Sci. Fd Agric.* **14**:501.

Jones, L. E., Clanton, D. C., Zimmerman, D. R., Tribble, R. L. and Christenson R. K., (1966) Grass hay vs. corn as energy for wintering beef cows, *J. Anim. Sci.* **25**:599 Abs.

Joubert, D. M. (1954a) Influence of winter nutritional depression on the growth, reproduction and production of cattle, *J. Agric. Sci.* **44**:5.

Joubert, D. M. (1954b) The influence of high and low nutritional planes on the oestrus cycle and conception rate of heifers, *J. Agric. Sci.* **45**:164.

Joubert, D. M. (1956a) An analysis of factors influencing post-natal growth and development of the muscle fiber, *J. Agric. Sci.* **47**:59.

Joubert, D. M. (1956b) Relation between body size and muscle-fibre diameter in the newborn lamb, *J. Agric. Sci.* **47**:449.

Joubert, D. M. (1957) On reproduction and growth in the South Devon breed, *Sth. Dev. Herd Breed Soc. Ann.* **11**:1.

Joubert, D. M. (1961) Duration of pregnancy of South African Friesland cattle, *S. Afr. J. Agric. Sci.* **4**:467.

Joubert, D. M. and Bonsma, F. N. (1957) The effect of nutrition on the birth weight of calves, *Sci. Bull. Dep. Agric. S. Afr.* **371**.

Joubert, D. M. and Hammond, J. (1958) A crossbreeding experiment with cattle with special reference to the maternal effect in South Devon Dexter crosses, *J. Agric. Sci.* **51**:325.

Judge, M. D., Martin, T. G., Bramblett, V. D. and Barton, J. A. (1965) Comparison of dairy and dual purpose carcasses with beef-type carcasses from animals of similar and younger ages, *J. Dairy Sci.* **48**:509.

Juhasz, B. (1965) Endogenous nitrogen cycle in ruminants, *Acta Vet. hung.* **15**:25.

Kail, I. J., Amir, S. and Bleiberg, G. M. (1968) Influence of the level of crude fibre in the ration of dairy cows on conception, *J. Dairy Sci.* **51**:954.

Kaltenbach, C. C. and Wiltbank, J. N. (1962) Heterotic effects on age and weight at puberty in beef heifers, *J. Anim. Sci.* **21**:662 Abs.

Kannan, A. and Jeness, R. (1961) *J. Dairy Sci.* **44**:808.

Karr, M. R. and Hodge, D. E. (1968) Oyster shell as roughage for finishing cattle, *J. Anim. Sci.* **27**:1166 Abs.

Karr, M. R., Little, C. O. and Mitchell, G. E. (1966) Starch disappearance from different segments of the digestive tract of steers, *J. Anim. Sci.* **25**:654.

KASPAR, A. and WILLIS, M. B. (1968) Rate of gain of different beef breeds and crosses on supplemented pasture in Cuba, *Rev. cubana Cienc. Agric.* (Eng. ed.), **2**:253.

KASTELIC, J., BENTLEY, O. G. and PHILLIPS, P. H. (1950) *J. Dairy Sci.* **33**:725.

KASTELIC, J., HOMEYER, P. and KLINE, E. A. (1956) The influence of oral administration of diethylstilboestrol on certain carcass characteristics of beef cattle, *J. Anim. Sci.* **15**:689.

KAUFFMAN, R. G. (1961) Ph.D. thesis, Univ. of Wisconsin.

KAUFFMAN, R. G., SUESS, G. G., BRAY, R. W. and SCARTH, R. D. (1968) Incidence of marbling of the bovine and porcine longissimus, *J. Anim. Sci.* **27**:969.

KAY, M., BOWERS, H. B. and MCKIDDIE, G. (1968) The protein requirements of rapidly growing steers, *Anim. Prod.* **10**:37.

KAY, M., MACLEOD, N. A., MCKIDDIE, G. and PHILIP, E. B. (1967) The nutrition of the early weaned calf, X: The effect of replacement of fish meal with either urea or ammonium acetate on growth rate and nitrogen retention in calves fed *ad libitum*, *Anim. Prod.* **9**:197.

KAY, M., PRESTON, T. R., MACLEOD, N. A. and PHILIP, E. B. (1966a) Intensive beef production, 7: The effect on nitrogen retention of diets containing barley processed by four different methods, *Anim. Prod.* **8**:39.

KAY, M., PRESTON, T. R., MACLEOD, N. A. and PHILIP, E. B. (1966b) Nutrition of the early weaned calf, 9: Nitrogen retention from different protein sources in calves fed *ad libitum*, *Anim. Prod.* **8**:43.

KAY, R. N. B. (1966) The influence of saliva on digestion in ruminants, *Wld Rev. Nutr. Diet.* **6**:292.

KEARL, L. C., BUTCHER, J. E. and HARRIS, L. E. (1965) Effects of protein and shelter on finishing cattle, *J. Anim. Sci.* **24**:856.

KEITH, T. B., DAHMEN, J. J. and BELL, T. D. (1965) Diethylstilbestrol in steer-finishing rations as affected by level of protein intake, Idaho Agric. Exp. Sta. Res. Bull. 68.

KEITH, T. B., JOHNSON, R. J. and LEHRER, W. P. (1955) Optimum ratio of concentrate and roughage for steers as affected by corn silage and protein level, Idaho Agric. Exp. Sta. Res. Bull. 32.

KELLY, R. F., FONTENOT, J. P., GRAHAM, P. P., WILKINSON, W. S. and KINCAID, C. M. (1968) Estimates of carcass composition of beef cattle fed at different planes of nutrition, *J. Anim. Sci.* **27**:620.

KELLY, R. F., GRAHAM, P. P. and FONTENOT, J. P. (1963) Effects of protein level of steer fattening rations, 11: Composition, cooking characteristics and taste panel evaluation of the meat, *J. Anim. Sci.* **22**:247 Abs.

KEMPTHORNE, O. and TANDON, O. B. (1953) The estimation of heritability by the regression of offspring on parent, *Biometrics* **9**:90.

KENNEDY, W. J., DINSMORE, W., RUTHERFORD, W. J. and SMITH, W. W. (1903) Experiment in beef production—beef type versus dairy type, Ia. Agr. Exp. Sta. Bull. 81.

KENNICK, W. H. and ENGLAND, D. C. (1960) A method of estimating the percentage of protein and fat in the edible portion of steer carcasses, *J. Anim. Sci.* **19**:1190.

KENNICK, W. H., ENGLAND, D. C. and ANGLEMIER, A. F. (1963) Method of estimating percent of protein and fat in the boneless portion of steer carcasses, *J. Anim. Sci.* **22**:989.

KENNICK, W. H., ENGLAND, D. C. and SATHER, L. A. (1961a) A comparison of the organoleptic scores and cooking losses of fresh frozen and frozen stored beef rib-roasts as affected by implanted hormones, *J. Anim. Sci.* **20**:674 Abs.

KENNICK, W. H., ENGLAND, D. C. and SATHER, L. A. (1961b) The effect of implanted hormones on cooking losses and organoleptic scores of fresh frozen beef rib roasts, *J. Anim. Sci.* **20**:674 Abs.

KENNICK, W. H., WALLACE, J. D., RALEIGH, R. G. and SATHER, L. A. (1965) A comparison of carcass and meat characteristics of Hereford and Hereford Charolais steers, *J. Anim. Sci.* **24**:587 Abs.

KERCHER, C. J. (1959) The use of tranquilizers for fat beef cattle going to slaughter, *J. Anim. Sci.* **18**:1172.

KERCHER, C. J. (1960a) Tranquilizers for fat beef cattle going to slaughter, *J. Anim. Sci.* **19**:964.

KERCHER, C. J. (1960b) Value of diallylstilbestrol and zymo-Pabst enzyme preparation for fattening yearling steers, *J. Anim. Sci.* **19**:966 Abs.

KERCHER, C. J. and BISHOP, D. V. (1963) The influence of all-concentrate feeding on the growth and carcass characteristics of beef cattle, *J. Anim. Sci.* **22**:839 Abs.

KERCHER, C. J. and PAULES, L. H. (1968a) Conditioning of beef calves, *J. Anim. Sci.* **27**:1112 Abs.

KERCHER, C. J. and PAULES, L. (1968b) Urea and phosphorus supplements for fattening steers, *J. Anim. Sci.* **27**:1166 Abs.

KERCHER, C. J., SMITH, W. and PAULES, L. (1966) Barley, corn and beet pulp in low fibre rations for fattening cattle, *J. Anim. Sci.* **25**:904.

KERCHER, C. J., STRATTON, P. O., SCHOONOVER, C. O., GORMAN, J. A. and HILSTON, N. W. (1958) A comparison of feedlot performance and carcass value of spayed vs. open heifers, Wyo. Agric. Exp. Sta. Mimeo. Circ. **99**:7.

KIBLER, H. H. (1962) Environmental physiology and shelter engineering with special reference to domestic animals, 61: Energy metabolism and related thermoregulatory reactions to thermal stress in 50° and 80° acclimatized dairy heifers, Mo. Agric. Exp. Sta. Res. Bull. 793.

KIBLER, H. H., JOHNSON, H. D., SHANKLIN, M. D. and HAHN, L. (1965) Environmental physiology and shelter engineering with special reference to domestic animals, 69: Acclimation of Holstein cattle to 84°F (29°C) temperature; changes in heat producing and heat dissipating functions, Miss. Agric. Exp. Sta. Res. Bull. No. 893, p. 28.

KIDDER, H. E., BARRETT, G. K. and CASIDA, L. E. (1952) *J. Dairy Sci.* **35**:436.

KIDDER, R. W., KOGER, M., MEADE, J. H. and CROCHETT, J. R. (1964) Systems of crossbreeding for beef production in Florida, Fla. Agric. Exp. Sta. Bull. 673.

KIDWELL, J. F., HUNTER, J. E., TERNAN, P. R., HARPER, J. E., SHELBY, C. E. and CLARK, R. T. (1959) Relation of production factors to conformation scores and body measurement associations among production factors and the relation of carcass grade and fatness to consumer preferences in yearling steers, *J. Anim. Sci.* **18**:894.

KIDWELL, J. F. and McCORMICK, J. A. (1956) The influence of size and type on growth and development of cattle, *J. Anim. Sci.* **15**:109.

KIDWELL, J. F., McCORMICK, J. A. and McCARTNEY, L. O. (1955) Bull indexing, Univ. Nev. Agric. Exp. Sta. Circ. 6.

KIDWELL, J. F., VERNON, E. M., CROWN, R. M. and SINGLETARY, C. B. (1952) Muscular hypertrophy in cattle, *J. Hered.* **43**:62.

KIEFFER, N. M. (1959) Inheritance of certain maternal traits in beef cattle, Ph.D. thesis, Okla. State Univ., Stillwater.

KIEFFER, N. M., CHAMBERS, D. and STEPHENS, D. F. (1959) Inheritance of certain maternal traits in beef cattle, *J. Anim. Sci.* **18**:1464 Abs.

KIEFFER, N. M., HENDRICKSON, R. L., CHAMBERS, D. and STEPHENS, D. F. (1958) The influence of sire upon some carcass characteristics of Angus steers and heifers, *J. Anim. Sci.* **17**:1137 Abs.

KINCAID, C. M. (1957) Calving percentage in S-10 Experiment Station herds based on a survey of all stations, Rep. of Ann. Meeting of the S-10 Technical Committee, Gainesville, Fla.

KINCAID, C. M. (1962) Breed crosses with beef cattle in the south, Southern Coop. Series Bull. 81.

KINCAID, C. M. and CARTER, R. C. (1958) Estimates of genetic and phenotypic parameters in beef cattle, 1: Heritability of growth rate estimated from response to sire selection, *J. Anim. Sci.* **17**:675.

KING, G. T., BUTLER, O. D. and SIMMS, P. L. (1958) Beef acceptability as rated by a panel of families and the Warner–Bratzler shear, using loin steaks and chuck roasts from cattle of known history, *J. Anim. Sci.* **17**:1152.

KING, G. T., BUTLER, O. D. and WYTHE, L. D., JR. (1959) A new method of cutting beef carcasses to determine accurately the yield of red meat in the carcass, *J. Anim. Sci.* **18**:1479 Abs.

KING, G. T., CARPENTER, Z. L., CUNNINGHAM, N. L. and ORTS, F. A. (1964) Cutability of Santa Gertrudis cow carcasses, *J. Anim. Sci.* **23**:858 Abs.

KING, G. T., LEGG, W. E., CARPENTER, Z. L. and CUNNINGHAM, N. L. (1965) Cutability of bull, heifer and steer carcasses, *J. Anim. Sci.* **24**:291 Abs.

KING, G. T., ORTS, F. A. and BUTLER, O. D. (1968) Factors affecting beef tenderness, *J. Anim. Sci.* **27**:1142 Abs.

KING, J. O. L. (1968) Feeding for fertility in dairy cows, *Farms Wkly*, 5th April, p. 95.

KING, J. W. B. and SMITH, C. (1968) Development of a pig sire line by selection with immigration, *J. Anim. Prod.* **10**:245 Abs.

KING, J. W. B. and YOUNG, G. B. (1955) A study of three breeds of sheep wintered in four environments, *J. Agic. Sci.* **45**:331.

KIRCHNER, V. E., CARPENTER, Z. L. and KING, G. T. (1968) Estimates of beef carcass cutability, *J. Anim. Sci.* **27**:1142 Abs.

KIRTON, A. H. (1964a) Some relations between the potassium and sodium contents of animals and their composition, *Tech. Conf. Carcass Composition and Appraisal of Meat Animals* (ed. D. E. Tribe), CSIRO, Melbourne.

KIRTON, A. H. (1964b) Assessment of body composition in the live animal, *Proc. NZ. Soc. Anim. Prod.* **24**:77.

KIRTON, A. H. and PEARSON, A. M. (1963) Comparison of methods of measuring potassium in pork and lamb and prediction of their composition from sodium and potassium, *J. Anim. Sci.* **22**:125.

KLINE, R. C., SINK, J. D., BEERY, K. E., ZIEGLER, J. H. and WILSON, L. L. (1968) Genetic influences on bovine skeletal muscle properties, *J. Anim. Sci.* **27**:1513 Abs.

KLOPFENSTEIN, T. J., PURSER, D. B. and TYZNIK, W. J. (1966) Effects of defaunation on feed digestibility; rumen metabolism and blood metabolites, *J. Anim. Sci.* **25**:765.

KLOSTERMAN, E. W. (1956) Diethylstilbestrol feeding and implantation, *Proc. Ohio Anim. Nut. Conf.*

KLOSTERMAN, E. W. (1966) Fattening cattle on slatted floors, *Feedstuffs*, 15th Jan., p. 38.

KLOSTERMAN, E. W., BENTLEY, O. G., MOXON, A. L. and KUNKLE, L. E. (1956) Relationships between level of protein, molasses trace minerals and quality of hay in rations for fattening cattle, *J. Anim. Sci.* **15**:456.

KLOSTERMAN, E. W., CAHILL, V. R., KUNKLE, L. E. and MOXON, A. L. (1955) The subcutaneous implantation of stilboestrol in fattening bulls and steers, *J. Anim. Sci.* **14**:1050.

KLOSTERMAN, E. W., CAHILL, V. R., KUNKLE, L. E. and MOXON, A. L. (1958) Influence of sex hormones upon feedlot performance and carcass quality of fattening cattle, Ohio Agr. Exp. Sta. Bull. 802.

KLOSTERMAN, E. W., CAHILL, V. R., PARKER, C. F. and HARVEY, W. R. (1965a) A comparison of the Hereford and Charolais breeds and their crosses under two systems of management, Ohio Agric. Exp. Sta. Res. Summary **7**:22.

KLOSTERMAN, E. W., JOHNSON, L. J. and ROLER, W. L. (1965b) Fattening cattle on steel slatted floors, Ohio Agric. Res. and Dev. Centre Res. Summary **7**:19.

KLOSTERMAN, E. W., KUNKLE, L. E., BENTLEY, O. G. and BURROUGHS, W. (1953) Supplements to poor quality hay for fattening cattle, Ohio Agric. Exp. Sta. Res. Bull. 732.

KLOSTERMAN, E. W., KUNKLE, L. E., GERLAUGH, P. and CAHILL, V. R. (1954) The effect of age of castration upon rate and economy of gain and carcass quality of beef calves, *J. Anim. Sci.* **13**:817.

KLOSTERMAN, E. W., MOXON, A. L. and CAHILL, V. R. (1959) Effect of stilboestrol and amount of corn silage in the ration upon the protein requirement of fattening steer calves, *J. Anim. Sci.* **18**: 1243.

KLOSTERMAN, E. W., SANFORD, L. G. and PARKER, C. F. (1968) Effect of cow size and condition and ration protein content upon maintenance requirements of mature beef cows, *J. Anim. Sci.* **27**:242.

KNAPP, B., BAKER, A. L. and PHILLIPS, R. W. (1943) Variations in the occurrence of bloat in the steer progeny of beef bulls, *J. Anim. Sci.* **2**:221.

KNAPP, B. J., BAKER, A. L., QUESENBERRY, J. R. and CLARK, R. T. (1942) Growth and production factors in range cattle, Mont. Agr. Exp. Sta. Bull. 400.

KNAPP, B., JR. and BLACK, W. H. (1941) Factors influencing rate of gain of beef calves during the suckling period, *J. Agr. Res.* **63**:249.

KNAPP, B., JR. and CLARK, R. T. (1950) Revised estimates of heritability of economic characteristics of beef cattle, *J. Anim. Sci.* **9**:582.

KNAPP, B., JR. and CLARK, R. T. (1951) Genetic and environmental correlation between weaning scores and subsequent gains in the feedlot with record of performance steers, *J. Anim. Sci.* **10**:365.

KNAPP, B., JR., LAMBERT, W. V. and BLACK, W. H. (1940) Factors influencing length of gestation and birth weight in cattle, *J. Agric. Res.* **61**:277.

KNAPP, B., JR. and NORDSKOG, A. W. (1946a) Heritability of growth and efficiency of beef cattle, *J. Anim. Sci.* **5**:62.

KNAPP, B., JR. and NORDSKOG, A. W. (1946b) Heritability of live animal scores grades and certain carcass characteristics in beef cattle, *J. Anim. Sci.* **5**:194.

KNEEBONE, H., MARKS, T., MCMEEKAN, C. P. and WALKER, D. E. (1950) Evaluation of the chiller beef carcass, *NZ J. Sci. Tech.* A, **31** (5), 3.

KNOX, J. H. and KOGER, M. (1945) Effect of age on the weight and production of range cows, N. Mex. Agric. Exp. Sta. Bull. 1004.

KNOX, J. H. and WATKINS, W. E. (1958) Supplements for range cows, N. Mex. Agric. Exp. Sta. Bull. 425.

KNOX, K. L. and WARD, G. M. (1961) Rumen concentrations of volatile fatty acids as affected by feeding frequency, *J. Dairy Sci.* **44:**1550.

KOCH, B. A., McCARTER, M. M., SMITH, E. F. and RICHARDSON, D. (1959a) Tranquilizers (with and without diethylstilboestrol) in beef cattle fattening rations, *J. Anim. Sci.* **18:**1499 Abs.

KOCH, R. M. (1953) Heritability of economic characters in beef cattle, Ph.D. thesis, Iowa Sta. College, Ames.

KOCH, R. M. and CLARK, R. T. (1955a) Influence of sex, season of birth, and age of dam on economic traits in range beef cattle, *J. Anim. Sci.* **14:**386.

KOCH, R. M. and CLARK, R. T. (1955b) Genetic and environmental relationship among economic characters in beef cattle, 1: Correlation among paternal and maternal half-sibs, *J. Anim. Sci.* **14:**775.

KOCH, R. M. and CLARK, R. T. (1955c) Genetic and environmental relationships among economic characters in beef cattle, 2: Correlations between offspring and dam and offspring and sire, *J. Anim. Sci.* **14:**786.

KOCH, R. M., GREGORY, K. E., CUNDIFF, L. V. and DICKERSON, G. E. (1968) Selection response in three lines of Hereford cattle, *J. Anim. Sci.* **27:**1127 Abs.

KOCH, R. M., GREGORY, K. E., INGALLS, J. E. and ARTHAUD, R. L. (1959b) Evaluating the influence of sex on birth weight and preweaning gain in beef cattle, *J. Anim. Sci.* **18:**738.

KOCH, R. M., GREGORY, K. E., INGALLS, J. E. and ARTHAUD, V. H. (1959c) Influence of hormone implants on gains made on native pasture and in the feedlot and on carcass characteristics of yearling steers, *J. Anim. Sci.* **18:**1010.

KOCH, R. M., SWIGER, L. A., CHAMBERS, D. and GREGORY, K. E. (1963) Efficiency of feed use in beef cattle, *J. Anim. Sci.* **22:**486.

KOGER, M. (1968) Personal communication.

KOGER, M., HARGROOVE, D. D., PEACOCK, F. M., CUNHA, T. J. and PALMER, A. Z. (1962a) Feed conversion in straight breed and crossbreed calves, *J. Anim. Sci.* **21:**973 Abs.

KOGER, M., KIDDER, R. W., CLUM, H. V. and LIDDON, J. M. (1957) The relationship of birth weights to growth at various stages of development in cattle of various breeds at the Florida Everglades Experiment Station, *J. Anim. Sci.* **16:**1018.

KOGER, M., KIDDER, R. W., PEACOCK, F. M., KIRK, W. G. and HAMMOND, M. W. (1961) Crossbreeding systems in beef cattle, *J. Anim. Sci.* **20:**908 Abs.

KOGER, M. and KNOX, J. H. (1945) A Method for estimating weaning weights of range calves at a constant age, *J. Anim. Sci.* **4:**285.

KOGER, M. and KNOX, J. H. (1952) Heritability of grade and type in range beef cattle, *J. Anim. Sci.* **11:**361.

KOGER, M., MITCHELL, J. S., KIDDER, R. W., BURNS, W. C., HENTGES, J. F., JR. and WARNICK, A. C. (1967) Factors influencing survival in beef calves, *J. Anim. Sci.* **26:**205 Abs.

KOGER, M., REYNOLDS, W. L., KIRK, W. G., PEACOCK, F. M. and WARNICK, A. C. (1962b) Reproductive performance of crossbred and straightbred cattle on different pasture programs in Florida, *J. Anim. Sci.* **21:**14.

KOGER, M., REYNOLDS, W. L., MEADE, J. H., KIRK, W. G., PEACOCK, F. M. and KIDDER, R. W. (1962c) Environment, sex and age of dam effects, *J. Anim. Sci.* **21:**973 Abs.

KOGER, T., ELLIOTT, H., HARBAUGH, F. G. and DURHAM, R. M. (1960) Sex effects on carcass and productive traits in fattening beef calves, *J. Anim. Sci.* **19:**1238 Abs.

KOHLER, P. H. (1963) Late season treatment for cattle grub control, *J. Anim. Sci.* **22:**1111 Abs.

KOHLMEIR, R. H. and BURROUGHS, W. (1963) Vitamin A and E interrelationships in high concentrate finishing rations for beef cattle, *J. Anim. Sci.* **22:**1125 Abs.

KOLARI, O. E., HARVEY, A. L., MEISKE, J. C. and AUNAN, W. J. (1961a) Linseed oil meal and lysine for cattle fed high corn silage rations, *J. Anim. Sci.* **20:**939.

KOLARI, O. E., HARVEY, A. L., MEISKE, J. C., AUNAN, W. J. and HANSON, L. E. (1959) Pelleted hay, pelleted ear corn and a tranquilizer for fattening beef cattle, *J. Anim. Sci.* **18:**1509 Abs.

KOLARI, O. E., HARVEY, A. L., MEISKE, J. C., AUNAN, W. J. and HANSON, L. E. (1960) Diethylstilbestrol, oxytetracycline, linseed oil meal, soybean oil meal and levels of corn silage in cattle fattening ration, *J. Anim. Sci.* **19**:1041.

KOLARI, O. E., HARVEY, A. L., MEISKE, J. C., AUNAN, W. J. and HANSON, L. E. (1961b) The effect of feeding pelleted hay, pelleted ear corn and a tranquilizer to fattening cattle, *J. Anim. Sci.* **20**:109.

KOONCE, K. L. and DILLARD, E. U. (1967) Some environmental effects on birth weight and gestation length in Hereford cattle, *J. Anim. Sci.* **26**:205.

KORKMAN, N. (1953) Versuok einer Vergluchenden Nachkommenschaftsuntersucking van Bullen die in Herden mit Verschueden starker Füttering wirker, *Z. Tierzücht. ZüchtBiol.* **61**:375.

KORKMAN, N. (1957) Selection with regard to the sex difference of body weight in mice, *Hereditas* (*Lund*) **43**:665.

KORKMAN, N. (1961) Selection for size in mice in different nutritional environments, *Hereditas* (*Lund*) **47**:342.

KORTSTEE, G. J. J. (1963) The gestation period of Meuse–Rhine–Yssel and Dutch Friesian cattle in the Netherlands, *Veeteelt en Zuivelber.* **6**:88.

KRAMLICH, W. E. and PEARSON, A. M. (1958) *Fd Res.* **23**:567.

KRAYBILL, H. F., BITTER, H. L. and HANKINS, O. G. (1952) Body composition of cattle, 2: Determination of fat and water content from measurement of body specific gravity, *J. Appl. Physiol.* **4**:575.

KREFT, H. W. (1962) Production qualities of heifers of different beef breeds and types, *S. Afr. J. Agric. Sci.* **5**:483.

KREHBIEL, E., BROWN, C. J., GIFFORD, W. and MABRY, C. (1958) The effectiveness of selection for type by scorecard in a small herd of Aberdeen Angus cattle, *J. Anim. Sci.* **17**:1138 Abs.

KRESS, D. D., HAUSER, E. R. and CHAPMAN, A. B. (1968) Factors affecting weaning weight in beef cattle, *J. Anim. Sci.* **27**:1128 Abs.

KRISTJANSSON, F. K. (1957) Observations on genotype–environmental interactions in swine, *Can. J. Anim. Sci.* **37**:179.

KROMANN, R. P. and MEYER, J. H. (1966) Rumen metabolism in sheep as influenced by the ration energy content, physical form and buffers, *J. Anim. Sci.* **25**:905 Abs.

KROPF, D. H. (1959) Relationships of certain muscle and bone characteristics in beef carcasses, *J. Anim. Sci.* **18**:1154 Abs.

KROPF, D. H. and GRAF, R. L. (1959a) Effect of grade, weight and class of beef carcasses on certain chemical and sensory evaluations for beef quality, *Fd Technol.* **13**:721.

KROPF, D. H. and GRAF, R. L. (1959b) The effect of carcass grade, weight and classification upon boneless beef yield, *J. Anim. Sci.* **18**:95.

KRUGER, L. and MEYER, F. (1967) Investigations of the problem of production and evaluation of beef, 1: Comparison of the fattening performance and carcass value of Herefords and Black Pied Lowlands fattened similarly to a final weight of 450 kg, *Z. Tierzücht. ZüchtBiol.* **83**:135.

KUHLMAN, L. R., FURR, R. D. and NELSON, A. B. (1961) Creep feeds and creep-feeding fall calves until spring vs. weaning, *J. Anim. Sci.* **20**:399 Abs.

KUMAZAKI, K. and MATSUKAWA, T. (1964) Statistical and genetic studies on meat productivity of the Japanese breed of cattle, III: Repeatability estimates for birth weight, weaning weight and gain from birth to weaning, *Bull. Chugoku–Shikoku Agric. Exp. Sta.* **12**:19.

KUNKLE, L. E. and CAHILL, V. R. (1959) Dairy beef production, 2: Evaluation of dairy beef carcasses, Ohio Agric. Exp. Sta. Res. Bull. 833.

KYOMO, M. L., STONAKER, H. H., RIDDLE, K., CRAMER, D. A. and RICHARDSON, G. (1966) Carcass characteristics of Hereford cows, *J. Anim. Sci.* **25**:588 Abs.

LABEN, R. C., CUPPS, P. T., MEAD, S. W. and ROJAN, W. M. (1955) Some effects of inbreeding and evidence of heterosis through outcrossing in a Holstein-Friesian herd, *J. Dairy Sci.* **38**:525.

LAGERLOF, N. (1929) *Skand. VetTidskr.* **19**:253.

LAGOS, F. and CARTWRIGHT, T. C. (1963) Sire environmental interaction of gain in cattle, *J. Anim. Sci.* **22**:820 Abs.

LAING, J. A. (1949) Infertility in cattle associated with death of ova at early stages after fertilization, *J. Comp. Path. Therap.* **59**:97.

LAL, P., MATHER, R. E. and PFAU, K. O. (1966) Factors affecting calf size in a Holstein herd, *J. Anim. Sci.* **25**:879 Abs.

LAMBERT, M. R., JACOBSON, N. L., ALLEN, R. S. and ZALHL, J. H. (1954) *J. Nutr.* **52**:259.

LAMMING, G. E., SWAN, H. and CLARKE, R. T. (1966) Studies on the nutrition of ruminants. 1: Substitution of maize by milled barley straw in a beef fattening diet and its effect on performance and carcass quality, *Anim. Prod.* **8**:303.

LAMMING, G. E., SWAN, H. and PICHARD, D. W. (1967) The substitution of urea for soyabean meal in a beef ration, *Anim. Prod.* **9**:270 Abs.

LAMPKIN, G. H. and KENNEDY, J. F. (1965) Some observations on reproduction weight change under lactation stress and the mothering ability of British and crossbred Zebu cattle in the tropics, *J. Agric. Sci.* **64**:407.

LAMPKIN, K. and LAMPKIN, G. H. (1960) Studies on the production of beef from Zebu cattle in East Africa, 2: Milk production in suckled cows and its effect on calf growth, *J. Agric. Sci.* **55**: 233.

LAMPO, P. and WILLEM, A. (1965) Causes of variation in birth weight of calves, *Vlaams diergeneesk Tijdschr.* **34**:79.

LANDAGORA, F. T., RUSOFF, L. L. and HARRIS, B., JR. (1957) Effect of aureomycin on young dairy calves raised in a new environment, *J. Dairy Sci.* **40**:50.

LANDMANN, W. A. and BATZER, O. F. (1966) Influence of processing procedures on the chemistry of meat flavours, *J. Agric. Fd Chem.* **14**:210.

LANE, A. (1964) Vitamin A injections for range cows, *Univ. Ariz. Cattle Feeders Day*, p. 28.

LANE, G. T., ALBRIGHT, J. L. and MARTIN, T. G. (1966) Effect of dietary regime on growth and body composition of dairy steers, *J. Anim. Sci.* **25**:905 Abs.

LANGLET, J. F. (1962) Some aspects of selection with regard to the improvement of beef production, *NATO 3rd Summer Course in Organization and Education of Anim. Prod. in Larger Areas, Wageningen.*

LANGLET, J. (1965) Review of existing knowledge of genetic relationship of meat and milk production with special emphasis on experimental techniques and design, *Wld Rev. Anim. Prod.* **1**:31.

LANGLET, J., GRAVERT, H. O. and ROSENHAHN, E. (1963) Progeny Testing for fattening performance and carcass value in cattle, *Report of Results for 1962 and 1963*, Kiel Inst. Tierzücht. Turheit. Christian-Albrechts Univ.

LANGLET, J. F., GRAVERT, H. O. and ROSENHAHN, E. (1967) Investigations on heredity of beef production in Friesians, *Z. Tierzücht. ZüchtBiol.* **83**:358.

LARSEN, H. J., STODDARD, G. E., JACOBSON, N. L. and ALLEN, R. S. (1956) Digestion and absorption of various carbohydrates posterior to the rumino-reticular area of the young bovine, *J. Anim. Sci.* **15**:473.

LARSEN, J. B. (1966) Danish work on the production of beef from young bulls, in *Feeding for Beef Production*, US Feed Grains Coun. Tech. Rept., p. 60.

LARSON, W. M., EMBRY, L. B. and LUTHER, R. M. (1968a) Feedlot performance, carcass characteristics and rumen fermentation of beef cattle fed diets with oyster shells or various levels of roughage, *J. Anim. Sci.* **27**:1168 Abs.

LARSON, W. M., LUTHER, R. M. and EMBRY, L. B. (1968b) Digestibility and rumen fermentation in beef cattle fed oyster shells or various levels of roughage, *J. Anim. Sci.* **27**:1167 Abs.

LARSON, W. M., EMBRY, L. B. and NYGAARD, L. J. (1966) Dry and high moisture corn fed once and twice daily to beef steers, *J. Anim. Sci.* **25**:1245.

LASLEY, J. F. and BOGART, R. W. (1943) Some factors influencing reproductive efficiency of range cattle under artificial and natural breeding conditions, Mo. Agr. Exp. Sta. Res. Bull. 376.

LASLEY, J. F., DAY, B. N. and COMFORT, J. E. (1961) Some genetic aspects of gestation length and birth and weaning weights in Hereford cattle, *J. Anim. Sci.* **20**:737.

LASSITER, C. A. (1955) Antibiotics as growth stimulants for dairy cattle—a review, *J. Dairy Sci.* **38**:1102.

LATHAM, J. O. and ROGERS, C. (1961) The influence of breed and sex on carcass characteristics of beef cattle bred in dairy herds, *Anim. Prod.* **3**:171.

LATOUSH, H. and WOODS, W. (1968) Effect of various levels of roughage and oyster shell in beef cattle finishing rations, *J. Anim. Sci.* **27**:1168 Abs.

LAUPRECHT, E. (1961) Production of a population with equal frequency of genes from three parental sources, *J. Anim. Sci.* **20**:426.

LAUPRECHT, E., SCHEPER, J. and SCHRODER, J. (1957) Messungen de speckdieck lebender schweine noch dem echolotvertfahren, *Mitt. dtsch. Lander. Ges.* **72**:881.

LAWRENCE, T. L. J. and PEARCE, J. (1964a, b) Some effects of wintering yearling beef cattle on different planes of nutrition, 1 and 2, *J. Agric. Sci.* **63**:5,23.

LAWRIE, R. A. (1960) Analysis of longissimus dorsi muscles from cattle implanted with hexoestrol, *Brit. J. Nutr.* **14**:255.

LAWRIE, R. A. (1966) *Meat Science*, Pergamon Press, Oxford.

LAWSON, J. E. and PETERS, H. F. (1964) The birth and weaning weights of Highland and Hereford cattle and their reciprocal crosses, *Can. J. Anim. Sci.* **44**:174.

LEDGER, H. P. (1965) The body and carcass composition of East African ruminants, 1: The composition of "Improved Boran" *Bos indicus* steer carcasses, *J. Agric. Sci.* **65**:261.

LEDGER, H. P. and HUTCHISON, H. G. (1962) The value of the tenth rib as a sample joint for the estimation of lean, fat and bone in carcasses of East African zebu cattle, *J. Agric. Sci.* **58**:81.

LEE, D. H. K. (1953) Manual of field studies on the heat tolerance of domestic animals, FAO Development paper No. 38, Rome.

LEE, D. H. K. and PHILLIPS, R. W. (1948) *J. Anim. Sci.* **7**:391.

LEGATES, J. E. (1962) Heritability of fat yields in herds with different production levels, *J. Dairy Sci.* **45**:990.

LEGAULT, C. R. and TOUCHBERRY, R. W. (1962) Heritability of birth weight and its relationship with production in dairy cattle, *J. Dairy Sci.* **45**:1226.

LEGG, W. E., KING, G. T., CARPENTER, Z. L. and CUNNINGHAM, N. L. (1965) Palatability of bull, heifer and steer carcasses, *J. Anim. Sci.* **24**:292 Abs.

LE GUELTE, P., DUMONT, B. L. and ARNOUX, J. (1964) Étude biometrique des bovins de boucherie, III: Variabilité de composition en marceaux et des caractere de conformation de la carcasse des boeufs Charolais, *Ann. Zootech.* **13**:255.

LEHMANN, R. P., GAINES, J. A., CARTER, R. C., BOVARD, K. P. and KINCAID, C. M. (1961) Selection indexes for weanling traits in beef calves, *J. Anim. Sci.* **20**:53.

LEIBHOLZ, J. (1967) The use of protein in calf diets, 1: A comparison of dried skim milk and meat meal, *Aust. J. Agric. Res.* **18**:149.

LEIBHOLZ, J. and MOSS, F. P. (1967) The use of protein in calf diets, 2: Meat meal quality, *Aust. J. Agric. Res.* **18**:157.

LENGEMANN, F. W. and ALLEN, N. N. (1955) The development of rumen function in the dairy calf, 1: Some characteristics of the rumen contents of cattle of various ages, *J. Dairy Sci.* **38**:651.

LENGEMANN, F. W. and ALLEN, N. N. (1959) Development of rumen function in the dairy calf, 2: Effect of diet upon characteristics of the rumen flora and fauna of young calves, *J. Dairy Sci.* **42**:1171.

LEONARD, B. E., CARTER, R. C., GAINES, J. A. and MCLURE, W. H. (1967) Maternal differences among reciprocal crossbred cows, *J. Anim. Sci.* **26**:205 Abs.

LERNER, I. M. (1950) *Population Genetics and Animal Improvement*, Camb. Univ. Press.

LERNER, I. M. (1954) *Genetic Homeostasis*, Oliver & Boyd, Edinburgh.

LERNER, I. M. and DONALD, H. P. (1966) *Modern Developments in Animal Breeding*, Academic Press, London.

LE ROY, H. L. (1958) Die Abstammungsbewertung, *Z. Tierzücht. ZüchtBiol.* **71**:328.

LEVI, D., SOLLER, M. and SHILO, A. (1967) The effect of age, live weight and rate of gain on dressing percentage and non-saleable fat content of Israel–Friesian bull calves, *Anim. Prod.* **9**:115.

LEWIS, D. (1961) The fate of nitrogenous compounds in the rumen, in *Digestive Physiology and Nutrition of the Ruminants* (ed. D. Lewis), Butterworths, London.

LEWIS, D., HILL, K. J. and ANNISON, E. F. (1957) Studies on the portal blood of sheep, 1: Absorption of ammonia from the rumen of the sheep, *Biochem. J.* **66**:587.

LEWIS, P. K., JR., BROWN, C. J. and HECK, M. C. (1962) Effect of pre-slaughter treatments on certain chemical and physical characteristics of certain beef muscles, *J. Anim. Sci.* **21**:433.

LEWIS, P. K., JR., BROWN, C. J. and HECK, M. C. (1964a) The effect of pre-slaughter stress, post mortem aging and method of cooking on the organoleptic characteristics of beef, *J. Anim. Sci.* **23**:861 Abs.

Lewis, P. K., Jr., Brown, C. J. and Heck, M. C. (1965) Effects of pre-slaughter treatment and castration on certain organoleptic and carcass characteristics of beef, Ark. Agr. Exp. Sta. Bull. 697.

Lewis, P. K., Jr., Brown, C. J. and Heck, M. C. (1968a) Effect of frozen storage on the colour of raw beef, *J. Anim. Sci.* **27**:1143 Abs.

Lewis, R. W., Brungardt, V. H. and Bray, R. W. (1964b) Estimating retail yield from the four major wholesale cuts in heifer carcasses, *J. Anim. Sci.* **23**:861 Abs.

Lewis, T. R., Suess, G. G. and Kauffman, R. G. (1968b) Subjective appraisal of carcass traits in live market animals, *J. Anim. Sci.* **27**:1134 Abs.

Lewis, W. H. E. (1966) Report on the 1965/66 Hereford Bull performance test, Beef Rec. Assoc. Tech. Rep. No. 3.

Lickley, C. R., Stonaker, H. H., Sutherland, T. M. and Riddle, K. H. (1960) Relationship between mature size, daily gain and efficiency of feed utilization in beef cattle, *J. Anim. Sci.* **19**:957 Abs.

Lima, J. O. A., Schuh, J. D., Hale, W. H. and Theurer, C. B. (1968) Steam process flaked grains for dairy calves, *J. Dairy Sci.* **51**:972.

Linares, T. and Plasse, D. (1966) Caracteres reproductivos en un hato Brahman de Venezuela, Mem. 1er reunion Latinoamer. Prod. Anim. 155.

Lindahl, I. L., Davis, R. E., Jacobson, D. R. and Shaw, J. C. (1957) Feedlot bloat studies, 1: Animal and dietary factors, *J. Anim. Sci.* **16**:165.

Lindholm, H. B. and Stonaker, H. H. (1957) Economic importance of traits and selection indexes for beef cattle, *J. Anim. Sci.* **16**:998.

Lindley, C. E., Easley, G. T., Whatley, J. A., Jr. and Chambers, D. (1958) A study of the reproductive performance of a purebred Hereford herd, *J. Anim. Sci.* **17**:336.

Link, B. A., Carsens, R. G., Bray, R. W. and Kowalczyk, T. (1967) Fatty degeneration of bovine longissimus, *J. Anim. Sci.* **26**:694.

Linton, A. C., Brinks, J. S., Stonaker, H. H., Sutherland, T. M. and Faulkner, L. C. (1968) Factors affecting weaning weights of cattle, *J. Anim. Sci.* **27**:1104 Abs.

Little, C. O., Bradley, N. W. and Mitchell, G. E., Jr. (1966) Plasma amino acids in steers fed urea supplements, *J. Anim. Sci.* **25**:260 Abs.

Little, C. O., Burroughs, W. and Woods, W. (1963) Nutritional significance of soluble nitrogen in dietary proteins for ruminants, *J. Anim. Sci.* **22**:358.

Little, C. O., Laster, D. B., Bradley, N. W. and Mitchell, G. E., Jr. (1968a) Digestive tract nitrogen and feedlot performance of steers fed soyabean meal or urea, *J. Anim. Sci.* **27**:1169 Abs.

Little, C. O., Mitchell, G. E., Jr. and Potter, G. D. (1965) Dietary influence on ruminal fluid proteins, *J. Anim. Sci.* **24**:893 Abs.

Little, C. O., Mitchell, G. E. Jr. and Reitnour, C. M. (1968b) Post ruminal digestion of corn starch in steers, *J. Anim. Sci.* **27**:790.

Little, C. O., Potter, G. D., Mitchell, G. E., Jr. and Bradley, N. W. (1968c) Amino acids reaching the abomasum of steers fed soyabean meal or urea, *J. Anim. Sci.* **27**:1169 Abs.

Livesay, E. A. and Bee, V. G. (1945) A study of the gestation periods of five breeds of cattle, *J. Anim. Sci.* **4**:13.

Livingston, H. R. (1965) Slatted floors, ARC Exp. Farm Buildings Rep. 3.

Lloyd, L. E. and Crampton, E. W. (1957) The relation between certain characteristics of fats and oils and their apparent digestibility by young pigs, young guinea pigs and pups, *J. Anim. Sci.* **16**:377.

Locker, R. H. (1960) Degree of muscular contraction as a factor in tenderness of beef, *J. Fd Sci.* **25**:304.

Lofgreen, G. P. (1961) The all-concentrate ration for beef cattle, *Feedstuffs*, 12th Aug., p. 50.

Lofgreen, G. P. and Garrett, W. N. (1954) Creatinine excretion and specific gravity as related to the composition of the 9th, 10th and 11th rib cut in Hereford steers, *J. Anim. Sci.* **13**:496.

Lofgreen, G. P. and Garrett, W. N. (1968) A system for expressing net energy requirements and feed values for growing and finishing beef cattle, *J. Anim. Sci.* **27**:793.

Lofgreen, G. P. and Otagaki, K. K. (1960) The net energy of blackstrap molasses for fattening steers as determined by a comparative slaughter technique, *J. Anim. Sci.* **19**:392.

LOGANATHAN, S., COOPER, R. J. and HOBBS, C. S. (1965) Factors affecting preweaning performance of Hereford calves, *J. Anim. Sci.* **24**:849 Abs.

LOMBARD, J. H. (1963) Heritabilities of pre-weaning and weaning characteristics of beef cattle, *Proc. S. Afri. Soc. Anim. Prod.* **2** (2), 121.

LONG, J. F., GERLAUGH, P. and RIFE, D. C. (1948) A genetic study of gestation in cattle, *Genetics* **33**:618.

LONG, T. A., FREAR, D. E. H., RUGH, M. and MILLER, J. (1968) Effect of source of nitrogen on feedlot performance of steers, *J. Anim. Sci.* **27**:1509 Abs.

LOOSLI, J. K. (1966) Problems and prospects in animal science research, *J. Anim. Sci.* **25**:244.

LOOSMORE, R. M. (1964) Health problems, *Proc. Conf. Farm Bldgs Centre, Kenilworth, Warwicks.*

LOOSMORE, R. M. and MARKSON, L. M. (1961) Poisoning of cattle by Brazilian groundnut meal, *Vet. Rec.* **73**:813.

LOPEZ SAUBIDET, C., CAVANDOLI, H., IGARTUA, O. A., JOANDET, G., CABRINI, E. J., VILLAR, J. A., SIVORI, I. H., HERNANDEZ, O., COVAS, G. and KUGLER, W. F. (1963) Cruzas con Charoles en la region Pampeana, INTA Est. Exp. Agropec. Balcarce, Bol. Tec. 6.

LOVELL, R. and HILL, A. B. (1940) A study of the mortality rate of calves in 335 herds in England and Wales (together with some limited observations for Scotland) *J. Dairy Res.* **11**:225.

LOY, R. G., ZIMBELMAN, R. G. and CASIDA, L. E. (1960) Effects of injected ovarian hormones on the corpeus luteum of the estrual cycle in cattle, *J. Anim. Sci.* **19**:175.

LOYD, E. J. and HINER, R. L. (1959) Relation between hydroxyproline of alkali-insoluble protein and tenderness of bovine muscle, *J. Agric. Fd Chem.* **7**:860.

LUITINGH, H. C. (1962) Developmental changes in beef steers as influenced by fattening, age and type of ration, *J. Agric. Sci.* **58**:1.

LUITINGH, H. C. (1963) The efficiency of beef production in terms of carcass weight increase as influenced by the ration concentration and the age of steers, *J. Agric. Sci.* **61**:127.

LUSH, J. L. (1932) The relationship of body shape of feeder steers to rate of gain, to dressing percentage and to the value of the dressed carcass, Tex. Agr. Exp. Sta. Bull. 471.

LUSH, J. L. (1935) Progeny test and individual performance as indicators of an animal's breeding value, *J. Dairy Sci.* **18**:1.

LUSH, J. L. (1945) *Animal Breeding Plans*, Iowa State Coll. Press, Ames.

LUSH, J. L. and COPELAND, O. C. (1930) *J. Agric. Res.* **41**:37.

LUSH, J. L., SHEARER, P. S. and CULBERTSON, C. C. (1939) Crossbreeding hogs for pork production, Ia. Agric. Exp. Sta. Bull. 380.

LUSH, J. L. and SHRODE, R. L. (1950) Changes in milk production with age and milking frequency, *J. Dairy Sci.* **33**:338.

LUTHER, R. M., EMBRY, L. B., WHETZAL, F. W. and HOELSCHER, M. A. (1959) Effects of a tranquilizer (perphenazine) on shrinkage and feedlot adaptation of yearling feeder steers, *J. Anim. Sci.* **18**:1491 Abs.

LUTHER, R. M. and TRENKLE, A. (1967) Ruminal acid production in lambs fed pelleted diets containing different levels of concentrates, *J. Anim. Sci.* **26**:590.

LUTHER, R., TRENKLE, A. and BURROUGHS, W. (1966) Influence of rumen protozoa on volatile fatty acid production and ration digestibility in lambs, *J. Anim. Sci.* **25**:1116.

LYMARJ, F. M. (1956) Crossing Red Steppe cattle with Semmental on the left bank of the Forest Steppe of the Ukraine, *Biul. naut.-tech Inform naukissled. Inst. Zivotn. Lesost. Polesj. USSR* (*Harjkov*) **18**.

MACDEARMID, A. (1967) Intensive beef production: The effect of the low level inclusion of antibiotics in diets for beef cattle, *Proc. of the Holmenhollen Symp. Antibiotics in Animal Nutrition, Oslo*, p. 45

MACDONALD, D., BRADLEY, R. and MCCREA, L. T. (1962) Mortality in barley fed cattle, *Vet Rec.* **74**:280.

MACDONALD, M. A. (1954) Relationship between type and production factors in beef cattle, *Proc. Ruakura Farmer's Conf. Week, New Zealand.*

MACKELLOR, J. C. (1960) The occurrence of muscular hypertrophy in South Devon cattle, *Vet rec.* **72**:507.

MACLEAN, C. W. (1966) Observations on laminitis in intensive beef units. *Vet. Rec.* **78**:223.
MACLEOD, N. A., MACDEARMID, A. and KAY, M. (1968) Intensive beef production, 9: A note on the performance of Friesian and Ayrshire steers fattened on a cereal diet, *Anim. Prod.* **10**:487.
MAGEE, W. T. (1965a) Estimating response to selection, *J. Anim. Sci.* **24**:242.
MAGEE, W. T. (1965b) Relationship between carcass traits in beef bulls, *J. Anim. Sci.* **24**:850 Abs.
MAGEE, W. T., BRATZLER, L. J., DEANS, R. J. and PEARSON, A. M. (1960) Relationship between carcass traits used in a beef selection program, *J. Anim. Sci.* **19**:1222.
MAGEE, W. T., BRINKS, J. S., NELSON, R. H. and BRANAMAN, G. A. (1961) Some factors affecting weaning weight and score of beef calves, Mich. Agric. Exp. Sta. Quart. Bull. **43**:556.
MAGEE, W. T., MERKEL, R. A., BRATZLER, L. J., PEARSON, A. M. and KEMP, K. E. (1968) Relationship among performance traits of grade Hereford bulls, *J. Anim. Sci.* **27**:13.
MAGEE, W. T., NELSON, R. H., BRANAMAN, G. A., BRATZLER, L. J. and PEARSON, A. M. (1958) Some factors affecting carcass grade in steers, *J. Anim. Sci.* **17**:649.
MAGRUDER, N. D. and NELSON, J. W. (1964) The performance and carcass evaluation of dairy bulls to market weight, *J. Anim. Sci.* **23**:83 Abs.
MAHADEVAN, P. (1966) *Breeding for Milk Production in Tropical Cattle* Comm. Agric. Bureaux, Farnham Royal, UK.
MAKELA, A. (1958) On the importance of free access to water in calf feeding, *Maatalouslieleillines Aikakauskirja*.
MAHMUD, A. and COBB, E. H. (1963) Factors affecting weaning weight, pre-weaning gain and conformation scores of beef calves in Hawaii, *J. Anim. Sci.* **22**:820 Abs.
MAIJALA, K. (1964) Fertility as a breeding problem in artificially bred populations of dairy cattle, 1: Registration and heritability of female fertility, *Ann. Agric. Fenn.* **3** (Suppl. 1), 94.
MALES, J. R., GREATHOUSE, T. R., HENDERSON, H. E. and BECK, C. C. (1968) Factors causing stress conditions involved in weaning and moving feeder cattle, *J. Anim. Sci.* **27**:1134 Abs.
MALTOS, J., AGUILAR, C., LAREDO, M. and DE ALBA, J. (1961) Progeny testing in tropical feedlots and pastures, *J. Anim. Sci.* **20**:908 Abs.
MANN, S. O., MASSON, F. M. and OXFORD, A. E. (1954) Effect of feeding aureomycin to calves upon the establishment of their normal rumen microflora and microfauna, *Brit. J. Nutr.* **8**:246.
MANUNTA, G. and NUVOLE, P. (1966) Carbohydrate-splitting activity of intestinal mucosa in the adult sheep, *Boll. Soc. ital. Biol. sper.* **42**:1014.
MAPLES, B. E., KIDDER, R. W., WARNICK, A. C. and KOGER, M. (1968) Heterosis and feed efficiency in beef cows, *J. Anim. Sci.* **27**:302 Abs.
MARCHELLO, J. A., BLACKMORE, D. W. and URICK, J. J. (1960) Heritability of 18 month weight of heifers and its relationship to birth weight and weaning weight of their first calf, *J. Anim. Sci.* **19**:956 Abs.
MARION, P. T. (1959) Effects of stilbestrol implants and tranquilizers on rate of gain, shrink, yield and carcass grade of beef steers, *J. Anim. Sci.* **18**:1173 Abs.
MARION, P. T. (1960) Influence of two levels of tapazole on gain and carcass grade of steers fed stilbestrol, *J. Anim. Sci.* **19**:645 Abs.
MARION, P. T. and JONES, H. J. (1961) Lysine and stilbestrol in sorghum rations for fattening steers, *J. Anim. Sci.* **20**:666 Abs.
MARION, P. T., JONES, J. H. and HUGHES, E. E. (1960a) Hydroxyzine and terramycin as feed additives for steers implanted or fed stilbestrol, *J. Anim. Sci.* **19**:965 Abs.
MARION, P. T., JONES, J. H. and HUGHES, E. E. (1960b) The value of tapazole in rations with oral stilbestrol for yearling steers, *J. Anim. Sci.* **19**:965 Abs.
MARION, P. T., JONES, J. H. and RIGGS, J. K. (1962) Energy levels for cows maintained on native pasture and in drylot, *J. Anim. Sci.* **21**:669 Abs.
MARION, P. T., ROBISON, E. D., MCGINTY, D. D. and RIGGS, J. K. (1968) Calving performance of pasture and drylot cows, *J. Anim. Sci.* **27**:1183 Abs.
MARION, P. T., ROBISON, E. D. and RIGGS, J. K. (1964) Drylot and pasture performance of beef cows, *J. Anim. Sci.* **23**:899 Abs.
MARLOWE, T. J. (1962) Weights and grades of beef cattle and their relation to performance, Va. Agric. Exp. Sta. Bull. 537.
MARLOWE, T. J. (1964) Evidence of selection for the snorter dwarf gene in cattle, *J. Anim. Sci.* **23**:454.

MARLOWE, T. J. and GAINES, J. A. (1958) The influence of age, sex, season of birth of calf and age of dam on pre-weaning growth rate and type score of beef calves, *J. Anim. Sci.* **17**:706.

MARLOWE, T. J., MAST, C. C. and SCHALLES, R. R. (1965) Some non-genetic influences on calf performances, *J. Anim. Sci.* **24**:494.

MARLOWE, T. J. and MORROW, G. A. (1967) Factors influencing the sale price of ROP bulls, *J. Anim. Sci.* **26**:201 Abs.

MARLOWE, T. J., ROONEY, J. R. and MERTANZA, W. F. (1962) A study of dwarfism in beef cattle, Va. Agric. Exp. Sta. Bull. 545.

MARLOWE, T. J. and VOGT, D. W. (1964) Within sex heritability estimates on beef calves, *J. Anim. Sci.* **23**:852 Abs.

MARLOWE, T. J. and VOGT, D. W. (1965) Heritability, phenotypic correlations and genetic correlations involving pre-weaning gain and weaning grade of beef calves, *J. Anim. Sci.* **24**:502.

MARQUART, W. R. (1964) Dairy beef in the packing industry, *J. Dairy Sci.* **47**:1145.

MARSH, B. B. (1952) *Biochim. biophys. Acta* **9**:129.

MARSH, B. B. (1964) Meat quality and rigor mortis, *Proc. Conf. Carcass Comp. and Appraisal of Meat Animals* (ed. D. E. Tribe), CSIRO, Melbourne.

MARTIN, A. K. and BLAXTER, K. L. (1961) The utilization of the energy of proteins by ruminants, *Proc. Sec. Conf. on Energy Metabolism, Wageningen.*

MARTIN, E. L., WALTERS, L. E. and WHITEMAN, J. V. (1966a) Association of beef carcass conformation with thick and thin muscle yields, *J. Anim. Sci.* **25**:682.

MARTIN, E. M. and LAMMING, G. E. (1958) The effect of hexoestrol on the nucleic-acid content of the anterior pituitary gland of yearling male sheep, *Proc. Nutr. Soc.* **17**:xlviii.

MARTIN, J. L., PRESTON, T. R. and ELÍAS, A. (1968a) Intensive beef production from sugar cane, 5: Nitrogen retention and dietary digestibility in calves given molasses/urea diets and different forages, *Rev. cubana Cienc. Agric.* (Eng ed.) **2**:65.

MARTIN, J. L., PRESTON, T. R. and WILLIS, M. B. (1968b) Intensive beef production from sugar cane, 6: Napier or maize as forage sources at two levels in diets based on molasses/urea, *Rev. cubana Cienc. Agric.* (Eng. ed.) **2**:175.

MARTIN, J. L., PRESTON, T. R. and WILLIS, M. B. (1969) Unpublished data.

MARTIN, J. L. and WILLIS, M. B. (1969) Interrelationships among carcass components of Brahman bulls fed high molasses/urea diets. *Rev. cubana Cienc. Agric.* (Eng. ed.) **31**:75 Abs.

MARTIN, T. G. (1968) Associations among estimators of beef carcass composition, *J. Anim. Sci.* **27**:1122 Abs.

MARTIN, T. G., DRAKE, M. K., GARRIGUS, R. R., PERRY, T. W. and BEESON, M. (1965) Carcass traits of Hereford and Charolais–Hereford heifers, *J. Anim. Sci.* **24**:866 Abs.

MARTIN, T. G., HOWARD, R. D., LANE, G. T., JUDGE, M. D. and ALBRIGHT, J. L. (1966b) Effect of dietary regime on Holstein steer carcasses, *J. Anim. Sci.* **25**:885 Abs.

MARTIN, T. G., JACOBSON, N. L., MCGILLIARD, L. D. and HOMEYER, P. G. (1962) Factors related to weight gain of dairy calves, *J. Dairy Sci.* **45**:886.

MARTIN, T. G. and STARKENBURG, R. T. (1965) Genetic correlations between beef and dairy traits in dual purpose cattle, *Wld Rev. Anim. Prod.* **1**:45.

MARTIN, W. G., RAMSEY, H. A., MATRONE, G. and WISE, G. H. (1959) Responses of young calves to a diet containing salts of volatile fatty acids, *J. Dairy Sci.* **42**:1377.

MASON, I. L. (1957) *A World Dictionary of Breeds, Types and Varieties of Livestock.*, Comm. Agric. Bureaux, Farnham Royal, UK.

MASON, I. L. (1961) How big are our beef breeds?, *Agriculture* **68**:71.

MASON, I. L. (1962a) Contribution of the dairy farm to beef production, *NATO 3rd Summer Course on Organization and Evaluation of Animal Production in Larger Areas, Wageningen.*

MASON, I. L. (1963) Symptoms of muscular hypertrophy in heterozygous steers, *Anim. Prod.* **5**:57.

MASON, I. L. (1964) Genetic relations between milk and beef characters in dual purpose cattle breeds, *Anim. Prod.* **6**:31.

MASON, I. L. (1966) Hybrid vigour in beef cattle, *Anim. Breed. Abst.* **34**:453.

MASON, I. L., OLIVER, S. A. C. and SCOTT, J. H. (1962) Progeny testing of beef bulls used in natural service, *Exp. Husb.* **7**:40.

MASON, I. L. and ROBERTSON, A. (1956) The progeny testing of dairy bulls at different levels of production, *J. Agric. Sci.* **47**:367.

MATASSINO, D. and MARATI, M. A. (1964) Live weight at birth of calves of the Marche breed and factors affecting it, *Prod. anim.* (*Napoli*) **3**:263.

MATHEWS, C. S., SCHWABE, E. L. and EMERY, F. E. (1942) *Growth* **6**:7.

MATTHEWS, D. J. and BENNETT, J. A. (1962) Effect of pre-slaughter rate of gain upon tenderness and other carcass characteristics of beef, *J. Anim. Sci.* **21**:738.

MATHIS, G. W. and KOTHMANN, M. M. (1968) Cow and calf response to grazing treatments on native range, *J. Anim. Sci.* **27**:1184 Abs.

MATRONE, G., BUNN, C. R. and MCNEILL, J. J. (1964) *J. Nutr.* **84**:215.

MATRONE, G., BUNN, C. R. and MCNEILL, J. J. (1965) Study of purified diets for growth and reproduction of the ruminant, *J. Nutr.* **86**:154.

MATRONE, G., RAMSEY, H. A. and WISE, G. H. (1957) Purified diets for ruminants, *Proc. Soc. Exp. Biol. Med.* **95**:731.

MATRONE, G., RAMSEY, H. A. and WISE, G. H. (1959) Effect of volatile fatty acids, $NaHCO_3$ and $KHCO_3$ in purified diets for ruminants, *Proc. Soc. Exp. Biol. Med.* **100**:8.

MATSUSHIMA, J. K. (1966) Grain processing, *Proc. 21st Ann. Tex. Nutr. Conf. Coll. Sta.*, p. 144.

MATSUSHIMA, J. K. (1967) *Feedstuffs* **39,** 11th March, p. 2.

MATSUSHIMA, J. K. (1968a) *Feedstuffs* **40,** 27th April, p. 44.

MATSUSHIMA, J. K. (1968b) *Feedstuffs* **40,** 5th Oct., p. 12.

MATSUSHIMA, J. K., CLANTON, D. C. and ARTHAUD, V. H. (1959) Hormones, hormone like substances and tranquilizers for fattening calves, Nebr. Agric. Exp. Sta. Cattle Progress Rep. 253.

MATSUSHIMA, J. K., MCCANN, C. P., STENQUIST, N. J. and MCLAREN, R. J. (1968) Oyster shells in beef finishing rations, *J. Anim. Sci.* **27**:1170 Abs.

MATSUSHIMA, J. K. and SPRAGUE, J. I. (1963) Bulls produce leaner and lower grading carcasses in Colorado State Univ. Feeding Study, Anim. Sci. Res. Highlights Colorado State Univ. Agr. Exp. Sta. Gen. Series. 785.

MATSUSHIMA, J. K. and STENQUIST, N. J. (1967) Reconstituted ensiled and flaked corn for cattle, *J. Anim. Sci.* **26**:925 Abs.

MAYER, J. (1966) Some aspects of the problem of regulation of food intake and obesity, *New Eng. J. Med.* **276**:610.

MAYNARD, L. A. (1937) *Animal Nutrition*, 1st edn., McGraw-Hill, New York.

MAYNARD, L. A. and LOOSLI, J. K. (1962) *Animal Nutrition*, McGraw-Hill, New York.

MCBEE, J. L. and NAUMANN, H. D. (1959) The influence of freezing on shear and taste panel evaluations of beef, *J. Anim. Sci.* **18**:1477 Abs.

MCBEE, J. L. and WILES, J. A. (1967) Influence of marbling and carcass grade on the physical and chemical characteristics of beef, *J. Anim. Sci.* **26**:701.

MCBRIDE, G. (1958) The environment and animal breeding problems, *Anim. Breed. Abst.* **26**:349.

MCBRIDE, G. (1964) Social behaviour of domestic animals, 2: Effect of the peck order on poultry productivity, *Anim. Prod.* **6**:1.

MCCANDLISH, A. C. (1923) Studies on the growth and nutrition of dairy cows, V: Milk as the sole ration for calves, *J. Dairy Sci.* **6**:54.

MCCARTHY, R. D. and KESSLER, E. M. (1956) Relation between age of calf, blood glucose, blood and rumen levels of volatile fatty acids and in vitro cellulose digestion, *J. Dairy Sci.* **39**:1280.

MCCARTOR, M. M., ENGLAND, M. W. and HEFLEY, H. M. (1964) High concentrate rations and beef steer performance, *J. Anim. Sci.* **23**:304 Abs.

MCCARTOR, M. M., ENGLAND, M. W. and WOODWARD, K. E. (1967) Performance on isonitrogenous, isomineral rations, *J. Anim. Sci.* **26**:923 Abs.

MCCARTOR, M. M. and HEFLEY, H. M. (1965) Effect of high concentrate rations on performance and rumen epithelium, *J. Anim. Sci.* **24**:895 Abs.

MCCLAIN, P. E. (1965) Relationships of stroma protein, water binding and pH to tenderness of bovine muscles, MS. thesis, Louisiana State Univ., Baton Rouge.

MCCLURE, T. J. (1965) A nutritional cause of low non-return rates in dairy herds, *Aust. Vet. J.* **41:** 119.

MCCORMICK, W. C., CLYBURN, T. M., WARWICK, E. J., CARMON, J. L. and SOUTHWELL, B. L. (1963) Grading, crisscrossing and rotational crossing as breeding systems, *J. Anim. Sci.* **22:**820 Abs.

MCCORMICK, W. C. and SOUTHWELL, B. L. (1957) A comparison of Brahman crossbred and British crossbred cattle, *J. Anim. Sci.* **16**:207.

McCoy, G., Williams, J. and Hunter, A. (1967) Serum protein changes in calves fed different sources of non-fat dried milk, *J. Anim. Sci.* **26**:1484 Abs.

McCroskey, J. E., Pope, L. S., Stephens, D. F. and Waller, G. (1961) Effect of pelleting steer fattening rations of different concentrates to roughage ratio, *J. Anim. Sci.* **20**:42.

McCullough, M. E. (1968) Influence of hay or silage and ratio of flaked corn or beet pulp to forage on cellulose disappearance *in vitro*, *J. Anim. Sci.* **27**:780.

McCullough, T. A. and Chestnutt, D. M. B. (1965) The performance of Friesian and Shorthorn steers given concentrate diets with or without hay, *Rec. Agric. Res.* **14** (2), 9.

McDaniel, A. H. and Roark, C. B. (1956) Performance and grazing habits of Hereford and Aberdeen–Angus cows and calves on improved pastures as related to types of shade, *J. Anim. Sci.* **15**:59.

McDonald, I. and Kay, M. (1967) A note on the composition of live weight gains estimated by regression analysis, *Anim Prod.* **9**:553.

McDonald, I. W. (1948) The absorption of ammonia from the rumen of the sheep, *Biochem. J.* **42**:584.

McDonald, L., Nichols, R. E. and McNutt, S. H. (1952) *Am. J. vet. Res.* **13**:446.

McDonald, P., Edwards, R. A. and Greenhalgh, J. F. (1966) *Animal Nutrition*, Oliver & Boyd, Edinburgh.

McDowell, R. E. (1958) Physiological approaches to animal climatology. *J. Hered.* **49**:52.

McDowell, R. E., Fletcher, J. L. and Johnson, J. C. (1959) Gestation length birth weight and age at first calving of crossbred cattle with varying amounts of Red Sindhi and Jersey breeding, *J. Anim. Sci.* **18**:1430.

McDowell, R. E., Roby, T. O., Fletcher, J. L., Foote, L. E., Branton, C. and High, J. W. (1964) Impact of anaplasmosis in a dairy herd, *J. Anim. Sci.* **23**:168.

McGinty, D. D., Breuer, L. H. and Riggs, J. K. (1967) Digestibility of dry and reconstituted sorghum grain by cattle, *J. Anim. Sci.* **26**:223 Abs.

McGinty, D. D. and Marion, P. T. (1965) Drylot performance of bulls, steers and heifers, *J. Anim. Sci.* **24**:279 Abs.

McGinty, D. D., Penic, P. and Bowers, E. J. (1968) Moist grain for finishing beef cattle, *J. Anim. Sci.* **27**:1170 Abs.

McGinty, D. D. and Riggs, J. K. (1967) Moist sorghum grains for finishing cattle, *J. Anim. Sci.* **26**:925 Abs.

McGinty, D. D., Schake, L. M. and Marion, P. T. (1966a) Feeding studies with cattle fed all grain rations containing protein sources, *Proc. 21st Ann. Tex. Nutr. Conf.*, p. 108.

McGinty, D. D., Schake, L. M. and Marion, P. T. (1966b) Protein supplements for all-concentrate rations, *J. Anim. Sci.* **25**:260 Abs.

McKean, H. E. and Bohren, B. B. (1961) Numerical aspects of regression of offspring on parent, *Biometrics* **17**:626.

McLaren, G. A. (1964) Symposium on microbial digestion in ruminants: Nitrogen metabolism in the rumen, *J. Anim. Sci.* **23**:577.

McLaren, G. A., Anderson, G. C. and Barth, K. M. (1965a) Influence of methionine and tryptophan on nitrogen utilization by lambs fed high levels of non-protein nitrogen, *J. Anim. Sci.* **24**:231.

McLaren, G. A., Anderson, G. C. and Barth, K. M. (1965b) Influence of folic acid, vitamin B12 and creatine on nitrogen utilization by lambs fed high levels of non-protein nitrogen, *J. Anim. Sci.* **24**:329.

McLaren, G. A., Anderson, G. C., Barth, K. M. and Welch, J. A. (1962) Casein and its degradation products in the utilization of urea nitrogen by lambs, *J. Anim. Sci.* **21**:258.

McLaren, G. A., Anderson, G. C., Martin, W. G. and Cooper, W. K. (1961) Fixation of ammonia nitrogen by rumen mucosa, *J. Anim. Sci.* **20**:942 Abs.

McLaren, R. J. and Matsushima, J. K. (1968) Digestion of ensiled reconstituted corn, *J. Anim. Sci.* **27**:1171 Abs.

McMeekan, C. P. (1940, a, b, c) Growth and development in the pig with special reference to carcass quality characters, *J. Agric. Sci.* **30**:276, 387, 511.

McMeekan, C. P. (1941) Growth and development in the pig with special reference to carcass quality characters, IV: The use of sample joints and of carcass measurements as indices of the composition of the bacon pig, *J. Agric. Sci.* **31**:1.

McMeekan, C. P. (1956) Beef carcass judging by measurement, *Pastoral Rev. Grazier Rec.* **66:** 1273.

McNaught, M. L., Smith, J. A. B., Henry, K. M. and Kon, S. K. (1950) The utilization of non-protein nitrogen in the bovine rumen, 5: The isolation and nutritive value of a preparation of dried rumen bacteria, *Biochem. J.* **46**:32.

McNitt, J. I., Stonaker, H. H. and Carroll, E. J. (1966) Breeding soundness in beef bulls, *J. Anim. Sci.* **25**:583 Abs.

McPhee, C. P., McBride, G. and James, J. W. (1964) Social behaviour of domestic animals, 3: Steers in small yards, *Anim. Prod.* **6**:9.

Meacham, T. N., Bovard, K. P. and Priode, B. M. (1964) Influence of vitamin A supplementation of beef cows on calf vitality and survival, *J. Anim. Sci.* **23**:308 Abs.

Mead, S. W. and Regan, W. M. (1931) Differences in rations devoid of roughages for calves, 1: The effect of the addition of cod liver oil and alfalfa ash, *J. Dairy Sci.* **14**:283.

Meade, J. H., Jr., Dollahan, J. C., Taylor, J. C. and Lindley, C. E. (1959a) Factors influencing weaning weights of Hereford and Angus cattle in Mississippi, *J. Anim. Sci.* **18**:1149 Abs.

Meade, J. H., Jr., Hammond, M. E. and Koger, M. (1961) Factors influencing performance in a Brahman herd, *J. Anim. Sci.* **20**:392 Abs.

Meade, J. H., Jr., Warnick, A. C., Koger, M. and Reynolds, W. L. (1959b) Genetic and environmental influences on pregnancy rate in beef cattle, *J. Anim. Sci.* **18**:1549 Abs.

Means, R. H. and King, G. T. (1959) The effect of sire on tenderness of beef loin steaks as measured by a panel of families and the Warner–Bratzler shear machine, *J. Anim. Sci.* **18**:1475 Abs.

Mechling, E. A. and Carter, R. C. (1962) Selection for twinning in a grade Angus herd, *J. Anim. Sci.* **21**:974 Abs.

Megown, J. W. (1967) Some basic concepts involving trace minerals, *Feedstuffs*, 18 Feb., p. 61.

Mehen, S. M., Hale, W. H., Theurer, B., Little, M. and Taylor, B. (1966) Effect of dry rolling, fine grinding, steam processing and pressure cooking on the digestion of milo rations by steers, *J. Anim. Sci.* **25**:593 Abs.

Meiske, J. C., Enfield, F. D. and Harvey, A. L. (1964) Effect of cow weight and other factors on performance of beef calves, *J. Anim. Sci.* **23**:1197 Abs.

Meiske, J. C., Harvey, A. L. and Kolari, O. E. (1960) Grain preference and response to stilbestrol implants by creep fed beef calves, *J. Anim. Sci.* **19**:1276 Abs.

Meiske, J. C., Van Ardsell, W. J., Leucke, R. W. and Hoefer, J. A. (1955) The utilization of urea and biuret as sources of nitrogen for growing fattening lambs, *J. Anim. Sci.* **14**:941.

Melampy, R. M., Gurland, J. and Rakes, J. M. (1959) Estrogen excretion by cows after oral administration of diethylstilbestrol, *J. Anim. Sci.* **18**:178.

Melton, C. C., Brown, C. J., Lewis, P. K., Jr., Heck, M. C. (1967a) Beef bull performance and secondary sex characteristics, *J. Anim. Sci.* **26**:244.

Melton, A. A., Cartwright, T. C. and Nelson, L. A. (1967b) Cow size as related to efficiency of calf gain, *J. Anim. Sci.* **26**:206 Abs.

Melton, A. A., Riggs, J. K., Nelson, L. A. and Cartwright, T. C. (1967c) Milk production, composition and calf gains of Angus, Charolais and Hereford cows, *J. Anim. Sci.* **26**:804.

Mendoza, M., Rojas, S. and Bacigalupo, A. (1968) El uso de pasta de algodon harina de pescado y anchovita fresca en engorde de novillos, *Proc. 2nd Reunion ALPA, Peru*, p. 40.

Meyer, B., Thomas, J., Buckley, R. and Cole, J. W. (1960a) The quality of grain finished and grass finished beef as affected by ripening, *Fd. Technol.* **14**:4.

Meyer, J. H., Hull, J. L., Weitkamp, W. H. and Bonilla, S. (1965) Compensatory growth responses of fattening steers following various low energy intake regimes on hay or irrigated pasture, *J. Anim. Sci.* **24**:29.

Meyer, J. H., Lofgreen, G. P. and Garret, W. N. (1960b) A proposed method for removing sources of error in beef cattle feeding experiments, *J. Anim. Sci.* **19**:1123.

Meyer, W. E. (1966) Sex associated characteristics of the beef carcass and muscle growth in the live animal, *Dissertation Absts.* B, **27**:1673.

Meyerhoeffer, D. C., Carter, R. C. and Priode, B. M. (1960) Early selection of beef calves, *J. Anim. Sci.* **19**:1222 Abs.

Meyerhoeffer, D. C., Carter, R. C. and Priode, B. M. (1963) Sex differences in heritability of traits in beef calves, *J. Anim. Sci.* **22**:240 Abs.

MI, M. P., CHAPMAN, A. B. and TYLER, W. J. (1962) Genetic variation in birth weights and measurements of Holsteins, *J. Anim. Sci.* **21**:975 Abs.

MICHELENA, J., PRESTON, T. R. and MACLEOD, N. A. (1968) The digestibility of grain sorghum reconstituted and ensiled for different periods of time, *Rev. cubana Cienc. Agric.* (Eng. ed.) **2**:71.

MIGUEL, C. and CARTWRIGHT, T. C. (1963) Comparison of heritabilities in crossbred and purebred cattle, *J. Anim. Sci.* **22**:821 Abs.

MILLER, J. C., HEDRICK, H. B., THOMPSON, G. B., FREITAG, R. R., MEYER, W. E., DYER, A. J. and NAUMANN, H. D. (1965) Factors affecting longissimus dorsi and subcutaneous fat measurements and indices of beef carcass cut-out, Miss. Agric. Exp. Sta. Res. Bull. 880.

MILLER, J. K. and MILLER, W. J. (1960) Development of zinc deficiency in Holstein calves fed a purified diet, *J. Dairy Sci.* **43**:1854.

MILLER, K. P. and FREDERICK, E. C. (1966) Relationships between feedlot bloat and daily gain with dairy steers, *J. Anim. Sci.* **25**:1254 Abs.

MILLER, K. P., GOODRICH, R. D., FREDERICK, E. C., YOUNG, C. W., MEISKE, J. C. and COLE, C. L. (1967) Effects of ratios of concentrate and hay on performance and carcass quality of Holstein steers, *J. Anim. Sci.* **26**:926 Abs.

MILLER, P., VAN VLECK, L. D. and HENDERSON, C. R. (1966) Interrelationships among herd life, milk production and calving interval, *J. Anim. Sci.* **25**:879 Abs.

MILLER, R. H. and MCGILLIARD, L. D. (1959) Relations between weight at first calving and milk production during the first lactation, *J. Dairy Sci.* **42**:1932.

MILLER, W. J., CARMON, J. L. and DALTON, H. L. (1958) Influence of anise oils on the palatability of calf starters, *J. Dairy Sci.* **41**:1262.

MILLS, C. F., DALGARNO, A., WILLIAMS, R. B. and QUARTERMAN, J. (1967) Zinc deficiency and the zinc requirements of calves and lambs, *Brit. J. Nutr.* **21**:751.

MILL, J. H. L. and LUGINBUHL, R. E. (1965) Incidence of bovine mucosal disease in Connecticut, *Cornell Vet.* **55**:583.

MINYARD, J. A. and DINKEL, C. A. (1965a) Weaning weight of beef calves as affected by age and sex of calf and age of dam, *J. Anim. Sci.* **24**:1067.

MINYARD, J. A. and DINKEL, C. A. (1965b) Heritability and repeatability of weaning weight in beef cattle, *J. Anim. Sci.* **24**:1072.

MITCHELL, G. E., NEUMANN, A. L. and DRAPER, H. H. (1956) Metabolism of tritium labelled diethylstilbestrol by steers, *J. Anim. Sci.* **15**:1285 Abs.

MITCHELL, H. H. and HAMILTON, T. S. (1933) Effect of long continued exercise upon the chemical composition of the muscle and other tissues of cattle, *J. Agric. Res.* **46**:917.

MITCHELL, H. H., HAMILTON, T. S. and HAINES, W. T. (1928) Some factors affecting the connective tissue content of beef muscle, *J. Nutr.* **1**:165.

MITCHELL, R. G., CORLEY, E. L. and TYLER, W. J. (1961) Heritability, phenotypic and genetic correlations between type ratings and milk and fat production in Holstein/Friesian cattle, *J. Dairy Sci.* **44**:1502.

MMB (1950) Report of the Production Division, No. 1.

MMB (1955) *The National Herd 1955 Census*, Prod. Div., MMB, Thames Ditton.

MMB (1959) Report of the Production Division, No. 9.

MMB (1960a) *The National Dairy Herd: Interim Census 1960*, Production Division, MMB, Thames Ditton.

MMB (1960b) Unpublished data.

MMB (1960c) *The Incidence of Difficult Calving in Ayrshire and Friesian Heifers*, Prod. Div. Report No. 10. p. 98, MMB Thames Ditton.

MMB (1965) *Dairy Herd (1965) Census*, Breeding and Production Organization, MMB, Thames Ditton.

MMB (1966) *Progeny Testing Dairy Beef*, Report Breeding and Production Organization, MMB, No. 16, p. 54.

MMB (1967) Report of the Breeding and Production Organization, No. 17, MMB, Thames Ditton.

MMB (1968) Report of the Breeding and Production Division, No. 18, MMB, Thames Ditton.

MOCHRIE, R. D. (1964) Feeding patterns and efficiency in ruminants, *Fed. Proc.* **23**:85.

MOCHRIE, R. D. and MURLEY, W. R. (1957) Changing dairy calves onto all dry feed at an early age, *J. Anim. Sci.* **16**:1079 Abs.

Moe, D. R., Kropf, D. H., Mackintosh, D. L., Harrison, D. L. and Anderson, L. (1964) The relationship of certain physical and chemical factors to cooking and sensory evaluations of beef, *J. Anim. Sci.* **23**:862 Abs.

Mohrman, R. K., Albert, W. W., Neumann, A. L. and Mitchell, G. E., Jr. (1959) The influence of hand-feeding, self-feeding and frequent interval feeding on performance and behaviour of beef cattle, *J. Anim. Sci.* **18**:1489 Abs.

Montgomery, M. J. and Baumgardt, B. R. (1965) Regulation of food intake in ruminants, 1: Pelleted rations varying in energy concentration, *J. Dairy Sci.* **48**:569.

Montgomery, M. J., Schultz, L. H. and Baumgardt, B. R. (1963) Effect of intraruminal infusion of volatile fatty acids and lactic acid on voluntary hay intake, *J. Dairy Sci.* **46**:1380.

Montsma, G. (1960) Observations of milk yield and calf growth and conversion rate in three types of cattle in Ghana, *Trop. Agric.* **37**:293.

Moody, W. G., Jacobs, J. A. and Kemp, J. D. (1965) Effects of texture on beef rib desirability, *J. Anim. Sci.* **24**:866 Abs.

Moody, W. G. and Kemp, J. D. (1965) Separable components as related to area of beef rib, *J. Anim. Sci.* **24**:866 Abs.

Moore, D. B., Stonaker, H. H., and Riddle, K. R. (1961) Factors influencing comparisons of Hereford bulls for rate of gain, *J. Anim. Sci.* **20**:255.

Moore, D. G., Chambers, D., Whatley, J. A., Jr. and Campbell, W. D. (1956) Some factors affecting difficulty at parturition of 2-year-old Hereford heifers, *J. Anim. Sci.* **15**:1225 Abs.

Morgan, J. H. L. (1967) Taste panel relationships, *Proc. NZ Soc. Anim. Prod.* **27**:71.

Morgan, J. T. and Parker, J. E. (1964) The control of climatic environment in intensive beef lots, *Proc. Conf. Intensive Housing of Beef Cattle, Farm Bldgs Centre, Warwick.*

Morley, F. W. (1956) Selection for economic characters in Australian Merino sheep, 7: Interactions between genotype and plane of nutrition, *Aust. J. Agric. Res.* **6**:77.

Morris, J. G. (1966) Finishing steers on sorghum grain and sorghum silage: Effects of grain-to-roughage ratio, urea supplementation and hexoestrol implantation on rate of body weight gain, feed efficiency and carcass compositions, *J. Agric. Sci.* **67**:191.

Morris, J. G., Gartner, R. J. W. and Pepper, P. M. (1967) Finishing steers on high grain rations: The effects of three roughages and of urea, vitamin A cobalt and sodium chloride supplements, *Aust. J. Exp. Agric. Anim. Husb.* **7**:144.

Morris, J. G. and Moir, K. W. (1964) Methods of determining the chemical composition of dead animals, *Tech. Conf. Carcass Composition and Appraisal of Meat Animals* (ed. D. E. Tribe) CSIRO, Melbourne.

Morrison, F. B. (1956) *Feeds and Feeding*, 22nd edn. Morrison, Ithaca, New York.

Morrison, S. H. (1967) 1967–8 ingredient analysis and estimated feed value tables for beef, sheep rations, *Feedstuffs*, 25 Nov., p. 39.

Morrow, G. A. and Marlowe, T. J. (1966) Genetics of mature traits in Angus cows, *J. Anim. Sci.* **25**:888 Abs.

Mott, G. O., Quinn, L. R., Bisschoff, W. V. A. and da Rocha, G. L. (1967) Molasses for pasture fed Zebu steers in Brazil, *J. Anim. Sci.* **26**:937 Abs.

Moulton, C. R., Trowbridge, P. F. and Haigh, L. D. (1922) Changes in proportion of carcass and offal on different planes of nutrition, Mo. Agric. Exp. Sta. Res. Bull. 54.

Mueller-Haller, B., Plasse, D., Gil, R., Koger, M., Butterworth, M. and Linares, T. (1968) Birth weight and pre-weaning gain in Criollos, Brahmans and their reciprocal crosses, *Proc. 2nd Reunion ALPA, Lima*, p. 75.

Muñoz, M. J. and Kaspar, A. (1967) The Zebu breed and its crosses in Cuba, in *Zootecnia y sanidad animal en Cuba*, Inst. de libros, Havana.

Muñoz, H., De Alba, J. and Luna, J. A. (1964) Comparison of weight in pure and crossbred bull calves, *J. Anim. Sci.* **23**:852 Abs.

Muñoz, H. and Martin, T. G. (1968) Pre- and post-weaning growth in Criollo, Brahman and Santa Gertrudis cattle and their reciprocal crosses, *Proc. 2nd Reunion ALPA, Lima*, p. 79.

Munro, S. S. (1962) Spurious negative correlations between age and weight per day of age in beef calves, *Nature* **196**: 1010.

Murphey, C. E., Hallet, D. K., Tyler, W. E. and Pierce, J. C., Jr. (1960) Estimating yields of retail cuts from beef carcasses, *J. Anim. Sci.* **19**:1240 Abs.

MURPHEY, C. E., HALLET, D. K., HOHE, K. E. and BREIDENSTEIN, B. C. (1963) Factors affecting yields of cuts from beef carcasses, *J. Anim. Sci.* **22**:828 Abs.

MURRAY, D. M. (1966) A comparison of the cutaneous evaporation rates in cattle exposed to heat in a climate laboratory and in the field, *J. Agric. Sci.* **66**:175.

NALBANDOV, A. V. (1963) Symposium on growth: Endocrine causes of growth and growth stasis, *J. Anim. Sci.* **22**:558.

NATZ, D. C. (1968) Californians go into dairy beef feeding in a big way, *Feedstuffs*, 20 July, p. 26.

NAUMANN, H. D. (1952) A recommended procedure for measuring and grading beef carcass evaluation, *Proc. Reciprocal Meat Conf.* **5**:108.

NAY, T. (1959) Sweat glands in cattle: Histology, morphology and evolutionary trends, *Aust. J. Agric. Res.* **10**:121.

NEHRING, K., SCHIEMANN, R. and HOFFMAN, L. (1961) The utilization of energy in feed in relation to plane of nutrition, 3: Experiments with bullocks and wethers, *Arch. Tierernähr.* **11**:157.

NELLOR, J. E. and COLE, H. H. (1956) The hormonal control of estrus and ovulation in the beef heifer, *J. Anim. Sci.* **15**:650.

NELMS, G. E. and BOGART, R. (1956) The effect of birth weight, age of dam and time of birth on suckling gains of beef calves, *J. Anim. Sci.* **15**:662.

NELMS, G. E., SCHOONOVER, C. O. and DRAKE, M. K. (1968) Predicting the muscle:bone ratio of bull carcasses, *J. Anim. Sci.* **27**:1107 Abs.

NELMS, G. E. and STRATTON, P. O. (1967) Selection practice and phenotypic change in a closed line of beef cattle, *J. Anim. Sci.* **26**:274.

NELSON, A. B., GREELEY, M. G., MILLER, J. A. and WALLER, G. R. (1957) Protein supplements for wintering beef cattle, *J. Anim. Sci.* **16**:1085 Abs.

NELSON, A. B. and POPE, L. S. (1959) Subsequent performance of stilbestrol implanted cattle on pasture and in the feedlot, *J. Anim. Sci.* **18**:1151 Abs.

NELSON, A. B. and WALLER, G. R. (1962) Urea in winter supplements for range beef cattle, *J. Anim. Sci.* **21**:387 Abs.

NELSON, D. K., BRYANT, J. M., JACOBSON, N. L., MCGILLIARD, A. D. and FROST, G. R. (1966) Effect of protein quality on growth of calves, *J. Anim. Sci.* **25**:1256 Abs.

NELSON, L. A. and CARTWRIGHT, T. C. (1967) Growth of calf as related to weight of dam, *J. Anim. Sci.* **26**:1464 Abs.

NELSON, L. A. and CARTWRIGHT, T. C. (1968) Inter-age correlations among weights of heifers, *J. Anim. Sci.* **27**:284 Abs.

NELSON, L. A., CARTWRIGHT, T. C. and FITZHUGH, H. A., JR. (1967) Weight-age curves of Angus and Hereford cows, *J. Anim. Sci.* **26**:206 Abs.

NELSON, P. M., LOWE, B. and HELSER, M. D. (1930) Influence of animal's age upon the quality and palatability of beef, 2: The roast beef preparation, quality and palatability, Ia. Agric. Exp. Sta. Bull. 273.

NEUMANN, A. L., ALBERT, W. W. and BREIDENSTEIN, B. C. (1956) A study of time and method of hormone administration for beef heifers, *J. Anim. Sci.* **15**:1285 Abs.

NEUVY, A. and VISSAC, B. (1962) *A Contribution to the Study of the Cullard Factor*, Union Nationale des Levres Genealogigues, Paris.

NEVILLE, W. E., JR. (1962) Influence of dam's milk production and other factors on 120- and 240-day weight of Hereford calves, *J. Anim. Sci.* **21**:315.

NEVILLE, W. E., JR., and MCCULLOUGH, M. E. (1968) Feed requirements of beef cows, *J. Anim. Sci.* **27**:295 Abs.

NEWLAND, H. W. and HENDERSON, H. E. (1966) Melengestrol and stilbestrol for finishing yearling steers, *J. Anim. Sci.* **25**:1254 Abs.

NEWLAND, H. W., HENDERSON, H. E. and ULLREY, D. E. (1966) Injectable vitamins A and E for finishing cattle, *J. Anim. Sci.* **25**:907 Abs.

NEWLAND, H. W., MAGEE, W. T., BRANAMAN, G. A. and BLAKESLEE, L. H. (1962) Effect of heat-processing and pelleting corn for steers and lambs, *J. Anim. Sci.* **21**:711.

NEWMAN, C. W. and OAKES, J. Y. (1961) Feedlot response of steers to stilbestrol implants following stilbestrol implants on pasture, *J. Anim. Sci.* **20**:399 Abs.

NEWSOM, I. E. (1938) A bacteriological study of liver abscesses in cattle, *J. Infect. Dis.* **63**:232.

NICHOLS, J. R. and WHITE, J. M. (1964) Correlation of meat and milk traits in dairy cattle, *J. Dairy Sci.* **47**:1149.

NICHOLS, J. R., ZEIGLER, J. H., WHITE, J. M., KESLER, E. M. and WATKINS, T. L. (1964) Production and carcass characteristics of Holstein–Friesian bulls and steers slaughtered at 800 or 1000 lb, *J. Dairy Sci.* **47**:179.

NICHOLSON, J. W. G. and CUNNINGHAM, H. M. (1965) Retained placenta, abortions and abnormal calves from beef cows fed all-barley rations, *Can. Vet. J.* **6**:275.

NICHOLSON, J. W. G., CUNNINGHAM, H. M. and FRIEND, D. W. (1962) The addition of buffers to ruminant rations, 2: Additional observations on weight gains, efficiency of gains and consumption by steers of all-concentrate rations, *Can. J. Anim. Sci.* **42**:75.

NICHOLSON, J. W. G., CUNNINGHAM, H. M. and FRIEND, D. W. (1963) Effect of adding buffers to all-concentrate rations on feedlot performance of steers, ration digestibility and intra-rumen environment, *J. Anim. Sci.* **22**:368.

NICKERSON, D. (1946) Colour measurement and its application to the grading of agricultural products, USDA Misc. Publ. 580.

NOLAND, P. R., FORD, B. F. and RAY, M. L. (1955) The use of ground chicken litter as a source of nitrogen for gestating-lactating ewes and for fattening steers, *J. Anim. Sci.* **14**:860.

NOLLER, C. H. and DICKSON, I. A. (1953) Value of hay and rumen inoculation in early weaning of calves, *J. Dairy Sci.* **36**:582.

NÖRING, L. (1962) Untersuchungen uber Korperentwichlung und Leistungen van Schwarzbunten Niederungsvich in der Höhenlange unter Berichsichtigung verschiedener Haltungsformen bei optimal Aufzuchtbedingungen, *Arch. Tierz.* **5**:251.

NORTON, C. L. and EATON, H. D. (1946) Dry calf starters for dairy calves, Cornell Agric. Exp. Sta. Bull. 835.

NORTON, H. W., JR. (1956) Gestation period for Holstein–Friesian cattle, *J. Dairy Sci.* **39**:1619.

NRC (1963) Nutrient requirements of domestic animals. 4: Nutrient requirements of beef cattle, Nat. Acad. Sci./Nat. Res. Council Publ. 1137.

OBRACEVIC, C. (1956) Comparison of some characters of Simmental and Holstein–Friesian cows, *Ark. poljopr. Nauk.* **9** (24), 3.

OBRACEVIC, C., SLJIVOVACKI, K., PLAZINA, P. and IVOS, R. (1966) Value of adding limited amounts of lucerne hay in concentrate fattening of young bulls, *Zborn. Rad. poljopriv. Fak.* **14** (426), 9.

OBRACEVIC, C., ZEREMSKI, D. and SLJIVOVACKI, K. (1961) Effect of hydroxyzine combined with stilboestrol in young fattening bulls, *Ark. poljopr. Nauk.* **14** (46), 26.

O'BRIEN, C. A. and ARNDT, B. F. (1968) Attempts at multiple conception in heifers following variable-term treatment with melengestrol acetate, *J. Anim. Sci.* **27**:1195 Abs.

O'BRIEN, C. A. and BAUMGARDNER, J. H. (1967) Effect of melengestrol acetate (MGA) on the reproductive physiology and feedlot performance of heifers, *J. Anim. Sci.* **26**:229 Abs.

O'BRIEN, C. A., BLOSS, R. E. and NICKS, E. F. (1968) Effect of melengestrol acetate on the growth and reproductive physiology of fattening heifers, *J. Anim. Sci.* **27**:664.

O'CONNOR, L. K., WOOD, P. D. P. and SMITH, G. F. (1968) A note on the differences between geographical areas in the gestation length and birth weight of British Friesian calves, *Anim. Prod.* **10**: 125.

O'CONNOR, L. K. and WILLIS, M. B. (1967) The effect of artificial insemination on the breed structure of British Friesian cattle, *Anim. Prod.* **9**:287.

ODEGARD, A. K. (1965) A study of some factors affecting reproductive efficiency in Norwegian Red cattle, *Acta agric. scand.* **15**:204.

OGILVIE, M. L., FALTIN, E. C., HAUSER, E. R., BRAY, R. W. and HOEKSTRA, W. G. (1960) Effects of stilbestrol in altering carcass composition and feedlot performance of beef steers, *J. Anim. Sci.* **19**:991.

OGLESBY, W. T. (1962) Financial losses from anaplasmosis, *Proc. 4th Nat. Anaplasmosis Conf. Reno*, p. 1.
OKAMOTO, S., KOGA, O., GOTO, I. and OKAMOTO, S. (1966) Genetic analysis of body size in Japanese Brown cattle, *Sci. Bull. Fac. Agric. Kyushu Univ.* **22**:151.
OLSEN, R. H. (1959) Feeding protein, phosphorus and energy supplements to beef cows on Utah desert range, MS thesis, Utah State Univ.
OLTJEN, R. R., BOND, J. and RICHARDSON, G. V. (1967) Performance of calves fed purified and natural diets, *J. Anim. Sci.* **26**:927 Abs.
OLTJEN, R. R. and DAVIS, R. E. (1963) Zinc, urea and buffers in all-concentrate steer rations, *J. Anim. Sci.* **22**:842 Abs.
OLTJEN, R. R. and DAVIS, R. E. (1965) Factors affecting the ruminal characteristics of cattle fed all-concentrate rations, *J. Anim. Sci.* **24**:198.
OLTJEN, R. R., DAVIS, R. E. and HINER, R. L. (1965) Factors affecting performance and carcass characteristics of cattle fed all-concentrate rations, *J. Anim. Sci.* **24**:192.
OLTJEN, R. R. and PUTNAM, P. A. (1966) Plasma amino acids and nitrogen retention by steers fed purified diets containing urea or isolated soy protein, *J. Nutr.* **89**:385.
OLTJEN, R. R., PUTNAM, P. A., WILLIAMS, E. E., JR. and DAVIS, R. E. (1966) Wheat versus corn in all-concentrate cattle rations, *J. Anim. Sci.* **25**:1000.
OLTJEN, R. R., ROBBINS, J. D. and DAVIS, R. E. (1964) Studies involving the use of glutamic acid in ruminant nutrition, *J. Anim. Sci.* **23**:767.
OLTJEN, R. R., SMITH, E. F., KOCH, B. A. and BAKER, F. H. (1959) The value of supplemented trace minerals in cattle fattening rations, *J. Anim. Sci.* **18**:1196.
OLTJEN, R. R., WALLER, G. R., NELSON, A. B. and TILLMAN, A. D. (1963) Ruminant studies with diammonium phosphate and urea, *J. Anim. Sci.* **22**:36.
OMAR, A. R. (1966) The aetiology and pathology of pneumonia in calves, *Vet. Bull.* **36**:259.
O'MARY, C. C. and AMENT, D. (1961) Comparison of two methods of adjusting weaning weights of calves for age of dam and sex of calf, *J. Anim. Sci.* **20**:673 Abs.
O'MARY, C. C., BROWN, T. L. and ENSMINGER, M. E. (1959a) Correlation of cow measurements to 180-day adjusted weaning weights of their calves, *J. Anim. Sci.* **18**:1471 Abs.
O'MARY, C. C., CULLISON, A. E. and CARMON, J. L. (1959b) Implanted and oral stilbestrol for fattening steers, *J. Anim. Sci.* **18**:14.
O'MARY, C. C., VANCE, D. W. and ENSMINGER, M. E. (1959c) Comparison of three systems of performance testing beef cattle, *J. Anim. Sci.* **18**:1465. Abs.
O'MARY, C. C., WARREN, E. P., DAVIS, T. J. and PIERCE, H. H., JR. (1956) Effects of low level implantations of stilbestrol in steers fattened on dry lot rations, *J. Anim. Sci.* **15**:52.
OMTVEDT, I. T., WHATLEY, J. A., JR., WHITEMAN, J. V. and MORRISON, R. D. (1962) Genotype–environment interactions in feedlot performance and carcass traits in swine, *J. Anim. Sci.* **21**:41.
ORME, L. E., COLE, J. W., KINCAID, C. M. and COOPER, R. J. (1960) Predicting total carcass lean in mature beef from weights of certain entire muscles, *J. Anim. Sci.* **19**:726.
ORME, L. E., PEARSON, A. M., BRATZLER, L. J. and MAGEE, W. T. (1958) Specific gravity as an objective measure of marbling, *J. Anim. Sci.* **17**:693.
ORME, L. E., PEARSON, A. M., BRATZLER, L. J., MAGEE, W. T. and WHEELER, A. C. (1959a) The muscle bone relationship in beef, *J. Anim. Sci.* **18**:1271.
ORME, L. E., PEARSON, A. M., MAGEE, W. T. and BRATZLER, L. J. (1959b) Relationship of live animal measurements to various carcass measurements in beef, *J. Anim. Sci.* **18**:991.
ØRSKOV, E. R. and ALLEN, A. M. (1966a) Utilization of salts of volatile fatty acids by grazing sheep, 3: Effect of frequency of feeding on the utilization of acetate and propionate by young growing lambs, *Br. J. Nutr.* **20**:509.
ØRSKOV, E. R. and ALLEN, A. M. (1966b) Utilization of salts of volatile fatty acids by growing sheep, 1: Acetate, propionate and butyrate as sources of energy for young growing lambs, *Br. J. Nutr.* **20**:295.
ORTS, F. A. and KING, G. T. (1959) Cannon bone characteristics as related to muscle in beef carcasses, *J. Anim. Sci.* **18**:1479 Abs.
ORTS, F. A., KING, G. T. and BUTLER, O. D. (1968) Cutability measures in the bovine carcass, *J. Anim. Sci.* **27**:1145 Abs.
OSMAN, A. H. and BRADFORD, G. E. (1965) Effects of environment on phenotypic and genetic variation in sheep, *J. Anim. Sci.* **24**:766.

OSMAN, A. H. and BRADFORD, G. E. (1967) Genotype–environment interactions and compensatory growth in sheep, *J. Anim. Sci.* **26**:1239.

OSMAN, H. F., THEURER, B., HALE, W. H. and MEHEN, S. M. (1966) Influence of grain processing on *in vitro* enzymatic starch digestion of barley and milo, *J. Anim. Sci.* **25**:593 Abs.

OTT, E. A., SMITH, W. H., HARRINGTON, R. B. and BEESON, W. M. (1966) Zinc toxicity in ruminants, 2: Effect of high levels of dietary zinc on gains, feed consumption and feed efficiency of beef cattle, *J. Anim. Sci.* **25**:419.

OTT, E. A., SMITH, W. H., STOB, M., PARKER, H. E. and BEESON, W. M. (1965) Zinc deficiency syndrome in the young calf, *J. Anim. Sci.* **24**:735.

OTTERSBY, D. E. and RUST, J. W. (1965) Effects of age and diet on rumen and blood components of the young calf, *J. Dairy Sci.* **48**:1716.

OWEN, F., PLUM, M. and HARRIS, L. (1965) Once versus twice daily feeding of milk to calves weaned at 21 or 42 days of age, *J. Dairy Sci.* **48**:824 Abs.

PAGOT, J. R. (1951–2) Crossing *Bos taurus* with Zebu: Statistical study of results obtained in French Nigeria, *Rev. Elev. Med. Vet. Pays. Trop.* **5**:53.

PAGOT, J. R. (1967) Personal communication.

PAHNISH, O. F., ROBERSON, R. L., TAYLOR, R. L., BRINKS, J. S., CLARK, R. T. and ROUBICEK, C. B. (1964) Genetic analyses of economic traits measured in range-raised Herefords at pre-weaning and weaning ages, *J. Anim. Sci.* **23**:562.

PAHNISH, O. F., BRINKS, J. S., CLARK, R. T. and QUESENBERRY, J. R. (1961a) Range performance of progeny of Miles City sires, *J. Anim. Sci.* **20**:909 Abs.

PAHNISH, O. F., STANLEY, E. B., BOGART, R. and ROUBICEK, C. B. (1961b) Influence of sex and sire on weaning weights of Southwestern range cattle, *J. Anim. Sci.* **20**:454.

PAHNISH, O. F., STANLEY, E. B. and SHILLINGBURY, C. G., JR. (1956) Effects of roughage on fattening cattle in Arizona, Ariz, Agric. Exp. Sta. Bull. 272.

PALMER, A. Z. (1963) Relation of age, breed, sex and feeding practice on beef and pork tenderness, *Proc. Meat Tenderness Symp.*, Campbell Soup Co., Camden, NJ, p. 161.

PALMER, A. Z., CARPENTER, J. W., ALSMEYER, R. H., CHAPMAN, H. L. and KIRK, W. G. (1958) Simple correlations between carcass grade, marbling, ether extract of loin eye and beef tenderness, *J. Anim. Sci.* **17**:1153 Abs.

PALMER, A. Z., CARPENTER, J. W., REDDISH, R. L., MURPHEY, C. E. and HALLETT, D. K. (1961) Estimated and actual yields of boneless retail cuts from Brahman crossbred cattle and carcasses, *J. Anim. Sci.* **20**:919 Abs.

PALMER, A. Z., CHAPMAN, H. L., CARPENTER, J. W. and ALSMEYER, R. H. (1957) Slaughter, carcass and tenderness characteristics as influenced by feed intake of steers fed chlortetracycline and/or diethylstilbestrol on pasture and in drylot, *J. Anim. Sci.* **16**:1075.

PALSSON, H. (1955) Conformation and body composition, in *Progress in the Physiology of Farm Animals* (ed. J. Hammond), Butterworths, London.

PALSSON, H. and VERGES, J. B. (1952a, b) Effects of plane of nutrition on growth and development of carcass quality in lambs, Parts 1 and 2, *J. Agric. Sci.* **42**:1.

PANARETTO, B. A. (1964) Estimation of body composition in living animals, *Tech. Cong. Carcass Composition and Appraisal of Meat Animals* (ed. D. E. Tribe), CSIRO, Melbourne.

PANARETTO, B. A. and TILL, A. R. (1963) Body composition *in vivo*, 2: The composition of mature goats and its relationship to the antipyrine tritiated water and *N*-acetyl-4-aminoantipyrine spaces, *Aust. J. Agric. Res.* **14**:926.

PANI, P. K., MAGEE, W. T. and KEMP, K. E. (1967) Factors affecting fertility in an AI beef herd, *J. Anim. Sci.* **26**:887 Abs.

PARKER, E. E., WALDRIP, W. J. and MARION, P. T. (1966) Effects of grazing rates and levels of winter supplement on cow–calf performance, *J. Anim. Sci.* **25**:599 Abs.

PARKER, J. L. (1968) Confinement feeding, cattle breeding research aimed at producing uniform quality beef for McDonald drive-ins, *Feedstuffs*, 14th Sept., p. 34.

PARRETT, N. A. and RIGGS, J. K. (1967) Dry, reconstituted and early harvested sorghum grain for cattle, *J. Anim. Sci.* **26**:224 Abs.

PARRETT, N. A., MCGINTY, D. D., BREUER, L. H. and RIGGS, J. K. (1966) Dry, reconstituted and early harvested sorghum grain for finishing cattle, *Tex. 21st Nutr. Conf.*, p. 100.

PATTERSON, R. E., CARTWRIGHT, T. C., JONES, J. H. and BAYLES, J. J. (1955) Performance testing of beef breeding stock, *J. Anim. Sci.* **14**:1034.

PATTON, W. R. and RALSTON, A. T. (1968) Early diethylstilbestrol treatment of bull calves, *J. Anim. Sci.* **27**:1117 Abs.

PAYNE, W. J. A. (1949) *Br. J. Nutr.* **3**:i.

PAUL, P., BRATZLER, L. J., FARWELL, E. D. and KNIGHT, K. (1952) Studies on tenderness of meat, 1: Rate and heat penetration, *Fd Res.* **17**:504.

PEACOCK, F. M., KIRK, W. G., HODGES, E. M., REYNOLDS, W. L. KOGER, M. (1960) Genetic and environmental influences on weaning weight and slaughter grade of Brahman, Shorthorn and Brahman–Shorthorn crossbred calves, Fla. Agric. Exp. Sta. Bull. 624.

PEACOCK, F. M., KIRK, W. G., HODGES, E. M., PALMER, A. Z. and CARPENTER, J. W. (1965) Influence of summer pasture, diethylstilbestrol and shade on fattening cattle in South Florida, Fla. Agric. Exp. Sta. Bull. 700.

PEARSON, A. M. (1960) Beef for tomorrow, Nat. Acad. Sci./Nat. Res. Council. Publ. 751.

PEARSON, A. M. (1963a) Quality meat production—factors affecting the eating characteristics of meat, Livestock Nutr. Feed Show, Graham Cherry Org., London.

PEARSON, A. M. (1963b) Objective and subjective methods for beef tenderness, *Proc. Meat Tenderness Symp.*, Campbell Soup Co., Camden, NJ.

PEARSON, A. M. (1966) Desirability of beef—its characteristics and their measurement, *J. Anim. Sci.* **25**:843.

PEARSON, A. M. and KIRK, W. G. (1954) Selecting and using beef or veal, Fla. Agric. Exp. Sta. Bull. 541.

PEPITO, N. N., CHAMBERS, D., WHITEMAN, J. V. and STEPHENS, D. F. (1961) Predicting feed efficiency in beef bulls, *J. Anim. Sci.* **20**:910 Abs.

PEREGONCUK, S. T. (1962) Intensive fattening of entire bulls, *Zivotnovodstvo* **24**(10):58.

PEREZ, C. B., WARNER, R. G. and LOOSLI, J. K. (1967) Evaluation of ureaphosphate as a source of nitrogen and phosphorus for ruminants, *J. Anim. Sci.* **26**:810.

PERKINS, J. L. and LUTHER, R. M. (1967) Effects of defaunation and energy level on ration utilization in sheep, *J. Anim. Sci.* **26**: 928 Abs.

PERRY, T. W., BEESON, W. M., ANDREWS, F. N. and STOB, M. (1955) The effects of oral administration of hormones on growth rate and deposition in the carcass of fattening steers, *J. Anim. Sci.* **14**: 329.

PERRY, T. W., BEESON, W. M., ANDREWS, F. N., STOB, M. and MOHLER, M. T. (1958) The comparative effectiveness of oral and subcutaneous implantation of diethylstilbestrol in combination with chlortetracycline, *J. Anim. Sci.* **17**:164.

PERRY, T. W., BEESON, W. M. and MOHLER, M. T. (1967) A comparison of high-urea supplements with natural protein supplements for growing and fattening beef cattle, *J. Anim. Sci.* **26**:1434.

PERRY, T. W., BEESON, W. M., MOHLER, M. T. and SMITH, W. H. (1962) Levels of supplemental vitamin A with and without suncured alfalfa meal for fattening steer calves, *J. Anim. Sci.* **21**:333.

PERRY, T. W., BEESON, W. M., SMITH, W. H., HARRINGTON, R. B. and MOHLER, M. T. (1968a) Interrelationships among vitamins A, E and K when added to the rations of fattening beef cattle, *J. Anim. Sci.* **27**:190.

PERRY, T. W., BEESON, W. M., SMITH, W. H. and MOHLER, M. T. (1965) Vitamins A, E and K and dehydrated alfalfa meal for fattening beef cattle, *J. Anim. Sci.* **24**:899 Abs.

PERRY, T. W., MOHLER, M. T. and BEESON, W. M. (1960) Effect of feeding different tranquilizers in combination with implanted diethylstilbestrol or oral antibiotic on fattening beef steers, *J. Anim. Sci.* **19**:533.

PERRY, T. W. and MUDD, C. A. (1957) Raw and gelatinized corn for beef cattle, *J. Anim. Sci.* **26**:1489 Abs.

PERRY, T. W., PURKLISER, E. D. and BEESON, W. M. (1966a) Effects of supplemental enzymes on nitrogen balance, 1: Digestibility of energy and nutrients and on growth and feed efficiency of cattle, *J. Anim. Sci.* **25**:760.

PERRY, T. W., SMITH, W. H., BEESON, W. M. and MOHLER, M. T. (1966b) Value of supplemental vitamin A for fattening beef cattle on pasture, *J. Anim. Sci.* **25**:814.

PERRY, T. W., TROUTT, H. F., PETERSON, R. C. and BEESON, W. M. (1968b) Oyster shell as a roughage replacer in fattening beef cattle, *J. Anim. Sci.* **27**:185.

PETROVIC, V. (1952) The gestation period of Simmentals, *God. poljopr. Fak. Zemun* (*Beograd*) **4**:363.

PHARR, L. D., COLVIN, H. W., JR., and NOLAND, P. R. (1967) Rumen motility of sheep as affected by the physical form of oat hay, *J. Anim. Sci.* **26**:414.

PHAR, P. (1968) Report in *Feedstuffs*, 27th April, p. 39.

PHILLIPS, R. W. (1961) World distribution of the major types of cattle, *J. Hered.* **52**:207.

PHILLIPSON, A. T. (1964) The digestion and absorption of nitrogenous compounds in the ruminant, in *Mammalian Protein Metabolism* (eds. H. N. Munro and J. B. Allison), Academic Press, New York.

PHILLIPSON, A. T. and MCANALLY, R. A. (1942) Studies on the fate of carbohydrates in the rumen of the sheep, *J. Exp. Biol.* **19**:199.

PIATKOWSKI, B. (1966) Feeding studies on calves, 3, *Arch Tierernähr.* **16**:41.

PIATKOWSKI, B. and STEGER, H. (1967) Feeding studies on calves, 5: Effect of sugar containing feed or pelleted rations on metabolism and growth of early-weaned calves, *Arch. Tierernähr.* **17**:209.

PIATKOWSKI, B., STEGER, H. and VOIGT, J. (1967) Pellets containing urea for ruminants, 1: Growth and feed conversion of calves weaned early, *Arch. Tierzücht.* **10**:313.

PIERCE, A. E. (1962) In *Animal Health and Production* (eds. C. S. Grunsell and A. I. Wright), Butterworths, London.

PIERCE, C. D., AVERY, H. G., BURRIS, M. and BOGART, R. (1954) Rate and efficiency of gain in beef cattle, 2: Some factors affecting performance testing, Oreg. Agric. Exp. Sta. Tech. Bull, 33.

PIERCE, J. C. (1957) The influence of conformation, finish and carcass weight on the percentage yield of wholesale and retail cuts of beef, *Proc. 10th Recip. Meat Conf, Chicago.*

PILKINGTON, D. H., WALTERS, L. E. and POPE, L. S. (1959) Carcass studies with steers, bulls and stilbestrol-implanted bulls sold as slaughtered calves, *J. Anim. Sci.* **18**:1154.

PILKINGTON, D. H., WALTERS, L. E. and WHITEMAN, J. V. (1960) Firmness of beef rib steaks as related to tenderness and fat content, *J. Anim. Sci.* **19**:1241 Abs.

PINCUS, G. and THIMANN, K. V. (1955) *The Hormones: Physiology, Chemistry and Applications*, 3, Academic Press, New York.

PINNEY, D. O., BRADLEY, N. W., LITTLE, C. O. and OVERFIELD, J. R. (1966) Urea and soybean meal supplementation of corn/corn silage rations containing different levels of energy, *J. Anim. Sci.* **25**:260 Abs.

PINNEY, D. O., MALKIES, L. E., POPE, L. S. and URBAN, K. (1962a) Effect of pre-weaning plane of nutrition on subsequent feedlot performance and carcass composition of beef calves, *J. Anim. Sci.* **21**:388.

PINNEY, D. O., POPE, L. S. and STEPHENS, D. F. (1963) Alternate low and high planes of nutrition on growth and performance of beef heifers, *J. Anim. Sci.* **22**:238 Abs.

PINNEY, D. O., POPE, L. S., STEPHENS, D. F. and WALLER, G. R. (1962b) Winter nutrition and age at calving on lifetime performance of beef cows, *J. Anim. Sci.* **21**:1009 Abs.

PITMAN, J. (1968) Report in *Feedstuffs*, 22nd June, p. 9.

PLASSE, D. (1968) Mating systems in beef cattle, 2: Breed crossing, *Ganagrinco* **3** (13), 10.

PLASSE, D. and KOGER, M. (1967) Studies on birth and weaning weight in a pedigree Santa Gertrudis herd, Mem. ALPA **2**:7.

PLASSE, D., WARNICK, A. C. and KOGER, M. (1965) Age at sexual maturity and dependance of ovulation rate on season of Brahman and crossbred heifers in Florida, *Z. Tierzücht. ZüchtBiol.* **81**:231.

PLASSE, D., WARNICK, A. C. and KOGER, M. (1968a) Reproductive behaviour of *Bos indicus* females in a subtropical environment, 1: Puberty and ovulation frequency in Brahman and Brahman × British heifers, *J. Anim. Sci.* **27**:94.

PLASSE, D., WARNICK, A. C., REESE, R. E. and KOGER, M. (1968b) Reproductive behaviour of *Bos indicus* females in a subtropical environment, 2: Gestation length in Brahman cattle, *J. Anim. Sci.* **27**:101.

PLASSE, D., KOGER, M. and WARNICK, A. C. (1968c) Reproductive behaviour of *Bos indicus* females in a subtropical environment, 3: Calving intervals from first exposure to conception and intervals from parturition to conception, *J. Anim. Sci.* **27**:105.

PLUM, M., ANDERSEN, H. and SWIGER, L. A. (1965) Heritability estimates of gestation length and birth weight in Holstein–Friesian cattle and their use in selection indexes, *J. Dairy Sci.* **48**:1672.

PLUM, M. and HARRIS, L. (1968) Rearing intensity and milk production of Holstein heifers, *J. Anim. Sci.* **27**:1128 Abs.

POLEY, G. E. and TRENKLE, A. H. (1963) Influence of nitrogen source on amino acid patterns in plasma and abomasal ingesta from sheep, *J. Anim. Sci.* **22**:1139 Abs.

POPE, L. S., HUMPHREY, K. D., WALTERS, L. and WALLER, G. R. (1957) Fattening steers and heifers on rations containing different levels of concentrates, Ohio Agric. Exp. Sta. Misc. Publ. MP **48**:64.

POPE, L. S., TURMAN, E. J., WALTERS, L. E., URBAN, K. and HALBERT, J. (1960) Implanting steer, bull and heifer calves in a fat slaughter-calf program, Okla. Agric. Exp. Sta. Misc. Publ. MP 57.

POPE, L. S., URBAN, K. and WALLER, G. R. (1959a) Rolling vs, pelleting grains, protein levels and certain feed additives in beef cattle fattening rations, *J. Anim. Sci.* **18**:1509 Abs.

POPE, L. S., WALTERS, L. E., WALLER, G. R. and CAMPBELL, W. D. (1959b) Rolled versus pelleted milo and certain feed additives for fattening steer calves., Okla. Agric. Exp. Sta. Misc. Publ. MP **55**:119.

POUJARDIEU, B. and VISSAC, B. (1966) Genetic variation in the performance of crossbred veal calves, *9th Int. Congr. Anim. Prod. Edinburgh*, p. 17.

POUNDEN, W. D. and HIBBS, J. W. (1948a) *J. Dairy Sci.* **31**:1041.

POUNDEN, W. D. and HIBBS, J. W. (1948b) *J. Dairy Sci.* **31**:1051.

POWELL, D., DURHAM, R. M. and GANN, G. (1968a) Liver Abscess effects on performance traits in fattening beef cattle, *J. Anim. Sci.* **27**:1174 Abs.

POWELL, D., KENT, W., ELLIOTT, H. and ZINN, D. W. (1961) Comparison of carcass traits of Angus and Hereford Steers, *J. Anim. Sci.* **20**:910 Abs.

POWELL, W. E., HUFFMAN, D. L. and PATTERSON, T. B. (1968b) Quantitative estimates of beef carcass composition, *J. Anim. Sci.* **27**:285 Abs.

PRESCOTT, J. H. D. and HINKS, C. E. (1968) *System of management and carcass quality of steers*, Univ. Newcastle Dep. Agric. Market, Rep. 8.

PRESCOTT, J. H. D. and LAMMING, G. E. (1964) The effects of castration on meat production in cattle, sheep and pigs, *J. Agric. Sci.* **63**:341.

PRESTON, R. L. (1966) Protein requirements of growing finishing cattle and lambs, *J. Nutr.* **90**: 157.

PRESTON, R. L. (1968) What is needed to break through the efficiency barrier in beef cattle, *Feedstuffs* 30th March, p. 20.

PRESTON, R. L. and BURROUGHS, W. (1958) Stilbestrol response in lambs fed rations differing in calorie to protein ratios, *J. Anim. Sci.* **17**:140.

PRESTON, R. L., CHENG, E., STORY, C. D., HOMEYER, P., PAULS, J. and BURROUGHS, W. (1956) The influence of oral administration of diethylstilbestrol upon estrogenic residues in the tissues of beef cattle, *J. Anim. Sci.* **15**:3.

PRESTON, T. R. (1956a) Unpublished data.

PRESTON, T. R. (1956b) Dry feeding of calves, *Agriculture* (*London*) **62**:462.

PRESTON, T. R. (1956c) The rearing of calves weaned at between two and four weeks of age, *Proc. Brit. Soc. Anim. Prod.*, p. 67.

PRESTON, T. R. (1958) The value of rumen inoculations and of diets containing sweetening agents for calves weaned on to dry food at three weeks of age, *Proc. Brit. Soc. Anim. Prod.*, p. 33.

PRESTON, T. R. (1960) Unpublished data.

PRESTON, T. R. (1962a) Antibiotics for the young ruminant, in *Antibiotics in Agriculture, Proc., Nottingham Univ. 9th Easter school* (ed. M. Woodbine,) Butterworths, London, p. 214.

PRESTON, T. R. (1962b) Unpublished data.

PRESTON, T. R. (1963a) Acute overeating with cereals in ruminants, *Vet. Rec.* **75**:125.

PRESTON, T. R. (1963b) The nutrition of the early weaned calf, in *World Review of Nutrition and Dietetics* (ed. G. H. Bourne), Pitmans, London, **4**:119.

PRESTON, T. R. (1963c) Unpublished data.

PRESTON, T. R. (1963d) Barley beef production, *Vet. Rec.* **75**:1399.

PRESTON, T. R. (1964) Barley beef production, *Feedstuffs* No. **40**:66.

PRESTON, T. R. (1967) Calf rearing, Min. Agric. Fish. Fd Bull, 10. HMSO, London.

PRESTON, T. R. and AITKEN, J. N. (1963) Unpublished data.

PRESTON, T. R., AITKEN, J. N., MACLEOD, N. A., MACDEARMID, A. and ROSEN, G. D. (1960a) An initial investigation on the effects of low level feeding of hydroxyzine dihydrochloride on growth, endocrines and carcass measurements of fattening cattle, *Anim. Prod.* **2**:27.

Preston, T. R., Aitken, J. N., Whitelaw, F. G., Macdearmid, A. and Philip, E. B. (1963a) Intensive beef production, 3: Performance of Friesian steers given low-fibre diets, *Anim. Prod.* **5**: 245.

Preston, T. R., Archibald, J. D. H. and Tinkler, W. (1957) The digestibility of grass by young calves, *J. Agric. Sci.* **48**:259.

Preston, T. R., Bowers, H. B., MacLeod, N. A. and Philip, E. B. (1965a) Intensive beef production, 6: A note on the nutritive value of high moisture barley stored anaerobically, *Anim. Prod.* **7**: 385.

Preston, T. R., Elias, A. and Willis, M. B. (1968a) Intensive beef production from sugar cane, 7: The performance of bulls given high levels of molasses/urea at different dilutions, *Rev. cubana Cienc. Agric.* (Eng. ed.) **2**:263.

Preston, T. R., Elias, A., Willis, M. B. and Sutherland, T. M. (1967a) Intensive beef production from molasses and urea, *Nature* **216**:721.

Preston, T. R. and Gee, I. (1957) Effect of hexoestrol on carcass composition and efficiency of food utilization in fattening lambs, *Nature* **179**:247.

Preston, T. R., Greenhalgh, I. and MacLeod, N. A. (1960b) The effect of hexoestrol on growth, carcass quality, endocrine and reproductive organs of ram, wether and female lambs, *Anim. Prod.* **2**:11.

Preston, T. R., Greenhalgh, I., Boyne, A. A., Crichton, J. A., Rolfe, E. J., Brown, A. and Dodsworth, T. L. (1961) The effect of hexoestrol on the eating quality of beef and lamb, *Anim. Prod.* **3**:233.

Preston, T. R., Kay, M., Walker, T., Bowers, H. B., MacLeod, N. A., Macdearmid, A., Philip, E. B. and Hargreave, K. (1965b) The effect of different sources of dietary nitrogen on performance of intensive beef cattle, *Anim. Prod.* **7**:288 Abs.

Preston, T. R., Macdearmid, A., Aitken, J. N., MacLeod, N. A. and Philip, E. B. (1968) The effect of castration on growth, feed conversion and carcass quality of Friesian male cattle given all-concentrate diets, *Rev. cubana Cienc. Agric.* (Eng. ed.) **2**:183.

Preston, T. R., Macdearmid, A. and MacLeod, N. A. (1963b) Intensive beef production: A study of feed processing and the value of supplementary roughage, *Anim. Prod.* **5**:216 Abs.

Preston, T. R., MacLeod, N. A. and Dinda, P. K. (1959) The effect of chlortetracycline on growth of early weaned calves, *Anim. Prod.* **1**:13.

Preston, T. R. and Whitelaw, F. G. (1962) Unpublished data.

Preston, T. R., Whitelaw, F. G., Aitken, J. N., Macdearmid, A. and Charleson, E. B. (1963c) Intensive beef production, 1: Performance of cattle given complete ground diets, *Anim. Prod.* **5**:47.

Preston, T. R., Whitelaw, F. G. and MacLeod, N. A. (1963d) The nutrition of the early weaned calf, 4: Ruminal ammonia formation from soluble and insoluble protein sources, *Anim. Prod.* **5**:147.

Preston, T. R., Whitelaw, F. G. and MacLeod, N. A. (1964) The nutrition of the early weaned calf. 6: The effect of supplemental lysine and methionine on the utilization of groundnut protein, *Anim. Prod.* **6**:17.

Preston, T. R., Whitelaw, F. G., MacLeod, N. A. and Philip, E. B. (1965c) The nutrition of the early weaned calf. 8: The effect on nitrogen retention of diets containing different amounts of fish meal, *Anim. Prod.* **7**:53.

Preston, T. R., Whitelaw, F. G., Ndumbe, R. D. and Charleson, E. B. (1960c) The effect of including stabilized tallow in the concentrate mixture fed to early weaned calves, *Proc. Nutr. Soc.* **19**:xviii.

Preston, T. R. and Willis, M. B. (1969) Sugar cane as an energy source for the production of meat, *Outlook in Agric.* **6**:29.

Preston, T. R., Willis, M. B. and Elias, A. (1967b) Intensive beef production from sugar cane, 1: Different levels of urea in molasses given *ad libitum* to fattening bulls as a supplement to a grain diet, *Rev. cubana Cienc. Agric.* (Eng. ed.) **1**:33.

Preston, T. R., Willis, M. B. and Elias, A. (1967c) Intensive beef production from sugar cane, 2: Comparison between normal and invert molasses as a supplement to forage or concentrates, *Rev. cubana Cienc. Agric.* (Eng. ed.) **1**:41.

Preston, T. R., Willis, M. B. and Elias, A. (1969a) Intensive beef production from sugar cane, 9:

Performance of two breeds given different amounts and sources of protein in a high-molasses diet, *Anim. Prod.* **11**:In press.

PRESTON, T. R., WILLIS, M. B. and ELIAS, A. (1969b) Intensive beef production from sugar cane, 11: High test or final molasses and the effect of selenium for fattening bulls, *Rev. cubana Cienc. Agric.* (Eng. ed.) **3**:In press.

PRESTON, T. R., WILLIS, M. B. and MARTIN, J. L. (1969c) Efficiency of utilization for fattening of the metabolizable energy of molasses-based diets, *J. Anim. Sci.* **28**:796.

PRICE, J. F., PEARSON, A. M. and BENNE, E. J. (1957) Specific gravity and chemical composition of the untrimmed ham as related to leanness of pork carcasses, *J. Anim. Sci.* **16**:85.

PRICE, W. D. and SMITH, W. H. (1968) Factors affecting Zn requirements of cattle, *J. Anim. Sci.* **27**: 1174 Abs.

PURSER, D. B. and BUECHLER, S. M. (1966) Amino-acid composition of rumen organisms, *J. Dairy Sci.* **49**:81.

PURSER, D. B., KLOPFENSTEIN, T. J. and CLINE, J. H. (1966) Dietary and defaunation effects upon plasma amino-acid concentrations in sheep, *J. Nutr.* **89**:226.

PURSER, D. B. and MOIR, R. J. (1959) Rumen flora studies in the sheep, 9: The effect of pH on the ciliate population of the rumen *in vivo*. *Aust. J. Agric. Res.* **10**:555.

PUTNAM, P. A., BOVARD, K. P., PRIODE, B. M. and LEHMANN, R. P. (1965) Rumen volatile fatty acids and gains of record-of-performance bulls, *J. Anim. Sci.* **24**:166.

PUTNAM, P. A. and DAVIS, R. E. (1963) Ration effects on drylot steer feeding patterns, *J. Anim. Sci.* **22**:437.

PUTNAM, P. A. and DAVIS, R. E. (1964) Physical form of barley–alfalfa steer rations, *J. Anim. Sci.* **23**: 1232 Abs.

PUTNAM, P. A. and DAVIS, R. E. (1965) Postrumen fiber digestibility, J. *Anim. Sci.* **24**:826.

PUTNAM, P. A., GUTIERREZ, J. and DAVIS, R. E. (1961) Effects of frequency of feeding upon rumen voltatile fatty acids, protozoal populations and weight gains in Angus heifer calves, *J. Dairy Sci.* **44**:1364.

PUTNAM, P. A., LEHMANN, R. P. and DAVIS, R. E. (1967a) Ration selection and feeding patterns of steers fed in drylot, *J. Anim. Sci.* **26**:647.

PUTNAM, P. A., OLTJEN, R. R. and BOND, J. J. (1967b) Soyabean oil in finishing rations for cattle, *J. Anim. Sci.* **26**:879 Abs.

QUARTERMAN, J. (1966) Vitamin A requirements of intensively fed beef cattle, *Vet. Rec.* **79**:855.

QUARTERMAN, J. and MILLS, C. F. (1964) Vitamin A and riboflavin concentrations in livers of intensively fattened cattle, *Proc. Nutr. Soc.* **23**:x.

QUAYLE, P. D. (1956) Unpublished data.

QUAYLE, P. D. (1958) A study of the effects of dietary aureomycin and methods of weaning in early weaned calves, *J. Agric. Sci.* **50**:335.

QUIÑONES, M. and PRESTON, T. R. (1968) Early weaning of dairy calves with different quantities of whole milk and with or without alfalfa in the diet, *Rev. cubana Cienc. Agric.* (Eng. ed.) **2**:191.

QUINTANA, F. O. (1968) A system for production of beef under actual Cuban conditions of 1967, Ing. Agron. thesis, Univ. Havana.

RAGAB, M. T. and ABD-EL-SALAM, M. F. (1963) Heritability and repeatability of body weight and growth rate of Egyptian buffaloes and cattle, *J. Anim. Prod. UAR* **3**:15.

RAGSDALE, A. C., THOMPSON, A. J., WORSTELL, D. M. and BRODY, S. (1953) The effect of humidity on milk production and composition, feed and water consumption and body weight in cattle, Mo. Agric. Exp. Sta. Res. Bull. 521.

RAIMONDI, R. (1955) Effect of castration on somatic growth and carcass character of fattening Piedmontese cattle, Parts 1 and 2, *Ann. Sper. Agrar.* **9**:1247, 1453.

RAIMONDI, R. (1961) A comparative study of fattening and musculature of Piedmontese and double-muscled calves, *Ann. Sper. Agrar.* **15**:105.

RAIMONDI, R. (1965) Comparative fattening trial between double-muscled Piedmontese × Friesian crossbred young bulls and Friesian young bulls, *Riv. Zootec.* **38**:111.

RAKES, A. H., HARDISON, W. A., ALBERT, J., MOORE, W. E. C. and GRAF, G. C. (1957) Response of growing dairy heifers to frequency of feeding, *J. Dairy Sci.* **40**:1621.

RALEIGH, R. J. and WALLACE, D. J. (1962) Response of weaner calves to various levels of energy and protein supplementation, *J. Anim. Sci.* **21**:668 Abs.

RALEIGH, R. J. and WALLACE, D. J. (1965) Frequency of feeding and urea utilization by ruminants, *J. Anim. Sci.* **24**:595 Abs.

RALSTON, A. T. (1965) Wheat in current beef cattle rations, *Feedstuffs*, 17th April, p. 18.

RALSTON, A. T., CASTER, J. E., KENNICK, W. H. and DAVIDSON, T. (1968) Response of feedlot heifers to certain exogenous hormones, *J. Anim. Sci.* **27**:1117 Abs.

RALSTON, A. T., CHURCH, D. C., KENNICK, W. H. and TAYLOR, N. O. (1963) Effect of varying milo-barley levels, ration preparation and intraruminal injections of vitamin A upon feedlot performance of steers, *J. Anim. Sci.* **22**:943.

RALSTON, A. T. and DYER, I. A. (1959) Effect of varying levels of hydroxyzine on blood characteristics and feedlot performance of steers, *J. Anim. Sci.* **18**:1181 Abs.

RALSTON, A. T., KENNICK, W. H., DAVIDSON, T. P. and ROWE, K. E. (1966) Effect of pre-finishing treatment upon finishing performance and carcass characteristics of beef cattle, *J. Anim. Sci.* **25**:29.

RALSTON, A. T., KENNICK, W. H. and TAYLOR, N. O. (1962) Effect of "high" concentrate diets upon performance, *J. Anim. Sci.* **21**:666 Abs.

RAMIREZ, D. V. and MCCANN, S. M. (1963) Comparison of the regulation of luteinizing hormone (LH) secretion in immature and adult rats, *Endocrinology* **72**:452.

RAMSBOTTOM, J. M. and STRANDINE, E. J. (1949) Initial physical and chemical changes in beef as related to tenderness, *J. Anim. Sci.* **8**:398.

RAMSBOTTOM, J. M., STRANDINE, E. J. and KOONZ, C. H. (1945) Comparative tenderness of representative beef muscles, *Fd Res.* **23**:32.

RAMSEY, C. B., COLE, J. W., BACKUS, W. R. and REYNOLDS, A. E. (1967) Ultrasonic estimates of muscle thickness in live cattle as predictors of carcass retail yield, *J. Anim. Sci.* **26**:899.

RAMSEY, C. B., COLE, J. W. and HOBBS, C. S. (1962) Relation of beef carcass grades, proposed yield grades and fat thickness to separable lean, fat and bone, *J. Anim. Sci.* **21**:193.

RAMSEY, C. B., COLE, J. W., MEYER, B. H. and TEMPLE, R. S. (1963) Effects of type and breed of British, Zebu and dairy cattle on production, palatability and composition, 2: Palatability differences and cooking losses as determined by laboratory and family panels, *J. Anim. Sci.* **22**:1001.

RAMSEY, C. B., COLE, J. W., TEMPLE, R. S. and HOBBS, C. S. (1966) Prediction of separable muscle in carcasses of seven breeds of steers, *J. Anim. Sci.* **25**:256 Abs.

RANATUNGA, P. (1965) Calf mortality in some government farms in Ceylon, *Ceylon Vet. J.* **13**:90.

RANDEL, P. F. (1966) A comparison of whole milk vs. milk replacer and of weaning at 6 or 9 weeks in raising dairy calves, Puerto Rica Agric. Exp. Sta. Bull. 198.

RANKIN, J. E. F. (1959) Abortions in heifers which had been fed silage containing hexoestrol, *Vet. Rec.* **71**:924.

RAPPEN, W. H. (1965) Birth weight in Black Pied cattle, *Tierzüchter*, **17**:435.

RATCLIFF, L., BOYD, L. J. and PLOWMAN, R. D. (1962) Performance and interactions of dairy sire groups on two systems of feeding, *J. Anim. Sci.* **21**:975 Abs.

RAUN, A. P., MCASKILL, J. W., WAGNER, J. F. and TOMKINSON, L. (1967) Effect of CAP on gains and feed consumption of open and bred heifers, *J. Anim. Sci.* **26**:950.

RAUN, A. P., MEANS, T. M., MCASKILL, J. W. and JORDAN, C. E. (1963) The effect of tylosin on performance of fattening steer and heifer calves, *J. Anim. Sci.* **22**:845 Abs.

RAUN, N. S. (1968) Professional animal scientists throughout the world, *J. Anim. Sci.* **27**:267.

RAUN, N. S., RENBARGER, R., STABLES, G. and POPE, L. S. (1965) Trace mineral supplementation of all-barley rations for fattening steers, *J. Anim. Sci.* **24**:279 Abs.

RAVEN, A. M. and ROBINSON, K. L. (1958) Studies on the nutrition of the young calf: A comparison of starch, lactose and hydrogenated palm oil with butterfat in milk diets, *Br. J. Nutr.* **12**:469.

RAVEN, A. M. and ROBINSON, K. L. (1961) Comparative effects of wet and dry feeding on the utilization of protein by calves, *Nature* **192**:1256.

RAVEN, A. M., ROBINSON, K. L., IRWIN, J. H. D. and FORBES, T. J. (1966) Beef production from bulls and steers, 2: The evaluation of carcasses of animals fed experimental high-concentrate diets, *Rec. Agric. Res.* **15**:129.

RAY, D. E., EMMERSON, M. A. and MELAMPY, R. M. (1961) Effect of exogenous progesterone in reproductive activity in the beef heifer, *J. Anim. Sci.* **20**:373.

RAY, D. E., ROUBICEK, C. B., PAHNISH, O. F. and BRINKS, J. S. (1968) Breeding merit of topcross progeny of inbred beef sires, *J. Anim. Sci.* **27**:1104 Abs.

RAY, M. L. and CHILD, R. D. (1964) Wintering steers on broiler house litter, *Ark. Farm Res.* **13** (5).

RAY, M. L. and MCBRIDE, W. M. (1961) Effect of Synovex-S on steer gains and carcass values, *J. Anim. Sci.* **20**:400 Abs.

REDDY, B. G., TUMA, H. J., GRANT, D. L. and COVINGTON, R. C. (1968) Relationship of intramuscular fat and the vascular system to beef tenderness, *J. Anim. Sci.* **27**:1146 Abs.

REED, W. D. C., ELLIOTT, R. C. and TOPPS, J. H. (1965) Phosphorus excretion of cattle fed on high energy diets, *Nature* **208**:953.

REID, J. T. (1953a) Urea as a protein replacement: A review, *J. Dairy Sci.* **36**:955.

REID, J. T. (1953b) Effects of several levels of nutrition upon growth, reproduction and lactation in cattle, *Proc. Cornell Nutr. Conf.*

REID, J. T. (1956) Some nutritional effects of varying concentrate-roughage ratios in relation to feed input—milk output by dairy cows, Mem. Cornell Agric. Exp. Sta. No. 344.

REID, J. T., BENSADOUN, A., PALADINES, O. L. and VAN NIEKERK, B. D. H. (1963) Body water estimations in relation to body composition and indirect calorimetry in ruminants, *Ann. NY Acad. Sci.* **110**:327.

REID, J. T., WELLINGTON, G. H. and DUNN, H. O. (1955) Some relationships among the major chemical components of the bovine body and their application to nutritional investigations, *J. Dairy Sci.* **38**:1344.

REID, R. L. (1961) Digestive physiology and nutrition of the ruminant, *Proc. 7th Easter School in Agric. Sci. Univ. Nottingham*, p. 138, Butterworths, London.

REILLY, G. (1957) Bonsmara cattle now passing through critical test, *Fmrs Wkly (Bloemfontein)*, 15th May, p. 18.

REISER, R. (1951) Hydrogenation of polyunsaturated fatty acids by the ruminant, *Fd Proc.* **10**:236.

REISINGER, R. C., HEDDLESTON, K. L. and MANTHEI, C. A. (1959) A myxovirus (SF 4) associated with shipping fever of cattle, *J. Am. Vet. Med. Ass.* **135**:147.

RENBARGER, R. E., SMITHSON, L. J., STEPHENS, D. F. and POPE, L. S. (1964) Effects of nutrition before and after calving on performance of beef heifers, *J. Anim. Sci.* **23**:293 Abs.

RENDEL, J. (1959) Factors influencing gestation length in Swedish breeds of cattle, *Z. Tierzücht. ZüchtBiol.* **73**:117.

RENDEL, J. M. and ROBERTSON, A. (1950) Estimation of genetic gain in milk yield by selection in a closed herd of dairy cattle, *J. Genet.* **50**:1.

RENOU, Y. (1964) Studies on the tenderness of meat, 1: Comparison of tenderness estimations obtained with a Warner-Bratzler apparatus and taste panels, *Ann. Zootech.* **13**:93.

REPP, W. W., HALE, W. H., CHENG, E. W. and BURROUGHS, W. (1955) Influence of oral administration of non-protein nitrogen feeding compounds upon blood ammonia and urea levels in lambs, *J. Anim. Sci.* **14**:118.

REY, J. (1968) Synchronization, oestrus response and fertility in heifers after a shortened period of inhibition of sexual activity by means of fluorogestone acetate, *Proc. 6th Congr. Rep. AI Paris*, p. 296.

REYNEKE, J. and BONSMA, J. C. (1964) An interaction between post-natal environment and heredity on weaning weight of beef calves *Proc. S. Afr. Soc. Anim. Prod.* **3**:170.

REYNEKE, J. and PENZHORN, E. J. (1964) Birth weights and related phenomena in Charolais: Frieslands with special reference to dystokia. *Proc. S. Afr. Soc. Anim. Prod.* **3**:166.

REYNOLDS, W. L., DEROUEN, T. M. and HIGH, J. W. (1963) The effect of growth rate on calving percent of Brangus and Africander Angus heifers, *J. Anim. Sci.* **22**:821 Abs.

REYNOLDS, W. L., DEROUEN, T. M., HIGH, J. W. and TEMPLE, R. S. (1964a) Relationship of pre-weaning to post-weaning performance of fed steers and replacement heifers, *J. Anim. Sci.* **23**:305 Abs.

Reynolds, W. L., DeRouen, T. M., High, J. W., Wiltbank, J. N., Warwick, E. J. and Temple, R. S. (1964b) Evaluation of pastures in terms of reproduction of beef cattle, *J. Anim. Sci.* **23**:890 Abs.

Reynolds, W. L., DeRouen, T. M. and Meyerhoeffer, D. C. (1967a) Milk production of Angus, Brahman and Zebu-cross cows, *J. Anim. Sci.* **26**:206 Abs.

Reynolds, W. L., DeRouen, T. M., Meyerhoeffer, D. C., Wiltbank, J. N. and Temple, R. S. (1965a) Birth weight and gestation length of beef cattle, *J. Anim. Sci.* **24**:851 Abs.

Reynolds, W. L., DeRouen, T. M., Temple, R. S. and Meyerhoeffer, D. C. (1965b) Reproductive performance of Angus and Brahman bulls mated to straightbred and Angus–Zebu cross cows, *J. Anim. Sci.* **24**:287 Abs.

Reynolds, W. L., DeRouen, T. M., Temple, R. S. and Meyerhoeffer, D. C. (1966) Reproductive traits of Angus, Zebu and Zebu-cross cows, *J. Anim. Sci.* **25**:252 Abs.

Reynolds, W. L., DeRouen, T. M., Temple, R. S. and Meyerhoeffer, D. C. (1967b) Winter feed and growth of Angus, Brahman and crossbred heifers, *J. Anim. Sci.* **26**:888 Abs.

Reynolds, W. L., Koger, M., Kirk, W. G. and Peacock, F. M. (1959) Expression of hybrid vigor in birth weights of beef calves, *J. Anim. Sci.* **18**:1467 Abs.

Reynolds, W. M., Hale, W. H., Sherman, W. C. and Luther, H. G. (1958) Studies of oleandomycin at nutritional levels in lamb and steer rations, *J. Anim. Sci.* **17**:1174 Abs.

Reynolds, W. M., Sherman, W. C., Appel, P. P. and Luther, H. G. (1956) Effect of protein level upon response of beef cattle to oxytetracycline and stilbestrol, *J. Anim. Sci.* **15**:1242 Abs.

Rhodes, R. W. and Woods, W. (1962) Volatile fatty acid measurements on the rumen contents of lambs fed rations of various physical form, *J. Anim. Sci.* **21**:483.

Rice, R. W. and Paules, L. H. (1965) Comparison of fifty percent hay and no hay ration with or without supplemental vitamin A for beef production from young dairy calves, *J. Dairy Sci.* **48**:1668.

Richardson, D., Perry, H. B., Dunn, L. L., Smith, E. F. and Harbers, L. H. (1966) Sources of non-protein nitrogen for ruminants, *J. Anim. Sci.* **25**:908 Abs.

Richardson, D., Smith, E. F., Baker, F. H. and Cox, R. F. (1961) Effects of roughage/concentrate ratio in cattle fattening rations on gains, feed efficiency, digestion and carcass, *J. Anim. Sci.* **20**:316.

Richter, K. (1963) The potential for increasing efficiency of feed utilization through newer knowledge of animal nutrition, *World Conf. Anim. Prod. Rome*, **1**:147.

Richter, K., Cranz, K. L. and Schmidt, K. H. (1960) Fattening trials with young bulls and young bullocks, 1: The influence of early castration on the fattening capacity, slaughter quality and carcass value, *Zuchtungskunde* **32**:5.

Ridler, B., Broster, W. H. and Foot, A. S. (1963) The growth rate of heifers in a dairy breed, *J. Agric. Sci.* **61**:1.

Riedel, B. B. and Arnold, J. L. (1956) The effect of pasture crops with and without supplemental corn feeding and drylot management for beef production and nematode control, *J. Anim. Sci.* **15**:537.

Riek, R. F. (1956) Factors affecting the susceptibility of cattle to tick infestation, *Aust. Vet. J.* **32**:204.

Riemenschneider, M. N. (1962) Report of the committee on Anaplasmosis, *J. Am. Vet. Med. Ass.* **141**:1461.

Riemerschmid, G. and Elder, J. S. (1945) The absorptivity for solar radiation of different coloured hairy coats of cattle, *Onderstepoort J. Vet. Sci. Anim. Ind.* **20**:223.

Riggs, J. K. (1965) Moist sorghum grain preserved in sealed storage for growing and fattening beef cattle, *Proc. 20th Annual Tex. Nutr. Conf.*, p. 141.

Riggs, J. K. (1966) Climatic environmental effects on feedlot performance and physiological responses of beef cattle, *J. Anim. Sci.* **25**:253 Abs.

Riggs, J. K., Conrad, B. E., Marion, P. T. and Allen, J. H. (1967) Young bulls, steers and heifers for slaughter beef production, *J. Anim. Sci.* **26**:211 Abs.

Riggs, J. K. and Crookshank, H. R. (1960) Moisture content of sorghum grain and urinary calculi in steers, *J. Anim. Sci.* **19**:1290 Abs.

Riggs, J. K. and Maddox, L. A. (1955) Tex. Agric. Exp. Sta. Bull. 809.

RILEY, J. G., HEDRICK, H. B., THOMPSON, G. B., DYER, A. J. and GEHRKE, C. W. (1968) Comparison of methods for determining beef carcass composition, *J. Anim. Sci.* **27**:1147 Abs.

RILEY, J. G., THOMPSON, G. B. and DYER, A. J. (1967) Accuracy of 28 and 56 day gains for culling feedlot cattle, *J. Anim. Sci.* **26**:1469 Abs.

RILEY, M. L., FIELD, R. A. and NELMS, G. E. (1966) Comparison of two methods of measuring the area of longissimus dorsi muscle, *J. Anim. Sci.* **25**:587 Abs.

RILEY, P. W., CARDON, B. P., BROWN, W. H. and STULL, J. W. (1965) Effects on cattle performance of intense moist cooking of the rolled grain portion of fattening rations, *J. Anim. Sci.* **24**:599 Abs.

RIPP, J. K. (1959) Tex. Agric. Exp. Sta. Prog. Rep. 2160.

RITCHEY, S. J. and HOSTETLER, R. L. (1964) Characterization of the eating quality of four beef muscles from animals of different ages by panel scores, shear-force values, extensibility of the muscle fibres and collagen content, *Fd Tech.* **18**:1067.

RITZMAN, E. G. and BENEDICT, F. G. (1938) Nutritional physiology of the adult ruminant, Publ. Carnegie Inst. 494.

ROB, O. and KRPATOVA, J. (1967) An outbreak of bovine abortion caused by *Aspergillus fumigatus*, *Veterinarstvi* **17**:443.

ROBERSON, R. L., PAHNISH, O. F., TAYLOR, R. L., BRINKS, J. S., CLARK, R. T. and LANE, A. M. (1963) Genetics of grade condition and weight in range cattle, *J. Anim. Sci.* **22**:822 Abs.

ROBERTS, R. C. (1965) Some contributions of the laboratory mouse to animal breeding research, Part 1, *Anim. Breed. Abst.* **33**:339.

ROBERTS, W. K. and MCKIRDY, J. A. (1964) Weight gains, carcass fat characteristics and ration digestibility in steers as affected by dietary rapeseed oil, sunflowerseed oil and animal tallow, *J. Anim. Sci.* **23**:682.

ROBERTS, W. K. and OMER, V. V. E. (1965) Dietary potassium requirement of fattening steers, *J. Anim. Sci.* **24**:902 Abs.

ROBERTSON, A. (1954) Inbreeding and performance in British Friesian cattle, *Proc. Br. Soc. Anim. Prod.*, p. 87.

ROBERTSON, A. (1955) Prediction equations in quantitative genetics, *Biometrics* **11**:95.

ROBERTSON, A. (1957) Optimum group size in progeny testing and family selection, *Biometrics* **13**:442.

ROBERTSON, A. (1959) A simple method of pedigree evaluation in dairy cattle, *Anim. Prod.* **1**:167.

ROBERTSON, A. (1960) The progeny testing of dairy bulls—a comparison of tests of father and son, *J. Agric. Sci.* **54**:100.

ROBERTSON, A., O'CONNOR, L. K. and EDWARDS, J. (1960) The progeny testing of dairy bulls at different management levels, *Anim. Prod.* **2**:141.

ROBERTSON, A. and RENDEL, J. M. (1950) The use of progeny testing with AI in dairy cattle, *J. Genet.* **50**:21.

ROBERTSON, K. E. and LIPPER, R. I. (1963) Effect of lighting on beef cattle performance, *Proc. Am. Soc. Agric. Engineers, Chicago.*

ROBERTSON, I. S. and LAING, A. (1965) A comparison of entire, partially and fully castrated beef cattle housed in stalls and yards, *Anim. Prod.* **7**:279 Abs.

ROBINSON, E. D. and MARION, P. T. (1966) Beef production following mesquite control, *J. Anim. Sci.* **25**:599 Abs.

ROBINSON, D. W. and LAMBOURNE, J. L. (1968) Muscular depletion in animals utilizing arid ranges, *J. Anim. Sci.* **27**:1123 Abs.

ROBINSON, N. W., HANSARD, S. L., JOHNS, D. M. and ROBERTSON, G. L. (1960) Excess dietary manganese and feedlot performance of beef cattle, *J. Anim. Sci.* **19**:1290 Abs.

ROBY, T. O. (1962) Natural transmission of bovine anaplasmosis, *The Southwestern Vet.* **16**:17.

ROGERS, R. W., HOWSE, G. W., LINDLEY, C. E., BACHUS, W. R. and TAYLOR, J. C. (1966) Beef tenderness as affected by marbling, *J. Anim. Sci.* **25**:886 Abs.

ROJAS, J., SCHWEIGERT, B. S. and RUPEL, I. W. (1948) *J. Dairy Sci.* **31**:81.

ROLLINS, W. C., CARROLL, F. D., POLLOCK, J. W. T. and KUDODA, M. N. (1962) Beef cattle performance and progeny tests for gain, efficiency, carcass conformation and earliness of maturity, *J. Anim. Sci.* **21**:200.

ROLLINS, W. C. and WAGNON, K. A. (1956a) A genetic analysis of weaning weights in a range beef herd operated under optimum and suboptimum nutritional regimes, *J. Anim. Sci.* **15**:125.

Rollins, W. C. and Wagnon, K. A. (1956b) Heritability of weaning grade in range beef cattle, *J. Anim. Sci.* **15**:529.

Romans, J. R., Tuma, H. J. and Tucker, W. L. (1965a) Influence of carcass maturity and marbling on the physical and chemical characteristics of beef, 1: Palatability, fibre diameter and proximate analysis, *J. Anim. Sci.* **24**:681.

Romans, J. R., Tuma, H. J. and Tucker, W. L. (1965b) Influence of carcass maturity and marbling on the physical and chemical characteristics of beef, 2: Muscle pigments and colour, *J. Anim. Sci.* **24**:686.

Rook, J. A. F., Balch, C. C., Campling, R. C. and Fisher, L. J. (1963) The utilization of acetic, propionic and butyric acids by growing heifers, *Br. J. Nutr.* **17**:399.

Rosochowicz, J. (1965) Preliminary observations of losses of calves at birth in Black Pied Lowland heifers, *Med. Vet.* **21**:110.

Ross, J. G., Armour, J. and Lee, R. P. (1960) Further observations on the influence of genetical factors in resistance to helminthiasis in Nigerian Zebu cattle, *Vet Rec.* **72**:119.

Rostovcev, N. F., Svarc, V. E. and Davydova, Z. M. (1964) The quality of bull and steer meat. *Dokl. Akad. Nauk Lenin.* **4**:29.

Roubicek, C. B., Erwin, E. S., Nelms, G. E. and Taylor, B. (1960) Response of beef steers to multiple stilbestrol implants pre-weaning, weaning, grazing and feedlot, *J. Anim. Sci.* **19**:966 Abs.

Roy, J. H. B. (1958) The nutrition of the early weaned dairy calf: A review, *Dairy Sci. Abst.* **20**:2.

Roy, J. H. B. (1959) Some nutritional and physiological aspects of calf rearing, *Outlook on Agric.* **2**:219.

Roy, J. H. B. (1964) The nutrition of intensively reared calves, *Vet. Rec.* **76**:511.

Roy, J. H. B., Palmer, J., Shillam, K. W. G., Ingram, P. L. and Wood, P. C. (1955) The nutritive value of colostrum for the calf, 10: The relationship between the period of time that a calf house has been occupied and the incidence of scouring and mortality in young calves, *Br. J. Nutr.* **9**:11.

Roy, J. H. B., Shillam, K. W. G., Hawkins, G. M. and Lang, J. M. (1958) The milk requirements of the newborn calf, *Br. J. Nutr.* **12**:123.

RRI (1964) *Annual Open Day Cattle Section*, Rowett Res. Inst., Aberdeen.

RRI (1965) *Annual Open Day Cattle Section*, Rowett Res. Inst., Aberdeen.

Rummler, H., Lane, J. W. and Berschneider, F. (1962) Biochemical changes and therapeutic methods in urea poisoning in cattle, *Monatsschr. Vet.* **17**:156.

Rupel, I. W., Bohstedt, G. and Hart, E. B. (1943) The comparative value of urea and linseed meal for milk production, *J. Dairy Sci.* **26**:647.

Rusnak, J. J., Long, T. A. and King, T. B. (1966) Hydrolysed poultry waste as a feed for cattle, *J. Anim. Sci.* **25**:909 Abs.

Russell, E. L., Hale, W. H. and Hubbert, F., Jr. (1962) Evaluation of di-ammonium phosphate as a source of nitrogen for ruminants, *J. Anim. Sci.* **21**:523.

Rutherford, J., Wilson, L. L., Garrigus, R. R. and Drewry, K. J. (1966) Beef bull selection criteria used by southern Indiana commercial beef producers, *J. Anim. Sci.* **25**:1279 Abs.

Saba, W. J., Hale, W. H., Hubbert, F., Jr., Kiernat, J. and Taylor, B. (1964) Digestion of milo and barley by cattle, *J. Anim. Sci.* **23**:533.

Sabin, S. W., Stratton, P. O. and Bogart, R. (1961) Genetic–environment study of calf growth, *J. Anim. Sci.* **20**:911 Abs.

Saffle, R. L. and Bratzler, L. J. (1959) The effect of fatness on some processing and palatability characteristics of pork carcasses, *Fd Technol.* **13**:236.

Sagebiel, J. A., Krause, G. F., Sibbit, W. R., Langford, L., Comfort, J. E., Dyer, A. J. and Lasley, J. F. (1968) Dystocia in reciprocally crossing Angus, Charolais and Herefords, *J. Anim. Sci.* **27**:1128 Abs.

Sagebiel, J. A., Langford, L. L., Sibbit, W. R., Comfort, J. E., Dyer, A. J. and Lasley, J. F. (1967a) Heterosis in pre-weaning traits in beef cattle, *J. Anim. Sci.* **26**:888 Abs.

Sagebiel, J. A., Sibbit, W. R., Langford, L. L., Dyer, A. J., Comfort, J. E. and Lasley, J. F.

(1967b) Heterosis in weaning, post-weaning and slaughter traits of beef heifers, *J. Anim. Sci.* **26**:889 Abs.

SAIDUDDIN, S., QUEVEDO, M. M. and FOOTE, W. D. (1968) Response of beef cows to exogenous progesterone and estradiol at various stages *post-partum*, *J. Anim. Sci.* **27**:1015.

SAIDUDDIN, S., RIESEN, J. W., GRAVES, W. E., TYLER, W. J. and CASIDA, L. E. (1967) Effect of suckling on the interval from parturition to first oestrus in dairy cows, *J. Anim. Sci.* **26**:950 Abs.

SAINSBURY, D. W. B. (1967) Intensive animal production—problems of disease, *Proc. 9th Int. Congr. Anim. Prod. Edinburgh*, p. 104 (invited papers).

SALMELA, A. B., REMPEL, W. E. and COMSTOCK, R. E. (1960) The reaction of three kinds of single cross pigs to three levels of feed intake, 1: Feedlot performance, *J. Anim. Sci.* **19**:84.

SAMSON-HIMMELSTJERNA, D. VON (1965) Correlations between milk yield, fat percentage and weight gain of Oldenburg Black Pied Lowland cattle, *Zuchtungskunde* **37**:323.

SAN CLEMENTE, C. L. and MACKENZIE, R. D. (1957) The bacteriostatic effect of diethylstilbestrol, Mich. Agric. Exp. Sta. Quart. Bull. **39**:438.

SANDER, E. G., WARNER, R. G., HARRISON, H. N. and LOOSLI, J. K. (1959) The stimulatory effect of sodium butyrate and sodium propionate on the development of rumen mucosa in the young calf, *J. Dairy Sci.* **42**:1600.

SANDERS, W. L. (1968) Relationship between change in condition of beef cows during the pasture season and the weaning performance of their calves, *J. Anim. Sci.* **27**:297 Abs.

SARGEANT, K., O'KELLY, J., CARNAGHAN, R. B. A. and ALLCROFT, R. (1961a) The assay of a toxin principle in certain groundnut meals, *Vet. Rec.* **73**:1215.

SARGEANT, K., SHERIDAN, A., O'KELLY, J. and CARNAGHAN, R. B. A. (1961b) Toxicity associated with certain samples of groundnuts, *Nature* **192**:1096.

SAWYER, W. A., BOGART, R., WALLACE, J. D., RALEIGH, R. J., BRINKS, J. S. and CLARK, R. T. (1963) Relationship among weights of dam and progeny performance, *J. Anim. Sci.* **22**:822 Abs.

SAYRE, R. N., BRISKEY, E. J., HOCKSTRA, W. G. and BRAY, R. W. (1961) Effect of preslaughter change to a cold environment on characteristics of pork muscle, *J. Anim. Sci.* **20**:487.

SCARTH, R. D. and BRAY, R. W. (1967) Correlations among traits from nine years of International beef carcass data, *J. Anim. Sci.* **26**:901 Abs.

SCARTH, R. D., PHILLIPS, R. J., SHERRITT, G. W., ZIEGLER, J. H. and KING, T. B. (1965) Estimating genetic and phenotypic parameters for performance traits, carcass traits and live measurements from selected groups of beef sires, *J. Anim. Sci.* **24**:1219 Abs.

SCARTH, R. D., PHILLIPS, P. J., SHERRITT, G. W., ZIEGLER, J. H. and KING, T. B. (1966) Associations of certain performance traits and live measurements with carcass composition and quality, *J. Anim. Sci.* **25**:886.

SCHAKE, L. M., RIGGS, J. K., MCGINTY, D. D. and MARION, P. T. (1966) Effects of feed intake levels upon yield and composition of milk from confined beef cows, *J. Anim. Sci.* **25**:248 Abs.

SCHALLES, R. R. (1967) Reproductive and genetic patterns in a herd of Angus cows, *Diss. Abstr.* **27**:3361B.

SCHALLES, R. R. and MARLOWE, T. J. (1967) Factors affecting test performance of beef bulls, *J. Anim. Sci.* **26**:21.

SCHELLING, G. T. and HATFIELD, E. E. (1967) Abomasal infusion of amino acids to growing lambs, *J. Anim. Sci.* **26**:1484 Abs.

SCHELLING, G. T., HINDS, F. C. and HATFIELD, E. E. (1967) Effect of dietary protein levels, amino-acid supplementation and nitrogen source upon the plasma free amino acid concentrations in growing lambs, *J. Nutr.* **92**:339.

SCHEPER, J. (1965) Possibilities of influencing meat production in young bulls by breeding, *Züchtungskunde* **37**:251.

SCHILLING, P. E. and ENGLAND, N. C. (1968) Some factors affecting reproduction in beef cattle, *J. Anim. Sci.* **27**:1363.

SCHMIDT, K. (1958) On the estimation of heritability of fertility in cattle, 2: *Dtsch. tierärztl. Wschr.* **65**:679.

SCHMIDT-NIELSEN, B. and OSAKI, H. (1958) Renal responses to changes in nitrogen metabolism in sheep, *Am. J. Physiol.* **193**:657.

SCHNEEBERGER, H. (1966) Problems of carcass evaluation in cattle, *Proc. 9th Int. Congr. Anim. Prod. Edinburgh.*

SCNOENAERS, F. and KAECKENBEERK, A. (1960) Studies of colibacillosis in calves, 3: Immunization, *Ann. Méd. vét.* **104**:117.

SCHÖMMUTH, G. (1965) Genetic basis for the fertility of Black Pied Lowland cattle, *Arch. Tierz.* **8**:429.

SCHOONOVER, C. O. and STRATTON, P. O. (1957) A photographic grid used to measure rib-eye areas, *J. Anim. Sci.* **16**:957.

SCHULTZ, H. W. (1957) *Proc. 10th Annual Reciprocal Meat Conf. Chicago.*

SCHULTZ, T. M. (1966) Increasing world food supplies: The economic requirements, *Proc. Natl. Acad. Sci.* **56**:322.

SCHULTZE, A. B. (1965) Can big calves affect breeding performance, *AI Digest* **13** (5), 8.

SCHWULST, F. J., SUMPTION, L. J., SWIGER, L. A. and ARTHAUD, V. H. (1966) Use of oxytocin for estimating milk production of beef cows, *J. Anim. Sci.* **25**:1045.

SCHWULST, F. J., KOCH, R. M., GREGORY, K. E., CUNDIFF, L. V. and SUMPTION, L. J. (1968) Heterosis of milk production in beef cows, *J. Anim. Sci.* **27**:1129 Abs.

SCOTT, L. M. and MARTIN, T. G. (1959) Effect of crossbreeding on body measurements of dual purpose calves, *J. Anim. Sci.* **18**:1466 Abs.

SEARLE, S. R. (1962) Numbers of paired observations needed for estimating repeatability and heritability from regression analysis, *J. Anim. Sci.* **21**:426.

SEEBECK, R. M. and TULLOH, N. M. (1966) The representation of yield of dressed carcass, *Anim. Prod.* **8**:281.

SEIFERT, G. W. and KENNEDY, J. F. (1966) Some observations on the birth weight of beef cattle, *Proc. Aust. Soc. Anim. Prod.* **6**:257.

SELF, H. L. (1967) Environment—what is it and how does it affect the cattle feeder, *Feedstuffs*, 16th Sept., p. 28.

SELF, H. L., SUMMERS, C. E., ROTH, F., HULL, D. and ZMOLEK, W. G. (1963) Environmental influence on rate and economy of gain in yearling steers, *J. Anim. Sci.* **22**:1111.

SELLERS, K., SMITH, G. F. and WOOD, P. D. P. (1968) An investigation into calf mortality in the first eight weeks of life in England and Wales, *Br. Vet. J.* **124**:89.

SELTZER, R. E. (1955) Consumer preference for beef, Ariz. Agric. Exp. Sta. Bull. 267.

SHAH, S. K. and O'MARY, C. C. (1964) Specific age–weight relationships in beef cattle, *J. Anim. Sci.* **23**:854.

SHANNON, F. P., SALISBURY, G. W. and VAN DENMARK, N. L. (1952) The fertility of cows inseminated at various intervals after calving, *J. Anim. Sci.* **11**:355.

SHARMAR, T. C. (1968) Intake and digestion of nutrients by the bovine and climatic stress, *J. Nutr.* **94**:317.

SHARRAH, N., KUNZE, M. S. and PANGBORNE, R. M. (1965) Beef tenderness, 1: Sensory and mechanical evaluation of animals of different breeds, *Fd Technol.* **19**:131.

SHAW, J. C., ENSOR, W. L., TELLECHEA, H. F. and LEE, S. D. (1960) Relation of diet to rumen volatile fatty acids, digestibility, efficiency of gain and degree of unsaturation of body fat in steers, *J. Nutr.* **71**:203.

SHAW, R. W., WOODWARD, T. E. and NORTON, R. P. (1918) *J. Agric. Res.* **12**:575.

SHEEHY, E. J. and SENIOR, B. J. (1942) Storing cattle at different levels of nutrition, *J. Dep. Agric. Eire* **39**:245.

SHELBY, C. E., CLARK, R. T., QUESENBERRY, J. R. and WOODWARD, R. R. (1957) Heritability of some economic traits in record of performance bulls, *J. Anim. Sci.* **16**:1019 Abs.

SHELBY, C. E., CLARK, R. T., QUESENBERRY, J. R. and WOODWARD, R. R. (1960) Heritability of some economic characteristics in record of performance bulls, *J. Anim. Sci.* **19**:450.

SHELBY, C. E., CLARK, R. T. and WOODWARD, R. R. (1955) The heritability of some economic characteristics of beef cattle, *J. Anim. Sci.* **14**:372.

SHELBY, C. E., HARVEY, W. R., CLARK, R. T., QUESENBERRY, J. R. and WOODWARD, R. R. (1963) Estimates of phenotypic and genetic parameters in ten years of Miles City ROP steer data, *J. Anim. Sci.* **22**:346.

SHELTON, M. (1968) An evaluation of some newer anthelmintics, *J. Anim. Sci.* **27**:1136 Abs.

SHERMAN, W. C., HALE, W. H., REYNOLDS, W. M. and LUTHER, H. G. (1959) The effect of tranquilizers, diethylstilbestrol and oxytetracycline alone and in combination on performance of steers, *J. Anim. Sci.* **18**:198.

Sherrod, B. L. and Tillman, D. A. (1962) Effects of varying the processing temperatures upon the nutritive values for sheep of solvent-extracted soyabean and cottonseed meals, *J. Anim. Sci.* **21**:901.

Sherrod, L. B. and Tillman, A. D. (1964) Effect of heating on the utilization of cottonseed meal by sheep, *J. Anim. Sci.* **23**:294 Abs.

Shillam, K. W. G. (1960) Studies on the nutrition of the young calf with special reference to the incidence of *Escherichia coli* infections, Ph.D. thesis, Univ. Reading.

Shillam, K. W. G., Dawson, D. A. and Roy, J. H. B. (1960) The effect of heat treatment on the nutritive value of milk for the young calf, 1: The effect of ultra high temperature treatment and of pasteurization, *Br. J. Nutr.* **14**:403.

Shillam, K. W. G. and Roy, J. H. B. (1963a) The effect of heat treatment on the nutritive value of milk for the young calf, 5: A comparison of spray-dried skim milks prepared with different pre-heating treatments and roller-dried skim milk, and the effects of chlortetracycline supplementations of the spray-dried skim milks, *Br. J. Nutr.* **17**:171.

Shillam, K. W. G. and Roy, J. H. B. (1963b) The effect of heat treatment on the nutritive value of milk for the young calf, 6: The effect of the addition of calcium, *Br. J. Nutr.* **17**:183.

Shillam, K. W. G., Roy, J. H. B. and Ingram, P. L. (1962a) The effect of heat treatment on the nutritive value of milk for the young calf, 2: The factor in a milk substitute associated with a high incidence of scouring and mortality, *Br. J. Nutr.* **16**:267.

Shillam, K. W. G., Roy, J. H. B. and Ingram, P. L. (1962b) The effect of heat treatment on the nutritive value of milk for the young calf, 3: The effect of the pre-heating treatment of spray-dried skim milk and a study of the effect of ultra high temperature, *Br. J. Nutr.* **16**:585.

Shillam, K. W. G., Roy, J. H. B. and Ingram, P. L. (1962c) The effect of heat treatment on the nutritive value of milk for the young calf, 4: Further studies on the effects of the preheating treatment of spray-dried skim milk and of ultra high temperature treatment, *Br. J. Nutr.* **16**: 593.

Shirley, R. L., Easley, J. F., Ammerman, C. B., Kirk, W. G., Palmer, A. Z. and Cunha, T. J. (1964) Some observations of urinary calculi in cattle, *J. Anim. Sci.* **23**:298 Abs.

Shirley, R. L., Palmer, A. Z., Carpenter, J. W., Peacock, F. N., Kirk, W. G. and Davis, G. K. (1957) Effect of grade and breed of cattle on glycogen, lactic acid, nucleic acids and phospholipid phosphorus, *J. Anim. Sci.* **16**:1088 Abs.

Shively, S., Wolf, D., Trenkle, A. and Burroughs, W. (1966) Sulfur additions to high urea finishing rations, *J. Anim. Sci.* **25**:1256 Abs.

Shope, R. E., Jr. (1965) Experimental studies on viral diarrhoea of cattle, *Diss. Abstr.* **26**:634.

Siddons, R. C. (1968) Intestinal disaccharidases in the calf, *Proc. Nutr. Soc.* **27**:18A.

Simkins, K. L., Jr. (1965) Relationship of blood and rumen metabolites to food intake in ruminants, Ph.D. thesis, Univ. Wisconsin.

Simkins, K. L., Jr., Suttie, J. W. and Baumgardt, B. R. (1965) Regulation of food intake in ruminants, 4: Effect of acetate, propionate, butyrate and glucose on voluntary food intake in dairy cattle, *J. Dairy Sci.* **48**:1623.

Simone, M., Carroll, F. D. and Clegg, M. T. (1958a) Effect of degree of finish in differences in quality factors of beef, *Fd Res.* **23**:32.

Simone, M., Clegg, M. T. and Carroll, F. D. (1958b) Effect of methods of stilbestrol administration on quality factors of beef, *J. Anim. Sci.* **17**:834.

Simone, M., Carroll, F. D. and Chichester, C. O. (1959) Differences in eating quality factors for beef from 18- and 30-month steers, *Fd Technol.* **13**:337.

Simone, M., Carroll, F. D., Chichester, C. O. and Whitaker, J. R. (1961) Quality factors of beef as affected by delayed growth due to protein deficiency, *J. Anim. Sci.* **20**:353.

Simpson, M. E., Asling, C. W. and Evans, H. M. (1950) Some endocrine influence on skeletal growth and differentiation, *Yale J. Biol. Med.* **23**:1.

Singh, O. N., Sinha, B. D. and Singh, P. P. S. R. (1958) Environmental and hereditary causes of variation in length of gestation of Tharparkar cows, *Indian J. Dairy Sci.* **11**:109.

Singh, O. N., Singh, R. N. and Srivastava, R. R. P. (1965) Study on *post-partum* interval to first service in Tharparkar cattle, *Indian J. Vet. Sci.* **35**:245.

Skelley, G. C., Stanford, W. C. and Edwards, R. L. (1968) Effect of ration and vitamin A on beef carcass and fat composition, *J. Anim. Sci.* **27**:288 Abs.

SKINNER, J. D. and JOUBERT, D. M. (1963) A further note on the duration of pregnancy and birth weight in beef cattle in the sub-tropics, *Proc. S. Afr. Soc. Anim. Prod.* **2** (2), 104.

SKINNER, J. D. and ZIERVOGELL, M. A. (1962) On duration of pregnancy and weight at birth in South Devon, Afrikaner and crossbred South Devon cattle, *Proc. S. Afri. Soc. Anim. Prod.* **1**:84.

SKINNER, P. E., HENRICKSON, R. L., CHAMBERS, D. and STEPHENS, D. F. (1959) Carcass characteristics of comprest and conventional type of Herefords, *J. Anim. Sci.* **18**:1469 Abs.

SKJERVOLD, H. and GRAVIR, K. (1961) Interaction between genotype and environment in selection for rate of gain in cattle, *Meld. Norg. Landbrukshogsk.* **40** (3), 8.

SKVORCOV, A. V. and ZILOV, V. N. (1966) Pregnancy duration in cows, *Zhivotnovodstvo, Mosk.* **28** (2), 44.

SLINGER, R. L., RAMSEY, C. B., COLE, J. W. and HOBBS, C. S. (1966) The relationship of chronological and physiological age of beef females to carcass and palatability characteristics, *J. Anim. Sci.* **25**:255 Abs.

SLJIVOVACKI, K., OBRACEVIC, C., PAVLICEVIC, A. and IVOS, R. (1966) The effect of oxytetracycline combined with stilboestrol in the fattening of young cattle, *Ark. poljopr. Nauk.* **19** (65), 23.

SLOOP, F., KIEHL, E. and BRADY, D. E. (1952) Preferences for self-service meat among household consumers in metropolitan St. Louis, Mo. Agric. Exp. Sta. Bull. 512.

SMART, L. I. and DRAKE, C. L. (1968) Effects of MGA and varying levels of sorghum grain on silage fed heifers, *J. Anim. Sci.* **27**:1176 Abs.

SMIRNOV, D. A. (1965) The effectiveness of commercial crossing of Black Pied cows with Charolais bulls, *Zhivotnovodstvo, Mosk.* **27** (5) 75.

SMITH, E. F. and PARRISH, D. B. (1953) A comparison of rolled, coarsely ground and finely ground milo grain for fattening yearling steers, Kan. Agric. Exp. Sta. Circ. 297.

SMITH, G. C., CARPENTER, Z. L. and KING, G. T. (1968) Differences in tenderness among beef longissimus dorsi core positions, *J. Anim. Sci.* **27**:1147 Abs.

SMITH, G. C. and O'MARY, C. C. (1962) Effects of management systems in performance testing beef calves, *J. Anim. Sci.* **21**:1041 Abs.

SMITH, G. C., O'MARY, C. C. and ENSMINGER, M. E. (1961) Rate of gain and feed efficiency within specific weight increments in growing beef cattle, *J. Anim. Sci.* **20**:911 Abs.

SMITH, G. E., SMITH, W. H. and BEESON, W. M. (1966) Effects of different levels of cellulose in purified diets for calves, *J. Anim. Sci.* **25**:355.

SMITH, G. M. and FITZHUGH, H. A., JR. (1968) Homogeneity of relationships between dam and progeny weights, *J. Anim. Sci.* **27**:1129 Abs.

SMITH, G. S., DUNBAR, R. S., MCLAREN, G. A., ANDERSON, G. C. and WELCH, J. A. (1960) Measurement of the adaptation response to urea–nitrogen utilization in the ruminant, *J. Nutr.* **71**:20.

SMITH, H. A. (1944) Ulcerative lesions of the bovine rumen and their possible relation to hepatic abscesses, *Am. J. Vet. Res.* **5**:234.

SMITH, H. W. (1962) Observations on the aetiology of neonatal diarrhoea (scour) in calves, *J. Path. Bact.* **84**:147.

SMITH, H. W. (1965) The development of the flora of the alimentary tract in young animals, *J. Path. Bact.* **90**:495.

SMITH, H. W. and CRABB, W. E. (1956a) *Vet. Rec.* **68**:274.

SMITH, H. W. and CRABB, W. E. (1956b) *J. gen. Microbiol.* **15**:556.

SMITH, H. W., O'NEIL, J. A. and SIMMONS, E. J. (1967a) The immune globulin content of the serum of calves in England, *Vet. Rec.* **80**:664.

SMITH, L. A., ANTHONY, W. B., STARLING, J. G. and GRIMES, H. W., JR. (1964) Response of nursed beef calves to small grain grazing supplied by creep, *J. Anim. Sci.* **23**:293 Abs.

SMITH, L. A., GRIMES, H. W., JR. and ANTHONY, W. B. (1967b) Creep feeding systems for beef calves, *J. Anim. Sci.* **26**:208 Abs.

SMITH, M. E., SCHIED, H. and WILSON, L. T. (1956) Stilbestrol and stilbestrol oxytetracycline combinations for steers fattened on corn silage, *J. Anim. Sci.* **15**:1239 Abs.

SMITHSON, L., EWING, S. A. and RENBARGER, B. (1966) Influence of level of nutrition of the dams on birth weight of beef calves, *J. Anim. Sci.* **25**:909 Abs.

SNYDER, J. C. and GUTHRIE, T. L. (1968) *Feedstuffs*,

SOLLER, M., BAR ANNAN, R. and PASTERNACK, H. (1966a) Selection of dairy cattle for growth rate and milk production, *Anim. Prod.* **8**:109.

SOLLER, M., SHILO, A. and BAR ANAN, R. (1966b) A note on heritability of live weights for age in Israeli Friesian dairy bull calves and its genetic correlation with milk production, *Anim. Prod.* **8**:157.

SORENSEN, A. M. and FOSTER, J. H. (1963) Natural and artificial breeding of synchronized cattle, *J. Anim. Sci.* **22**:865 Abs.

SORENSEN, A. M., HANSEL, W., HAUGH, W. H., ARMSTRONG, D. T. MCGINTIE, K. and BRATTON, R. W. (1959) Causes and prevention of reproductive failures in dairy cattle, Cornell Agric. Exp. Sta. Bull. 936.

SOUTHWELL, B. L., HALE, O. M. and MCCORMICK, W. C. (1958) Poultry house litter as a protein supplement in steer fattening rations, Ga. Agric. Exp. Sta. Mim. Ser. NS 55.

SPETH, C. F., BOHMAN, V. R., MELENDY, H. and WADE, M. A. (1962) Effect of dietary supplements on cows on a semi-desert range, *J. Anim. Sci.* **21**:444.

SPRADBROW, P. B. (1967) A microbiological study of bovine conjunctivitis and keratoconjunctivitis, *Aust. Vet. J.* **43**:55.

STAHELI, D. L., NEUMANN, A. L., ACORD, C. R. and ALBERT, W. W. (1956) The value of antibiotics in grain rations fed to beef cattle on lush pasture with hormone relationships, *J. Anim. Sci.* **15**:1239 Abs.

STALLCUP, O. T., BROWN, C. J. and ROUSSEL, J. D. (1967) Histiology of parathyroids of Herefords having a hoof anomaly, *J. Anim. Sci.* **26**:206 Abs.

STARCHENKOV, V. M., BYKOVSKII, I. F. and ANDRIYANOV, A. V. (1967) Clinical manifestations and treatment of aspergillotoxicus in cattle, *Veterinariya* (*Moscow*) **4**:64.

STEENSBERG, V. (1947) The feeding requirements of young cattle, *Br. J. Nutr.* **1**:139.

STEGENGA, T. (1961) The influence of young versus old dams on development in cattle, *Veeteelt en Zuivelber.* **4**:319.

STEGER, H., PIATKOWSKI, B., PUSCHEL, F. and VOIGT, J. (1966) Feeding studies on calves, 4: Effect of early weaning on growth, volatile fatty acid content in the rumen and blood composition of calves, *Arch. Tierernähr.* **16**:162.

STEVENS, C. E. and STETTLER, B. K. (1966) Factors affecting the transport of volatile fatty acids across rumen epithelium, *Am. J. Physiol.* **210**:365.

STOB, M. (1956) Fecal elimination of hormones in sheep and cattle treated with synthetic estrogens, *J. Anim. Sci.* **15**:990.

STOB, M. (1966) Hormones in growth and fattening, in *Hormonal Relationships and Applications in the Production of Meat, Milk and Eggs*, Nat. Acad. Sci. NRC Pub. 1415.

STOB, M., PERRY, T. W., ANDREWS, F. N. and BEESON, W. M. (1956) Residual estrogen in the tissue of cattle treated orally with diethylstilbestrol, dienestrol hexestrol and chlortetracycline, *J. Anim. Sci.* **15**:997.

STOBBS, T. H. (1966a) The improvement of small East African Zebu cattle, *Exp. Agric.* **2**:287.

STOBBS, T. H. (1966b) The introduction of Boran cattle into an ECF endemic area, *E. Afr. Agric. For. J.* **31**:298.

STOBBS, T. H. (1967) Management of small East African Zebu in relation to milk yield, calf growth and mortality, *E. Afr. Agric. For. J.* **32**:250.

STOBO, I. J. F. (1961) Rep. Nat. Inst. Res. Dairy. Reading, p. 47.

STOBO, I. J. F. (1964) Studies in the nutrition of young cattle with special reference to rumen development and protein requirements of the early weaned calf, Ph.D. thesis, Univ. Reading.

STOBO, I. J. F. and ROY, J. H. B. (1963) Rept. Nat. Inst. Res. Dairy. Reading, p. 47.

STOBO, I. J. F. and ROY, J. H. B. (1964) The effect of rumen development on digestive efficiency in the calf, *Anim. Prod.* **6**:253. Abs.

STOBO, I. J. F., ROY, J. H. B. and GASTON, H. (1966) Rumen development in the calf, 1: The effects of diets containing different proportions of concentrates to hay on rumen development, *Br. J. Nutr.* **20**:171.

STOBO, I. J. F., ROY, J. H. B. and GASTON, H. J. (1967a) The protein requirement of the ruminant calf, 1: The effect of protein content of the concentrate mixture on the performance of calves weaned at an early age, *Anim. Prod.* **9**:7.

STOBO, I. J. F., ROY, J. H. B. and GASTON, H. J. (1967b) The protein requirement of the ruminant calf, 2: Further studies on the effect of protein content of the concentrate mixture on the performance of calves weaned at an early age, *Anim. Prod.* **9**:23.

STOBO, I. J. F., ROY, J. H. B. and GASTON, H. J. (1967c) The protein requirement of the ruminant calf, 3: The ability of the calf weaned at five weeks of age to utilize urea given as a supplement to a low protein concentrate, *Anim. Prod.* **9**:155.

STOBO, I. J. F., ROY, J. H. B. and GASTON, H. J. (1967d) The effect of different levels of protein and fat in milk substitute diets for veal production, *Anim. Prod.* **9**:267 Abs.

STONAKER, H. H. (1958) Breeding for beef, Colo. Agric. Exp. Sta. Bull. 501 S.

STONAKER, H. H. (1963) A genetic hypothesis for sex mating system interactions in growth of cattle and poultry, *J. Anim. Sci.* **22**:320.

STONAKER, H. H., HAZALEUS, M. H. and WHEELER, S. S. (1952) Feedlot and carcass characteristics of individually fed comprest and conventional type Hereford steers, *J. Anim. Sci.* **11**:17.

STORER, N. W. (1963) The coming changes in American science, *Sci.* **142**:464.

STORY, C. D., CHENG, E. W., PAULS, J. and HALE, W. H. (1957) Estrogenic activity of feces and urine following oral administration of diethylstilbestrol to lambs, *J. Anim. Sci.* **16**:307.

STOTHERS, S. C. and STRINGHAM, E. W. (1956) Effect of chlortetracycline (aureomycin) diethylstilbestrol and chlortetracycline-diethylstilbestrol in combination on feeder calves fed a finishing ration, *J. Anim. Sci.* **15**:1293 Abs.

STOUFFER, J. R., WALLENTINE, M. V., WELLINGTON, G. H. and DIEKMANN, A. (1961) Development and application of ultrasonic methods for measuring fat thickness and the eye area in cattle and hogs, *J. Anim. Sci.* **20**:759.

STRANDINE, E. J., KOONZ, C. H. and RAMSBOTTOM, J. M. (1949) A study of variations in muscles of beef and chickens, *J. Anim. Sci.* **8**:483.

STRINGER, W. C., CRAMER, C. L., ZOELLNER, K. O., RHODES, V. J. and NAUMANN, H. D. (1963) Retail yield estimates of market steers and carcasses, *J. Anim. Sci.* **22**:829 Abs.

STRINGER, W. C., HEDRICK, H. B., CRAMER, C. L., EPLEY, R. J., DYER, A. J., WHITE, R. H. and NAUMANN, H. D. (1967) Effect of extended feeding on retail value of beef, *J. Anim. Sci.* **26**:902 Abs.

STRUEMPLAR, A. W. and BURROUGHS, W. (1959) Stilbestrol feeding and growth hormone stimulation in immature ruminants, *J. Anim. Sci.* **18**:427.

STUEDEMANN, J. A., GUENTHER, J. J., EWING, S. A., MORRISON, R. D. and ODELL, G. V. (1968) Effect of nutritional level imposed from birth to eight months of age on subsequent growth and development pattern of full-fed beef calves, *J. Anim. Sci.* **27**:234.

STUFFLEBEAM, C. E., LASLEY, J. F., MAYER, D. T., WILSON, L. L. and COMFORT, J. E. (1963) Value of certain blood components as selection tools for feedlot gains, *J. Anim. Sci.* **22**:1110 Abs.

SUAREZ, M. F. (1963) Economic importance of the control of cattle ticks in Argentina, *Vet. med. Nachr.* **4**:359.

SUDWEEKS, E. M. and SMITH, C. R. (1968) Three preconditioning rations for feeder calves, *J. Anim. Sci.* **27**:1114 Abs.

SUESS, G. G., BRAY, R. W., LEWIS, R. W. and BRUNGARDT, V. H. (1966a) Sire sex and weight effects upon beef carcass traits and palatability, *J. Anim. Sci.* **25**:1197.

SUESS, G. G., BRAY, R. W., LEWIS, R. W. and BRUNGARDT, V. H. (1966b) Influence of certain live and quantitative carcass traits upon beef palatability, *J. Anim. Sci.* **25**:1203.

SUESS, G. G., TYLER, W. J. and BRUNGARDT, V. H. (1968) Relationship between carcass characteristics of Holstein steers and genetic level for milk production, *J. Anim. Sci.* **27**:972.

SULLIVAN, J. S., ENGLAND, N. and FARTHING, B. R. (1964) Effect of type of dam and type of calf on growth rate of beef calves from birth to weaning, *J. Anim. Sci.* **23**:854 Abs.

SUMMERS, C. E., BURROUGHS, W., KLINE, E. A. and WOODS, W. (1960) Carcass grade and dressing percent of cattle fed different levels of protein in high grain rations, *J. Anim. Sci.* **19**:1242 Abs.

SUTHERLAND, T. M., BIONDINI, P. E., HAVERLAND, L. H. and PETTUS, D. (1968) Growth rate and efficiency of feed utilization in mice, *J. Anim. Sci.* (In press).

SUTTON, J. D., MCGILLIARD, A. D. and JACOBSON, N. L. (1963a) Functional development of rumen mucosa, 1: Absorptive ability, *J. Dairy Sci.* **46**:426.

SUTTON, J. D., MCGILLIARD, A. D., RICHARD, M. and JACOBSON, N. L. (1963b) Functional development of rumen mucosa, 2: Metabolic activity, *J. Dairy Sci.* **46**:530.

SWAFFER, P. (1967) Purebred association's stake in operating record of performance programs for beef cattle, *J. Anim. Sci.* **26**:1264.

SWAN, H. and LAMMING, G. E. (1967) Studies on the nutrition of ruminants, 2: The effect of level of crude fibre in maize-based rations on the carcass composition of Friesian steers, *Anim. Prod.* **9**:203.

SWANSON, L. A., KLINE, E. A. and GOLL, D. E. (1965) Variability on muscle fibres size in bovine longissimus dorsi, *J. Anim. Sci.* **24**:97.

SWIFT, C. E. (1954) The diethylstilbestrol content of tissues of treated steers, lambs and poultry, *Fd Res.* **19**:402.

SWIFT, C. E. and BERMAN, M. D. (1959) Factors affecting the water retention of beef, 1: Variations in composition and properties among eight muscles, *Fd Technol.* **8**:305.

SWIFT, R. F., THACKER, E. J., BLACK, A., BRATZLER, J. W. and JAMES, W. H. (1947) Digestibility of rations for ruminants as affected by proportion of nutrients, *J. Anim. Sci.* **6**:432.

SWIGER, L. A. (1961) Genetic and environmental influences on gain of beef cattle during various periods of life, *J. Anim. Sci.* **20**:183.

SWIGER, L. A., GREGORY, K. E., ARTHAUD, V. H., BRIEDENSTEIN, B. C., KOCH, R. M. SUMPTION, L. J. and ROWDEN, W. W. (1966) Adjustment factors for carcass, gain and feed traits of beef cattle, *J. Anim. Sci.* **25**:69.

SWIGER, L. A., GREGORY, K. E., KOCH, R. M. and ARTHAUD, V. H. (1961a) Effect of inbreeding on performance traits of beef cattle, *J. Anim. Sci.* **20**:626.

SWIGER, L. A., GREGORY, K. E., KOCH, R. M., ROWDEN, W. W., ARTHAUD, V. H. and INGALLS, J. E. (1963) Evaluating post-weaning gain of beef calves, *J. Anim. Sci.* **22**:514.

SWIGER, L. A., GREGORY, K. E., SUMPTION, L. J. and BREIDENSTEIN, B. C. (1964) The importance of measuring cut out in cattle, *J. Anim. Sci.* **23**:854 Abs.

SWIGER, L. A., GREGORY, K. E., SUMPTION, L. V., BREIDENSTEIN, B. C. and ARTHAUD, V. A. (1965) Selection indexes for efficiency of beef production, *J. Anim. Sci.* **24**:418.

SWIGER, L. A. and HAZEL, L. N. (1961) Optimum length of feeding period in selecting for gain of beef cattle, *J. Anim. Sci.* **20**:189.

SWIGER, L. A., KOCH, R. M., GREGORY, K. E. and ARTHAUD, V. H. (1961b) Effect of length of the feeding period on accuracy of selection for gain and feed consumption in beef cattle, *J. Anim. Sci.* **20**:802.

SWIGER, L. A. KOCH, R. M., GREGORY, K. E. and ARTHAUD, V. H. (1962) Selecting beef cattle for economical gain, *J. Anim. Sci.* **21**:588.

SYKES, J. A., SCANLON, M., RUSSELL, W. O. and DMOCHOWSKI, L. (1964) Experimental induction of infectious bovine hetero-conjunctivitis, *Tex. Rep. Biol. Med.* **22**:741.

SZANTO, J., MOHAN, R. N. and LEVINE, N. D. (1964) Prevalence of coccidia and gastrointestinal nematodes in beef cattle in Illinois and their relation to shipping fever, *J. Am. Vet. Med. Assoc.* **144**:741.

SZENT-GYORGYI, A. (1945) *Acta physiol. scand.* **9,** Supp., 25.

TALLACK, R. C. M. (1967) Lincoln Red cattle weight recording scheme 1961–1967, the Beef Rec. Assoc. Tech. Rep. 7.

TALLIS, G. M., KLOSTERMAN, E. W. and CAHILL, V. R. (1959) Body measurements in relation to beef type and to certain carcass characteristics, *J. Anim. Sci.* **18**:108.

TALLIS, G. M., MOORE, R. W. and GREAM, B. D. (1963) Specific gravity in live sheep, *Nature* (*Lond.*) **198**:214.

TANDON, O. B. (1951) Differences in milk production and age at first calving among Indian and crossbred dairy cattle in India, Ph.D. thesis, Iowa State Coll. Ames.

TANNER, J. E., COOPER, R. J. and KRUSE, W. E. (1965) Relationships between weaning weights of calves and weights and measurements of their dams, *J. Anim. Sci.* **24**:280 Abs.

TANNER, J. E., RICHEY, J. A., WILLHAM, R. L. and WHITEMAN, J. V. (1967) *Prog. Rep. 41st Ann. Livestock Feeders Day*, Okla. State Univ.

TAYLER, J. C. (1959) A relationship between weight of internal fat, fill and the herbage intake of grazing cattle, *Nature* **184**:2021.

TAYLER, J. C. (1964) The relationship between growth and carcass quality in cattle and sheep: A review, *Emp. J. Exp. Agric.* **32**:191.

TAYLER, J. C., ALDER, F. E. and RUDMAN, J. E. (1957) Fill and carcass changes of yard and pasture fed cattle turned into spring pasture, *Nature*, **179**:197.

TAYLER, J. C., RUDMAN, J. E. and KEMP, C. D. (1961) Relationships between certain carcass measurements, weights of wholesale joints and sample joint composition of Hereford cross-bred steers, *J. Agric. Sci.* **57**:347.

TAYLOR, B., HALE, W. H. and HUBBERT, F., JR. (1964) Fat additions to Arizona feedlot rations, *J. Anim. Sci.* **23**:601 Abs.

TAYLOR, B. R. (1967) The Hereford cattle recording scheme, Beef Rec. Assoc. Tech. Rep. 6.

TAYLOR, C. R., and LYMAN, C. P. (1967) A comparative study of the environmental physiology of an East African antelope, the Eland and the Hereford steer, *Physiol. Zoöl.* **40**:280.

TAYLOR, J. C., CARTER, R. C., KINCAID, C. M., PRIODE, B. M. and GAINES, J. A. (1960a) Estimates of genetic and phenotypic parameters in beef cattle, 4: Repeatability of cow performance, *J. Anim. Sci.* **19**:700.

TAYLOR, J. C., DOLLAHON, J. C., TRAVIS, H. G. and LINDLEY, C. E. (1960b) Correlations of various factors with the sale price of performance tested and non-performance tested beef bulls, *J. Anim. Sci.* **19**:1227 Abs.

TAYLOR, R. D., KOHLER, G. D., MADDY, K. H. and ENOCHIAN, R. V. (1968) Alfalfa meal in poultry feeds—an economic evaluation during parametric linear programming, Market. Econ. Div. USDA Agric. Econ. Rep. 130.

TAYLOR, ST., C. S. (1963) Accuracy in measuring cattle with special reference to identical twins, *Anim. Prod.* **5**:105.

TAYLOR, ST., C. S. (1965) Pathways to maturity, ARC Anim. Breed. Res. Org. Rep., p. 20.

TAYLOR, ST., C. S. (1966) Genetic studies on twin cattle, *Proc. 9th Int. Congr. Anim. Prod.*, Edinburgh, p. 3.

TAYLOR, ST., C. S. and CRAIG, J. (1967) Variation during growth of twin cattle, *Anim. Prod.* **9**:35.

TAYLOR, ST., C. S. and FITZHUGH, H. A., JR. (1968) Genetic relations among maturing rate, growth rate and feed efficiency, *J. Anim. Sci.* **27**:286 Abs.

TAYLOR, ST., C. S. and YOUNG, G. B. (1966) Variation of growth and efficiency in twin cattle with live weight and feed intake controlled, *J. Agric. Sci.* **66**:67.

TEMPLE, R. S., JAMESON, M. and KINCAID, C. M. (1964) Reproductive performance of beef cattle in the South, *J. Anim. Sci.* **23**:305 Abs.

TEMPLE, R. S. and ROBERTSON, G. L. (1961) Effect of creep feeding on growth rate, grade and economy of production of crossbred beef calves in the Gulf coast region, *J. Anim. Sci.* **20**:399 Abs.

TEMPLE, R. S., SULLIVAN, J. S., JR., FARTHING, B. R. and ROBERTSON, G. L. (1961) Genetic and environmental effects in purebred and backcross calves, *J. Anim. Sci.* **20**:912 Abs.

TEPPERMAN, J. and TEPPERMAN, H. M. (1960) Some effects of hormones on cells and cell constituents, *Pharmacol. Rev.* **12**:301.

TERBLANCHE, H. J. J. (1967) Methyl-thio-uracil in fattening rations of young and mature steers, *J.S. Afr. Vet. Med. Assoc.* **38**:3.

TERNAN, P. R., KIDWELL, J. F., HUNTER, J. E., SHELBY, C. E. and CLARK, R. T. (1959) Associations among conformation scores among body measurements and the relations between scores and measurements in yearling steers, *J. Anim. Sci.* **18**:880.

TEZEBAEV, N. (1967) A valuable beef breed—the Galloway, *Zhivotnovodstvo, Mosk.* **29** (3), 65.

THACKSTON, G. R., COLE, J. W., RAMSEY, C. B. and HOBBS, C. S. (1967) Comparison of three beef quantity prediction equations, *J. Anim. Sci.* **26**:212 Abs.

THEURER, B., TREI, J. E. and HALE, W. H. (1967) *In vitro* VFA production as influenced by steam processing and flaking milo and barley, *J. Anim. Sci.* **26**:930 Abs.

THOMAS, O. O., CLARK, J. L., MATZ, J. J., JR. and YOUNG, L. G. (1964) Effect of trace mineral additions to beef cattle fattening rations, *J. Anim. Sci.* **23**:894 Abs.

THOMAS, O. O. and GEISSLER, B. R. (1968) Substitution of wheat for barley in cattle fattening rations, *J. Anim. Sci.* **27**:1115 Abs.

THOMAS, O. O., JORDAN, H. WILLSON, F. S. (1958) Dynafac and stilbestrol implants when used with completely pelleted rations for fattening cattle, *J. Anim. Sci.* **17**:1172 Abs.

THOMAS, O. O. and MYERS, L. L. (1961) Steam- or dry-rolled barley in high concentrate rations for fattening beef steers, *J. Anim. Sci.* **20**:953 Abs.

THOMAS, O. O., WOODWARD, R. R., DOTY, J. T. and QUESENBERRY, J. R. (1959) Effect of 3,3′-

diallyldiethylstilbestrol in rations for steers wintered in the range and subsequent summer grazing and feedlot trials and in feedlot rations for heifers, *J. Anim. Sci.* **18**:1498 Abs.

Thomas, O. O., Woodward, R. R., Quesenberry, J. R. and Willson, F. S. (1957) Stilbestrol implants for yearling cattle grazed on native summer range, *J. Anim. Sci.* **16**:1031 Abs.

Thomas, R. C. and Cartwright, T. C. (1962) Factors affecting feedlot gain of Hereford bulls, *J. Anim. Sci.* **21**:976 Abs.

Thomas, R. D. and Klatte, F. J. (1967) High concentrate ration effects on ruminant blood lactate, *J. Anim. Sci.* **26**:931 Abs.

Thompson, G. B., Hedrick, H. B., Preston, R. L. and Schake, L. M. (1962) Winter feeding for quality beef, Miss. Agric. Exp. Sta. Spec. Rep. **14**:1.

Thompson, G. B., Preston, R. L. and Hedrick, H. B. (1961) Winter feeding for quality beef production, Miss. Agric. Exp. Sta. Spec. Rep. **5**:10.

Thompson, J. T., Bradley, N. W. and Little, C. O. (1965) Ruminal volatile fatty acid concentrations and performance of steers fed different levels and forms of hay and grain, *J. Anim. Sci.* **24**:1179.

Thompson, J. T., Bradley, N. W. and Little, C. O. (1967) Utilization of urea and fat in meal and pelleted rations for steers, *J. Anim. Sci.* **26**:830.

Thompson, R. C. and Kercher, C. J. (1959) Effect of hormone implants in stocker steers and subsequent feedlot gains, *J. Anim. Sci.* **18**:1176 Abs.

Thornton, J. W. (1960) Estimates of genetic, phenotypic and environmental parameters of growth in beef heifers, MS thesis Virginia Polytechnic Inst. Blacksburg, Va.

Thornton, J. W., Gaines, J. A. and Kincaid, C. M. (1960) Estimates of parameters of growth in beef heifers, *J. Anim. Sci.* **19**:1228 Abs.

Thornton, J. W. and Hiner, R. L. (1965) Volume of beef round related to carcass composition, *J. Anim. Sci.* **24**:301.

Thornton, J. W. and Wiltbank, J. N. (1959) Breed and sire differences in gestation length of beef cattle, *J. Anim. Sci.* **18**:1153.

Thrasher, D. M., Brown, P. B., Mullins, A. M. and Hansard, S. L. (1964a) Conventional vs. all-concentrate, low-fiber fattening rations for steers, *J. Anim. Sci.* **23**:307 Abs.

Thrasher, D. M., Hansard, S. L., Mullins, A. M. and Brown, P. B. (1964b) Effect of an all-concentrate diet, source of protein and B vitamins on performance of steers, *J. Anim. Sci.* **23**:895 Abs.

Thrasher, D. M., Scott, V. B., England, N. C., Farthing, B. R. and Hansard, S. L. (1965) Effect of an all-concentrate ration and selenium on steers, *J. Anim. Sci.* **24**:906 Abs.

Thrasher, D. M., Scott, V. B. and Hansard, S. L. (1967) Protein supplementation of conventional and all-concentrate rations for steer calves, *J. Anim. Sci.* **26**:225 Abs.

Thrift, F. A. (1964) Weaning weight of calves as affected by age, sex, season of birth and age of dam, MS thesis, Univ. of Georgia, Athens.

Thurber, H. E., Strong, H. T. and Clegg, M. T. (1959) Relative value of different oestrogens and estrogen–steroid combinations upon growth in beef cattle, *J. Anim. Sci.* **18**:1176 Abs.

Tillman, A. D., Gallup, W. D., Pope, L. S., McLaren, G. A. and Price, W. (1957) Utilization of ammoniated industrial products by cattle, *J. Anim. Sci.* **16**:179.

Tobin, W. C. (1962) Cattle scabies can be costly, *J. Am. Vet. Med. Assoc.* 1 **41**:845.

Todd, J. C., Riggs, J. K. and Smith, J. C. (1968) Milk yields and calf weight from Brahman, Hereford and crossbred cows in the gulf coast prairie, *J. Anim. Sci.* **27**:286 Abs.

Topps, J. H., Kay, R. N. B., Goodall, E. D., Whitelaw, F. G. and Reid, R. S. (1968) Digestion of concentrate and of hay diets in the stomach and intestines of ruminants, 2: Young steers, *Br. J. Nutr.* **22**:281.

Topps, J. H., Reed, W. D. C. and Elliott, R. C. (1966) Studies of the metabolism of cattle given high concentrate diets, *J. Agric. Sci.* **66**:233.

Totusek, R. (1967) *Okla. Prog. Rep.* 1966–7, p. 79.

Totusek, R., Franks, L., Baller, W. and Renbarger, R. (1967) *Okla. State Univ. 41st Ann. Livestock Feeders Day.*

Totusek, R. and Hall, G. A. B. (1967) Autoclaved soybean meals in milo rations, *J. Anim. Sci.* **26**:931 Abs.

Touchberry, R. W. (1963) Heritability of milk and fat yield and fat percent at different levels of milk yield, *J. Dairy Sci.* **46**:620 Abs.

TOVAR, J., RIGGS, J. K. and COOPER, R. J. (1966) Factors affecting weaning weights of Hereford and rotational crossbred calves, *J. Anim. Sci.* **25**:264 Abs.

TREI, J. E., HALE, W. H., SABA, W. J., KEATING, E. K. and TAYLOR, B. R. (1964) Digestion of milo and barley by ruminants, *J. Anim. Sci.* **23**:895 Abs.

TREI, J. E., HALE, W. H. and THEURER, B. (1966) Influence of grain processing factors on *in vitro* fermentation rate, *J. Anim. Sci.* **25**:910 Abs.

TRIBE, G. W., KANAREK, A. D. and WHITE, G. (1968) Preliminary studies on the development of a bovine parainfluenza, 3: Virus vaccine, *Res. Vet. Sci.* **9**:152.

TRIMBERGER, G. W. (1954) Conception rates in dairy cattle from service at various intervals after parturition, *J. Dairy Sci.* **37**:1042.

TRIMBERGER, G. W. and HANSEL, W. (1955) Conception rate and ovarian function following estrus control by progesterone injection in dairy cattle, *J. Anim. Sci.* **14**:224.

TUCKER, R. E., LITTLE, C. O., MITCHELL, G. E., JR., HAYES, B. W. and KARR, M. R. (1966) Starch digestion in different sections of the digestive tract of sheep, *J. Anim. Sci.* **25**:911.

TULLOH, N. M. (1961) Skin and skinfold thickness in relation to the depth of subcutaneous fat in beef cattle, *Aust. J. Exp. Agric. Anim. Husb.* **1**:27.

TULLOH, N. M. (1964) The carcass compositions of sheep, cattle and pigs as functions of body weight, *Tech. Conf. on Carcass Composition and Meat Appraisal of Meat Animals* (ed D. E. Tribe), CSIRO, Melbourne.

TUMA, H. J., CORINGTON, R. C., GRANT, D. L. and KROPT, D. H. (1967) Effect of bovine marbling and maturity on chemical and histological traits and tenderness, *J. Anim. Sci.* **26**:1471 Abs.

TUMA, H. J., HENRICKSON, R. L., ODELL, G. V. and STEPHENS, D. F. (1963) Variation in the physical and chemical characteristics of the longissimus dorsi muscle from animals differing in age, *J. Anim. Sci.* **22**:354.

TUMA, H. J., HENRICKSON, R. L., STEPHENS, D. F. and MOORE, R. (1962a) Influence of marbling and animal age on factors associated with beef quality, *J. Anim. Sci.* **21**:848.

TUMA, H. J., VENABLE, J. H., WUTHIER, P. R. and HENRICKSON, R. L. (1962b) Relationship of fibre diameter to tenderness and meatiness as influenced by bovine age, *J. Anim. Sci.* **21**:33.

TURMAN, E. J., RENBARGER, R. E. and STEPHENS, D. F. (1968) Multiple births in beef cows treated with PMS, *J. Anim. Sci.* **27**:1198 Abs.

TURNER, J. W., FARTHING, B. R. and ROBINSON, G. L. (1968) Heterosis in reproductive performance of beef cows, *J. Anim. Sci.* **27**:336.

TURNER, C. W. (1956) Biological assay of beef steer carcasses for estrogenic activity following the feeding of diethylstilbestrol at a level of 10 mg per day in the ration, *J. Anim. Sci.* **15**:13.

TURNER, H. G. and SCHLEGER, A. V. (1960) The significance of coat type in cattle, *Aust. J. Agric. Res.* **11**:645.

TURTON, J. D. (1962) The effect of castration on meat production and quality in cattle, sheep and pigs, *Anim. Breed. Abs.* **30**:447.

UDALL, R. H., DEEM, A. W. and MAAG, D. D. (1958) Studies on urolithiasis, 1: Experimental production associated with feeding in steers, *Am. J. Vet. Res.* **19**:825.

UHART, B. A. and CARROLL, R. D. (1967) Acidosis in beef steers, *J. Anim. Sci.* **26**:1195.

ULBERG, L. C., CHRISTIAN, R. E. and CASIDA, L. E. (1951) Ovarian response in heifers to progesterone injections, *J. Anim. Sci.* **10**:752.

ULBERG, L. C. and LINDLEY, L. E. (1960) Use of progesterone and estrogen in the control of reproductive activities in beef cattle, *J. Anim. Sci.* **19**:1132.

ULYATT, M. J. (1965) The effects of intra-ruminal infusions of volatile fatty acids on food intake of sheep, *NZ J. Agric. Res.* **8**:397.

UMBERGER, E. J., CURTIS, J. M. and GASS, G. H. (1959) Failure to detect residual estrogenic activity in the edible tissues of steers fed stilbestrol, *J. Anim. Sci.* **18**:221.

URICK, J. J., BRINKS, J. S., CLARK, R. T., PAHNISH, O. F. and WILLSON, F. S. (1966) History and performance of inbred lines of Hereford cattle developed at the United States Range Livestock Experiment Station, Mont. Agric. Exp. Sta. Bull. 602.

Urick, J. J., Brinks, J. S., Pahnish, O. F., Knapp, B. W. and Riley, T. M. (1968) Heterosis in post-weaning traits among lines of Hereford cattle, *J. Anim. Sci.* **27**:323.

Urick, J. J., Flower, A. E., Willson, F. S. and Shelby, C. E. (1957) A genetic study of steer progeny groups during successive growth periods, *J. Anim. Sci.* **16**:217.

USDA (1962) Summary of activities of meat inspection division, USDA, ARS.

USDA (1968) Number of cattle feedlots by size, groups and number of feedlot cattle marketed, 1962–67.

Vaccaro, R. and Dillard, E. U. (1966) Relationship of dams weight and weight changes to calf's growth rate in Hereford cattle, *J. Anim. Sci.* **25**:1063.

Van Arsdel, III. W. C. and Bogart, R. (1962) Ambient temperature, heart rates and rectal temperatures of Hereford calves, *J. Anim. Sci.* **21**:656 Abs.

Van Demark, N. L. and Salisbury, G. W. (1950) The relation of the *post-partum* breeding interval to reproductive efficiency in the dairy cow, *J. Anim. Sci.* **9**:307.

Vandeplassche, M., Herman, J., Bouters, R. and Spincemaille, J. (1965) Preventive obstetrics in cattle, *Vlaams diergeneesk. Tijdschr.* **34**:161.

Van Dieten, S. W. J. (1964) Calf mortality at birth, *Veeteelt en Zuivelber.* **7**:20.

Van Dieten, S. W. J. (1966) Fertility following stillbirths in cattle, *Veeteelt en Zuivelber.* **9**:69.

Van Es, A. J. H. (1961) Between animal variation in the amount of energy required for the maintenance of cows, *Versl. landbouwk. Onder z.*, No. 675, p. 124.

Van Es, A. J. H. and Nijkamp, H. J. (1967) Energy requirements of cattle, *Proc. 4th Symp. Energy Metab. Warsaw.*

Van Graan, B., Jr. and Joubert, D. M. (1961) Duration of pregnancy in Afrikaner cattle, *Emp. J. Exp. Agric.* **29**:225.

Van Loen, A. and Van Dieten, S. W. J. (1962) Anatomical defects, stillbirths and birth registration relative to AI in bovine cattle, *Tijdschr. Diergeneesf.* **87**:1566.

Van Syckle, C. and Brough, O. L. (1958) Customer acceptance of fat characteristics of beef, Wash. Agr. Exp. Sta. Tech. Bull. 27.

Van Vleck, L. D. (1963) Genotype and environment in sire evaluation, *J. Dairy Sci.* **46**:983.

Van Vleck, L. D. and Bradford, G. E. (1964) Heritability of milk yield at different environmental levels, *Anim. Prod.* **6**:285.

Van Vleck, L. D., Searle, S. R. and Henderson, C. R. (1960) The number of daughter-dam pairs needed for estimating heritability, *J. Anim. Sci.* **19**:916.

Vara, M., Bacigalupo, A. and Téllez, J. (1968) Use of cotton wood in fattening cattle, *J. Anim. Sci.* **27**:1137 Abs.

Veenhuizen, E. L. and Wagner, J. F. (1964) Synchronization of estrus in the beef heifer and *post-partum* cow, *J. Anim. Sci.* **23**:1229 Abs.

Vegors, H. H., Baird, D. M., Sell, O. E. and Stewart, T. B. (1956) Parasitism in beef yearlings as related to forage availability and levels of protein feeding, *J. Anim. Sci.* **15**:1199.

Veiga, J. S., Chieffi, A. and Paiva, O. M. (1946) Duracao do periodo de gostacao en femeas de raca Nalare e idade na epoca da primeira cria, *Rev. Fac. Med. Vet. S. Paulo* **3**:55.

Verley, F. A. and Touchberry, R. W. (1961) Effects of crossbreeding on reproductive performance of dairy cattle, *J. Dairy Sci.* **44**:2058.

Vernon, E. H., Damon, R. A., Jr., Harvey, W. R., Warwick, E. J. and Kincaid, C. M. (1959). Relation of heat tolerance determination to productivity in beef cattle, *J. Anim. Sci.* **19**:91.

Vernon, E. H., Harvey, W. R. and Warwick, E. J. (1964) Factors affecting weight and score of crossbred type calves, *J. Anim. Sci.* **23**:21.

Verzor, F. (1963) *Lectures on Experimental Gerentology*, p. 36, Charles C. Thomas, Springfield, Ill.

Viall, V. E. and Mason, I. L. (1961) Heritability estimates for growth and carcass characteristics in Friesian steers, *Proc. 8th Int. Cong. Anim. Prod. Hamburg.*

Vianna, A. T., De Alba, J., Paez, G. and Magofle, C. (1964a) Mode of inheritance of birth weight and gestation length in Charolais cattle, *Turrialba* **14**:120.

VIANNA, A. T., DE ALBA, J., PAEZ, G. and MAGOFLE, C. (1964b) A genetic study of birthweight and gestation periods in Charolais cattle, *Min. da Agric. estudies tecn.* **26**:24.

VIDACS, G. and WARD, G. M. (1960) Parakeratosis condition of rumen epithelium produced by an all-concentrate ration, *J. Dairy Sci.* **43**:875.

VILSTRUP, R. H. (1964) Report in *Feedstuffs*, 5th Dec., p. 64.

VINNICUK, D. T. (1966) The heritability of some measurements of the exterior of Simmental cattle, *Zhivotnovodstvo, Mosk.* **28** (4), 63.

VIRTANEN, A. I. (1966) Milk production of cows on protein free feed, *Science* **153**:1603.

VITLO, P. D. and MAGEE, W. T. (1965) Live animal estimations of carcass traits, *J. Anim. Sci.* **24**:853 Abs.

VOGT, D. W., ANDERSON, D. E. and EASLEY, G. T. (1963) Studies on bovine ocular squamous carcinoma (cancer eye), 14: Heritabilities, phenotypic correlation and genetic correlations involving corneoscleral and lid pigmentation, *J. Anim. Sci.* **22**:762.

VOGT, D. W., GAINES, J. A., CARTER, R. C., MCCLURE, W. H. and KINCAID, C. M. (1967) Heterosis from crosses among British breeds of beef cattle post weaning performance to slaughter, *J. Anim. Sci.* **26**:443.

VOGT, D. W. and MARLOWE, T. J. (1966) A further study of the genetic parameters involving pre-weaning growth rate and weaning grade in beef calves, *J. Anim. Sci.* **25**:265 Abs.

WAGNER, J. F., MCASKILL, J. W. and MEANS, A. T. (1963) Synchronization of estrus in the bovine, *J. Amin. Sci.* **22**:866 Abs.

WAGNON, K. A., GUILBERT, H. R. and HART, G. H. (1959) Beef cattle investigations in the San Joaquin experimental range, Calif. Agric. Exp. Sta. Bull. 765.

WAGNON, K. A. and ROLLINS, W. C. (1959) Heritability estimates of post-weaning growth to long yearling age of range beef heifers raised on grain, *J. Anim. Sci.* **18**:918.

WALDO, D. R. (1967) Factors that influence roughage intake, *Feedstuffs*, 11th Feb., p. 26.

WALDRIP, W. J. and MARION, P. T. (1963) Effect of winter feed and grazing systems on cow performance, *J. Anim. Sci.* **22**:853 Abs.

WALKER, C. A. (1960) The population morphology and evolutionary trends of aprocrine sweat glands of African indigenous cattle, *J. Agric. Sci.* **55**:119.

WALKER, C. A. (1964) The growth and development of the beef qualities of Angoni cattle (East African Shorthorn Zebu), 1: Live weight, *J. Agric. Sci.* **63**:135.

WALKER, D. E. (1961) A study of the growth and development of Jersey cattle, 1: A new carcass disection technique, *NZ J. Agric. Res.* **4**:99.

WALKER, D. M. (1948) Studies on the nutrition of young dairy stock, Ph.D. thesis, Univ. of Reading.

WALKER, D. M. (1950) *Bull. Anim. Behav.* **8**:5.

WALKER, D. M. and HEPBURN, W. R. (1955) The nutritive value of roughages for sheep, *J. Agric. Sci.* **45**:298.

WALKER, D. M., THOMPSON, S. Y., BARTLETT, S. and KON, S. K. (1949) *Int. Dairy Cong. XII, Stockholm* **1**:83.

WALKER, T. W. (1968) Personal communication.

WALKER, T. W., KAY, M., PRESTON, T. R., MACDONALD, I., MACLEOD, N. A. and MACDEARMID, A. (1968) The performance of beef cattle given diets of barley supplemented with either vegetable protein or non-protein nitrogen, *Anim. Prod.* **10**:381.

WALLACE, J. D. and RALEIGH, R. J. (1961) Effect of time of weaning on winter performance of Hereford calves, *J. Anim. Sci.* **20**:665 Abs.

WALLACE, J. D., and RALEIGH, R. J. (1967) Protein intake and exercise for pregnant heifers, *J. Anim. Sci.* **26**:931 Abs.

WALLACE, L. R. (1948) The growth of lambs before and after birth in relation to the level of nutrition *J. Agric. Sci.* **38**:243.

WALLENTINE, M. V., DRAIN, J. J., WELLINGTON, G. H. and MILLER, J. I. (1961) Some effects on beef carcasses from feeding stilbestrol, *J. Anim. Sci.* **20**:792.

WALTER, M. J., GOLL, D. E., ANDERSON, L. P. and KLINE, E. A. (1963) Effect of marbling and maturity on beef tenderness, *J. Anim. Sci.* **22**:1115 Abs.

WALTER, M. J., GOLL, D. E., KLINE, E. A., ANDERSON, L. P. and CARLIN, E. A. (1965a) Effect of marbling and maturity on beef muscle characteristics, 1: Objective measurements of tenderness and chemical properties, *Fd. Technol.* **19**:159.

WALTER, M. J., GOLL, D. E., KLINE, E. A., ANDERSON, L. P. and CARLIN, E. A. (1965b) Effect of marbling and maturity on beef muscle characteristics, 2: Physical, chemical and sensory evaluation of steak, *Fd. Technol.* **19**:163.

WANG, H., RASCH, E., BATES, V., BEARD, F. J., PIERCE, J. C. and HANKINS, G. O. (1954) Histological observations on fat loci and distribution in cooked beef, *Fd Res.* **19**:314.

WANG, H., DOTY, D. M., BEARD, F. J., PIERCE, J. C. and HANKINS, O. G. (1956) Extensibility of single beef muscle fibers, *J. Anim. Sci.* **15**:97.

WARD, G. (1968) Report in *Feedstuffs*.

WARD, G. M. and MORRILL, J. L. (1966) Digestibility and nitrogen utilization of rolled and moist-heat-treated sorghum grain, *J. Dairy Sci.* **49**:392.

WARD, J. K., RICHARDSON, D. and TSIEN, W. S. (1960) Value of added enzyme preparation in beef cattle rations, *J. Anim. Sci.* **19**:1298 Abs.

WARDROP, I. D. (1966) The effects of the plane of nutrition in early post-natal life on the subsequent growth and development of cattle, *Aust. J. Agric. Res.* **17**:375.

WARNER, R. G., FLATT, W. P. and LOOSLI, J. K. (1956) Dietary factors influencing the development of the ruminant stomach, *J. Agric. Fd Chem.* **4**:788.

WARNER, R. L., MEYER, W. E., THOMPSON, G. B. and HEDRICK, H. B. (1965) Performance and carcass characteristics of beef bulls, steers and heifers, *J. Anim. Sci.* **24**:869 Abs.

WARNER, R. L., MITCHELL, G. E., JR., LITTLE, C. O. and ALDERSON, N. E. (1968) Pre-intestinal disappearance of vitamin A in steers fed varying levels of concentrate, *J. Anim. Sci.* **27**:298 Abs.

WARNICK, A. C., KIRST, R. C., BURNS, W. C. and KOGER, M. (1967) Factors influencing pregnancy in beef cows, *J. Anim. Sci.* **26**:231 Abs.

WARNICK, A. C., MEADE, J. H., JR., and KOGER, M. (1960) Factors influencing pregnancy rate in Florida beef cattle, Fla. Agric. Exp. Sta. Bull. 623.

WARREN, E. P., THRIFT, F. A. and CARMEN, J. L. (1965a) Factors influencing weaning weights of Georgia beef calves, *J. Anim. Sci.* **24**:853 Abs.

WARREN, E. P., THRIFT, F. A. and CARMEN, J. L. (1965b) Estimates of the effect of certain environmental factors on weaning weight of Georgia beef calves, Ga. Agric. Exp. Sta. Tech. Bull. 47.

WARREN, R. B., ARTHAUD, U. H., ADAMS, C. H. and KOCH, R. M. (1959) Thermister thermometer for estimating fat thickness on live beef cattle, *J. Anim. Sci.* **18**:1469 Abs.

WARWICK, B. L. and CARTWRIGHT, T. C. (1955) Heritability of gain in young growing beef cattle, *J. Anim. Sci.* **14**:363.

WARWICK, E. J. (1958) Fifty years of progress in breeding beef cattle, *J. Anim. Sci.* **17**:922.

WARWICK, E. J., DAVIS, R. E. and HINER, R. L. (1964) Response of monozygotic bovine twins to high and low concentrate rations, *J. Anim. Sci.* **23**:78.

WASHBURN, L. E. (1963) Mycosis and brisket disease in cattle, *J. Anim. Sci.* **22**:866 Abs.

WATKINS, J. L., SHERRITT, G. W. and ZIEGLER, J. H. (1967) Predicting body tissue characteristics using ultrasonic techniques, *J. Anim. Sci.* **26**:470.

WATSON, R. H. (1944) *CSIRO Res. Bull.* **180**:1.

WAWRZYNCZAK, S. (1965) The effect of partial castration on the fattening of young bulls, *Medycyna wet.* **21**:359.

WAYMACK, L. B., BILKOVICH, F. R. and HANSARD, S. L. (1968) Phosphorus absorption in the young calf following induced parasitism by *Osteragia* spp., *J. Anim. Sci.* **27**:298 Abs.

WEBB, N. B., KAHLENBERG, O. J. and NAUMANN, H. D. (1964) Factors influencing beef tenderness, *J. Anim. Sci.* **23**:1027.

WEBB, R. J., CMARIK, G. F. and CATE, H. A. (1957) The comparative effects of diethylstilbestrol and progesterone estradiol benzoate implant on fattening steers fed varying ratios of concentrate and roughages, *J. Anim. Sci.* **16**:1089 Abs.

WEBSTER, C. C. and WILSON, P. N. (1966) *Agriculture in the Tropics*, Longmans, London.

WEICHENTHAL, B. A., EMBRY, L. B., EMERICK, R. J. and WHETZAL, F. W. (1963) Influence of sodium nitrate, vitamin A and protein level on feedlot performance and vitamin A status of fattening cattle, *J. Anim. Sci.* **22**:979.

WEILAND, G. (1966) Observations on age at first calving, *Terzucht* **20**:299.

WEILAND, G. and KLOSE, J. (1962) *Terzucht* **16**:472.

WEINER, J. S. and HELLMANN, K. (1960) *Biol. Rev.* **35**:141.

WEIR, C. E. (1960) *The Science of Meat and Meat Products* (ed. Am. Meat Inst. Foundation), Reinhold, New York.

WEISS, R. L., BAUMGARDT, B. R., BARR, G. R. and BRUNGARDT, V. H. (1967) Some influences of rumen volatile fatty acids upon carcass composition and performance in growing fattening steers, *J. Anim. Sci.* **26**:389.

WELDY, J. R., MCDOWELL, R. E. and VANSOEST, P. J. (1962) Influence of heat stress on rumen VFA levels, *J. Anim. Sci.* **21**:1031 Abs.

WELLER, R. A. (1957) The amino acid composition of hydrolysates of microbial preparations from the rumen of sheep, *Aust. J. Biol. Sci.* **10**:384.

WELLINGTON, G. H. (1968) Marbling in intensively produced Holstein steers, J. *Anim. Sci.* **27**:1149 Abs.

WELLINGTON, G. H., REID, J. T., BRATZLER, L. J. and MILLER, L. J. (1954) Body composition and carcass changes in young cattle, *J. Anim. Sci.* **13**:973 Abs.

WELLINGTON, G. H. and STOUFFER, J. R. (1959) Beef marbling—its estimation and influence on tenderness and juiciness, Cornell Agr. Exp. Sta. Res. Bull. 941.

WESELI, J. D., GOOD, D. L. and HOLLAND, L. A. (1958) Relationships among live and carcass characteristics of slaughter steers, Kans. Agri. Exp. Sta. Circ. **358**:55.

WESTBYE, O. and NAESS, B. (1967) Charolaisrasen og charolaiskrysninger, Inst. anatomi. Norges Vet. Tech. comm.

WESTER, J. (1930) *Br. Vet. J.* **86**:401.

WHEAT, J. D. and HOLLAND, L. A. (1960) Relationship between slaughter and carcass grades in beef cattle, *J. Anim. Sci.* **19**:722.

WHEAT, J. D. and RIGGS, J. K. (1958) Heritability and repeatibility of gestation length in beef cattle, *J. Anim. Sci.* **17**:249.

WHEELER, R. R., WESWIG, P. H., BRANNON, W. F., HUBBERT, F. E., JR. and SAWYER, W. A. (1957) The carotene and vitamin A content of plasma and liver of range Hereford cows and their calves in the Northern Great Basin, *J. Anim. Sci.* **16**:525.

WHETZAL, F. W., EMBRY, L. B., DITTMAN, A. E. and GASTLER, G. F. (1962) Value of hay, molasses and protein supplement in barley rations for fattening cattle, *J. Anim. Sci.* **21**:1016 Abs.

WHITAKER, R. J., MILLER, W. J., CARMEN, J. L. and DALTON, H. L. (1957) Influence of level and source of crude fiber in calf starters on weight and feed consumption, *J. Dairy Sci.* **40**:887.

WHITE, F. E. and GREEN, W. W. (1952) Relationships of measurements of live animals to weight of wholesale cuts of beef, *J. Anim. Sci.* **11**:370.

WHITE, T. W. and REYNOLDS, W. L. (1968) Sources and levels of roughage in steer rations, *J. Anim. Sci.* **27**:298 Abs.

WHITELAW, F. G. and PRESTON, T. R. (1963) The nutrition of the early weaned calf, 3: Protein solubility and amino acid composition as factors affecting protein utilization, *Anim. Prod.* **5**: 131.

WHITELAW, F. G., PRESTON, T. R., DAWSON, G. S. (1961) The nutrition of the early weaned calf, 2: A comparison of commercial groundnut meal, heat-treated groundnut meal and fish meal as the major protein source in the diet, *Anim. Prod.* **3**:127.

WHITELAW, F. G., PRESTON, T. R. and MACLEOD, N. A. (1962) Further studies on protein quality in the diet of the early weaned calf, *Anim. Prod.* **4**:300 Abs.

WHITELAW, F. G., PRESTON, T. R. and MACLEOD, N. A. (1963) The nutrition of the early weaned calf, 5: The effect of protein quality, antibiotics and level of feeding on growth and feed conversion, *Anim. Prod.* **5**:227.

WHITELAW, F. G., PRESTON, T. R. and MACLEOD, N. A. (1964) The nutrition of the early weaned calf, 7: The relative value of four different fish meal products as the major protein source in the diet, *Anim. Prod.* **6**:25.

WHITING, F. and CLARK, R. D. (1955) Raising dairy calves with a limited amount of milk, *Can. J. Anim. Sci.* **35**:454.

WIBERG, G. S. and STEPHENSON, N. R. (1957) The detection of estrogenic activity in tissues of steers which have been fed diethylstilbestrol, *Can. J. Biochem. Physiol.* **35**:1107.

WIERBICKI, E., CAHILL, V. R., KUNKLE, L. E. and DEATHERAGE, P. E. (1956) *Fd Technol.* **10**:80.

Wierbicki, E., Cahill, V. R., Kunkle, L. E., Klosterman, E. W. and Deatherage, F. E. (1955) Meat quality: Effect of castration on biochemistry and quality of meat, *J. Agric. Fd Chem.* **3:** 244.

Wierbicki, E. and Deatherage, F. E. (1954) Meat assay: Hydroxyproline as an index of connective tissue in muscle, *J. Agric. Fd Chem.* **2**:878.

Wierbicki, E. and Deatherage, F. E. (1958) Determination of waterholding capacity of fresh meats, *J. Agric. Fd Chem.* **6**:387.

Wierbicki, E., Kunkle, L. E., Cahill, V. R. and Deatherage, F. E. (1954) The relation of tenderness to protein alterations during post-mortem ageing, *Fd Technol.* **8**:507.

Wieser, M. F., Preston, T. R., Macdearmid, A. and Rowland, A. G. (1966) Intensive beef production, 8: The effect of chlortetracycline on growth, feed utilization and incidence of liver abscesses in barley beef cattle, *Anim. Prod.* **8**:411.

Wilcox, G. E. (1968) Infectious bovine kerato-conjunctivitis: A review, *Vet. Bull.* **38**:349.

Wilcox, J. C. (1967) The influence of plane of nutrition during rearing on the milking potential of Hereford cows suckling calves, *Anim. Prod.* **9:** 285 Abs.

Wilk, J. C., Young, C. W. and Cole, C. L. (1963) Genetic and phenotypic relationships between certain body measurements and first lactation milk production in dairy cattle, *J. Dairy Sci.* **46:** 1273.

Willard, H. S. (1948) Effect of Holstein birth weight on calf gain and final weight, Wyo. Agric. Exp. Sta. Bull. 286.

Willett, M. D. J. (1950) The influence of the bull on the gestation period of his offspring, *Landbouwk. Tijdschr.* **62**:636.

Willey, N. B., Butler, O. D., Riggs, J. K., Jones, J. H. and Lyerley, P. J. (1951) The influence of type in feedlot performance and killing qualities of Hereford steers, *J. Anim. Sci.* **10**:195.

Williams, D. B., Bradley, N. W., Little, C. O. and Crowe, W. M. (1968a) Effects of oyster shells with and without roughage in beef finishing rations, *J. Anim. Sci.* **27**:299 Abs.

Williams, D. L., Whiteman, J. V. and Tillman, A. D. (1968b) Cottonseed meal vs, urea in cattle supplements, *J. Anim. Sci.* **27**:1180 Abs.

Williams, J. N. II, Hobbs, C. S., Ramsey, L. B. and Temple, R. S. (1965) Gains, efficiency and carcass differences between bulls, steers and heifers, *J. Anim. Sci.* **24**:283 Abs.

Williams, L. G. (1959) A preliminary note on the effect of implantation of stilboestrol and hexoestrol on the growth and carcass characteristics of beef steers and young wethers, *Proc. 2nd Conf. Aust. Soc. Anim. Prod.*

Williams, L. W. and Baker, B., Jr. (1961) Effects of stilbestrol implants on reproduction and market qualities of beef heifers, *J. Anim. Sci.* **20**:394 Abs.

Williams, S. and Edgar, C. D. (1966) *Planned Beef Production*, Crosby Lockwood, London.

Williamson, G. and Payne, W. J. A. (1959) *An Introduction to Animal Husbandry in the Tropics*, Longmans, London.

Williamson, J. L., Geurin, H. B., Thompson, J. C., Teter, W. S., Hotchkiss, D. E., Wilcke, H. L. and Bethke, R. M. (1961) Pelleted low-roughage complete rations for steers, *J. Anim. Sci.* **20**:956 Abs.

Willis, M. B. (1960) A study of nicking and of sire interaction through female families in a herd of British–Friesian cattle, Ph.D. thesis, Univ. Edinburgh.

Willis, M. B. (1962) Unpublished data.

Willis, M. B. (1966) The progeny testing of dairy bulls, Inst. Cienc. Animal, Havana, Tech, Comm. 1.

Willis, M. B. and Preston, T. R. (1967) Some aspects of performance-testing in the Charolais breed, *Rev. cubana Cienc. Agric.* (Eng. ed.) **1**:21.

Willis, M. B. and Preston, T. R. (1968a) The performance of different breeds of beef cattle in Cuba, *Anim. Prod.* **10**:77.

Willis, M. B. and Preston, T. R. (1968b) Unpublished data.

Willis, M. B. and Preston, T. R. (1969a) Unpublished data.

Willis, M. B. and Preston, T. R. (1969b) The performance of beef breeds in Cuba: Growth carcass composition of bulls, *Rev. cubana Cienc. Agric.* (Eng. ed.) **3**:71 Abs.

Willis, M. B. and Preston, T. R. (1969c) The effect of using Brown Swiss, Charolais, Criollo and Holstein on Brahman cows—growth and carcass composition, *Anim. Prod.* **11**:277 Abs.

WILLIS, M. B. and PRESTON, T. R. (1969d) The reproductive performance of four breeds of beef cows in Cuba, *Rev. cubana Cienc. Agric.* (Eng. ed.) **3**:78 Abs.

WILLIS, M. B. and PRESTON, T. R. (1970) Performance testing for beef: interrelationships among traits in bulls weaned early, *Anim. Prod.* **12**:In press.

WILLIS, M. B., PRESTON, T. R., MARTIN, J. L. and VELAZQUEZ, M. (1968) Carcass composition of Brahman bulls fed high energy diets and slaughtered at different live weights, *Rev. cubana Cienc. Agric.* (Eng. ed.) **2**:83.

WILLSON, F. S., FLOWER, A. E., KIEFFER, N. M. and MILLER, R. W. (1963) Topcross tests of ROP and visually selected herds of Hereford cattle, *J. Anim. Sci.* **22**:823 Abs.

WILLSON, F. S., URICK, J. J. and FLOWER, A. E. (1954) Genetic studies of steer progeny groups slaughtered following three successive feeding treatments, *J. Anim. Sci.* **13**:965 Abs.

WILSON, A. D. (1963) The effect of diet on the secretion of parotid saliva by sheep, 2: Variations in the rate of salivary secretion. *Aust. J. Agric. Res.* **14**:680.

WILSON, B. B. and WOODS, W. (1967) Effect of increasing levels of gelatinized corn upon rumen metabolites, *J. Anim. Sci.* **26**:932 Abs.

WILSON, C. D., BRAY, R. W. and PHILLIPS, P. H. (1954) The effects of age and grade on the collagen and elastin content of beef and veal, *J. Anim. Sci.* **13**:826.

WILSON, G. D., BROWN, P. D., CHESBRO, W. R., GINGER, B. and WEIR, C. E. (1960) The use of antibiotics and gamma irradiation in the ageing of steaks at high temperatures, *Fd Technol.* **14**:143.

WILSON, L. L., DINKEL, C. A. and RAY, D. E. (1962) Genetic parameters and selection indexes for beef cattle, *J. Anim. Sci.* **21**:977 Abs.

WILSON, L. L., DINKEL, C. A., RAY, D. E. and MINYARD, J. A. (1963a) Beef carcass composition as influenced by diethylstilbestrol, *J. Anim. Sci.* **22**:699.

WILSON, L. L., DINKEL, C. A., RAY, D. E. and MINYARD, J. A. (1963b) Beef cattle selection indexes involving conformation and weight, *J. Anim. Sci.* **22**:1086.

WILSON, L. L., DINKEL, C. A., TUMA, H. J. and MINYARD, J. A. (1964) Live animal prediction of cutability and other beef carcass characteristics by several judges, *J. Anim. Sci.* **23**:1102.

WILSON, L. L., GILLOOLY, J. E., PUGH, M. C., THOMPSON, C. E. and PURDY, H. R. (1968) Relation of milk and progeny growth traits of Angus-Holstein cows, *J. Anim. Sci.* **27**:1512 Abs.

WILSON, L. L., KAISER, C. J. and HAWKINS, K. (1966) Comparison of early weaning, creep feeding and noncreep feeding for fall calves, *J. Anim. Sci.* **25**:1274 Abs.

WILSON, L. L., ZIEGLER, J. H., THOMPSON, C. E., WATKINS, J. L. and PURDY, H. R. (1967) Sire and sex effects on beef growth and carcass characteristics, *J. Anim. Sci.* **26**:1465 Abs.

WILSON, P. N. and HOUGHTON, T. R. (1962) The development of the herd of Holstein–Zebu cattle at the Imperial College of Tropical Agriculture, Trinidad, *Emp. J. Exp. Agric.* **30**:159.

WILSON, P. N. and OSBOURN, D. F. (1960) Compensatory growth after undernutrition in mammals and birds, *Biol. Rev.* **35**:324.

WILTBANK, J. N., BURRIS, M. J. and PRIODE, B. M. (1956) The occurrence of estrus and the conception rate in a herd of 450 beef cows bred during a limited breeding season, *J. Anim. Sci.* **15**:1216 Abs.

WILTBANK, J. N. and COOK, A. C. (1958) The comparative reproductive performance of nursed cows and milked cows, *J. Anim. Sci.* **17**:640.

WILTBANK, J. N., COOK, A. C., DAVIS, R. E. and WARWICK, E. J. (1957) The effect of different combinations of energy and protein on the occurrence of estrus, length of the estrous period and time of conception in beef heifers, *J. Amin. Sci.* **16**:1100 Abs.

WILTBANK, J. N., GREGORY, K. E., SWIGER, L. A., INGALLS, J. E., ROTHLISBERGER, J. A. and KOCH, R. M. (1966) Effects of heterosis on age and weight at puberty in beef heifers, *J. Anim. Sci.* **25**: 744.

WILTBANK, J. N., GREGORY, K. E., ROTHLISBERGER, J. A., INGALLS, J. E. and KASSON, C. W. (1967a). Fertility in beef cows bred to produce straightbred and crossbred calves, *J. Anim. Sci.* **26**:1005.

WILTBANK, J. N. and HARVEY, W. R. (1963) Reproductive performance of beef cows in Louisiana, *J. Anim. Sci.* **22**:823 Abs.

WILTBANK, J. N. and KASSON, C. W. (1968) Synchronization of estrus in cattle with an oral progesteronal agent and an injection of an estrogen, *J. Anim. Sci.* **27**:113.

WILTBANK, J. N., ROWDEN, W. W. and INGALLS, J. E. (1959) The age and weight at puberty in Hereford heifers, *J. Anim. Sci.* **18**:1562 Abs.

WILTBANK, J. N., ROWDEN, W. W., INGALLS, J. E., GREGORY, K. E. and KOCH, R. M. (1962) Effect of energy level on reproductive phenomena of mature Hereford cows, *J. Anim. Sci.* **21**:219.

WILTBANK, J. N., ROWDEN, W. W., INGALLS, J. E. and ZIMMERMAN, D. R. (1964) Influence of *post-partum* energy level on reproductive performance of Hereford cows restricted in energy intake prior to calving, *J. Anim. Sci.* **23**:1049.

WILTBANK, J. N., SHUMWAY, R. P., PARKER, W. R. and ZIMMERMAN, D. R. (1967b) Duration of estrus, time of ovulation and fertilization rate in beef heifers synchronized with dihydroxy progesterone acetophenide, *J. Anim. Sci.* **26**:764.

WILTBANK, J. N., WARWICK, E. J., VERNON, E. H. and PRIODE, B. M. (1961) Factors affecting net calf crop in beef cattle, *J. Anim. Sci.* **20**:409.

WILTBANK, J. N., ZIMMERMAN, D. R., INGALLS, J. E. and ROWDEN, W. W. (1965) Use of progestational compounds alone or in combination with estrogen for synchronization of estrus, *J. Anim. Sci.* **24**:990.

WINCHESTER, C. F. (1964) Symposium on growth; environment and growth, *J. Anim. Sci.* **23**:254.

WINCHESTER, C. F. and ELLIS, N. R. (1956) Delayed growth of beef cattle, USDA Tech. Bull. 1159.

WINCHESTER, C. F. and HARVEY, W. R. (1966) Effects of protein and energy intake on nitrogen retention and growth of cattle, USDA Tech. Bull. 1364.

WINCHESTER, C. F., HINER, R. L. and SCARBOROUGH, V. C. (1957) Some effects on beef cattle of protein and energy restriction, *J. Anim. Sci.* **16**:426.

WINCHESTER, C. F. and HOWE, P. E. (1955) Relative effects of continuous and interrupted growth in beef steers, USDA Tech. Bull. 1108.

WINCHESTER, C. F. and MORRIS, M. J. (1956) Water intake rates of cattle, *J. Anim. Sci.* **15**:722.

WIPF, V. K., CARPENTER, J. W., CHAPMAN, H. L., JR., PALMER, A. Z. and CUNHA, T. J. (1964) Effects of slaughter age and diethylstilbestrol implants on feedlot performance and carcass characteristics of bulls and steers, *J. Anim. Sci.* **23**:865 Abs.

WISE, M. B., BLUMER, T. N. and BARRICK, E. R. (1963) Influence of urea, fat and alfalfa meal on performance, rumen epithelium and livers of steers fed all-concentrate diets, *J. Anim. Sci.* **22**:849.

WISE, M. B., BLUMER, T. N., CRAIG, H. B. and BARRICK, E. R. (1965) Influence of rumen buffering agents and hay on performance and carcass characteristics of steers fed all-concentrate rations, *J. Anim. Sci.* **24**:83.

WISE, M. B., BLUMER, T. N., MATRONE, G. and BARRICK, E. R. (1961) Investigations on the feeding of all-concentrate rations to beef cattle, *J. Anim. Sci.* **20**:561.

WISE, M. B., BLUMER, T. N., MATRONE, G. and BARRICK, E. R. (1962) Further investigations on all-concentrate rations for beef cattle, *J. Anim. Sci.* **21**:1017 Abs.

WISE, M. B. and LA MASTER, J. C. (1968) *J. Dairy Sci.* **51**:452.

WISE, M. B., SMITH, S. E. and BARNES, L. L. (1958) The phosphorus requirements of calves, *J. Anim. Sci.* **17**:89.

WISMER-PEDERSEN, J. (1959) *Fd Res.* **24**:711.

WISMER-PEDERSEN, J. and BRISKEY, E. J. (1961) Rate of anerobic glycolysis versus structure in pork muscle, *Nature* **189**:318.

WISTRAND, G. C. and RIGGS, J. K. (1966) Milk production of Santa Gertrudis cows as measured by calf nursing and machine milking methods, *J. Anim. Sci.* **25**:263 Abs.

WITHERS, F. W. (1952) Mortality rate and disease incidence in calves in relation to feeding, management and other environmental factors, *Br. Vet. J.* **108**:315.

WITHERS, F. W. (1953) Mortality rate and disease incidence in calves as related to feeding, management and other environmental factors, Part 4, *Br. Vet. J.* **109**:122.

WITT, H. G., WARNICK, A. C., KOGER, M. and CUNHA, T. J. (1958) The effect of level of protein intake and alfalfa meal on reproduction and gains in beef cows, *J. Anim. Sci.* **17**:1211 Abs.

WOLLNER, H. (1968) Personal communication.

WOODHAM, P. R. and TROWER, S. J. (1965) Palatability characteristics of rib-steaks from Aberdeen Angus steers and bulls, *NZ J. Agric. Res.* **8**:921.

WOOD, A. (1962) Personal communication.

WOOD, P. D. P. (1965) Survey of Charolais calf births in England and Wales, MMB Mimeo.

WOODS, W. (1962) Effect of implantation followed by feeding of stilbestrol on steer performance and carcass characteristics, *J. Anim. Sci.* **21**:533.

WOODS, W., BURROUGHS, W., RAUN, N. S., COOLEY, R. and BOCKHOP, C. (1961) High concentrate–low fibre finishing rations for beef cattle, *Feedstuffs*, 24th June, p. 36.

WOODS, W. and LUTHER, R. (1962) Further observations on the effect of physical preparation of the ration on volatile fatty acid production, *J. Anim. Sci.* **21**:809.

WOODS, W. and RHODES, R. W. (1962) Effect of varying roughage to concentrate ratios on the utilization by lambs of rations differing in physical form, *J. Anim. Sci.* **21**:479.

WOODS, W. and SCHOLL, J. M. (1962) Substitution of corn for forage in the fattening ration of steers, *J. Anim. Sci.* **21**:69.

WOODS, W. and WILSON, B. B. (1967) Influence of level of particle size of gelatinized corn on animal performance and rumen fermentation, *J. Anim. Sci.* **26**:933 Abs.

WOODWARD, R. R. and CLARK, R. T. (1959) A study of stillbirths in a herd of range cattle, *J. Anim. Sci.* **18**:85.

WOODWARD, R. R. and RICE, F. J. (1958) Variation in weight–constant body length measurements of Hereford bulls, *J. Anim. Sci.* **17**:1146 Abs.

WOODWARD, R. R., RICE, F. J., QUESENBERRY, J. R., HINER, R. L., CLARK, R. T. and WILLSON, F. S. (1959) Relationships between measures of performance, body form and carcass quality of beef cattle, Mont. Agric. Exp. Sta. Bull. 550.

WORD, J. D., JR., WILLIAMS, D. L., MARTIN, L. C., WILLIAMS, E. I., PANCIERA, R. J., NELSON, T. E., BYRD, K. L. and TILLMAN, A. D. (1968) Urea toxicity studies with the pregnant bovine, *J. Anim. Sci.* **27**:1180 Abs.

WORSTELL, D. M. and BRODY, S. (1953) Comparative physiological reactions of European and Indian cattle to changing temperature, Mo. Agric. Exp. Sta. Res. Bull. 515.

WRIGHT, P. L., GRAINGER, R. B. and MARCO, G. J. (1966) Post-ruminal degradation and absorption of carbohydrate by the mature ruminant, *J. Nutr.* **89**:241.

WRIGHT, S. (1931) Evolution in Mendelian populations, *Genetics* **16**:97.

WUTHIER, P. R. and STRATTON, P. O. (1957) The creatine level of blood serum as an indicator of carcass composition, *J. Anim. Sci.* **16**:961.

WYTHE, L. D., JR., ORTS, F. A. and KING, G. T. (1961) Bone–muscle relationships in beef carcasses, *J. Anim. Sci.* **20**:3.

YAO, T. S., DAWSON, W. M. and COOK, A. C. (1953) Relationships between meat production characters and body measurements in Beef and Milking Shorthorn steers, *J. Anim. Sci.* **12**:775.

YEATES, N. T. M. (1952) The quantitative definition of cattle carcasses, *Aust. J. Agric. Res.* **3**:68.

YEATES, N. T. N. (1964) Starvation changes and subsequent recovery of adult beef muscles, *J. Agric. Sci.* **62**:267.

YEATES, N. T. M. (1965) *Modern Aspects of Animal Production*, Butterworths, London.

YECK, R. G. and KIBLER, H. H. (1958) Predicting heat tolerance from calf vaporization rates, *J. Anim. Sci.* **17**:1228 Abs.

YECK, R. G. and STEWART, R. E. (1959) *Proc. Aust. Soc. Agric. Engineers* **2**:71.

YODER, R. D., TRENKLE, A. and BURROUGHS, W. (1966) Influence of rumen protozoa and bacteria upon cellulose digestion *in vitro*, *J. Anim. Sci.* **25**:609.

YOUNG, A. W., BRADLEY, N. W., and CUNDIFF, L. V. (1967) Effects of an oral progesterone on feedlot heifers, *J. Anim. Sci.* **26**:231 Abs.

YOUNG, G. B. (1953) A study of genotype–environment interaction in mice, *J. Agric. Sci.* **43**:218.

YEUH, M. H. and STRONG, F. M. (1960) Some volatile constituents of cooked beef, *J. Agric. Fd Chem.* **8**:491.

ZAVERTJAEV, B. P. (1966) The character of the inheritance and variability of body weight in calves, *Zhivotnovodstvo, Mosk.* **28** (12), 66.

ZEREBCOV, P. I. and SOLNCEV, A. O. (1966) Effect of some organic acids on N metabolism in the rumen, *Inz. Timirjazev. Sel'skohoz Akad.* **1**:168.

ZEREMSKI, D. and KOLJAJIC, V. (1966) Effect of high concentrate rations on fattening in some breeds of cattle, *Zborn. Rad. poljopriv. Fak.* **14** (417), 9.

ZEIGLER, J. H., BEERY, K. E., ERB, W. W. and WILSON, L. L. (1968) Variations in consumer acceptability of beef, *J. Anim. Sci.* **27:** 1513 Abs.

ZIMBELMAN, R. G. (1963) Determination of the minimal effective dose of 6 α methyl-17α-acetoxyprogesterone for control of the estrual cycle of cattle, *J. Anim. Sci.* **22:**1051.

ZIMMERMAN, D. R., CLANTON, D. C. and MATSUSHIMA, J. K. (1961a) *Post-partum* reproductive performance in beef heifers as affected by protein and energy intake during gestation, *J. Anim. Sci.* **20:**957 Abs.

ZIMMERMAN, J. E., DAVIS, S. L. SHOEMAKER, B. E. and LAMB, P. E. (1966) Gain, efficiency and carcass merit of steers fed to different market weights, *J. Amin. Sci.* **25:**1253 Abs.

ZIMMERMAN, J. E., DEEBLE, F. K. and NEUMANN, A. L. (1961b) Protein requirements and protein energy interrelationships in beef cattle, *J. Anim. Sci.* **20:**958 Abs.

ZINN, D. W., DURHAM, R. M. and STOVALL, R. (1963a) Muscle growth and development in the beef animal during the feeding period, *J. Anim. Sci.* **22:**829 Abs.

ZINN, D. W., ELLIOTT, H., BURNETT, D. and DURHAM, R. M. (1961) Evaluation of USDA beef grading methods, *J. Anim. Sci.* **20:**922.

ZINN, D. W., MONTGOMERY, T. H., BELCHER, G. and KENT, W. (1963b) Effects of length of feeding period on fat deposition and tenderness in the beef carcass, *J. Amin. Sci.* **22:**830 Abs.

ZINN, D. W., STOVALL, R., MILLER, J. C. and DURHAM, R. M. (1962) Effects of length of time on feed on carcass conformation and grade of beef, *J. Anim. Sci.* **21:**986 Abs.

ZIOLECKI, A. and BRIGGS, C. A. E. (1961) The microflora of the rumen of the young calf, 2: Source, nature and development, *J. Appl. Bacteriol.* **24:**148.

ZURCHER, T. D. and BEESON, W. M. (1968) Studies on the zinc requirements of beef cattle *J. Anim. Sci.* **27:**1181 Abs.

ZURKOWSKA, K. (1962) The estimation of fertility and length of gestation period in Black Pied Lowland cows from the Poznan region. *Zesz. nauk. Szkel. glów. Gosp. wiejsk. Zootech.* **3**(3), 15.

APPENDIX I

*Rearing by Suckling**

The rearing of dairy calves by double or multiple suckling has been practised for many years (e.g. Williams and Edgar, 1966). However, as a system it has found little acceptability to specialized rearers who, in the main, have gone for artificial rearing by weaning or use of milk replacers.

There is now reason to think that this trend may show signs of reversal. The arguments for change are several. There has been, in the 70s, an increasing demand for milk products for human consumption—particularly skim milk powder, which is the basis for most milk replacers. Thus in many countries prices for reconstituted milk replacers are not so far below, and occasionally superior to, those of fresh cow's milk. Secondly, there has been a sharp rise in the price, or rather the value, of calves to the dairyman following the world-wide increases in beef prices. Thus, in many situations the dairy farmer can earn as much for his milk, marketing it in the form of calf live weight, as selling it to the milk factory. Thirdly, in countries which do not have milk surpluses, to purchase milk powder on the world market involves expenditure of foreign exchange, and in the context of developing countries this is an important constraint. Besides, in such countries there is usually a shortage of milk in the human diet, and in such circumstances it is difficult to justify use of the same supplies of milk powder for calf feeding. Finally, recent research has shown that there are important physiological benefits both to the calf and the cow from suckling. The process of obtaining milk from the cow by machine/hand milking, or by suckling, is not the same as has often been supposed.

Everitt *et al.* (1968) used a system of multiple suckling to rear Friesian calves on Jersey cows in early lactation, the latter being reintroduced into the milking herd when the calves were weaned—usually after 70 days. In their experiments they used identical twin pairs of cows, one member being used for the suckling system, the other remaining in the milking herd throughout lactation. Their findings showed that, when reintroduced into the milking herd after weaning, cows which had been suckled gave significantly more milk in the remaining weeks of lactation than their pair mates which had never been suckled. Incidence of subclinical mastitis was also less in the suckled milked cows. Calf growth rate by suckling, at 4 calves per cow, was superior to that recorded for rearing on milk replacers; moreover, mortality was considerably reduced. The only disadvantage of the system was with respect to the difficulties encountered in persuading the foster cows to accept "alien" calves. The plan was also aimed basically at specialized dairy farmers—whose Jersey calves were not suitable—to encourage them to engage in rearing for beef production.

* See supplementary list of references, p. 545

Under conditions of most developing countries, management inputs such as those required for fostering calves are not always readily available. For instance, in Cuba, Ugarte and Preston (1970, unpublished data) found that multiple suckling was feasible at the level of an experimental station, but found no acceptance when applied to large-scale commercial farms. They therefore evolved a simpler procedure whereby the cow was allowed to suckle her own calf for a restricted period after each milking. It was found that in most large commercial herds, some 20 to 30 minutes on average elapsed between the end of milking and the cow actually leaving the milking shed or parlour. Time spent in suckling her calf after this interval rarely exceeded 15 minutes; moreover, there was no difficulty in separating cow and calf when suckling was finished, possibly because for the rest of the day each was confined in different corrals or pastures.

Results of an experiment comparing this restricted suckling system with conventional artificial rearing are set out in Tables I.1 and I.2. Holstein and Holstein ×

TABLE I.1 REARING DAIRY CALVES BY RESTRICTED SUCKLING: EFFECTS ON CALF[1] GROWTH RATE (FROM UGARTE AND PRESTON, 1972A)

	Live weight (kg)		
	Birth	Weaning (70 days)	Daily gain
Holstein × Zebu dams			
1 × day suckling	35.2	91.2	0.80
2 × day suckling	34.2	107.0	1.03
Holstein dams			
1 × day suckling	39.5	81.5	0.60
2 × day suckling	42.1	102.0	0.86

[1] The calves were by a variety of sires, balanced over each treatment.

TABLE I.2 REARING DAIRY CALVES BY RESTRICTED SUCKLING: EFFECTS ON MILK YIELD OF THEIR DAMS (FROM UGARTE AND PRESTON, 1972A)

	Amount of milk daily (litres)			Increase over control (%)
	At milking	Drunk by calf	Total	
Holstein × Zebu				
1 × day suckling	5.1	5.5	10.6	73
2 × day suckling	2.7	8.2	10.9	68
Control[1]	6.3		6.3	
Holstein				
1 × day suckling	9.6	5.7	15.3	57
2 × day suckling	6.3	8.7	15.0	53
Control[1]	9.8		9.8	

[1] Average values from 5th to 70th (weaning) day of lactation. Calves from control cows were suckled for first 3 days of lactation only and then reared artificially.

Zebu dams, and suckling after only one, or after both milkings, were other factors studied. The outstanding features of the results were the extremely high growth rates of the calves (1 kg daily for twice daily suckling), and the stimulation in milk yield observed in the milking/suckling system compared with the "milking only" control. In part, the increase in milk yield on the former may have reflected bad machine milking techniques, but this is often the rule rather than the exception, in conditions of development, where almost everyone is a trainee, and where skilled workers are a scarcity. In this case the calf acts as a safety factor so that milk is not left unutilized.

In Zebu crossbred cows, combined milking and suckling was particularly beneficial; for milking alone, some 17% of lactations terminated before 70 days, while none of the suckled cows went dry in this period. The reduced clinical and subclinical mastitis in milked/suckled cows (Table I.3) confirms the New Zealand work, and is an important attribute for the system, especially in countries where drugs and veterinarians are both in short supply. In a subsequent trial, Ugarte and Preston (1973) investigated a procedure of letting the calf be suckled twice daily for the first month of lactation, then only once daily until weaning at 70 days. Growth rate of the calves was slightly reduced for the modified plan compared with twice daily suckling throughout (Table I.4), however, as would be expected, saleable milk yield increased (Fig. I.1). In fact, on the modified plan, saleable milk yield was the same

TABLE I.3 REARING DAIRY CALVES BY RESTRICTED SUCKLING: EFFECT ON INCIDENCE OF MASTITIS (UGARTE AND PRESTON, 1972A)

	No. of cows	Quarters affected by mastitis	
		Clinical	Subclinical[1]
Milking/suckling	36	5	14
Milking only	36	18	52

[1] Mean values for 5 samples.

TABLE I.4 REARING DAIRY CALVES BY RESTRICTED SUCKLING: EFFECT OF SUCKLING FREQUENCY ON CALF GROWTH RATE (FROM UGARTE AND PRESTON, 1973)

	Suckling frequency	
	2X daily for 10 weeks	2X daily for 4 weeks then 1X daily for 6 weeks
Average daily gain in live weight to weaning at 10 weeks, kg	0.86	0.53

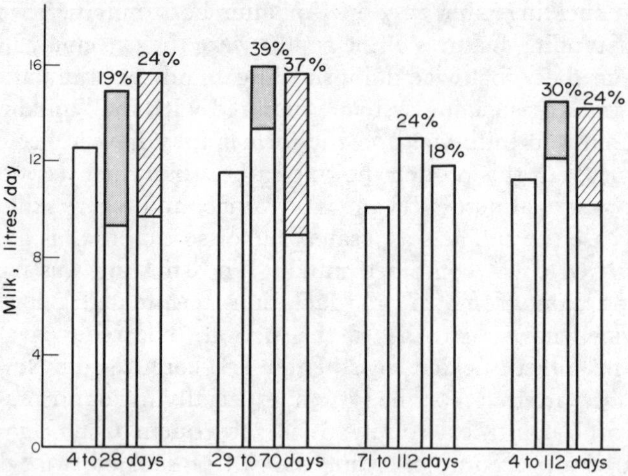

FIG. I.1 Rearing dairy calves by restricted suckling: milk yield of cows milked and suckled twice daily to weaning at 70 days (hatched), milked and suckled twice daily to 28 days and then milked cows twice daily but suckled only once daily to weaning at 70 days (shaded), and control cows milked twice daily but not suckled (open) (from Ugarte and Preston, 1973).

as for control cows which were never allowed to suckle—yet with the former plan the calf was reared as an integral part of the system. Milk yield after weaning in milked/suckled cows also appeared to be at a higher rate than in controls, in agreement with the New Zealand findings.

The interval between milking and suckling is obviously a critical factor, in determining the amount of milk available to the calf. However, the total yield (milked plus suckled), and presumably the stimulatory effect, was overall the same, whether the interval was short (20 minutes) or long (2 hours) (see Table I.5).

For crossbred cows, particularly those with Zebu breeding, even simpler pro-

TABLE I.5 REARING DAIRY CALVES BY RESTRICTED SUCKLING: EFFECT OF THE INTERVAL BETWEEN MILKING AND SUCKLING ON COW MILK YIELD AND CALF GROWTH (UGARTE AND PRESTON, 1972B)

Interval from milking to suckling	Amount of milk			Daily LW gain	Conversion of milk to gain
	At milking	Consumed by calf	Total		
		litres		kg	Litres/kg
20 minutes	13.85[a]	3.81[a]	17.66	0.55	6.9
120 minutes	12.41[b]	5.21[b]	17.62	0.62	8.0

[a,b] Values within each column with different superscripts differ significantly at $P < 0.01$.

cedures have been developed (Veitia and Simon, 1972). Milk yields and calf growth were similar when such animals were milked only once daily, and allowed to suckle their calves instead of being milked a second time, than when twice daily milking and suckling were employed (see Table I.6). The labour costs are obviously much lower with the former system.

TABLE I.6 REARING DAIRY CALVES BY RESTRICTED SUCKLING: TWICE A DAY MILKING AND SUCKLING VERSUS A SIMPLIFIED PROCEDURE OF MILKING ONCE DAILY IN THE AFTERNOON (FROM VEITIA AND SIMON, 1972)

	Milking/suckling twice daily	Milking morning suckling afternoon
To weaning at 60 days		
Wt at birth, kg	33.3	34.4
Wt at 60 days, kg	71.6	79.4
Live wt gain, kg/day	0.63	0.75
Milk, litres/day		
At milking	4.1	5.7
Drunk by calf	6.6	7.0
Total	10.7	12.7
Post-weaning, 60 to 120 days		
Calf live wt gain, kg/day	0.65	0.73
Daily milk yield, litres	9.5	10.3

APPENDIX II

Supplementary List of References

ANON. (1970) Unpublished data, Institute of Animal Science, Havana.

BROWN, P. B. (1962) Sugar cane bagasse—Blackstrap molasses rations for beef cattle, *Proceedings 11th Congress I.S.S.C.T.*, Mauritius, pp. 1216–1224.

BURROUGHS, W., TERNUS, G. S., TRENKLE, A. H., VETTER, R. L. and COOPER, C. (1970) Amino acids and proteins added to corn-urea rations (abstr.), *J. Anim. Sci.* **31:**1037.

CLARK, J. (1971) Molasses for milk production. M.Cs. Thesis, Universidad de la Habana.

CLEASBY, T. G. (1963) The feeding value of molasses: *Proceedings of the South African Sugar Technologists' Association*, pp. 113–117.

DION, H. G. (1973) Barbados breakthrough, *Proc. CIDA Seminar on Sugar Cane as Livestock Feed*, Barbados, Jan. 30–31.

EVERITT, G. C., PHILLIPS, S. D. M. and WHITEMAN, D. P. (1968) Suckling: effects on the calf and the cow, *Proc. Ruakura Farmers' Conf. Week*, N.Z

FAO (1969) *Production yearbook 1968–1969*, FAO, Rome.

FINCHMAN, J. E. (1966) Notes on the nutritional value of Rhodesian molasses, *Rhodesia agric. J.* **63:**106.

GEERKEN, C. M. and SUTHERLAND, T. M. (1969) Rumen liquid volume, liquid outflow, and the onward passage of soluble carbohydrate from this organ in animals fed high molasses diets, *Rev. cuba. Cienc. agric.* (Eng. ed.) **3:**217.

HATCH, M. D. and SLACK, C. R. (1966) Photosynthesis by sugar cane leaves, *Biochem. J.* **101:**103.

HUME, I. D., MOIR, J. J. and SOMERS, M. (1970) Synthesis of microbial protein in the rumen: I. Influence of the level of nitrogen intake, *Aust. J. agric. Res.* **21:**283.

JAMES, L. A. (1973) Comfith in rations for livestock, *Proc. CIDA Seminar on Sugar Cane as Livestock Feed*, Barbados, Jan. 30–31.

KOWLACZYK, J., RAMÍREZ, A. and GEERKEN, C. M. (1969) Studies on a composition and flow of duodenal contents in cattle fed diets high in molasses and urea, *Rev. cuba. Cienc. agric.* (Engl. ed.) **3:**221.

LOSADA, H., DIXON, F. and PRESTON, T. R. (1971) Thiamine and molasses toxicity. 1. Effects with roughage-free diets, *Rev. cuba. Cienc. agric.* (Engl. ed.) **5:**369.

LOSADA, H. and PRESTON, T. R. (1973) Effect of forage on some rumen parameters in calves fed molasses-based diets, *Cuba J. Agric. Sci.* (Engl. ed.) **7:**185.

MARTIN, J. L. and PRESTON, T. R. Different forage sources for bulls fed a molasses-based diet, *Cuba J. Agric. Sci.* In press.

MARTY, R. J. and SUTHERLAND, T. M. (1970) Changes in sucrose and lactic acid metabolism in the rumen of cattle during adaptation to a high-molasses diet, *Rev. cuba. Cienc. agric.* (Engl. ed.) **4:**45.

MARTY, R. J. and PRESTON, T. R. (1970) Molar proportions of the short chain volatile fatty acids (VFA) produced in the rumen of cattle given high-molasses diet, *Rev. cuba. Cienc. agric.* (Engl. ed.) **4:**183.

MORCIEGO, S., MUÑOZ, F. and PRESTON, T. R. (1970) Commercial fattening of bulls with molasses/urea and restricted grazing, *Rev. cuba. Cienc. agric.* (Engl. ed.) **4:**97.

MORCIEGO, S., MUÑOZ, F., MARTIN, J. L. and PRESTON, T. R. A note on the effect of different levels of fish meal and urea in a molasses-based diet for fattening bulls under commercial conditions, *Cuba. J. Agric. Sci.* In press.

MSIRI (1961) Mauritius Sugar Industry Research Institute Technical Circular No. 18, *By-products of the Sugar Industry in Mauritius*, p. 147.

Muñoz, F., Morciego, F. and Preston, T. R. (1970) Commercial fattening of bulls with molasses-urea, fish meal and restricted forage under feedlot conditions, *Rev. cuba. Cienc. agric.* (Engl. ed. **4**:91.

NRC (1956) National Research Council Publ. No. 449 (NRC, Washington).

Perón, N. and Preston, T. R. (1971) Effect of synthetic and natural roughage on tissue weights and contents of the intestinal tract in bulls fed liquid diets based on molasses/urea, *Rev. cuba. Cienc. agric.* (Engl. ed.) **5**:49.

Pigden, W. J. (1972) Evaluation of Comfith as a commercial livestock feed in the Caribbean, *Proc. CIDA Seminar on Sugar Cane as Livestock Feed*, Barbados, Jan. 30–31.

Preston, T. R. and Martin, J. L. Different forage sources for bulls fed a molasses-based diet, *Cuba J. Agric. Sci.* In press.

Preston, T. R. and Molina, A. Rapeseed meal in molasses/urea-based diets for fattening cattle, *Cuba J. Agric. Sci.* In press.

Preston, T. R. and Muñoz, F. (1971) The effect of giving increasing quantities of torula yeast protein to bulls fattened on a molasses-based diet, *Rev. cuba. Cienc. agric.* **5**:9.

Preston, T. R., Sansoucy, R., Nielsen, S. A. and Delaitre, C. (1973) Effect of supplementary maize grain on performance of Zebu bulls fed a molasses-urea based ration. In preparation

Ramírez, A. and Kowalczyk, J. (1971) Synthesis of microbial protein in young bulls fed a protein-free diet based on molasses/urea, *Rev. cuba. Cienc. Agric.* **5**:21.

Redferne, D. (1972) Personal communication.

Sansoucy, R., Nielsen, S. A., Delaitre, C. and Preston, T. R. (1973) Bagasse as a source of roughage in molasses-based diets. In preparation.

Turner, A. W. and Hodgetts, V. E. (1955) Buffer systems in the rumen of the sheep. II. Buffering properties in relation to composition, *Austr. J. agric. Res.* **6**:125.

Ugarte, J. and Preston, T. R. (1972a) Rearing dairy calves by restricted suckling. 1. Effect of suckling once or twice daily on milk production and calf growth, *Rev. cuba. Cienc. agric.* (Engl. ed.) **6**:173.

Ugarte, J. and Preston, T. R. (1972b) Rearing dairy calves by restricted suckling. 2. Milk production and calf growth as affected by the length of the interval between milking and suckling, *Rev. cuba. Cienc. agric.* (Engl. ed.) **6**:331.

Ugarte, J. and Preston, T. R. (1973) Rearing dairy calves by restricted suckling. 3. Effect of suckling frequency on calf growth and milk yield, *Cuban J. Agric. Sci.* **7**: in press.

Veitia, J. L. and Simon, L. (1972) Effect of two restricted suckling systems of calf rearing on milk production and calf growth, *Rev. cuba. Cienc. Agric.* (Engl. ed.) **6**:189.

Glossary

Abbreviations used in the text and in tables

Breed abbreviations

A	Angus
Af	Africander
Ay	Ayrshire
B	Brahman
BA	Brangus
BPL	Black Pied Lowland
Br	British
BS	Brown Swiss
C	Charolais
Cr	Criollo
D	Devon
DS	Dairy Shorthorn
F	Friesian
G	Guernsey
H	Hereford
HF	Holstein–Friesian
HL	Highland
J	Jersey
MRY	Meuse–Rhine–Yssel
NR	Norwegian Red
PH	Polled Hereford
RD	Red Dane
RP	Red Poll
S	Shorthorn
SD	South Devon
SG	Santa Gertrudis

Other abbreviations

AI	Artificial insemination
ARC	Agricultural Research Council
ATP	Adenosine triphosphate
BRA	Beef Recording Association (UK)
CAP	6-chloro-Δ^6-17-acetoxyprogesterone
DE	Digestible energy
DES	Diethylstilboestrol
DHIA	Dairy Herd Improvement Association (US)
DCP	Digestible crude protein
DM	Dry matter
EEC	European Economic Community
FAO	Food and Agriculture Organization
FCM	Fat-corrected milk
FSH	Follicle-stimulating hormone
FU	Feed unit
GE	Gross energy
IU	International Unit
LH	Luteinizing hormone
MAP	6-α-methyl-17-α-acetoxyprogesterone
ME	Metabolizable energy
MGA	Melengestrol acetate
MLC	Meat and Livestock Commission (UK)
MMB	Milk Marketing Board of England and Wales
MTU	Methyl-thio-uracil
N	Nitrogen
NE	Net energy
NFE	Nitrogen-free extract
NIRD	National Institute for Research in Dairying (UK)
NPN	Non-protein nitrogen
NRC	National Research Council (US)
PIDA	Pig Industry Development Authority (UK)
PMS	Pregnant mare serum
RLR	Rump, loin, round
RLRC	Rump, loin, round, chuck
SD	Standard deviation
TDN	Total digestible nutrients
USDA	United States Department of Agriculture
VFA	Volatile fatty acids

Index

Biographical Details

M. B. Willis, B.Sc., Ph.D.

is Lecturer in Animal Production at the University of Newcastle upon Tyne. He was a geneticist with the Milk Marketing Board from 1960–65 and from 1965 to the end of 1971 Head of Animal Science Division at the Instituto de Ciencia Animal, Havana. His main field of interest lies with beef cattle and particularly in the development of testing systems and breeding methods and in the more fundamental studies of growth. He is the author of some 44 scientific papers and has had over 20 communications presented at scientific congresses. He has also produced one other book on beef cattle.

T. R. Preston, Ph.D., D.Sc.

is Technical Adviser and Director of Research to 'proyecto Nutricional Ganadero' Comision Nacional de la Industria Azucarera, Humboldt No. 56–1er piso, Mexico 1, D.F. He was Director of the Instituto de Ciencia Animal, Havana, Cuba, from 1965 to 1971 and from 1972–73 spent one year with FAO, Rome, as Nutrition Officer. He is well known as the originator of the early weaning system of calf rearing and the intensive "barley beef" system, both in general use in the UK and elsewhere. His work at the Instituto de Ciencia Animal in Cuba was concerned with the development of feeding systems for cattle, pigs and poultry based on sugar-cane by-products. It is estimated that as a result of this research some half a million head of beef cattle are intensively fattened each year in Cuba using molasses-based rations. With Dr. M. B. Willis he collaborated on the development of performance testing and breeding systems in beef cattle. Dr. Preston has travelled extensively in tropical countries in Africa, South and Central America and Asia, and serves as International Consultant in tropical animal production through the agencies of International Organizations such as the World Bank and FAO. Dr. Preston has published over 150 papers in some 20 scientific journals together with over one hundred research communications presented at scientific congresses and has lectured extensively.